Noble gases

Atomic weights are based on carbon-12. Atomic weights in parentheses indicate the most stable or best-known isotope. Slight disagreement exists as to the exact electronic configuration of several of the high-atomic-number elements.

IIIA	IVA	VA	VIA	VIIA	
					2 Helium **He** 4.00260
5 Boron **B** 10.81	**6** Carbon **C** 12.011	**7** Nitrogen **N** 14.0067	**8** Oxygen **O** 15.9994	**9** Fluorine **F** 18.99840	**10** Neon **Ne** 20.179
13 Aluminum **Al** 26.98154	**14** Silicon **Si** 28.086	**15** Phosphorus **P** 30.97376	**16** Sulfur **S** 32.06	**17** Chlorine **Cl** 35.453	**18** Argon **Ar** 39.948

	IB	IIB					

			IIIA	IVA	VA	VIA	VIIA	
28 Nickel **Ni** 58.71	**29** Copper **Cu** 63.546	**30** Zinc **Zn** 65.38	**31** Gallium **Ga** 69.72	**32** Germanium **Ge** 72.59	**33** Arsenic **As** 74.9216	**34** Selenium **Se** 78.96	**35** Bromine **Br** 79.904	**36** Krypton **Kr** 83.80
46 Palladium **Pd** 106.4	**47** Silver **Ag** 107.868	**48** Cadmium **Cd** 112.40	**49** Indium **In** 114.82	**50** Tin **Sn** 118.69	**51** Antimony **Sb** 121.75	**52** Tellurium **Te** 127.60	**53** Iodine **I** 126.9045	**54** Xenon **Xe** 131.30
78 Platinum **Pt** 195.09	**79** Gold **Au** 196.9665	**80** Mercury **Hg** 200.59	**81** Thallium **Tl** 204.37	**82** Lead **Pb** 207.2	**83** Bismuth **Bi** 208.9804	**84** Polonium **Po** (210)[a]	**85** Astatine **At** (210)[a]	**86** Radon **Rn** (222)[a]

Inner transition elements

63 Europium **Eu** 151.96	**64** Gadolinium **Gd** 157.25	**65** Terbium **Tb** 158.9254	**66** Dysprosium **Dy** 162.50	**67** Holmium **Ho** 164.9304	**68** Erbium **Er** 167.26	**69** Thulium **Tm** 168.9342	**70** Ytterbium **Yb** 173.04	**71** Lutetium **Lu** 174.97
95 Americium **Am** (243)[a]	**96** Curium **Cm** (247)[a]	**97** Berkelium **Bk** (249)[a]	**98** Californium **Cf** (251)[a]	**99** Einsteinium **Es** (254)[a]	**100** Fermium **Fm** (253)[a]	**101** Mendelevium **Md** (256)[a]	**102** Nobelium **No** (254)[a]	**103** Lawrencium **Lr** (257)[a]

College Chemistry

An Introduction to General, Organic, and Biochemistry

Fourth Edition

College Chemistry

An Introduction to General, Organic, and Biochemistry

Fourth Edition

Morris Hein

Leo R. Best

Scott Pattison

Brooks/Cole Publishing Company
Pacific Grove, California

Brooks/Cole Publishing Company
A Division of Wadsworth, Inc.

Printed in the United States of America
10 9 8 7 6 5 4 3 2

Library of Congress Cataloging in Publication Data
Hein, Morris.
  College chemistry: an introduction to general, organic, and biochemistry / Morris Hein, Leo R. Best, Scott Pattison.
      p. cm.
  Includes index.
  ISBN 0-534-08562-8
  1. Chemistry. I. Best, Leo R. II. Pattison, Scott, [date].
III. Title.
QD31.2.H43 1988
540—dc19   87-24633
                                            CIP

Sponsoring and Production Editor: Sue Ewing
Editorial Assistant: Heidi Wieland
Production Assistants: Linda Loba and Dorothy Bell
Manuscript Editor: Patricia E. Cain
Permissions Editor: Carline Haga
Interior Design: Flora Pomercy/Katherine Minerva
Cover Design: Katherine Minerva
Cover Photo: Courtesy of Nelson Max, Lawrence Livermore National Laboratory
Art Coordinator: Lisa Torri
Interior Illustration: John Foster
Typesetting: Polyglot, Singapore
Cover Printing: The Lehigh Press Company, Pennsauken, New Jersey
Printing and Binding: R. R. Donnelley & Sons Company, Crawfordsville, Indiana

About the cover: The photo is a computer-generated image of two base pairs of DNA. One pair is represented by a ball-and-stick model; the other is a space-filling model. A CDC 7600 was used to calculate which spheres, balls, and sticks would be visible. A Sperry-UNIVAC V75 was used to color the visible regions. The images were superimposed by double exposing them in a Dicomed film recorder. Courtesy of Nelson Max, Lawrence Livermore National Laboratory.

To Edna, Louise, and Joan

Preface

As in the previous editions, the primary purpose of this edition of *College Chemistry* is to instruct students in the basic concepts of chemistry. This book is intended for students who, although not majoring in chemistry, require a basic course in the subject that includes an introduction to organic chemistry and biochemistry. The text is written with the assumption that the students have not taken a previous chemistry course.

Many students are somewhat apprehensive about beginning the study of chemistry. Accordingly, one of our major goals has been to present the subject in a well-organized and readily understandable fashion. Each chapter was written with this thought in mind: Is our language clear—will the student be able to understand this material?

A fair amount of quantitative reasoning is essential to the study of chemistry. Therefore, another major goal has been to provide careful, step-by-step explanations of the topics that require quantitative reasoning. These explanations are then illustrated by one or more problems. These example problems are generally set up and worked by the conversion-factor dimensional analysis approach. This approach has proven to be an effective tool and requires no mathematics beyond arithmetic and elementary algebra. From experience, however, we know that to develop sufficient skill in quantitative reasoning, most students need considerable practice in working numerical problems. Consequently, we have provided many end-of-chapter problems. To save student time, an inexpensive electronic calculator is recommended for the calculations needed in these problems.

In preparation for this revision, a number of instructors who are actual or potential users of the text submitted detailed reviews and comments on the text. These colleagues provided many suggestions for changes both in content and arrangement; a number of changes in the present text were based on these helpful suggestions.

Learning Aids

The following features are intended to serve as learning aids and to make the text convenient to use—a book that students can read, understand, and study by themselves.

- A list of achievement goals is given at the beginning of each chapter as a guide to students.
- Important new terms are set in boldface type where they are defined in the text, and they are also printed in color in the margin.
- A detailed discussion of significant figures, rounding off numbers, scientific notation of numbers, and the use of dimensional analysis in calculations is given in Chapter 2. Appendix I contains a concise review of the mathematics pertinent to *College Chemistry*.
- Numerous questions and problems are given in separate groups at the end of each chapter. These questions are generally arranged in the order in which the topics are discussed. A few of the more challenging problems are marked with asterisks. Answers to all mathematical problems are given in Appendix V.
- All chapters have at least one self-evaluation question that contains a fairly large number of "correct" or "not correct" statements. Answers to these questions are given in Appendix V.
- The mole is used as a unifying chemical concept wherever possible.
- Material on inorganic nomenclature appears in several chapters, but for convenient reference the basic rules for naming inorganic compounds are brought together in Chapter 8.
- Examples relating to health topics are used extensively.

Supplementary Materials

Supplementary materials that accompany *College Chemistry* are a student study guide, a laboratory manual, and a solutions manual.

Major Changes and Additions

- The concepts of the mole and Avogadro's number have been moved from Chapter 5 to Chapter 9 where they complement the material on quantitative composition of compounds.
- The sections on oxidation numbers and oxidation number tables have been moved from the end of Chapter 7 (Chemical Bonds) to the beginning of Chapter 8 (Nomenclature).

- The biochemistry section, especially Chapters 30 through 34, has been revised extensively.
- A chapter, Chapter 19, on the chemistry of some selected metals and non-metals has been added.
- Most of the end-of-chapter problems have been modified or are new.
- Both the joule and calorie are used as energy units, with emphasis on the joule.
- A more extensive discussion of enzymes has been added to Chapter 29.
- New material on viruses and genetic engineering has been introduced.
- The significance of processed foods, food additives, and dieting in relation to good nutrition is treated in more detail.
- A section on hydrolysis has been added to Chapter 16.
- Several pressure units are introduced in discussing the properties of gases, but emphasis is given to atmospheres and torrs in problems.
- A different method of balancing oxidation–reduction equations in alkaline solutions is given.
- Ionic bond is used in place of electrochemical bond.
- Much of the material on cell structure and function, formerly found in Chapter 30, has been integrated into Chapter 32, Bioenergetics.
- The use of K, L, M, . . . for atomic orbitals has been deleted.
- The periodic table most recently recommended by the American Chemical Society is shown in Appendix VI.

Acknowledgments

It is impossible to thank by name each of the many people who have been involved and helpful in making this revision of *College Chemistry*. We are grateful for the friendship and many helpful comments and suggestions from our colleagues and students who, over the years, have made this book possible. We appreciate the many helpful comments and suggestions made by the following reviewers of this manuscript: Robert Bruce Banks, *University of North Carolina, Greensboro*; Robert K. Boggess, *Radford University*; Edward J. Cowles, *University of Minnesota, Duluth*; David A. Darnall, *Shelby State Community College*; Karen E. Eichstadt, *Ohio University*; Edwin J. Gollier, *Virginia Military Institute*; John Pearsley, *Grossmont College*; and John K. Ruff, *University of Georgia*.

No textbook can be completed without the untiring effort of many professionals in publishing. Special thanks are due to Sue Ewing, Kath Minerva, Trisha Cain, Lisa Torri, and Flora Pomeroy of Brooks/Cole Publishing. All have contributed to making this edition.

Last, but certainly not least, we are grateful to our wives, Edna, Louise, and Joan, for their patience and understanding during this revision.

Morris Hein
Leo R. Best
Scott Pattison

Contents

3   Properties of Matter   44

4   Elements and Compounds   60

5   Atomic Theory and Structure   80

6   The Periodic Arrangement of the Elements   108

7   Chemical Bonds: The Formation of Compounds from Atoms   125

15   Ionization: Acids, Bases, Salts; Colloids   331

16   Chemical Equilibrium   364

23 Aldehydes and Ketones   580

24 Carboxylic Acids, Their Derivatives, and Amines   602

25 Polymers: Macromolecules   640

26   Stereoisomerism   655

27   Carbohydrates   673

28   Lipids   703

29   Amino Acids, Polypeptides, and Proteins   722

30   Nucleic Acids and Heredity   757

31   Nutrition and Digestion   783

1 Introduction

1.1 The Nature of Chemistry

What is chemistry? A popular dictionary gives this definition: Chemistry is the science of the composition, structure, properties, and reactions of matter, especially of atomic and molecular systems. Another, somewhat simpler dictionary definition is: Chemistry is the science dealing with the composition of matter and the changes in composition that matter undergoes. Neither of these definitions is entirely adequate. Chemistry, along with the closely related science of physics, is a fundamental branch of knowledge. Chemistry is also closely related to biology, not only because living organisms are made of material substances but also because life itself is essentially a complicated system of interrelated chemical processes.

The scope of chemistry is extremely broad: It includes the whole universe and everything, animate and inanimate, in the universe. Chemistry is concerned not only with the composition and changes of composition of matter, but also with the energy and energy changes associated with matter. Through chemistry we seek to learn and to understand the general principles that govern the behavior of all matter.

The chemist, like other scientists, observes nature and attempts to understand its secrets: What makes a rose red? Why is sugar sweet? What is occurring when iron rusts? Why is carbon monoxide poisonous? Why do people wither with age?

Problems such as these—some of which have been solved, some of which are still to be solved—are part of what we call chemistry.

A chemist may interpret natural phenomena, devise experiments that will reveal the composition and structure of complex substances, study methods for improving natural processes, or, sometimes, synthesize substances unknown in nature. Ultimately, the efforts of successful chemists advance the frontiers of knowledge and at the same time contribute to the well-being of humanity. Chemistry can help us to understand nature; however, one need not be a professional chemist or scientist to enjoy natural phenomena. Nature and its beauty, its simplicity within complexity, are for all to appreciate.

The body of chemical knowledge is so vast that no one can hope to master it all, even in a lifetime of study. However, many of the basic concepts can be learned in a relatively short period of time. These basic concepts have become part of the education required for many professionals, including agriculturists, biologists, dental hygienists, dentists, medical technologists, microbiologists, nurses, nutritionists, pharmacists, physicians, and veterinarians, to name a few.

1.2   History of Chemistry

People have practiced empirical chemistry from the earliest times. Ancient civilizations were practicing the art of chemistry in such processes as wine-making, glass-making, pottery-making, dyeing, and elementary metallurgy. The early Egyptians, for example, had considerable knowledge of certain chemical processes. Excavations into ancient tombs dated about 3000 B.C. have uncovered workings of gold, silver, copper, and iron, pottery from clay, glass beads, and beautiful dyes and paints, as well as bodies of Egyptian kings in remarkably well-preserved states. Many other cultures made significant developments in chemistry. However, all these developments were empirical; that is, they were achieved by trial and error and did not rest on any valid theory of matter.

Philosophical ideas relating to the properties of matter (chemistry) did not develop as early as those relating to astronomy and mathematics. The Greek philosophers made great strides in philosophical speculation concerning materialistic ideas about chemistry. They led the way to placing chemistry on an intellectual, scientific basis. They introduced the concepts of elements, atoms, shapes of atoms, and chemical combination. They believed that all matter was derived from four elements: earth, air, fire, and water. The Greek philosophers had keen minds and perhaps came very close to establishing chemistry on a sound basis similar to the one that was to develop about 2000 years later. The main shortcoming of the Greek approach to scientific work was a failure to carry out systematic experimentation.

Greek civilization was succeeded by the Roman civilization. The Romans were outstanding in military, political, and economic affairs. They practiced empirical chemical arts such as metallurgy, enameling, glass-making, and pottery-making, but they did very little to advance new and theoretical knowledge. Eventually the Roman civilization was succeeded in Europe by the Dark Ages. During this period European civilization and learning were at a very low ebb.

In the Middle East and in North Africa, knowledge did not decline during the Dark Ages as it did in Western Europe. At this time Arabic cultures made contributions that were of great value to the development of modern chemistry. In particular, the Arabic number system, including the use of zero, gained acceptance; the branch of mathematics known as *algebra* was developed; and alchemy, a sort of pseudochemistry, was practiced extensively.

One of the more interesting periods in the history of chemistry was that of the alchemists (500–1600 A.D.). People have long had a lust for gold, and in those days gold was considered the ultimate, most perfect metal formed in nature. The principal goals of the alchemists were to find a method of prolonging human life indefinitely and to change the base metals, such as iron, zinc, and copper, into gold. They searched for a universal solvent to transmute base metals into gold and for the "philosopher's stone" to rid the body of all diseases and to renew life. In the course of their labors they learned a great deal of chemistry. Unfortunately, much of their work was done secretly because of the mysticism that shrouded their activity, and very few records remain.

Although the alchemists were not guided by sound theoretical reasoning and were clearly not in the intellectual class of the Greek philosophers, they did something that the philosophers had not considered worthwhile. They subjected various materials to prescribed treatments under what might be loosely described as laboratory methods. These manipulations, carried out in alchemical laboratories, not only uncovered many facts of nature but also paved the way for the systematic experimentation that is characteristic of modern science.

Alchemy began to decline in the 16th century when Paracelsus (1493–1541), a Swiss physician and outspoken revolutionary leader in chemistry, strongly advocated that the objectives of chemistry be directed toward the needs of medicine and the curing of human ailments. He openly condemned the mercenary efforts of alchemists to convert cheaper metals to gold.

But the real beginning of modern science can be traced to astronomy during the Renaissance. Nicolaus Copernicus (1473–1543), a Polish astronomer, began the downfall of the generally accepted belief in a geocentric universe. Although not all the Greek philosophers had believed that the sun and the stars revolved about the earth, the geocentric concept had come to be generally accepted. The heliocentric (sun-centered) universe concept of Copernicus was based on direct astronomical observation and represented a radical departure from the concepts handed down from Greek and Roman times. The ideas of Copernicus and the invention of the telescope stimulated additional work in astronomy. This work, especially that of Galileo Galilei (1564–1642) and Johannes Kepler (1571–1630), led directly to a rational explanation by Sir Isaac Newton (1642–1727) of the general laws of motion, which he formulated between about 1665 and 1685.

Modern chemistry was slower to develop than astronomy and physics; it began in the 17th and 18th centuries when Joseph Priestley (1733–1804), who discovered oxygen in 1774, and Robert Boyle (1627–1691) began to record and publish the results of their experiments and to discuss their theories openly. Boyle, who has been called the founder of modern chemistry, was one of the first to practice chemistry as a true science. He believed in the experimental method.

In his most important book, *The Sceptical Chymist*, he clearly distinguished between an element and a compound or mixture. Boyle is best known today for the gas law that bears his name. A French chemist, Antoine Lavoisier (1743–1794), placed the science on a firm foundation with experiments in which he used a chemical balance to make quantitative measurements of the weights of substances involved in chemical reactions.

The use of the chemical balance by Lavoisier and others later in the 18th century was almost as revolutionary in chemistry as the use of the telescope had been in astronomy. Thereafter, chemistry became a quantitative experimental science. Lavoisier also contributed greatly to the organization of chemical data, to chemical nomenclature, and to the establishment of the Law of Conservation of Mass in chemical changes. During the period from 1803 to 1810, John Dalton (1766–1844), an English schoolteacher, advanced his atomic theory. This theory (see Section 5.2) placed the atomistic concept of matter on a valid rational basis. It remains today as a tremendously important general concept of modern science.

Since the time of Dalton, knowledge of chemistry has advanced in great strides, with the most rapid advancement occurring at the end of the 19th century and during the 20th century. Especially outstanding achievements have been made in determining the structure of the atom, understanding the biochemical fundamentals of life, developing chemical technology, and the mass production of chemicals and related products.

1.3   The Branches of Chemistry

Chemistry may be broadly classified into two main branches: *organic* chemistry and *inorganic* chemistry. Organic chemistry is concerned with compounds containing the element carbon. The term *organic* was originally derived from the chemistry of living organisms: plants and animals. Inorganic chemistry deals with all the other elements as well as with some carbon compounds. Substances classified as inorganic are derived mainly from mineral sources rather than from animal or vegetable sources.

Other subdivisions of chemistry, such as analytical chemistry, physical chemistry, biochemistry, electrochemistry, geochemistry, and radiochemistry, may be considered specialized fields of, or auxiliary fields to, the two main branches.

Chemical engineering is the branch of engineering that deals with the development, design, and operation of chemical processes. A chemical engineer usually begins with a chemist's laboratory-scale process and develops it into an industrial-scale operation.

1.4   Relationship of Chemistry to Other Sciences and Industry

Besides being a science in its own right, chemistry is the servant of other sciences and industry. Chemical principles contribute to the study of physics, biology, agriculture, engineering, medicine, space research, oceanography, and many other sciences. Chemistry and physics are overlapping sciences, since both are based on the properties and behavior of matter. Biological processes are chemical in nature. The metabolism of food to provide energy to living organisms is a chemical process. Knowledge of molecular structure of proteins, hormones, enzymes, and the nucleic acids is assisting biologists in their investigations of the composition, development, and reproduction of living cells.

Chemistry is playing an important role in alleviating the growing shortage of food in the world. Agricultural production has been increased with the use of chemical fertilizers, pesticides, and improved varieties of seeds. Chemical refrigerants make possible the frozen food industry, which preserves large amounts of food that might otherwise spoil. Chemistry is also producing synthetic nutrients, but much remains to be done as the world population increases relative to the land available for cultivation. Expanding energy needs have brought about difficult environmental problems in the form of air and water pollution. Chemists and other scientists are working diligently to alleviate these problems.

Advances in medicine and chemotherapy, through the development of new drugs, have contributed to prolonged life and the relief of human suffering. More than 90% of the drugs and pharmaceuticals being used in the United States today have been developed commercially within the past 45 years. The plastics and polymer industry, unknown 60 years ago, has revolutionized the packaging and textile industries and is producing durable and useful construction materials. Energy derived from chemical processes is used for heating, lighting, and transportation. Virtually every industry is dependent on chemicals—for example, the petroleum, steel, rubber, pharmaceutical, electronic, transportation, cosmetic, garment, aircraft, and television industries. (The list could go on.) Figure 1.1 illustrates the conversion of natural resources by the chemical industry into useful products for commerce, industry, and human needs.

1.5   Scientific Method

Chemistry, as a science or field of knowledge, is concerned with ideas and concepts relating to the behavior of matter. Although these concepts are abstract, their application has had a concrete impact on human culture. This impact is due to modern technology, which may be said to have begun about 200 years ago and which has grown at an accelerating rate ever since.

An important difference between science and technology is that science represents an abstract body of knowledge, and technology represents the physical application of this knowledge to the world in which we live.

Why has the science of chemistry and its associated technology flourished in the last two centuries? Is it because we are growing more intelligent? No, we have absolutely no reason to believe that the general level of human intelligence is any higher today than it was in the Dark Ages. The use of the scientific method is usually credited with being the most important single factor in the amazing development of chemistry and technology. Although complete agreement is

Raw Materials

from mine, forest, sea, air, farm, oil, brine, and gas wells

The Chemical Industry

in more than 13,500 plants in the United States
converts these raw materials into more than 50,000

Chemicals

such as acids and alkalies, salts, organic compounds, solvents, compressed gases, pigments, and dyes,
which are used

By the chemical industry itself   **By other industries**

to produce   **in the production of**

Cosmetics
Detergents and soap
Drugs and medicines
Dyes and inks   *Durable Goods*
Explosives   Aircraft and equipment   *Nondurable Goods*
Fertilizers   Building materials   Beverages
Paints   Pesticides   Electrical equipment   Food products
Plastic materials   Hardware   Leather and leather products
Sanitizing chemicals   Machinery   Packaging
Synthetic fibers   Metal products   Paper and paper products
Synthetic rubber   Motor vehicles and equipment   Petroleum and coal products
And many others   Other products of   Rubber products
                                        metal, glass, paper, and wood   Textiles

The Ultimate Market

Health, food, clothing, shelter, transportation, communication, defense, and other needs.

Figure 1.1 Broad scope of the chemical industry today. (*Courtesy Chemical Manufacturers Association.*)

lacking on exactly what is meant by "using the scientific method," the general approach is as follows:

1. Collect facts or data that are relevant to the problem or question at hand, which is usually done by planned experimentation.
2. Analyze the data to find trends (regularities) that are pertinent to the problem. Formulate a hypothesis that will account for the data that have been accumulated and that can be tested by further experimentation.
3. Plan and do additional experiments to test the hypothesis. Such experiments extend beyond the range that is covered in Step 1.
4. Modify the hypothesis as necessary so that it is compatible with all the pertinent experimental data.

Confusion sometimes arises regarding the exact meanings of the words *hypothesis, theory,* and *law*. A hypothesis is a tentative explanation of certain facts that provides a basis for further experimentation. A well-established hypothesis is often called a theory. Thus a theory is an explanation of the general principles of certain phenomena with considerable evidence or facts to support it. Hypotheses and theories explain natural phenomena, whereas scientific laws are simple statements of natural phenomena to which no exceptions are known under the given conditions.

Although the four steps listed in the preceding paragraph are a broad outline of the general procedure that is followed in much scientific work, they are not a recipe for doing chemistry or any other science. But chemistry is an experimental science, and much of its progress has been due to application of the scientific method through systematic research. Occasionally a great discovery is made by accident, but the majority of scientific achievements are accomplished by well-planned experiments.

Many theories and laws are studied in chemistry. They make the study of chemistry or any science easier, because they summarize particular aspects of the science. The student will note that some of the theories advanced by great scientists in the past have since been substantially altered and modified. Such changes do not mean that the discoveries of the past are less significant than those of today. Modification of existing theories in the light of new experimental evidence is essential to the growth and evolution of scientific knowledge.

1.6 How to Study Chemistry

How do you as a student approach a subject such as chemistry with its unfamiliar terminology, symbols, formulas, theories, and laws? All the generally accepted habits of good study are applicable to the study of chemistry. Budget your study time and spend it wisely. In particular, you can spend your time more profitably in regular, relatively short periods of study rather than in one prolonged cram session.

Chemistry has its own language, and learning this language is of prime importance to the successful study of chemistry. Chemistry is a subject of many facts. At first you will simply have to memorize some of them. However, you will also learn these facts by referring to them frequently in your studies and by repetitive use. For example, you must learn the symbols of 30 or 40 common elements in order to be able to write chemical formulas and equations. As with the alphabet, repetitive use of these symbols will soon make them part of your vocabulary.

The need for careful reading of assigned material cannot be overemphasized. You should read each chapter at least twice. The first time, read the chapter rapidly, noting especially topic headings, diagrams, and other outstanding features. Then read more thoroughly and deliberately for better understanding. It may be profitable to underline and abstract material during the second reading. Isolated reading may be sufficient for some subjects, but it is not sufficient for learning chemistry. During the lectures, become an active mental participant and try to think along with your instructor; do not just occupy a seat. Lecture and laboratory sessions will be much more meaningful if you have already read the assigned material.

Your studies must include a good deal of written chemistry. Chemical symbolism, equations, problem solving, and so on, require much written practice for proficiency. One does not become an accomplished pianist by merely reading or listening to music—it takes practice. One does not become a good baseball player by reading the rules and watching baseball games—it takes practice. So it is with chemistry. One does not become proficient in chemistry by only reading about it—it takes practice.

You will encounter many mathematical problems as you progress through this text. To solve a numerical problem, you should read the problem carefully to determine what is being asked. Then develop a plan for solving the problem. It is a good idea to start by writing down the pertinent material—a formula, a diagram, an equation, the data given in the problem. This information will give you something to work with, to think about, to modify, and finally to expand into an answer. When you have arrived at an answer, consider it carefully to make sure that it is a reasonable one. The solutions to problems should be recorded in a neat, orderly, stepwise fashion. Fewer errors and saved time are the rewards of a neat and orderly approach to problem solving. If you need to read and study still further for complete understanding, do it!

QUESTIONS

Review questions

1. Was the concept of a geocentric universe necessarily based on incorrect astronomical observations? Explain.
2. What were the principal goals of the alchemists?
3. What instrument, when first used by chemists, can be considered to be analogous to the use of the telescope by early astronomers? Explain the analogy.
4. Classify the following statements as observation,

law, hypothesis, or theory:
(a) When the pressure remains constant, the volume of a gas is directly proportional to the absolute temperature.
(b) The water in a closed test tube boiled at 83°C.
(c) Iron gets heavier when it rusts because it attracts particles of rust from the air.
(d) All matter is composed of tiny particles called atoms.
(e) As it approaches its melting point, glass turns a flame yellow.

(f) Molecules in a gas are always moving.

(g) When wood burns it decomposes to its elements, which all escape as gas.

5. Name at least three products of chemical research you use regularly that probably did not exist 35 years ago.

6. Which of the following statements are correct?

(a) Chemistry is the science that deals with the composition of substances and the transformations they undergo.

(b) Robert Boyle, in the 17th century, clearly distinguished between an element and a compound or mixture.

(c) Both the knowledge and intellectual capacity of Western European people decreased markedly during the Dark Ages.

(d) From 1803 to 1810, John Dalton advanced his atomic theory.

(e) Most of the drugs and pharmaceuticals used in the United States today have been available for at least a century.

(f) A key feature of the scientific method is to plan and do additional experiments to test a hypothesis.

(g) Scientific laws are simple statements of natural phenomena to which no exceptions are known.

(h) Antoine Lavoisier was one of the first chemists to make quantitative measurements using a chemical balance.

(i) The two main branches of chemistry are organic and biochemistry.

2

Standards for Measurement

After studying Chapter 2, you should be able to

1. Understand the terms listed in Question A at the end of the chapter.
2. Differentiate clearly between mass and weight.
3. Know the basic metric units of mass, length, and volume.
4. Give the numerical equivalents of the metric prefixes deci, centi, milli, micro, deka, hecto, kilo, and mega.
5. Express any number in exponential-notation form.
6. Express the results of arithmetic operations to the proper number of significant figures.
7. Set up and solve problems by the dimensional analysis, or factor-label, method.
8. Convert any measurement of mass, length, or volume in American units to metric units and vice versa.
9. Make conversions between Fahrenheit, Celsius, and Kelvin temperatures.
10. Differentiate clearly between temperature and heat.
11. Make calculations using the equation

    joules = (grams of substance) × (specific heat of substance) × (Δt)

12. Calculate the density, mass, or volume of an object or substance from appropriate data.
13. Calculate the specific gravity when given the density of a substance and vice versa.
14. Recognize the common laboratory measuring instruments illustrated in this chapter.

2.1   Mass and Weight

Chemistry is an experimental science. The results of experiments are usually determined by making measurements. In elementary experiments the quantities that are commonly measured are mass (weight), length, volume, pressure, temperature, and time. Measurements of electrical and optical quantities may also be needed in more sophisticated experimental work.

mass

Although *mass* and *weight* are often used interchangeably, the two words have quite different meanings. The **mass** of a body is defined as the amount of matter in that body. The mass of an object is a fixed and unvarying quantity that is independent of the object's location.

weight

The **weight** of a body is the measure of the earth's gravitational attraction for that body. Unlike mass, weight varies in relation to (1) the position of an object on or its distance from the earth and (2) whether the rate of motion of the object is changing with respect to the motion of the earth. Consider an astronaut of mass 70.0 kilograms (154 pounds) who is being shot into orbit. At the instant before blast-off, the weight of the astronaut is also 70.0 kilograms. As the distance from the earth increases and the rocket turns into an orbiting course, the gravitational pull on the astronaut's body decreases until a state of weightlessness (zero weight) is attained. However, the mass of the astronaut's body has remained constant at 70.0 kilograms during the entire event.

The mass of an object may be measured on a chemical balance by comparing it with other known masses. Two objects of equal mass will have equal weights if they are measured in the same place. Thus, under these conditions the terms *mass* and *weight* are used interchangeably. Although the chemical balance is used to determine mass, it is said to *weigh* objects, and we often speak of the *weight* of an object when we really mean its mass.

2.2   Measurement and Significant Figures

To understand certain aspects of chemistry it is necessary to set up and solve problems. Problem solving requires an understanding of the elementary mathematical operations used to manipulate numbers. Numerical values or data are obtained from measurements made in an experiment. A chemist may use these data to calculate the extent of the physical and chemical changes occurring in the substances that are being studied. By appropriate calculations the results of an experiment may be compared with those of other experiments and summarized in ways that are meaningful.

The result of a measurement is expressed by a numerical value together with a unit of that measurement. For example,

$$\overset{\frown}{\text{Numerical value}}$$
70.0 kilograms = 154 pounds
$$\underset{\text{Unit}}{\smile}$$

Numbers obtained from a measurement are never exact values. They always have some degree of uncertainty due to the limitations of the measuring instrument and the skill of the individual making the measurement. The numerical value recorded for a measurement should give some indication of its reliability (precision). To express maximum precision this number should contain all the digits that are known plus one digit that is estimated. This last estimated digit introduces some uncertainty. Because of this uncertainty every number that expresses a measurement can have only a limited number of digits. These digits, used to express a measured quantity, are known as **significant figures**, or **significant digits**.

significant figures

Suppose we weigh an object on a balance that is calibrated in grams, and we observe that the balance scale stops between 15 and 16 (see Figure 2.1). We then know that the weight of the object is at least 15 grams but less than 16 grams. To express the weight with greater precision, we estimate that the indicator on the balance is about four-tenths the distance between 15 and 16. The weight of the object is, therefore, recorded as 15.4 grams. The last digit (4) has some uncertainty, because it is an estimated value. The recorded weight, 15.4 grams, is said to have three significant figures. Now suppose the balance scale shown in Figure 2.1 stops right on 15. The weight of the object should be recorded as 15.0 grams. It is necessary to use the zero to indicate that the object was weighed to a precision of one-tenth gram. The weight of the object is 15.0 grams, not 14.9 grams or 15.1 grams or 15 grams.

Some numbers are exact and have an infinite number of significant figures. Exact numbers occur in simple counting operations; when you count 25 dollars, you have exactly 25 dollars. Defined numbers, such as 12 inches in 1 foot, 60 minutes in 1 hour, and 100 centimeters in 1 meter, are also considered to be exact numbers. Exact numbers have no uncertainty.

(a)   (b)

Figure 2.1   (a) Scale on a balance indicating a weight of 15.4 grams. (b) Scale on a balance indicating a weight of 15.0 grams.

Evaluating Zeros

In any measurement all nonzero numbers are significant. However, zeros may or may not be significant, depending on their position in the number. Rules for determining when zero is significant in a measurement follow.

1. Zeros between nonzero digits are significant:

   205 has three significant figures.
   2.05 has three significant figures.
   61.09 has four significant figures.

2. Zeros that precede the first nonzero digit are not significant. These zeros are used to locate a decimal point:

   0.0025 has two significant figures (2, 5).
   0.0108 has three significant figures (1, 0, 8).

3. Zeros at the end of a number that includes a decimal point are significant:

   0.500 has three significant figures (5, 0, 0).
   25.160 has five significant figures.
   3.00 has three significant figures.
   20. has two significant figures.

4. Zeros at the end of a number without a decimal point are ambiguous and may or may not be significant:

   1000 (The zeros may or may not be significant.)
   590 (The zero may or may not be significant.)

One way of indicating whether these zeros are significant is to write the number using a decimal point and a power of 10. Thus, if the value 1000 has been determined to four significant figures, it is written as 1.000×10^3. If 590 has only two significant figures, it is written as 5.9×10^2 (in this case the zero is not significant).

PROBLEM

2.1

How many significant figures are in each of these numbers?

(a) 4.5 inches   (e) 25.0 grams
(b) 3.025 feet   (f) 12.20 liters
(c) 125.0 meters   (g) 100,000 people
(d) 0.001 mile   (h) 205 birds

Answers: (a) 2   (b) 4   (c) 4   (d) 1   (e) 3   (f) 4   (g) unknown but probably 2   (h) 3

2.3   Rounding Off Numbers

In calculations we often obtain answers that have more digits than we are justified in using. It is necessary, therefore, to drop the nonsignificant digits in order to express the answer with the proper number of significant figures. When

rounding off numbers

digits are dropped from a number, the value of the last digit retained is determined by a process known as **rounding off numbers.** Two rules will be used in this book for rounding off numbers:

Rule 1. When the first digit after those you want to retain is 4 or less, that digit and all others to its right are dropped. The last digit retained is not changed.

Examples rounded off to four digits:

74.693 = 74.69

This digit is dropped.

1.00629 = 1.006

These two digits are dropped.

Rule 2. When the first digit after those you want to retain is 5 or greater, that digit and all others to the right of it are dropped and the last digit retained is increased by one.

Examples rounded off to four digits:

1.026868 = 1.027

These three digits are dropped.
This digit is changed to 7.

18.03500 = 18.04

These three digits are dropped.
This digit is changed to 4.

12.899 = 12.90

This digit is dropped.
These two digits are changed to 90.

PROBLEM

2.2

Round off these numbers to the number of significant digits indicated:
(a) 42.246 (four digits)   (d) 0.08965 (two digits)
(b) 88.015 (three digits)   (e) 225.3 (three digits)
(c) 0.08965 (three digits)   (f) 14.150 (three digits)

Answers: (a) 42.25 (Rule 2)   (b) 88.0 (Rule 1)   (c) 0.0897 (Rule 2)
(d) 0.090 (Rule 2)   (e) 225 (Rule 1)   (f) 14.2 (Rule 2)

2.4   ## Scientific Notation of Numbers

The age of the earth has been estimated as about 4,500,000,000 (4.5 billion) years. Because this is an estimated value, let us say to the nearest 0.1 billion years, we are justified in using only two significant figures to express it. To express this number with two significant figures we write it using a power of 10 as 4.5×10^9 years.

Very large and very small numbers are often used in chemistry. These numbers can be simplified and conveniently written using a power of 10. Writing a number as a power of 10 is called scientific notation of numbers.

To write a number in scientific notation, move the decimal point in the original number so that it is located after the first nonzero digit. This new number is multiplied by 10 raised to the proper power (exponent). The power of 10 is equal to the number of places that the decimal point has been moved. If the decimal was moved to the left, the power of 10 will be a positive number. If the decimal was moved to the right, the power of 10 will be a negative number.

scientific notation

The **scientific notation** of a number is the number written as a factor between 1 and 10 multiplied by 10 raised to a power. For example,

$$2468 = 2.468 \times 10^3 \qquad 0.0562 = 5.62 \times 10^{-2}$$

Number   Scientific notation   Number   Scientific notation
         of the number   of the number

Study the examples that follow.

EXAMPLE

2.1

Write 5283 in scientific notation.

5283.   Place the decimal between the 5 and the 2. Since the decimal was moved three
3 2 1   places to the left, the power of 10 will be 3, and the number 5.283 is multiplied
        by 10^3.

5.283×10^3 (Correct scientific notation)

EXAMPLE

2.2

Write 4,500,000,000 in scientific notation (two significant figures).

4 500 000 000.   Place the decimal between the 4 and the 5. Since the decimal was
9   1   moved nine places to the left, the power of 10 will be 9, and the
                 number 4.5 is multiplied by 10^9.

4.5×10^9 (Correct scientific notation)

EXAMPLE

2.3

Write 0.000123 in scientific notation.

0.000123   Place the decimal between the 1 and the 2. Since the decimal was moved
4   four places to the right, the power of 10 will be −4, and the number 1.23 is
           multiplied by 10^{-4}.

1.23×10^{-4} (Correct scientific notation)

PROBLEM

2.3

Write the following numbers in scientific notation:
(a) 1200 (four digits)   (c) 0.0468
(b) 6,600,000 (two digits) (d) 0.00003

a) 1.200×10^3

b) 6.6×10^6

c) 4.68×10^{-2}

d) 3.0×10^{-5}

Answers: (a) $1200 = 1.200 \times 10^3$ (b) $6\,600\,000 = 6.6 \times 10^6$
                     3   6

(c) $0.0468 = 4.68 \times 10^{-2}$ (d) $0.00003 = 3 \times 10^{-5}$
         2   5

2.5   Significant Figures in Calculations

The results of a calculation based on measurements cannot be more precise than the least precise measurement.

Multiplication or division. In calculations involving multiplication or division, the answer must contain the same number of significant figures as in the measurement that has the least number of significant figures. Consider the following calculations:

(a) 134 in. × 25 in. = 3350 in.^{2}

The answer should contain only two significant figures because the factor 25 has two significant figures. The answer, therefore, is rounded off and expressed in scientific notation:

$$134 \text{ in.} \times 25 \text{ in.} = 3.4 \times 10^3 \text{ in.}^2 \quad \text{(Answer)}$$

(b) $\dfrac{213 \text{ miles}}{4.20 \text{ hours}} = 50.714285 \text{ miles/hour}$

A hand calculator was used to obtain the eight-digit answer given. Since each factor in the problem has three digits, only three digits can be used in the answer:

$$\frac{213 \text{ miles}}{4.20 \text{ hours}} = 50.7 \text{ miles/hour} \quad \text{(Answer)}$$

(c) $\dfrac{2.2 \times 273}{760} = 0.79026315 = 0.79 \quad \text{(Answer)}$

The answer should be rounded off to two significant figures (2.2 is the limiting factor). The correct, rounded-off answer is 0.79.

Addition or subtraction. The results of an addition or a subtraction must contain the same number of digits to the right of the decimal point as in the term with the least number of digits to the right of the decimal point. Consider the following calculations:

(a) Add 125.17, 129.2, and 52.24.

    125.17   The number with the greatest uncertainty is 129.2. Therefore the
    129.2   answer is rounded off to a value having one decimal place.
     52.24
    306.61

    306.6 (Answer)

(b) Subtract 14.1 from 132.56.

$$\begin{array}{r} 132.56 \\ -\ 14.1 \\ \hline 118.46 \end{array}$$

14.1 contains the least number of digits to the right of the decimal point. Therefore the answer is rounded off to a value having one decimal place.

118.5 (Answer)

PROBLEM

2.4

How many significant figures should the answer contain in each of these calculations?
(a) $14.0 \times 5.2 = 2$
(d) $8.2 + 0.125 = 2$
(b) $0.1682 \times 8.2 = 4$
(e) $119.1 - 3.44 = 4$
(c) $\dfrac{160 \times 33}{4} = 1$
(f) $\dfrac{94.5}{1.2} = 2$

Answers: (a) 2   (b) 2   (c) 1   (d) 2 (one decimal place)   (e) 4 (one decimal place)   (f) 2

PROBLEM

2.5

Do the following calculations, and round off your answers to the proper number of significant figures.

(a) $190.6 \times 2.3 = 438.38$

The value 438.38 was obtained with a hand calculator. The answer should have two significant figures, because 2.3, the number with the fewest significant figures, has only two significant figures. The answer must, therefore, be expressed in scientific notation.

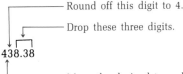

— Round off this digit to 4.

— Drop these three digits.

438.38

— Move the decimal two places to the left.

The correct answer is 4.4×10^2.

(b) $\dfrac{13.59 \times 6.3}{12} = 7.13475$

The value 7.13475 was obtained with a hand calculator. The answer should contain two significant figures because 6.3 and 12 have only two significant figures.

— Drop these four digits.

7.13475

— This digit remains the same.

The correct answer is 7.1.

(c) $\dfrac{1.039 - 1.020}{1.039} = 0.018286814$

The value 0.018286814 was obtained with a hand calculator. When the subtraction in the numerator is done,

$$1.039 - 1.020 = 0.019$$

the number of significant figures changes from four to two. Therefore the answer should contain two significant figures after the division is carried out:

```
                  ┌──── Drop these six digits.
                  ↓
                ┌───┐
    0.018286814
           ↑
           └──────── This digit remains the same.
```

The correct answer is 0.018, or 1.8×10^{-2}.

Additional material on mathematical operations is given in the Mathematical Review in Appendix I. You are urged to review Appendix I and to study carefully any portions that are not familiar to you. This study may be done at various times during the course as the need for additional knowledge of mathematical operations arises.

2.6   The Metric System

metric system or SI

The **metric system,** or **International System** (**SI**, from *Système International*), is a decimal system of units for measurements of mass, length, time, and other physical quantities. It is built around a set of base units and uses factors of 10 to express larger or smaller numbers of these units. To express quantities that are larger or smaller than the base units, prefixes are added to the names of the units. These prefixes represent multiples of 10, making the metric system a decimal system of measurements. Table 2.1 shows the names, symbols, and numerical values of the prefixes. These are also shown in Appendix III. Some of the more commonly used prefixes are

mega   One million (1,000,000) times the unit expressed
kilo   One thousand (1000) times the unit expressed
deci   One-tenth (0.1) of the unit expressed
centi   One-hundredth (0.01) of the unit expressed
milli   One-thousandth (0.001) of the unit expressed
micro   One-millionth (0.000001) of the unit expressed
nano   One-billionth (0.000000001) of the unit expressed

Examples are

1 kilometer   = 1000 meters
1 kilogram   = 1000 grams
1 microsecond = 0.000001 second

The seven base units in the International System, their abbreviations, and the quantities they measure are given in Table 2.2. Other units are derived from these base units.

Table 2.1 Prefixes used in the metric system and their numerical values (The more commonly used prefixes are in color.)

Prefix	Symbol	Numerical value		
tera	T	1,000,000,000,000	or	10^{12}
giga	G	1,000,000,000	or	10^9
mega	M	1,000,000	or	10^6
kilo	k	1,000	or	10^3
hecto	h	100	or	10^2
deka	da	10	or	10^1
deci	d	0.1	or	10^{-1}
centi	c	0.01	or	10^{-2}
milli	m	0.001	or	10^{-3}
micro	μ	0.000001	or	10^{-6}
nano	n	0.000000001	or	10^{-9}
pico	p	0.000000000001	or	10^{-12}
femto	f	0.000000000000001	or	10^{-15}
atto	a	0.000000000000000001	or	10^{-18}

Table 2.2 International System base units of measurement

Quantity	Name of unit	Abbreviation
Length	Meter	m
Mass	Kilogram (grsm)	kg
Temperature	Kelvin (F -C)	K
Time	Second	s
Amount of substance	Mole	mol
Electric current	Ampere	A
Luminous intensity	Candela	cd
energy	Joule	
volume	— (liter)	

The metric system, or International System, is currently used by most of the countries in the world, not only for scientific and technical work, but also in commerce and industry. The United States is currently in the process of changing to the metric system of weights and measurements.

2.7   Measurement of Length

Standards for the measurement of length have an interesting historical development. The Old Testament mentions such units as the *cubit* (the distance from a man's elbow to the tip of his outstretched hand). In ancient Scotland the inch was once defined as a distance equal to the width of a man's thumb.

Reference standards of measurements have undergone continuous improvements in precision. The standard unit of length in the metric system is the **meter.** When the metric system was first introduced in the 1790s, the meter was defined as one ten-millionth of the distance from the equator to the North Pole measured

meter

along the meridian passing through Dunkirk, France. In 1889 the meter was redefined as the distance between two engraved lines on a platinum–iridium alloy bar maintained at 0° Celsius. This international meter bar is stored in a vault at Sèvres near Paris. Duplicate meter bars have been made and are used as standards by many nations.

By the 1950s length could be measured with such precision that a new standard was needed. Accordingly, the length of the meter was redefined in 1960 and again in 1983. The latest definition is: A meter is the distance that light travels in a vacuum during 1/299,792,458 of a second.

A meter is 39.37 inches, a little longer than 1 yard. One meter contains 10 decimeters, 100 centimeters, or 1000 millimeters (see Figure 2.2). A kilometer contains 1000 meters. Table 2.3 shows the relationships of these units.

The angstrom unit (10^{-10} m, abbreviated Å) is used extensively in expressing

Table 2.3 **Units of length**

Unit	Abbreviation	Meter equivalent	Exponential equivalent
Kilometer	km	1000 m	10^3 m
Meter	m	1 m	10^0 m
Decimeter	dm	0.1 m	10^{-1} m
Centimeter	cm	0.01 m	10^{-2} m
Millimeter	mm	0.001 m	10^{-3} m
Micrometer	μm	0.000001 m	10^{-6} m
Nanometer	nm	0.000000001 m	10^{-9} m
Angstrom	Å	0.0000000001 m	10^{-10} m

Figure 2.2 Comparison of the metric and American systems of length measurement: 2.54 cm = 1 in.

the wavelength of light and in atomic dimensions. Other important relationships are

$$1 \text{ m} = 100 \text{ cm} = 1000 \text{ mm} = 10^6 \text{ } \mu\text{m} = 10^{10} \text{ Å}$$

$$1 \text{ cm} = 10 \text{ mm} = 0.01 \text{ m}$$

$$1 \text{ in.} = 2.54 \text{ cm}$$

$$1 \text{ mile} = 1.61 \text{ km}$$

2.8 Problem Solving

Many chemical principles are illustrated by mathematical concepts. Learning how to set up and solve numerical problems in a systematic fashion is essential in the study of chemistry. This skill, once acquired, is also very rewarding in other study areas. An electronic calculator will save you much time in computation.

Usually a problem can be solved by several methods. But in all methods it is best, especially for beginners, to use a systematic, orderly approach. The dimensional analysis, or factor-label, method is stressed in this book because

1. It provides a systematic, straightforward way to set up problems.
2. It gives a clear understanding of the principles involved.
3. It helps in learning to organize and evaluate data.
4. It helps to identify errors because unwanted units are not eliminated if the setup of the problem is incorrect.

The basic steps for solving problems are

1. Read the problem very carefully to determine what is to be solved for, and write it down.
2. Tabulate the data given in the problem. Even in tabulating data it is important to label all factors and measurements with the proper units.
3. Determine which principles are involved and which unit relationships are needed to solve the problem. Sometimes it is necessary to refer to tables for needed data.
4. Set up the problem in a neat, organized, and logical fashion, making sure that unwanted units cancel. Use sample problems in the text as guides for making setups.
5. Proceed with the necessary mathematical operations. Make certain that the answer contains the proper number of significant figures.
6. Check the answer to see if it is reasonable.

> **Label all factors with the proper units.**

Just a few more words about problem solving. Don't allow any formal method of problem solving to limit your use of common sense and intuition. If a problem is clear to you and its solution seems simpler by another method, by all means use it. But in the long run you should be able to solve many otherwise difficult problems by using the dimensional analysis method.

The dimensional analysis method of problem solving converts one unit to another unit by the use of conversion factors:

$$\text{unit}_1 \times \text{conversion factor} = \text{unit}_2$$

If you want to know how many millimeters are in 2.5 meters, you need to convert meters (m) to millimeters (mm). Therefore, you start by writing

$$\text{m} \times \text{conversion factor} = \text{mm}$$

This conversion factor must accomplish two things. It must cancel, or eliminate, meters; and it must introduce millimeters, the unit wanted in the answer. Such a conversion factor will be in fractional form and have meters in the denominator and millimeters in the numerator:

$$\cancel{\text{m}} \times \frac{\text{mm}}{\cancel{\text{m}}} = \text{mm}$$

We know that 1 m = 1000 mm. From this relationship we can write two factors, 1 m per 1000 mm and 1000 mm per 1 m:

$$\frac{1\ \text{m}}{1000\ \text{mm}} \quad \text{and} \quad \frac{1000\ \text{mm}}{1\ \text{m}}$$

Using the factor 1000 mm/1 m, we can set up the calculation for the conversion of 2.5 m to millimeters:

$$2.5\ \cancel{\text{m}} \times \frac{1000\ \text{mm}}{1\ \cancel{\text{m}}} = 2500\ \text{mm} \quad \text{or} \quad 2.5 \times 10^3\ \text{mm}$$

(Two significant figures)

Note that, in making this calculation, units are treated as numbers; meters in the numerator are canceled by meters in the denominator.

Now suppose you need to change 215 centimeters to meters. First you must determine that you need to convert centimeters to meters. We start with

$$\text{cm} \times \text{conversion factor} = \text{m}$$

The conversion factor must have centimeters in the denominator and meters in the numerator:

$$\cancel{\text{cm}} \times \frac{\text{m}}{\cancel{\text{cm}}} = \text{m}$$

From the relationship 100 cm = 1 m, we can write a factor that will accomplish this conversion:

$$\frac{1\ \text{m}}{100\ \text{cm}}$$

Now set up the calculation using all the data given:

$$215\ \cancel{\text{cm}} \times \frac{1\ \text{m}}{100\ \cancel{\text{cm}}} = \frac{215\ \text{m}}{100} = 2.15\ \text{m}$$

Some problems may require a series of conversions to reach the correct units in the answer. For example, suppose we want to know the number of seconds in 1 day. We need to go from the unit of days to seconds in this manner:

$$\text{day} \rightarrow \text{hours} \rightarrow \text{minutes} \rightarrow \text{seconds}$$

This series requires three conversion factors, one for each step. We convert days to hours (hr), hours to minutes (min), and minutes to seconds (s). The conversions can be done individually or in a continuous sequence

$$\cancel{\text{day}} \times \frac{\text{hr}}{\cancel{\text{day}}} \qquad \cancel{\text{hr}} \times \frac{\text{min}}{\cancel{\text{hr}}} \qquad \cancel{\text{min}} \times \frac{\text{s}}{\cancel{\text{min}}}$$

$$\cancel{\text{day}} \times \frac{\cancel{\text{hr}}}{\cancel{\text{day}}} \times \frac{\cancel{\text{min}}}{\cancel{\text{hr}}} \times \frac{\text{s}}{\cancel{\text{min}}} = \text{s}$$

Inserting the proper factors we calculate the number of seconds in 1 day to be

$$1 \ \cancel{\text{day}} \times \frac{24 \ \cancel{\text{hr}}}{1 \ \cancel{\text{day}}} \times \frac{60 \ \cancel{\text{min}}}{1 \ \cancel{\text{hr}}} \times \frac{60 \ \text{s}}{1 \ \cancel{\text{min}}} = 86{,}400. \ \text{s}$$

All five digits in 86,400 are significant, since all the factors in the calculation are exact numbers.

The dimensional analysis, or factor-label, method used in the preceding work shows how unit conversion factors are derived and used in calculations. After you become more proficient with the terms, you can save steps by writing the factors directly in the calculation. The problems that follow give examples of the conversion from American to metric units.

PROBLEM

2.6

How many centimeters are in 2.00 ft?

The stepwise conversion of units from feet to centimeters may be done in this manner: Convert feet to inches; then convert inches to centimeters.

$$\text{ft} \rightarrow \text{in.} \rightarrow \text{cm}$$

The conversion factors needed are

$$\frac{12 \ \text{in.}}{1 \ \text{ft}} \qquad \text{and} \qquad \frac{2.54 \ \text{cm}}{1 \ \text{in.}}$$

$$2.00 \ \cancel{\text{ft}} \times \frac{12 \ \text{in.}}{1 \ \cancel{\text{ft}}} = 24.0 \ \text{in.}$$

$$24.0 \ \cancel{\text{in.}} \times \frac{2.54 \ \text{cm}}{1 \ \cancel{\text{in.}}} = 61.0 \ \text{cm} \quad \text{(Answer)}$$

Since 1 ft and 12 in. are exact numbers, the number of significant figures allowed in the answer is three, based on the number 2.00.

PROBLEM

2.7

How many meters are in a 100 yd football field? The stepwise conversion of units from yards to meters may be done in this manner, using the proper conversion factors.

$$yd \rightarrow ft \rightarrow in. \rightarrow cm \rightarrow m$$

$$100 \text{ yd} \times \frac{3 \text{ ft}}{1 \text{ yd}} = 300 \text{ ft} \qquad\qquad (3 \text{ ft/yd})$$

$$300 \text{ ft} \times \frac{12 \text{ in.}}{1 \text{ ft}} = 3.60 \times 10^3 \text{ in.} \qquad\qquad (12 \text{ in./ft})$$

$$3.60 \times 10^3 \text{ in.} \times \frac{2.54 \text{ cm}}{1 \text{ in.}} = 9.14 \times 10^3 \text{ cm} \qquad (2.54 \text{ cm/in.})$$

$$9.14 \times 10^3 \text{ cm} \times \frac{1 \text{ m}}{100 \text{ cm}} = 9.14 \text{ m} \qquad\qquad (1 \text{ m/100 cm}) \qquad \text{(Three significant figures)}$$

Problems 2.6 and 2.7 may be solved using a running linear expression and writing down conversion factors in succession. This method often saves one or two calculation steps and allows numerical values to be reduced to simpler terms, leading to simpler calculations. The single linear expressions for Problems 2.6 and 2.7 are

$$2.00 \text{ ft} \times \frac{12 \text{ in.}}{1 \text{ ft}} \times \frac{2.54 \text{ cm}}{1 \text{ in.}} \times 61.0 \text{ cm}$$

$$100 \text{ yd} \times \frac{3 \text{ ft}}{1 \text{ yd}} \times \frac{12 \text{ in.}}{1 \text{ ft}} \times \frac{2.54 \text{ cm}}{1 \text{ in.}} \times \frac{1 \text{ m}}{100 \text{ cm}} = 91.4 \text{ m}$$

Using the units alone (Problem 2.7), we see that the stepwise cancellation proceeds in succession until the desired unit is reached.

$$yd \times \frac{ft}{yd} \times \frac{in.}{ft} \times \frac{cm}{in.} \times \frac{m}{cm} = m$$

PROBLEM

2.8

How many cubic centimeters (cm^3) are in a box that measures 2.20 in. by 4.00 in. by 6.00 in.? First we need to determine the volume of the box in cubic inches ($in.^3$) by multiplying together the length times the width times the height.

$$2.20 \text{ in.} \times 4.00 \text{ in.} \times 6.00 \text{ in.} = 52.8 \text{ in.}^3$$

Now we need to convert $in.^3$ to cm^3, which can be done by using the inches and centimeters relationship three times.

$$\text{in.}^3 \times \frac{\text{cm}}{\text{in.}} \times \frac{\text{cm}}{\text{in.}} \times \frac{\text{cm}}{\text{in.}} = \text{cm}^3$$

$$52.8 \text{ in.}^3 \times \frac{2.54 \text{ cm}}{1 \text{ in.}} \times \frac{2.54 \text{ cm}}{1 \text{ in.}} \times \frac{2.54 \text{ cm}}{1 \text{ in.}} = 865 \text{ cm}^3$$

| **2.9** | ## Measurement of Mass |

kilogram

The gram is used as a unit of mass measurement, but it is a tiny amount of mass; for instance, a nickel has a mass of about 5 grams. Therefore the *standard* unit of mass in the SI system is the **kilogram** (equal to 1000 grams). The amount of mass in a kilogram is defined by international agreement as exactly equal to the mass of a platinum–iridium weight (international prototype kilogram) kept in a vault at Sèvres, France. Comparing this unit of mass to 1 pound (16 ounces), we find that a kilogram is equal to 2.2 pounds. A pound is equal to 454 grams (0.454 kilogram). The same prefixes used in length measurement are used to indicate larger and smaller gram units (see Table 2.4).

It is convenient to remember that

1 g = 1000 mg

1 kg = 1000 g

1 kg = 2.2 lb

1 lb = 454 g

To change grams to milligrams, multiply grams by the conversion factor 1000 mg/g. The setup for converting 25 g to milligrams is

$$25 \text{ g} \times \frac{1000 \text{ mg}}{1 \text{ g}} = 25{,}000 \text{ mg} \quad (2.5 \times 10^4 \text{ mg}) \quad \text{(Answer)}$$

Note that multiplying a number by 1000 is the same as multiplying the number

Table 2.4   Metric units of mass

Unit	Abbreviation	Gram equivalent	Exponential equivalent
Kilogram	kg	1000 g	10^3 g
Gram	g	1 g	10^0 g
Decigram	dg	0.1 g	10^{-1} g
Centigram	cg	0.01 g	10^{-2} g
Milligram	mg	0.001 g	10^{-3} g
Microgram	μg	0.000001 g	10^{-6} g

by 10^3 and can be done by moving the decimal point three places to the right:

$$6.428 \times 1000 = 6428 \qquad \underset{3}{\underbrace{(6.428)}}$$

To change milligrams to grams, multiply milligrams by the conversion factor 1 g/1000 mg. For example, to convert 155 mg to grams:

$$155 \; \cancel{mg} \times \frac{1 \text{ g}}{1000 \; \cancel{mg}} = 0.155 \text{ g} \quad \text{(Answer)}$$

Examples of converting weights from American to metric units are shown in Problems 2.9 and 2.10.

PROBLEM

2.9

A 1.50 lb package of sodium bicarbonate costs 80 cents. How many grams of this substance are in this package?

   We are solving for the number of grams equivalent to 1.50 lb. Since 1 lb = 454 g, the factor to convert pounds to grams is 454 g/lb.

$$1.50 \; \cancel{lb} \times \frac{454 \text{ g}}{1 \; \cancel{lb}} = 681 \text{ g} \quad \text{(Answer)}$$

Note: The cost of the sodium bicarbonate has no bearing on the question asked in this problem.

PROBLEM

2.10

Suppose four ostrich feathers weigh 1.00 lb. Assuming that each feather is equal in weight, how many milligrams does a single feather weigh? The unit conversion in this problem is from 1.00 lb/4 feathers to milligrams per feather. Since the unit *feathers* occurs in the denominator of both the starting unit and the desired unit, the unit conversions needed are

$$\text{lb} \rightarrow \text{g} \rightarrow \text{mg}$$

$$\frac{1.00 \; \cancel{lb}}{4 \text{ feathers}} \times \frac{454 \; \cancel{g}}{1 \; \cancel{lb}} \times \frac{1000 \text{ mg}}{1 \; \cancel{g}} = \frac{113{,}500 \text{ mg}}{1 \text{ feather}} \qquad (1.14 \times 10^5 \text{ mg/feather})$$

2.10   **Measurement of Volume**

volume

Volume, as used here, is the amount of space occupied by matter. The SI unit of volume is the cubic meter (m^3). However, the liter (pronounced *leeter* and abbreviated L) and the milliliter (abbreviated mL) are the standard units of volume used in most chemical laboratories.

   One liter is a little larger than one U.S. quart (see Figure 2.3). One liter is also equal to 1000 milliliters, and one milliliter is equal to one cubic centimeter (1 cm^3).

Figure 2.3 Comparison of the volume of a liter (1000 mL) and a quart (946 mL). The flasks shown are called volumetric flasks.

It is convenient to remember that

1 L = 1000 mL = 1000 cm^3

1 mL = 1 cm^3

1 L = 1.057 qt

946 mL = 1 qt

The volume of a cubic or rectangular container can be determined by multiplying its length times width times height. Thus a 10 cm square box has a volume of 10 cm × 10 cm × 10 cm = 1000 cm^3.

Examples of volume conversions are shown below.

PROBLEM

2.11

How many milliliters are contained in 3.5 liters?
    The conversion factor to change liters to milliliters is 1000 mL/L.

$$3.5 \; \cancel{L} \times \frac{1000 \; mL}{\cancel{L}} = 3500 \; mL \qquad (3.5 \times 10^3 \; mL)$$

Liters may be changed to milliliters by moving the decimal point three places to the right and changing the units to milliliters.

    1.500 L = 1500. mL

PROBLEM

2.12

How many cubic centimeters are in a cube that is 11.1 inches on a side?
    First change inches to centimeters. The conversion factor is 2.54 cm/in.

$$11.1 \; \cancel{in.} \times \frac{2.54 \; cm}{1 \; \cancel{in.}} = 28.2 \; cm \; on \; a \; side$$

Then change to cubic volume (length × width × height).

    28.2 cm × 28.2 cm × 28.2 cm = 22,426 cm^3 \qquad (2.24 × 10^4 cm^3)

2.11 Heat and Temperature Scales

heat

Heat is a form of energy associated with the motion of small particles of matter. The term *heat* refers to the quantity of energy within a system or to a quantity of energy added to or taken away from a system. *System* as used here simply refers to the entity that is being heated or cooled. Depending on the amount of heat energy present, a given system is said to be hot or cold. **Temperature** is a measure of the intensity of heat, or how hot a system is, regardless of its size. Heat always flows from a region of higher temperature to one of lower temperature. The SI unit of temperature is the Kelvin.

temperature

The temperature of a system can be expressed by several different scales. Three commonly used temperature scales are the Celsius scale (pronounced *sell-see-us*), the Kelvin (absolute) scale, and the Fahrenheit scale. The unit of temperature on the Celsius and Fahrenheit scales is called a *degree*, but the size of the Celsius and the Fahrenheit degree is not the same. The symbol for the Celsius and Fahrenheit degrees is °, and it is placed as a superscript after the number and before the symbol for the scales. Thus, 100°C means 100 *degrees Celsius*. The degree sign is not used with Kelvin temperatures.

degrees Celsius = °C

Kelvin (absolute) = K

degrees Fahrenheit = °F

On the Celsius scale the interval between the freezing and boiling temperatures of water is divided into 100 equal parts, or degrees. The freezing point of water is assigned a temperature of 0°C and the boiling point of water a temperature of 100°C. The Kelvin temperature scale is also known as the absolute temperature scale, because 0 K is the lowest temperature theoretically attainable. The Kelvin zero is 273.16 degrees below the Celsius zero. A kelvin is equal in size to a Celsius degree. The freezing point of water on the Kelvin scale is 273.16 K (usually rounded to 273 K). The Fahrenheit scale has 180 degrees between the freezing and boiling temperatures of water. On this scale the freezing point of water is 32°F and the boiling point is 212°F.

0°C ≅ 273 K ≅ 32°F

The three scales are compared in Figure 2.4. Although absolute zero (0 K) is the lower limit of temperature on these scales, temperature has no known upper limit. (Temperatures of several million degrees are known to exist in the sun and in other stars.)

By examining Figure 2.4 we can see that there are 100 Celsius degrees and 100 kelvins between the freezing and boiling points of water. But there are 180 Fahrenheit degrees between these two temperatures. Hence, the size of a degree on the Celsius scale is the same as the size of one kelvin, but one Celsius degree corresponds to 1.8 degrees on the Fahrenheit scale.

From these data, mathematical formulas have been derived to convert a temperature on one scale to the corresponding temperature on another scale.

Figure 2.4   Comparison of Celsius, Kelvin, and Fahrenheit temperature scales

These formulas are

$$K = °C + 273 \tag{1}$$

$$°F = (1.8 \times °C) + 32 \tag{2}$$

$$°C = \frac{(°F - 32)}{1.8} \tag{3}$$

Interpretation: Formula (1) states that the addition of 273 to the degrees Celsius converts the temperature to kelvins. Formula (2) states that, to obtain the Fahrenheit temperature corresponding to a given Celsius temperature, we multiply the degrees Celsius by 1.8 and then add 32. Formula (3) states that, to obtain the corresponding Celsius temperature, we subtract 32 from the degrees Fahrenheit and then divide this answer by 1.8. Examples of temperature conversions follow.

PROBLEM

2.13

The temperature at which table salt (sodium chloride) melts is 800°C. What is this temperature on the Kelvin and Fahrenheit scales?

We need to calculate K from °C, so we use formula (1) above. We also need to calculate °F from °C; for this calculation we use formula (2).

$$K = °C + 273$$

$$K = 800°C + 273 = 1073 \ K$$

$$°F = (1.8 \times °C) + 32$$

$$°F = (1.8 \times 800°C) + 32$$

$$°F = 1440 + 32 = 1472°F$$

$$800°C = 1073 \ K = 1472°F$$

PROBLEM
2.14

The temperature for December 1 was 110°F, a new record. Calculate this temperature in °C. Formula (3) applies here.

$$°C = \frac{(°F - 32)}{1.8}$$

$$°C = \frac{(110 - 32)}{1.8} = \frac{78}{1.8} = 43°C$$

PROBLEM
2.15

What temperature on the Fahrenheit scale corresponds to −8.0°C? (Be alert to the presence of the minus sign in this problem.)

$$°F = (1.8 \times °C) + 32$$

$$°F = [1.8 \times (-8.0)] + 32 = -14.4 + 32$$

$$°F = 18 \qquad \text{(2 significant figures)}$$

Temperatures used in this book are in degrees Celsius (°C) unless specified otherwise.

2.12   Heat: Quantitative Measurement

The SI-derived unit for heat is the joule (pronounced *jool* and abbreviated J). Another unit for heat, which has been used for many years, is the calorie (abbreviated cal). The relationship between joules and calories is

$$4.184 \ J = 1 \ cal \qquad \text{(exactly)}$$

joule

calorie

To give you some idea of the magnitude of these heat units, 4.184 **J** or 1 **cal** is the quantity of heat energy required to change the temperature of 1 g of water by 1°C, usually measured from 14.5°C to 15.5°C.

Since joule and calorie are rather small units, the use of kilojoules (kJ) and kilocalories (kcal) are used to express heat energy in many chemical processes. The kilocalorie is also known as the nutritional or large Calorie (spelled with a capital C and abbreviated Cal). In this book heat energy will be expressed in joules with parenthetical values in calories.

1 kJ = 1000 J

1 kcal = 1000 cal

The difference in the meanings of the terms *heat* and *temperature* can be seen by this example: Visualize two beakers, A and B. Beaker A contains 100 g of water at 20°C, and beaker B contains 200 g of water also at 20°C. The beakers are heated until the temperature of the water in each reaches 30°C. The *temperature* of the water in the beakers was raised by exactly the same amount, 10°C. But twice as much *heat* (8368 J or 2000 cal) was required to raise the temperature of the water in beaker B as was required in beaker A (4184 J or 1000 cal).

In the middle of the 18th century, Joseph Black, a Scottish chemist, heated and cooled equal masses of iron and lead through the same temperature range. Black noted that much more heat was needed for the iron than for the lead. He had discovered a fundamental property of matter—namely, that every substance has a characteristic heat capacity. Heat capacities may be compared in terms of **specific heat**   specific heats. The **specific heat** of a substance is the quantity of heat (lost or gained) required to change the temperature of 1 g of that substance by 1°C. It follows then that the specific heat of water is 4.184 J/g°C (1 cal/g°C). The specific heat of water is high compared with that of most substances. Aluminum and copper, for example, have specific heats of 0.900 and 0.385 J/g°C, respectively (see Table 2.5). The relation of mass, specific heat, temperature change (Δt), and quantity of heat lost or gained by a system is expressed by this general equation:

$$\begin{pmatrix} \text{grams of} \\ \text{substance} \end{pmatrix} \times \begin{pmatrix} \text{specific heat} \\ \text{of substance} \end{pmatrix} \times \Delta t = \text{joules or calories} \qquad (4)$$

Thus, the amount of heat needed to raise the temperature of 200 g of water by 10°C can be calculated as follows:

$$200 \text{ g} \times \frac{4.184 \text{ J}}{\text{g°C}} \times 10°\text{C} = 8368 \text{ J} \qquad (2000 \text{ cal})$$

Examples of specific-heat problems follow.

Table 2.5   Specific heat of selected substances

Substance	Specific heat J/g°C	Specific heat cal/g°C
Water	4.184	1.00
Ethyl alcohol	2.138	0.511
Ice	2.059	0.492
Aluminum	0.900	0.215
Iron	0.473	0.113
Copper	0.385	0.0921
Gold	0.131	0.0312
Lead	0.128	0.0305

PROBLEM

2.16

Calculate the specific heat of a solid in J/g°C and cal/g°C if 1638 J raise the temperature of 125 g of the solid from 25.0°C to 52.6°C.

First solve equation (4) to obtain an equation for specific heat.

$$\text{specific heat} = \frac{J}{g \times \Delta t}$$

Now substitute in the data:

$$J = 1638; \quad g = 125; \quad \Delta t = 52.6 - 25.0°C = 27.6°C$$

$$\text{specific heat} = \frac{1638 \text{ J}}{125 \text{ g} \times 27.6°C} = 0.475 \text{ J/g°C}$$

Now convert joules to calories using 1 cal/4.184 J:

$$\text{specific heat} = \frac{0.475 \text{ J}}{g°C} \times \frac{1 \text{ cal}}{4.184 \text{ J}} = 0.114 \text{ cal/g°C}$$

PROBLEM

2.17

A sample of a metal weighing 212 g is heated to 125.0°C and then dropped into 375 g of water at 24.0°C. If the final temperature of the water is 34.2°C, what is the specific heat of the metal? (Assume no heat losses to the surroundings.)

When the metal enters the water it begins to cool, losing heat to the water. At the same time the temperature of the water rises. This process continues until the temperature of the metal and the temperature of the water are equal, at which point (34.2°C) no net flow of heat occurs.

The heat lost or gained by a system is given by equation (4). We use this equation first to calculate the heat gained by the water and then to calculate the specific heat of the metal.

$$\text{temperature rise of the water } (\Delta t) = 34.2°C - 24.0°C = 10.2°C$$

$$\text{heat gained by the water} = 375 \text{ g} \times \frac{4.184 \text{ J}}{g°C} \times 10.2°C = 1.60 \times 10^4 \text{ J}$$

The metal dropped into the water must have a final temperature the same as the water (34.2°C).

$$\text{temperature drop of the metal } (\Delta t) = 125.0°C - 34.2°C = 90.8°C$$

$$\text{heat lost by the metal} = \text{heat gained by the water} = 1.60 \times 10^4 \text{ J}$$

Rearranging equation (4) we get

$$\text{specific heat} = \frac{J}{g \times \Delta t}$$

$$\text{specific heat of the metal} = \frac{1.60 \times 10^4 \text{ J}}{212 \text{ g} \times 90.8°C} = 0.831 \text{ J/g°C}$$

2.13 Tools for Measurement

Common measuring instruments used in chemical laboratories are illustrated in Figures 2.5 and 2.6. A balance is used to measure mass. Some balances will weigh objects to the nearest microgram. The choice of the balance depends on the accuracy required and the amount of material being weighed. Three standard balances are shown in Figure 2.5: a quadruple-beam balance with precision up to 0.01 g; a single-pan, top-loading balance with a precision of 0.001 g (1 mg); and a single-pan analytical balance with a precision up to 0.0001 g. Automatic-recording and electronic balances are also available.

The most common instruments or equipment for measuring liquids are the graduated cylinder, volumetric flask, buret, pipet, and syringe, which are shown in Figure 2.6. These calibrated pieces are usually made of glass and are available in various sizes

The common laboratory instrument for measuring temperature is a thermometer (see Figure 2.4).

(a)   (b)   (c)

Figure 2.5 (a) A Cent-O-Gram R311 balance has four calibrated horizontal beams, each fitted with a movable weight. The weight of the object placed on the pan is determined by moving the weights along the beams until the swinging beam is in balance, as shown by the indicator on the right. (*Courtesy Ohaus Scale Corporation.*) (b) A single-pan, top-loading, rapid-weighing balance with direct readout to the nearest milligram (for example, 125.456 g). (*Courtesy Sartorius Balance Div., Brinkmann Instruments Inc.*) (c) A single-pan analytical balance for high-precision weighing. The precision of this balance is 0.1 mg (0.0001 g). (*Courtesy Mettler Instrument Corporation, Hightstown, N.J.*)

Graduated   Volumetric   Buret   Pipet   Syringe
cylinder   flask

Figure 2.6   Calibrated glassware for measuring the volume of liquids

2.14   Density

density

Density (d) is the ratio of the mass of a substance to the volume occupied by that mass; it is the mass per unit of volume and is given by the equation

$$d = \frac{mass}{volume} \tag{5}$$

Density is a physical characteristic of a substance and may be used as an aid to its identification. When the density of a solid or a liquid is given, the mass is usually expressed in grams and the volume in milliliters or cubic centimeters.

$$d = \frac{mass}{volume} = \frac{g}{mL} \quad or \quad d = \frac{g}{cm^3}$$

Since the volume of a substance (especially liquids and gases) varies with temperature, it is important to state the temperature along with the density. For example, the volume of 1.0000 g water at 4°C is 1.0000 mL, at 20°C it is 1.0018 mL, and at 80°C it is 1.0290 mL. Density, therefore, also varies with temperature.

The density of water at 4°C is 1.0000 g/mL, but at 80°C the density of water is 0.9718 g/mL.

$$d^{4°C} = \frac{1.0000 \text{ g}}{1.0000 \text{ mL}} = 1.0000 \text{ g/mL}$$

$$d^{80°C} = \frac{1.0000 \text{ g}}{1.0290 \text{ mL}} = 0.9718 \text{ g/mL}$$

The density of iron at 20°C is 7.86 g/mL.

$$d^{20°C} = \frac{7.86 \text{ g}}{1.00 \text{ mL}} = 7.86 \text{ g/mL}$$

The density of iron indicates that is is about eight times as heavy as water per unit of volume. The densities of water, sulfur, lead, and gold are compared in Figure 2.7.

Densities for liquids and solids are usually represented in terms of grams per milliliter (g/mL) or grams per cubic centimeter (g/cm³). The density of gases, however, is expressed in terms of grams per liter (g/L). Unless otherwise stated, gas densities are given for 0°C and 1 atmosphere pressure (discussed further in Chapter 12). Table 2.6 lists the densities of a number of common materials.

Suppose that water, carbon tetrachloride, and cottonseed oil are successively poured into a graduated cylinder. The result is a layered three-liquid system (Figure 2.8). Can we predict the order of the liquid layers? Yes, by looking up the densities in Table 2.6. Carbon tetrachloride has the greatest density (1.595 g/mL), and cottonseed oil has the lowest density (0.926 g/mL). Carbon tetrachloride will be the bottom layer, and cottonseed oil will be the top layer. Water, with a density between the other two liquids, will form the middle layer. This information can also be determined by experiment. Add a few milliliters of carbon tetrachloride to a beaker of water. The carbon tetrachloride, being more dense than the water, will sink. Cottonseed oil, being less dense than water, will float when added to the beaker. Direct comparisons of density in this manner can be made only with liquids that are *immiscible* (do not mix with or dissolve in one another).

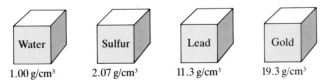

Figure 2.7 Comparison of the masses of equal volumes (1.00 cm³) of water, sulfur, lead, and gold. The mass of each substance per cubic centimeter is its density. (Water is at 4°C; the three solids, at 20°C.)

Table 2.6 Densities of some selected materials. For comparing densities the density of water is the reference for solids and liquids; air is the reference for gases.

Liquids and solids		Gases	
Substance	Density (g/mL at 20°C)	Substance	Density (g/L at 0°C)
Wood (Douglas fir)	0.512	Hydrogen	0.090
Ethyl alcohol	0.789	Helium	0.178
Cottonseed oil	0.926	Methane	0.714
Water (4°C)	**1.000**	Ammonia	0.771
Sugar	1.59	Neon	0.90
Carbon tetrachloride	1.595	Carbon monoxide	1.25
Magnesium	1.74	Nitrogen	1.251
Sulfuric acid	1.84	**Air**	**1.293**
Sulfur	2.07	Oxygen	1.429
Salt	2.16	Hydrogen chloride	1.63
Aluminum	2.70	Argon	1.78
Silver	10.5	Carbon dioxide	1.963
Lead	11.34	Chlorine	3.17
Mercury	13.55		
Gold	19.3		

Figure 2.8 Relative density of liquids. When three immiscible (not capable of mixing) liquids are poured together, the liquid with the highest density will be the bottom layer. In the case of cottonseed oil, water, and carbon tetrachloride, cottonseed oil is the top layer.

Cottonseed oil

Water

Carbon tetrachloride

The density of air at 0°C is approximately 1.293 g/L. Gases with densities less that this value are said to be "lighter than air." A helium-filled balloon will rise rapidly in air, because the density of helium is only 0.178 g/L.

When an insoluble solid object is dropped into water, it will sink or float, depending on its density. If the object is less dense than water, it will float, displacing a *mass* of water equal to the mass of the object. If the object is more dense than water, it will sink, displacing a *volume* of water equal to the volume of the object. This information can be utilized to determine the volume (and density) of irregularly shaped objects.

Sample calculations of density problems follow.

PROBLEM

2.18

What is the density of a mineral if 427 g of the mineral occupy a volume of 35.0 mL? We need to solve for density, so we start by writing the formula for calculating density.

$$d = \frac{\text{mass}}{\text{volume}}$$

Then we substitute the data given in the problem into the equation and solve.

mass = 427 g   volume = 35.0 mL

$$d = \frac{\text{mass}}{\text{volume}} = \frac{427 \text{ g}}{35.0 \text{ mL}} = 12.2 \text{ g/mL}   \text{(Answer)}$$

PROBLEM

2.19

The density of gold is 19.3 g/mL. What is the mass of 25.0 mL of gold?

Two ways to solve this problem are: (1) Solve the density equation for mass, then substitute the density and volume data into the new equation and calculate; (2) Solve by dimensional analysis.

Method 1. **(a)** Solve the density equation for mass:

$$d = \frac{\text{mass}}{\text{volume}}   \text{mass} = d \times \text{volume}$$

(b) Substitute the data and calculate:

$$\text{mass} = \frac{19.3 \text{ g}}{\text{mL}} \times 25.0 \text{ mL} = 482 \text{ g}   \text{(Answer)}$$

Method 2. Dimensional analysis: Use density as a conversion factor, converting mL → g

The conversion of units is

$$\text{mL} \times \frac{\text{g}}{\text{mL}} = \text{g}$$

$$25.0 \text{ mL} \times \frac{19.3 \text{ g}}{\text{mL}} = 482 \text{ g}   \text{(Mass of gold)}$$

PROBLEM

2.20

Calculate the volume (in mL) of 100 g of ethyl alcohol.

From Table 2.6 we see that the density of ethyl alcohol is 0.789 g/mL. This density also means that 1 mL of the alcohol weighs 0.789 g (1 mL/0.789 g). For a conversion factor, we can use either

$$\frac{\text{g}}{\text{mL}} \quad \text{or} \quad \frac{\text{mL}}{\text{g}}$$

In this case the conversion is from g → mL, so we use mL/g. Substituting the data, we get

$$100 \ \cancel{g} \times \frac{1 \ \text{mL}}{0.789 \ \cancel{g}} = 127 \ \text{mL of ethyl alcohol}$$

This problem may also be done by solving the density equation for volume and then substituting the data in the new equation.

PROBLEM

2.21

The water level in a graduated cylinder stands at 20.0 mL before and at 26.2 mL after a 16.74 metal bolt is submerged in the water. (a) What is the volume of the bolt? (b) What is the density of the bolt?

(a) The bolt will displace a volume equal to its volume. Thus the increase in volume is the volume of the bolt.

$$
\begin{array}{ll}
26.2 \ \text{mL} = & \text{volume of water plus bolt} \\
-20.0 \ \text{mL} = & \text{volume of water} \\
\hline
6.2 \ \text{mL} = & \text{volume of bolt} \quad \text{(Answer)}
\end{array}
$$

(b) $d = \dfrac{\text{mass of bolt}}{\text{volume of bolt}} = \dfrac{16.74 \ \text{g}}{6.2 \ \text{mL}} = 2.7 \ \text{g/mL}$ (Answer)

2.15   **Specific Gravity**

specific gravity

The **specific gravity** (sp gr) of a substance is a ratio of the density of that substance to the density of another substance. Water is usually used as the reference standard for solids and liquids. Air is usually used as the reference standard for gases. Specific gravity has no units because the density units cancel. The specific gravity tells us how many times as heavy a liquid, a solid, or a gas is as compared to the reference material.

$$\text{sp gr} = \frac{\text{density of a liquid or solid}}{\text{density of water}} \qquad \text{or} \qquad \frac{\text{density of a gas}}{\text{density of air}} \qquad (6)$$

PROBLEM

2.22

What is the specific gravity of mercury with respect to water at 4°C? (Density of water at 4°C is 1.000 g/mL.)

$$\text{sp gr} = \frac{\text{density of mercury}}{\text{density of water}} = \frac{13.55 \ \text{g/mL}}{1.000 \ \text{g/mL}}$$

sp gr of mercury = 13.55

The value for the specific gravity of mercury (13.55) tells us that, per unit volume, mercury is 13.55 times as heavy as water. Do you think that you could readily lift a liter of mercury?

Figure 2.9 Specific gravity determination using hydrometers. The hydrometer in (a) is floating in water, showing a specific gravity of 1.0. The hydrometer in (b) is floating in dilute sulfuric acid (battery acid), showing a specific gravity of 1.3.

(a) Water   (b) Sulfuric acid

hydrometer   A **hydrometer** consists of a weighted bulb at the end of a sealed, calibrated tube. This instrument is used to measure the specific gravity of a liquid (see Figure 2.9). When a hydrometer is floated in a liquid, the specific gravity is indicated on the scale at the surface of the liquid.

QUESTIONS

An asterisk indicates a more challenging question or problem.

A. *Review the meanings of the new terms introduced in this chapter.*

The terms listed in Section A of each set of Questions are new terms defined in the chapter. They appear in boldface type and occur in the chapter in the order listed in Question A.

1. Mass
2. Weight
3. Significant figures
4. Rounding off numbers
5. Scientific notation
6. Metric system, or SI
7. Meter
8. Kilogram
9. Volume
10. Heat
11. Temperature
12. Joule
13. A calorie
14. Specific heat
15. Density
16. Specific gravity
17. Hydrometer

B. *Information useful in answering these questions will be found in the tables and figures.*

1. Use Table 2.3 to determine how many decimeters make up 1 km.
2. What is the temperature difference in Fahrenheit degrees between 25°C and 100°C? (See Figure 2.4.)
3. Which metal will become warmer when 10 joules of energy are absorbed by one gram each of aluminum and iron? (See Table 2.5.)
4. Why do you suppose the neck of a 100 mL volumetric flask is narrower than the top of a 100 mL graduated cylinder? (See Figure 2.6.)
5. Refer to Table 2.6 and describe the arrangement that would be seen if these three immiscible substances were placed in a 100 mL graduated cylinder: 25 mL mercury, 25 mL carbon tetrachloride, and a cube of magnesium measuring 2.0 cm on an edge.

6. Arrange these materials in order of increasing density: salt, cottonseed oil, sulfur, aluminum, and ethyl alcohol.
7. Will an argon-filled balloon rise or sink in a methane atmosphere? Explain.
8. Ice floats in cottonseed oil and sinks in ethyl alcohol. The density of ice must therefore lie between what numerical values?

C. *Review questions*

1. What are some of the important advantages of the metric system over the American system of weights and measurements?
2. What are the abbreviations for the following?
   (a) Gram   (g) Micrometer
   (b) Kilogram   (h) Angstrom
   (c) Milligram   (i) Milliliter
   (d) Microgram   (j) Microliter
   (e) Centimeter   (k) Liter
   (f) Millimeter
3. For the following numbers tell whether the zeros are significant, are not significant, or may or may not be significant.
   (a) 503   (c) 4200   (e) 100.00
   (b) 0.007   (d) 3.0030   (f) 8.00×10^2
4. State the rules for rounding off numbers.
5. Distinguish between heat and temperature.
6. Will water or ethyl alcohol become hotter when 100 joules of energy are added to 25 g samples of these substances initially at 20°C?
7. Distinguish between density and specific gravity.
8. Which of the following statements are correct?
   (a) The prefix *micro* indicates one-millionth of the unit expressed.
   (b) The length 10 cm is equal to 1000 mm.
   (c) The number 383.263 rounded to four significant figures becomes 383.3.
   (d) The number of significant figures in the number 29,004 is five.
   (e) The number 0.00723 contains three significant figures.
   (f) The sum of 32.276 + 2.134 should contain four significant figures.
   (g) The product of 18.42 cm × 3.40 cm should contain three significant figures.
   (h) One microsecond is 10^{-6} second.
   (i) One thousand meters is a longer distance than 1000 yards.
   (j) One liter is a larger volume than one quart.
   (k) One centimeter is longer than one inch.
   (l) One cubic centimeter (cm^3) is equal to one milliliter.
   (m) The number 0.0002983 in scientific notation is 2.983×10^{-3}.
   (n) $3.0 \times 10^4 \times 6.0 \times 10^6 = 1.8 \times 10^{11}$
   (o) The direction of heat flow is from hot to cold.
   (p) A joule is a unit of temperature.
   (q) Temperature is a form of energy.
   (r) The density of water at 4°C is 1.00 g/ml.
   (s) A pipet is a more accurate instrument for measuring 10.0 mL of water than is a graduated cylinder.
   (t) A hydrometer is an instrument used to measure the specific heat of liquids.

D. *Review problems*

Significant Figures, Rounding, Scientific Notation, and Mathematical Review

1. How many significant figures are in each of the following numbers?
   (a) 0.025   (d) 0.0081   (g) 5.50×10^3
   (b) 40.0   (e) 0.0404   (h) 4.090×10^{-3}
   (c) 22.4   (f) 129,042
2. Round off the following numbers to three significant figures:
   (a) 93.246   (e) 4.644
   (b) 8.8726   (f) 129.509
   (c) 0.02854   (g) 34.250
   (d) 21.25   (h) 1.995×10^6
3. Express each of the following numbers in scientific notation:
   (a) 2,900,000   (d) 4082.2   (g) 12,000,000
   (b) 0.0456   (e) 0.00840   (h) 0.0000055
   (c) 0.58   (f) 40.30
4. Solve the following mathematical problems, stating answers to the proper number of significant figures:
   (a) $12.62 + 1.5 + 0.25 =$
   (b) $4.68 \times 12.5 =$
   (c) $2.25 \times 10^3 \times 4.80 \times 10^4 =$
   (d) $\dfrac{182.6}{4.6} =$
   (e) $\dfrac{452 \times 6.2}{14.3} =$
   (f) $1986 + 23.48 + 0.012 =$
   (g) $0.0394 \times 12.8 =$

(h) $2.92 \times 10^{-3} \times 6.14 \times 10^5 =$

(i) $\dfrac{0.4278}{59.6} =$

(j) $\dfrac{29.3}{284 \times 415} =$

5. Change these fractions to decimals. Express each answer to three significant figures.

(a) $\dfrac{5}{6}$ (b) $\dfrac{3}{7}$ (c) $\dfrac{12}{16}$ (d) $\dfrac{9}{18}$

6. Solve each equation for X:

(a) $3.42X = 6.5$ (d) $0.298X = 15.3$

(b) $\dfrac{X}{12.3} = 7.05$ (e) $\dfrac{X}{0.819} = 10.9$

(c) $\dfrac{0.525}{X} = 0.25$ (f) $\dfrac{8.4}{X} = 282$

7. Solve each equation for the unknown:

(a) $°C = \dfrac{212 - 32}{1.8}$ (c) $K = 25 + 293$

(b) $°F = 1.8(22) + 32$ (d) $\dfrac{8.9\ g}{1\ mL} = \dfrac{40.90\ g}{volume}$

Unit Conversions

8. Make the following conversions, showing mathematical setups:

(a) 28.0 cm to m (l) 12 nm to cm
(b) 1000. m to km (m) 0.520 km to cm
(c) 9.28 cm to mm (n) 3.884 Å to nm
(d) 150 mm to km (o) 42.2 in. to cm
(e) 0.606 cm to km (p) 0.64 mile to in.
(f) 4.5 cm to Å (q) 504 miles to km
(g) 6.5×10^{-7} m to Å (r) 2.00 in.^{2} to cm^2
(h) 12.1 m to cm (s) 35.6 m to ft
(i) 8.0 km to m (t) 16.5 km to miles
(j) 315 mm to cm (u) 4.5 in.^{3} to mm^3
(k) 25 km to mm (v) 3.00 miles^3 to mm^3

9. Make the following conversions, showing mathematical setups:

(a) 10.68 g to mg (e) 164 mg to g
(b) 6.8×10^4 mg to kg (f) 0.65 kg to mg
(c) 8.54 g to kg (g) 5.5 kg to g
(d) 42.8 kg to lb (h) 95 lb to g

10. Make the following conversions, showing mathematical setups:

(a) 25.0 mL to L (e) 0.468 L to mL
(b) 22.4 L to mL (f) 35.6 L to gal
(c) 3.5 qt to mL (g) 9.0 μL to mL
(d) 4.5×10^4 ft^3 to m^3 (h) 20.0 gal to L

11. An automobile traveling at 55 miles per hour is moving at what speed in (a) kilometers per hour and (b) feet per second?

12. A sprinter in the Olympic Games ran the 100 m dash in 9.82 s. What was his speed in (a) feet per second and (b) miles per hour?

13. A lab experiment requires each student to use 6.55 g of sodium chloride. The instructor opens a new 1.00 lb jar of the salt. If 24 students each take exactly the assigned amount of salt, how much should be left in the bottle at the end of the lab period?

14. When the space satellite Voyager I, which gave us new data on the planet Saturn, reaches the planet Neptune in 1989 it will be traveling at an average speed of 13 miles per second. What will be its speed in (a) miles per hour and (b) kilometers per hour?

15. How many kilograms does a 170 lb man weigh?

16. The usual aspirin tablet contains 5.0 grains of aspirin. How many grams of aspirin are in one tablet (1 grain = $\frac{1}{7000}$ lb)?

17. The sun is approximately 93 million miles from the earth. How many seconds will it take light to travel from the sun to the earth if the velocity of light is 3.00×10^{10} cm per second?

18. The average mass of the heart of a human baby is about 1 ounce. What is the mass in milligrams?

19. How much would 1.0 kg of potatoes cost if the price is $1.78 for 10 pounds?

20. The price of gold varies greatly and has been as high as $800 per ounce. What is the value of 227 g of gold at $345 per ounce? Gold is priced per troy ounce [1 lb (avoirdupois) = 14.58 oz (troy)].

21. An adult ruby-throated hummingbird has an average weight of 3.2 g, whereas an adult California condor may attain a weight of 21 lb. How many times heavier than the hummingbird is the condor?

22. At 35 cents per liter how much will it cost to fill a 15.8 gal tank with gasoline?

23. How many liters of gasoline will be used to drive 500 miles in a car that averages 34 miles per gallon?

24. Calculate the volume, in liters, of a box 75 cm long by 55 cm wide by 55 cm high.

25. Assuming that there are 20 drops in 1.0 mL, how many drops are in one gallon?

26. How many liters of oil are in a 42 gallon barrel of oil?

27. How many milliliters will be delivered by a filled 5.0 μL syringe?

*28. Calculate the number of milliliters of water in 1.00 cubic foot of water.

*29. Oil spreads in a thin layer on water and is called an "oil slick." How much area in square meters (m^2) will 200 cm^3 of oil cover if it forms a layer 5 Å in thickness?

Temperature Conversions and Specific Heat

30. Make the following conversions, showing mathematical setups:
    (a) 162°F to °C   (e) 32°C to °F
    (b) 0.0°F to °C   (f) −8.6°F to °C
    (c) 0.0°F to K   (g) 273°C to K
    (d) − 18°C to °F   (h) 212 K to °C

31. Normal body temperature for humans is 37.0°C. What is this temperature on the Fahrenheit scale?

32. Which is colder, −100°C or −138°F

*33. (a) At what temperature are the Fahrenheit and Celsius temperatures exactly equal?
    (b) At what temperature are they numerically equal but opposite in sign?

34. How many joules of heat are required to raise the temperature of 80 g of water from 20°C to 70°C?

35. How many joules are required to raise the temperature of 80 g of iron from 20°C to 70°C? How many calories?

36. A 250. g metal bar requires 5.866 kJ to change its temperature from 22°C to 100°C. What is the specific heat of the metal in J/g°C?

*37. A 20.0 g piece of a metal at 203°C is dropped into 100. g of water at 25.0°C. The water temperature rises to 29.0°C. Calculate the specific heat (J/g°C) of the metal. Assume that all the heat lost by the metal is transferred to the water and no heat is lost to the surroundings.

*38. Assuming no heat losses by the system, what will be the final temperature when 50 g of water at 10°C are mixed with 10 g of water at 50°C?

*39. A 325 g piece of gold at 427°C is dropped into 200 mL of water at 22.0°C. The specific heat of gold is 0.131 J/g°C. Calculate the final temperature of the mixture. (Assume no heat losses to the surroundings.)

Density and Specific Gravity

40. Calculate the density of a liquid if 50.00 mL of the liquid weigh 78.26 g.

41. A 12.8 mL sample of bromine weighs 39.9 g. What is the density of bromine?

42. When a 32.7 g piece of chromium metal was placed into a graduated cylinder containing 25.0 mL of water, the water level rose to 29.6 mL. Calculate the density of the chromium.

43. Concentrated sulfuric acid has a density of 1.84 g/mL. Calculate the weight, in grams, of 500. mL of this acid.

44. An empty graduated cylinder weighs 42.817 g. When filled with 50.0 mL of an unknown liquid it weighs 106.773 g. What is the density of the liquid?

45. What weight of mercury ($d = 13.6$ g/mL) will occupy a volume of 25.0 mL?

46. A 35.0 mL sample of ethyl alcohol ($d = 0.789$ g/mL) is added to a graduated cylinder that weighs 49.28 g. What will be the weight of the cylinder plus the alcohol?

47. You are given three cubes, A, B, and C; one is magnesium, one is aluminum, and the third is silver. All three cubes weigh the same, but cube A has a volume of 25.9 mL, cube B has a volume of 16.7 mL, and cube C has a volume of 4.29 mL. Identify cubes A, B, and C.

*48. A cube of aluminum weighs 500 g. What will be the weight of a cube of gold of the same dimensions?

49. A 25.0 mL sample of water at 80°C weighs 24.30 g. Calculate (a) the density of water at this temperature and (b) the volume per gram.

50. Calculate (a) the density and (b) the specific gravity of a solid that weighs 136 g and has a volume of 50.0 mL.

51. The mass of an empty container is 88.25 g. The mass of the container when filled with a liquid ($d = 1.25$ g/mL) is 150.50 g. What is the volume of the container?

52. Which liquid will occupy the greater volume, 50 g of water or 50 g of ethyl alcohol? Explain.

53. A gold bullion dealer advertised a bar of pure gold for sale. The gold bar weighed 3300 g and measured 2.00 cm by 15.0 cm by 6.00 cm. Was the gold bar pure gold? Show evidence for your answer.

54. The largest nugget of gold on record was found

in 1872 in New South Wales, Australia, and weighed 93.3 kg. Assuming the nugget is pure gold, what is its volume in cubic centimeters?

*55. Forgetful Freddie placed 25.0 mL of a liquid in a graduated cylinder that weighed 89.450 g when empty. When Freddie placed a metal slug weighing 15.434 g into the cylinder, the volume rose to 30.7 mL. Freddie was asked to calculate the density of the liquid and of the metal slug from his data, but he forgot to obtain the weight of the liquid. He was told that if he weighed the cylinder containing the liquid and the slug, he would have enough data for the calculations. He did so and found it weighed 125.934 g. Calculate the density of the liquid and of the metal slug.

*56. A solution made by adding 143 g of sulfuric acid to 500 mL of water had a volume of 554 mL.

(a) What value will a hydrometer read when placed in this solution?
(b) What volume of concentrated sulfuric acid (d = 1.84 g/mL) was added?

57. A solution made by adding 500 g of sulfuric acid to 500 mL of water had a volume of 717 mL.
(a) What value will a hydrometer read when placed in this solution?
(b) What volume of concentrated sulfuric acid (d = 1.84 g/mL) was added?

58. Two hundred milliliters of gasoline weigh 144 g. Is the specific gravity of gasoline greater or less than that of water? Show evidence for your answer.

$\Delta T = 100 - 22$
(78)

36. $Q = m \cdot \Delta T \cdot SH$

$5.866 KJ = (250.g)(78°C)(S.H)$

$S.H. = \dfrac{5.866 KJ}{(250.g)(78°C)} = 3.0 \times 10^{4}$

$= \dfrac{5866 J}{(250.g)(78)} = .30 \; J/g \, °C$

$5.866 KJ \cdot \dfrac{1000 \; J}{1 \; KJ} = 5866 \; J$

3 Properties of Matter

After studying
Chapter 3,
you should be
able to

1. Understand the new terms listed in Question A at the end of the chapter.
2. Identify the three physical states of matter and list the physical properties that characterize each state.
3. Distinguish between the physical and chemical properties of matter.
4. Classify the changes undergone by matter as either physical or chemical.
5. Distinguish between substances and mixtures.
6. Distinguish between kinetic and potential energy.
7. State the Law of Conservation of Mass.
8. State the Law of Conservation of Energy.
9. Explain why the laws dealing with the conservation of mass and energy may be combined into a single, more accurate general statement.
10. Calculate the percent composition of compounds from the weights of the elements involved in a chemical reaction and vice versa.

3.1 Matter Defined

The entire universe consists of matter and energy. Every day we come into contact with countless kinds of matter. Air, food, water, rocks, soil, glass, and this book are all different types of matter. Broadly defined, **matter** is *anything that has mass and occupies space.*

matter

44

speed of light

3×10^{10} cm/sec.

3×10^{8} m/sec.

Figure 3.1   An apparently empty test tube is submerged, mouth downward, in water. Only a small volume of water rises into the tube, which is actually filled with air. This experiment proves that air, which is matter, occupies space.

Matter may be quite invisible. If an apparently empty test tube is submerged, mouth downward, in a beaker of water, the water rises only slightly into the tube. The water cannot rise farther because the tube is filled with invisible matter: air (see Figure 3.1).

To the eye, matter appears to be continuous and unbroken. However, it is actually discontinuous and is composed of discrete, tiny particles called *atoms*. The particulate nature of matter will become evident when we study atomic structure and the properties of gases.

3.2   Physical States of Matter

solid

Matter exists in three physical states: solid, liquid, and gas. A **solid** has a definite shape and volume, with particles that cohere rigidly to one another. The shape of a solid can be independent of its container. For example, a crystal of sulfur has the same shape and volume whether it is placed in a beaker or simply laid on a glass plate.

Most commonly occurring solids, such as salt, sugar, quartz, and metals, are *crystalline*. Crystalline materials exist in regular, repeating, three-dimensional, geometric patterns. Solids such as plastics, glass, and gels, because they do not have any particular regular internal geometric pattern, are called **amorphous solids**. (*Amorphous* means without shape or form.) Figure 3.2 illustrates three crystalline solids: salt, quartz, and gypsum.

amorphous

liquid

A **liquid** has a definite volume but not a definite shape, with particles that cohere firmly but not rigidly. Although the particles are held together by strong attractive forces and are in close contact with one another, they are able to move freely. Particle mobility gives a liquid fluidity and causes it to take the shape of the container in which it is stored. Figure 3.3 shows equal amounts of liquid in differently shaped containers.

gas

A **gas** has indefinite volume and no fixed shape, with particles that are moving independently of one another. Particles in the gaseous state have gained enough energy to overcome the attractive forces that held them together as liquids or solids. A gas presses continuously in all directions on the walls of any container.

(a)

(b)

(c)

Figure 3.2   These three naturally occurring substances are examples of regular geometric formations that are characteristic of crystalline solids: (a) halite (salt), (b) quartz, and (c) gypsum.

Figure 3.3   Liquids have the property of fluidity and assume the shape of their container, as illustrated in each of the three different calibrated containers.

Table 3.1 Common materials in the solid, liquid, and gaseous states of matter

Solids	Liquids	Gases
Aluminum	Alcohol	Acetylene
Copper	Blood	Air
Gold	Gasoline	Butane
Polyethylene	Honey	Carbon dioxide
Salt	Mercury	Chlorine
Sand	Oil	Helium
Steel	Vinegar	Methane
Sulfur	Water	Oxygen

Table 3.2 Physical properties of solids, liquids, and gases

State	Shape	Volume	Particles	Compressibility
Solid	Definite	Definite	Rigidly cohering; tightly packed	Very slight
Liquid	Indefinite	Definite	Mobile; cohering	Slight
Gas	Indefinite	Indefinite	Independent of one another and relatively far apart	High

Because of this quality a gas completely fills a container. The particles of a gas are relatively far apart compared with those of solids and liquids. The actual volume of the gas particles is usually very small in comparison with the volume of the space occupied by the gas. A gas therefore may be compressed into a very small volume or expanded almost indefinitely. Liquids cannot be compressed to any great extent, and solids are even less compressible than liquids.

When a bottle of ammonia solution is opened in one corner of the laboratory, one can soon smell its familiar odor in all parts of the room. The ammonia gas escaping from the solution demonstrates that gaseous particles move freely and rapidly and tend to permeate the entire area into which they are released.

Although matter is discontinuous, attractive forces exist that hold the particles together and give matter its appearance of continuity. These attractive forces are strongest in solids, giving them rigidity; they are weaker in liquids but still strong enough to hold liquids to definite volumes. In gases the attractive forces are so weak that the particles of a gas are practically independent of one another. Table 3.1 lists a number of common materials that exist as solids, liquids, and gases. Table 3.2 summarizes comparative properties of solids, liquids, and gases.

3.3   Substances and Mixtures

The term *matter* refers to all materials or material things that make up the universe. Many thousands of different and distinct kinds of matter or substances substance

exist. A **substance** is a particular kind of matter with a definite, fixed composition. A substance, sometimes known as a *pure substance*, is either an element or a compound. Familiar examples of elements are copper, gold, and oxygen. Familiar compounds are salt, sugar, and water. Elements and compounds are discussed in more detail in Chapter 4.

We can classify a sample of matter as either *homogeneous* or *heterogeneous* by examining it. **Homogeneous** matter is uniform in appearance and has the same properties throughout. Matter consisting of two or more physically distinct phases is **heterogeneous**. A **phase** is a homogeneous part of a system separated from other parts by physical boundaries. A system is simply the body of matter under consideration. Whenever we have a system in which visible boundaries exist between the parts or components, that system has more than one phase and is heterogeneous. It does not matter whether the components are in the solid, liquid, or gaseous states.

homogeneous

heterogeneous

phase

An important fact to keep in mind is that a pure substance, an element or compound, is always *homogeneous* in composition. However, a pure substance may exist as different phases in a heterogeneous system. Ice floating in water, for example, is a two-phase system made up of solid water and liquid water. The water in each phase is *homogeneous* in composition; but because two phases are present, the system is *heterogeneous*.

mixture

A **mixture** is a material containing two or more substances and can be either heterogeneous or homogeneous. Mixtures are variable in composition. If we add a tablespoonful of sugar to a glass of water, a heterogeneous mixture is formed immediately. The two phases are a solid (sugar) and a liquid (water). But upon stirring the sugar dissolves to form a homogeneous mixture or solution. Both substances are still present: All parts of the solution are sweet and wet. The proportions of sugar and water can be varied simply by adding more sugar and stirring to dissolve.

Many substances do not form homogeneous mixtures. If we mix sugar and fine white sand, a heterogeneous mixture is formed. Careful examination may be needed to decide that the mixture is heterogeneous because the two phases (sugar and sand) are both white solids. Ordinary matter exists mostly as mixtures. If we examine soil, granite, iron ore, or other naturally occurring mineral deposits, we find them to be heterogeneous mixtures. Seawater is a homogeneous mixture (solution) containing many substances. Air is a homogeneous mixture (solution) of several gases. We shall consider mixtures further in Chapter 4. Figure 3.4 illustrates the relationships of substances and mixtures.

3.4 Properties of Substances

properties

How do we recognize substances? Each substance has a set of **properties** that is characteristic of that substance and gives it a unique identity. Properties are the personality traits of substances and are classified as either physical or chemical. **Physical properties** are the inherent characteristics of a substance that can be determined without altering its composition; they are associated with its

physical properties

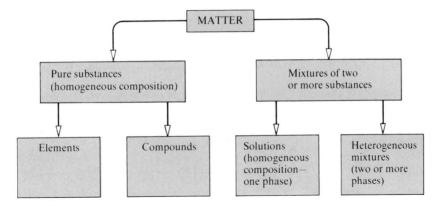

Figure 3.4 Classification of matter: A pure substance is always homogeneous in composition, whereas a mixture always contains two or more substances and may be either homogeneous (a solution) or heterogeneous.

chemical properties

physical existence. Common physical properties are color, taste, odor, state of matter (solid, liquid, or gas), density, melting point, and boiling point. **Chemical properties** describe the ability of a substance to form new substances, either by reaction with other substances or by decomposition.

We can select a few of the physical and chemical properties of chlorine as an example. Physically, chlorine is a gas about 2.4 times heavier than air. It is yellowish-green in color and has a disagreeable odor. Chemically, chlorine will not burn but will support the combustion of certain other substances. It can be used as a bleaching agent, as a disinfectant for water, and in many chlorinated substances such as refrigerants and insecticides. When chlorine combines with the metal sodium, it forms a salt called sodium chloride. These properties, among others, help to characterize and identify chlorine.

Substances, then, are recognized and differentiated by their properties. Table 3.3 lists four substances and tabulates several of their common physical properties. Information about common physical properties, such as that given in Table 3.3, is available in handbooks of chemistry and physics. Scientists do not pretend to know all the answers or to remember voluminous amounts of data,

Table 3.3 Physical properties of chlorine, water, sugar, and acetic acid

Substance	Color	Odor	Taste	Physical state	Boiling point (°C)	Melting point (°C)
Chlorine	Yellowish-green	Sharp, suffocating	Sharp, sour	Gas	−34.6	−101.6
Water	Colorless	Odorless	Tasteless	Liquid	100.0	0.0
Sugar	White	Odorless	Sweet	Solid	Decomposes 170–186	—
Acetic acid	Colorless	Like vinegar	Sour	Liquid	118.0	16.7

Figure 3.5 Physical changes in the appearance and state of water

but it is important for them to know where to look for data in the literature. Handbooks are one of the most widely used resources for scientific data.*

> **No two substances will have identical physical and chemical properties.**

3.5   Physical Changes

physical change

Matter can undergo two types of changes, physical and chemical. **Physical changes** are changes in physical properties (such as size, shape, and density) or changes in state of matter without an accompanying change in composition. The changing of ice into water and water into steam are physical changes from one state of matter into another. No new substances are formed in these physical changes (see Figure 3.5).

When a clean platinum wire is heated in a burner flame, the appearance of the platinum changes from silvery metallic to glowing red. This change is physical because the platinum can be restored to its original metallic appearance by cooling and, more importantly, because the composition of the platinum is not changed by heating and cooling.

3.6   Chemical Changes

chemical change

In a **chemical change**, new substances are formed that have different properties and composition from the original material. The new substances need not in any way resemble the initial material.

When a clean copper wire is heated in a burner flame, the appearance of the copper changes from coppery metallic to glowing red. Unlike the platinum previously mentioned, the copper is not restored to its original appearance by cooling but has become a black material. This black material is a new substance

---

* Robert C. Weast, ed., *Handbook of Chemistry and Physics*, 68th ed. (Cleveland: Chemical Rubber Company, 1987). Norbert A. Lange, comp., *Handbook of Chemistry*, 13th ed. (New York: McGraw-Hill, 1985).

Before heating
wire is copper-colored

Copper and oxygen
from the air combine
chemically on heating

After heating,
wire is black

Copper wire: 1.00 g
(100% copper)

Copper (II) oxide:1.251 g
79.9% copper: 1.00 g
20.1% oxygen: 0.251 g

Figure 3.6 Chemical change: Formation of copper(II) oxide from copper and oxygen

called copper(II) oxide. It was formed by chemical change when copper combined with oxygen in the air during the heating process. The unheated wire was essentially 100% copper, but the copper(II) oxide is 79.9% copper and 20.1% oxygen. One gram of copper will yield 1.251 g of copper(II) oxide (see Figure 3.6). The platinum was changed only physically when heated, but the copper was changed both physically and chemically when heated.

When 1.000 g of copper reacts with oxygen to yield 1.251 g of copper(II) oxide, the copper must have combined with 0.251 g of oxygen. The percentage of copper and oxygen can be calculated from these data, the copper and oxygen each being a percent of the total weight of copper(II) oxide:

$$1.000 \text{ g copper} + 0.251 \text{ g oxygen} \longrightarrow 1.251 \text{ g copper(II) oxide}$$

$$\frac{1.000 \text{ g copper}}{1.251 \text{ g copper(II) oxide}} \times 100\% = 79.9\% \text{ copper}$$

$$\frac{0.251 \text{ g oxygen}}{1.251 \text{ g copper(II) oxide}} \times 100\% = 20.1\% \text{ oxygen}$$

Mercury(II) oxide is an orange-red powder that, when subjected to high temperature (500–600°C), decomposes into a colorless gas (oxygen) and a silvery, liquid metal (mercury). The composition and physical appearance of each product are noticeably different from those of the starting compound. When mercury(II) oxide is heated in a test tube (see Figure 3.7), small globules of mercury are observed collecting on the cooler part of the tube. Evidence that oxygen forms is observed when a glowing wood splint, lowered into the tube, bursts into flame. Oxygen supports and intensifies the combustion of the wood. From these observations we conclude that a chemical change has taken place.

Chemists have devised *chemical equations* as a shorthand method for expressing chemical changes. The two previous examples of chemical changes can be

Mercury

Mercury (II) oxide

Figure 3.7 Heating mercury(II) oxide causes it to decompose into mercury and oxygen. Observation of the mercury and oxygen with properties different from those of mercury(II) oxide is evidence that a chemical change has occurred.

represented by the following word equations:

$$\text{Copper} + \text{Oxygen} \xrightarrow{\Delta} \text{Copper(II) oxide} \text{(Cupric oxide)} \tag{1}$$

$$\text{Mercury(II) oxide} \xrightarrow{\Delta} \text{Mercury} + \text{Oxygen} \tag{2}$$

Equation (1) states: Copper plus oxygen when heated produce copper(II) oxide. Equation (2) states: Mercury(II) oxide when heated produces mercury plus oxygen. The arrow means "produces"; it points to the products. The Greek letter delta (Δ) represents heat. The starting substances [copper, oxygen, and mercury(II) oxide] are called the *reactants*, and the substances produced [copper(II) oxide, mercury, and oxygen] are called the *products*. In later chapters equations are presented in a still more abbreviated form, with symbols to represent substances.

Physical change usually accompanies a chemical change. Table 3.4 lists some common physical and chemical changes. In the examples given in the table, you will note that, wherever a chemical change occurs, a physical change occurs also. However, wherever a physical change is listed, only a physical change occurs.

Table 3.4 Examples of processes involving physical or chemical changes

Process taking place	Type of change	Accompanying physical changes
Rusting of iron	Chemical	Shiny, bright metal changes to reddish-brown rust.
Boiling of water	Physical	Liquid changes to vapor.
Burning of sulfur in air	Chemical	Yellow solid sulfur changes to gaseous, choking sulfur dioxide.
Boiling an egg	Chemical	Liquid white and yolk change to solids.
Combustion of gasoline	Chemical	Liquid gasoline burns to gaseous carbon monoxide, carbon dioxide, and water.
Digesting food	Chemical	Food changes to liquid nutrients and partially solid wastes.
Sawing of wood	Physical	Smaller pieces of wood and sawdust are made from a larger piece of wood.
Burning of wood	Chemical	Wood burns to ashes, gaseous carbon dioxide, and water.
Heating of glass	Physical	Solid becomes pliable during heating, and the glass may change its shape.

3.7 Conservation of Mass

Law of Conservation of Mass

The **Law of Conservation of Mass** states that no detectable change is observed in the total mass of the substances involved in a chemical change. This law, tested by extensive laboratory experimentation, is the basis for the quantitative weight relationships among reactants and products.

The decomposition of mercury(II) oxide into mercury and oxygen illustrates this law. One hundred grams of mercury(II) oxide decomposes into 92.6 g of mercury and 7.39 g of oxygen:

Mercury(II) oxide $\longrightarrow$ Mercury + Oxygen

    100. g   92.6 g   7.39 g

100. g Reactant

100. g Products

Operation of the ordinary photographic flashbulb also illustrates the law. Sealed within the bulb are fine wires of magnesium (a metal) and oxygen (a gas). When these reactants are energized, they combine chemically, producing magnesium oxide, a blinding white light, and considerable heat. The chemical change may be represented by this equation

Magnesium + Oxygen $\longrightarrow$ Magnesium oxide + Heat + Light

When weighed before and after the chemical change, as illustrated in Figure 3.8, the bulb shows no increase or decrease in weight.

Mass of reactants = Mass of products

Figure 3.8 The flashbulb, containing magnesium and oxygen, weighs the same (a) before and (b) after the bulb is flashed. When the bulb is flashed, a chemical change occurs, and the original substances change into the white powder magnesium oxide.

3.8   Energy

From the prehistoric discovery that fire could be used to warm shelters and cook food to the modern-day discovery that nuclear reactors can be used to produce vast amounts of controlled energy, man's technical progress has been directed by the ability to produce, harness, and utilize energy. **Energy** is the capacity of matter to do work. Energy exists in several forms; some of the more familiar forms are mechanical, chemical, electrical, heat, nuclear, and radiant or light energy. Matter can have both potential and kinetic energy.

energy

Potential energy is stored energy, or energy an object possesses due to its relative position. For example, a ball located 20 ft above the ground has more potential energy than when located 10 ft above the ground and will bounce higher when allowed to fall. Water backed up behind a dam represents potential energy that can be converted into useful work in the form of electrical or mechanical energy. Gasoline is a source of chemical potential energy. When gasoline burns (combines with oxygen), the heat released is associated with a decrease in potential energy. The new substances formed by burning have less chemical potential energy than the gasoline and oxygen did.

potential energy

Kinetic energy is the energy that matter possesses due to its motion. When the water behind the dam is released and allowed to flow, its potential energy is changed into kinetic energy, which can be used to drive generators and produce electricity. All moving bodies possess kinetic energy. The pressure exerted by a confined gas is due to the kinetic energy of rapidly moving gas particles. We all know the results when two moving vehicles collide: Their kinetic energy is expended in the crash that occurs.

kinetic energy

Energy can be converted from one form to another form. Some kinds of energy can be converted to other forms easily and efficiently. For example, mechanical energy can be converted to electrical energy with an electric generator at better than 90% efficiency. On the other hand, solar energy has thus far been directly converted to electrical energy at an efficiency of only about 15%.

3.9 Energy in Chemical Changes

In all chemical changes matter either absorbs or releases energy. Chemical changes can produce different forms of energy. Electrical energy to start automobiles is produced by chemical changes in the lead storage battery. Light energy for photographic purposes occurs as a flash during the chemical change in the magnesium flashbulb. Heat and light energies are released from the combustion of fuels. All the energy needed for our life processes—breathing, muscle contraction, blood circulation, and so on—is produced by chemical changes occurring within the cells of our bodies.

Conversely, energy is used to cause chemical changes. For example, a chemical change occurs in the electroplating of metals when electrical energy is passed through a salt solution in which the metal is submerged. A chemical change also occurs when radiant energy from the sun is used by green plants in the process of photosynthesis. And, as we saw, a chemical change occurs when heat causes mercury(II) oxide to decompose into mercury and oxygen. Chemical changes are often used primarily to produce energy rather than to produce new substances. The heat or thrust generated by the combustion of fuels is more important than the new substances formed.

3.10 Conservation of Energy

An energy transformation occurs whenever a chemical change occurs. If energy is absorbed during the change, the products will have more chemical potential energy than the reactants. Conversely, if energy is given off in a chemical change, the products will have less chemical potential energy than the reactants. Water, for example, can be decomposed in an electrolytic cell. Electrical energy is absorbed in the decomposition, and the products, hydrogen and oxygen, have a greater chemical potential energy level than that of water. This potential energy is released in the form of heat and light when the hydrogen and oxygen are burned to form water again (see Figure 3.9). Thus, energy can be changed from one form to another or from one substance to another and therefore is not lost.

The energy changes occurring in many systems have been thoroughly studied by many investigators. No system has been found to acquire energy except at the

Law of Conservation of Energy

expense of energy possessed by another system. This principle is stated in other words as the **Law of Conservation of Energy**: Energy can be neither created nor destroyed though it can be transformed from one form to another.

3.11 Interchangeability of Matter and Energy

Sections 3.7–3.10 dealt with matter and energy, which are clearly related; any attempt to deal with one inevitably involves the other. The nature of this relationship eluded the most able scientists until the beginning of the 20th century. Then, in 1905, Albert Einstein (Figure 3.10) presented one of the most original scientific concepts ever devised.

Figure 3.9 Energy transformations during the electrolysis of water and the combustion of hydrogen and oxygen: Electrical energy is converted to chemical energy in the electrolysis, and chemical energy is converted to heat and light energy in the combustion.

Figure 3.10   Albert Einstein (1879–1955), world-renowned physicist and author of the theory of relativity and the interrelationship between matter and energy: $E = mc^2$ (*Courtesy of the Bettmann Archives.*)

Einstein stated that the quantity of energy E equivalent to the mass m could be calculated by the equation $E = mc^2$. In this equation the energy units of E are ergs (1 erg = 1×10^{-7} J), m is in grams, and c is the velocity of light (3.0×10^{10} cm/s). According to Einstein's equation, whenever energy is absorbed or released by a substance, mass is lost or gained. Although the energy changes in chemical reactions are measurable and may appear to be large, the amounts are relatively small. The accompanying difference in mass between reactants and products in chemical changes is so small that it cannot be detected by available measuring instruments. According to Einstein's equation 9.2×10^7 J (9.2×10^{14} ergs) of energy are equivalent to 0.0000010 g (1.0 μg) of mass:

$$1 \ \mu\text{g mass} = 9.2 \times 10^7 \text{ J energy} \ (9.2 \times 10^{14} \text{ ergs})$$

In a more practical sense, when 2.8×10^3 g of carbon are burned to carbon dioxide, 9.2×10^7 J of energy are released. Of this very large amount of carbon, only about one-millionth of a gram, which is 3.6×10^{-8} % of the starting mass, is converted to energy. Therefore, in actual practice we may treat the reactants and products of chemical changes as having constant mass. However, because mass and energy are interchangeable, the two laws dealing with the conservation of matter may be combined into a single and generally more accurate statement:

The total amount of mass and energy remains constant during chemical change.

QUESTIONS

A. *Review the meanings of the new terms introduced in this chapter.*

1. Matter
2. Solid
3. Amorphous
4. Liquid
5. Gas
6. Substance
7. Homogeneous
8. Heterogeneous
9. Phase
10. Mixture
11. Properties
12. Physical properties
13. Chemical properties
14. Physical change
15. Chemical change
16. Law of Conservation of Mass
17. Energy
18. Potential energy
19. Kinetic energy
20. Law of Conservation of Energy

B. *Information useful in answering these questions will be found in the tables and figures.*

1. What evidence can you find in Figure 3.1 that gases occupy space?
2. Which three liquids listed in Table 3.1 are not mixtures?
3. Which of the gases listed in Table 3.1 is not a pure substance?
4. In what physical state does acetic acid exist at 10°C? (See Table 3.3.)
5. In what physical state does chlorine exist at 102 K? (See Table 3.3.)

6. What evidence of chemical change is visible when mercury(II) oxide is heated as shown in Figure 3.7?
7. What chemical changes occur to the matter in the flashbulb of Figure 3.8 when the bulb is fllashed?
8. What physical changes occur during the electrolysis of water? (See Figure 3.9.)

C. *Review questions*

1. List four different substances in each of the three states of matter.
2. In terms of the properties of the ultimate particles of a substance, explain
   (a) Why a solid has a definite shape but a liquid does not.
   (b) Why a liquid has a definite volume but a gas does not.
   (c) Why a gas can be compressed rather easily but a solid cannot be compressed appreciably.
3. When the stopper is removed from a partly filled bottle containing solid and liquid acetic acid at 16.7°C, a strong vinegarlike odor is noticeable immediately. How many acetic acid phases must be present in the bottle? Explain.

4. Is the system enclosed in the bottle of Question 3 homogeneous or heterogeneous? Explain.
5. Is a system that contains only one substance necessarily homogeneous? Explain.
6. Is a system that contains two or more substances necessarily heterogeneous? Explain.
7. Distinguish between physical and chemical properties.
8. What is the fundamental difference between a chemical change and a physical change?
*9. Classify the following as being primarily physical or primarily chemical changes:
   (a) Formation of a snowflake
   (b) Freezing ice cream
   (c) Boiling water
   (d) Boiling an egg
   (e) Churning cream to make butter
   (f) Souring milk
10. Classify the following as being primarily physical or chemical changes:
   (a) Lighting a candle
   (b) Stirring cake batter
   (c) Dissolving sugar in water
   (d) Decomposition of limestone by heat
   (e) A leaf turning yellow
   (f) Gas escaping from a freshly opened bottle of soda pop
11. Cite the evidence that indicated that only physical changes occurred when a platinum wire was heated in a burner flame.
12. Cite the evidence that indicated that both physical and chemical changes occurred when a copper wire was heated in a burner flame.
13. Cite the evidence that heating mercury(II) oxide brings about a chemical change.
14. Identify the reactants and products for each of the following:
   (a) Heating a copper wire in a burner flame
   (b) Heating mercury(II) oxide as shown in Figure 3.7
   (c) Flashing the flashbulb shown in Figure 3.8
15. In a chemical change why can we consider that mass is neither lost nor gained (for practical purposes)?
16. Distinguish between potential and kinetic energy.
17. What happens to the kinetic energy of a speeding automobile when the automobile is braked to a stop?
18. What energy transformation is responsible for the fiery reentry of a returning space vehicle?
19. When the flashbulb of Figure 3.8 is flashed, energy is given off to the surroundings. Explain why the mass of the bulb appears to be the same after flashing as it was before, even though (according to Einstein) energy is equivalent to mass.
20. Which of the following statements are correct? (Try to answer this question without referring to the text.)
   (a) Liquids are the least compact state of matter.
   (b) Liquids have a definite volume and a definite shape.
   (c) Matter in the solid state is discontinuous; that is, it is made up of discrete particles.
   (d) Wood is homogeneous.
   (e) Wood is a substance.
   (f) Dirt is a mixture.
   (g) Seawater, although homogeneous, is a mixture.
   (h) Any system made up of only one substance is homogeneous.
   (i) Any system containing two or more substances is heterogeneous.
   (j) A solution, although it contains dissolved material, is homogeneous.
   (k) Boiling water represents a chemical change, because a change of state occurs.
   (l) All the following represent chemical changes: baking a cake, frying an egg, leaves changing color, iron changing to rust.
   (m) All of the following represent physical changes: breaking a stick, melting wax, folding a napkin, burning hydrogen to form water.
   (n) Chemical changes can produce electrical energy.
   (o) Electrical energy can produce chemical changes.
   (p) A stretched rubber band possesses kinetic energy.
   (q) An automobile rolling down a hill possesses both kinetic and potential energy.
   (r) When heated in the air, a platinum wire gains weight.
   (s) When heated in the air, a copper wire loses weight.
   (t) The two kinds of pure substances are elements and compounds.

D. *Review problems*

1. Calculate the boiling point of acetic acid in (a) Kelvins and (b) degrees Fahrenheit. (See Table 3.3)

2. What is the percentage of iron in a mixture that contains 15.0 g of iron, 16.0 g of sulfur, and 18.5 g of sand?

3. How many grams of copper(II) oxide can be obtained from 2.80 g of copper? (See Figure 3.6)

4. How many grams of copper will combine with 5.50 g of oxygen to form copper(II) oxide?

5. How many grams of mercury can be obtained from 85.0 g of mercury(II) oxide?

6. If 60.0 g of a meat sample contain 6.40 g of fat, what percentage fat is present?

7. When 13.0 g of magnesium was heated in air, 21.5 g of magnesium oxide was produced. Given the chemical reaction

Magnesium + Oxygen $\longrightarrow$ Magnesium oxide

(a) What weight of oxygen has combined with the magnesium?

(b) What percentage of the magnesium oxide is oxygen?

8. When aluminum combines with chlorine gas, they produce the substance aluminum chloride. If 4.94 g of aluminum chloride is formed from 1.00 g of aluminum, how many grams of chlorine will combine with 5.50 g of aluminum?

*9. If a U.S. 25-cent coin weighs about 5.5 g,

(a) How many joules would be released by the complete conversion of a 25-cent coin to energy? How many calories?

(b) The energy calculated in (a) could heat how many gallons of water from room temperature to the boiling point if 1.27×10^6 J are needed to heat a gallon of water from room temperature (20°C) to boiling (100°C)?

4

Elements and Compounds

**After studying
Chapter 4,
you should be
able to**

1. Understand the new terms listed in Question A at the end of the chapter.
2. List in order of abundance the five most abundant elements in the earth's crust, seawater, and atmosphere.
3. List in order of abundance the six most abundant elements in the human body.
4. Classify common materials as elements, compounds, or mixtures.
5. Write the symbols when given the names or write the names when given the symbols of the common elements listed in Table 4.3
6. State the Law of Definite Composition.
7. Understand how symbols, including subscripts and parentheses, are used to write chemical formulas.
8. Differentiate among atoms, molecules, and ions.
9. List the characteristics of metals and nonmetals.
10. Name binary compounds from their formulas.
11. Balance simple chemical equations when the formulas are given.
12. List the elements that occur as diatomic molecules.

4.1 Elements

All the words in the English dictionary are formed from an alphabet consisting of only 26 letters. All known substances on earth—and most probably in the element

universe, too—are formed from a sort of "chemical alphabet" consisting of 108 presently known elements. An **element** is a fundamental or elementary substance that cannot be broken down by chemical means to simpler substances. Elements are the building blocks of all substances. The elements are numbered in order of increasing complexity beginning with hydrogen, number 1. Of the first 92 elements, 88 are known to occur in nature. The other four—technetium (43), promethium (61), astatine (85), and francium (87)—either do not occur in nature or have only transitory existences during radioactive decay. With the exception of number 94, plutonium, elements above number 92 are not known to occur naturally but have been synthesized, usually in very small quantities, in laboratories. The discovery of trace amounts of element 94 (plutonium) in nature has been reported recently. The syntheses of elements 107 and 109 were reported in 1981 and 1982; element 108 has not been reported. No elements other than those on the earth have been detected on other bodies in the universe.

Most substances can be decomposed into two or more simpler substances. We have seen that mercury(II) oxide can be decomposed into mercury and oxygen and that water can be decomposed into hydrogen and oxygen. Sugar can be decomposed into carbon, hydrogen, and oxygen. Table salt is easily decomposed into sodium and chlorine. An element, however, cannot be decomposed into simpler substances by ordinary chemical changes.

If we could take a small piece of an element, say copper, and divide it and subdivide it into smaller and smaller particles, we finally would come to a single unit of copper that we could no longer divide and still have copper. This ultimate particle, the smallest particle of an element that can exist, is called an

atom

atom. An atom is also the smallest unit of an element that can enter into a chemical reaction. Atoms are made up of still smaller subatomic particles. But these subatomic particles (described in Chapter 5) do not have the properties of elements.

4.2   Distribution of Elements

Elements are distributed very unequally in nature. At normal room temperature two of the elements, bromine and mercury, are liquids; eleven elements, hydrogen, nitrogen, oxygen, fluorine, chlorine, helium, neon, argon, krypton, xenon, and radon, are gases; all the other elements are solids.

Ten elements make up about 99% of the weight of the earth's crust, seawater, and atmosphere. Oxygen, the most abundant of these, constitutes about 50% of this mass. The distribution of the elements shown in Table 4.1 includes the earth's crust to a depth of about 10 miles, the oceans, fresh water, and the atmosphere but does not include the mantle and core of the earth, which are believed to consist of metallic iron and nickel. Because the atmosphere contains relatively little matter, its inclusion has almost no effect on the distribution shown in Table 4.1. But the inclusion of fresh and salt water does have an appreciable effect since water contains about 11.1% hydrogen. Nearly all of the 0.87% hydrogen shown is from water.

Table 4.1 Distribution of the elements in the earth's crust, seawater, and atmosphere

Element	Weight percent	Element	Weight percent
Oxygen	49.20	Chlorine	0.19
Silicon	25.67	Phosphorus	0.11
Aluminum	7.50	Manganese	0.09
Iron	4.71	Carbon	0.08
Calcium	3.39	Sulfur	0.06
Sodium	2.63	Barium	0.04
Potassium	2.40	Nitrogen	0.03
Magnesium	1.93	Fluorine	0.03
Hydrogen	0.87		
Titanium	0.58	All others	0.47

Table 4.2 Average elemental composition of the human body

Element	Weight percent
Oxygen	65.0
Carbon	18.0
Hydrogen	10.0
Nitrogen	3.0
Calcium	2.0
Phosphorus	1.0
Traces of several other elements	1.0

The average distribution of the elements in the human body is shown in Table 4.2. Note again the high percentage of oxygen.

4.3 Names of the Elements

The names of the elements came to us from various sources. Many are derived from early Greek, Latin, or German words that generally described some property of the element. For example, iodine is taken from the Greek word *iodes,* meaning violetlike. Iodine, indeed, is violet in the vapor state. The name of the metal bismuth had its origin from the German words *weisse masse,* which means white mass. Miners called it *wismat;* it was later changed to *bismat,* and finally to bismuth. Some elements are named for the location of their discovery—for example, germanium, discovered in 1886 by Winkler, a German chemist. Others are named in commemoration of famous scientists, such as einsteinium and curium, named for Albert Einstein and Marie Curie, respectively.

4.4 Symbols of the Elements

symbol

We all recognize Mr., N. Y., and Ave. as abbreviations for mister, New York, and avenue. In like manner chemists have assigned an abbreviation to each element; these are called **symbols** of the elements. Fourteen of the elements have a single letter as their symbol, five have three-letter symbols, and the rest have two letters. A symbol stands for the element itself, for one atom of the element, and (as we shall see later) for a particular quantity of the element.

Rules governing symbols of elements are as follows:

1. Symbols are composed of one, two, or three letters.
2. If one letter is used, it is capitalized.
3. If two or three letters are used, the first is capitalized and the others are lowercase letters.

Examples: Sulfur S   Barium Ba

The symbols and names of all the elements are given in the table on the inside back cover of this book. Table 4.3 lists the more commonly used symbols. If we examine this table carefully, we note that most of the symbols start with the same letter as the name of the element that is represented. A number of symbols, however, appear to have no connection with the names of the elements they represent (see Table 4.4). These symbols have been carried over from earlier names (usually in Latin) of the elements and are so firmly implanted in the literature that their use is continued today.

Special care must be used in writing symbols. Begin each with a capital letter and use a lowercase second letter if needed. For example, consider Co, the symbol for the element cobalt. If through error CO (capital C and capital O) is

Table 4.3 Symbols of the most common elements

Element	Symbol	Element	Symbol	Element	Symbol
Aluminum	Al	Fluorine	F	Phosphorus	P
Antimony	Sb	Gold	Au	Platinum	Pt
Argon	Ar	Helium	He	Potassium	K
Arsenic	As	Hydrogen	H	Radium	Ra
Barium	Ba	Iodine	I	Silicon	Si
Bismuth	Bi	Iron	Fe	Silver	Ag
Boron	B	Lead	Pb	Sodium	Na
Bromine	Br	Lithium	Li	Strontium	Sr
Cadmium	Cd	Magnesium	Mg	Sulfur	S
Calcium	Ca	Manganese	Mn	Tin	Sn
Carbon	C	Mercury	Hg	Titanium	Ti
Chlorine	Cl	Neon	Ne	Tungsten	W
Chromium	Cr	Nickel	Ni	Uranium	U
Cobalt	Co	Nitrogen	N	Zinc	Zn
Copper	Cu	Oxygen	O		

Table 4.4 Symbols of the elements derived from early names: These symbols are in use today even though they do not correspond to the current name of the element.

Present name	Symbol	Former name
Antimony	Sb	Stibium
Copper	Cu	Cuprum
Gold	Au	Aurum
Iron	Fe	Ferrum
Lead	Pb	Plumbum
Mercury	Hg	Hydrargyrum
Potassium	K	Kalium
Silver	Ag	Argentum
Sodium	Na	Natrium
Tin	Sn	Stannum
Tungsten	W	Wolfram

written, the two elements carbon and oxygen (the *formula* for carbon monoxide) are represented instead of the single element cobalt. Another example of the need for care in writing symbols is the symbol Ca for calcium versus Co for cobalt. The letters must be distinct or else the symbol for the element may be misinterpreted.

Knowledge of symbols is essential for writing chemical formulas and equations. You should begin to learn the symbols immediately because they will be used extensively in the remainder of this book and in any future chemistry courses you may take. One way to learn the symbols is to practice a few minutes a day by making side-by-side lists of names and symbols and then covering each list alternately and writing the corresponding name or symbol. Initially it is a good plan to learn the symbols of the most common elements shown in Table 4.3.

The experiments of alchemists paved the way for the development of chemistry. Alchemists surrounded their work with mysticism, partly by devising a system of symbols known only to practitioners of alchemy (see Figure 4.1). The symbol ℞ (from the Latin *recipe*) is still used in medicine and was established during this time. In the early 1800s the Swedish chemist J. J. Berzelius (1779–1848) made a great contribution to chemistry by devising the present system of symbols using letters of the alphabet.

Gold   Silver   Iron   Mercury   Sulfur   Lead   Nickel   Copper   Sugar   Glass   Nitric acid

Figure 4.1 Some typical alchemists' symbols

4.5 Compounds

compound
A **compound** is a distinct substance containing two or more elements chemically combined in definite proportions by weight. Compounds, unlike elements, can be decomposed chemically into simpler substances—that is, into simpler compounds and/or elements. Atoms of the elements in a compound are combined in whole-number ratios, never as fractional parts of atoms. Compounds fall into two general types, *molecular* and *ionic*.

molecule
A **molecule** is the smallest uncharged individual unit of a compound formed by the union of two or more atoms. Water is a typical molecular compound. If we divide a drop of water into smaller and smaller particles, we finally obtain a single molecule of water consisting of two hydrogen atoms bonded to one oxygen atom. This molecule is the ultimate particle of water; it cannot be further subdivided without destroying the water and forming hydrogen and oxygen.

ion

cation
anion
An **ion** is a positively or negatively charged atom or group of atoms. An ionic compound is held together by attractive forces that exist between positively and negatively charged ions. A positively charged ion is called a **cation** (pronounced *cat-eye-on*); a negatively charged ion is called an **anion** (pronounced *an-eye-on*).

Compounds

Molecular
Exist as molecules that consist of two or more elements bonded together

Ionic
Exist in the form of cations and anions held together by the attractive force of their positive and negative charges

---

Sodium chloride is a typical ionic compound. The ultimate particles of sodium chloride are positively charged sodium ions and negatively charged chloride ions. Sodium chloride is held together in a crystalline structure by the attractive forces existing between these oppositely charged ions. Although ionic compounds consist of large aggregates of cations and anions, their formulas are normally represented by the simplest possible ratio of the atoms in the compound. For example, in sodium chloride the ratio is one sodium ion to one chlorine ion, and the formula is NaCl (see Section 4.7). The two types of compounds, molecular and ionic, are illustrated in Figure 4.2.

There are more than 6 million known registered compounds, with no end in sight as to the number that will be prepared in the future. Each compound is unique and has characteristic physical and chemical properties. Let us consider two compounds, water and mercury(II) oxide in some detail. Water is a colorless, odorless, tasteless liquid that can be changed to a solid (ice) at 0°C and to a gas (steam) at 100°C. Composed of two atoms of hydrogen and one atom of oxygen per

(a) H_2O (b) NaCl

Figure 4.2   Representation of molecular and ionic (nonmolecular) compounds: (a) Two hydrogen atoms combined with an oxygen atom to form a molecule of water. (b) A positively charged sodium ion and a negatively charged chloride ion form the compound sodium chloride.

molecule, water is 11.2% hydrogen and 88.8% oxygen by weight. Water reacts chemically with sodium to produce hydrogen gas and sodium hydroxide, with lime to produce calcium hydroxide, and with sulfur trioxide to produce sulfuric acid. No other compound has all these exact physical and chemical properties; they are characteristic of water alone.

Mercury(II) oxide is a dense, orange-red powder having a ratio of one atom of mercury to one atom of oxygen. Its composition by weight is 92.6% mercury and 7.4% oxygen. When it is heated to temperatures greater than 360°C, a colorless gas (oxygen) and a silvery, liquid metal (mercury) are produced. These specific physical and chemical properties belong to mercury(II) oxide and to no other substance. Thus, a compound may be identified and distinguished from all other compounds by its characteristic properties.

4.6 Law of Definite Composition of Compounds

A large number of experiments extending over a long period of time have established the fact that a particular compound always contains the same elements in the same proportions by weight. For example, water will always contain 11.2% hydrogen and 88.8% oxygen by weight. The fact that water contains hydrogen and oxygen in this particular ratio does not mean that hydrogen and oxygen cannot combine in some other ratio. However, a compound with a different ratio would not be water. In fact, hydrogen peroxide is made up of two atoms of hydrogen and two atoms of oxygen per molecule and contains 5.9% hydrogen and 94.1% oxygen by weight; its properties are markedly different from those of water.

	Water	*Hydrogen peroxide*
Percent H	11.2	5.9
Percent O	88.8	94.1
Atomic composition	2 H + 1 O	2 H + 2 O

Law of Definite Composition

The **Law of Definite Composition** states: A compound always contains two or more elements combined in a definite proportion by weight. The reliability of this law, which in essence states that the composition of a substance will always be the same no matter what its origin or how it is formed, is the cornerstone of the science of chemistry.

4.7 Chemical Formulas

chemical formula

Chemical formulas are used as abbreviations for compounds. A **chemical formula** shows the symbols and the ratio of the atoms of the elements in a compound. Sodium chloride contains one atom of sodium per atom of chlorine; its formula is NaCl. The formula for water is H_2O; it shows that a molecule of water contains two atoms of hydrogen and one atom of oxygen.

The formula of a compound tells us which elements it is composed of and how many atoms of each element are present in a formula unit. For example, a molecule of sulfuric acid is composed of two atoms of hydrogen, one atom of sulfur, and four atoms of oxygen. We could express this compound as HHSOOOO, but the usual formula for writing sulfuric acid is H_2SO_4. The formula may be expressed verbally as "H-two-S-O-four." Numbers that appear partially below the line and to the right of a symbol of an element are called *subscripts*. Thus the 2 and the 4 in H_2SO_4 are subscripts. Characteristics of chemical formulas are

1. The formula of a compound contains the symbols of all the elements in the compound.
2. When the formula contains one atom of an element, the symbol of that element represents that one atom. The number one (1) is not used as a subscript to indicate one atom of an element.
3. When the formula contains more than one atom of an element, the number of atoms is indicated by a subscript written to the right of the symbol of that atom. For example, the two (2) in H_2O indicates two atoms of H in the formula.
4. When the formula contains more than one of a group of atoms that occurs as a unit, parentheses are placed around the group, and the number of units of the group are indicated by a subscript placed to the right of the parentheses. Consider the nitrate group, NO_3^-. The formula for sodium nitrate, $NaNO_3$, has only one nitrate group; therefore no parentheses are needed. Calcium nitrate, $Ca(NO_3)_2$, has two nitrate groups, as indicated by the use of parentheses and the subscript 2. $Ca(NO_3)_2$ has a total of nine atoms: one Ca, two N, and six O atoms. The formula $Ca(NO_3)_2$ is read as "C-A [pause] N-O-three-taken twice."
5. Formulas written as H_2O, H_2SO_4, $Ca(NO_3)_2$, and $C_{12}H_{22}O_{11}$ show only the number and kind of each atom contained in the compound; they do not show the arrangement of the atoms in the compound or how they are chemically bonded to one another.

Figure 4.3 illustrates how symbols and numbers are used in chemical formulas.

Figure 4.3 Explanation of the formulas NaCl, H_2SO_4, and $Ca(NO_3)_2$

PROBLEM

4.1

Write formulas for the following compounds, the atom composition of which is given. **(a)** Hydrogen chloride: 1 atom hydrogen + 1 atom chlorine; **(b)** Methane: 1 atom carbon + 4 atoms hydrogen; **(c)** Glucose: 6 atoms carbon + 12 atoms hydrogen + 6 atoms oxygen.

(a) First write the symbols of the atoms in the formula: H   Cl   Since the ratio of atoms is one to one, we merely bring the symbols together to give the formula for hydrogen chloride as HCl.

(b) Write the symbols of the atoms: C   H   Now bring the symbols together and place a subscript 4 after the hydrogen atom. The formula is CH_4.

(c) Write the symbols of the atoms: C   H   O   Now write the formula, bringing together the symbols followed by the correct subscripts according to the data given (six C, twelve H, six O). The formula is $C_6H_{12}O_6$.

4.8   **Mixtures**

Single substances—elements or compounds—seldom occur naturally in the pure state. Air is a mixture of gases; seawater is a mixture containing a variety of dissolved minerals; ordinary soil is a complex mixture of minerals and various organic materials.

How is a mixture distinguished from a pure substance? A mixture (see Section 3.3) always contains two or more substances that can be present in varying concentrations. Let us consider an example of a homogeneous mixture and an example of a heterogeneous mixture. Homogeneous mixtures (solutions) containing either 5% or 10% salt in water can be prepared simply by mixing the correct amounts of salt and water. These mixtures can be separated by boiling away the water, leaving the salt as a residue. The composition of a heterogeneous mixture of sulfur crystals and iron filings can be varied by merely blending in either more sulfur or more iron filings. This mixture can be separated physically by using a magnet to attract the iron or by adding carbon disulfide to dissolve the sulfur.

Iron(II) sulfide (FeS) contains 63.5% Fe and 36.5% S by weight. If we mix iron and sulfur in this proportion, do we have iron(II) sulfide? No, it is still a mixture; the iron is still attracted by a magnet. But if this mixture is heated strongly, a chemical change (reaction) occurs in which the reacting substances, iron and sulfur, form a new substance, iron(II) sulfide. Iron(II) sulfide, FeS, is a compound of iron and sulfur and has properties that are different from those of either iron or sulfur: It is neither attracted by a magnet nor dissolved by carbon disulfide. The differences between the iron and sulfur *mixture* and the iron(II) sulfide *compound* are as follows:

Mixture of iron and sulfur	*Compound of iron and sulfur*
Formula: mixture has no definite formula; consists of Fe and S.	Formula: FeS
Composition: mixture contains Fe and S in any proportion by weight.	Composition: compound contains 63.5% Fe and 36.5% S by weight.
Separation: Fe and S can be separated by physical means.	Separation: Fe and S can be separated only by chemical changes.

The general characteristics of mixtures and compounds are compared in Table 4.5.

Table 4.5 Comparison of mixtures and compounds

	Mixture	*Compound*
Composition	May be composed of elements, compounds, or both in variable composition.	Composed of two or more elements in a definite, fixed proportion by weight.
Separation of components	Separation may be made by physical or mechanical means.	Elements can be separated by chemical changes only.
Identification of components	Components do not lose their identity.	A compound does not resemble the elements from which it is formed.

4.9 Metals, Nonmetals, and Metalloids

Three primary classifications of the elements are metals, nonmetals, and metalloids. Most of the elements are metals. We are familiar with metals because of their widespread use in tools, materials of construction, automobiles, and so on. But nonmetals are equally useful in our everyday life as major components of such items as clothing, food, fuel, glass, plastics, and wood.

metals

The **metals** are solids at room temperature (mercury is an exception). They have high luster, are good conductors of heat and electricity, are *malleable* (can be rolled or hammered into sheets), and are *ductile* (can be drawn into wires). Most metals have a high melting point and high density. Familiar metals are aluminum, chromium, copper, gold, iron, lead, magnesium, mercury, nickel, platinum, silver, tin, and zinc. Less familiar but still important metals are calcium, cobalt, potassium, sodium, uranium, and titanium.

Metals have little tendency to combine with each other to form compounds. But many metals readily combine with nonmetals such as chlorine, oxygen, and sulfur to form mainly ionic compounds such as metallic chlorides, oxides, and sulfides. In nature the more active metals are found combined with other elements as minerals. A few of the less active ones such as copper, gold, and silver are sometimes found in a native, or free, state.

nonmetals

Nonmetals, unlike metals, are not lustrous, have relatively low melting points and densities, and are generally poor conductors of heat and electricity. Carbon, phosphorus, sulfur, selenium, and iodine are solids; bromine is a liquid; the rest of the nonmetals are gases. Common nonmetals found uncombined in nature are carbon (graphite and diamond), nitrogen, oxygen, sulfur, and the noble gases (helium, neon, argon, krypton, xenon, and radon).

Nonmetals combine with one another to form molecular compounds such as carbon dioxide (CO_2), methane (CH_4), butane (C_4H_{10}), and sulfur dioxide (SO_2). Fluorine, the most reactive nonmetal, combines readily with almost all the other elements.

metalloids

Several elements (boron, silicon, germanium, arsenic, antimony, tellurium, and polonium) are classified as **metalloids** and have properties that are intermediate between those of metals and those of nonmetals. The intermediate position of these elements is shown in Table 4.6, which lists and classifies all the elements as metals, nonmetals, or metalloids. Certain metalloids, such as boron, silicon, and germanium, are the raw materials for the semiconductor devices that make our modern electronics industry possible.

4.10 Elements That Exist as Diatomic Molecules

Seven of the elements (all nonmetals) occur as *diatomic molecules*. These elements and their symbols, formulas, and brief descriptions are listed in Table 4.7. Whether found free in nature or prepared in the laboratory, the molecules of these elements always contain two atoms. The formulas of the free elements are therefore always written to show this molecular composition: H_2, N_2, O_2, F_2, Cl_2, Br_2, and I_2.

Table 4.6 Classification of the elements into metals, metalloids, and nonmetals

1 H																	2 He
3 Li	4 Be											5 B	6 C	7 N	8 O	9 F	10 Ne
11 Na	12 Mg											13 Al	14 Si	15 P	16 S	17 Cl	18 Ar
19 K	20 Ca	21 Sc	22 Ti	23 V	24 Cr	25 Mn	26 Fe	27 Co	28 Ni	29 Cu	30 Zn	31 Ga	32 Ge	33 As	34 Se	35 Br	36 Kr
37 Rb	38 Sr	39 Y	40 Zr	41 Nb	42 Mo	43 Tc	44 Ru	45 Rh	46 Pd	47 Ag	48 Cd	49 In	50 Sn	51 Sb	52 Te	53 I	54 Xe
55 Cs	56 Ba	57 La	72 Hf	73 Ta	74 W	75 Re	76 Os	77 Ir	78 Pt	79 Au	80 Hg	81 Tl	82 Pb	83 Bi	84 Po	85 At	86 Rn
87 Fr	88 Ra	89 Ac	104 Unq	105 Unp	106 Unh	107 —		109 —									

Key
☐ Metals
▨ Metalloids
▩ Nonmetals

58 Ce	59 Pr	60 Nd	61 Pm	62 Sm	63 Eu	64 Gd	65 Tb	66 Dy	67 Ho	68 Er	69 Tm	70 Yb	71 Lu
90 Th	91 Pa	92 U	93 Np	94 Pu	95 Am	96 Cm	97 Bk	98 Cf	99 Es	100 Fm	101 Md	102 No	103 Lr

Table 4.7 Elements that exist as diatomic molecules

Element	Symbol	Molecular formula	Normal state
Hydrogen	H	H_2	Colorless gas
Nitrogen	N	N_2	Colorless gas
Oxygen	O	O_2	Colorless gas
Fluorine	F	F_2	Pale yellow gas
Chlorine	Cl	Cl_2	Yellow-green gas
Bromine	Br	Br_2	Reddish-brown liquid
Iodine	I	I_2	Bluish-black solid

It is important to see how symbols are used to designate either an atom or a molecule of an element. Consider hydrogen and oxygen. Hydrogen gas is present in volcanic gases and can be prepared by many chemical reactions. Regardless of their source, all samples of free hydrogen gas consist of diatomic molecules. Free hydrogen is designated and its composition is expressed by the formula H_2. Oxygen makes up about 21% by volume of the air that we breathe. This free oxygen is constantly being replenished by photosynthesis; it can also be prepared in the laboratory by several reactions. All free oxygen is diatomic and is designated by the formula O_2. Now consider water, a compound designated by the formula H_2O (sometimes HOH). Water contains neither free hydrogen (H_2) nor free oxygen (O_2). The H_2 part of the formula H_2O simply indicates that two atoms of hydrogen are combined with one atom of oxygen to form water. Thus symbols are used to designate elements, show the composition of molecules of elements, and give the elemental composition of compounds.

4.11   Nomenclature and Chemical Equations

Knowledge of chemical names and of the writing and balancing of chemical equations is vital to the study of chemistry. This section serves only as an introduction to the naming of compounds and the writing of equations. More complete details of the systematic methods of naming inorganic compounds are given in Chapter 8, and a more detailed explanation of chemical equations is given in Chapter 10. Refer to these two chapters often, as needed. Neither chapter is intended to be studied only in the sequence given in the text; rather, they are common depositories of information on chemical nomenclature and equations.

Nomenclature

We have already used such names as hydrogen chloride (HCl), mercury(II) oxide (HgO), magnesium oxide (MgO), and sodium chloride (NaCl). Note that all four names end in *ide*. This *ide* ending is characteristic of the names of *binary compounds*—that is, compounds composed of atoms of two different elements. Some compounds contain several atoms of the same element (for example, CCl_4, carbon tetrachloride), but as long as only two different kinds of atoms are present, the compound is considered to be binary.

When a compound consisting of a metal and a nonmetal is named, the name of the metal is given first, followed by the name of the nonmetal, which is modified to end in *ide* (see Table 4.8).

There are exceptions to the rule that all names ending in *ide* are for binary compounds. Some compounds containing more than two elements also have names that end in *ide* (for example, NH_4Cl, ammonium chloride; NaOH, sodium hydroxide). Refer to Section 8.7 for more details on naming binary compounds.

Table 4.8   Names of selected nonmetals modified to end in *ide*, for use in naming binary compounds

Nonmetal	Modified name used in binary compounds
Oxygen	Oxide
Fluorine	Fluoride
Chlorine	Chloride
Bromine	Bromide
Iodine	Iodide
Sulfur	Sulfide
Nitrogen	Nitride

Examples of binary compounds with names ending in *ide* are

NaCl	Sodium chloride	H_2S	Hydrogen sulfide
$BaBr_2$	Barium bromide	$AlBr_3$	Aluminum bromide
NaI	Sodium iodide	K_2S	Potassium sulfide
CaF_2	Calcium fluoride	Mg_3N_2	Magnesium nitride

Other names and formulas that you should become familiar with early in your study of chemistry are the commonly used acids and bases shown below. Methods used for naming these compounds are discussed in Chapter 8.

HCl	Hydrochloric acid	NaOH	Sodium hydroxide
H_2SO_4	Sulfuric acid	KOH	Potassium hydroxide
HNO_3	Nitric acid	$Ca(OH)_2$	Calcium hydroxide
$HC_2H_3O_2$	Acetic acid	NH_4OH	Ammonium hydroxide
H_3PO_4	Phosphoric acid		

PROBLEM

4.2

Name the binary compounds having the formulas NaCl and MgO.

The name is sodium chloride.

The name is magnesium oxide.

Chemical Equations

chemical equation

Chemical changes, or reactions, form substances with compositions that are different from those of the starting substances. A **chemical equation** is a shorthand expression for a chemical reaction. Substances in the reaction are represented by their symbols or formulas in the equation. The equation indicates both the reactants (starting substances) and the products and often shows the conditions necessary to facilitate the chemical change. The reactants are written on the left side and the products on the right side of the equation. An arrow ($\rightarrow$) pointing to the products separates the reactants from the products. A plus sign (+) is used to separate one reactant (or product) from another.

Reactants ⟶ Products

We shall see in Chapter 5 that every atom has a specific mass. In an equation the symbols or formulas that represent a substance also represent a specific mass of that substance. Because no detectable change in mass results from a chemical change, the mass of the products must equal the mass of the reactants. When a chemical change is represented by an equation, this conservation of mass is attained by balancing the equation. After the correct formulas for the reactants and products are established, an equation is balanced by placing integral numbers (as needed) in front of the formulas of the substances in the equation. We use these numbers to obtain an equation that has the same number of atoms of each kind of element on each side of the equation.

> **A balanced chemical equation contains the same number of atoms of each kind of element on each side of the equation.**

Consider, again, the reaction of metallic copper heated in air. The chemical change may be represented by the following equations:

$$\text{Copper} + \text{Oxygen} \xrightarrow{\Delta} \text{Copper(II) oxide} \tag{1}$$

$$\text{Cu} + \text{O}_2 \xrightarrow{\Delta} \text{CuO} \quad \text{(unbalanced)} \tag{2}$$

Copper and oxygen are the reactants, and copper(II) oxide is the product. Equation (2) as written is not balanced because two oxygen atoms appear on the left side and only one on the right side. We place a 2 in front of Cu and a 2 in front of CuO to obtain the balanced equation:

$$2\,\text{Cu} + \text{O}_2 \xrightarrow{\Delta} 2\,\text{CuO} \quad \text{(balanced)} \tag{3}$$

This balanced equation contains 2 Cu atoms and 2 O atoms on each side of the equation.

A very important factor to remember when balancing equations is that you must not change the subscripts of a correct formula for the convenience of balancing the equation. In the unbalanced equation (2) we cannot change the formula of CuO to CuO_2 to balance the equation, even though by doing so we balance the number of atoms of each element on each side of the equation. The formula CuO_2 is not the correct formula for the true product. It is also important to be aware that a number in front of a formula multiplies every atom in that formula by that number. Thus,

2 CuO   means 2 Cu atoms and 2 O atoms

3 H_2O means 6 H atoms and 3 O atoms

4 H_2SO_4 means 8 H atoms, 4 S atoms, and 16 O atoms

> **Once a correct formula is written, it must not be changed during the balancing of an equation.**

PROBLEM

4.3

How many atoms of each element are in each of these expressions?
(a) CH_4 **(b)** $2 CH_4$ **(c)** $3 Ca(OH)_2$

(a) CH_4
           ↗ ↖
      1 atom C   4 atoms H

Each molecule of CH_4 contains one C atom and four H atoms.
(b) $2 CH_4$ means two molecules of CH_4. Since one molecule of CH_4 contains one C atom and four H atoms, two CH_4 molecules contain two C atoms and eight H atoms.

(c) $Ca(OH)_2$
           ↗ ↖
      1 atom Ca   2 units of OH

Each unit of OH contains one atom of O and one atom of H. Therefore $(OH)_2$ contains two O atoms and two H atoms. One formula unit of $Ca(OH)_2$ contains one Ca atom, two O atoms, and two H atoms; $3 Ca(OH)_2$ indicates three formula units of $Ca(OH)_2$. Therefore $3 Ca(OH)_2$ contains three Ca atoms, six O atoms, and six H atoms.

PROBLEM

4.4

When methane gas (CH_4) is burned in air, it reacts with oxygen to yield carbon dioxide and water. The equation for the reaction is

$$CH_4 + O_2 \longrightarrow CO_2 + H_2O \quad \text{(unbalanced)}$$

Balance the equation for this reaction.
    Inspecting each side of the equation we observe

Left side: 1 C atom   Right side: 1 C atom
             4 H atoms   2 H atoms
             2 O atoms   3 O atoms

The numbers of H and O atoms on each side of the equation are not equal, so the equation is unbalanced. To balance the equation, first place a 2 in front of the H_2O. This balances the H atoms, giving four H atoms on each side:

$$CH_4 + O_2 \longrightarrow CO_2 + 2 H_2O \quad \text{(unbalanced)}$$

The oxygen atoms are still unbalanced, with two O atoms on the left and four O atoms on the right. Place a 2 in front of the O_2, and the equation is balanced:

$$CH_4 + 2 O_2 \longrightarrow CO_2 + 2 H_2O \quad \text{(balanced)}$$

The balanced equation contains one C, four H, and four O atoms on each side.

PROBLEM

4.5

Balance the following equation:

$$2 Al + 3 Cl_2 \longrightarrow 2 AlCl_3 \quad \text{(unbalanced)}$$

In this equation the Cl atoms are not in balance (two Cl atoms on the left and three Cl atoms on the right side of the equation). Placing integral numbers in front of Cl_2 will always result in an even number of Cl atoms on the left side of the equation. Therefore the number in front of $AlCl_3$ will have to be an even number (2, 4, 6, ...). The number of Cl atoms needed on each side of the equation is 6, the lowest common multiple of 2 and 3. Placing a 3 in front of Cl_2 and a 2 in front of $AlCl_3$ will give 6 Cl atoms on each side of the equation:

$$Al + 3\,Cl_2 \longrightarrow 2\,AlCl_3 \quad \text{(unbalanced)}$$

By balancing the Cl atoms we have unbalanced the Al atoms. But we can correct this imbalance by placing a 2 in front of Al to give the balanced equation:

$$2\,Al + 3\,Cl_2 \longrightarrow 2\,AlCl_3 \quad \text{(balanced)}$$

Each side of the balanced equation has two Al and six Cl atoms.

QUESTIONS

A. *Review the meanings of the new terms introduced in this chapter.*

1. Element
2. Atom
3. Symbol
4. Compound
5. Molecule
6. Ion
7. Cation
8. Anion
9. Law of Definite Composition
10. Chemical formula
11. Metal
12. Nonmetal
13. Metalloid
14. Chemical equation

B. *Information useful in answering these questions will be found in the tables and figures.*

1. Of the ten most abundant elements in the earth's crust, seawater, and atmosphere, how many are metals? Nonmetals? Metalloids?
2. Of the six most abundant elements in the human body, how many are metals? Nonmetals? Metalloids?
3. Why is the symbol for gold Au rather than G or Go?
4. Give the names of (a) the solid diatomic nonmetal and (b) the liquid diatomic nonmetal.
5. What would be the modified names of the two elements of Question 4 when they are combined with metals in binary compounds?
6. Are there more atoms of silicon or hydrogen in the earth's crust, seawater, and atmosphere? Use Table 4.1 and the fact that the mass of the silicon atom is about 28 times that of a hydrogen atom.

7. How many metals are there? Nonmetals? Metalloids? (See Table 4.6.)

C. *Review questions*

1. What does the symbol of an element stand for?
2. Write down what you believe to be the symbols for the elements phosphorus, aluminum, hydrogen, potassium, magnesium, sodium, nitrogen, nickel, silver, and plutonium. Now look up the correct symbols and rewrite them, comparing the two sets.
3. Interpret the difference in meanings for each of these pairs:
   (a) Si and SI   (b) Pb and PB   (c) 4 P and P_4
4. List six elements and their symbols in which the first letter of the symbol is different from that of the name.
5. Write the names and symbols for the 14 elements that have only one letter as their symbol. (See table on inside back cover.)
6. Distinguish between an element and a compound.
7. Explain why the Law of Definite Composition does not pertain to mixtures.
8. What are the two general types of compounds? How do they differ from each other?
9. What is the basis for distinguishing one compound from another?
10. Given the following list of compounds and their

formulas, what elements are present in each compound?

(a) Potassium iodide   KI
(b) Sodium carbonate Na_2CO_3
(c) Aluminum oxide Al_2O_3
(d) Calcium bromide $CaBr_2$
(e) Carbon tetrachloride CCl_4
(f) Magnesium bromide $MgBr_2$
(g) Nitric acid HNO_3
(h) Barium sulfate $BaSO_4$
(i) Aluminum phosphate $AlPO_4$
(j) Acetic acid $HC_2H_3O_2$

11. Write the formula for each of the following compounds, the composition of which is given after each name:

(a) Zinc oxide   1 atom Zn,
    ZnO   1 atom O
(b) Potassium chlorate   1 atom K,
    K ClO₃   1 atom Cl,
     3 atoms O
(c) Sodium hydroxide   1 atom Na,
     1 atom O,
    NaOH   1 atom H
(d) Aluminum bromide   1 atom Al,
    Al Br₃   3 atoms Br
(e) Calcium fluoride   1 atom Ca,
    CaF₂   2 atoms F
(f) Lead(II) chromate   1 atom Pb,
     1 atom Cr,
    PbCrO₄   4 atoms O
(g) Ethyl alcohol   2 atoms C,
     6 atoms H,
    C₂H₆O O,   1 atom O
(h) Benzene   6 atoms C,
    (CH)₆   6 atoms H

12. Explain the meaning of each symbol and number in the following formulas:

(a) H_2O (d) $Ni(NO_3)_2$
(b) $AlBr_3$ (e) $C_{12}H_{22}O_{11}$ (sucrose)
(c) Na_2SO_4

13. How many atoms are represented in each of these formulas?

(a) KF   (f) $NaC_2H_3O_2$
(b) $CaCO_3$ (g) CCl_2F_2 (Freon)
(c) N_2 (h) $Al_2(SO_4)_3$
(d) $Ba(ClO_3)_2$ (i) $(NH_4)_2C_2O_4$
(e) $K_2Cr_2O_7$

14. How many atoms are contained in (a) one molecule of hydrogen, (b) one molecule of water, and (c) one molecule of sulfuric acid?

15. What is the major difference between a cation and an anion?

16. Write the names and formulas of the elements that exist as diatomic molecules.

17. How many atoms of oxygen are represented in each expression?

(a) $4 H_2O$ (c) H_2O_2 (e) $Al(ClO_3)_3$
(b) $3 CuSO_4$ (d) $3 Fe(OH)_3$

18. How many atoms of hydrogen are represented in each expression?

(a) $5 H_2$ (c) $2 C_6H_{12}O_6$
(b) $2 Ba(C_2H_3O_2)_2$ (d) $2 HC_2H_3O_2$

19. Distinguish between homogeneous and heterogeneous mixtures.

20. Classify each of the following materials as an element, compound, or mixture:

(a) Air   (e) Wine
(b) Oxygen   (f) Iodine
(c) Sodium chloride   (g) Sulfuric acid
(d) Platinum   (h) Crude oil

21. Classify each of the following materials as an element, compound, or mixture:

(a) Paint   (e) Sulfuric acid
(b) Salt   (f) Silver
(c) Copper   (g) Milk
(d) Beer   (h) Sodium hydroxide

22. A white solid, on heating, formed a colorless gas and a yellow solid. Assuming that there was no reaction with the air, is the original solid an element or a compound? Explain.

23. Tabulate the properties that characterize metals and nonmetals.

24. Which of the following are diatomic molecules?

(a) H_2 (c) HCl   (e) NO   (g) $MgCl_2$
(b) SO_2 (d) H_2O (f) NO_2

25. Name the following binary compounds. Refer to Chapter 8 if necessary.

(a) AgBr   (e) NaF   (h) BN
(b) HI   (f) K_2O (i) $BaCl_2$
(c) $MgBr_2$ (g) LiCl   (j) Al_2S_3
(d) CaS

What is common to the names of these binary compounds?

26. An atom of silver is represented by the symbol Ag; a hydrogen molecule by the formula H_2; a water molecule by H_2O. Write the expressions to represent:

(a) Five silver atoms
(b) Four hydrogen molecules
(c) Three water molecules

27. Balance these equations (all formulas are correct as written):
    (a) $H_2 + Cl_2 \longrightarrow HCl$
    (b) $Zn + CuSO_4 \longrightarrow Cu + ZnSO_4$
    (c) $HCl + NaOH \longrightarrow NaCl + H_2O$
    (d) $Ca + O_2 \longrightarrow CaO$
    (e) $Fe + HCl \longrightarrow FeCl_2 + H_2$
    (f) $P + I_2 \longrightarrow PI_3$
    (g) $MgO + HCl \longrightarrow MgCl_2 + H_2O$
    (h) $HNO_3 + Ba(OH)_2 \longrightarrow Ba(NO_3)_2 + H_2O$
    (i) $BiCl_3 + H_2S \longrightarrow Bi_2S_3 + HCl$
    (j) $Mg_3N_2 + H_2O \longrightarrow Mg(OH)_2 + NH_3$

28. Balance the following equations, each of which represents a method of preparing oxygen gas:
    (a) $H_2O_2 \longrightarrow H_2O + O_2$
    (b) $KClO_3 \xrightarrow{\Delta} KCl + O_2$
    (c) $KNO_3 \xrightarrow{\Delta} KNO_2 + O_2$
    (d) $Na_2O_2 + H_2O \longrightarrow NaOH + O_2$
    (e) $H_2O \xrightarrow[H_2SO_4]{\text{Electrical energy}} H_2 + O_2$

29. Balance the following equations, each of which represents a method of preparing hydrogen gas:
    (a) $Zn + HCl \longrightarrow ZnCl_2 + H_2$
    (b) $Al + H_2SO_4 \longrightarrow Al_2(SO_4)_3 + H_2$
    (c) $Na + H_2O \longrightarrow NaOH + H_2$
    (d) $C + H_2O \text{ (steam)} \longrightarrow CO + H_2$
    (e) $Fe + H_2O \text{ (steam)} \longrightarrow Fe_3O_4 + H_2$

30. Which of the following statements are correct?
    (a) The smallest unit of an element that can exist and enter into a chemical reaction is called a molecule.
    (b) The basic building blocks of all substances, which cannot be decomposed into simpler substances by ordinary chemical change, are compounds.
    (c) The most abundant element in the earth's crust, seawater, and atmosphere by weight is oxygen.
    (d) The most abundant element in the human body, by weight, is carbon.
    (e) Most of the elements are represented by symbols consisting of one or two letters.
    (f) The symbol for copper is Co.
    (g) The symbol for sodium is Na.
    (h) The symbol for potassium is P.
    (i) The symbol for lead is Le.
    (j) Early names for some elements led to unlikely symbols, such as Fe for iron.
    (k) A compound is a distinct substance that contains two or more elements combined in a definite proportion by weight.
    (l) The smallest uncharged individual unit of a compound formed by the union of two or more atoms is called a substance.
    (m) An ion is a positive or negative electrically charged atom or group of atoms.
    (n) The Law of Definite Composition states that a compound always contains two or more elements combined in a definite proportion by weight.
    (o) A chemical formula is a shorthand expression for a chemical reaction.
    (p) The formula Na_2CO_3 indicates a total of six atoms, including three oxygen atoms.
    (q) A general property of nonmetals is that they are good conductors of heat and electricity.
    (r) Metals have the properties of ductility and malleability.
    (s) *Malleable* means that when struck a hard blow the substance will shatter.
    (t) Elements that have properties intermediate between metals and nonmetals are called mixtures.
    (u) More of the elements are metals than nonmetals.
    (v) In a balanced chemical equation, the mass of the products is equal to the mass of the reactants.
    (w) Bromine is an element that occurs as a diatomic molecule, Br_2.
    (x) The binary compound CaS is called calcium sulfate.
    (y) The substances on the left side of the arrow in a chemical equation are called reactants and those on the right side are called products.
    (z) The equation $2C_2H_2 + 4\ O_2 \longrightarrow 4\ CO_2 + 2\ H_2O$ is balanced.

D. *Review problems*

1. Common table salt, NaCl, contains 39.3% sodium and 60.7% chlorine by weight. What weight of sodium is present in 25.0 g of salt?
2. Red brass is a homogeneous mixture of 90% copper and 10% zinc. If 40 g of zinc is added to 100 g of red brass, what will be the new composition?
3. Calcium oxide, CaO, contains 71.5% calcium.

What size sample of CaO would contain 12.0 g of calcium?

*4. What would be the density of a solution made by mixing 2.50 mL of carbon tetrachloride (CCl_4, $d = 1.595$ g/mL) and 3.50 mL of carbon tetrabromide (CBr_4, $d = 3.420$ g/mL)? Assume that the volume of the mixed liquids is the sum of the two volumes used.

*5. Only two elements, Br_2 ($d = 3.12$ g/mL) and Hg ($d = 13.6$ g/mL), are liquids at room temperature. How many milliliters of Br_2 will have the same mass as 12.5 mL Hg?

*6. When 14.5 g of calcium and 14.5 g of sulfur were mixed and reacted to give the compound calcium sulfide (CaS), 2.90 g of sulfur remained unreacted.
   (a) What percentage of the compound is sulfur?
   (b) An atom of which element, Ca or S, has the greater mass? Explain.
   (c) How many grams of sulfur will combine with 30.0 g of calcium?

7. Pure gold is too soft a metal for many uses, so it is alloyed to give it more mechanical strength. One particular alloy is made by mixing 60 g of gold, 8.0 g of silver, and 12 g of copper. What carat gold is this alloy if pure gold is considered to be 24 carat?

*8. Methane, the chief component of natural gas, has the formula CH_4. Each atom of carbon weighs 12 times as much as an atom of hydrogen. Calculate the weight percent of carbon in methane.

9. White gold is a homogeneous solution of 90% gold and 10% palladium. How much gold is present in a bar of white gold weighing 9420 g?

*10. The metal used to make the U.S. nickel coin is an alloy of 75% copper and 25% nickel. What maximum weight of alloy could be produced if only 450 kg of nickel and 1180 kg of copper were on hand?

Atomic Theory and Structure

After studying Chapter 5, you should be able to

1. Understand the new terms listed in Question A at the end of the chapter.
2. State the major provisions of Dalton's atomic theory.
3. Give the names, symbols, charges, and relative masses of the three principal subatomic particles.
4. Describe the atom as conceived by Ernest Rutherford after his alpha scattering experiments.
5. Describe the atom as conceived by Niels Bohr.
6. Discuss the contributions to atomic theory made by Dalton, Thomson, Rutherford, Bohr, Chadwick, and Schrödinger.
7. Describe what is meant by an electron orbital.
8. Determine the maximum number of electrons that can exist in the principal energy levels and sublevels.
9. Determine the atomic number, mass number, or number of neutrons of any isotope when given the values of any two of these three items.
10. Draw the diagram of any isotope of the first 56 elements, showing the composition of the nucleus and the numbers of electrons in the main energy levels.
11. Write the electron structure ($1s^2 2s^2 2p^6 \ldots$) for any of the first 56 elements.
12. Explain what is represented by the Lewis-dot (electron-dot) structure of an element.

13. Write Lewis-dot (electron-dot) symbols for the first 20 elements.
14. Understand the basis for the Octet Rule.
15. Name and distinguish among the three isotopes of hydrogen.
16. Calculate the average atomic mass (weight) of an element, given the isotopic masses and abundance of its isotopes.

5.1   Early Thoughts

The structure of matter has long intrigued and engaged the minds of people. The seed of modern atomic theory was sown during the time of the ancient Greek philosophers. About 440 B.C. Empedocles stated that all matter was composed of four "elements"—earth, air, water, and fire. Democritus (about 470–370 B.C.), one of the early atomistic philosophers, thought that all forms of matter were finitely divisible into invisible particles, which he called atoms. He held that atoms were in constant motion and that they combined with one another in various ways. This purely speculative hypothesis was not based on scientific observations. Shortly thereafter, Aristotle (384–322 B.C.) opposed the theory of Democritus and endorsed and advanced the Empedoclean theory. So strong was the influence of Aristotle that his theory dominated the thinking of scientists and philosophers until the beginning of the 17th century. The term *atom* is derived from the Greek word *atomos*, meaning indivisible.

5.2   Dalton's Atomic Theory

More than 2000 years after Democritus, the English schoolmaster John Dalton (1766–1844) revived the concept of atoms and proposed an atomic theory based on facts and experimental evidence. This theory, described in a series of papers published during the period 1803–1810, rested on the idea of a different kind of atom for each element. The essence of **Dalton's atomic theory** may be summed up as follows:

Dalton's atomic theory

1. Elements are composed of minute, indivisible particles called atoms.
2. Atoms of the same element are alike in mass and size.
3. Atoms of different elements have different masses and sizes.
4. Chemical compounds are formed by the union of two or more atoms of different elements.
5. Atoms combine to form compounds in simple numerical ratios such as one to one, two to one, two to three, and so on.
6. Atoms of two elements may combine in different ratios to form more than one compound.

Dalton's atomic theory stands as a landmark in the development of chemistry. The major premises of his theory are still valid today. However, some of the statements must be modified or qualified because investigations since Dalton's time have shown that (1) atoms are composed of subatomic particles; (2) not all the atoms of a specific element have the same mass; and (3) atoms, under special circumstances, can be decomposed.

5.3 Subatomic Parts of the Atom

The concept of the atom—a particle so small that it could not be seen even with the most powerful microscope—and the subsequent determination of its structure stand among the very greatest creative intellectual human achievements.

Any visible quantity of an element contains a vast number of identical atoms. But when we refer to an atom of an element, we isolate a single atom from the multitude in order to present that element in its simplest form. Figure 5.1 illustrates the hypothetical isolation of a single copper atom from its crystal lattice.

Let us examine this tiny particle we call the atom. The diameter of a single atom ranges from 0.1 to 0.5 nanometers (1 nm = 1×10^{-9} m). Hydrogen, the smallest atom, has a diameter of about 0.1 nm. To arrive at some idea of how small an atom is, consider this dot (•), which has a diameter of about 1 mm, or 1×10^6 nm. It would take 10 million hydrogen atoms to form a line of atoms across this dot. As inconceivably small as atoms are, they contain even smaller particles, the **subatomic particles,** such as electrons, protons, and neutrons.

subatomic *particles* *electron*

The experimental discovery of the electron (e^-) was made in 1897 by J. J. Thomson (1856–1940). The **electron** is a particle with a negative electrical charge and a mass of 9.110×10^{-28} g. This mass is 1/1837 the mass of a hydrogen atom and corresponds to 0.0005486 atomic mass unit (amu) (defined in Section 5.17). One atomic mass unit has a mass of 1.6606×10^{-24} g. Although the actual electrical charge of an electron is known, its value is too cumbersome for practical use. Therefore, the electron has been assigned a relative electrical charge of -1. The size of an electron has not been determined exactly, but its diameter is believed to be less than 10^{-12} cm.

Single atom of Cu

Crystalline structure of copper

Figure 5.1   A single atom of copper compared with copper as it occurs in its regular crystalline lattice structure: Billions of atoms are present in a cross section of even the smallest strand of copper wire.

Table 5.1 Electrical charge and relative mass of electrons, protons, and neutrons

Particle	Symbol	Relative electrical charge	Relative mass (amu)	Actual mass (g)
Electron	e^-	-1	$\dfrac{1}{1837}$	9.110×10^{-28}
Proton	p	$+1$	1	1.673×10^{-24}
Neutron	n	0	1	1.675×10^{-24}

proton

Protons were first observed by E. Goldstein (1850–1930) in 1886. However, it was J. J. Thomson who discovered the nature of the proton. He showed that the proton is a particle, and he calculated its mass to be about 1837 times that of an electron. The **proton** (p) is a particle with a relative mass of 1 amu and an actual mass of 1.673×10^{-24} g. Its relative charge ($+1$) is equal in magnitude but of opposite sign to the charge on the electron. The mass of a proton is only very slightly less than that of a hydrogen atom.

neutron

The third major subatomic particle was discovered in 1932 by James Chadwick (1891–1974). This particle, the **neutron** (n), bears neither a positive nor a negative charge and has a relative mass of about 1 amu. Its actual mass (1.675×10^{-24} g) is only very slightly greater than that of a proton. The properties of these three subatomic particles are summarized in Table 5.1.

Nearly all the ordinary chemical properties of matter can be explained in terms of atoms consisting of electrons, protons, and neutrons. The discussion of atomic structure that follows is based on the assumption that atoms contain only these principal subatomic particles. Many other subatomic particles such as mesons, positrons, neutrinos, and antiprotons have been discovered. At this time it is not clear whether all these particles are actually present in the atom or whether they are produced by reactions occurring within the nucleus. The fields of atomic and particle or high-energy physics are fascinating and have attracted many young scientists in recent years. This interest has resulted in a great deal of research that is producing a long list of subatomic particles. Descriptions of the properties of many of these particles are to be found in recent physics textbooks and in various articles appearing in *Scientific American* over the past several years.

5.4 The Nuclear Atom

The discovery that positively charged particles were present in atoms came soon after the discovery of radioactivity by Henri Becquerel in 1896. Radioactive elements spontaneously emit alpha, beta, and gamma rays from their nuclei (see Chapter 18).

Ernest Rutherford (Figure 5.2) had, by 1907, established that the positively charged alpha particles emitted by certain radioactive elements were ions of the

E. Rutherford

Figure 5.2   Ernest Rutherford (1871–1937), British physicist who identified two of the three principal rays emanating from radioactive substances: His experiments with alpha particles led to the first laboratory transmutation of an element and to his formulation of the nuclear atom. Rutherford was awarded the Nobel prize in 1908 for his work on transmutation. *(Courtesy Rutherford Museum, McGill University.)*

element helium. Rutherford used these alpha particles to establish the nuclear nature of atoms. In some experiments performed in 1911, he directed a stream of positively charged helium ions (alpha particles) at a very thin sheet of gold foil (about 1000 atoms thick). He observed that most of the alpha particles passed through the foil with little or no deflection; but a few of the particles were deflected at large angles, and occasionally one even bounced back from the foil (see Figure 5.3). It was known that like charges repel each other and that an electron with a mass of 1/1837 amu could not possibly have an appreciable effect on the path of a 4 amu alpha particle, which is about 7350 times more massive than an electron. Rutherford therefore reasoned that each gold atom must contain a positively charged mass occupying a relatively tiny volume and that, when an alpha particle approached close enough to this positive mass, it was deflected. Rutherford spoke of this positively charged mass as the *nucleus of*

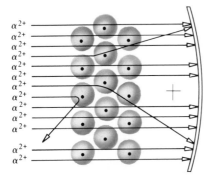

Figure 5.3 Diagram representing Rutherford's experiment on alpha particle scattering: Positive alpha particles (α^{2+}), emanating from a radioactive source, were directed at a thin metal foil. Diagram illustrates the deflection and repulsion of the positive alpha particles by the positive nuclei of the metal atoms.

the atom. Because alpha particles have relatively high masses, the extent of the deflections (some actually bounced back) indicated to Rutherford that the nucleus is relatively very heavy and dense. (The density of the nucleus of a hydrogen atom is about 10^{12} g/cm^3, about one trillion times the density of water.) Because most of the alpha particles passed through the thousand or so gold atoms without any apparent deflection, he further concluded that most of an atom consists of empty space.

When we speak of the mass of an atom, we are, for practical purposes, referring primarily to the mass of the nucleus. The nucleus contains all the protons and neutrons, which represent more than 99.9% of the total mass of any atom (see Table 5.1). By way of illustration, the largest number of electrons known to exist in an atom is 109. The mass of even 109 electrons is only about 1/17 of the mass of a single proton or neutron. The mass of an atom, therefore, is primarily determined by the combined masses of its protons and neutrons.

5.5 General Arrangement of Subatomic Particles

The alpha particle scattering experiments of Rutherford established that the atom contains a dense, positively charged nucleus. The later work of Chadwick demonstrated that the atom contains neutrons, which are particles with mass but no charge. Light, negatively charged electrons are also present and offset the positive charges in the nucleus. Based on this experimental evidence, a general description of the atom and the location of its subatomic particles was devised. Each atom consists of a **nucleus** surrounded by electrons. The nucleus contains protons and neutrons but not electrons. In a neutral atom the postive charge of the nucleus (due to protons) is exactly offset by the negative electrons. Because the charge of an electron is equal but of opposite sign to the charge of a proton, a neutral atom must contain exactly the same number of electrons as protons. However, this generalized picture of atomic structure provides no information on the arrangement of electrons within the atom.

nucleus

A neutral atom contains the same number of protons and electrons.

5.6   The Bohr Atom

At high temperatures or when subjected to high voltages, elements in the gaseous state give off colored light. Brightly colored neon signs illustrate this property of matter very well. When passed through the prism or the grating of a spectroscope, the light emitted by a gas appears as a set of brightly colored lines and is called a line spectrum. These colored lines indicate that the light is being emitted only at certain wavelengths, or frequencies, that correspond to specific colors. Each element possesses a unique set of these spectral lines that is different from the sets of all the other elements.

In 1912–1913, while studying the line spectra of hydrogen, Niels Bohr (1885–1962), a Danish physicist, made a significant contribution to the rapidly growing knowledge of atomic structure. His research led him to believe that electrons in an atom exist in specific regions at various distances from the nucleus. He also visualized the electrons as rotating in orbits around the nucleus, like planets rotating around the sun.

Bohr's first paper in this field dealt with the hydrogen atom, which he described as a single electron rotating in an orbit about a relatively heavy nucleus. He applied the concept of energy quanta, proposed in 1900 by the German physicist Max Planck (1858–1947), to the observed line spectra of hydrogen. Planck stated that energy is never emitted in a continuous stream but only in small discrete packets called quanta (Latin, *quantus*, how much). Bohr theorized that electrons have several possible orbits at different distances from the nucleus and that an electron had to be in one specific orbit (energy level) or another; it could not exist between orbits. In other words, the energy of the electron is said to be quantized. Bohr also stated that, when a hydrogen atom absorbed one or more quanta of energy, its electron would "jump" to an orbit at a greater distance from the nucleus.

Bohr was able to account for spectral lines this way. A number of orbits are available, each corresponding to a different energy level. The orbit closest to the nucleus is the lowest, or ground-state, energy level; orbits at increasing distances are the second, third, fourth, etc., energy levels. When an electron falls from a high-energy orbit to a lower one (say, from the fourth to the second), a quantum of energy is emitted as light at a specific frequency, or wavelength. This light corresponds to one of the lines visible in the hydrogen spectrum (see Figure 5.4). Several lines are visible in this spectrum. Each line corresponds to a specific electron energy-level shift within the hydrogen atom.

The chemical properties of an element and its position in the periodic table (Chapter 6) depend on electron behavior within the atoms. In turn much of our knowledge of the behavior of electrons within atoms is based on spectroscopy. Niels Bohr contributed a great deal to our knowledge of atomic structure by (1) suggesting quantized energy levels for electrons and (2) showing that spectral lines result from the radiation of small increments of energy (Planck's quanta) when electrons shift from one energy level to another. Bohr's calculations succeeded very well in correlating the experimentally observed spectral lines with electron energy levels for the hydrogen atom. However, Bohr's

Figure 5.4 Line spectrum of hydrogen: Each line corresponds to the wavelength of the energy emitted when the electron of a hydrogen atom, which has absorbed energy, falls back to a lower energy level.

methods of calculation did not succeed for heavier atoms. More theoretical work on atomic structure was needed.

In 1924 the French physicist Louis de Broglie suggested that moving electrons had properties of waves as well as mass. In 1926 Erwin Schrödinger, an Austrian physicist, introduced a new method of calculation—quantum mechanics, or wave mechanics. By Schrödinger's method electrons are described in mathematical terms as having dual characteristics; that is, some electron properties are best described in terms of waves (like light) and others in terms of particles having mass.

Since the late 1920s quantum mechanical concepts have generally replaced Bohr's ideas in theoretical considerations of atomic structure. One important difference between the Bohr and the quantum mechanics concepts is in the treatment of electrons. Quantum mechanics retains the concept of electrons being in specific energy levels. But the electrons are treated not as revolving about the nucleus in *orbits* but as being located in *orbitals*. An **orbital** is simply a region in space about the nucleus where there is a high probability of finding a given electron.

orbital

5.7 Energy Levels of Electrons

Not all the electrons in an atom are located the same distance from the nucleus. As pointed out by both the Bohr theory and quantum mechanics, the probability of finding electrons is greatest at certain specified distances from the nucleus, called **energy levels**. Energy levels are also referred to as **electron shells** and may contain only a limited number of electrons. The main or principal energy levels (**n**) are numbered, starting with **n** = 1 as the energy level nearest to the nucleus and going to **n** = 7, for the known elements. (Theoretically, the number of energy levels is infinite.) Each succeeding energy level is located farther from the nucleus. The electrons in energy levels at increasing distances from the nucleus have increasingly higher energies. The order of energy for the principal energy levels **n** is

**energy levels
of electrons**

**electron
shells**

Principal energy levels: $1 < 2 < 3 < 4 < 5 < 6 < 7$

Table 5.2   Maximum number of electrons
that can occupy each principal energy level

Principal energy level, n	Maximum number of electrons in each energy level, $2n^2$
1	$2 \times 1^2 = 2$
2	$2 \times 2^2 = 8$
3	$2 \times 3^2 = 18$
4	$2 \times 4^2 = 32$
5	$2 \times 5^2 = 50^a$

^{a} The theoretical value of 50 electrons in energy level 5
has never been attained in any element known to date.

The number of electrons that can exist in each energy level is limited. The maximum number of electrons for a specific energy level can be calculated from the formula $2n^2$, where **n** is the number of the principal energy level. For example, energy level 1 (**n** = 1) can have a maximum of two electrons ($2 \times 1^2 = 2$), energy level 2 (**n** = 2) can have a maximum of eight electrons ($2 \times 2^2 = 8$), and so on. Table 5.2 shows the maximum number of electrons that can exist in each of the first five energy levels.

5.8   Energy Sublevels

The principal energy levels contain sublevels designated by the letters s, p, d, and f. These orbitals are the ones in which electrons are located. The s sublevel consists of one orbital; the p sublevel consists of three orbitals; the d sublevel consists of five orbitals; and the f sublevel consists of seven orbitals. An electron spins on its own axis in one of only two directions, clockwise or counterclockwise. As a result, only two electrons can occupy the same orbital, one spinning clockwise and the other spinning counterclockwise. When an orbital contains two electrons, the electrons are said to be paired. Because no more than two electrons can exist in an orbital, the maximum numbers of electrons that can exist in the sublevels are 2 in the s orbital, 6 in the three p orbitals, 10 in the five d orbitals, and 14 in the seven f orbitals.

Type of sublevel	Number of orbitals possible	Number of electrons possible
s	1	2
p	3	6
d	5	10
f	7	14

The order of energy of the sublevels within a principal energy level is the following: s electrons are lower in energy than p electrons, which are lower than *d* electrons, which are lower than *f* electrons. This order may be expressed in the following manner:

Sublevel energy: $s < p < d < f$

Not all principal energy levels contain each and every type of sublevel. To determine what types of sublevels occur in any given energy level, we need to know the maximum number of electrons possible in that energy level (see Table 5.2), and we need to use these three rules:

1. No more than two electrons can occupy one orbital.
2. Electrons occupy the lowest possible energy sublevels; they enter a higher sublevel only when the lower sublevels are filled.
3. Orbitals in a given sublevel of equal energy are each occupied by a single electron before a second electron enters them. For example, all three p orbitals must contain one electron before a second electron enters a p orbital.

The maximum number of electrons in the first energy level is two; both are s orbital electrons, designated as $1s^2$. (The s orbital in the second energy level (**n** = 2) is written as 2s, in the third energy level as 3s, and so on.) The second energy level, with a maximum of eight electrons, contains only s and p electrons—namely, a maximum of two s and six p electrons, designated as $2s^2 2p^6$. The following diagram shows how to read these electron designations:

If each orbital contains two electrons, the second energy level can have four orbitals (8 electrons): one s orbital and three individual p orbitals. These three p orbitals are energetically equivalent to each other and are labeled $2p_x$, $2p_y$, and $2p_z$ to indicate their orientation in space (see Figure 5.5). The symbols $3s^2$, $3p^6$, and $3d^{10}$ show the sublevel breakdown of electrons in the third energy level. From this line of reasoning, we can see that, if an atom has sufficient electrons, *f* electrons first appear in the fourth energy level. Table 5.3 shows the type of sublevel electron orbitals and the maximum number of orbitals and electrons in each energy level. No elements in the fifth, sixth, and seventh energy levels contain the calculated maximum number of electrons.

Since the *spdf* atomic orbitals have definite orientations in space, they are represented by particular spatial shapes. At this time we will consider only the s and p orbitals. The s orbitals are spherically symmetrical about the nucleus, as illustrated in Figure 5.5. A 2s orbital is a larger sphere than a 1s orbital. The p orbitals (p_x, p_y, p_z) are dumbbell shaped and are oriented at right angles to each other along the x, y, and z axes in space. An electron has an equal probability of being located in either lobe of the p orbital. In illustrations such as Figure 5.5,

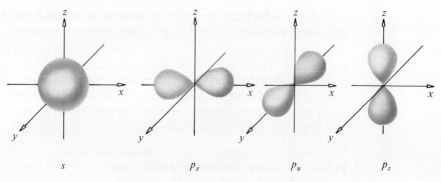

Figure 5.5   Perspective representation of the s, p_x, p_y, and p_z atomic orbitals

Table 5.3   Sublevel electron orbitals in each principal energy level and the maximum number of orbitals and electrons in each energy level

Principal energy level	Sublevel electron orbitals	Maximum number of orbitals	Maximum number of electrons
1	s	1	2
2	s, p	4	8
3	s, p, d	9	18
4	s, p, d, f	16	32
5	s, p, d, f	Incomplete[a]	(50)[a]
6	s, p, d	Incomplete[a]	(72)[a]
7	s	Incomplete[a]	(96)[a]

[a] Insufficient electrons to complete the shell.

the boundaries of the orbitals enclose the region of the greatest probability (about a 90% chance) of finding an electron. In the ground-state, or lowest energy level of a hydrogen atom, this region is a sphere having a radius of 0.053 nm.

Pauli Exclusion Principle

The assignment of electrons in an atom is summarized by the **Pauli Exclusion Principle,** which states that no two electrons in a single atom can (1) occupy the same principal energy level, (2) occupy the same energy sublevel, (3) have the same sublevel orientation in space, and (4) have the same direction of spin. Thus, according to the Pauli Exclusion Principle, only two electrons can occupy an electron orbital, but these electrons must have opposite spins.

5.9   Atomic Numbers of the Elements

atomic number

The **atomic number** of an element is the number of protons in the nucleus of an atom of that element. The atomic number determines the identity of an atom. For example, every atom with an atomic number of 1 is a hydrogen atom; it contains one proton in its nucleus. Every atom with an atomic number of 8 is an oxygen atom; it contains 8 protons in its nucleus. Every atom with an atomic number of 92 is a uranium atom; it contains 92 protons in its nucleus. The atomic number tells us not only the number of positive charges in the nucleus but also the number of electrons in the neutral atom.

Atomic number = Number of protons in the nucleus

5.10 The Simplest Atom: Hydrogen

The common hydrogen atom, consisting of a nucleus containing one proton and an electron orbital containing one electron, is the simplest known atom. (Some hydrogen atoms are known to contain one or two neutrons in their nucleus. See Section 5.16 on isotopes). The electron in hydrogen occupies an s orbital in the first energy level. This electron does not move in any definite path but rather in a rapid random motion throughout its entire orbital, forming an electron "cloud" about the nucleus. The diameter of the nucleus is believed to be about 10^{-13} cm, and the diameter of the electron orbital to be about 10^{-8} cm. Hence, the diameter of the electron orbital of a hydrogen atom is about 100,000 times greater than the diameter of the nucleus.

What we have, then, is a positive nucleus surrounded by an electron cloud formed by an electron in an s orbital. The net electrical charge on the hydrogen atom is zero; it is called a *neutral atom*. Figure 5.6 shows two methods of representing a hydrogen atom.

5.11 Atomic Structures of the First Twenty Elements

Starting with hydrogen and progressing in order of increasing atomic number to helium, lithium, beryllium, and so on, the atoms of each successive element

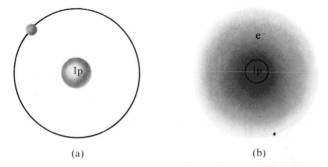

(a) (b)

Figure 5.6 The hydrogen atom: (a) Illustration of the Bohr description, indicating a discrete electron moving around its nucleus of one proton. (b) Illustration of the modern concept of a hydrogen atom consisting of an electron in an s orbital as a cloud of negative charge surrounding the proton in the nucleus.

contain one more proton and one more electron than do the atoms of the preceding element. This sequence continues, without exception, through the entire list of known elements. It is one of the most impressive examples of order in nature.

The number of neutrons also increases as we progress through the list of elements. But this number, unlike the number of protons and electrons, does not increase in a perfectly uniform manner. Furthermore, atoms of the same element may contain different numbers of neutrons; such atoms are called *isotopes*. For example, three different hydrogen isotopes are described in Section 5.16. The most abundant helium isotope (element number 2) contains two neutrons, but two other helium isotopes exist, containing one and four neutrons, respectively.

The ground-state electron structures of the first 20 elements fall into a regular pattern. The one hydrogen electron is in the first energy level as are both helium electrons. The electron structures for hydrogen and helium are written $1s^1$ and $1s^2$, respectively. The maximum number of electrons in the first energy level is two ($2\mathbf{n}^2 = 2 \times 1^2 = 2$; see Section 5.7), so the two electrons fill the first energy level of helium.

An atom with three electrons will have its third electron in the second energy level because the first level can contain only two electrons. Thus in lithium (atomic number 3) the third electron is in the 2s sublevel of the second energy level. Lithium has the electron structure $1s^2 2s^1$.

In succession, the atoms of beryllium (4), boron (5), carbon (6), nitrogen (7), oxygen (8), fluorine (9), and neon (10) have one more proton and one more electron than the preceding element until, in neon, both the first and second energy levels are filled to capacity, with two and eight electrons, respectively.

H	$1s^1$	C	$1s^2 2s^2 2p^2$
He	$1s^2$	N	$1s^2 2s^2 2p^3$
Li	$1s^2 2s^1$	O	$1s^2 2s^2 2p^4$
Be	$1s^2 2s^2$	F	$1s^2 2s^2 2p^5$
B	$1s^2 2s^2 2p^1$	Ne	$1s^2 2s^2 2p^6$

Element 11, sodium (Na), has two electrons in the first energy level and eight electrons in the second energy level, with the remaining electron occupying the 3s orbital in the third energy level. The electron structure of sodium is $1s^2 2s^2 2p^6 3s^1$. Magnesium (12), aluminum (13), silicon (14), phosphorus (15), sulfur (16), chlorine (17), and argon (18) follow in order, each adding one electron to the third energy level up to argon, which has eight electrons in the third energy level.

Up through the 3p level, the sequence of filling the sublevels is exactly as expected, based on the increasing principle of sublevel energy levels. However, after the 3p level is filled, variations occur. The third energy level might logically be expected to fill to its capacity of 18 electrons with 3d electrons before electrons enter the 4s sublevel. However, this order of filling the third energy level does not occur because the 4s sublevel is at a lower energy than the 3d sublevel (see Figure 5.7). Consequently, because the sublevels fill in order of

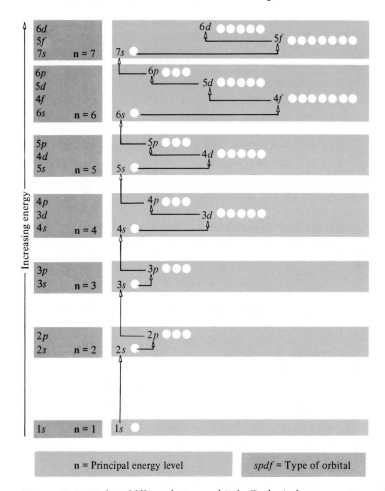

| n = Principal energy level | *spdf* = Type of orbital |

Figure 5.7 Order of filling electron orbitals: Each circle represents an orbital, which can contain two electrons. The progression of electrons filling the energy sublevels is shown, starting with 1s and going to 6d. All lower sublevels must be filled before an electron enters the next higher sublevel. For example, all three 2p orbitals must be filled before an electron enters the 3s sublevel. (Some exceptions to this order are known.)

increasing energy, the last electron in potassium (19) and the last two electrons in calcium (20) are in the 4s sublevel. The electron structures for potassium and calcium are

$$\text{K} \quad 1s^2 2s^2 2p^6 3s^2 3p^6 4s^1 \qquad \text{Ca} \quad 1s^2 2s^2 2p^6 3s^2 3p^6 4s^2$$

This break in sequence does not invalidate the formula $2n^2$, which prescribes the maximum number of electrons that each shell can contain but not the order in

Table 5.4   Electron structure of the first 20 elements

Element	Number of protons (atomic number)	Number of electrons	Electron structure
H	1	1	$1s^1$
He	2	2	$1s^2$
Li	3	3	$1s^2 2s^1$
Be	4	4	$1s^2 2s^2$
B	5	5	$1s^2 2s^2 2p^1$
C	6	6	$1s^2 2s^2 2p^2$
N	7	7	$1s^2 2s^2 2p^3$
O	8	8	$1s^2 2s^2 2p^4$
F	9	9	$1s^2 2s^2 2p^5$
Ne	10	10	$1s^2 2s^2 2p^6$
Na	11	11	$1s^2 2s^2 2p^6 3s^1$
Mg	12	12	$1s^2 2s^2 2p^6 3s^2$
Al	13	13	$1s^2 2s^2 2p^6 3s^2 3p^1$
Si	14	14	$1s^2 2s^2 2p^6 3s^2 3p^2$
P	15	15	$1s^2 2s^2 2p^6 3s^2 3p^3$
S	16	16	$1s^2 2s^2 2p^6 3s^2 3p^4$
Cl	17	17	$1s^2 2s^2 2p^6 3s^2 3p^5$
Ar	18	18	$1s^2 2s^2 2p^6 3s^2 3p^6$
K	19	19	$1s^2 2s^2 2p^6 3s^2 3p^6 4s^1$
Ca	20	20	$1s^2 2s^2 2p^6 3s^2 3p^6 4s^2$

which the shells are filled. Table 5.4 shows the electron structure of the first 20 elements.

The relative energies of the electron orbitals are shown in Figure 5.7. The order given can be used to determine the electron distribution in the atoms of the elements, although some exceptions to the pattern are known. Suppose we wish to determine the electron structure of a chlorine atom (atomic number 17), which has 17 electrons. Following the order in Figure 5.7, we begin by placing two electrons in the 1s orbital, then two electrons in the 2s orbital, and then six electrons in the 2p orbitals. We now have used ten electrons.

$$1s^2 2s^2 2p^6$$

Finally we place the next two electrons in the 3s orbital and the remaining five electrons in the 3p orbitals, which uses all 17 electrons, giving the electron structure for a chlorine atom as $1s^2 2s^2 2p^6 3s^2 3p^5$. The sum of the superscripts equals 17, the number of electrons in the atom. This procedure is summarized below.

Order of orbitals to be filled: 1s2s2p3s3p

Distribution of the 17 electrons in a chlorine atom: $1s^2 2s^2 2p^6 3s^2 3p^5$

PROBLEM

5.1

What is the electron distribution in a phosphorus atom?

First determine the number of electrons contained in a phosphorus atom. The atomic number of phosphorus is 15; therefore each atom contains 15 protons and 15 electrons. Now tabulate the number of electrons in each principal and subenergy level until all 15 electrons are assigned. The electron distribution in phosphorus is $1s^2 2s^2 2p^6 3s^2 3p^3$.

Sublevel	Number of e⁻	Total e⁻
1s orbital	2e⁻	2
2s orbital	2e⁻	4
2p orbital	6e⁻	10
3s orbital	2e⁻	12
3p orbital	3e⁻	15

5.12   Electron Structures of the Elements beyond Calcium

The elements following calcium have a less regular pattern of adding electrons. The lowest energy level available for the 21st electron is the $3d$ sublevel. Scandium (21) has one more electron than calcium (20). Its electron structure will be the same as calcium plus one electron in the $3d$ sublevel. The electron structure for scandium is $1s^2 2s^2 2p^6 3s^2 3p^6 4s^2 3d^1$. The elements following scandium, titanium (22) through copper (29), continue to add d electrons until the third energy level has its maximum of 18. Two exceptions in the orderly electron addition are chromium (24) and copper (29), the structures of which are given in Table 5.5. The third energy level of electrons is first completed in the element copper. Table 5.5 shows the order of filling of the electron orbitals and the electron configuration of all the elements through number 106.

PROBLEM

5.2

What is the electron structure for a sulfur atom (atomic number 16) and for an iron atom (atomic number 26)?

Look in Table 5.5 for the element with atomic number 16 and write down its structure, $[Ne]3s^2 3p^4$. $[Ne]$ is an abbreviated structure for neon, which is $1s^2 2s^2 2p^6$. Therefore, the electron structure for a sulfur atom is $1s^2 2s^2 2p^6 3s^2 3p^4$.

For an iron atom, Table 5.5 shows a structure of $[Ar]4s^2 3d^6$. This notation means that the electron structure of iron consists of the electron structure for argon plus $4s^2 3d^6$. The table shows that the structure for $[Ar]$ is $[Ne]3s^2 3p^6$, which is equal to $1s^2 2s^2 2p^6 3s^2 3p^6$. Therefore, the electron structure for iron is $1s^2 2s^2 2p^6 3s^2 3p^6 4s^2 3d^6$.

If Table 5.5 is not available, the structure can be determined by tabulating electrons as in Problem 5.1 and using Figure 5.7. Structures for all the noble gases, He, Ne, Ar, and so on, are also given in Table 5.6 in Section 5.15.

Table 5.5   Electron structures of the elements

Element	Atomic number	Electron structure	Element	Atomic number	Electron structure
H	1	$1s^1$	Zn	30	$[Ar]\,4s^23d^{10}$
He	2	$1s^2$	Ga	31	$[Ar]\,4s^23d^{10}4p^1$
Li	3	$1s^22s^1$	Ge	32	$[Ar]\,4s^23d^{10}4p^2$
Be	4	$1s^22s^2$	As	33	$[Ar]\,4s^23d^{10}4p^3$
B	5	$1s^22s^22p^1$	Se	34	$[Ar]\,4s^23d^{10}4p^4$
C	6	$1s^22s^22p^2$	Br	35	$[Ar]\,4s^23d^{10}4p^5$
N	7	$1s^22s^22p^3$	Kr	36	$[Ar]\,4s^23d^{10}4p^6$
O	8	$1s^22s^22p^4$	Rb	37	$[Kr]\,5s^1$
F	9	$1s^22s^22p^5$	Sr	38	$[Kr]\,5s^2$
Ne	10	$1s^22s^22p^6$	Y	39	$[Kr]\,5s^24d^1$
Na	11	$[Ne]\,3s^1$	Zr	40	$[Kr]\,5s^24d^2$
Mg	12	$[Ne]\,3s^2$	Nb	41	$[Kr]\,5s^14d^4$
Al	13	$[Ne]\,3s^23p^1$	Mo	42	$[Kr]\,5s^14d^5$
Si	14	$[Ne]\,3s^23p^2$	Tc	43	$[Kr]\,5s^24d^5$
P	15	$[Ne]\,3s^23p^3$	Ru	44	$[Kr]\,5s^14d^7$
S	16	$[Ne]\,3s^23p^4$	Rh	45	$[Kr]\,5s^14d^8$
Cl	17	$[Ne]\,3s^23p^5$	Pd	46	$[Kr]\,4d^{10}$
Ar	18	$[Ne]\,3s^23p^6$	Ag	47	$[Kr]\,5s^14d^{10}$
K	19	$[Ar]\,4s^1$	Cd	48	$[Kr]\,5s^24d^{10}$
Ca	20	$[Ar]\,4s^2$	In	49	$[Kr]\,5s^24d^{10}5p^1$
Sc	21	$[Ar]\,4s^23d^1$	Sn	50	$[Kr]\,5s^24d^{10}5p^2$
Ti	22	$[Ar]\,4s^23d^2$	Sb	51	$[Kr]\,5s^24d^{10}5p^3$
V	23	$[Ar]\,4s^23d^3$	Te	52	$[Kr]\,5s^24d^{10}5p^4$
Cr	24	$[Ar]\,4s^13d^5$	I	53	$[Kr]\,5s^24d^{10}5p^5$
Mn	25	$[Ar]\,4s^23d^5$	Xe	54	$[Kr]\,5s^24d^{10}5p^6$
Fe	26	$[Ar]\,4s^23d^6$	Cs	55	$[Xe]\,6s^1$
Co	27	$[Ar]\,4s^23d^7$	Ba	56	$[Xe]\,6s^2$
Ni	28	$[Ar]\,4s^23d^8$	La	57	$[Xe]\,6s^25d^1$
Cu	29	$[Ar]\,4s^13d^{10}$	Ce	58	$[Xe]\,6s^24f^15d^1$

5.13   Diagramming Atomic Structures

We can use several methods to diagram the atomic structures of atoms, depending on what we are trying to illustrate. When we want to show both the nuclear makeup and the electron structure of each energy level (without orbital detail), we can use a diagram such as Figure 5.8.

A method of diagramming subenergy levels is shown in Figure 5.9. Each orbital is represented by a square □. When the orbital contains one electron, an arrow (↑) is placed in the square. A second arrow, pointing downward (↓), indicates the second electron in that orbital.

Table 5.5 (*continued*)

Element	Atomic number	Electron structure	Element	Atomic number	Electron structure
Pr	59	[Xe] $6s^24f^3$	Bi	83	[Xe] $6s^24f^{14}5d^{10}6p^3$
Nd	60	[Xe] $6s^24f^4$	Po	84	[Xe] $6s^24f^{14}5d^{10}6p^4$
Pm	61	[Xe] $6s^24f^5$	At	85	[Xe] $6s^24f^{14}5d^{10}6p^5$
Sm	62	[Xe] $6s^24f^6$	Rn	86	[Xe] $6s^24f^{14}5d^{10}6p^6$
Eu	63	[Xe] $6s^24f^7$	Fr	87	[Rn] $7s^1$
Gd	64	[Xe] $6s^2f^75d^1$	Ra	88	[Rn] $7s^2$
Tb	65	[Xe] $6s^24f^9$	Ac	89	[Rn] $7s^26d^1$
Dy	66	[Xe] $6s^24f^{10}$	Th	90	[Rn] $7s^26d^2$
Ho	67	[Xe] $6s^24f^{11}$	Pa	91	[Rn] $7s^25f^26d^1$
Er	68	[Xe] $6s^24f^{12}$	U	92	[Rn] $7s^25f^36d^1$
Tm	69	[Xe] $6s^24f^{13}$	Np	93	[Rn] $7s^25f^46d^1$
Yb	70	[Xe] $6s^24f^{14}$	Pu	94	[Rn] $7s^25f^6$
Lu	71	[Xe] $6s^24f^{14}5d^1$	Am	95	[Rn] $7s^25f^7$
Hf	72	[Xe] $6s^24f^{14}5d^2$	Cm	96	[Rn] $7s^25f^76d^1$
Ta	73	[Xe] $6s^24f^{14}5d^3$	Bk	97	[Rn] $7s^25f^9$
W	74	[Xe] $6s^24f^{14}5d^4$	Cf	98	[Rn] $7s^25f^{10}$
Re	75	[Xe] $6s^24f^{14}5d^5$	Es	99	[Rn] $7s^25f^{11}$
Os	76	[Xe] $6s^24f^{14}5d^6$	Fm	100	[Rn] $7s^25f^{12}$
Ir	77	[Xe] $6s^24f^{14}5d^7$	Md	101	[Rn] $7s^25f^{13}$
Pt	78	[Xe] $6s^14f^{14}5d^9$	No	102	[Rn] $7s^25f^{14}$
Au	79	[Xe] $6s^14f^{14}5d^{10}$	Lr	103	[Rn] $7s^25f^{14}6d^1$
Hg	80	[Xe] $6s^24f^{14}5d^{10}$	Unq	104	[Rn] $7s^25f^{14}6d^2$
Tl	81	[Xe] $6s^24f^{14}5d^{10}6p^1$	Unp	105	[Rn] $7s^25f^{14}6d^3$
Pb	82	[Xe] $6s^24f^{14}5d^{10}6p^1$	Unh	106	[Rn] $7s^25f^{14}6d^4$

Note: For simplicity of expression, symbols of the chemically stable noble gases are used as a portion of the electron structure for the elements beyond neon. For example, the electron structure of a sodium atom, Na, consists of ten electrons, as in neon [Ne], plus a $3s^1$ electron. Detailed electron structures for the noble gases are given in Table 5.6.

The diagram for hydrogen is [↑]. Helium, with two electrons, is drawn as [↑↓]; both electrons are 1s electrons. The diagram for lithium shows three electrons in two energy levels, $1s^22s^1$. All four electrons for beryllium are s electrons, $1s^22s^2$. Boron has the first p electron, which is located in the $2p_x$ orbital. Because it is

Fluorine atom   Sodium atom   Magnesium atom

Figure 5.8 Atomic structure diagrams of fluorine, sodium, and magnesium atoms. The numbers of protons and neutrons are shown in the nucleus. The number of electrons is shown in each principal energy level outside the nucleus.

Element	Orbital electron structure						Linear expression of electron structure
	$1s$	$2s$	$2p_x$	$2p_y$	$2p_z$	$3s$	
H	↑						$1s^1$
He	↑↓						$1s^2$
Li	↑↓	↑					$1s^2 2s^1$
Be	↑↓	↑↓					$1s^2 2s^2$
B	↑↓	↑↓	↑				$1s^2 2s^2 2p_x^1$
C	↑↓	↑↓	↑	↑			$1s^2 2s^2 2p_x^1 2p_y^1$
N	↑↓	↑↓	↑	↑	↑		$1s^2 2s^2 2p_x^1 2p_y^1 2p_z^1$
O	↑↓	↑↓	↑↓	↑	↑		$1s^2 2s^2 2p_x^2 2p_y^1 2p_z^1$
F	↑↓	↑↓	↑↓	↑↓	↑		$1s^2 2s^2 2p_x^2 2p_y^2 2p_z^1$
Ne	↑↓	↑↓	↑↓	↑↓	↑↓		$1s^2 2s^2 2p_x^2 2p_y^2 2p_z^2$
Na	↑↓	↑↓	↑↓	↑↓	↑↓	↑	$1s^2 2s^2 2p_x^2 2p_y^2 2p_z^2 3s^1$

Figure 5.9 Subenergy-level electron structure of hydrogen through sodium atoms. Each electron is indicated by an arrow placed in the square, which represents the orbital.

energetically more difficult for the next p electron to pair up with the electron in the p_x orbital than to occupy a second p orbital, the second p electron in carbon is located in the $2p_y$ orbital. The third p electron in nitrogen is still unpaired and is found in the $2p_z$ orbital. This filling order is in accordance with **Hund's Rule,** which states that an electron cannot enter a half-filled orbital if an empty orbital of the same energy sublevel is available. The next three electrons pair with each of the 2p electrons through the element neon. Also shown in Figure 5.9 are the equivalent linear expressions for these orbital electron structures.

Hund's Rule

The electrons in successive elements are found in sublevels of increasing energy. The general sequence of increasing energy of sublevels and the order of filling sublevels with electrons is

1s 2s 2p 3s 3p 4s 3d 4p 5s 4d 5p 6s 4f 5d 6p 7s 5f 6d

Minor variations from the electron structure predicted by the foregoing general sequence are found in a number of atoms. Table 5.5 shows the accepted ground-state electron structure for the elements.

PROBLEM

5.3

Diagram the electron structure of a zinc atom and a rubidium atom. Use the $1s^2 2s^2 2p^6$, etc., method.

The atomic number of zinc is 30; therefore it has 30 protons and 30 electrons in a neutral atom. Using Figure 5.7, tabulate the 30 electrons as follows:

Orbital	Number of e⁻	Total e⁻
1s	2e⁻	2
2s	2e⁻	4
2p	6e⁻	10
3s	2e⁻	12
3p	6e⁻	18
4s	2e⁻	20
3d	10e⁻	30

The electron structure of a zinc atom is $1s^2 2s^2 2p^6 3s^2 3p^6 4s^2 3d^{10}$. Check by adding the superscripts, which should equal 30.

The atomic number of rubidium is 37; therefore it has 37 protons and 37 electrons in a neutral atom. With a little practice, and using Figure 5.7, the electron structure may be written directly in the linear form. The electron structure of a rubidium atom is $1s^2 2s^2 2p^6 3s^2 3p^6 4s^2 3d^{10} 4p^6 5s^1$. Check by adding the superscripts, which should equal 37.

5.14 Lewis-Dot Representation of Atoms

The Lewis-dot (or electron-dot) method of representing atoms, proposed by the American chemist G. N. Lewis (1875–1946), uses the symbol for the element and dots for electrons. The number of dots placed around the symbol equals the number of s and p electrons in the outermost enegy level of the atom. Paired dots represent paired electrons; unpaired dots represent unpaired electrons. For example, **H·** is the Lewis-dot structure for a hydrogen atom, $1s^1$; **:Ḃ** is the Lewis-dot structure for a boron atom, $1s^2 2s^2 2p^1$; **:İ·** is an iodine atom, which has seven electrons in its outermost energy level. In the case of boron, the symbol B represents the boron nucleus and the $1s^2$ electrons; the dots represent only the $2s^2 2p^1$ electrons.

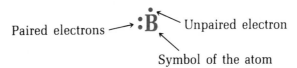

Paired electrons ⟶ :Ḃ ⟵ Unpaired electron

Symbol of the atom

The Lewis-dot method is often used, not only because of its simplicity of expression, but also because much of the chemistry of the atom is directly associated with the electrons in the outermost energy level. This association is

H·   He: Li·   Be: :B·   :C·   :N·   ·O·   :F·   :Ne:

Na·   Mg: :Al·   :Si·   :P·   ·S·   :Cl·   :Ar:

K·   Ca:

Figure 5.10   Lewis-dot structures of the first 20 elements. Dots represent electrons in the outermost energy level only.

especially true for the first 20 elements and the remaining Group A elements of the periodic table (see Chapter 6). Figure 5.10 shows Lewis-dot structures for the elements hydrogen through calcium.

PROBLEM

5.4

Write the Lewis-dot structure for a phosphorus atom.

First establish the electron structure for a phosphorus atom. It is $1s^2 2s^2 2p^6 3s^2 3p^3$. Note that there are five electrons in the outermost principal energy level; they are $3s^2 3p^3$. Write the symbol for phosphorus and place the five electrons as dots around it:

The $3s^2$ electrons are paired and are represented by the paired dots. The $3p^3$ electrons, which are unpaired, are represented by the single dots.

5.15   **The Octet Rule**

noble gases

The family of elements consisting of helium, neon, argon, krypton, xenon, and radon is known as the **noble gases**. These elements, formerly called *inert gases*, have almost no chemical reactivity; in fact, no compounds of any of them were known before 1962.

Each of these elements, except helium, has an outer shell of eight electrons, two *s* and six *p* (see Table 5.6). The only shell of helium is an *s* orbital filled with two electrons. The electron structure of the noble gases is such that the outer shell *s* and *p* orbitals are filled with paired electrons. This arrangement is very stable and makes the atoms of the noble gases chemically unreactive. Recogni-

Octet Rule

tion of the extraordinary stability of this structure led to the **Octet Rule:** Through chemical changes many of the elements tend to attain an electron structure of eight electrons in their outermost energy level, identical to that of the chemically stable noble gases. Although the Octet Rule is useful and applies to the behavior of many elements and compounds, it is not universally applicable:

Table 5.6   Arrangement of electrons in the noble gases. Each gas except helium has eight electrons in its outermost energy level.

		Electron structure					
Noble gas	Symbol	$n = 1$	2	3	4	5	6
Helium	He	$1s^2$					
Neon	Ne	$1s^2$	$2s^22p^6$				
Argon	Ar	$1s^2$	$2s^22p^6$	$3s^23p^6$			
Krypton	Kr	$1s^2$	$2s^22p^6$	$3s^23p^63d^{10}$	$4s^24p^6$		
Xenon	Xe	$1s^2$	$2s^22p^6$	$3s^23p^63d^{10}$	$4s^24p^64d^{10}$	$5s^25p^6$	
Radon	Rn	$1s^2$	$2s^22p^6$	$3s^23p^63d^{10}$	$4s^24p^64d^{10}4f^{14}$	$5s^25p^65d^{10}$	$6s^26p^6$

some elements do not obey this rule. Applications of the Octet Rule are given in Chapter 7.

5.16   Isotopes of the Elements

Shortly after Rutherford's conception of the nuclear atom, experiments were performed to determine the masses of individual atoms. These experiments showed that the masses of nearly all atoms were greater than could be accounted for by simply adding up the masses of all the protons and electrons that were known to be present in an atom. This fact led to the concept of the neutron, a particle with no charge but with a mass about the same as that of a proton. Because this particle has no charge, it was very difficult to detect, and the existence of the neutron was not proven experimentally until 1932. All atomic nuclei except that of the simplest hydrogen atom are now believed to contain neutrons.

All atoms of a given element have the same number of protons, but experimental evidence has shown that, in most cases, all atoms of a given element do not have identical masses because atoms of the same element may have different numbers of neutrons in their nuclei.

isotopes

Atoms of an element having the same atomic number but different atomic masses are called **isotopes** of that element. Atoms of the various isotopes of an element, therefore, have the same number of protons and electrons but different numbers of neutrons.

Three isotopes of hydrogen (atomic number 1) are known. Each has one proton in the nucleus and one electron in the first energy level. The first isotope (protium), without a neutron, has a mass of 1 amu; the second isotope (deuterium), with one neutron in the nucleus, has a mass of 2 amu; the third isotope (tritium), with two neutrons, has a mass of 3 amu (see Figure 5.11).

The three isotopes of hydrogen may be represented by the symbols ^1_1H, ^2_1H, and ^3_1H, indicating an atomic number of 1 and mass numbers of 1, 2, and 3, respectively. This method of representing atoms is called *isotopic notation*. The

mass number

subscript (Z) is the atomic number; the superscript (A) is the **mass number,**

$^1_1$H $^2_1$H, D $^3_1$H, T
Protium   Deuterium   Tritium

Figure 5.11 Schematic diagram of the isotopes of hydrogen: The number of protons (p) and neutrons (n) are shown within the nucleus. The electron (e⁻) exists in an orbital outside the nucleus.

which is the sum of the number of protons and the number of neutrons in the nucleus. The hydrogen isotopes may also be referred to as hydrogen-1, hydrogen-2, and hydrogen-3.

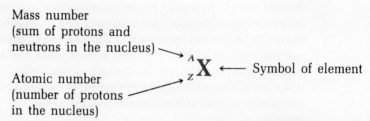

Mass number
(sum of protons and
neutrons in the nucleus)

Atomic number
(number of protons
in the nucleus)

$$^A_Z X$$

← Symbol of element

Most of the elements occur in nature as mixtures of isotopes. However, not all isotopes are stable; some are radioactive and are continuously decomposing to form other elements. For example, of the seven known isotopes of carbon, only two, carbon-12 and carbon-13, are stable. Of the seven known isotopes of oxygen, only three, $^{16}_8O$, $^{17}_8O$, and $^{18}_8O$, are stable. Of the fifteen known isotopes of arsenic, $^{75}_{33}As$ is the only one that is stable.

5.17   Atomic Weight (Atomic Mass)

Single atoms are far too small to weigh individually on a balance. But fairly precise determinations of the masses of individual atoms can be made with an instrument called a *mass spectrometer*. The mass of a single hydrogen atom is 1.6736×10^{-24} g. However, it is neither convenient nor practical to compare the actual weights of atoms expressed in grams; therefore a table of relative atomic weights using *atomic mass units* was devised. (The term *atomic mass* is often used instead of atomic weight.) The carbon isotope having six protons and six neutrons and designated carbon-12, or $^{12}_6C$, was chosen as the standard for

**atomic
mass unit**

atomic weights. This reference isotope was assigned a value of exactly 12 atomic mass units (amu). Thus one **atomic mass unit** is defined as equal to exactly 1/12 of the mass of a carbon-12 atom. The actual mass of a carbon-12 atom is 1.9927×10^{-23} g, and that of one atomic mass unit is 1.6606×10^{-24} g. In the table of atomic weights, all elements then have values that are relative to the mass assigned to the reference isotope carbon-12.

A table of atomic weights is given on the inside back cover of this book. Hydrogen atoms, with a mass of about 1/12 that of a carbon atom, have an average atomic mass of 1.00797 amu on this relative scale. Magnesium atoms, which are about twice as heavy as carbon, have an average mass of 24.305 amu. The average atomic mass of oxygen is 15.9994 amu (usually rounded off to 16.0 amu for calculations).

Since most elements occur as mixtures of isotopes with different masses, the atomic weight determined for an element represents the average relative mass of all the naturally occurring isotopes of that element. The atomic weights of the individual isotopes are approximately whole numbers, because the relative masses of the protons and neutrons are approximately 1.0 amu each. Yet we find that the atomic weights given for many of the elements deviate considerably from whole numbers. For example, the atomic weight of rubidium is 85.4678 amu, that of copper is 63.546 amu, and that of magnesium is 24.305 amu. The deviation of an atomic weight from a whole number is due mainly to the unequal occurrence of the various isotopes of an element. It is also due partly to the difference between the mass of a free proton or neutron and the mass of these same particles in the nucleus. For example, the two principal isotopes of copper are $^{63}_{29}$Cu and $^{65}_{29}$Cu. It is apparent that copper-63 atoms are the more abundant isotope, since the atomic weight of copper, 63.546 amu, is closer to 63 than to 65 amu. The actual values of the copper isotopes observed by mass spectra determination are shown in the following table:

Isotope	Isotopic mass (amu)	Abundance (%)	Average atomic mass (amu)
$^{63}_{29}$Cu	62.9298	69.09	63.55
$^{65}_{29}$Cu	64.9278	30.91	

The average atomic mass can be calculated by multiplying the atomic mass of each isotope by the fraction of each isotope present and adding the results. The calculation for copper is

62.9298 amu $\times$ 0.6909 = 43.48 amu
64.9278 amu $\times$ 0.3091 = $\underline{20.07}$ amu

63.55 amu

atomic weight

The **atomic weight** of an element is the average relative mass of the isotopes of that element referred to the atomic mass of carbon-12 (exactly 12.0000 amu).

The relationship between mass number and atomic number is such that if we subtract the atomic number from the mass number of a given isotope, we obtain

Table 5.7 Determination of the number of neutrons in an atom by subtracting the atomic number from the mass number

	Hydrogen ($_1^1$H)	Oxygen ($_8^{16}$O)	Sulfur ($_{16}^{32}$S)	Fluorine ($_9^{19}$F)	Iron ($_{26}^{56}$Fe)
Mass number	1	16	32	19	56
Atomic number	-1	-8	-16	-9	-26
Number of neutrons	0	8	16	10	30

the number of neutrons in the nucleus of an atom of that isotope. Table 5.7 shows the application of this method of determining the number of neutrons. For example, the fluorine atom ($_9^{19}$F), atomic number 9, having a mass of 19 amu, contains 10 neutrons:

Mass number − Atomic number = Number of neutrons

$$19 \quad - \quad 9 \quad = \quad 10$$

The atomic weights given in the table on the inside back cover of this book are values accepted by international agreement. You need not memorize atomic weights. In most of the calculations needed in this book, use of atomic weights to the first decimal place will give results of sufficient accuracy.

QUESTIONS

A. *Review the meanings of the new terms introduced in this chapter.*

1. Dalton's atomic theory?
2. Subatomic particles
3. Electron
4. Proton
5. Neutron
6. Nucleus
7. Orbital
8. Energy levels of electrons
9. Electron shells
10. Pauli Exclusion Principle
11. Atomic number
12. Hund's Rule
13. Noble gases
14. Octet Rule
15. Isotopes
16. Mass number
17. Atomic mass unit
18. Atomic weight

B. *Information useful in answering these questions will be found in the tables and figures.*

1. What are the atomic numbers of (a) copper, (b) nitrogen, (c) phosphorus, (d) radium, and (e) zinc?
2. A neutron is approximately how many times heavier than an electron?

3. Explain why, in Rutherford's experiments, some alpha particles were scattered at large angles by the gold foil or even bounced back from it.
4. How many electrons can be present in the fourth energy level?
5. How many orbitals can exist in the third energy level? What are they?
6. Sketch the s, p_x, p_y, and p_z orbitals.
7. Diagram the atomic structures of the following atoms:
   (a) $_7^{14}$N (b) $_{17}^{35}$Cl (c) $_{30}^{65}$Zn (d) $_{40}^{91}$Zr
   (e) $_{53}^{127}$I
8. Show the Lewis-dot structures for C, Mg, Al, Cl, and K.
9. In the designation $3d^7$, give the significance of the 3, the d, and the 7.
10. Using the method shown in Figure 5.9, show the orbital electron structure for an atom of:
    (a) Si (b) S (c) Ar (d) V
11. What electron structure do the noble gases have in common?

C. *Review questions*

Atomic Structure

1. From the point of view of a chemist, what are the essential differences among a proton, a neutron, and an electron?
2. Describe the general arrangement of subatomic particles in the atom.
3. What part of the atom contains practically all its mass?
4. What experimental evidence led Rutherford to conclude each of the following?
   (a) The nucleus of the atom contains most of the atomic mass.
   (b) The nucleus of the atom is positively charged.
   (c) The atom consists of mostly empty space.
5. What contribution did each of the following scientists make to the atomic theory?
   (a) Dalton   (c) Rutherford (e) Bohr
   (b) Thomson   (d) Chadwick
6. What is the major difference between an orbital and a Bohr orbit?
7. Explain how the spectral lines of hydrogen occur.
8. Which of the following statements are correct?
   (a) John Dalton developed an important atomic theory in the early 1800s.
   (b) Dalton said that elements are composed of minute, indivisible particles called *atoms*.
   (c) Dalton said that when atoms combine to form compounds, they do so in simple numerical ratios.
   (d) Dalton said that atoms are composed of protons, neutrons, and electrons.
   (e) All of Dalton's theory is still considered valid today.
   (f) Hydrogen is the smallest atom.
   (g) A proton is about 1837 times as heavy as an electron.
   (h) The nucleus of an atom contains protons, neutrons, and electrons.
   (i) The Bohr theory proposed that electrons move around the nucleus in circular orbits.
   (j) Bohr concluded from his experiment that the positive charge and almost all the mass were concentrated in a very small nucleus.

Electron Structure

9. What is an electron orbital?

10. Under which conditions can a second electron enter an orbital already containing one electron?
11. What is meant when we say that the electron structure of an atom is in its ground state?
12. How do 1s and 2s orbitals differ? How are they alike?
13. What letters are used to designate the energy sublevels?
14. List the following electron sublevels in order of increasing energy: 2s, 2p, 4s, 1s, 3d, 3p, 4p, 3s.
15. How many s electrons, p electrons, and d electrons are possible in any electron shell?
16. How many protons are in the nucleus of an atom of each of these elements: H, B, F, Sc, Ag, U, Br, Sb, and Pb?
17. Give the electron structure $(1s^2 2s^2 2p^6 \ldots)$ for B, Ti, Zn, Br, and Sr.
18. Why is the eleventh electron of the sodium atom located in the third energy level rather than in the second energy level?
19. Why is the last electron in potassium located in the fourth energy level rather than in the third energy level?
20. Which atoms have the following electron structures?
    (a) $1s^2 2s^2 2p^6 3s^2$
    (b) $1s^2 2s^2 2p^5$
    (c) $1s^2 2s^2 2p^6 3s^2 3p^6 4s^2 3d^8$
    (d) $1s^2 2s^2 2p^6 3s^2 3p^6 4s^2 3d^5$
    (e) $1s^2 2s^2 2p^6 3s^2 3p^6 4s^2 3d^{10} 4p^6 5s^1 4d^5$
21. Show the electron structures $(1s^2 2s^2 2p^6 \ldots)$ for elements of atomic numbers 8, 11, 17, 23, 28, and 34.
22. Using only Table 5.5 show the electron structures $(1s^2 2s^2 2p^6 \ldots)$ for the elements having the following numbers of electrons:
    (a) 9 (b) 26 (c) 31 (d) 39 (e) 52
23. Which elements have the following electron structures?
    (a) [Ar]$4s^2 3d^1$ (c) [Kr]$5s^2 4d^{10} 5p^2$
    (b) [Ar]$4s^2 3d^{10} 4p^6$ (d) [Xe]$6s^1$
24. Identify these atoms from their atomic structure diagrams:

    (a) $\left(\begin{array}{c}16p\\16n\end{array}\right)$ $2e^-$ $8e^-$ $6e^-$

    (b) $\left(\begin{array}{c}28p\\32n\end{array}\right)$ $2e^-$ $8e^-$ $16e^-$ $2e^-$

25. Diagram the atomic structures (as in Question 24) for these atoms:
    (a) $^{27}_{13}$Al (b) $^{51}_{23}$V
26. State the Octet Rule and its relationship to the noble gases.
27. Write Lewis-dot structures for these atoms: He, B, O, Na, Si, Ar, Ga, Ca, Br, and Kr.
28. Which of the following statements are correct?
    (a) In the ground state, electrons tend to occupy orbitals having the lowest possible energy.
    (b) The maximum number of p electrons in the first energy level is six.
    (c) A 2s electron is in a lower energy state than a 2p electron.
    (d) The electron structure for a carbon atom is $1s^2 2s^2 2p^2$.
    (e) The $2p_x$, $2p_y$, and $2p_z$ electron orbitals are all in the same energy state.
    (f) The energy level of a 3d electron is higher than that of a 4s electron.
    (g) The electron structure for a calcium atom is $1s^2 2s^2 2p^6 3s^2 3p^6 3d^2$.
    (h) There are seven principal energy levels for the known elements.
    (i) The third energy level can have a maximum of 18 electrons.
    (j) The number of possible d electrons in the third energy level is ten.
    (k) The first f electron occurs in the fourth principal energy level.
    (l) The Lewis-dot symbol for nitrogen is $:\overset{\bullet}{N}\cdot$
    (m) The Lewis-dot symbol for potassium is $P\cdot$
    (n) Atoms of all the noble gases (except helium) have eight electrons in their outermost energy level.
    (o) A p orbital is spherically symmetrical around the nucleus.
    (p) An atom of nitrogen has two electrons in a 1s orbital, two electrons in a 2s orbital, and one electron in each of three different 2p orbitals.
    (q) The maximum number of electrons that can occupy a specific energy level **n** is given by $2\mathbf{n}^2$.
    (r) $^{12}_{6}$C is an isotope of carbon that is used as the reference standard for the atomic mass system.
    (s) The Lewis-dot symbol for the noble gas helium is $:\overset{\bullet\bullet}{\underset{\bullet\bullet}{He}}:$

(t) When an orbital contains two electrons, the electrons are spinning in the same direction.

Isotopes, Isotopic Notation

29. In what ways are isotopes alike? In what ways are they different?
30. What special names are given to the isotopes of hydrogen?
31. List the similarities and differences in the three isotopes of hydrogen.
32. What is the symbol and name of the element that has an atomic number of 24 and a mass number of 52?
33. An atom of an element has a mass number of 201 and has 121 neutrons in its nucleus.
    (a) What is the electrical charge of the nucleus?
    (b) What is the symbol and name of the element?
34. How many protons and neutrons are in each of the six naturally occurring isotopes of calcium having mass numbers of 40, 42, 43, 44, 46, and 48?
35. What are the numbers of protons, neutrons, and electrons in each of the following?
    (a) $^{79}_{35}$Br (b) $^{131}_{56}$Ba (c) $^{238}_{92}$U (d) $^{56}_{26}$Fe
36. What letters are used to designate atomic number and mass number in isotopic notation of atoms?
37. Write isotopic notation symbols for the following:
    (a) $Z = 26$, $A = 55$ (d) $Z = 14$, $A = 29$
    (b) $Z = 12$, $A = 26$ (e) $Z = 79$, $A = 188$
    (c) $Z = 3$, $A = 6$
38. Give the isotopic notation ($^{73}_{32}$Ge, for example) for:
    (a) An atom containing 27 protons, 32 neutrons, and 27 electrons.
    (b) An atom containing 110 neutrons, 74 electrons, and 74 protons.
39. Which of the following statements are correct?
    (a) An element with an atomic number of 39 has 39 protons, 39 neutrons, and 39 electrons.
    (b) An atom of the isotope $^{60}_{26}$Fe has 34 neutrons in its nucleus.
    (c) $^{2}_{1}$H is a symbol for the isotope deuterium.
    (d) An atom of $^{31}_{15}$P contains 15 protons, 16 neutrons, and 31 electrons.
    (e) In the isotope $^{6}_{3}$Li, $Z = 3$ and $A = 3$.
    (f) Isotopes of a given element have the same

number of protons but differ in the number of neutrons.

(g) The three isotopes of hydrogen are called protium, deuterium, and tritium.

(h) $^{23}_{11}Na$ and $^{24}_{11}Na$ are isotopes.

(i) $^{24}_{11}Na$ has one more electron than $^{23}_{11}Na$.

(j) $^{24}_{11}Na$ has one more proton than $^{23}_{11}Na$.

(k) $^{24}_{11}Na$ has one more neutron than $^{23}_{11}Na$.

(l) Only a few of the elements exist in nature as mixtures of isotopes.

Atomic Weight (Atomic Mass)

40. Explain why the atomic weights of elements are not whole numbers.

41. Is the isotopic mass of a given isotope ever an exact whole number? Is it always? In answering, consider the masses of $^{12}_{6}C$ and $^{63}_{29}Cu$.

42. Which of the isotopes of calcium in Question 34 is the most abundant isotope? Can you be sure? Explain your choice.

43. Which of the following statements are correct?

(a) One atomic mass unit weighs 12 times as much as one carbon-12 atom.

(b) The atomic masses of protium and deuterium differ by about 100%.

(c) $^{23}_{11}Na$ and $^{24}_{11}Na$ have the same atomic masses.

(d) The atomic weight of an element represents the average relative atomic mass of all the naturally occurring isotopes of that element.

D. *Review problems*

1. Change the following to powers of 10 (scientific notation):

(a) 510,000   (c) $(0.0001)^2$

(b) 0.000274   (d) $(8.0)^3$

2. Using the formula $2n^2$, calculate the number of electrons that can exist in the principal energy levels $n = 1, 2, 3, 4, 5,$ and 6.

3. Complete the following table with the appropriate data for each isotope given:

Atomic number	Mass number	Symbol of element	Number of protons	Number of neutrons
(a) 8	16			
(b)		Ni		30
(c)	199		80	

4. The actual mass of one atom of an unknown isotope is 2.18×10^{-22} amu. Calculate the atomic mass of this isotope.

5. Naturally occurring silver exists as two stable isotopes, ^{107}Ag with a mass of 106.9041 amu (51.82%) and ^{109}Ag with a mass of 108.9047 amu (48.18%). Calculate the average atomic weight of silver.

6. Naturally occurring magnesium consists of three stable isotopes: ^{24}Mg, 23.985 amu (78.99%); ^{25}Mg, 24.986 amu (10.00%); and ^{26}Mg, 25.983 amu (11.01%). Calculate the average atomic weight of magnesium.

$$(23.985)(.7899) = 18.946$$
$$(24.986)(.10) = 2.499$$
$$(25.983)(.1101) = 2.861$$
$$\overline{ 24.306}$$

6

The Periodic Arrangement of the Elements

After studying Chapter 6, you should be able to

1. Understand the new terms listed in Question A at the end of the chapter.
2. Describe briefly the contributions of Döbereiner, Newlands, Mendeleev, Meyer, and Moseley to the development of the periodic law.
3. State the periodic law in its modern form.
4. Indicate the locations of the metals, nonmetals, metalloids, and noble gases in the periodic table.
5. Indicate in the periodic table the areas where the s, p, d, and f orbitals are being filled.
6. Describe how atomic radii vary (a) from left to right in a period and (b) from top to bottom in a group or family of elements.
7. Distinguish between representative elements and transition elements.
8. Identify groups of elements by their special names.
9. Describe the changes in outer-level electron structure when (a) moving from left to right in a period and (b) going from top to bottom in a group.
10. Explain the relationship between group number and the number of outer-shell electrons for the representative elements.
11. List the general characteristics of group properties.
12. Write Lewis-dot structures for the representative elements from their position in the periodic table.

13. Predict formulas of simple compounds formed between the representative (Group A) elements using the periodic table.
14. Point out how the change in electron structure between adjacent transition elements differs from that between representative elements.

6.1   Early Attempts to Classify the Elements

Chemists of the early 19th century had sufficient knowledge of the properties of elements to recognize similarities among groups of elements. As early as 1817 J. W. Döbereiner (1780–1849), professor at the University of Jena in Germany, observed the existence of *triads* of similarly behaving elements, in which the middle element had an atomic weight approximating the average of the other two elements. He also noted that for many other properties the value for the central element was approximately the average of the values for the other two elements. Table 6.1 presents comparative data on atomic weight and density for two sets of Döbereiner's triads.

In 1864, J. A. R. Newlands (1837–1898), an English chemist, reported his *Law of Octaves*. In his studies Newlands observed that, when the elements were arranged according to increasing atomic weights, every eighth element had similar properties. (The noble gases were not yet discovered at that time.) Newlands' theory was ridiculed by his contemporaries in the Royal Chemical Society, and they refused to publish his work. Many years later, however, Newlands was awarded the highest honor of the society for this important contribution to the development of the periodic law.

In 1869 Dmitri Ivanovitch Mendeleev (1834–1907) of Russia and Lothar Meyer (1830–1895) of Germany independently published their periodic arrangements of the elements that were based on increasing atomic weights. Because his arrangement was published slightly earlier and was in a somewhat more useful form than that of Meyer, Mendeleev's name is usually associated with the modern periodic table.

Table 6.1   Döbereiner's triads

Triads	Atomic weight	Density (g/mL at 4°C)
Chlorine	35.5	1.56[a]
Bromine	79.9	3.12
Iodine	126.9	4.95
Average of chlorine and iodine	81.2	3.26
Calcium	40.1	1.55
Strontium	87.6	2.6
Barium	137.4	3.5
Average of calcium and barium	88.8	2.52

[a]Density at −34°C (liquid)

6.2   The Periodic Law

Only about 63 elements were known when Mendeleev constructed his table. He arranged these elements so that those with similar chemical properties fitted into columns to form family groups. The arrangement left many gaps between elements, and Mendeleev predicted that these spaces would be filled as new elements were discovered. For example, spaces for undiscovered elements were left after calcium, under aluminum, and under silicon. He called these unknown elements eka-boron, eka-aluminum, and eka-silicon. The term *eka* comes from Sanskrit meaning "one" and was used to indicate that the missing element was one place away in the table from the element indicated. Mendeleev even went so far as to predict with high accuracy the physical and chemical properties of these undiscovered elements. The three elements, scandium (atomic number 21), gallium (31), and germanium (32), were in fact discovered during Mendeleev's lifetime and were found to have properties agreeing very closely with the predictions that he had made for eka-boron, eka-aluminum, and eka-silicon. The amazing way in which Mendeleev's predictions were fulfilled is illustrated in Table 6.2, which compares the predicted properties of eka-silicon with those of germanium, discovered by the German chemist C. Winkler in 1886.

Two major additions have been made to the periodic table since Mendeleev's time: (1) A new family of elements, the noble gases, was discovered and added; and (2) elements having atomic numbers greater than 92 have been discovered and fitted into the table.

The term *periodic* means recurring at regular intervals. The original periodic tables were based on the premise that the properties of the elements are periodic functions of their atomic weights. However, this basic premise had some disturbing discrepancies. For example, the atomic weight for argon is greater than that of potassium, yet argon had to be placed before potassium, because argon is certainly a noble gas, and potassium behaves like the other alkali metals.

Table 6.2   Comparison of the properties of eka-silicon predicted by Mendeleev with the properties of germanium

Property	Mendeleev's predictions in 1871 for eka-silicon (Es)	Observed properties for germanium (Ge)
Atomic weight	72	72.6
Color of metal	Dirty gray	Grayish-white
Density	5.5 g/mL	5.35 g/mL
Oxide formula	EsO_2	GeO_2
Oxide density	4.7 g/mL	4.70 g/mL
Chloride formula	$EsCl_4$	$GeCl_4$
Chloride density	1.9 g/mL	1.87 g/mL
Boiling temperature of chloride	Under 100°C	86°C

These discrepancies were resolved by the work of the British physicist H. G. J. Moseley (1887–1915) and by the discovery of the existence of isotopes. Moseley noted that the X-ray emission frequencies of the elements increased in a regular, stepwise fashion each time the nuclear charge (atomic number) increased by one unit. This observation meant that the periodic table must be based on a revised premise—namely, that the properties of the elements are a periodic function of their *atomic numbers*. Under this revised premise, argon (18) properly comes before potassium (19), even though the atomic weight of argon is greater than the atomic weight of potassium. The current statement of the **periodic law** is

periodic law

> **The properties of the chemical elements recur periodically when the elements are arranged in increasing order of their atomic numbers.**

As the format of the periodic table is studied, it becomes evident that the periodicity of the properties of the elements is due to the recurring similarities of their electron structures.

6.3 Arrangement of the Periodic Table

periodic table

The modern **periodic table** is shown in Table 6.3 and on the inside front cover of this book. In this table the elements are arranged horizontally in numerical sequence according to their atomic numbers; the result is seven horizontal rows called **periods.** Each period, with the exception of the first, starts with an alkali metal and ends with a noble gas. This arrangement forms vertical columns of elements that have identical or similar outer-shell electron structures and thus similar chemical properties. These columns are known as **groups** or **families of elements.**

periods of elements

groups or families of elements

The heavy zigzag line starting at boron and running diagonally down the table separates the elements into metals and nonmetals. The elements to the right of the line are nonmetallic, and those to the left are metallic. The elements bordering the zigzag line are the metalloids, which show both metallic and nonmetallic properties. With some exceptions the characteristic electron arrangement of metals is that their atoms have one, two, or three electrons in the outer energy level, whereas nonmetals have five, six, or seven electrons in the outer energy level.

In this periodic arrangement the elements also fall into blocks according to the sublevel of electrons that is being filled. The grouping of the elements into *spdf* blocks is shown in Table 6.4. The *s* and *p* blocks are made up of Group A elements and noble gases. The *s* block consists of the Group IA and IIA elements and helium; each element in this block has one or two *s* electrons in its outer energy level. The *p* block contains the Group IIIA through VIIA elements and the noble gases (except helium). In the *p* block, electrons are filling the *p* sublevel orbitals. Each *p* block element has two *s* electrons and from one to six *p* electrons in its outermost energy level.

Table 6.3 Periodic table of the elements

Table 6.3 (*continued*)

Atomic weights are based on carbon-12. Atomic weights in parentheses indicate the most stable or best-known isotope. Slight disagreement exists as to the exact electronic configuration of several of the high-atomic-number elements.

Noble gases

		IIIA	IVA	VA	VIA	VIIA	2 Helium **He** 2 4.00260
		5 Boron **B** 2,3 10.81	6 Carbon **C** 2,4 12.011	7 Nitrogen **N** 2,5 14.0067	8 Oxygen **O** 2,6 15.9994	9 Fluorine **F** 2,7 18.99840	10 Neon **Ne** 2,8 20.179

IB	IIB		13 Aluminum **Al** 2,8,3 26.98154	14 Silicon **Si** 2,8,4 28.086	15 Phosphorus **P** 2,8,5 30.97376	16 Sulfur **S** 2,8,6 32.06	17 Chlorine **Cl** 2,8,7 35.453	18 Argon **Ar** 2,8,8 39.948

28 Nickel **Ni** 2,8,16,2 58.71	29 Copper **Cu** 2,8,18,1 63.546	30 Zinc **Zn** 2,8,18,2 65.38	31 Gallium **Ga** 2,8,18,3 69.72	32 Germanium **Ge** 2,8,18,4 72.59	33 Arsenic **As** 2,8,18,5 74.9216	34 Selenium **Se** 2,8,18,6 78.96	35 Bromine **Br** 2,8,18,7 79.904	36 Krypton **Kr** 2,8,18,8 83.80
46 Palladium **Pd** 2,8,18,18,0 106.4	47 Silver **Ag** 2,8,18,18,1 107.868	48 Cadmium **Cd** 2,8,18,18,2 112.40	49 Indium **In** 2,8,18,18,3 114.82	50 Tin **Sn** 2,8,18,18,4 118.69	51 Antimony **Sb** 2,8,18,18,5 121.75	52 Telurium **Te** 2,8,18,18,6 127.60	53 Iodine **I** 2,8,18,18,7 126.9045	54 Xenon **Xe** 2,8,18,18,8 131.30
78 Platinum **Pt** 2,8,18,32,17,1 195.09	79 Gold **Au** 2,8,18,32,18,1 196.9665	80 Mercury **Hg** 2,8,18,32,18,2 200.59	81 Thallium **Tl** 2,8,18,32,18,3 204.37	82 Lead **Pb** 2,8,18,32,18,4 207.2	83 Bismuth **Bi** 2,8,18,32,18,5 208.9804	84 Polonium **Po** 2,8,18,32,18,6 $(210)^a$	85 Astatine **At** 2,8,18,32,18,7 $(210)^a$	86 Radon **Rn** 2,8,18,32,18,8 $(222)^a$

Inner transition elements

63 Europium **Eu** 2,8,18,25,8,2 151.96	64 Gadolinium **Gd** 2,8,18,25,9,2 157.25	65 Terbium **Tb** 2,8,18,27,8,2 158.9254	66 Dysprosium **Dy** 2,8,18,28,8,2 162.50	67 Holmium **Ho** 2,8,18,29,8,2 164.9304	68 Erbium **Er** 2,8,18,30,8,2 167.26	69 Thulium **Tm** 2,8,18,31,8,2 168.9342	70 Ytterbium **Yb** 2,8,18,32,8,2 173.04	71 Lutetium **Lu** 2,8,18,32,9,2 174.97
95 Americium **Am** 2,8,18,32,25,8,2 $(243)^a$	96 Curium **Cm** 2,8,18,32,25,9,2 $(247)^a$	97 Berkelium **Bk** 2,8,18,32,26,9,2 $(249)^a$	98 Californium **Cf** 2,8,18,32,27,9,2 $(251)^a$	99 Einsteinium **Es** 2,8,18,32,28,9,2 $(254)^a$	100 Fermium **Fm** 2,8,18,32,29,9,2 $(253)^a$	101 Mendelevium **Md** 2,8,18,32,30,9,2 $(256)^a$	102 Nobelium **No** 2,8,18,32,31,9,2 $(254)^a$	103 Lawrencium **Lr** 2,8,18,32,32,9,2 $(257)^a$

Table 6.4 Arrangement of the elements into blocks according to the sublevel of electrons being filled in their atomic structure

Period	s block IA		d block Transition elements											p block					Noble gases
		IIA	IIIB	IVB	VB	VIB	VIIB	⌐—VIII—⌐			IB	IIB	IIIA	IVA	VA	VIA	VIIA		
1	1s H																		1s He
2	2s Li	Be											2p B	C	N	O	F		Ne
3	3s Na	Mg											3p Al	Si	P	S	Cl		Ar
4	4s K	Ca	3d Sc	Ti	V	Cr	Mn	Fe	Co	Ni	Cu	Zn	4p Ga	Ge	As	Se	Br		Kr
5	5s Rb	Sr	4d Y	Zr	Nb	Mo	Tc	Ru	Rh	Pd	Ag	Cd	5p In	Sn	Sb	Te	I		Xe
6	6s Cs	Ba	5d La	Hf	Ta	W	Re	Os	Ir	Pt	Au	Hg	6p Tl	Pb	Bi	Po	At		Rn
7	7s Fr	Ra	6d Ac	Unq	Unp	Unh	Uns		Une										

f block Inner transition elements

	s block		4f Ce	Pr	Nd	Pm	Sm	Eu	Gd	Tb	Dy	Ho	Er	Tm	Yb	Lu
	p block		5f Th	Pa	U	Np	Pu	Am	Cm	Bk	Cf	Es	Fm	Md	No	Lr
	d block															
	f block															

The d block includes the transition elements of Groups IB through VIIB and Group VIII (see Section 6.7). In this block electrons are filling the d sublevel orbitals. Each period beginning with period 4 can have ten d block elements. Periods 4, 5, and 6 each have ten; period 7 is incomplete (see Table 6.4).

The f block consists of the inner transition elements and includes two series of 14 elements in periods 6 and 7. The first series, found in period 6, is the lanthanide series (Ce to Lu); the second, found in period 7, is the actinide series (Th to Lr). Electrons are filling the $4f$ sublevel orbitals in the lanthanide series and the $5f$ orbitals in the actinide series.

6.4   Periods of Elements

Of the seven periods of elements (see Tables 6.4 and 6.5), the first three are known as *short periods*, and the remaining four as *long periods*. The first period contains 2 elements, hydrogen and helium. Period 2 contains 8 elements, starting with lithium and ending with neon. Period 3 also contains 8 elements, sodium to argon. Periods 4 and 5 each contain 18 elements; period 6 has 32 elements; and period 7, which is incomplete, contains the remaining elements.

The number of each period corresponds to the number of the outermost energy level that contains electrons of the elements in that period. For example, the period 1 elements contain electrons in the first energy level only; period 2

Table 6.5 The number of elements in each period

Period number	Number of elements	Electron orbitals being filled in each period
1	2	1
2	8	2s2p
3	8	3s3p
4	18	4s3d4p
5	18	5s4d5p
6	32	6s4f5d6p
7	22	7s5f6d

elements contain electrons in the first and second energy levels; period 3 elements contain electrons in the first, second, and third levels; and so on.

From the standpoint of properties, we find that the two elements in the first period are gases; hydrogen (1) is reactive, and helium (2) is a noble gas. Thereafter, as we move from left to right across the successive periods from 2 to 6, we find that the elements vary from strongly metallic at the beginning to nonmetallic at the end of each period. Period 7 is incomplete but begins with a strongly metallic element, francium (87).

Starting with the third element of the long periods, 4, 5, 6, and 7 (scandium, Sc; yttrium, Y; lanthanum, La; actinium, Ac), the inner shells of d and f orbital electrons begin to fill in, forming the transition and inner transition elements (d and f blocks). Both the transition and inner transition elements are metallic.

In general the atomic radii of the elements within a period decrease with increasing nuclear charge. This decrease occurs because, as the positive charge on the nucleus increases, it exerts a greater attractive force on the electrons, causing the atom to become smaller. Therefore the size of the atoms becomes progressively smaller from left to right within each period (see Figure 6.1). Because the noble gases do not readily combine with other elements to form compounds, the radii of their atoms are not determined in the same comparative manner as are those of the other elements. However, calculations have shown that the radii of the noble gas atoms are about the same as, or slightly smaller

Na	Mg	Al	Si	P	S	Cl
0.186 nm	0.160 nm	0.143 nm	0.118 nm	0.110 nm	0.104 nm	0.099 nm

Figure 6.1 Radii of period 3 elements: In general the size of the atoms in a period decreases with increasing nuclear charge.

than, the element immediately preceding them. Slight deviations in atomic radii occur in the middle of the long periods of the elements.

6.5 Groups or Families of Elements

representative elements

transition elements

The groups, or families, of elements are numbered IA through VIIA, IB through VIIB, VIII, and noble gases. Group A elements are often referred to as the **representative,** or *main,* groups of **elements.** They are filling in electrons in the *s* and *p* orbitals. Group B and Group VIII elements are known as the **transition elements.** They are filling in electrons in the *d* and *f* orbitals.

The elements comprising each family have similar electron structures in their outer energy level. In the atoms of Group A elements, the number of electrons in the outer energy level is identical to the group number. Group IA is known as the *alkali metals.* Each atom of this family of elements has one *s* electron in its outer energy level. Group IIA atoms, known as the *alkaline earth metals,* each have two *s* electrons in their outer energy level. Group VIIA is known as the *halogens;* their atoms each have seven electrons (two *s* and five *p*) in their outer energy level. The noble gases (except helium) have eight electrons in their outer energy level.

Each alkali metal starts a new period of elements in which the *s* electron occupies a principal energy level one greater than in the previous period. As a result the size of the atoms of this and other families of elements increases from the top to the bottom of the family. (This generality has some exceptions.) The relative size of the alkali metal atoms is illustrated in Figure 6.2.

One major distinction between groups is the energy level to which the last electron is added. In the elements of Groups IA through VIIA, IB, IIB, and the noble gases, the last electron is added either to an *s* or to a *p* orbital located in the outermost energy level. (This rule has some exceptions; see Table 5.5.) In the elements of Groups IIIB through VIIB and VIII, the last electron goes to a *d* or to an *f* orbital located in an inner energy level. For examples see Figure 6.3.

The general characteristics of group properties are as follows:

1. The number of electrons in the outer energy level of Groups IA through VIIA, IB, and IIB elements is the same as the group number. The other B groups and Group VIII do not show this characteristic. Each noble gas except helium has eight electrons in its outer energy level.
2. The groups on the left and in the middle sections of the table tend to be metallic in nature. The groups on the right tend to be nonmetallic.
3. The radii of the elements increase from top to bottom within a particular group (for example, from lithium to francium).
4. Elements at the bottom of a group tend to be more metallic in their properties than those at the top. This tendency is especially noticeable in Groups IVA through VIIA.
5. Elements within an A group have the same number of electrons in their outer shell and show closely related chemical properties.
6. Elements within a B group have some similarity in electron structure and also show some similarities in chemical properties.

A new format for numbering the groups in the periodic table has been recommended by the American Chemical Society Committee on Nomenclature

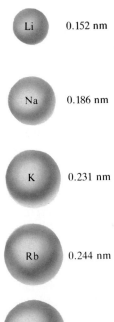

Li   0.152 nm

Na   0.186 nm

K   0.231 nm

Rb   0.244 nm

Cs   0.262 nm

Figure 6.2   Radii of the atoms of the alkali metal family: The size of the atoms in a family increases from top to bottom, because each atom progressively contains electrons in a higher principal energy level.

Group	Noble gas	IA	IIA	IIIB	IVB
Element	Ar	K	Ca	Sc	Ti
Electron structure	2,8,8	2,8,8,1	2,8,8,2	2,8,9,2	2,8,10,2
Energy level	1,2,3	1,2,3,4	1,2,3,4	1,2,3,4	1,2,3,4
Last electron added	↑	↑	↑	↑	↑

Figure 6.3   Comparison of the placement of the last electron in Group A and Group B elements: The energy level to which the last electron is added is indicated by the arrow, an outer level for Group A elements and an inner level for Group B elements.

and by the International Union of Pure and Applied Chemistry (IUPAC) Commission on the Nomenclature of Inorganic Chemistry. The new format numbers the groups from 1 to 18 going from left to right. A periodic table using this numbering method is given in Appendix VI.

PROBLEM

6.1

Write Lewis-dot symbols for the representative elements Na, K, Sr, Se, and Br.

First we need to locate these elements in the periodic table. They are all Group A elements. Then, knowing that Group A numbers are the same as the number of outer-shell electrons and that Lewis-dot structures show only the outer-shell electrons, we can proceed to write the Lewis-dot structures.

Na, K	Group IA	$(1e^-)$	Na· K·
Sr	Group IIA	$(2e^-)$	Sr:
Se	Group VIA	$(6e^-)$	·S̈e:
Br	Group VIIA	$(7e^-)$	:B̈r:

6.6 Predicting Formulas by Use of the Periodic Table

The periodic table can be used to predict the formulas of simple compounds. As we shall see in Chapter 7, the chemical properties of the elements are dependent on their electrons. The representative (Group A) elements ordinarily form compounds using only the electrons in their outer energy level. If we examine Group IA, the alkali metals, we see that all of them have one electron in their outer energy level; all follow a noble gas in the table; and all, except lithium, have eight electrons in their next inner shell. These likenesses suggest that these metals should have a great deal of similarity in their chemistry, since their chemical properties are vested primarily in their outer-shell electron. And they do have similarity: All readily lose their outer electron and attain a noble gas electron structure. In doing so they form compounds with similar atomic compositions. For example, all the monoxides of Group IA contain two atoms of the alkali metal to one atom of oxygen. Their formulas are Li_2O, Na_2O, K_2O, Rb_2O, Cs_2O, and Fr_2O.

How can we use the table to predict formulas of other compounds? Because of similar electron structures, the elements in a family generally form compounds with the same atomic ratios, as was shown in the preceding paragraph for the oxides of the Group IA metals. In general, if we know the atomic ratio of a particular compound, say sodium chloride (NaCl), we can predict the atomic ratios and formulas of the other alkali metal chlorides. These formulas are LiCl, KCl, RbCl, CsCl, and FrCl (see Table 6.6).

In a similar way, if we know that the formula of the oxide of hydrogen is H_2O, we can predict that the formula of the sulfide will be H_2S, because sulfur has the same outer-shell electron structure as oxygen. It must be recognized, however, that these are only predictions; it does not necessarily follow that every element in a group will behave like the others or even that a predicted compound will actually exist. Knowing the formulas for potassium chlorate, bromate, and iodate to be $KClO_3$, $KBrO_3$, and KIO_3, we can correctly predict the corresponding sodium compounds to have the formulas $NaClO_3$, $NaBrO_3$, and $NaIO_3$. Fluorine belongs to the same family of elements (Group VIIA) as chlorine, bromine, and iodine. So we can predict that potassium and sodium fluorates will have the formulas KFO_3 and $NaFO_3$. But this prediction would not be correct, because potassium and sodium fluorates are not known to exist. However, if they did

Table 6.6 Elements in Group A families have the same outer-shell electron structure and are likely to form compounds with the same atomic ratios. Shown, for example, are the monoxides, chlorides, bromides, and sulfates of the alkali metals.

Lewis-dot structure	Monoxides	Chlorides	Bromides	Sulfates
Li·	Li_2O	LiCl	LiBr	Li_2SO_4
Na·	Na_2O	NaCl	NaBr	Na_2SO_4
K·	K_2O	KCl	KBr	K_2SO_4
Rb·	Rb_2O	RbCl	RbBr	Rb_2SO_4
Cs·	Cs_2O	CsCl	CsBr	Cs_2SO_4

exist, the formulas could very well be correct, for these predictions are based on comparisons with known formulas and similar electron structures.

Predicting formulas using this type of analogy is not as reliable for the transition (Group B) elements.

PROBLEM

6.2

The formula for calcium sulfate is $CaSO_4$ and that for lithium carbonate is Li_2CO_3. Predict formulas for **(a)** magnesium sulfate, **(b)** potassium carbonate, and **(c)** magnesium selenate.

(a) Look in the periodic table for calcium and magnesium. They are both in Group IIA. Since the formula for calcium sulfate is $CaSO_4$, it is reasonable to predict that the formula for magnesium sulfate is $MgSO_4$.

(b) Find lithium and potassium in the periodic table. They are in Group IA. Since the formula for lithium carbonate is Li_2CO_3, it is reasonable to predict that K_2CO_3 is the formula for potassium carbonate.

(c) Find selenium in the periodic table. It is in Group VIA just below sulfur. Therefore it is reasonable to assume that selenium forms selenate in the same way that sulfur forms sulfate. Since $MgSO_4$ was the predicted formula for magnesium sulfate in part (a), it is reasonable to assume that the formula for magnesium selenate is $MgSeO_4$.

6.7 Transition Elements

Elements in Groups IB, IIIB through VIIB, and VIII are known as the transition elements. Transition elements occur in periods 4, 5, 6, and 7. The transition elements are characterized by an increasing number of d or f electrons in an inner shell; they all have either one or two electrons in their outer shell. In period 4, electrons enter the $3d$ sublevel. In period 5, electrons enter the $4d$ sublevel. The transition elements in period 6 include the lanthanide series (or *rare earth elements*, Ce to Lu), in which electrons are entering the $4f$ sublevel.

The 5d sublevel also fills up in the sixth period. The seventh period of elements is an incomplete period. It includes the actinide series (Th to Lr), in which electrons are entering the 5f and 6d sublevels.

All of the transition elements are metals. In the formation of transition element compounds, electrons may come from more than one energy level. For this reason many of these metals form multiple series of compounds. These compounds often occur in the form of some of the most beautifully colored crystals to be found in nature.

6.8   Noble Gases

The noble gases are the last group in the periodic table and are sometimes called the zero group. These gases are characterized by extremely low chemical reactivity and were, in fact, formerly known as the inert gases because they were believed to be chemically inert. Their low reactivity is associated with a stable electron outer shell consisting of filled s orbitals and (except for helium) filled p orbitals (see Section 5.15).

All the noble gases except radon are normally present in the atmosphere. Argon is the most abundant, about 1% by volume. The others are present only in trace amounts. Argon was discovered in 1894 by Lord Raleigh (1842–1919) and Sir William Ramsay (1852–1916). Helium was first observed in the spectrum of the sun during an eclipse in 1868. It was not until 1894 that Ramsay recognized that helium exists in the earth's atmosphere. In 1898 he and his co-worker, Morris W. Travers (1872–1961), announced the discovery of neon, krypton, and xenon, having isolated them from liquid air. Friedrich E. Dorn (1848–1916) first identified radon, the heaviest member of the noble gases, as a radioactive gas emanating from the element radium.

Because of its low density and nonflammability, helium has been used for filling balloons and dirigibles. Only hydrogen surpasses helium in lifting power. Helium mixed with oxygen is used by deep-sea divers for breathing. This mixture reduces the danger of acquiring the "bends" (caisson disease), pains and paralysis suffered by divers on returning from the ocean depths to normal atmospheric pressure. Helium is also used in heliarc welding, to supply an inert atmosphere for the welding of active metals such as magnesium. Helium is found in some natural gas wells in the southwestern United States. As a liquid it is used to study the properties of substances at very low temperatures. The boiling point of liquid helium, 4.2 K, is not far above absolute zero.

We are all familiar with the neon sign, in which a characteristic red color is produced when an electric discharge is passed through a tube filled with neon. This color may be modified by mixing the neon with other gases or by changing the color of the glass. Argon is used primarily in gas-filled electric light bulbs and other types of electronic tubes to provide an inert atmosphere for prolonging tube life. Argon is also used in some welding applications where an inert atmosphere is needed. Krypton and xenon have not been used extensively because of their limited availability. Radon is radioactive; it has been used medicinally in the treatment of cancer. Most recently, radon has been shown to be a hazardous cancer-producing pollutant in the air.

For many years it was believed that the noble gases could not be made to combine chemically with any other element. Then, in 1962, Neil Bartlett at the University of British Columbia, Vancouver, synthesized the first noble gas compound, xenon hexafluoroplatinate, $XePtF_6$. This outstanding discovery opened a new field in the techniques of preparing noble gas compounds and investigating their chemical bonding and properties. Other compounds of xenon and compounds of krypton and radon have been prepared. Some of these are XeF_2, XeF_4, XeF_6, $XeOF_4$, $Xe(OH)_6$, and KrF_2.

6.9 New Elements

Mendeleev allowed gaps in his orderly periodic table for elements whose discovery he predicted. These were actually discovered, as were all the elements up to atomic number 92 that occur naturally on the earth. Sixteen elements beyond uranium (atomic numbers 93–107 and 109) have been discovered or synthesized since 1939. All these elements have unstable nuclei and are radioactive. Beyond element 101 the isotopes synthesized thus far have such short lives that chemical identification has not been accomplished.

Intensive research is continuing on the synthesis of still heavier elements to extend the periodic table beyond the presently known elements. It is predicted that elements 110 through 118 will be very stable but still radioactive. Element 114 will lie below lead (82) in the periodic table and should be exceptionally stable. Element 118 should be a member of the noble gas family. Elements 119 and 120 should be in Groups IA and IIA, respectively, and have electrons in the 8s sublevel.

6.10 Summary

The arrangement of the elements into the modern periodic table has been and continues to be of great value to chemists and chemistry students. This value increases with your knowledge of chemistry. For a given element the following data can usually be obtained directly from the table: name, symbol, atomic number, atomic weight, electron structure, group number, period number, and whether it is a metal, nonmetal, or metalloid. From the location of the element in the periodic table, one can estimate and compare many of its properties—such as ionization energy, density, atomic radius, atomic volume, oxidation states, electrical conductance, and electronegativity—with those of other elements.

The periodic table is still used as a guide in predicting the synthesis of possible new elements. It presents a very large amount of chemical information in compact form and correlates the properties and relationships of all the elements. The table is so useful that a copy hangs in nearly every chemistry lecture hall and laboratory in the world. Refer to it often.

QUESTIONS

A. *Review the meanings of the new terms introduced in this chapter.*

1. Periodic law
2. Periodic table
3. Periods of elements
4. Groups or families of elements
5. Representative elements
6. Transition elements

B. *Information useful in answering these questions will be found in the tables and figures.*

1. From the standpoint of electron structure, what do the elements in the s block have in common?
2. Write the symbols for the elements having atomic numbers 8, 16, 34, 52, and 84. What do these elements have in common?
3. Mendeleev described a then-undiscovered element as eka-silicon. When this element was discovered, (a) what was it named and (b) how did the actual density agree with that predicted by Mendeleev?
4. How does the size of the atoms of the elements in the third period vary from left to right?
5. Write the symbols of the family of elements that have seven electrons in their outer energy level.
6. Write the symbols of the alkali metal family in order of increasing atomic size.
7. What is the greatest number of elements to be found in any period? Which periods have this number?
8. From the standpoint of energy level, how does the placement of the last electron differ in Group A elements from that of Group B elements?

C. *Review questions*

1. What were Döbereiner's triads? In what way did they lead to later developments in periodicity?
2. What do you think is the basis for Newlands' Law of Octaves?
3. Given that the noble gases were not discovered at the time of Newlands' Law of Octaves, could his law be extended as far as the element bromine? Explain.
4. What is meant by the term *periodicity* as applied to the elements?

5. Why are some missing elements in Mendeleev's periodic table considered a victory for his table rather than a defeat?
6. How does our modern periodic table differ from Mendeleev's?
7. What additonal understanding of periodic properties was added by the work of H. G. J. Moseley?
8. State the periodic law in its current form. How is this law different from the law as stated by Mendeleev?
9. Find the places in the modern periodic table where elements are not in proper sequence according to atomic weight.
10. How are elements in a period related to one another?
11. How are elements in a group related to one another?
12. What is common about the electron structures of the alkali metals?
13. Why would you expect the elements zinc, cadmium, and mercury to be in the same chemical family?
14. Draw the Lewis-dot structures for Cs, Ba, Tl, Pb, Po, At, and Rn. How do these structures correlate with the group in which each element occurs?
15. Pick the electron structures below that represent elements in the same chemical family:
    (a) $1s^2 2s^1$
    (b) $1s^2 2s^2 2p^4$
    (c) $1s^2 2s^2 2p^2$
    (d) $1s^2 2s^2 2p^6 3s^2 3p^4$
    (e) $1s^2 2s^2 2p^6 3s^2 3p^6$
    (f) $1s^2 2s^2 2p^6 3s^2 3p^6 4s^2$
    (g) $1s^2 2s^2 2p^6 3s^2 3p^6 4s^1$
    (h) $1s^2 2s^2 2p^6 3s^2 3p^6 4s^2 3d^1$
16. Pick the electron structures below that represent elements in the same chemical family:
    (a) $[He]2s^2 2p^6$ (e) $[Ar]4s^1 3d^{10}$
    (b) $[Ne]3s^1$ (f) $[Ar]4s^2 3d^{10} 4p^6$
    (c) $[Ne]3s^2$ (g) $[Ar]4s^2 3d^5$
    (d) $[Ne]3s^2 3p^3$ (h) $[Kr]5s^1 4d^{10}$
17. In the periodic table, calcium (element 20), is surrounded by elements 12, 19, 21, and 38. Which of these have physical and chemical properties most resembling calcium?
18. Oxygen is a gas. Sulfur is a solid. What is it about

their electron structures that causes them to be grouped in the same chemical family?

19. Classify each of the following elements as metals, nonmetals, or metalloids:
    (a) Potassium   (e) Iodine
    (b) Plutonium   (f) Tungsten
    (c) Sulfur   (g) Molybdenum
    (d) Antimony   (h) Germanium

20. In which period and group does an electron first appear in a d orbital?

21. How many electrons occur in the outer shell of Group IIIA and IIIB elements? Why are they different?

22. In which groups are transition elements located?

23. How do the electron structures of the transition elements differ from representative elements?

24. Which element in each of the following pairs has the larger atomic radius?
    (a) Na or K   (c) O or F   (e) Ti or Zr
    (b) Na or Mg   (d) Br or I

25. Which element in each of Groups IA–VIIA has the smallest atomic radius?

26. Why does the atomic size increase in going down any family of the periodic table?

27. All the atoms within each Group A family of elements can be represented by the same Lewis-dot structure. Complete the table, expressing the Lewis-dot structure for each group. Use E to represent the elements.

Group	IA	IIA	IIIA	IVA	VA	VIA	VIIA
	E·						

28. Let E be any representative element. Following the pattern in the table, write the formulas for the hydrogen and oxygen compounds of
    (a) Na   (c) Al   (e) Sb   (g) Cl
    (b) Ca   (d) Sn   (f) Se

Group IA	IIA	IIIA	IVA	VA	VIA	VIIA
EH	EH_2	EH_3	EH_4	EH_3	H_2E	HE
E_2O	EO	E_2O_3	EO_2	E_2O_5	EO_3	E_2O_7

29. Group IB elements have one electron in their outer shell, as do Group IA elements. Would you expect them to form compounds such as CuCl, AgCl, and AuCl? Explain.

30. The formula for lead(II) bromide is $PbBr_2$; predict formulas for tin(II) and germanium(II) bromides. (If needed, see Section 8.7, part (b), for the use of Roman numerals in naming compounds.)

31. The formula for sodium sulfate is Na_2SO_4. Write the names and formulas for the other alkali metal sulfates.

32. The formula for calcium bromide is $CaBr_2$. Write formulas for magnesium bromide, strontium bromide, and barium bromide.

33. Why should the discovery of the existence of isotopes have any bearing on the fact that the periodicity of the elements is a function of their atomic numbers and not their atomic weights?

Try to answer Questions 34–36 without referring to the periodic table.

34. The atomic numbers of the noble gases are 2, 10, 18, 36, 54, and 86. What are the atomic numbers for the elements with six electrons in their outer electron shells?

35. Element number 87 is in Group IA, period 7. Describe its outermost energy level. How many energy levels of electrons does it have?

36. If element 36 is a noble gas, in which groups would you expect elements 35 and 37 to occur?

37. Write a paragraph describing the general features of the periodic table.

38. Rank the following five elements according to the radii of their atoms, from smallest to largest: Na, Mg, Cl, K, and Rb.

39. Which of the following statements are correct?
    (a) Properties of the elements are periodic functions of their atomic numbers.
    (b) There are more nonmetallic elements than metallic elements.
    (c) Metallic properties of the elements increase from left to right across a period.
    (d) Metallic properties of the elements increase from top to bottom in a family of elements.
    (e) Calcium is a member of the alkaline earth metal family.
    (f) Iron belongs to the alkali metal family.
    (g) Bromine belongs to the halogen family.
    (h) Neon is a noble gas.
    (i) Group A elements do not contain partially filled d or f sublevels.

(j) An atom of oxygen is larger than an atom of lithium.

(k) An atom of sulfur is larger than an atom of oxygen.

(l) An atom of aluminum (Group IIIA) has five electrons in its outer shell.

(m) If the formula for calcium iodide is CaI_2, then the formula for cesium iodide is CsI_2.

(n) If the formula for aluminum oxide is Al_2O_3, then the formula for gallium oxide is Ga_2O_3.

(o) Uranium is an inner transition element.

(p) The element $[Ar]4s^2 3d^{10} 4p^5$ is a halogen.

(q) The element $[Kr]5s^2$ is a nonmetal.

(r) The element with $Z = 12$ forms compounds similar to the element with $Z = 37$.

(s) Nitrogen, fluorine, neon, gallium, and bromine are all nonmetals.

(t) The Lewis-dot structure for tin is $:\overset{\cdot}{Sn}\cdot$

(u) The atom having an outer-shell electron structure of $5s^2 5p^2$ would be in period 6, Group IVA.

(v) The yet-to-be-discovered element with an atomic number of 118 would be a noble gas.

(w) The most metallic element of Group VIIA is iodine.

7

Chemical Bonds: The Formation of Compounds from Atoms

After studying Chapter 7, you should be able to

1. Understand the new terms listed in Question A at the end of the chapter.
2. Describe how the ionization energies of the elements vary with respect to (a) position in the periodic table and (b) the removal of successive electrons.
3. Determine the number of valence electrons in an atom for any Group A element.
4. Describe (a) the formation of ions by electron transfer and (b) the nature of the chemical bond formed by electron transfer.
5. Show by means of Lewis-dot structures the formation of an ionic compound from atoms.
6. Describe a crystal of sodium chloride.
7. Predict the formulas of the monatomic ions of Group A metals and nonmetals.
8. Predict the relative sizes of an atom and a monatomic ion for a given element.
9. Describe the covalent bond and predict whether a given covalent bond would be polar or nonpolar.
10. Draw Lewis-dot structures for the diatomic elements.
11. Identify single, double, and triple covalent bonds.
12. Describe the changes in electronegativity in (1) moving across a period and (2) moving down a group in the periodic table.

13. Describe the effect of electronegativity on the type of chemical bonds in a compound.
14. Draw Lewis-dot structures for (a) the molecules of covalent compounds and (b) polyatomic ions.
15. Describe the difference between polar and nonpolar bonds.
16. Distinguish clearly between ionic and molecular substances.
17. Predict whether the bonding in a compound will be primarily ionic or covalent.
18. Distinguish coordinate covalent bonds from covalent bonds in a Lewis structure.

7.1 Chemical Bonds

chemical bonds

Except in very rare instances, matter does not fly apart spontaneously. It is prevented from doing so by forces acting at the ionic and molecular levels. Through chemical reactions atoms tend to attain more stable states at lower chemical potential energy levels. Atoms react chemically by losing, gaining, or sharing electrons. Forces arise from electron-transferring and electron-sharing interactions. Those forces that hold oppositely charged ions together or that bind atoms together in molecules are called **chemical bonds.** The two principal types of bonds are: the ionic bond and the covalent bond.

7.2 Ionization Energy and Electron Affinity

According to Niels Bohr's concept, electrons exist at various discrete energy levels depending on the amount of energy that the atom has absorbed. If sufficient energy is applied to an atom, it is possible to remove completely (or "knock out") one or more electrons from its structure, thereby forming a positive ion:

$$\text{Atom} + \text{Energy} \longrightarrow \text{Positive ion} + \text{Electron } (e^-)$$

ionization energy

The amount of energy required to remove one electron from an atom or an ion is called the **ionization energy.** The *first* ionization energy is the amount of energy required to remove the first electron from an atom, the *second* ionization energy is the amount needed to remove the second electron from that atom, and so on.

Ionization energies may be expressed in terms of various energy units such as electron volts, kilojoules, or kilocalories per mole. The mole (abbreviated mol), which is discussed in detail in Chapter 9, is the unit in the International System for expressing an amount of substance. One mole of a substance is 6.022×10^{23} individual particles of that substance. Thus a mole of atoms is 6.022×10^{23} atoms, or a mole of oranges is 6.022×10^{23} oranges (and that's a lot of oranges). In the following discussion ionization energy is expressed as kilojoules per mole (kJ/mol) indicating the number of kilojoules required to remove one electron from each atom in a mole of atoms.

Table 7.1 Ionization energies for selected elements: Values are expressed in kilojoules per mole, showing energies required to remove one to five electrons per atom. Color indicates the energy needed to remove an electron from a noble gas electron structure.

| Element | Required amounts of energy (kJ/mol) | | | | |
	1st e⁻	2nd e⁻	3rd e⁻	4th e⁻	5th e⁻
H	1,314				
He	2,372	5,247			
Li	520	7,297	11,810		
Be	900	1,757	14,845	21,000	
B	800	2,430	3,659	25,020	32,810
C	1,088	2,352	4,619	6,222	37,800
Ne	2,080	3,962	6,276	9,376	12,190
Na	496	4,565	6,912	9,540	13,355

$$\text{Na} \quad + 494 \text{ kJ} \longrightarrow \quad \text{Na}^+ \quad + \quad e^-$$

| 1 mol | 1 mol | 1 mol |
| sodium atoms | sodium ions | electrons |

Table 7.1 gives the ionization energies for the removal of one to five electrons from several elements. Thus, 1314 kJ are required to remove one electron from a mole of hydrogen atoms, but only 494 kJ are needed to remove the first electron from a mole of sodium atoms. The table shows that increasingly higher amounts of energy are required to remove the second, third, fourth, and fifth electrons. This sequence is logical, because the removal of electrons does not decrease the number of protons, or the amount of charge, in the nucleus. Therefore the remaining electrons are held more tightly. The data of Table 7.1 also show that an extra-large ionization energy is needed whenever an electron is pulled away from a noble gas electron structure, clearly demonstrating the high stability of this structure.

First ionization energies have been experimentally determined for most of the elements. Figure 7.1 is a graphic plot of the first ionization energies of the first 56 elements, H through Ba.

Certain periodic relationships are evident in Figure 7.1. In the Group A, or representative, elements, the first ionization energy generally decreases from top to bottom in groups or families. For example, in alkali metals (Group IA) the first ionization energy decreases from 520 kJ/mol for lithium to 376 kJ/mol for cesium. The two main reasons for this family trend are that (1) as we go from top to bottom in the family, the electron being removed is farther away from its nucleus, and (2) the electron is shielded from its nucleus by more inner shells of electrons. Furthermore all the alkali metals have relatively low first ionization energies, indicating that each has one electron that is easily removed.

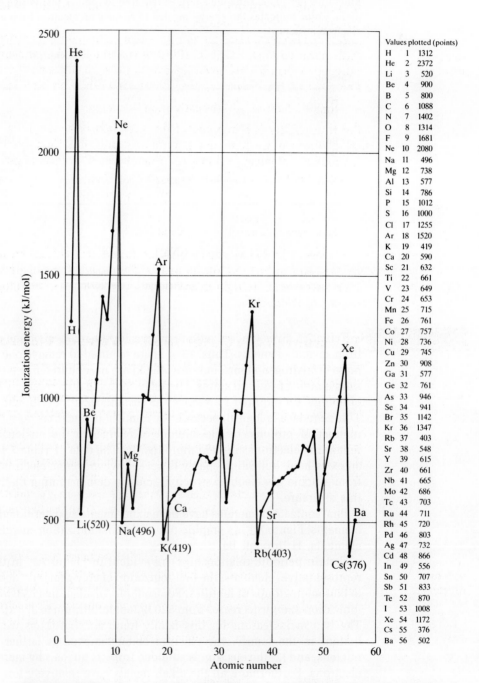

Values plotted (points)		
H	1	1312
He	2	2372
Li	3	520
Be	4	900
B	5	800
C	6	1088
N	7	1402
O	8	1314
F	9	1681
Ne	10	2080
Na	11	496
Mg	12	738
Al	13	577
Si	14	786
P	15	1012
S	16	1000
Cl	17	1255
Ar	18	1520
K	19	419
Ca	20	590
Sc	21	632
Ti	22	661
V	23	649
Cr	24	653
Mn	25	715
Fe	26	761
Co	27	757
Ni	28	736
Cu	29	745
Zn	30	908
Ga	31	577
Ge	32	761
As	33	946
Se	34	941
Br	35	1142
Kr	36	1347
Rb	37	403
Sr	38	548
Y	39	615
Zr	40	661
Nb	41	665
Mo	42	686
Tc	43	703
Ru	44	711
Rh	45	720
Pd	46	803
Ag	47	732
Cd	48	866
In	49	556
Sn	50	707
Sb	51	833
Te	52	870
I	53	1008
Xe	54	1172
Cs	55	376
Ba	56	502

Figure 7.1 Periodic relationship of the first ionization energy to the atomic number of the elements

From left to right within a period, the ionization energy gradually increases despite some irregularities. The noble gases have relatively high values, confirming the nonreactivity of this family and the stability of an eight-electron structure in the outer energy level.

electron affinity

Atoms also have *electron affinity*—that is, the ability to attract electrons and form negative ions. **Electron affinity** may be defined as the amount of energy released or absorbed when an electron is added to an atom to form a negative ion. For most of the elements, heat is released when an atom adds an electron.

Atom + Electron $\longrightarrow$ Negative ion + Energy

Electron affinity is a measure of the attraction of an atom for an electron—in other words, of the tendency to form a negative ion. Chlorine, for example, is a nonmetallic element and has a strong tendency to form negative ions. Consequently the electron affinity of chlorine is high.

$$\underset{\substack{\text{1 mol} \\ \text{chlorine atoms}}}{\text{Cl}} + \underset{\substack{\text{1 mol} \\ \text{electrons}}}{\text{e}^-} \longrightarrow \underset{\substack{\text{1 mol} \\ \text{chloride ions}}}{\text{Cl}^-} + 348 \text{ kJ (83 kcal)}$$

Electron affinity tends to be high for nonmetals (particularly for the halogens, oxygen, and sulfur) and low for metals. The general trend of electron affinity is to increase from left to right in any period and to decrease from top to bottom in a family of elements.

7.3 Electrons in the Outer Shell — Valence Electrons

One outstanding property of the elements is their tendency to form a stable outer-shell electron structure. For many elements this stable outer shell contains eight electrons (two s and six p) identical to the outer-shell electron structure of the noble gases. Atoms undergo rearrangements of electron structure to attain a state of greater stability. These rearrangements are accomplished by losing, gaining, or sharing electrons with other atoms. For example, a hydrogen atom has a tendency to accept another electron and thus attain an electron structure like that of the stable noble gas helium; a fluorine atom can acquire one more electron to attain a stable electron structure like neon; a sodium atom tends to lose one electron to attain a stable electron structure like neon.

Na + Energy $\longrightarrow$ Na$^+$ + 1e$^-$

valence electrons

The electrons in the outermost shell of an atom are responsible for most of this electron activity and are called the **valence electrons.** In Lewis-dot symbols of atoms, the dots represent the outer-shell electrons and thus also represent the valence electrons. For example, hydrogen has one valence electron; sodium, one; aluminum, three; and oxygen, six. When a rearrangement of these electrons takes place between atoms, a chemical change occurs.

$$\text{H·} \qquad \text{Al·} \qquad \text{·O:}$$

| One valence | Three valence | Six valence |
| electron | electrons | electrons |

7.4 The Ionic Bond: Transfer of Electrons from One Atom to Another

The chemistry of the elements, especially the representative ones, is to attain an outer-shell electron structure like that of the chemically stable noble gases. With the exception of helium, this stable structure consists of eight electrons in the outer shell (see Table 5.6).

Let us look at the electron structures of sodium and chlorine to see how each element can attain a structure of 8 electrons in its outer shell. A sodium atom has 11 electrons: 2 in the first energy level, 8 in the second energy level, and 1 in the third energy level. A chlorine atom has 17 electrons: 2 in the first energy level, 8 in the second energy level, and 7 in the third energy level. If a sodium atom transfers or loses its 3s electron, its third energy level becomes vacant, and it becomes a sodium ion with an electron configuration identical to that of the noble gas neon. This process absorbs energy.

$$11+ \quad 2e^- 8e^- 1e^- \longrightarrow \overset{1+}{11+} \quad 2e^- 8e^- \; + \; 1e^-$$

Na atom ($1s^2 2s^2 2p^6 3s^1$)   Na$^+$ ion ($1s^2 2s^2 2p^6$)

An atom that has lost or gained electrons will have a plus or minus electric charge, depending on which charged particles, protons or electrons, are in excess. Recall that a charged atom or group of atoms is called an *ion*.

By losing a negatively charged electron, the sodium atom becomes a positively charged particle known as a sodium ion. The charge, + 1, results because the nucleus still contains 11 positively charged protons, and the electron orbitals contain only 10 negatively charged electrons. The charge is indicated by a plus sign (+) and is written as a superscript after the symbol of the element (Na$^+$).

A chlorine atom with 7 electrons in the third energy level needs 1 electron to pair up with its one unpaired 3p electron to attain the stable outer-shell electron structure of argon. By gaining 1 electron the chlorine atom becomes a chloride ion (Cl$^-$), a negatively charged particle containing 17 protons and 18 electrons. This process releases energy.

$$17+ \quad 2e^- 8e^- 7e^- \; + \; 1e^- \longrightarrow \overset{1-}{17+} \quad 2e^- 8e^- 8e^-$$

Cl atom ($1s^2 2s^2 2p^6 3s^2 3p^5$)   Cl$^-$ ion ($1s^2 2s^2 2p^6 3s^2 3p^6$)

Consider the case in which sodium and chlorine atoms react with each other. The 3s electron from the sodium atom transfers to the half-filled 3p orbital in the chlorine atom to form a positive sodium ion and a negative chloride ion. The compound sodium chloride results because the Na^+ and Cl^- ions are strongly attracted to each other by their opposite electrostatic charges. The force holding the oppositely charged ions together is an ionic bond.

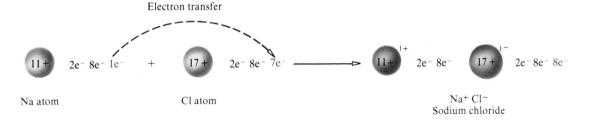

The Lewis-dot representation of sodium chloride formation is shown below:

$$Na \cdot + \cdot \overset{\cdot\cdot}{\underset{\cdot\cdot}{Cl}} : \longrightarrow Na^+ : \overset{\cdot\cdot}{\underset{\cdot\cdot}{Cl}} : ^-$$

The chemical reaction between sodium and chlorine is a very vigorous one, producing considerable heat energy in addition to the salt formed. When energy is released in a chemical reaction, the products are more stable than the reactants. Note that in NaCl both atoms attained a noble gas electron structure.

Sodium chloride is made up of cubic crystals in which each sodium ion is surrounded by six chloride ions and each chloride ion by six sodium ions, except at the crystal surface. A visible crystal is a regularly arranged aggregate of millions of these ions, but the ratio of sodium to chloride ions is one to one, hence the formula NaCl. The cubic crystalline lattice arrangement of sodium chloride is shown in Figure 7.2.

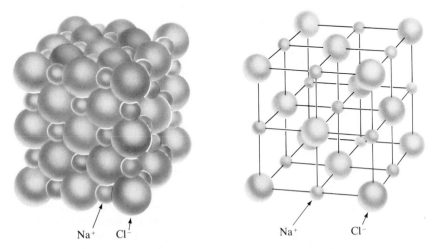

Figure 7.2 Sodium chloride crystal: Diagram represents a small fragment of sodium chloride, which forms cubic crystals. Each sodium ion is surrounded by six chloride ions, and each chloride ion is surrounded by six sodium ions.

0.186 nm   0.099 nm   0.095 nm   0.181 nm

Na atom   Cl atom   Na$^+$ ion   Cl$^-$ ion

Figure 7.3 Relative sizes of sodium and chlorine atoms and their ions

Figure 7.3 contrasts the relative sizes of sodium and chlorine atoms with those of their ions. The sodium ion is smaller than the atom due primarily to two factors: (1) The sodium atom has lost its outer shell of 1 electron, thereby reducing its size; and (2) the 10 remaining electrons are now attracted by 11 protons and are thus drawn closer to the nucleus. Conversely the chloride ion is larger than the atom because it has 18 electrons but only 17 protons; the nuclear attraction on each electron is thereby decreased, allowing the chlorine atom to expand as it forms an ion.

We have seen that when sodium reacts with chlorine, each atom becomes an electrically charged ion. Sodium chloride, like all ionic substances, is held together by the attraction existing between positive and negative charges. An **ionic bond** is the electrostatic attraction between oppositely charged ions.

Ionic bonds are formed whenever one or more electrons are transferred from one atom to another. The metals, which have relatively little attraction for their valence electrons, tend to form ionic bonds when they combine with nonmetals.

It is important to recognize that substances with ionic bonds do not exist as molecules. In sodium chloride, for example, the bond does not exist solely between a single sodium ion and a single chloride ion. Each sodium ion in the crystal attracts six near-neighbor negative chloride ions; in turn, each negative chloride ion attracts six near-neighbor positive sodium ions (see Figure 7.2).

A metal will usually have one, two, or three electrons in its outer energy level. In reacting, metal atoms characteristically lose these electrons, attain the electron structure of a noble gas, and become positive ions. A nonmetal, on the other hand, is only a few electrons short of having a complete octet in its outer energy level and thus has a tendency to gain electrons (electron affinity). In reacting with metals, nonmetal atoms characteristically gain one, two, or three electrons, attain the electron structure of a noble gas, and become negative ions. The ions formed by loss of electrons are much smaller than the corresponding metal atoms; the ions formed by gaining electrons are larger than the corresponding nonmetal atoms. The actual dimensions of the atomic and ionic radii of several metals and nonmetals are given in Table 7.2.

ionic bond

Table 7.2 Change in atomic radii of selected metals and nonmetals. The metals shown lose electrons to become positive ions. The nonmetals gain electrons to become negative ions.

Metals		Nonmetals	
Atomic radius (nm)	*Ionic radius (nm)*	*Ionic radius (nm)*	*Atomic radius (nm)*
Li 0.152	Li^+ 0.060	F 0.071	F^- 0.136
Na 0.186	Na^+ 0.095	Cl 0.099	Cl^- 0.181
K 0.227	K^+ 0.133	Br 0.114	Br^- 0.195
Mg 0.160	Mg^{2+} 0.065	O 0.074	O^{2-} 0.140
Al 0.143	Al^{3+} 0.050	S 0.103	S^{2-} 0.184

Study the following examples. Note the loss and gain of electrons between atoms; also note that the ions in each compound have a noble-gas electron structure.

EXAMPLE

7.1

Formation of magnesium chloride, $MgCl_2$

A magnesium atom of electron structure $1s^2 2s^2 2p^6 3s^2$ must lose two electrons or gain six electrons to reach a stable electron structure. If magnesium reacts with chlorine and each chlorine atom can accept only one electron, two chlorine atoms will be needed for the two electrons from one magnesium atom. The compound formed will contain one magnesium ion and two chloride ions. The magnesium atom, having lost two electrons, becomes a magnesium ion with a +2 charge. Each chloride ion will have a −1 charge. The transfer of electrons from a magnesium atom to two chlorine atoms is shown in the following illustration.

Mg atom   2 Cl atoms   Magnesium chloride

EXAMPLE

7.2

Formation of sodium fluoride, NaF

Na·   +   ·F̈:̈   Na⁺ :F̈:̈⁻

Sodium atom   Fluorine atom   Sodium fluoride

The fluorine atom, with seven electrons in its outer shell, behaves similarly to the chlorine atom.

EXAMPLE

7.3

Formation of aluminum chloride, $AlCl_3$

$$·\ddot{C}l:$$ $$:\ddot{C}l:^{-}$$

$$\ddot{A}l· \ + \ ·\ddot{C}l: \longrightarrow Al^{3+} \ :\ddot{C}l:^{-} \quad or \quad AlCl_3$$

$$·\ddot{C}l:$$ $$:\ddot{C}l:^{-}$$

Aluminum   Chlorine   Aluminum chloride
   atom   atoms

Each chlorine atom can accept only one electron. Therefore three chlorine atoms are needed to combine with the three outer-shell electrons of one aluminum atom. The aluminum atom has lost three electrons to become an aluminum ion, Al^{3+}, with a +3 charge.

EXAMPLE

7.4

Formation of magnesium oxide, MgO

12+ 2e⁻ 8e⁻ 2e⁻   +   8+ 2e⁻ 6e⁻   ⟶   12+²⁺ 2e⁻ 8e⁻   8+²⁻ 2e⁻ 8e⁻

Mg:̈   +   ·Ö:̈   Mg²⁺ :Ö:̈²⁻

Magnesium atom   Oxygen atom   Magnesium oxide

The magnesium atom, with two electrons in the outer energy level, exactly fills the need of two electrons of one oxygen atom. The resulting compound has a ratio of one atom of magnesium to one atom of oxygen. The oxygen (oxide) ion has a −2 charge, having gained two electrons. In combining with oxygen, magnesium behaves the same way as when combining with chlorine; it loses two electrons.

EXAMPLE

7.5

Formation of sodium sulfide, Na_2S

$$\begin{matrix} Na\cdot \\ Na\cdot \end{matrix} + \quad \cdot\ddot{S}: \quad \longrightarrow \quad \begin{matrix} Na^+ \\ Na^+ \end{matrix} \quad :\ddot{S}:^{2-} \quad \text{or} \quad Na_2S$$

Sodium   Sulfur   Sodium sulfide
atoms   atom

Two sodium atoms supply the electrons that one sulfur atom needs to make eight in its outer shell.

EXAMPLE

7.6

Formation of aluminum oxide, Al_2O_3

$$\begin{matrix} & & \cdot\ddot{O}: & & & :\ddot{O}:^{2-} \\ \ddot{Al}\cdot & & & & Al^{3+} & \\ & + & \cdot\ddot{O}: & \longrightarrow & & :\ddot{O}:^{2-} \quad \text{or} \quad Al_2O_3 \\ \ddot{Al}\cdot & & & & Al^{3+} & \\ & & \cdot\ddot{O}: & & & :\ddot{O}:^{2-} \end{matrix}$$

Aluminum   Oxygen   Aluminum oxide
atoms   atoms

One oxygen atom, needing two electrons, cannot accommodate the three electrons from one aluminum atom. One aluminum atom falls one electron short of the four electrons needed by two oxygen atoms. A ratio of two atoms of aluminum to three atoms of oxygen, involving the transfer of six electrons (two to each oxygen atom), gives each atom a stable electron configuration.

Note that in each of the examples above outer shells containing eight electrons were formed in all the negative ions. This formation resulted from the pairing of all the s and p electrons in these outer shells.

Chemistry would be considerably simpler if all compounds were made by the direct formation of ions as outlined in the examples just given. However, this method is only one of the two general methods of compound formation. The second general method will be outlined in the sections that follow.

7.5   The Covalent Bond: Sharing Electrons

Some atoms do not transfer electrons from one atom to another to form ions. Instead they form a chemical bond by sharing pairs of electrons between them.

covalent bond   A **covalent bond** consists of a pair of electrons shared between two atoms. This bonding concept was introduced in 1916 by G. N. Lewis of the University of California at Berkeley. In the millions of compounds that are known, the covalent bond is the predominant chemical bond.

True molecules exist in substances in which the atoms are covalently bonded. Hence, it is proper to refer to molecules of such substances as hydrogen, chlorine, hydrogen chloride, carbon dioxide, water, or sugar. These substances contain only covalent bonds and exist as aggregates of molecules. We do not use the term *molecule* when talking about ionically bonded compounds such as sodium chloride, because such substances exist as large aggregates of positive and negative ions, not as molecules.

A study of the hydrogen molecule will give an insight into the nature of the covalent bond and its formation. The formation of a hydrogen molecule, H_2, involves the overlapping and pairing of 1s electron orbitals from two hydrogen atoms. This overlapping and pairing is shown in Figure 7.4. Each atom contributes one electron of the pair that is shared jointly by two hydrogen nuclei. The orbital of the electrons now includes both hydrogen nuclei, but probability factors show that the most likely place to find the electrons (the point of highest electron density) is between the two nuclei. The two nuclei are shielded from each other by the pair of electrons, allowing the two nuclei to be drawn very close to each other. (The average bond length between the hydrogen nuclei is 7.4×10^{-9} cm or 7.4×10^{-2} nm.)

The tendency for hydrogen atoms to form a molecule is very strong. In the molecule, each electron is attracted by two positive nuclei. This attraction gives the hydrogen molecule a more stable structure than the individual hydrogen atoms had. Energy is released when a bond forms between two atoms. Consequently, the same amount of energy is needed to break that bond. Experimental evidence of stability is shown by the fact that 436 kJ are needed to break the bonds between the hydrogen atoms in 1 mole of hydrogen molecules. The strength of a bond may be determined by the energy required to break it. The energy required to break a covalent bond is known as the bond *dissociation*

Figure 7.4   The formation of a hydrogen molecule from two hydrogen atoms: The two 1s orbitals overlap, forming the H_2 molecule. In this molecule the two electrons are shared between the atoms, forming a covalent bond.

energy. The following bond dissociation energies illustrate relative bond strengths. (All substances are considered to be in the gaseous state and to form neutral atoms.)

Reaction	Bond dissociation energy (kJ/mol)
$H_2 \longrightarrow 2\ H$	435
$N_2 \longrightarrow 2\ N$	946
$O_2 \longrightarrow 2\ O$	595
$F_2 \longrightarrow 2\ F$	153
$Cl_2 \longrightarrow 2\ Cl$	243
$Br_2 \longrightarrow 2\ Br$	193
$I_2 \longrightarrow 2\ I$	151

The formula of chlorine gas is Cl_2. When the two atoms of chlorine combine to form this molecule, the electrons must interact in a manner that is similar to that shown in the preceding example. Each chlorine atom would be more stable with eight electrons in its outer shell. But chlorine atoms are identical, and neither is able to pull an electron away from the other. What happens is this: The unpaired $3p$ electron orbital of one chlorine atom overlaps the unpaired $3p$ electron orbital of the other atom, resulting in a pair of electrons that are mutually shared between the two atoms. Each atom furnishes one of the pair of shared electrons. Thus, each atom attains a stable structure of eight electrons by sharing an electron pair with the other atom. The pairing of the p electrons and formation of a chlorine molecule are illustrated in Figure 7.5. Neither chlorine atom has a positive or negative charge, since both contain the same number of protons and have equal attraction for the pair of electrons being shared. Other examples of molecules in which electrons are equally shared between two atoms are

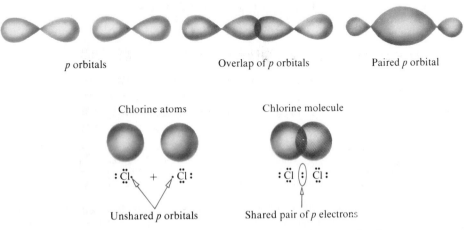

p orbitals Overlap of p orbitals Paired p orbital

Chlorine atoms Chlorine molecule

Unshared p orbitals Shared pair of p electrons

Figure 7.5   Pairing of p electrons in the formation of a chlorine molecule hydrogen, H_2; oxygen, O_2; nitrogen, N_2; fluorine, F_2; bromine, Br_2; and iodine, I_2. Note that more than one pair of electrons may be shared between atoms.

H:H   :F̈:F̈:   :B̈r:B̈r: :Ï:Ï: :Ö::Ö: :N:::N:

Hydrogen   Fluorine   Bromine   Iodine   Oxygen   Nitrogen

The Lewis structure given for oxygen does not adequately account for all the properties of the oxygen molecule. Experimentally, oxygen appears to have two unpaired electrons but also shows the characteristics of a double bond between the two atoms. Theories explaining the bonding in oxygen molecules are complex and beyond the scope of this book.

A common practice in writing structures is to replace a pair of dots (:) used to represent a shared pair of electrons by a dash (—). But you must remember that a dash represents a shared pair of electrons. One dash represents a single bond; two dashes, a double bond; and three dashes, a triple bond. The six structures just shown may be written thus:

H—H   :F̈—F̈:   :B̈r—B̈r: :Ï—Ï: :Ö=Ö: :N≡N:

Electronegativity

electro-negativity

When two different kinds of atoms share a pair of electrons, one atom assumes a partial positive charge and the other a partial negative charge with respect to each other. This difference in charge occurs because the two atoms exert unequal attraction for the pair of shared electrons. The attractive force that an atom of an element has for shared electrons in a molecule is known as its **electronegativity**. Elements differ in their electronegativities. For example, both hydrogen and chlorine need one electron to form stable electron configurations. They share a pair of electrons in hydrogen chloride, HCl. Chlorine is more electronegative and therefore has a greater attraction for the shared electrons than does hydrogen. As a result the pair of electrons is displaced toward the chlorine atom, giving it a partial negative charge and leaving the hydrogen atom with a partial positive charge. It should be understood that the electron is not transferred entirely to the chlorine atom, as in the case of sodium chloride, and no ions are formed. The entire molecule, HCl, is electrically neutral. A partial charge is usually indicated by the Greek letter delta, δ. Thus, a partial positive charge is represented by $\delta+$ and a partial negative charge by $\delta-$.

Hydrogen chloride

{ The pair of shared electrons in HCl is closer to the more electronegative chlorine atom than to the hydrogen atom, giving chlorine a partial negative charge with respect to the hydrogen atom.

The electronegativity, or ability of an atom to attract an electron, depends on several factors: (1) the charge on the nucleus, (2) the distance of the outer electrons from the nucleus, and (3) the amount the nucleus is shielded from the outer-shell electrons by intervening shells of electrons. A scale of relative

Table 7.3 Relative electronegativity of the elements: The electronegativity value is given below the symbol of each element.

Legend:
- 9 — Atomic number
- F — Symbol
- 4.0 — Electronegativity

1	2	3	4	5	6	7	8	9	10	11	12	13	14	15	16	17	18
1 **H** 2.1																	2 **He** —
3 **Li** 1.0	4 **Be** 1.5											5 **B** 2.0	6 **C** 2.5	7 **N** 3.0	8 **O** 3.5	9 **F** 4.0	10 **Ne** —
11 **Na** 0.9	12 **Mg** 1.2											13 **Al** 1.5	14 **Si** 1.8	15 **P** 2.1	16 **S** 2.5	17 **Cl** 3.0	18 **Ar** —
19 **K** 0.8	20 **Ca** 1.0	21 **Sc** 1.3	22 **Ti** 1.4	23 **V** 1.6	24 **Cr** 1.6	25 **Mn** 1.5	26 **Fe** 1.8	27 **Co** 1.8	28 **Ni** 1.8	29 **Cu** 1.9	30 **Zn** 1.6	31 **Ga** 1.6	32 **Ge** 1.8	33 **As** 2.0	34 **Se** 2.4	35 **Br** 2.8	36 **Kr** —
37 **Rb** 0.8	38 **Sr** 1.0	39 **Y** 1.2	40 **Zr** 1.4	41 **Nb** 1.6	42 **Mo** 1.8	43 **Tc** 1.9	44 **Ru** 2.2	45 **Rh** 2.2	46 **Pd** 2.2	47 **Ag** 1.9	48 **Cd** 1.7	49 **In** 1.7	50 **Sn** 1.8	51 **Sb** 1.9	52 **Te** 2.1	53 **I** 2.5	54 **Xe** —
55 **Cs** 0.7	56 **Ba** 0.9	57–71 **La-Lu** 1.1–1.2	72 **Hf** 1.3	73 **Ta** 1.5	74 **W** 1.7	75 **Re** 1.9	76 **Os** 2.2	77 **Ir** 2.2	78 **Pt** 2.2	79 **Au** 2.4	80 **Hg** 1.9	81 **Tl** 1.8	82 **Pb** 1.8	83 **Bi** 1.9	84 **Po** 2.0	85 **At** 2.2	86 **Rn** —
87 **Fr** 0.7	88 **Ra** 0.9	89– **Ac-** 1.1–1.7	104 **Unq**	105 **Unp**	106 **Unh**	107 **Uns**	—	109 **Une**									

electronegativities, in which the most electronegative element, fluorine, is assigned a value of 4.0, was developed by the Nobel laureate (1954 and 1962) Linus Pauling (b. 1901). Table 7.3 shows that the relative electronegativity of the nonmetals is high and that of the metals is low. These electronegativities indicate that atoms of metals have a greater tendency to lose electrons than do atoms of nonmetals and that nonmetals have a greater tendency to gain electrons than do metals. The higher the electronegativity value, the greater the attraction for electrons.

7.7 Writing Lewis Structures

As we have seen, Lewis structures are a convenient way of showing the covalent bonds in many molecules or ions of the representative elements. In writing Lewis structures the object is to connect the atoms in a molecule with covalent bonds by rearranging the valence electrons of the atoms so that each atom has eight outer-shell electrons around it. Exceptions to this rule are hydrogen, which requires only two electrons, and several other elements such as lithium, beryllium, and boron.

The most difficult part of writing Lewis structures is determining the arrangement of the atoms in a molecule or an ion. In simple molecules with more than two atoms, one atom will be the central atom surrounded by the other atoms. Thus Cl_2O has two possible arrangements, Cl—Cl—O or Cl—O—Cl. Usually, but not always, the single atom in the formula (except H) will be the central atom.

Although Lewis structures for many molecules and ions can be written by inspection, the following procedure will be helpful for learning to write these structures:

1. Obtain the total number of valence electrons to be used in the structure by adding the number of valence electrons in all of the atoms in the molecule or ion. If you are writing the structure of an ion, add one electron for each negative charge or subtract one electron for each positive charge on the ion. Remember, the number of valence electrons of Group A elements is the same as their group number in the periodic table.
2. Write down the skeletal arrangement of the atoms and connect them with a single covalent bond (two dots or one dash). Hydrogen, which contains only one bonding electron, can form only one covalent bond. Oxygen atoms are not normally bonded to each other, except in compounds known to be peroxides. Oxygen atoms normally have a maximum of two covalent bonds—either two single bonds or one double bond.
3. Subtract two electrons for each single bond you used in Step 2 from the total number of electrons calculated in Step 1. This subtraction gives you the net number of electrons available for completing the structure.
4. Distribute pairs of electrons (pairs of dots) around each atom (except hydrogen) to give each atom a total of eight electrons around it.
5. If there are not enough electrons to give these atoms eight electrons, change single bonds between atoms to double or triple bonds by shifting unbonded pairs of electrons as needed. Check to see that each atom (except H) has eight electrons around it. A double bond counts as four electrons for each atom to which it is bonded.

PROBLEM

7.1

How many valence electrons are in each of these atoms: Cl, H, C, O, N, S, P, I?
You can look in Table 5.5 for the electron structure, or, if the element is in Group A of the periodic table, the number of valence electrons is equal to the group number.

Atom	Periodic group	Valence electrons
Cl	VIIA	7
H	IA	1
C	IVA	4
O	VIA	6
N	VA	5
S	VIA	6
P	VA	5
I	VIIA	7

PROBLEM

7.2

Write the Lewis structure for water, H_2O.

Step 1. The total number of valence electrons is 8: 2 from the two hydrogen atoms and 6 from the oxygen atom.

Step 2. The two hydrogen atoms are connected to the oxygen atom. Write the skeletal structure:

H O

 H

Place two dots between the hydrogen and oxygen atoms to form the covalent bonds:

H:O

 Ḧ

Step 3. Subtract the 4 electrons used in Step 2 from 8 to obtain 4 electrons yet to be used.

Step 4. Distribute the 4 electrons around the oxygen atom. Hydrogen atoms cannot accommodate any more electrons.

H:Ö: or   H—Ö:
 Ḧ |
                          H

This arrangement is the Lewis structure. Each atom has a noble gas electron structure.

PROBLEM

7.3

Write Lewis structures for a molecule of **(a)** methane, CH_4, and **(b)** carbon tetrachloride, CCl_4.

(a) Step 1. The total number of valence electrons is 8: 1 from each hydrogen atom and 4 from the carbon atom.

   Step 2. The skeletal structure contains four H atoms around a central C atom. Place 2 electrons between the C and each H.

         H   H
      H C H   H:C:H
         H   H

   Step 3. Subtract the 8 electrons used in Step 2 from 8 to obtain zero electrons yet to be placed. Therefore, the Lewis structure must be as written in Step 2:

                                   H
         H |
      H:C:H   or   H—C—H
         H |
                                   H

(b) Step 1. The total number of valence electrons to be used is 32: 4 from the carbon atom and 7 from each of the four chlorine atoms.

   Step 2. The skeletal structure contains the four Cl atoms around a central C atom. Place 2 electrons between the C and each Cl:

         Cl   Cl
      Cl C Cl   Cl:C:Cl
         Cl   Cl

Step 3. Subtract the 8 electrons used in Step 2 from 32 to obtain 24 electrons yet to be placed.

Step 4. Distribute the 24 electrons (12 pairs) around the Cl atoms so that each Cl atom has 8 electrons around it:

$$:\ddot{\underset{..}{Cl}}:$$
$$:\ddot{\underset{..}{Cl}}:\ddot{\underset{..}{C}}:\ddot{\underset{..}{Cl}}: \quad \text{or} \quad :\ddot{\underset{..}{Cl}}-C-\ddot{\underset{..}{Cl}}:$$
$$:\ddot{\underset{..}{Cl}}: \qquad\qquad :\ddot{\underset{..}{Cl}}:$$

This arrangement is the Lewis structure; CCl_4 contains four covalent bonds.

PROBLEM

7.4

Write Lewis structures for **(a)** carbon dioxide, CO_2, and **(b)** nitric acid, HNO_3.

(a) Step 1. The total number of valence electrons is 16: 4 from the carbon atom and 6 from each oxygen atom.

Step 2. The two O atoms are bonded to a central C atom. Write the skeletal structure and place 2 electrons between the C and each O atom:

O:C:O

Step 3. Subtract the 4 electrons used in Step 2 from 16 to obtain 12 electrons yet to be placed.

Step 4. Distribute the 12 electrons around the C and O atoms. Several possibilities exist:

$$:\ddot{\underset{..}{O}}:C:\ddot{\underset{..}{O}}: \qquad :\ddot{\underset{..}{O}}:C:\ddot{\underset{..}{O}}: \qquad :\ddot{\underset{..}{O}}:\ddot{\underset{..}{C}}:O:$$
$$\quad\text{I} \qquad\qquad\quad \text{II} \qquad\qquad\quad \text{III}$$

Step 5. All the atoms do not have 8 electrons around them. Move one pair of unbonded electrons from each O atom in structure I and place one additional pair of electrons between each C and O atom, forming two double bonds:

$$:\ddot{O}::C::\ddot{O}: \quad \text{or} \quad :\ddot{O}=C=\ddot{O}:$$

Each atom now has 8 electrons around it. Carbon is sharing four pairs of electrons, and each oxygen is sharing two pairs.

(b) Step 1. The total number of valence electrons is 24: 1 from the hydrogen atom, 5 from the nitrogen atom, and 6 from each oxygen atom.

Step 2. The three O atoms are bonded to a central N atom. The H atom is bonded to one of the O atoms. Write the skeletal structure and place 2 electrons between each pair of atoms:

$$\qquad\text{O}$$
$$\qquad\ddot{}$$
$$H:O:N:O$$

Step 3. Subtract the 8 electrons used in Step 2 from 24 to obtain 16 electrons yet to be placed.

Step 4. Distribute the 16 electrons around the N and O atoms:

$$\ddot{:O}\ \longleftarrow\ \text{Electron deficient}$$
$$H\!:\!\ddot{\underset{..}{O}}\!:\!\ddot{\underset{..}{N}}\!:\!\ddot{\underset{..}{O}}\!:$$

Step 5. One pair of electrons is still needed to give all the N and O atoms 8 electrons. Move the unbonded pair of electrons from the N atom and place it between the N and the electron-deficient O atom, making a double bond:

$$\overset{\displaystyle :\ddot{O}}{H\!:\!\ddot{\underset{..}{O}}\!:\!\ddot{\underset{..}{N}}\!:\!\ddot{\underset{..}{O}}\!:}\qquad \text{or} \qquad H\!-\!\ddot{\underset{..}{O}}\!-\!N\!\overset{\displaystyle :\ddot{O}}{\underset{\displaystyle \parallel}{}}\!\ddot{\underset{..}{O}}\!:$$

This arrangement is the Lewis structure.

PROBLEM

7.5

Write the Lewis structure for a sulfate ion, SO_4^{2-}.

Step 1. These five atoms have 30 valence electrons (6 in each atom) plus 2 electrons from the -2 charge, which makes 32 electrons to be placed.

Step 2. In the sulfate ion the sulfur is the central atom surrounded by the four oxygen atoms. Write the skeletal structure and place 2 electrons between each pair of atoms:

$$\begin{array}{c} O \\ O\!:\!\ddot{S}\!:\!O \\ O \end{array}$$

Step 3. Subtract the 8 electrons used in Step 2 from 32 to give 24 electrons yet to be placed.

Step 4. Distribute the 24 electrons around the four O atoms and indicate that the sulfate ion has a -2 charge:

$$\left[\begin{array}{c} :\ddot{O}: \\ :\ddot{O}\!:\!\ddot{S}\!:\!\ddot{O}: \\ :\ddot{O}: \end{array}\right]^{2-} \qquad \text{or} \qquad \left[\begin{array}{c} :\ddot{O}: \\ | \\ :\ddot{O}\!-\!S\!-\!\ddot{O}: \\ | \\ :\ddot{O}: \end{array}\right]^{2-}$$

This arrangement is the Lewis structure. Each atom has 8 electrons around it.

Although many compounds follow the octet rule for covalent bonding, the rule has numerous exceptions. Sometimes it is impossible to write a structure in which each atom has 8 electrons around it. For example, in BF_3 the boron atom has only 6 electrons around it, and in SF_6 the sulfur atom has 12 electrons around it.

7.8 Nonpolar and Polar Covalent Bonds

nonpolar covalent bond

We have considered bonds to be either ionic or covalent depending on whether electrons are transferred from one atom to another or are shared between two atoms. In a **nonpolar covalent bond** the shared pair of electrons is attracted equally by the two atoms. Nonpolar covalent bonds form between the same kind of atoms. For example, the covalent bond in a hydrogen molecule or in a chlorine molecule is nonpolar because the electronegativity difference between identical atoms is zero. (See Figure 7.6.)

polar covalent bond

A covalent bond between two different kinds of atoms has a partial ionic character and is known as a **polar covalent bond.** This bond is polar because the two atoms have different electronegativities. The polarity is due to unequal sharing of the electrons because the more electronegative atom has a greater attraction for the shared pair of electrons. The more electronegative atom thus acquires a partial negative charge, and the other atom acquires a partial positive charge. When a polar covalent bond is present in a diatomic molecule such as HCl, the molecule is polar. By *polar* we mean an unequal distribution of electrical charge. Overall, however, the HCl molecule is neutral because the partial negative charge on the chlorine atom is exactly balanced by the partial positive charge on the hydrogen atom.

dipole

A **dipole** is a molecule that is electrically unsymmetrical, causing it to be oppositely charged at two points. A dipole is often written as $\oplus\ominus$. A hydrogen chloride molecule is polar and behaves as a small dipole. The HCl dipole may be written as $H \longrightarrow Cl$. The arrow points toward the negative end of the dipole. Molecules of H_2O, HBr, and ICl are polar.

$$\overset{\delta+}{H} + \!\!\longrightarrow \overset{\delta-}{Cl} \qquad \overset{\delta+}{H} + \!\!\longrightarrow \overset{\delta-}{Br} \qquad \overset{\delta+}{I} + \!\!\longrightarrow \overset{\delta-}{Cl} \qquad \overset{\delta-}{\underset{\overset{\delta+}{H} \quad \overset{\delta+}{H}}{O}}$$

How do we know whether a bond between two atoms is ionic or covalent? The difference in electronegativity between two atoms determines the character of the bond formed between them. As the difference in electronegativity increases, the polarity of the bond (or percentage ionic character) increases. As a rule, if the electronegativity difference between two bonded atoms is greater than 1.7–1.9,

H_2	Cl_2	HCl	Na^+Cl^-
Nonpolar molecules		Polar covalent molecule	Ionic compound

Figure 7.6 Nonpolar, polar covalent, and ionic compounds

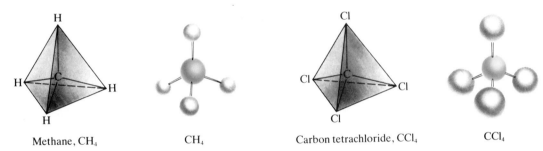

Methane, CH_4 CH_4 Carbon tetrachloride, CCl_4 CCl_4

Figure 7.7 Ball-and-stick models of methane and carbon tetrachloride. Methane and carbon tetrachloride are nonpolar molecules because their polar bonds cancel one another in the tetrahedral arrangement of their atoms. The carbon atoms are located in the centers of the tetrahedrons.

the bond will be more ionic than covalent. If the electronegativity difference is greater than 2.0, the bond is strongly ionic. If the electronegativity difference is less than 1.5, the bond is strongly covalent.

Care must be taken to distinguish between polar bonds and polar molecules. A covalent bond between different kinds of atoms is always polar. But a molecule containing different kinds of atoms may or may not be polar, depending on its shape or geometry. Molecules of HF, HCl, HBr, HI, and ICl are all polar because each contains a single polar bond. However, CO_2, CH_4, and CCl_4 are nonpolar molecules despite the fact that all three contain polar bonds. The carbon dioxide molecule, O=C=O, is nonpolar because the carbon–oxygen dipoles cancel each other by acting in opposite directions.

$$\overset{\longleftarrow + \quad +\longrightarrow}{O=C=O}$$

Dipoles in opposite directions

Methane (CH_4) and carbon tetrachloride (CCl_4) are nonpolar because the four C—H and C—Cl polar bonds are identical, and, because these bonds emanate from the center to the corners of a tetrahedron in the molecule, the effect of their polarities cancel one another (Figure 7.7).

We have said that water is a polar molecule. If the atoms in water were linear like those in carbon dioxide, the two O—H dipoles would cancel each other, and the molecule would be nonpolar. However, water is definitely polar and has a nonlinear (bent) structure with an angle of 105° between the two O—H bonds (see Figure 7.8).

7.9 Coordinate Covalent Bonds

In Section 7.5 we saw that a covalent bond was formed by the overlapping of electron orbitals between two atoms. The two atoms each furnish an electron to make a pair that is shared between them.

Figure 7.8 The polar water molecule, H_2O

coordinate
covalent bond

Covalent bonds can also be formed by one atom furnishing both electrons that are shared between the two atoms. The bond so formed is called a **coordinate covalent bond.** This bond is often designated by an arrow pointing away from the electron-pair donor. (For example, A $\longrightarrow$ B in a structure indicates that both electrons forming the covalent bond between A and B come from the A atom.) Once formed, a coordinate covalent bond cannot be distinguished from any other covalent bond; it is simply a pair of electrons shared between two atoms.

The Lewis structures of sulfurous and sulfuric acids show coordinate covalent bonds between the sulfur and the oxygen atoms that are not bonded to hydrogen atoms. The colored dots indicate the electrons of the sulfur atom.

The lone (unbonded) pair of electrons on the sulfur atom in sulfurous acid allows room for another oxygen atom with six valence electrons to fit perfectly into its structure to form sulfuric acid. Other atoms with six valence electrons in their outer shell, such as sulfur, could also fit into this pattern. The coordinate covalent bond explains the formation of many complex molecules.

7.10 Polyatomic Ions

polyatomic ion

A **polyatomic ion** is a stable group of atoms that has either a positive or a negative charge and behaves as a single unit in many chemical reactions. Sodium sulfate, Na_2SO_4, contains two sodium ions and a sulfate ion. The sulfate ion, SO_4^{2-}, is a polyatomic ion composed of one sulfur atom and four oxygen atoms and has a charge of -2. One sulfur and four oxygen atoms have a total of 30 electrons in their outer shells. The sulfate ion contains 32 outer-shell electrons and therefore has a charge of -2. In this case the two additional electrons come from the two sodium atoms, which are now sodium ions.

$$\text{Na}^+ \left[\begin{array}{c} :\ddot{\text{O}}: \\ :\ddot{\text{O}}:\text{S}:\ddot{\text{O}}: \\ :\ddot{\text{O}}: \end{array} \right]^{2-} \text{Na}^+ \qquad \left[\begin{array}{c} :\ddot{\text{O}}: \\ :\ddot{\text{O}}:\text{S}:\ddot{\text{O}}: \\ :\ddot{\text{O}}: \end{array} \right]^{2-}$$

Sodium sulfate   Sulfate ion

Sodium sulfate has both ionic and covalent bonds. Ionic bonds exist between each of the sodium ions and the sulfate ion. Covalent bonds are present between the sulfur and oxygen atoms within the sulfate ion. One important difference between the ionic and covalent bonds in this compound can be demonstrated by dissolving sodium sulfate in water. It dissolves in water forming three charged particles, two sodium ions and one sulfate ion, per formula unit of sodium sulfate:

$$\text{Na}_2\text{SO}_4 \xrightarrow{\text{Water}} 2\ \text{Na}^+ + \text{SO}_4^{2-}$$

Sodium sulfate   Sodium ions   Sulfate ion

The SO_4^{2-} ion remains as a unit, held together by covalent bonds; whereas, where the bonds were ionic, dissociation of the ions took place. Do not think, however, that polyatomic ions are so stable that they cannot be altered. Chemical reactions by which polyatomic ions can be changed to other substances do exist.

The Lewis structures for several common polyatomic ions are shown below:

Ammonium ion, NH_4^+ Nitrate ion, NO_3^- Phosphate ion, PO_4^{3-} Hydroxide ion, OH^-

QUESTIONS

A. *Review the meanings of the new terms introduced in this chapter.*

1. Chemical bonds
2. Ionization energy
3. Electron affinity
4. Valence electrons
5. Ionic bond
6. Covalent bond
7. Electronegativity
8. Nonpolar covalent bond
9. Polar covalent bond
10. Dipole
11. Coordinate covalent bond
12. Polyatomic ion

B. *Information useful in answering these questions will be found in the tables and figures.*

1. Explain why much more ionization energy is required to remove the first electron from neon than from sodium.
2. Explain the large increase in ionization energy needed to remove the third electron from beryllium compared with that needed for the second electron.
3. Does the first ionization energy increase or decrease from top to bottom in the periodic table for the alkali metal family? Explain.
4. Does the first ionization energy increase or decrease from top to bottom in the periodic table for

the noble gas family? Explain.

5. In which general areas of the periodic table are the elements with (a) the highest and (b) the lowest electronegativities found?

6. Which is larger, a magnesium atom or a magnesium ion? Explain.

7. Which is smaller, a bromine atom or a bromide ion? Explain.

8. Using the table of electronegativity values (Table 7.3), indicate which element is positive and which is negative in the following compounds:

   (a) H_2O (e) NO   (i) CCl_4
   (b) NaF   (f) Ch_4 (j) IBr
   (c) NH_3 (g) HCl   (k) MgH_2
   (d) PbS   (h) LiH   (l) OF_2

9. Classify the bond between the following pairs of elements as principally ionic or principally covalent (use Table 7.3):

   (a) Sodium and chlorine
   (b) Carbon and hydrogen
   (c) Chlorine and carbon
   (d) Calcium and oxygen
   (e) Hydrogen and sulfur
   (f) Barium and oxygen
   (g) Fluorine and fluorine
   (h) Potassium and fluorine

C. *Review questions*

1. Explain why, in general, the ionization energy decreases from top to bottom in a family of elements.

2. Why does barium (Ba) have a lower ionization energy than beryllium (Be)?

3. Why is there such a large increase in the ionization energy required to remove the second electron from a sodium atom as opposed to the removal of the first electron?

4. Explain how electron affinity differs from ionization energy.

5. Explain what happens to the electron structures of Mg and Cl atoms when they react to form $MgCl_2$.

6. Write an equation representing (a) the change of a fluorine atom to a fluoride ion (F^-) and (b) the change of a calcium atom to a calcium ion (Ca^{2+}).

7. Use Lewis-dot structures to show the electron

transfer for the formation of the following ionic compounds from the atoms.

   (a) MgF_2 (b) K_2O (c) CaO   (d) NaBr

8. What are valence electrons?

9. How many valence electrons are in each of these atoms?

   H, K, Mg, He, Al, Si, N, P, O, Cl

10. How many electrons must be gained or lost for each of the following to achieve a noble gas electron structure?

    (a) A calcium atom   (d) A chloride ion
    (b) A sulfur atom   (e) A nitrogen atom
    (c) A helium atom   (f) A potassium atom

11. Explain why potassium forms a K^+ ion but not a K^{2+} ion.

12. Why does an aluminum ion have a +3 charge?

13. Which is larger? Explain.

    (a) A potassium atom or a potassium ion
    (b) A bromine atom or a bromide ion
    (c) A magnesium ion or an aluminum ion
    (d) Fe^{2+} or Fe^{3+}

14. Write Lewis-dot structures for

    (a) Na (b) Br^- (c) O^{2-} (d) Ga (e) Ga^{3+}

15. Why is it not proper to speak of sodium chloride molecules?

16. What is a covalent bond? How does it differ from an ionic bond?

17. What is different about the formation of a coordinate covalent bond from that of an ordinary covalent bond?

18. Classify the bonding in each compound as ionic or covalent:

    (a) H_2O (c) MgO   (e) HCl   (g) NH_3
    (b) NaCl   (d) Br_2 (f) $BaCl_2$ (h) SO_2

19. Predict the type of bond that would be formed between each of the following pairs of atoms:

    (a) Na and N   (d) H and Si
    (b) N and S   (e) O and F
    (c) Br and I

20. Draw Lewis structures for:

    (a) H_2 (b) N_2 (c) Cl_2 (d) O_2 (e) Br_2

21. Draw Lewis structures for:

    (a) NCl_3 (c) H_3PO_4 (e) H_2S
    (b) H_2CO_3 (d) C_2H_6 (f) CS_2

22. Briefly comment on the structure Na:O:Na for the compound Na_2O.

23. What are the four most electronegative elements?

24. Draw Lewis structures for:

    (a) Ba^{2+} (b) Al^{3+} (c) I^-

(d) S^{2-} (g) CN^- (i) ClO_3^-
(e) SO_4^{2-} (h) CO_3^{2-} (j) NO_3^-
(f) SO_3^{2-}

25. The Lewis structure for chloric acid is

$$H:\overset{..}{\underset{..}{O}}:\overset{..}{\underset{..}{Cl}}:\overset{..}{\underset{..}{O}}:$$
$$:\overset{}{\underset{..}{O}}:$$

Point out the covalent and coordinate covalent bonds in this structure.

26. Draw the Lewis structure for ammonia (NH_3). What type of bond is present? Can this molecule form coordinate covalent bonds? If so, how many?

27. Rank these elements from highest electronegativity to lowest: Mg, S, F, H, O, Cs.

28. Classify the following molecules as polar or nonpolar:
    (a) H_2O (c) CF_4 (e) CO_2
    (b) HBr   (d) F_2 (f) NH_3

29. Is it possible for a molecule to be nonpolar even though it contains polar covalent bonds? Explain.

30. Why is CO_2 a nonpolar molecule, whereas CO is a polar molecule?

31. Which of these statements are correct? (Try to answer this question using only the periodic table.)
    (a) The amount of energy required to remove one electron from an atom is known as the ionization energy.
    (b) Metallic elements tend to have relatively low electronegativities.
    (c) Elements with a high ionization energy tend to have very metallic properties.
    (d) Sodium and chlorine react to form molecules of NaCl.
    (e) A chlorine atom has fewer electrons than a chloride ion.
    (f) The noble gases have a tendency to lose one electron to become positively charged ions.
    (g) The chemical bonds in a water molecule are ionic.
    (h) The chemical bonds in a water molecule are polar.
    (i) Valence electrons are those electrons in the outermost shell of an atom.
    (j) An atom with eight electrons in its outer shell has all its s and p orbitals filled.

(k) Fluorine has the lowest electronegativity of all the elements.
(l) Oxygen has a greater electronegativity than carbon.
(m) A cation is larger than its corresponding neutral atom.
(n) Cl_2 is more ionic in character than HCl.
(o) A neutral atom with eight electrons in its valence shell will likely be an atom of a noble gas.
(p) A nitrogen atom has four valence electrons.
(q) An aluminum atom must lose three electrons to become an aluminum ion, Al^{3+}.
(r) A stable group of atoms that has either a positive or a negative charge and behaves as a single unit in many chemical reactions is called a polyatomic ion.
(s) Sodium sulfate, Na_2SO_4, has covalent bonds between sulfur and the oxygen atoms, and ionic bonds between sodium ions and the sulfate ion.
(t) The water molecule is a dipole.
(u) In an ethylene molecule, C_2H_4,

two pairs of electrons are shared between the carbon atoms.
(v) The octet rule is mainly useful for atoms where only s and p electrons enter into bonding.
(w) When electrons are transferred from one atom to another, the resulting compound contains ionic bonds.
(x) A phosphorus atom, $\cdot\overset{..}{P}\cdot$, needs three additional electrons to attain a stable octet of electrons.
(y) The simplest compound between oxygen, $\cdot\overset{..}{O}\cdot$, and fluorine, $:\overset{..}{F}\cdot$, atoms is FO_2.
(z) The $H:\overset{..}{\underset{..}{Cl}}:$ molecule has three unshared pairs of electrons.
(aa) The smaller the difference in electronegativity between two atoms, the more ionic the bond between them will be.
(bb) Lewis structures are mainly useful for the representative elements.

(cc) The correct Lewis structure for NH_3 is

$$H:\overset{\cdot\cdot}{N}:H$$
$$\overset{|}{H}$$

(dd) The correct Lewis structure for CO_2 is

$$:\overset{\cdot\cdot}{O}:C:\overset{\cdot\cdot}{O}:$$

(ee) The correct Lewis structure for SO_4^{2-} is

$$:\overset{\cdot\cdot}{O}:\overset{\cdot\cdot}{O}:\overset{\cdot\cdot}{S}:\overset{\cdot\cdot}{O}:\overset{\cdot\cdot}{O}:^{2-}$$

(ff) In period 4 of the periodic table, the element having the lowest ionization energy is Xe.

(gg) An atom having an electron structure of $1s^2 2s^2 2p^6 3s^2 3p^2$ has four valence electrons.

(hh) When an atom of bromine becomes a bromide ion, its size increases.

(ii) The structures that show that H_2O is a dipole and that CO_2 is not a dipole are

$$H-\overset{\cdot\cdot}{\underset{\cdot\cdot}{O}}-H \quad \text{and} \quad :\overset{\cdot\cdot}{O}=C=\overset{\cdot\cdot}{O}:$$

(jj) The Cl^- and S^{2-} ions have the same electron structure.

8

Nomenclature of Inorganic Compounds

1. Understand the new terms listed in Question A at the end of the chapter.
2. State the rules for assigning oxidation numbers.
3. Assign oxidation numbers to the representative elements in binary compounds from their positions in the periodic table.
4. Write the formulas of compounds formed by combining the ions from Tables 8.2, 8.3, and 8.4 (or from the inside back cover of this book) in the correct ratios.
5. Assign the oxidation number to each element in a compound or ion.
6. Write the names and formulas for inorganic binary compounds in which the metal has only one common oxidation state.
7. Write the names and formulas for inorganic binary compounds that contain metals of variable oxidation state, using either the Stock System or classical nomenclature.
8. Write the names and formulas for inorganic binary compounds that contain two nonmetals.
9. Write the names and formulas for binary acids.
10. Write the names and formulas for ternary oxyacids.
11. Write the names and formulas for ternary salts.
12. Given the formula of a salt, write the name and formula of the acid from which the salt may be derived.

13. Write the names and formulas for salts that contain more than one kind of positive ion.
14. Write the names and formulas for inorganic bases.

8.1   Oxidation Numbers of Atoms

oxidation number

oxidation state

We have seen that atoms can combine to form compounds by losing, gaining, or sharing electrons. The **oxidation number** or **oxidation state** of an element is a number having a positive, a negative, or a zero value that may be assigned to an atom of that element in a compound. These positive and negative numbers are directly related to the positive and negative charges that result from the transfer of electrons from one atom to another in ionic compounds or from an unequal sharing of electrons between atoms forming covalent bonds. Oxidation numbers are assigned by a somewhat arbitrary system of rules. They are useful for writing formulas, naming compounds, and balancing chemical equations.

In a compound having ionic bonds, the oxidation number of an atom or group of atoms existing as an ion is the same as the *charge of the ion.* Thus, in sodium chloride, $NaCl$, the oxidation number of sodium is $+1$ and that of chlorine is -1; in magnesium oxide, MgO, the oxidation number of magnesium is $+2$ and that of oxygen is -2; in calcium chloride, $CaCl_2$, the oxidation number of calcium is $+2$ and that of chlorine is -1. The sum of the oxidation numbers of all the atoms in a compound is numerically equal to zero, because a compound is electrically neutral.

For practical purposes it is also convenient to assign oxidation numbers to the individual atoms making up molecules and polyatomic ions. Here the electrons have not been completely transferred from one atom to another, and the assignment cannot be done solely on the basis of ionic charges. However, oxidation numbers can be readily assigned to the atoms in either molecules or polyatomic ions by this general method: For each covalent bond, first assign the shared pair of electrons to the more electronegative atom. Then assign an oxidation number to each atom corresponding to its apparent net charge based on the number of electrons gained or lost and on the fact that the sum of the oxidation numbers must equal zero for a compound or must equal the charge on a polyatomic ion. Consider these substances: H_2, H_2O, CH_4, and CCl_4.

	H:H	H:Ö: ·· H	H ·· H:C:H ·· H	:Cl: ·· :Cl:C:Cl: ·· :Cl:
Oxidation number	H, 0	H, +1 O, −2	H, +1 C, −4	C, +4 Cl, −1

In H_2 the pair of electrons is shared equally between the two atoms; therefore, each H is assigned an oxidation number of zero. In H_2O, the oxygen is the more electronegative atom and is assigned the two pairs of shared electrons. The oxygen atom now has two more electrons than the neutral atom and therefore is assigned an oxidation number of -2. Each hydrogen atom in H_2O has one less electron than the neutral atom and is assigned an oxidation number of $+1$. In CH_4 all four shared pairs of electrons are assigned to the more electronegative carbon atom. The carbon atom then has an additional four electrons and is assigned an oxidation number of -4. Each hydrogen atom has one less electron than the neutral atom and is assigned an oxidation number of $+1$. In CCl_4 one pair of electrons is assigned to each of the four more electronegative chlorine atoms. The carbon atom therefore has four less electrons than the neutral atom and is assigned an oxidation number of $+4$. Each chlorine atom has one additional electron and is assigned an oxidation number of -1.

The following rules govern the assignment of oxidation numbers:

1. The oxidation number of any free element is zero, even when the atoms are combined with themselves. (*Examples:* Na, Mg, H_2, O_2, Cl_2)
2. Metals generally have positive oxidation numbers in compounds.
3. The oxidation number of hydrogen in a compound or an ion is $+1$ except in metal hydrides, where H is -1. (For example, NaH: Na, $+1$; H, -1).
4. The oxidation number of oxygen in a compound or an ion is -2 except in peroxides, where it is -1, and in OF_2, where it is $+2$.
5. The oxidation number of a monatomic ion is the same as the charge on the ion.
6. The oxidation number of an atom in a covalent compound is equal to the net apparent charge on the atom after each pair of shared electrons is assigned to the more electronegative element sharing the pair of electrons.
7. The algebraic sum of the oxidation numbers for all the atoms in a compound must equal zero.
8. The algebraic sum of the oxidation numbers for all the atoms in a polyatomic ion must equal the charge on the ion.

The oxidation numbers of many elements are predictable from their position in the periodic table. This predictability is especially true of the Group A elements because the number of electrons in their outer shells corresponds to the group number. Remember that metals lose electrons and become positively charged ions and nonmetals tend to gain electrons and become negatively charged ions. Nonmetals can also share electrons with other atoms to assume a positive or negative oxidation number. Hydrogen can have a $+1$ or -1 oxidation number, depending on the relative electronegativity of the element with which it is combined.

The predictable oxidation numbers of the Group A elements are given in the following table:

Group number	IA	IIA	IIIA	IVA	VA	VIA	VIIA
Oxidation number	+1	+2	+3	+4 to −4	−3 to +5	−2 to +6	−1 to +7

Table 8.1 illustrates the use of oxidation numbers to predict formulas of binary compounds from representative members of these groups.

Table 8.1   Selected binary hydrogen, oxygen, and chlorine compounds of Group A elements

	Group number						
	IA	IIA	IIIA	IVA	VA	VIA	VIIA
Hydrogen compound	NaH	CaH$_2$	AlH$_3$	CH$_4$	NH$_3$	H$_2$S	HCl
Oxygen compound	Na$_2$O	CaO	Al$_2$O$_3$	CO$_2$	N$_2$O$_5$	SO$_3$	Cl$_2$O
Chlorine compound	NaCl	CaCl$_2$	AlCl$_3$	CCl$_4$	NCl$_3$	SCl$_2$	Cl$_2$

8.2   Oxidation Number Tables

Writing formulas of compounds and chemical equations is facilitated by a knowledge of oxidation numbers and ionic charges. Table 8.2 lists the names and ionic charges of common monatomic ions. Monatomic ions of Groups IA and IIA elements are not given in Table 8.2 because the charges and oxidation numbers of these ions are readily determined from the periodic table. The charges and oxidation numbers of the Groups IA, IIA, and IIIA metal ions are positive and correspond to the group number (for example, Na$^+$, Ca^{2+}, Al^{3+}). The negative charges and oxidation numbers of Groups VA, VIA, and VIIA monatomic ions can be determined by subtracting eight from the group number. Sulfur, for example, is in Group VIA, and $6 - 8 = -2$. Therefore the oxidation number of the sulfide ion (S^{2-}) is -2. All the halogens (F, Cl, Br, and I) in binary compounds with metals or hydrogen have an oxidation number of -1. The charges for Zn^{2+} and Cd^{2+} ions (Group IIB) are always $+2$.

The names, formulas, and ionic charges of some common polyatomic ions are given in Table 8.3. A more comprehensive list of both monatomic and polyatomic ions is given on the inside back cover of this book. Table 8.4 lists the principal oxidation numbers of common elements that have variable oxidation states.

8.3   Formulas of Ionic Compounds

The sum of the oxidation numbers of all the atoms in a compound is zero. This statement applies to all substances, regardless of whether they are ionically or covalently bonded. For ionically bonded compounds the sum of the charges on all the ions in the compound must also be zero. Hence the formulas of ionic substances can easily be determined and written by simply combining the ions in the simplest proportion that makes the sum of the ionic charges add up to zero.

To illustrate: Sodium chloride consists of Na$^+$ and Cl$^-$ ions. Since $(+1) + (-1) = 0$, these ions combine in a one-to-one ratio, and the formula is written NaCl. Calcium fluoride is made up of Ca^{2+} and F$^-$ ions, therefore one Ca^{2+} ion $(+2)$ and two F$^-$ ions (-2) are needed to make zero, so the formula is CaF$_2$.

Table 8.2 Names, formulas, and charges of selected monatomic ions

Name	Formula	Oxidation number or charge	Name	Formula	Oxidation number or charge
Aluminum	Al^{3+}	+3	Lead(II)	Pb^{2+}	+2
Arsenic(III)	As^{3+}	+3	Magnesium	Mg^{2+}	+2
Barium	Ba^{2+}	+2	Manganese(II)	Mn^{2+}	+2
Cadmium	Cd^{2+}	+2	Mercury(I)	Hg^+	+1
Calcium	Ca^{2+}	+2	Mercury(II)	Hg^{2+}	+2
Chromium(III)	Cr^{3+}	+3	Nickel(II)	Ni^{2+}	+2
Copper(I)	Cu^+	+1	Silver	Ag^+	+1
Copper(II)	Cu^{2+}	+2	Tin(II)	Sn^{2+}	+2
Iron(II)	Fe^{2+}	+2	Tin(IV)	Sn^{4+}	+4
Iron(III)	Fe^{3+}	+3	Zinc	Zn^{2+}	+2
Bromide	Br^-	−1	Nitride	N^{3-}	−3
Chloride	Cl^-	−1	Oxide	O^{2-}	−2
Fluoride	F^-	−1	Sulfide	S^{2-}	−2
Iodide	I^-	−1			

Table 8.3 Names, formulas, and charges of some common polyatomic ions

Name	Formula	Charge	Name	Formula	Charge
Acetate	$C_2H_3O_2^-$	−1	Cyanide	CN^-	−1
Ammonium	NH_4^+	+1	Dichromate	$Cr_2O_7^{2-}$	−2
Arsenate	AsO_4^{3-}	−3	Hydroxide	OH^-	−1
Bicarbonate	HCO_3^-	−1	Nitrate	NO_3^-	−1
Bisulfate	HSO_4^-	−1	Nitrite	NO_2^-	−1
Bromate	BrO_3^-	−1	Permanganate	MnO_4^-	−1
Carbonate	CO_3^{2-}	−2	Phosphate	PO_4^{3-}	−3
Chlorate	ClO_3^-	−1	Sulfate	SO_4^{2-}	−2
Chromate	CrO_4^{2-}	−2	Sulfite	SO_3^{2-}	−2

Table 8.4 Principal oxidation numbers of some common elements that have variable oxidation states

Element	Oxidation number	Element	Oxidation number
Cu	+1, +2	Cl	−1, +1, +3, +5, +7
Hg	+1, +2	Br	−1, +1, +3, +5, +7
Sn	+2, +4	I	−1, +1, +3, +5, +7
Pb	+2, +4	S	−2, +4, +6
Fe	+2, +3	N	−3, +1, +2, +3, +4, +5
Au	+1, +3	P	−3, +3, +5
Ni	+2, +3	C	−4, +4
Co	+2, +3		
As	+3, +5		
Bi	+3, +5		
Cr	+2, +3, +6		

Aluminum oxide is a bit more complicated because it consists of Al^{3+} and O^{2-} ions. Since 6 is the lowest common multiple of 3 and 2, we have $2(+3) + 3(-2) = 0$; that is, two Al^{3+} ions $(+6)$ and three O^{2-} ions (-6) are needed; therefore, the formula is Al_2O_3.

The foregoing compounds all are made up of monatomic ions. The same procedure is used for polyatomic ions. Consider calcium hydroxide, which is made up of Ca^{2+} and OH^- ions. Since $(+2) + 2(-1) = 0$, one Ca^{2+} and two OH^- ions are needed, so the formula is $Ca(OH)_2$. The parentheses are used to enclose the OH^- so that two hydroxide ions can be shown. It is not correct to write CaO_2H_2 in place of $Ca(OH)_2$ because the identity of the compound would be lost by so doing. Note that the positive ion is written first in formulas. The following table provides examples of formula writing for ionic compounds.

Name of compound	Ions	Lowest common multiple	Sum of charges on ions	Formula
Sodium bromide	Na^+, Br^-	1	$(+1) + (-1) = 0$	$NaBr$
Potassium sulfide	K^+, S^{2-}	2	$2(+1) + (-2) = 0$	K_2S
Zinc sulfate	Zn^{2+}, SO_4^{2-}	2	$(+2) + (-2) = 0$	$ZnSO_4$
Ammonium phosphate	NH_4^+, PO_4^{3-}	3	$3(+1) + (-3) = 0$	$(NH_4)_3PO_4$
Aluminum chromate	Al^{3+}, CrO_4^{2-}	6	$2(+3) + 3(-2) = 0$	$Al_2(CrO_4)_3$

The sum of the charges on the ions of an ionically bonded compound must equal zero.

PROBLEM

8.1

Write formulas for **(a)** calcium chloride; **(b)** iron(III) sulfide; **(c)** aluminum sulfate. Refer to Tables 8.2, 8.3, and 8.4 as needed.

(a) Step 1. From the name we know that calcium chloride is composed of calcium and chloride ions. First write down the formulas of these ions.

$$Ca^{2+} \quad \text{and} \quad Cl^-$$

Step 2. To write the formula of the compound, combine the smallest numbers of Ca^{2+} and Cl^- ions to give a charge sum equal to zero. In this case the lowest common multiple of the charges is 2:

$$(Ca^{2+}) + 2(Cl^-) = 0$$

$$(+2) + 2(-1) = 0$$

Therefore, the formula is $CaCl_2$.

(b) Use the same procedure for iron(III) sulfide.

Step 1. Write down the formulas for the iron(III) and sulfide ions.

$$Fe^{3+} \quad \text{and} \quad S^{2-}$$

Step 2. Use the smallest numbers of these ions required to give a charge sum equal to zero. The lowest common multiple of the charges is 6:

$$2(Fe^{3+}) + 3(S^{2-}) = 0$$

$$2(+3) + 3(-2) = 0$$

Therefore, the formula is Fe_2S_3.

(c) Use the same procedure for aluminum sulfate.

Step 1. Write down the formulas for the aluminum and sulfate ions.

$$Al^{3+} \quad \text{and} \quad SO_4^{2-}$$

Step 2. Use the smallest numbers of these ions required to give a charge sum equal to zero. The lowest common multiple of the charges is 6:

$$2(Al^{3+}) + 3(SO_4^{2-}) = 0$$

$$2(+3) + 3(-2) = 0$$

Therefore, the formula is $Al_2(SO_4)_3$. Note the use of parentheses around the SO_4^{2-} ion.

8.4   Determining Oxidation Numbers and Ionic Charges from a Formula

If the formula of a compound is known, the oxidation number of an element or the charge on a polyatomic ion in the formula can often be determined by algebraic difference. To begin you must know the oxidation numbers of a few elements. Excellent ones with which to work are hydrogen, always +1 except in hydrides (a hydride is a compound of hydrogen combined with a metal); oxygen, always −2 except in peroxides; and sodium, always +1. Using the compound sulfuric acid, H_2SO_4, as an example, let us determine the charge of the sulfate ion and the oxidation number of the sulfur atom. The sulfate ion is combined with two hydrogen atoms, each with a +1 oxidation number. The sulfate ion must then have a −2 charge in order for the net charge in the compound to be zero.

$$
\begin{array}{ll}
H^+ & +1 \\
H^+ & +1 \\
SO_4^{2-} & \underline{-2} \\
& 0
\end{array}
$$

To find the oxidation number of sulfur, we proceed as follows:

Step 1. Write the oxidation number of a single atom of hydrogen and a single atom of oxygen below the atoms in the formula.

Step 2. Below this write the sums of the oxidation numbers of all the H and O atoms: $2(+1) = +2$ and $4(-2) = -8$.

Step 3. Then add together the total oxidation numbers of all the atoms, including the sulfur atom, and set them equal to zero: $+2 + S + (-8) = 0$. Solving the equation for S, we determine that the oxidation number of sulfur is $+6$, the value needed to give the sum of zero.

$$H_2 \ S \ O_4$$

Step 1. $+1$ -2

Step 2. $2(+1) = +2$ $4(-2) = -8$

Step 3. $+2 + S + (-8) = 0$

$$S = +6$$

The oxidation number of sulfur in H_2SO_4 is $+6$.

What is the oxidation number of chromium in sodium dichromate, $Na_2Cr_2O_7$? Using the same method as for H_2SO_4, we have

$$Na_2 \ Cr_2 \ O_7$$

Step 1. $+1$ -2

Step 2. $2(+1) = +2$ $7(-2) = -14$

Step 3. $+2 + 2 \ Cr + (-14) = 0$

$$2 \ Cr = +12$$

$$Cr = +6$$

The oxidation number of chromium in $Na_2Cr_2O_7$ is $+6$.

The formula of radium chloride is $RaCl_2$. What is the oxidation number of radium? If you remember that the oxidation number of chloride is -1, then the value for radium is $+2$, because one radium ion is combined with two Cl^- ions. If you do not remember the oxidation number of chloride, then you should try to recall the formula of another chloride. One that might come to mind is sodium chloride, NaCl, in which the chloride is -1 because of its combination with one sodium ion of $+1$. This recollection establishes the oxidation number of chloride, which then enables you to calculate the value for radium.

What is the oxidation number of phosphorus in the phosphate ion, PO_4^{3-}? First of all, note that this ion is polyatomic, with a charge of -3. The sum of the oxidation numbers of phosphorus and oxygen must equal -3 and not zero. Four oxygen atoms, each with a -2, give a total of -8. The oxidation number of the phosphorus atom must then be +5:

$$P\ O_4^{3-}$$

$$-2$$
$$P + 4(-2) = -3$$
$$P = +5$$

> **The sum of the oxidation numbers of the atoms in a polyatomic ion must equal the charge of the polyatomic ion.**

8.5   Common, or Trivial, Names of Substances

Chemical nomenclature is the system of names that chemists use to identify compounds. When a new substance is formulated, it must be named in order to distinguish it from all other substances. Before chemistry was systematized, a substance was given a name that generally associated it with one of its outstanding physical or chemical properties. For example, *quicksilver* is a common name for mercury translated from the Latin to mean *liquid silver*. Nitrous oxide, N_2O, used as an anesthetic in dentistry, has been called *laughing gas* because it induces laughter when inhaled. The name *nitrous oxide* is now giving way to the more systematic name *dinitrogen monoxide*. Nonsystematic names are called *common*, or *trivial*, names.

Common names for chemicals are widely used in many industries because the systematic name frequently is too long or too technical for everyday use. For example, CaO is called *lime*, not *calcium oxide*, by plasterers; photographers refer to $Na_2S_2O_3$ as *hypo*, rather than *sodium thiosulfate*; nutritionists refer to $C_{27}H_{44}O$ as *vitamin D_3*, not as 9,10-*secocholesta*-5,7,10(19)-*trien*-3β-*ol*. These examples, particularly that of vitamin D_3, show the practical need for short, common names. Table 8.5 lists the common names, formulas, and chemical names of some familiar substances.

8.6   Systematic Chemical Nomenclature

The trivial name is not entirely satisfactory to the chemist, who requires a name that will identify precisely the composition of each substance. Therefore, as the number of known compounds increased, it became necessary to develop a scientific, systematic method of identifying compounds by name. The systematic method of naming inorganic compounds considers the compound to be composed of two parts, one positive and one negative. The positive part (positive ion or least electronegative element) is named and written first. The negative part, generally nonmetallic, follows. The names of the elements are modified with suffixes and prefixes to identify the different types or classes of compounds. Thus the compound composed of sodium ions and chloride ions is named sodium

Table 8.5 Common or trivial names, formulas, and chemical names of some familiar substances

Common name	Formula	Chemical name
Acetylene	C_2H_2	Ethyne
Lime	CaO	Calcium oxide
Slaked lime	$Ca(OH)_2$	Calcium hydroxide
Water	H_2O	Water
Galena	PbS	Lead(II) sulfide
Alumina	Al_2O_3	Aluminum oxide
Baking soda	$NaHCO_3$	Sodium hydrogen carbonate
Cane or beet sugar	$C_{12}H_{22}O_{11}$	Sucrose
Blue stone, blue vitriol	$CuSO_4 \cdot 5H_2O$	Copper(II) sulfate pentahydrate
Borax	$Na_2B_4O_7 \cdot 10H_2O$	Sodium tetraborate decahydrate
Brimstone	S	Sulfur
Calcite, marble, limestone	$CaCO_3$	Calcium carbonate
Cream of tartar	$KHC_4H_4O_6$	Potassium hydrogen tartrate
Epsom salts	$MgSO_4 \cdot 7H_2O$	Magnesium sulfate heptahydrate
Gypsum	$CaSO_4 \cdot 2H_2O$	Calcium sulfate dihydrate
Grain alcohol	C_2H_5OH	Ethanol, ethyl alcohol
Hypo	$Na_2S_2O_3$	Sodium thiosulfate
Laughing gas	N_2O	Dinitrogen monoxide
Litharge	PbO	Lead(II) oxide
Lye, caustic soda	NaOH	Sodium hydroxide
Milk of magnesia	$Mg(OH)_2$	Magnesium hydroxide
Muriatic acid	HCl	Hydrochloric acid
Oil of vitriol	H_2SO_4	Sulfuric acid
Plaster of paris	$CaSO_4 \cdot \frac{1}{2} H_2O$	Calcium sulfate hemihydrate
Potash	K_2CO_3	Potassium carbonate
Pyrite (fool's gold)	FeS_2	Iron disulfide
Quicksilver	Hg	Mercury
Sal ammoniac	NH_4Cl	Ammonium chloride
Saltpeter (chile)	$NaNO_3$	Sodium nitrate
Table salt	NaCl	Sodium chloride
Washing soda	$Na_2CO_3 \cdot 10H_2O$	Sodium carbonate decahydrate
Wood alcohol	CH_3OH	Methanol, methyl alcohol

chloride; the covalent compound composed of carbon atoms and oxygen atoms in a 1:2 ratio is named carbon dioxide; the compound composed of iron(II) ions and chloride ions is named iron(II) chloride (read as "iron-two chloride").

We shall consider the naming of acids, bases, salts, and oxides. Refer to Tables 8.2, 8.3, and 8.4 for the names, formulas, and oxidation numbers of ions. For handy, quick reference, the names and formulas of some common ions are given on the inside back cover of this book.

These two general rules are very helpful in naming the different types of compounds:

Rule 1. The usual oxidation numbers of Groups IA, IIA, and IIIA elements are +1, +2, and +3, respectively. That is, for these elements the oxidation number is the same as the periodic table group number.

Rule 2. The oxidation numbers of elements in the other periodic groups are variable. However, in practically all compounds, combined oxygen has an oxidation number of −2; and the halogens (Group VIIA) have an oxidation number of −1 in binary compounds with metals.

8.7 Binary Compounds

Binary compounds contain two different elements, and their names have two parts: the name of the more positive element followed by the name of the more negative element modified to end in *ide*. [Some nonbinary compounds have names ending in *ide*, but they are exceptions to the rule and are discussed in part (d) of this section.]

(a) Binary compounds in which the positive element has a fixed oxidation state. Most of these compounds contain a metal and a nonmetal. The chemical name is composed of the name of the metal followed by the name of the nonmetal, which has been modified to an identifying stem plus the suffix *ide*. For example, sodium chloride, NaCl, is composed of one atom each of sodium and chlorine. The name of the metal, sodium, is written first and is not modified. The second part of the name is derived from the nonmetal, chlorine, by using the stem *chlor* and adding the ending *ide*; it is named *chloride*. The compound name is sodium chloride.

NaCl

Elements: Sodium (metal)
Chlorine (nonmetal)
name modified to the stem *chlor* + *ide*
Name of compound: Sodium chloride

Stems of the more common elements that form negative ions are shown in the following table. Table 8.6 shows some compounds with names ending in *ide*.

Symbol	Element	Stem	Binary name ending
B	Boron	Bor	Boride
Br	Bromine	Brom	Bromide
Cl	Chlorine	Chlor	Chloride
F	Fluorine	Fluor	Fluoride
H	Hydrogen	Hydr	Hydride
I	Iodine	Iod	Iodide
N	Nitrogen	Nitr	Nitride
O	Oxygen	Ox	Oxide
P	Phosphorus	Phosph	Phosphide
S	Sulfur	Sulf	Sulfide

Table 8.6   **Examples of compounds with names ending in** *ide*

Formula	Name	Formula	Name
$AlCl_3$	Aluminum chloride	PbS	Lead(II) sulfide
Al_2O_3	Aluminum oxide	LiI	Lithium iodide
CaC_2	Calcium carbide	$MgBr_2$	Magnesium bromide
HCl	Hydrogen chloride	NaH	Sodium hydride
HI	Hydrogen iodide	Na_2O	Sodium oxide

Compounds may contain more than one atom of the same element, but as long as they contain only two different elements and if only one compound of these two elements exists, the name follows the rule for binary compounds:

Examples: $CaBr_2$ Mg_3N_2 Ag_2O

Calcium bromide   Magnesium nitride   Silver oxide

(b) Binary compounds containing metals of variable oxidation numbers. Two systems are commonly used for compounds in this category. The official system, designated by the International Union of Pure and Applied Chemistry (IUPAC), is known as the *Stock System.* In the Stock System, when a compound contains a metal that can have more than one oxidation state, the oxidation number of the metal is designated by a Roman numeral placed in parentheses immediately following the name of the metal. The negative element is treated in the usual manner for binary compounds.

Oxidation number: +1   +2   +3   +4   +5   +6
Roman numeral: (I)   (II)   (III)   (IV)   (V)   (VI)

Examples: $FeCl_2$ Iron(II) chloride Fe^{2+}
              $FeCl_3$ Iron(III) chloride Fe^{3+}
              CuCl   Copper(I) chloride Cu^+
              $CuCl_2$ Copper(II) chloride Cu^{2+}

The fact that $FeCl_2$ has two chloride ions, each with a −1 charge, establishes that the oxidation number of Fe is +2. To distinguish between the two iron chlorides, $FeCl_2$ is named iron(II) chloride and $FeCl_3$ is named iron(III) chloride.

Iron(II) chloride   Iron(III) chloride
$FeCl_2$ $FeCl_3$

Oxidation number: +2   −1   +3   −1
Name: Iron(II)   chloride   Iron(III)   chloride

When a metal has only one possible oxidation state, we need not distinguish one oxidation state from another, so Roman numerals are not needed. Thus we do not say calcium(II) chloride for $CaCl_2$, but rather calcium chloride, since the oxidation number of calcium is understood to be $+2$.

In classical nomenclature, when the metallic ion has only two oxidation numbers, the name of the metal (usually the Latin name) is modified with the suffixes *ous* and *ic* to distinguish between the two. The lower oxidation state is given the *ous* ending, and the higher one, the *ic* ending.

Examples:	$FeCl_2$	Ferrous chloride	Fe^{2+}	(lower oxidation state)
	$FeCl_3$	Ferric chloride	Fe^{3+}	(higher oxidation state)
	$CuCl$	Cuprous chloride	Cu^+	(lower oxidation state)
	$CuCl_2$	Cupric chloride	Cu^{2+}	(higher oxidation state)

Table 8.7 lists some common metals that have more than one oxidation number.

Notice that the *ous–ic* naming system does not give the oxidation state of an element but merely indicates that at least two oxidation states exist. The Stock System avoids any possible uncertainty by clearly stating the oxidation number.

(c) Binary compounds containing two nonmetals. The chemical bond that exists between two nonmetals is predominantly covalent. In a covalent compound, positive and negative oxidation numbers are assigned to the elements according to their electronegativities. The least electronegative element is named first. The common nonmetals arranged in order of increasing electronegativity form this series:

Si, B, P, H, C, S, I, Br, N, Cl, O, F

In a compound between two of these elements, the element that occurs first in

Table 8.7 Names and oxidation states of some common metal ions that have more than one oxidation number

Formula	Stock System name	Classical name
Cu^+	Copper(I)	Cuprous
Cu^{2+}	Copper(II)	Cupric
Hg^+ $(Hg_2)^{2+}$	Mercury(I)	Mercurous
Hg^{2+}	Mercury(II)	Mercuric
Fe^{2+}	Iron(II)	Ferrous
Fe^{3+}	Iron(III)	Ferric
Sn^{2+}	Tin(II)	Stannous
Sn^{4+}	Tin(IV)	Stannic
Pb^{2+}	Lead(II)	Plumbous
Pb^{4+}	Lead(IV)	Plumbic
As^{3+}	Arsenic(III)	Arsenous
As^{5+}	Arsenic(V)	Arsenic
Ti^{3+}	Titanium(III)	Titanous
Ti^{4+}	Titanium(IV)	Titanic

the series is usually written and named first. The name of the second element retains the modified binary ending. A Latin or Greek prefix (*mono, di, tri,* and so on) is attached to the name of each element to indicate the number of atoms of that element in the molecule. The prefix *mono* is generally omitted except when needed to distinguish between two or more compounds, such as carbon monoxide, CO, and carbon dioxide, CO_2. Some common prefixes and their numerical equivalences follow.

Mono = 1	Hexa = 6
Di = 2	Hepta = 7
Tri = 3	Octa = 8
Tetra = 4	Nona = 9
Penta = 5	Deca = 10

Here are some examples of compounds that illustrate this system:

CO	Carbon monoxide	N_2O	Dinitrogen monoxide
CO_2	Carbon dioxide	N_2O_4	Dinitrogen tetroxide
PCl_3	Phosphorus trichloride	NO	Nitrogen oxide
PCl_5	Phosphorus pentachloride	N_2O_3	Dinitrogen trioxide
P_2O_5	Diphosphorus pentoxide	S_2Cl_2	Disulfur dichloride
CCl_4	Carbon tetrachloride	S_2F_{10}	Disulfur decafluoride

N_2O_3

(Di)nitrogen — Indicates two nitrogen atoms

(tri) oxide — Indicates three oxygen atoms

Some special names such as ammonia for NH_3 are exceptions to the system.

(d) Exceptions that use *ide* endings. Three notable exceptions that use the *ide* ending are hydroxides (OH^-), cyanides (CN^-), and ammonium (NH_4^+) compounds. These polyatomic ions, when combined with another element, take the ending *ide*, even though more than two elements are present in the compound.

NH_4I	Ammonium iodide
$Ca(OH)_2$	Calcium hydroxide
KCN	Potassium cyanide

(e) Acids derived from binary compounds. Certain binary hydrogen compounds, when dissolved in water, form solutions that have *acid* properties. Because of this property, these compounds are given acid names in addition to their regular *ide* names. For example, HCl is a gas and is called *hydrogen chloride*, but its water solution is known as *hydrochloric acid*. Binary acids are composed of hydrogen and one other nonmetallic element. However, not all binary hydrogen compounds are acids. To express the formula of a binary acid, it

Table 8.8 Names and formulas
of selected binary acids

Formula	Acid name
HF	Hydrofluoric acid
HCl	Hydrochloric acid
HBr	Hydrobromic acid
HI	Hydriodic acid
H_2S	Hydrosulfuric acid
H_2Se	Hydroselenic acid

is customary to write the symbol of hydrogen first, followed by the symbol of the second element (for example, HCl, HBr, H_2S). When we see formulas such as CH_4 or NH_3, we understand that these compounds are not normally considered to be acids.

To name a binary acid, place the prefix *hydro* in front of, and the suffix *ic* after, the stem of the nonmetal name. Then add the word *acid*.

Examples: HCl H_2S
                Hydro chlor/ic acid   *Hydro sulfur/ic acid*
                (Hydrochloric acid)   (Hydrosulfuric acid)

Acids are hydrogen-containing substances that liberate hydrogen ions when dissolved in water. The same formula is often used to express binary hydrogen compounds such as HCl, regardless of whether they are dissolved in water. Table 8.8 shows several examples of binary acids.

(f) Salts of binary acids.   Salts are ionic compounds of cations and anions. When the hydrogen of an acid is replaced by a metal ion or an ammonium ion, the compound formed is a *salt*. Salts are named by combining the names of the cation and anion, the name of the cation being given first. Thus table salt (NaCl), made of sodium ions (Na^+) and chloride ions (Cl^-), is named sodium chloride. It is the sodium salt of hydrochloric acid.

For salts of binary acids, the name of the negative ion is taken from the name of the compound from which the acid was derived. To illustrate, the name of hydrobromic acid (HBr) is derived from hydrogen *bromide*; therefore, the series of salts obtained from this acid are *bromides*. The names and formulas of the sodium, calcium, and aluminum salts of hydrobromic acid are:

NaBr $CaBr_2$ $AlBr_3$
Sodium bromide   Calcium bromide   Aluminum bromide

8.8 Ternary Compounds

Ternary compounds contain three elements and generally consist of an electropositive group, either hydrogen or a metal, combined with a polyatomic negative group or ion. Most ternary compounds are either ternary oxyacids or salts of ternary oxyacids. In general, when naming ternary compounds, the positive group is given first followed by the name of the negative ion. We shall consider the naming of compounds in which one of the three elements is oxygen.

(a) **Ternary oxyacids.** Inorganic ternary compounds containing hydrogen, oxygen, and one other element are called *oxyacids*. The element other than hydrogen or oxygen in these acids is usually a nonmetal, but in some cases it can be a metal. The *ous–ic* system is used in naming ternary acids. The suffixes *ous* and *ic* are used to indicate different oxidation states of the element other than hydrogen and oxygen. The *ous* ending again indicates the lower oxidation state, and the *ic* ending, the higher oxidation state.

To name these acids, we place the ending *ic* or *ous* after the stem of the element other than hydrogen and oxygen and add the word *acid*. If an element has only one usual oxidation state, the *ic* ending is used. Hydrogen in a ternary oxyacid is not specifically designated in the acid name, but its presence is implied by use of the word *acid*.

Examples: H_2SO_3 Sulfur/*ous acid*   (S is +4)

H_2SO_4 Sulfur/*ic acid*   (S is +6)

Once again, the acid name is associated with the water solution of the pure compound. In the pure state the usual ternary name may be used. Thus, H_2SO_4 is called both sulfuric acid and hydrogen sulfate.

In cases in which a series has more than two oxyacids, the *ous–ic* names are further modified with the prefixes *per* and *hypo*. *Per* is placed before the stem of the element other than hydrogen and oxygen when the element has a higher oxidation number than in the *ic* acid. *Hypo* is used as a prefix before the stem when the element has a lower oxidation number than in the *ous* acid. The complete system for naming ternary oxyacids is shown for the oxyacids of chlorine in Table 8.9.

The Lewis structures of the oxyacids of chlorine are

Hypochlorous acid   Chlorous acid   Chloric acid   Perchloric acid

Check the oxidation number of chlorine in each of these oxyacids using the method for assigning oxidation numbers.

Examples of other ternary oxyacids and their names are shown in Table 8.10.

(b) **Salts of ternary acids.** As with binary acids a salt is formed when the hydrogen of the acid is replaced by a metal or ammonium ion. These salts are named in much the same way as the salts of binary acids; that is, the name of the cation is given first, followed by the name of the polyatomic anion. The names of the anions are derived from the names of the corresponding ternary acids by

Table 8.9 Oxyacids and oxyanions of chlorine

Acid formula	Acid name	Chlorine oxidation number	Anion formula	Anion name
HClO	Hypochlorous acid	+1	ClO^-	Hypochlorite
$HClO_2$	Chlorous acid	+3	ClO_2^-	Chlorite
$HClO_3$	Chloric acid	+5	ClO_3^-	Chlorate
$HClO_4$	Perchloric acid	+7	ClO_4^-	Perchlorate

Table 8.10 Formulas and names of selected ternary oxyacids

Formula	Acid name	Formula	Acid name
H_2SO_3	Sulfurous acid	$HC_2H_3O_2$	Acetic acid
H_2SO_4	Sulfuric acid	$H_2C_2O_4$	Oxalic acid
HNO_2	Nitrous acid	H_2CO_3	Carbonic acid
HNO_3	Nitric acid	$HBrO_3$	Bromic acid
H_3PO_2	Hypophosphorous acid	HIO_3	Iodic acid
H_3PO_3	Phosphorous acid	H_3BO_3	Boric acid
H_3PO_4	Phosphoric acid		

changing the *ous* and *ic* endings to *ite* and *ate*, respectively. The stem portion of the acid name is not changed.

Ternary oxyacid   Ternary oxysalt
   ous ending of acid   becomes   *ite* ending in salt
    ic ending of acid   becomes   *ate* ending in salt

Thus the sulf*ite* ion (SO_3^{2-}) is derived from sulfur*ous* acid (H_2SO_3) and the sulf*ate* ion (SO_4^{2-}) from sulfur*ic* acid (H_2SO_4). The names and formulas of the sodium, calcium, and aluminum salts of sulfurous and sulfuric acids are:

     Na_2SO_3 $CaSO_3$ $Al_2(SO_3)_3$
   Sodium sulfite   Calcium sulfite   Aluminum sulfite

     Na_2SO_4 $CaSO_4$ $Al_2(SO_4)_3$
   Sodium sulfate   Calcium sulfate   Aluminum sulfate

The complete system for naming ternary acids and their anions, using the oxyacids of chlorine as a model, is shown in Table 8.9. A comparison of the acid, anion, and salt names for a number of ternary oxycompounds is presented in Table 8.11.

The endings *ous*, *ic*, *ite*, and *ate* are part of classical nomenclature; they are not used in the Stock System to indicate different oxidation states of the elements. These endings are still used, however, in naming many common compounds.

Table 8.11 Comparison of acid, anion, and salt names for selected ternary oxycompounds

Acid	Anion	Formulas and names of representative salts	
H_2SO_4 Sulfuric acid	SO_4^{2-} Sulfate ion	$CaSO_4$ $Fe_2(SO_4)_3$	Calcium sulfate Iron(III) sulfate or ferric sulfate
H_2SO_3 Sulfurous acid	SO_3^{2-} Sulfite ion	Na_2SO_3 Ag_2SO_3	Sodium sulfite Silver sulfite
HNO_3 Nitric acid	NO_3^- Nitrate ion	KNO_3 $Hg(NO_3)_2$	Potassium nitrate Mercury(II) nitrate or mercuric nitrate
HNO_2 Nitrous acid	NO_2^- Nitrite ion	KNO_2 $Co(NO_2)_2$	Potassium nitrite Cobalt(II) nitrite or cobaltous nitrite
H_2CO_3 Carbonic acid	CO_3^{2-} Carbonate ion	Li_2CO_3 $BaCO_3$	Lithium carbonate Barium carbonate
H_3PO_4 Phosphoric acid	PO_4^{3-} Phosphate ion	$AlPO_4$ $Zn_3(PO_4)_2$	Aluminum phosphate Zinc phosphate
H_3PO_3 Phosphorous acid	PO_3^{3-} Phosphite ion	Na_3PO_3 $Zn_3(PO_3)_2$	Sodium phosphite Zinc phosphite
HIO_3 Iodic acid	IO_3^- Iodate ion	$AgIO_3$ $Cu(IO_3)_2$	Silver iodate Copper(II) iodate or cupric iodate
$HC_2H_3O_2$ Acetic acid	$C_2H_3O_2^-$ Acetate ion	$Pb(C_2H_3O_2)_2$ $NH_4C_2H_3O_2$	Lead(II) acetate Ammonium acetate
$H_2C_2O_4$ Oxalic acid	$C_2O_4^{2-}$ Oxalate ion	CaC_2O_4 $(NH_4)_2C_2O_4$	Calcium oxalate Ammonium oxalate

The Stock name for H_2SO_4 is tetraoxosulfuric(VI) acid, and that for H_2SO_3 is trioxosulfuric(IV) acid. These Stock names are awkward and are not commonly used.

8.9 Salts with More than One Kind of Positive Ion

Salts can be formed from acids that contain two or more acid hydrogen atoms by replacing only one of the hydrogen atoms with a metal or by replacing both hydrogen atoms with different metals. Each positive group is named first, and then the appropriate salt ending is added.

Acid	Salt	Name of salt
H_2CO_3	$NaHCO_3$	Sodium hydrogen carbonate or sodium bicarbonate
H_2S	$NaHS$	Sodium hydrogen sulfide or sodium bisulfide
H_3PO_4	$MgNH_4PO_4$	Magnesium ammonium phosphate
H_2SO_4	$NaKSO_4$	Sodium potassium sulfate

Table 8.12 Names of selected salts that contain more than one kind of positive ion

Acid	Salt	Name of salt
H_2SO_4	$KHSO_4$	Potassium hydrogen sulfate or potassium bisulfate
H_2SO_3	$Ca(HSO_3)_2$	Calcium hydrogen sulfite or calcium bisulfite
H_2S	NH_4HS	Ammonium hydrogen sulfide or ammonium bisulfide
H_3PO_4	$MgNH_4PO_4$	Magnesium ammonium phosphate
H_3PO_4	NaH_2PO_4	Sodium dihydrogen phosphate
H_3PO_4	Na_2HPO_4	Disodium hydrogen phosphate
$H_2C_2O_4$	KHC_2O_4	Potassium hydrogen oxalate or potassium binoxalate
H_2SO_4	$KAl(SO_4)_2$	Potassium aluminum sulfate
H_2CO_3	$Al(HCO_3)_3$	Aluminum hydrogen carbonate or aluminum bicarbonate

Note the name *sodium bicarbonate* given in the table. The prefix *bi* is commonly used to indicate a compound in which one of two acid hydrogen atoms has been replaced by a metal. The HCO_3^- ion is known as the hydrogen carbonate ion or the bicarbonate ion. Another example is sodium bisulfate, which has the formula $NaHSO_4$. Table 8.12 shows examples of other salts that contain more than one kind of positive ion.

Note that prefixes are also used in chemical nomenclature to give special clarity or emphasis to certain compounds as well as to distinguish between two or more compounds.

Examples: Na_3PO_4 Trisodium phosphate

              Na_2HPO_4 Disodium hydrogen phosphate

              NaH_2PO_4 Sodium dihydrogen phosphate

8.10   Bases

Inorganic bases contain the hydroxide ion, OH^-, in chemical combination with a metal ion. These compounds are called *hydroxides*. The OH^- group is named as a single ion and is given the ending *ide*. Several common bases are listed below:

    NaOH   Sodium hydroxide

    KOH   Potassium hydroxide

    NH_4OH Ammonium hydroxide

    $Ca(OH)_2$ Calcium hydroxide

    $Ba(OH)_2$ Barium hydroxide

We have now looked at ways of naming a variety of inorganic compounds—binary compounds consisting of a metal and a nonmetal and of two nonmetals, and binary and ternary acids, salts, and bases. These compounds are just a small part of the classified chemical compounds. Most of the remaining classes are in the broad field of organic chemistry under such categories as hydrocarbons, alcohols, ethers, aldehydes, ketones, phenols, and carboxylic acids.

PROBLEM
8.2

Name the compound CaS.

Step 1. From the formula it is a two-element compound and follows the rules for binary compounds.

Step 2. The compound is composed of Ca, a Group IIA metal, and S, a nonmetal. Since Group IIA elements have only one oxidation state, we name the positive part of the compound *calcium*.

Step 3. Modify the name of the second element to the identifying stem *sulf* and add the binary ending *ide* to form the name of the negative part, *sulfide*.

Step 4. The name of the compound, therefore, is *calcium sulfide*.

PROBLEM
8.3

Name the compound FeS.

Step 1. This compound follows the rules for a binary compound and, like CaS, must be a sulfide.

Step 2. It is a compound of Fe, a metal, and S, a nonmetal. In the oxidation number tables, we see that Fe has two oxidation numbers. In sulfides, the oxidation number of S is -2. Therefore, the oxidation number of Fe must be $+2$, and the name of the positive part of the compound is *iron(II)* or *ferrous*.

Step 3. We have already determined that the name of the negative part of the compound will be *sulfide*.

Step 4. The name of FeS is *iron(II) sulfide*, or *ferrous sulfide*.

PROBLEM
8.4

Name the compound PCl_5.

Step 1. Phosphorus and chlorine are nonmetals, so the rules for naming binary compounds containing two nonmetals apply. Phosphorus is named first because it is less electronegative than chlorine. Therefore the compound is a chloride.

Step 2. No prefix is needed for phosphorus because each molecule has only one atom of phosphorus. The prefix *penta* is used with chloride to indicate the five chlorine atoms. (PCl_3 is also a known compound.)

Step 3. The name for PCl_5 is *phosphorus pentachloride*.

PROBLEM
8.5

(a) Name the salt KNO_3 and **(b)** name the acid HNO_3 from which this salt can be derived.

(a) Step 1. The compound contains three elements and follows the rules for ternary compounds.

Step 2. The salt is composed of a K^+ ion and a NO_3^- ion. The name of the positive part of the compound is *potassium*.

Step 3. Since it is a ternary salt, the name will end in *ite* or *ate*. In the oxidation number tables, we see that the name of the NO_3^- ion is *nitrate*.

Step 4. The name of the salt is *potassium nitrate*.

(b) The name of the acid follows the rules for ternary oxyacids. Because the name of the salt KNO_3 ends in *ate*, the name of the corresponding acid will end in *ic acid*. Change the *ate* ending of nitrate to *ic*. Thus *nitrate* becomes *nitric*, and the name of the acid is *nitric acid*.

QUESTIONS

A. *Review the meanings of the new terms introduced in this chapter.*

1. Oxidation state
2. Oxidation number

B. *In naming compounds be careful to use correct spelling.*

1. Using the principle employed in Table 8.1, write formulas for:
   (a) The hydrogen compounds of Li, C, I, N, Sr
   (b) The oxygen compounds of Ca, Si, Br, Al, P
   (c) The iodine compounds of Li, Al, C, Sr, S

2. Use the oxidation number tables and determine the formulas for compounds composed of the following ions:
   (a) Sodium and chlorate
   (b) Hydrogen and sulfate
   (c) Tin(II) and acetate
   (d) Copper(I) and oxide
   (e) Zinc and bicarbonate
   (f) Iron(III) and carbonate

3. Determine the oxidation number of the element underlined in each formula:
   (a) $\underline{Mn}CO_3$ (d) $K\underline{Mn}O_4$ (g) $\underline{W}Cl_5$
   (b) $\underline{Sn}F_4$ (e) $Ba\underline{C}O_3$ (h) $K_2\underline{Cr}_2O_7$
   (c) $K\underline{N}O_3$ (f) $\underline{P}Cl_3$

4. Determine the oxidation number of the element underlined in each formula:
   (a) $\underline{In}I_3$ (d) $\underline{C}_2H_5OH$ (g) $\underline{Fe}_2(CO_3)_3$
   (b) $K\underline{Cl}O_3$ (e) $Mg(\underline{N}O_3)_2$ (h) $Na\underline{Cl}O_4$
   (c) $Na_2\underline{S}O_4$ (f) $\underline{Sn}O_2$

5. Write the formula of the compound that would be formed between the given elements:
   (a) Na and I (c) Al and O (e) Cs and Cl
   (b) Ba and F (d) K and S (f) Sr and Br

6. Write the formula of the compound that would be formed between the given elements:
   (a) Ba and O (c) Ga and Cl (e) Li and Si
   (b) H and S (d) Be and Br (f) Mg and P

7. Does the fact that two elements combine in a one-to-one atomic ratio mean that their oxidation numbers are both 1? Explain.

8. What might be the formula of a compound formed between elements X and Z where:
   (a) X has 1 electron and Z has 6 electrons in the outer energy level.
   (b) X has 4 electrons and Z has 7 electrons in the outer energy level.
   (c) X has 1 electron and Z has 7 electrons in the outer energy level.

9. Write formulas for the following cations (remember to include the charges): sodium, magnesium, aluminum, copper(II), iron(II), ferric, lead(II), silver, cobalt(II), barium, hydrogen, mercury(II), tin(II), chromium(III), stannic, manganese(II), bismuth(III).

10. Write formulas for the following anions (do not forget to include the charges): chloride, bromide, fluoride, iodide, cyanide, oxide, hydroxide, sulfide, sulfate, bisulfate, bisulfite, chromate, carbonate, bicarbonate, acetate, chlorate, permanganate, oxalate.

11. Complete the table, filling in each box with the proper formula.

Anions

Cations	Br^-	O^{2-}	NO_3^-	PO_4^{3-}	CO_3^{2-}
K^+	KBr				
Mg^{2+}					
Al^{3+}					
Zn^{2+}				$Zn_3(PO_4)_2$	
H^+					

12. Complete the table, filling in each box with the proper formula.

Anions

Cations	SO_4^{2-}	Cl^-	AsO_4^{3-}	$C_2H_3O_2^-$	CrO_4^{2-}
NH_4^+			$(NH_4)_3AsO_4$		
Ca^{2+}					
Fe^{3+}	$Fe_2(SO_4)_3$				
Ag^+					
Cu^{2+}					

13. State how each of the following is used in naming inorganic compounds: *ide, ous, ic, hypo, per, ite, ate,* Roman numerals.

14. Write formulas for the following binary compounds, all of which are composed of nonmetals:
    (a) Carbon monoxide
    (b) Sulfur trioxide
    (c) Carbon tetrabromide
    (d) Phosphorus trichloride
    (e) Nitrogen dioxide
    (f) Dinitrogen pentoxide

15. Name the following binary compounds, all of which are composed of nonmetals:
    (a) CO_2 (d) CCl_4 (g) P_2O_5 (j) CS_2
    (b) N_2O (e) SO_2 (h) OF_2
    (c) PCl_5 (f) N_2O_4 (i) NF_3

16. Name the following compounds:
    (a) K_2O (d) $BaCO_3$ (g) $Zn(NO_3)_2$
    (b) NH_4Br (e) Na_3PO_4 (h) Ag_2SO_4
    (c) CaI_2 (f) Al_2O_3

17. Write formulas for the following compounds:
    (a) Sodium nitrate
    (b) Magnesium fluoride
    (c) Barium hydroxide
    (d) Ammonium sulfate
    (e) Silver carbonate
    (f) Calcium phosphate

18. Name each of the following compounds by both the Stock (IUPAC) System, and the *ous–ic* system:
    (a) $CuCl_2$ (d) $FeCl_3$ (g) $As(C_2H_3O_2)_3$
    (b) $CuBr$ (e) SnF_2 (h) TiI_3
    (c) $Fe(NO_3)_2$ (f) $HgCO_3$

19. Write formulas for the following compounds:
    (a) Tin(IV) bromide (d) Mercuric nitrite
    (b) Copper(I) sulfate (e) Titanic sulfide
    (c) Ferric carbonate (f) Iron(II) acetate
20. Write formulas for the following acids:
    (a) Hydrochloric acid (d) Carbonic acid
    (b) Chloric acid (e) Sulfurous acid
    (c) Nitric acid (f) Phosphoric acid
21. Name the following acids:
    (a) HNO_2 (d) HBr (g) HF
    (b) H_2SO_4 (e) H_3PO_3 (h) $HBrO_3$
    (c) $H_2C_2O_4$ (f) $HC_2H_3O_2$
22. Write formulas for the following acids:
    (a) Acetic acid
    (b) Hydrofluoric acid
    (c) Hypochlorous acid
    (d) Boric acid
    (e) Nitrous acid
    (f) Hydrosulfuric acid
23. Name the following acids:
    (a) H_3PO_4 (c) HIO_3 (e) HClO (g) HI
    (b) H_2CO_3 (d) HCl (f) HNO_3 (h) $HClO_4$
24. Name the following compounds:
    (a) $Ba(NO_3)_2$ (d) $MgSO_4$ (g) NiS
    (b) $NaC_2H_3O_2$ (e) $CdCrO_4$ (h) $Sn(NO_3)_4$
    (c) PbI_2 (f) $BiCl_3$ (i) $Ca(OH)_2$
25. Write formulas for the following compounds:
    (a) Silver sulfite
    (b) Cobalt(II) bromide
    (c) Tin(II) hydroxide
    (d) Aluminum sulfate
    (e) Manganese(II) fluoride
    (f) Ammonium carbonate
    (g) Chromium(III) oxide
    (h) Cupric chloride
    (i) Potassium permanganate
    (j) Barium nitrite
    (k) Sodium peroxide
    (l) Ferrous sulfate
    (m) Potassium dichromate
    (n) Bismuth(III) chromate
26. Write formulas for the following compounds:
    (a) Sodium chromate
    (b) Magnesium hydride
    (c) Nickel(II) acetate
    (d) Calcium chlorate
    (e) Lead(II) nitrate
    (f) Potassium dihydrogen phosphate
    (g) Manganese(II) hydroxide
    (h) Cobalt(II) bicarbonate

(i) Sodium hypochlorite
(j) Arsenic(V) carbonate
(k) Chromium(III) sulfite
(l) Antimony(III) sulfate
(m) Sodium oxalate
(n) Potassium thiocyanate

27. Write the name of each salt and the formula and name of the acid from which the salt may be derived. [*Example:* NiC_2O_4, nickel(II) oxalate, $H_2C_2O_4$, oxalic acid.]
    (a) $ZnSO_4$ (k) $Ca(HSO_4)_2$
    (b) $HgCl_2$ (l) $As_2(SO_3)_3$
    (c) $CuCO_3$ (m) $Sn(NO_2)_2$
    (d) $Cd(NO_3)_2$ (n) $FeBr_3$
    (e) $Al(C_2H_3O_2)_3$ (o) $KHCO_3$
    (f) CoF_2 (p) $BiAsO_4$
    (g) $Cr(ClO_3)_3$ (q) $Fe(BrO_3)_2$
    (h) Ag_3PO_4 (r) $(NH_4)_2HPO_4$
    (i) NiS (s) NaClO
    (j) $BaCrO_4$ (t) $KMnO_4$

28. Write the chemical formula for each of the following substances:
    (a) Baking soda (i) Fool's gold
    (b) Lime (j) Saltpeter
    (c) Epsom salts (k) Limestone
    (d) Muriatic acid (l) Cane sugar
    (e) Vinegar (m) Milk of magnesia
    (f) Potash (n) Washing soda
    (g) Lye (o) Grain alcohol
    (h) Quicksilver

29. Give the name and formula of three salts with *ide* endings that are not binary compounds. Do not use the exact salts used as examples in the chapter.

30. Which of these statements are correct?
    (a) An oxidation number can be positive, negative, or zero.
    (b) The oxidation number of Group IA elements is -1.
    (c) The sum of the oxidation numbers for all the atoms in a polyatomic ion is zero.
    (d) The formula for calcium hydride is CaH_2.
    (e) All the following compounds are acids: H_2SO_4, HCl, HNO_3, $NaC_2H_3O_2$.
    (f) The ions of all the following metals have an oxidation number of $+2$: Ca, Ba, Sr, Cd, Zn.
    (g) The formulas for nitrous and sulfurous acids are HNO_2 and H_2SO_3.
    (h) The formula for the compound between Fe^{3+} and O^{2-} is Fe_3O_2.

(i) The oxidation number of Cr in K_2CrO_4 is +6.

(j) The oxidation number of Sn in $SnCl_4$ is +4.

(k) The oxidation number of Co in $CoCl_2$ is +4.

(l) The name for $NaNO_2$ is sodium nitrite.

(m) The name for $Ca(ClO_3)_2$ is calcium chlorate.

(n) The name for CuO is copper(I) oxide.

(o) The name for SO_4^{2-} is sulfate ion.

(p) The name for N_2O_4 is dinitrogen tetroxide.

(q) The name for Na_2O is disodium oxide.

(r) If the name of an anion ends with *ide*, the name of the corresponding acid will start with *hydro*.

(s) If the name of an anion ends with *ite*, the corresponding acid name will end with *ic*.

(t) If the name of an acid ends with *ous*, the corresponding salt name will end with *ate*.

(u) In FeI_2, the iron is iron(II) because it is combined with two I^- ions.

(v) In Cu_2SO_4, the copper is copper(II) because there are two copper ions.

(w) In Ru_2O_3, we can deduce the oxidation state of Ru as +3 because two ions are combined with three oxide ions.

(x) When two nonmetals combine, prefixes of *di, tri, tetra*, and so on are used to specify how many atoms of each element are in a molecule.

(y) N_2O_3 is called dinitrogen trioxide.

(z) $Sn(CrO_4)_2$ is called tin dichromate.

(aa) In the Stock System of nomenclature, when a compound contains a metal that can have more than one oxidation number, the oxidation number of the metal is designated by a Roman numeral written immediately after the name of the metal.

9

Quantitative Composition of Compounds

After studying Chapter 9, you should be able to

1. Understand the new terms listed in Question A at the end of the chapter.
2. Explain the meaning of the mole.
3. Discuss the relationship between a mole and Avogadro's number.
4. Convert grams, atoms, molecules, molecular weights, and formula weights to moles, and vice versa.
5. Determine the formula weight or molecular weight of a compound from the formula.
6. Calculate the percentage composition by weight of a compound from its formula.
7. Calculate the percentage composition of a compound from experimental data on combining weights.
8. Explain the relationship between an empirical formula and a molecular formula.
9. Determine the empirical formula of a compound from its percentage composition.
10. Calculate the molecular formula of a compound from its percentage composition and molecular weight.

9.1 The Mole

In the laboratory we normally weigh substances on a balance in units of grams. But, when we run a chemical reaction, the reaction occurs between atoms and molecules. For example, in the reaction between magnesium and sulfur, one atom of sulfur reacts with one atom of magnesium:

$$Mg + S \longrightarrow MgS$$

However, when we measure the masses of these two elements that react, we find that 24.305 g of Mg are required to react with 32.06 g of S. Because magnesium and sulfur react in a 1:1 atom ratio, we can conclude from this experiment that 24.305 g of Mg contains the same number of atoms as 32.06 g of S. How many atoms are in 24.305 g of Mg or 32.06 g of S? These two amounts each contain one mole of atoms.

The mole (abbreviated mol) is one of the seven base units in the International System and is the unit for an amount of substance. The mole is a counting unit as in other things that we count, such as a dozen (12) eggs or a gross (144) of pencils. But a mole is a much larger number of things, namely 6.022×10^{23}. Thus one mole contains 6.022×10^{23} entities of anything. In reference to our reaction between magnesium and sulfur, 1 mol Mg (24.305 g) contains 6.022×10^{23} atoms of magnesium and 1 mol S (32.06 g) contains 6.022×10^{23} atoms of sulfur.

Avogadro's number

The number 6.022×10^{23} is known as **Avogadro's number** in honor of Amedeo Avogadro (1776–1856), an Italian physicist. Avogadro's number is an important constant in chemistry and physics and has been experimentally determined by several independent methods.

> **Avogadro's number = 6.022×10^{23}**

It is difficult to imagine how large Avogadro's number really is, but perhaps the following analogy will help express it: If 10,000 people started to count Avogadro's number and each counted at the rate of 100 numbers per minute each minute of the day, it would take them over 1 trillion (10^{12}) years to count the total number. So, even the minutest amount of matter contains extremely large numbers of atoms. For example, 1 mg (0.001 g) of sulfur contains 2×10^{19} atoms of sulfur.

mole

Avogadro's number is the basis for the amount of substance that is used to express a particular number of chemical species, such as atoms, molecules, formula units, ions, or electrons. This amount of substance is the mole. We define a **mole** as an amount of a substance containing the same number of formula units as there are atoms in exactly 12 g of carbon-12. (Recall that carbon-12 is the reference isotope for atomic weights.) Other definitions are used, but they all relate to a mole being Avogadro's number of formula units of a substance. A *formula unit* is the atom or molecule indicated by the formula of the substance under consideration—for example, Mg, MgS, H_2O, O_2, $^{75}_{33}As$.

From the above definition we can say that the atomic weight (abbreviated at. wt) in grams of any element contains one mole of atoms. For example,

1 mol H $=$ 1.0079 g H $= 6.022 \times 10^{23}$ atoms

1 mol Mg $=$ 24.305 g Mg $= 6.022 \times 10^{23}$ atoms

1 mol S $=$ 32.06 g S $= 6.022 \times 10^{23}$ atoms

1 mol O $=$ 15.9994 g O $= 6.022 \times 10^{23}$ atoms

1 mol Na $=$ 22.9898 g Na $= 6.022 \times 10^{23}$ atoms

1 atomic weight (g) = 1 mole of atoms
$\qquad$ **= Avogadro's number (6.022×10^{23}) of atoms**

The term *mole* is so commonplace in chemical jargon that chemists use it as freely as the words *atom* and *molecule*. The mole is used in conjunction with many different particles, such as atoms, molecules, ions, and electrons, to represent Avogadro's number of these particles. If we can speak of a mole of atoms, we can also speak of a mole of molecules, a mole of electrons, a mole of ions, understanding that in each case we mean 6.022×10^{23} formula units of these particles.

1 mole of atoms $= 6.022 \times 10^{23}$ atoms

1 mole of molecules $= 6.022 \times 10^{23}$ molecules

1 mole of ions $= 6.022 \times 10^{23}$ ions

We frequently encounter problems that require conversions involving quantities of mass, numbers, and moles of atoms of an element. Conversion factors that can be used for this purpose are

(a) Grams to atoms: $\dfrac{6.022 \times 10^{23} \text{ atoms of the element}}{1 \text{ at. wt of the element}}$

(b) Atoms to grams: $\dfrac{1 \text{ at. wt of the element}}{6.022 \times 10^{23} \text{ atoms of the element}}$

(c) Grams to moles: (Monatomic elements) $\dfrac{1 \text{ mole of the element}}{1 \text{ at. wt of the element}}$

(d) Moles to grams: (Monatomic elements) $\dfrac{1 \text{ at. wt of the element}}{1 \text{ mole of the element}}$

PROBLEM

9.1

How many moles of iron do 25.0 g of Fe represent?

The problem requires that we change grams of Fe to moles of Fe. We look up the atomic weight of Fe in the atomic weight table (inside the back cover) and find it to be 55.8. Then we use the proper conversion factor to obtain moles. The conversion factor is (c).

$$\text{grams Fe} \longrightarrow \text{moles Fe} \qquad \text{grams Fe} \times \frac{1 \text{ mole Fe}}{1 \text{ at. wt Fe}}$$

$$25.0 \text{ g Fe} \times \frac{1 \text{ mol Fe}}{55.8 \text{ g Fe}} = 0.448 \text{ mol Fe} \quad \text{(Answer)}$$

PROBLEM

9.2

How many magnesium atoms are contained in 5.00 g of Mg?

The problem requires that we change grams of magnesium to atoms of magnesium:

$$\text{grams Mg} \longrightarrow \text{atoms Mg}$$

We find the atomic weight of magnesium to be 24.3 and set up the calculation using conversion factor (a):

$$\text{grams Mg} \times \frac{6.022 \times 10^{23} \text{ atoms Mg}}{1 \text{ at. wt Mg}}$$

$$5.00 \text{ g Mg} \times \frac{6.022 \times 10^{23} \text{ atoms Mg}}{24.3 \text{ g Mg}} = 1.24 \times 10^{23} \text{ atoms Mg} \quad \text{(Answer)}$$

An alternative solution is first to convert grams of magnesium to moles of magnesium, which are then changed to atoms of magnesium:

$$\text{grams Mg} \longrightarrow \text{moles Mg} \longrightarrow \text{atoms Mg}$$

Use conversion factor (c) followed by (a). The calculation setup is

$$5.00 \text{ g Mg} \times \frac{1 \text{ mol Mg}}{24.3 \text{ g Mg}} \times \frac{6.022 \times 10^{23} \text{ atoms Mg}}{1 \text{ mol Mg}} = 1.24 \times 10^{23} \text{ atoms Mg}$$

Thus 1.24×10^{23} atoms of Mg are contained in 5.00 g of Mg.

PROBLEM

9.3

How many grams does one atom of carbon weigh?

From the table of atomic weights we see that the atomic weight of carbon is 12.0 g. The factor needed to convert atoms to grams is conversion factor (b).

$$\text{atoms C} \longrightarrow \text{grams C} \qquad \text{atoms C} \times \frac{1 \text{ at. wt C}}{6.022 \times 10^{23} \text{ atoms C}}$$

$$1 \text{ atom C} \times \frac{12.0 \text{ g C}}{6.022 \times 10^{23} \text{ atoms C}} = 1.99 \times 10^{-23} \text{ g C} \quad \text{(Answer)}$$

PROBLEM

9.4

How many grams do 3.01×10^{23} atoms of sodium weigh?

The information needed to solve this problem is the atomic weight of Na (23.0 g) and conversion factor (b).

$$\text{atoms Na} \longrightarrow \text{grams Na} \qquad \text{atoms Na} \times \frac{1 \text{ at. wt Na}}{6.022 \times 10^{23} \text{ atoms Na}}$$

$$3.01 \times 10^{23} \text{ atoms Na} \times \frac{23.0 \text{ g Na}}{6.022 \times 10^{23} \text{ atoms Na}} = 11.5 \text{ g Na} \quad \text{(Answer)}$$

PROBLEM

9.5

How many grams does 0.252 mol of Cu weigh?

The information needed to solve this problem is the atomic weight of Cu (63.5 g) and conversion factor (d).

$$\text{moles Cu} \longrightarrow \text{grams Cu} \qquad \text{moles Cu} \times \frac{1 \text{ at. wt Cu}}{1 \text{ mole Cu}}$$

$$0.252 \text{ mol Cu} \times \frac{63.5 \text{ g Cu}}{1 \text{ mol Cu}} = 16.0 \text{ g Cu} \quad \text{(Answer)}$$

PROBLEM

9.6

How many oxygen atoms are present in 1.00 mol of oxygen molecules?

Oxygen is a diatomic molecule with the formula O_2. Therefore a molecule of oxygen contains two atoms of oxygen:

$$\frac{2 \text{ atoms O}}{1 \text{ molecule O}_2}$$

The sequence of conversions is

$$\text{moles O}_2 \longrightarrow \text{molecules O}_2 \longrightarrow \text{atoms O}$$

Two conversion factors are needed; they are

$$\frac{6.022 \times 10^{23} \text{ molecules O}_2}{1 \text{ mol O}_2} \quad \text{and} \quad \frac{2 \text{ atoms O}}{1 \text{ molecule O}_2}$$

The calculation is

$$1.00 \text{ mol O}_2 \times \frac{6.022 \times 10^{23} \text{ molecules O}_2}{1 \text{ mol O}_2} \times \frac{2 \text{ atoms O}}{1 \text{ molecule O}_2} = 1.20 \times 10^{24} \text{ atoms O}$$

$$\text{(Answer)}$$

9.2   Formula Weight or Molecular Weight

formula weight

molecular weight

Because compounds are composed of atoms, their masses may be represented by the formula weight or the molecular weight. The **formula weight** (form. wt) of a substance is the total mass of all the atoms in the chemical formula of that substance. The **molecular weight** (mol. wt) of a substance is the total mass of all the atoms in a molecule of that substance. Formula weight and molecular weight are often used interchangeably. However, the term *formula weight* is more inclusive, since it includes both molecular and ionic substances.

If the formula of a substance is known, its formula weight or molecular weight may be determined by adding together the atomic weights of all the atoms in the formula. If more than one atom of any element is present, it must be added as many times as it is used in the formula. When atomic weights are in grams, the formula weight and molecular weight will also be in grams. We will continue to use atomic weights in grams in the future.

PROBLEM

9.7

The molecular formula for water is H_2O. What is its molecular weight?

Proceed by looking up the atomic weights of H (1.008) and O (15.999) and adding together the masses of all the atoms in the formula unit. Water contains two atoms of H and one atom of O. Thus,

$$
\begin{aligned}
2\,H &= 2 \times 1.008 = 2.016 \text{ g} \\
1\,O &= 1 \times 15.999 = \underline{15.999 \text{ g}} \\
&\qquad\qquad\quad 18.015 \text{ g} = \text{Molecular or formula weight}
\end{aligned}
$$

PROBLEM

9.8

Calculate the formula weight of calcium hydroxide, $Ca(OH)_2$.

The formula of this substance contains one atom of Ca and two atoms each of O and H. Proceed as in Problem 9.7. Thus

$$
\begin{aligned}
1\,Ca &= 1 \times 40.08 = 40.08 \text{ g} \\
2\,O &= 2 \times 15.999 = 31.998 \text{ g} \\
2\,H &= 2 \times 1.008 = \underline{2.016 \text{ g}} \\
&\qquad\qquad\quad 74.094 \text{ g} = \text{Formula weight}
\end{aligned}
$$

The atomic weights of elements are often rounded off to one decimal place to simplify calculations. (However, this simplification cannot be made in the more exacting chemical work.) If we calculate the formula weight of $Ca(OH)_2$ on the basis of one decimal place, we find the value to be 74.1 g instead of 74.094 g. The formula weight of $Ca(OH)_2$ would then be calculated as follows:

$$
\begin{aligned}
1\,Ca &= 1 \times 40.1 = 40.1 \text{ g} \\
2\,O &= 2 \times 16.0 = 32.0 \text{ g} \\
2\,H &= 2 \times 1.0 = \underline{2.0 \text{ g}} \\
&\qquad\qquad\;\; 74.1 \text{ g} = \text{Formula weight}
\end{aligned}
$$

A formula weight or molecular weight of a compound is one mole of that compound and therefore contains Avogadro's number of formula units or molecules.

As an illustration consider the compound hydrogen chloride, HCl. One atom of H combines with one atom of Cl to form one molecule of HCl. When 1 atomic weight of H (1.0 g of H representing 1 mol or 6.022×10^{23} H atoms) combines with 1 atomic weight of Cl (35.5 g of Cl representing 1 mol or 6.022×10^{23} Cl atoms), 1 molecular weight of HCl (36.5 g of HCl representing 1 mol or 6.022×10^{23} HCl molecules) is produced. Since 36.5 g of HCl contains 6.022×10^{23} molecules, we may refer to this quantity as a molecular weight, as a formula weight, or as a mole of HCl. These relationships are summarized in the following table.

H	Cl	HCl
6.022×10^{23} H *atoms*	6.022×10^{23} Cl *atoms*	6.022×10^{23} HCl *molecules*
1 mol H *atoms*	1 mol Cl *atoms*	1 mol HCl *molecules*
1.0 g H	35.5 g Cl	36.5 g HCl
1 at. wt H	1 at. wt Cl	1 mol. wt HCl or
		1 form. wt HCl

In dealing with diatomic elements (H_2, O_2, N_2, F_2, Cl_2, Br_2, and I_2), special care must be taken to distinguish between a mole of atoms (atomic weight) and a mole of molecules (molecular weight). For example consider *one* mole of oxygen molecules, which weighs 32.0 g. This quantity is equal to *two* atomic weights of the element oxygen and thus represents *two* moles of oxygen atoms. The key concept is that one mole represents Avogadro's number of the particular chemical entity—atoms, molecules, formula units, and so forth—that is under consideration.

$$1 \text{ mol } H_2O = 18.0 \text{ g } H_2O = 6.022 \times 10^{23} \text{ molecules}$$
$$1 \text{ mol NaCl} = 58.5 \text{ g NaCl} = 6.022 \times 10^{23} \text{ formula units}$$
$$1 \text{ mol } H_2 = 2.0 \text{ g } H_2 = 6.022 \times 10^{23} \text{ molecules}$$
$$1 \text{ mol } HNO_3 = 63.0 \text{ g } HNO_3 = 6.022 \times 10^{23} \text{ molecules}$$
$$1 \text{ mol } K_2SO_4 = 174.3 \text{ g } K_2SO_4 = 6.022 \times 10^{23} \text{ formula units}$$

1 mol = 6.022×10^{23} formula units or molecules
1 mol = 1 formula weight or 1 molecular weight of a compound

We often need to convert moles of a compound to grams, and grams of a compound to moles. The factors for these conversions are

Grams to moles: $\dfrac{1 \text{ mol of a substance}}{1 \text{ form. wt of the substance}}$

Moles to grams: $\dfrac{1 \text{ form. wt of a substance}}{1 \text{ mol of the substance}}$

PROBLEM

9.9

What is the weight of 1 mol of sulfuric acid, H_2SO_4?

One mole of H_2SO_4 is one formula weight of H_2SO_4. The problem, therefore, is solved in a similar manner to Problems 9.7 and 9.8. Look up the atomic weights of H, S, and O, and solve.

$$
\begin{aligned}
2\,H &= 2 \times 1.0 = \underline{2.0\,g} \\
1\,S &= 1 \times 32.1 = 32.1\,g \\
4\,O &= 4 \times 16.0 = \underline{64.0\,g} \\
&\qquad\qquad\quad 98.1\,g = \text{Weight of 1 mol (1 form. wt) of } H_2SO_4
\end{aligned}
$$

PROBLEM

9.10

How many moles of NaOH are there in 1.00 kg of sodium hydroxide?

First we know that

1 mol = 1 form. wt = (23.0 + 16.0 + 1.0 g) or 40.0 g NaOH

1 kg = 1000 g

To convert grams to moles we use the conversion factor

$$
\frac{1\ \text{mol}}{1\ \text{form. wt}} \quad \text{or} \quad \frac{1\ \text{mol NaOH}}{40.0\ \text{g NaOH}}
$$

Use this conversion sequence:

kg NaOH $\longrightarrow$ g NaOH $\longrightarrow$ mol NaOH

The calculation is

$$
1.00\ \cancel{\text{kg NaOH}} \times \frac{1000\ \cancel{\text{g NaOH}}}{\cancel{\text{kg NaOH}}} \times \frac{1\ \text{mol NaOH}}{40.0\ \cancel{\text{g NaOH}}} = 25.0\ \text{mol NaOH}
$$

$$
1.00\ \text{kg NaOH} = 25.0\ \text{mol NaOH}
$$

PROBLEM

9.11

How many grams do 5.00 moles of water weigh?

First we know that

1 mol H_2O = 18.0 g   (Problem 9.7)

To convert moles to grams, use the conversion factor

$$
\frac{1\ \text{mol. wt } H_2O}{1\ \text{mol } H_2O} \quad \text{or} \quad \frac{18.0\ \text{g } H_2O}{1\ \text{mol } H_2O}
$$

The conversion is

mol H_2O $\longrightarrow$ g H_2O

The calculation is

$$5.00 \text{ mol H}_2\text{O} \times \frac{18.0 \text{ g H}_2\text{O}}{1 \text{ mol H}_2\text{O}} = 90.0 \text{ g H}_2\text{O} \quad \text{(Answer)}$$

PROBLEM

9.12

How many molecules of HCl are there in 25.0 g of hydrogen chloride?

From the formula we find that the molecular weight of HCl is 36.5 g (1.0 + 35.5 g). The sequence of conversions is

$$\text{g HCl} \longrightarrow \text{mol HCl} \longrightarrow \text{molecules HCl}$$

using the conversion factors

$$\frac{1 \text{ mol HCl}}{36.5 \text{ g HCl}} \quad \text{and} \quad \frac{6.022 \times 10^{23} \text{ molecules HCl}}{1 \text{ mol HCl}}$$

$$25.0 \text{ g HCl} \times \frac{1 \text{ mol HCl}}{36.5 \text{ g HCl}} \times \frac{6.022 \times 10^{23} \text{ molecules HCl}}{1 \text{ mol HCl}} = 4.12 \times 10^{23} \text{ molecules HCl}$$

(Answer)

9.3 Percentage Composition of Compounds

percentage composition of a compound

Percent means parts per one hundred parts. Just as each piece of pie is a percentage of the whole pie, each element in a compound is a percentage of the whole compound. The **percentage composition of a compound** is the *weight-percent* of each element in the compound. The formula weight represents the total mass, or 100%, of the compound. Thus the percentage composition of water, H_2O, is 11.1% H and 88.9% O by weight. According to the Law of Definite Composition, the percentage composition must be the same no matter what size sample is taken.

The percentage composition of a compound can be determined if its formula is known or if the weights of two or more elements that have combined with each other are known or are experimentally determined.

If the formula is known, it is essentially a two-step process to determine the percentage composition.

Step 1. Calculate the formula weight as was done in Section 9.2.

Step 2. Divide the total weight of each element in the formula weight by the formula weight and multiply by 100%. This gives the percentage composition.

$$\frac{\text{Total weight of the element}}{\text{Formula weight}} \times 100\% = \text{Percentage of the element}$$

It is necessary to multiply by 100% and not just 100; otherwise the answer is unitless.

PROBLEM

9.13

Calculate the percentage composition of sodium chloride, NaCl.

Step 1. Calculate the formula weight of NaCl:

Atomic weights: Na, 23.0; Cl, 35.5

$$
\begin{array}{l}
1\ \text{Na} = 23.0\ \text{g} \\
1\ \text{Cl} = \underline{35.5\ \text{g}} \\
\phantom{1\ \text{Cl} = }58.5\ \text{g}\quad \text{(Formula weight)}
\end{array}
$$

Step 2. Now calculate the percentage composition. We know there are 23.0 g Na and 35.5 g Cl in 58.5 g NaCl.

$$
\text{Na:}\quad \frac{23.0\ \cancel{g}\ \text{Na}}{58.5\ \cancel{g}\ \text{NaCl}} \times 100\% = \ \ 39.3\%\ \text{Na}
$$

$$
\text{Cl:}\quad \frac{35.5\ \cancel{g}\ \text{Cl}}{58.5\ \cancel{g}\ \text{NaCl}} \times 100\% = \frac{60.7\%\ \text{Cl}}{100.0\%\ \text{total}}
$$

In any two-component system, if one percentage is known, the other is automatically defined by difference; that is, if Na = 39.3%, then Cl = 100% − 39.3% = 60.7%. However, the calculation of the percentage of each component should be carried out, since this provides a check against possible error. The percentage composition data should add up to 100 ± 0.2%.

PROBLEM

9.14

Calculate the percentage composition of potassium chloride, KCl.

Step 1. Calculate the formula weight of KCl:

Atomic weights: K, 39.1; Cl, 35.5

$$
\begin{array}{l}
1\ \text{K} = 39.1\ \text{g} \\
1\ \text{Cl} = \underline{35.5\ \text{g}} \\
\phantom{1\ \text{Cl} = }74.6\ \text{g}\quad \text{(Formula weight)}
\end{array}
$$

Step 2. Now calculate the percentage composition. We know there are 39.1 g K and 35.5 g Cl in 74.6 g KCl.

$$
\text{K:}\quad \frac{39.1\ \cancel{g}\ \text{K}}{74.6\ \cancel{g}\ \text{KCl}} \times 100\% = \ \ 52.4\%\ \text{K}
$$

$$
\text{Cl:}\quad \frac{35.5\ \cancel{g}\ \text{Cl}}{74.6\ \cancel{g}\ \text{KCl}} \times 100\% = \frac{47.6\%\ \text{Cl}}{100.0\%\ \text{total}}
$$

Comparing the data calculated for NaCl and for KCl, we see that NaCl contains a higher percentage of Cl by weight, although each compound has a one-to-one atom ratio of Cl to Na and K. The reason for this weight percentage difference is that Na and K do not have the same atomic weights.

It is important to realize that, when we compare 1 mole of NaCl with 1 mole of KCl, each quantity contains the same number of Cl atoms—namely, 1 mole of Cl atoms. However, if we compare equal masses of NaCl and KCl, there will be more Cl atoms in the mass of NaCl since NaCl has a higher weight percent of Cl.

1 mole NaCl *contains*	*100 g* NaCl *contains*	*1 mole* KCl *contains*	*100 g KCl* contains
1 mol Na		1 mol K	
1 mol Cl	39.3 g Na	1 mol Cl	52.4 g K
60.7% Cl	60.7 g Cl	47.6% Cl	47.6 g Cl

PROBLEM

9.15

Calculate the percentage composition of potassium sulfate, K_2SO_4.

Step 1. Calculate the formula weight of K_2SO_4:

Atomic weights: K, 39.1; S, 32.1; O, 16.0

$$2\ K = 2 \times 39.1 = 78.2\ g$$
$$1\ S = 1 \times 32.1 = 32.1\ g$$
$$4\ O = 4 \times 16.0 = \underline{64.0\ g}$$
$$174.3\ g \quad \text{(Formula weight)}$$

Step 2. Now calculate the percentage composition. We know there are 78.2 g of K, 32.1 g of S, and 64.0 g of O in 174.3 g of K_2SO_4.

$$\text{K:} \quad \frac{78.2\ g\ K}{174.3\ g\ K_2SO_4} \times 100\% = 44.9\%\ K$$

$$\text{S:} \quad \frac{32.1\ g\ S}{174.3\ g\ K_2SO_4} \times 100\% = 18.4\%\ S$$

$$\text{O:} \quad \frac{64.0\ g\ O}{174.3\ g\ K_2SO_4} \times 100\% = \frac{36.7\%\ O}{100.0\%\ \text{total}}$$

The percentage composition can be determined from experimental data without knowing the formula of a compound. This determination is done by calculating the weight of each element in a compound as a percentage of the total weight of the compound formed (see Problem 9.16).

PROBLEM

9.16

When heated in air, 1.63 g of zinc, Zn, combine with 0.40 g of oxygen, O_2, to form zinc oxide. Calculate the percentage composition of the compound formed.
First, calculate the total weight of the compound formed:

$$
\begin{array}{l}
1.63\ g\ Zn \\
\underline{0.40\ g\ O_2} \\
2.03\ g \quad = \text{Total weight of product}
\end{array}
$$

Then divide the weight of each element by the total weight (2.03 g) and multiply by 100%:

$$\frac{1.63 \text{ g}}{2.03 \text{ g}} \times 100\% = 80.3\% \text{ Zn}$$

$$\frac{0.40 \text{ g}}{2.03 \text{ g}} \times 100\% = \frac{19.7\% \text{ O}}{100.0\% \text{ total}}$$

The compound formed contains 80.3% Zn and 19.7% O.

9.4   Empirical Formula versus Molecular Formula

**empirical
formula**

The **empirical formula,** or *simplest formula,* gives the smallest whole-number ratio of the atoms that are present in a compound. This formula gives the relative number of atoms of each element in the compound.

**molecular
formula**

The **molecular formula** is the true formula, representing the total number of atoms of each element present in one molecule of a compound. It is entirely possible that two or more substances will have the same percentage composition, yet be distinctly different compounds. For example, acetylene, C_2H_2, is a common gas used in welding; benzene, C_6H_6, is an important solvent obtained from coal tar and is used in the synthesis of styrene and nylon. Both acetylene and benzene contain 92.3% C and 7.7% H. The smallest ratio of C and H corresponding to these percentages is CH (1:1). Therefore the empirical formula for both acetylene and benzene is CH, even though it is known that the molecular formulas are C_2H_2 and C_6H_6, respectively. It is not uncommon for the molecular formula to be the same as the empirical formula. If the molecular formula is not the same, it will be an integral (whole number) multiple of the empirical formula.

CH = Empirical formula

$(CH)_2 = C_2H_2 =$ Acetylene   (Molecular formula)

$(CH)_6 = C_6H_6 =$ Benzene   (Molecular formula)

Table 9.1 summarizes the data concerning these CH formulas. Table 9.2 shows empirical and molecular formula relationships of other compounds.

Table 9.1 Molecular formulas of two compounds having an empirical formula with a 1:1 ratio of carbon and hydrogen atoms

Formula	Composition		Formula weight
	%C	%H	
CH (empirical)	92.3	7.7	13.0 (empirical)
C_2H_2 (acetylene)	92.3	7.7	26.0 (2 × 13.0)
C_6H_6 (benzene)	92.3	7.7	78.0 (6 × 13.0)

Table 9.2 Some empirical and molecular formulas

Compound	Empirical formula	Molecular formula	Compound	Empirical formula	Molecular formula
Acetylene	CH	C_2H_2	Diborane	BH_3	B_2H_6
Benzene	CH	C_6H_6	Hydrazine	NH_2	N_2H_4
Ethylene	CH_2	C_2H_4	Hydrogen	H	H_2
Formaldehyde	CH_2O	CH_2O	Chlorine	Cl	Cl_2
Acetic acid	CH_2O	$C_2H_4O_2$	Bromine	Br	Br_2
Glucose	CH_2O	$C_6H_{12}O_6$	Oxygen	O	O_2
Hydrogen chloride	HCl	HCl	Nitrogen	N	N_2
Carbon dioxide	CO_2	CO_2			

9.5 Calculation of Empirical Formula

It is possible to establish an empirical formula because (1) the individual atoms in a compound are combined in whole-number ratios and (2) each element has a specific atomic weight.

In order to calculate the empirical formula we need to know (1) the elements that are combined, (2) their atomic weights, and (3) the ratio by weight or percentage in which they are combined. If elements A and B form a compound, we may represent the empirical formula as A_xB_y, where x and y are small whole numbers that represent the number of atoms of A and B. To write the empirical formula, we must determine x and y.

The solution to this problem requires three or four steps:

Step 1. Assume a definite starting quantity (usually 100 g) of the compound, if not given, and express the weight of each element in grams.

Step 2. Multiply the weight (in grams) of each element by the factor 1 mol/1 at. wt to convert grams to moles. This conversion gives the number of moles of atoms of each element in the quantity assumed. At this point these numbers will usually not be whole numbers.

Step 3. Divide each of the values obtained in Step 2 by the smallest of these values. If the numbers obtained by this procedure are whole numbers, use them as subscripts in writing the empirical formula. If the numbers obtained are not whole numbers, go on to Step 4.

Step 4. Multiply the values obtained in Step 3 by the smallest number that will convert them to whole numbers. Use these whole numbers as the subscripts in the empirical formula. For example, if the ratio of A to B is 1.0:1.5, multiply both numbers by 2 to obtain a ratio of 2:3. The empirical formula then is A_2B_3.

PROBLEM

9.17

Calculate the empirical formula of a compound containing 11.19% hydrogen, H, and 88.89% oxygen, O.

Step 1. Express each element in grams. If we assume that there are 100 g of material, then the percentage of each element is equal to the grams of each element in 100 g.

$$H = 11.19\% = \frac{11.19 \text{ g}}{100 \text{ g}}$$

$$O = 88.89\% = \frac{88.89 \text{ g}}{100 \text{ g}}$$

Step 2. Multiply the grams of each element by the proper mol/at. wt factor to obtain the relative number of moles of atoms:

$$H: \quad 11.19 \text{ g H} \times \frac{1 \text{ mol H atoms}}{1.01 \text{ g H}} = 11.1 \text{ mol H atoms}$$

$$O: \quad 88.89 \text{ g O} \times \frac{1 \text{ mol O atoms}}{16.0 \text{ g O}} = 5.55 \text{ mol O atoms}$$

The formula could be expressed as $H_{11.1}O_{5.55}$. However, it is customary to use the smallest whole-number ratio of atoms. This ratio is calculated in Step 3.

Step 3. Change these numbers to whole numbers by dividing each by the smaller.

$$H = \frac{11.1 \text{ mol}}{5.55 \text{ mol}} = 2 \qquad O = \frac{5.55 \text{ mol}}{5.55 \text{ mol}} = 1$$

In this step the ratio of atoms has not changed, because we divided the number of moles of each element by the same number.

The simplest ratio of H to O is 2:1.

Empirical formula = H_2O

PROBLEM

9.18

The analysis of a salt showed that it contained 56.58% potassium, K, 8.68% carbon, C, and 34.73% oxygen, O. Calculate the empirical formula for this substance.

Steps 1 and 2. After changing the percentage of each element to grams, find the relative number of moles of each element by multiplying by the proper mol/at. wt factor.

$$K: \quad 56.58 \text{ g K} \times \frac{1 \text{ mol K atoms}}{39.1 \text{ g K}} = 1.45 \text{ mol K atoms}$$

$$C: \quad 8.68 \text{ g C} \times \frac{1 \text{ mol C atoms}}{12.0 \text{ g C}} = 0.720 \text{ mol C atoms}$$

$$O: \quad 34.73 \text{ g O} \times \frac{1 \text{ mol O atoms}}{16.0 \text{ g O}} = 2.17 \text{ mol O atoms}$$

Step 3. Divide each number of moles by the smallest value:

$$K = \frac{1.45 \text{ mol}}{0.720 \text{ mol}} = 2.01$$

$$C = \frac{0.720 \text{ mol}}{0.720 \text{ mol}} = 1.00$$

$$O = \frac{2.17 \text{ mol}}{0.720 \text{ mol}} = 3.01$$

The simplest ratio of K:C:O is 2:1:3.

Empirical formula = K_2CO_3

PROBLEM

9.19

A sulfide of iron was formed by combining 2.233 g of iron, Fe, with 1.926 g of sulfur, S. What is the empirical formula of the compound?

Steps 1 and 2. The grams of each element are given, so we use them directly in our calculations. Calculate the relative number of moles of each element by multiplying grams of each element by the proper mol/at. wt factor.

$$\text{Fe:} \quad 2.233 \text{ g Fe} \times \frac{1 \text{ mol Fe atoms}}{55.8 \text{ g Fe}} = 0.0400 \text{ mol Fe atoms}$$

$$\text{S:} \quad 1.926 \text{ g S} \times \frac{1 \text{ mol S atoms}}{32.1 \text{ g S}} = 0.0600 \text{ mol S atoms}$$

Step 3. Divide each number of moles by the smaller of the two numbers:

$$\text{Fe} = \frac{0.0400 \text{ mol}}{0.0400 \text{ mol}} = 1.00$$

$$\text{S} = \frac{0.0600 \text{ mol}}{0.0400 \text{ mol}} = 1.50$$

Step 4. We still have not reached a ratio that will give a formula containing whole numbers of atoms, so we must double each value to obtain a ratio of 2.00 atoms of Fe to 3.00 atoms of S. Doubling both values does not change the ratio of Fe and S atoms.

Fe: $1.00 \times 2 = 2.00$

S: $1.50 \times 2 = 3.00$

Empirical formula = Fe_2S_3

In many of these calculations, results may vary somewhat from an exact whole number, which can be due to experimental errors in obtaining the data or from rounding off numbers. Calculations that vary by no more than ±0.1 from a whole number can usually be rounded off to the nearest whole number. Deviations greater than about 0.1 unit usually mean that the calculated ratios need to be multiplied by a factor to make them all whole numbers. For example, an atom ratio of 1 to 1.33 should be multiplied by 3 to make the ratio 3:4.

9.6   ## Calculation of the Molecular Formula from the Empirical Formula

The molecular formula can be calculated from the empirical formula if the molecular weight, in addition to data for calculating the empirical formula, is known. The molecular formula, as stated in Section 9.4, will be equal to or some multiple of the empirical formula. For example, if the empirical formula of a compound of hydrogen and fluorine is HF, the molecular formula can be expressed as $(HF)_n$, where $n = 1, 2, 3, 4, \ldots$. This n means that the molecular formula could be HF, H_2F_2, H_3F_3, H_4F_4, and so on. To determine the molecular formula, we must evaluate n.

$$n = \frac{\text{Molecular weight}}{\text{Empirical formula weight}} = \text{Number of empirical formula units}$$

What we actually calculate is the number of units of the empirical formula that are contained in the molecular formula.

PROBLEM

9.20

A compound of nitrogen and oxygen with a molecular weight of 92.0 g/mol was found to have an empirical formula of NO_2. What is its molecular formula?

Step 1. Let n be the number of (NO_2) units in a molecule; then the molecular formula is $(NO_2)_n$.

Step 2. Each (NO_2) unit weighs $[14 + (2 \times 16)]$ or 46.0 g. The molecular weight of $(NO_2)_n$ is 92.0 g and the number of (46.0) units in 92.0 is 2.

$$n = \frac{92.0 \text{ g}}{46.0 \text{ g}} = 2 \quad \text{(Empirical formula units)}$$

Step 3. The molecular formula is $(NO_2)_2$, or N_2O_4.

PROBLEM

9.21

The hydrocarbon propylene has a molecular weight of 42.0 g/mol and contains 14.3% H and 85.7% C. What is its molecular formula?

Step 1. First find the empirical formula:

$$C: \quad 85.7 \text{ g C} \times \frac{1 \text{ mol C atoms}}{12.0 \text{ g C}} = 7.14 \text{ mol C atoms}$$

$$H: \quad 14.3 \text{ g H} \times \frac{1 \text{ mol H atoms}}{1.0 \text{ g H}} = 14.3 \text{ mol H atoms}$$

Divide each value by the smaller number of moles:

$$C = \frac{7.14 \text{ mol}}{7.14 \text{ mol}} = 1.0$$

$$H = \frac{14.3 \text{ mol}}{7.14 \text{ mol}} = 2.0$$

Empirical formula $= CH_2$

Step 2. Determine the molecular formula from the empirical formula and molecular weight.

Molecular formula $= (CH_2)_n$

Molecular weight $= 42.0$

Each CH_2 unit weighs $(12.0 + 2.0)$ or 14.0. The number of CH_2 units in 42.0 is 3.

$$n = \frac{42.0}{14.0} = 3 \quad \text{(Empirical formula units)}$$

The molecular formula is $(CH_2)_3$, or C_3H_6.

QUESTIONS

A. *Review the meaning of the new terms introduced in this chapter.*

1. Avogadro's number
2. Mole
3. Formula weight
4. Molecular weight
5. Percentage composition of a compound
6. Empirical formula
7. Molecular formula

B. *Review questions*

1. What is a mole?
2. Which would weigh more: a mole of potassium atoms, or a mole of gold atoms?
3. Which would contain more atoms: a mole of potassium atoms, or a mole of gold atoms?
4. Which would contain more electrons: a mole of potassium atoms, or a mole of gold atoms?
*5. If the atomic weight scale had been defined differently, with an atom of $^{12}_{6}C$ being defined as weighing 50 amu, would this have any effect on the value of Avogadro's number? Explain.
6. What is the numerical value of Avogadro's number?
7. What is the relationship between Avogadro's number and the mole?

8. Complete the following statements, supplying the proper quantity:
   (a) A mole of oxygen atoms (O) contains_____ atoms.
   (b) A mole of oxygen molecules (O_2) contains _____ molecules.
   (c) A mole of oxygen molecules (O_2) contains _____ atoms.
   (d) A mole of oxygen atoms (O) weighs_____ grams.
   (e) A mole of oxygen molecules (O_2) weighs _____ grams.

9. Which of the following statements are correct?
   (a) One atomic weight of any element contains 6.022×10^{23} atoms.
   (b) The mass of one atom of chlorine is

   $$\frac{35.5 \text{ g}}{6.022 \times 10^{23} \text{ atoms}}$$

   (c) A mole of magnesium atoms (24.3 g) contains the same number of atoms as a mole of sodium atoms (23.0 g).
   (d) A mole of bromine atoms contains 6.022×10^{23} atoms of bromine.
   (e) A mole of chlorine molecules (Cl_2) contains 6.022×10^{23} atoms of chlorine.

(f)   A mole of aluminum atoms weighs the same as a mole of tin atoms.

(g)   A mole of H_2O contains 6.022×10^{23} atoms.

(h)   A mole of hydrogen molecules (H_2) contains 1.204×10^{24} electrons.

10. How are formula weight and molecular weight related to each other? In what respects are they different?

11. How many molecules are present in 1 mol. wt of sulfuric acid, H_2SO_4? How many atoms are present?

12. What is the relationship between the following?
(a) Mole and molecular weight
(b) Mole and formula weight

13. Why is it correct to refer to the weight of 1 mole of sodium chloride, but incorrect to refer to a molecular weight of sodium chloride?

14. In calculating the empirical formula of a compound from its percentage composition, why do we choose to start with 100 g of the compound?

15. Which of the following statements are correct?
(a)   A mole of sodium and a mole of sodium chloride contain the same number of sodium atoms.

(b)   A compound such as NaCl has a formula weight but no true molecular weight.

(c)   One mole of nitrogen gas (N_2) weighs 14.0 g.

(d)   The percentage of oxygen is higher in K_2CrO_4 than it is in Na_2CrO_4.

(e)   The number of Cr atoms is the same in a mole of K_2CrO_4 as it is in a mole of Na_2CrO_4.

(f)   Both K_2CrO_4 and Na_2CrO_4 contain the same percentage by weight of Cr.

(g)   A molecular weight of sucrose, $C_{12}H_{22}O_{11}$, contains 1 mole of sucrose molecules.

(h)   Two moles of nitric acid, HNO_3, contain 6 moles of oxygen atoms.

(i)   The empirical formula of sucrose, $C_{12}H_{22}O_{11}$, is CH_2O.

(j)   A hydrocarbon that has a molecular weight of 280 and an empirical formula of CH_2 has a molecular formula of $C_{22}H_{44}$.

(k)   The empirical formula is often called the simplest formula.

(l)   The empirical formula of a compound gives the smallest whole-number ratio of the atoms that are present in a compound.

(m)   If the molecular formula and the empirical formula of a compound are not the same, the empirical formula will be an integral multiple of the molecular formula.

(n)   The empirical formula of benzene, C_6H_6, is CH.

(o)   A compound having an empirical formula of CH_2O, and a molecular weight of 60, has a molecular formula of $C_3H_6O_3$.

C. *Problems*

Formula Weight, Molecular Weight

1. Determine the molecular or formula weight of the following compounds:
(a) CsBr   (f) Fe_2O_3
(b) K_2SO_4 (g) $C_{18}H_{36}O_{18}$
(c) $Ba(NO_3)_2$ (h) $Al_2(CrO_4)_3$
(d) C_3H_7OH (i) $(NH_4)_2CO_3$
(e) $H_2C_2O_4$ (j) $CaCl_2 \cdot 2\ H_2O$

2. Determine the formula weight of the following compounds:
(a) KOH   (f) $C_6H_5NO_2$
(b) Ag_2SO_4 (g) $C_{18}H_{36}O_{18}$
(c) $CrCl_3$ (h) $K_3Fe(CN)_6$
(d) $Cu(NO_3)_2$ (i) $Mg_3(AsO_4)_2$
(e) $Sr(HCO_3)_2$ (j) C_4H_9I

Moles and Avogadro's Number

3. How many moles of atoms are contained in the following?
(a) 22.5 g Zn
(b) 0.688 g Mg
(c) 4.5×10^{22} atoms Cu
(d) 382 g Co
(e) 0.055 g Sn
(f) 8.5×10^{24} molecules N_2

4. How many moles are contained in the following?
(a) 25.0 g NaOH   (d) 14.8 g CH_3OH
(b) 44.0 g Br_2 (e) 2.88 g Na_2SO_4
(c) 0.684 g $MgCl_2$ (f) 4.20 lb ZnI_2

5. Calculate the number of grams in each of the following:
(a) 0.550 mol Au
(b) 15.8 mol H_2O
(c) 12.5 mol Cl_2
(d) 3.15 mol NH_4NO_3
(e) 4.25×10^{-4} mol H_2SO_4
(f) 4.5×10^{22} molecules CCl_4
(g) 0.00255 mol Ti
(h) 1.5×10^{16} atoms S

6. How many molecules are contained in each of the following:
   (a) 1.26 mol O_2 (c) 16.0 g CH_4
   (b) 0.56 mol C_6H_6 (d) 1000. g HCl
7. Calculate the weight in grams of each of the following:
   (a) 1 atom Pb
   (b) 1 atom Ag
   (c) 1 molecule H_2O
   (d) 1 molecule $C_3H_5(NO_3)_3$
8. Make the following conversions:
   (a) 8.66 mol Cu to grams Cu
   (b) 125 mol Au to kilograms Au
   (c) 10 atoms C to moles C
   (d) 5000 molecules CO_2 to moles CO_2
   (e) 28.4 g S to moles S
   (f) 2.50 kg NaCl to moles NaCl
   (g) 42.4 g Mg to atoms Mg
   (h) 485 mL Br_2 ($d = 3.12$ g/mL) to moles Br_2
9. One mole of carbon disulfide (CS_2) contains
   (a) How many carbon disulfide molecules?
   (b) How many carbon atoms?
   (c) How many sulfur atoms?
   (d) How many total atoms of all kinds?
10. White phosphorus is one of several forms of phosphorus and exists as a waxy solid consisting of P_4 molecules. How many atoms are present in 0.350 mol of P_4?
11. How many grams of sodium contain the same number of atoms as 10.0 g of potassium?
12. One atom of an unknown element is found to have a mass of 1.79×10^{-23} g. What is the atomic weight of this element?
*13. If a stack of 500 sheets of paper is 4.60 cm high, what will be the height, in meters, of a stack of Avogadro's number of sheets of paper?
14. There are about 5.0 billion (5.0×10^9) people on earth. If 1 mole of dollars were distributed equally among these people, how many dollars would each person receive?
*15. If 20 drops of water equal 1.0 mL (1.0 cm^3),
   (a) How many drops of water are there in a cubic mile of water?
   (b) What would be the volume in cubic miles of a mole of drops of water?
*16. Silver has a density of 10.5 g/cm^3. If 1.00 mol of silver were shaped into a cube,
   (a) What would be the volume of the cube?
   (b) What would be the length of one side of the cube?

17. How many atoms of oxygen are contained in each of the following?
   (a) 16.0 g O_2
   (b) 0.622 mol MgO
   (c) 6.00×10^{22} molecules $C_6H_{12}O_6$
   (d) 5.0 mol MnO_2
   (e) 250 g $MgCO_3$
   (f) 5.0×10^{18} molecules H_2O
18. Calculate the number of:
   (a) Grams of silver in 25.0 g AgBr
   (b) Grams of chlorine in 5.00 g $PbCl_2$
   (c) Grams of nitrogen in 6.34 mol $(NH_4)_3PO_4$
   (d) Grams of oxygen in 8.45×10^{22} molecules SO_3
   (e) Grams of hydrogen in 45.0 g C_3H_8O
*19. A sulfuric acid solution contains 65.0% H_2SO_4 by weight and has a density of 1.55 g/mL. How many moles of the acid are present in 1.00 L of the solution?
*20. A nitric acid solution containing 72.0% HNO_3 by weight has a density of 1.42 g/mL. How many moles of HNO_3 are present in 100 mL of the solution?
21. Given 1.00 g samples of each of the following compounds: CO_2, O_2, H_2O, and CH_3OH
   (a) Which sample will contain the largest number of molecules?
   (b) Which sample will contain the largest number of atoms?
   Show proof for your answers.
22. How many grams of Fe_2S_3 will contain a total number of atoms equal to Avogadro's number?

Percentage Composition
23. Calculate the percentage composition by weight of the following compounds:
   (a) NaBr   (c) $FeCl_3$ (e) $Al_2(SO_4)_3$
   (b) $KHCO_3$ (d) $SiCl_4$ (f) $AgNO_3$
24. Calculate the percentage composition by weight of the following compounds:
   (a) $ZnCl_2$ (d) $(NH_4)_2SO_4$
   (b) $NH_4C_2H_3O_2$ (e) $Fe(NO_3)_3$
   (c) MgP_2O_7 (f) ICl_3
25. Calculate the percentage of iron, Fe, in the following compounds:
   (a) FeO   (c) Fe_3O_4
   (b) Fe_2O_3 (d) $K_4Fe(CN)_6$
26. Which of the following chlorides has the highest and which has the lowest percentage of chlorine, Cl, by weight, in its formula?

(a) KCl (b) $BaCl_2$ (c) $SiCl_4$ (d) LiCl

27. A 6.20 g sample of phosphorus was reacted with oxygen to form an oxide weighing 14.20 g. Calculate the percentage composition of the compound.

28. A sample of ethylene chloride was analyzed to contain 6.00 g of C, 1.00 g of H, and 17.75 g of Cl. Calculate the percentage composition of ethylene chloride.

29. How many grams of lithium will combine with 20.0 grams of sulfur to form the compound Li_2S?

30. Calculate the percentage of
    (a) Mercury in $HgCO_3$
    (b) Oxygen in $Ca(ClO_3)_2$
    (c) Nitrogen in $C_{10}H_{14}N_2$ (nicotine)
    (d) Mg in $C_{55}H_{72}MgN_4O_5$ (chlorophyll)

31. Answer the following by examination of the formulas. Check your answers by calculations if you wish. Which compound has the:
    (a) Higher percent by weight of hydrogen, H_2O or H_2O_2?
    (b) Lower percent by weight of nitrogen, NO or N_2O_3?
    (c) Higher percent by weight of oxygen, NO_2 or N_2O_4?
    (d) Lower percent by weight of chlorine, $NaClO_3$ or $KClO_3$?
    (e) Higher percent by weight of sulfur, $KHSO_4$ or K_2SO_4?
    (f) Lower percent by weight of chromium, Na_2CrO_4 or $Na_2Cr_2O_7$?

Empirical and Molecular Formulas

32. Calculate the empirical formula of each compound from the percentage compositions given:
    (a) 63.6% N, 36.4% O
    (b) 46.7% N, 53.3% O
    (c) 25.9% N, 74.1% O
    (d) 43.4% Na, 11.3% C, 45.3% O
    (e) 18.8% Na, 29.0% Cl, 52.3% O
    (f) 72.02% Mn, 27.98% O

33. Calculate the empirical formula of each compound from the percentage compositions given.
    (a) 64.1% Cu, 35.9% Cl
    (b) 47.2% Cu, 52.8% Cl
    (c) 51.9% Cr, 48.1% S
    (d) 55.3% K, 14.6% P, 30.1% O

(e) 38.9% Ba, 29.4% Cr, 31.7% O
(f) 3.99% P, 82.3% Br, 13.7% Cl

34. A sample of tin (Sn) weighing 3.996 g was oxidized and found to have combined with 1.077 g of oxygen. Calculate the empirical formula of this oxide of tin.

35. A 3.054 g sample of vanadium (V) combined with oxygen to form 5.454 g of product. Calculate the empirical formula for this compound.

*36. Zinc and sulfur react to form zinc sulfide, ZnS. If we mix 19.5 g of zinc and 9.40 g of sulfur, have we added sufficient sulfur to fully react all the zinc? Show evidence for your answer.

37. Hydroquinone is an organic compound commonly used as a photographic developer. It has a molecular weight of 110 g/mol and a composition of 65.45% C, 5.45% H, and 29.09% O. Calculate the molecular formula of hydroquinone.

38. Fructose is a very sweet natural sugar that is present in honey, fruits, and fruit juices. It has a molecular weight of 180 g/mol and a composition of 40.0% C, 6.7% H, and 53.3% O. Calculate the molecular formula of fructose.

39. Aspirin is well known as a pain reliever (analgesic) and as a fever reducer (antipyretic). It has a molecular weight of 180 and a composition of 60.0% C, 4.48% H, and 35.5% O. Calculate the molecular formula of aspirin.

40. How many grams of oxygen are contained in 8.50 g $Al_2(SO_4)_3$?

41. Gallium arsenide is one of the newer materials used to make semiconductor chips for use in supercomputers. Its composition is 48.2% Ga and 51.8% As. What is the empirical formula?

42. Listed below are the compositions of four different compounds of carbon and chlorine. Determine both the empirical formula and the molecular formula for each.

	Percentage C	Percentage Cl	Molecular weight
(a)	7.79	92.21	154
(b)	10.13	89.87	237
(c)	25.26	74.74	285
(d)	11.25	88.75	320

10

Chemical Equations

1. Understand the new terms listed in Question A at the end of the chapter.
2. Know the format used in setting up chemical equations.
3. Recognize the various symbols commonly used in writing chemical equations.
4. Balance simple chemical equations.
5. Interpret a balanced equation in terms of the relative numbers or amounts of molecules, atoms, grams, or moles of each substance represented.
6. Classify equations as representing combination, decomposition, single-displacement, or double-displacement reactions.
7. Use the activity series to predict whether a single-displacement reaction will occur.
8. Complete and balance equations for simple combination, decomposition, single-displacement, and double-displacement reactions when given the reactants.
9. Distinguish between exothermic and endothermic reactions, and relate the quantity of heat to the amounts of substances involved in the reaction.
10. Identify the major sources of chemical energy and their uses.

10.1 The Chemical Equation

Chemical reactions and equations were introduced in Chapter 4. We saw that in a chemical reaction the substances entering the reaction are called reactants and the substances formed are called the products. In a chemical reaction atoms, molecules, or ions interact and rearrange themselves to form the products. During this process chemical bonds are broken and new bonds are formed. The reactants and products may be in the solid, liquid, or gaseous state, or in solution.

chemical equation

A **chemical equation** is a shorthand expression for a chemical change or reaction. It shows, among other things, the rearrangement of the atoms that are involved in the reaction. A **word equation** states in words, in equation form, the substances involved in a chemical reaction. For example, when mercury(II) oxide is heated, it decomposes to form mercury and oxygen. The word equation for this decomposition is

word equation

$$\text{Mercury(II) oxide} + \text{Heat} \longrightarrow \text{Mercury} + \text{Oxygen}$$

From the chemist's point of view, this method of describing a chemical reaction is inadequate. It is bulky and cumbersome to use and does not give quantitative information. The chemical equation, using symbols and formulas, is a far better way to describe the decomposition of mercury(II) oxide:

$$2\ HgO \xrightarrow{\ \Delta\ } 2\ Hg + O_2 \uparrow$$

This equation gives all the information from the word equation plus formulas, composition, reactive amounts of all the substances involved in the reaction, and much additional information (see Section 10.4). Even though a chemical equation provides much quantitative information, it is still not a complete description; it does not tell us how much energy is needed to cause decomposition, what we observe during the reaction, or anything about the rate of reaction. This information must be obtained from other sources or from experimentation.

10.2   Format for Writing Chemical Equations

A chemical equation uses the chemical symbols and formulas of the reactants and products and other symbolic terms to represent a chemical reaction. Equations are written according to this general format:

1. The reactants are separated from the products by an arrow ($\rightarrow$) that indicates the direction of the reaction. A double arrow ($\rightleftarrows$) indicates that the reaction goes in both directions and establishes an equilibrium between the reactants and the products.
2. The reactants are placed to the left and the products to the right of the arrow. A plus sign ($+$) is placed between reactants and between products when needed.
3. Conditions required to carry out the reaction may, if desired, be placed above or below the arrow or equality sign. For example, a delta sign placed over the arrow ($\xrightarrow{\Delta}$) indicates that heat is supplied to the reaction.
4. Coefficients (small integral numbers) are placed in front of substances (for example, $2\ H_2O$) to balance the equation and to indicate the number of formula units (atoms, molecules, moles, ions) of each substance reacting or being produced. When no number is shown, it is understood that one formula unit of the substance is indicated.

Table 10.1   Symbols commonly used in chemical equations

Symbol	Meaning
$\rightarrow$	Yields; produces (points to products)
$\rightleftharpoons$	Reversible reaction; equilibrium between reactants and products
$\uparrow$	Gas evolved (written after a substance)
$\downarrow$	Solid or precipitate formed (written after a substance)
(s)	Solid state (written after a substance)
(l)	Liquid state (written after a substance)
(g)	Gaseous state (written after a substance)
(aq)	Aqueous solution (substance dissolved in water)
Δ	Heat
$+$	Plus or added to (placed between substances)

5. The physical state of a substance is indicated by the following symbols: (s) for solid state; (l) for liquid state; (g) for gaseous state; and (aq) for substances in aqueous solution.

Symbols commonly used in equations are given in Table 10.1.

10.3   Writing and Balancing Equations

balanced equation

To represent the quantitative relationships of a reaction, the chemical equation must be balanced. A **balanced equation** contains the same number of each kind of atom on each side of the equation. The balanced equation, therefore, obeys the Law of Conservation of Mass.

The ability to balance equations must be acquired by every chemistry student. Simple equations are easy to balance, but some care and attention to detail are required. The way to balance an equation is to adjust the number of atoms of each element so that it is the same on each side of the equation. But we must not change a correct formula in order to achieve a balanced equation. Each equation must be treated on its own merits; we have no simple "plug in" formula for balancing equations. The following outline gives a general procedure for balancing equations. Study this outline and refer to it as needed when working examples. There is no substitute for practice in learning to write and balance chemical equations.

1. Identify the reaction for which the equation is to be written.   Formulate a description or word equation for the reaction if needed (for example, mercury(II) oxide decomposes yielding mercury and oxygen).
2. Write the unbalanced, or skeleton, equation.   Make sure that the formula for each substance is correct and that the reactants are written to the left and the products to the right of the arrow (for example, $HgO \rightarrow Hg + O_2$). The correct formulas must be known or ascertained from the periodic table, oxidation numbers, lists of ions, or experimental data.

3. Balance the equation. Use the following steps as necessary:
   (a) Count and compare the number of atoms of each element on each side of the equation and determine those that must be balanced.
   (b) Balance each element, one at a time, by placing small whole numbers (coefficients) in front of the formulas containing the unbalanced element. It is usually best to balance metals first, then nonmetals, then hydrogen and oxygen. Select the smallest coefficients that will give the same number of atoms of the element on each side. A coefficient placed before a formula multiplies every atom in the formula by that number (for example, $2 H_2SO_4$ means two molecules of sulfuric acid and also means four H atoms, two S atoms, and eight O atoms.)
   (c) Check all other elements after each individual element is balanced to see whether, in balancing one, other elements have become unbalanced. Make adjustments as needed.
   (d) Balance polyatomic ions such as SO_4^{2-}, which remain unchanged from one side of the equation to the other, in the same way as individual atoms.
   (e) Do a final check, making sure that each element and/or polyatomic ion is balanced and that the smallest possible set of whole-number coefficients has been used.

$$4 HgO \longrightarrow 4 Hg + 2 O_2 \quad \text{(Incorrect form)}$$

$$2 HgO \longrightarrow 2 Hg + O_2 \quad \text{(Correct form)}$$

Not all chemical equations can be balanced by the simple method of inspection just described. The balancing of more complex equations is described in Chapter 17.

The following examples show stepwise sequences leading to balanced equations. Study each example carefully.

EXAMPLE

10.1

Write the balanced equation for the reaction that takes place when magnesium metal is burned in air to produce magnesium oxide.

1. *Word equation*

$$\text{Magnesium} + \text{Oxygen} \longrightarrow \text{Magnesium oxide}$$

2. *Skeleton equation*

$$Mg + O_2 \longrightarrow MgO \quad \text{(unbalanced)}$$

3. *Balance*
   (a) Oxygen is not balanced. Two O atoms appear on the left side and one on the right side.
   (b) Place the coefficient 2 before MgO.

$$Mg + O_2 \longrightarrow 2 MgO \quad \text{(unbalanced)}$$

   (c) Now Mg is not balanced. One Mg atom appears on the left side and two on the right side. Place a 2 before Mg.

$$2 Mg + O_2 \longrightarrow 2 MgO \quad \text{(balanced)}$$

   (d) *Check:* Each side has two Mg and two O atoms.

EXAMPLE

10.2

When methane, CH_4, undergoes complete combustion, it reacts with oxygen to produce carbon dioxide and water. Write the balanced equation for this reaction.

1. *Word equation*

Methane + Oxygen $\longrightarrow$ Carbon dioxide + Water

2. *Skeleton equation*

$CH_4 + O_2 \longrightarrow CO_2 + H_2O$ (unbalanced)

3. *Balance*
   (a) Carbon is balanced. Hydrogen and oxygen are not balanced.
   (b) Balance H atoms by placing a 2 before H_2O.

$CH_4 + O_2 \longrightarrow CO_2 + 2\ H_2O$ (unbalanced)

Each side of the equation has four H atoms; oxygen is still not balanced. Place a 2 before O_2 to balance the oxygen atoms.

$CH_4 + 2\ O_2 \longrightarrow CO_2 + 2\ H_2O$ (balanced)

   (c) *Check:*   The equation is correctly balanced; it has one C, four O, and four H atoms on each side.

EXAMPLE

10.3

Oxygen and potassium chloride are formed by heating potassium chlorate. Write a balanced equation for this reaction.

1. *Word equation*

Potassium chlorate $\xrightarrow{\Delta}$ Potassium chloride + Oxygen

2. *Skeleton equation*

$KClO_3 \xrightarrow{\Delta} KCl + O_2$ (unbalanced)

3. *Balance*
   (a) Oxygen is unbalanced (three O atoms on the left and two on the right side).
   (b) How many oxygen atoms are needed? The subscripts of oxygen (3 and 2) in $KClO_3$ and O_2 have a common denominator of 6. Therefore coefficients for $KClO_3$ and O_2 are needed to give six oxygen atoms on each side. Place a 2 before $KClO_3$ and a 3 before O_2 to give six O atoms on each side.

$2\ KClO_3 \xrightarrow{\Delta} KCl + 3\ O_2$ (unbalanced)

Now K and Cl are not balanced. Place a 2 before KCl, which balances both K and Cl at the same time.

$2\ KClO_3 \xrightarrow{\Delta} 2\ KCl + 3\ O_2$ (balanced)

   (c) *Check:*   Each side contains two K, two Cl, and six O atoms.

EXAMPLE

10.4

Balance by starting with the word equation given.

1. *Word equation*

   Silver nitrate + Hydrogen sulfide $\longrightarrow$ Silver sulfide + Nitric acid

2. *Skeleton equation*

   $AgNO_3 + H_2S \longrightarrow Ag_2S + HNO_3$ (unbalanced)

3. *Balance*
   (a) Ag and H are unbalanced.
   (b) Place a 2 in front of $AgNO_3$ to balance Ag.

   $2\ AgNO_3 + H_2S \longrightarrow Ag_2S + HNO_3$ (unbalanced)

   (c) H and NO_3^- are still unbalanced. Balance by placing a 2 in front of HNO_3.

   $2\ AgNO_3 + H_2S \longrightarrow Ag_2S + 2\ HNO_3$ (balanced)

   (d) In this example N and O atoms are balanced by balancing the NO_3^- ion as a unit.
   (e) *Check:* Each side has two Ag, two H, and one S atom. Also, each side has two NO_3^- ions.

EXAMPLE

10.5

Balance by starting with the word equation given.

1. *Word equation*

   Aluminum hydroxide + Sulfuric acid $\longrightarrow$ Aluminum sulfate + Water

2. *Skeleton equation*

   $Al(OH)_3 + H_2SO_4 \longrightarrow Al_2(SO_4)_3 + H_2O$ (unbalanced)

3. *Balance*
   (a) All elements are unbalanced.
   (b) Balance Al by placing a 2 in front of $Al(OH)_3$. Treat the unbalanced SO_4^{2-} ion as a unit and balance by placing a 3 before H_2SO_4. Note that Step 3(d) may sometimes be combined with Step 3(b).

   $2\ Al(OH)_3 + 3\ H_2SO_4 \longrightarrow Al_2(SO_4)_3 + H_2O$ (unbalanced)

   Balance the unbalanced H and O by placing a 6 in front of H_2O.

   $2\ Al(OH)_3 + 3\ H_2SO_4 \longrightarrow Al_2(SO_4)_3 + 6\ H_2O$ (balanced)

   (c) *Check:* Each side has two Al, twelve H, three S, and eighteen O atoms.

EXAMPLE

10.6

When the fuel in a butane gas stove undergoes complete combustion, it reacts with oxygen to form carbon dioxide and water. Write the balanced equation for this reaction.

1. *Word equation*

$$\text{Butane} + \text{Oxygen} \longrightarrow \text{Carbon dioxide} + \text{Water}$$

2. *Skeleton equation*

$$C_4H_{10} + O_2 \longrightarrow CO_2 + H_2O \quad \text{(unbalanced)}$$

3. *Balance*
   (a) All elements are unbalanced.
   (b) Balance C by placing a 4 in front of CO_2.

$$C_4H_{10} + O_2 \longrightarrow 4\ CO_2 + H_2O \quad \text{(unbalanced)}$$

   Balance H by placing a 5 in front of H_2O.

$$C_4H_{10} + O_2 \longrightarrow 4\ CO_2 + 5\ H_2O \quad \text{(unbalanced)}$$

   Oxygen remains unbalanced. The oxygen atoms on the right side are fixed, because 4 CO_2 and 5 H_2O are derived from the single C_4H_{10} molecule on the left. When we try to balance the O atoms, we find that there is no integer (whole number) that can be placed in front of O_2 to bring about a balance. The equation can be balanced if we use $6\frac{1}{2}$ O_2 and then double the coefficients of each substance, including the $6\frac{1}{2}$ O_2, to obtain the balanced equation.

$$C_4H_{10} + 6\tfrac{1}{2}\ O_2 \longrightarrow 4\ CO_2 + 5\ H_2O \quad \text{(balanced—incorrect form)}$$

$$2\ C_4H_{10} + 13\ O_2 \longrightarrow 8\ CO_2 + 10\ H_2O \quad \text{(balanced)}$$

   (c) *Check:* Each side now has eight C, twenty H, and twenty-six O atoms.

10.4   What Information Does an Equation Tell Us?

Depending on the particular context in which it is used, a formula can have different meanings. The meanings refer either to an individual chemical entity (atom, ion, molecule, or formula unit) or to a mole of that chemical entity. For example, the formula H_2O can be used to indicate either

(a) $H_2O = \begin{cases} \text{1 molecule of water} \\ \text{2 hydrogen atoms} + \text{1 oxygen atom} \\ \text{18 amu of water} \end{cases}$

(b) $H_2O = \begin{cases} \text{1 mole of water} \\ 6.022 \times 10^{23} \text{ molecules of water} \\ \text{18.0 grams of water} \end{cases}$

Formulas used in equations can be expressed in units of individual chemical entities or as moles, the latter being more commonly used. For example, in the reaction of hydrogen and oxygen to form water,

$$2 H_2(g) + O_2(g) \longrightarrow 2 H_2O(g)$$

the 2 H_2 can represent 2 molecules or 2 moles of hydrogen; the O_2, 1 molecule or 1 mole of oxygen; and the 2 H_2O, 2 molecules or 2 moles of water. In terms of moles, this equation is stated: 2 moles of H_2 react with 1 mole of O_2 to give 2 moles of H_2O.

As indicated earlier, a chemical equation is a shorthand description of a chemical reaction. Interpretation of the balanced equation gives us the following information:

1. What the reactants are and what the products are
2. The formulas of the reactants and products
3. The number of molecules or formula units of reactants and products in the reaction
4. The number of atoms of each element involved in the reaction
5. The number of molecular weights or formula weights of each substance used or produced
6. The number of moles of each substance
7. The number of grams of each substance used or produced

Consider the equation

$$H_2(g) + Cl_2(g) \longrightarrow 2 HCl(g)$$

This equation states that hydrogen gas reacts with chlorine gas to produce hydrogen chloride, also a gas. Let us summarize all the information relating to the equation. The information that can be stated about the relative amount of each substance, with respect to all other substances in the balanced equation, is written below its formula in the following equation:

$$H_2(g) \quad + \quad Cl_2(g) \quad \longrightarrow \quad 2 HCl(g)$$

Hydrogen	*Chlorine*	*Hydrogen chloride*
1 molecule	1 molecule	2 molecules
2 atoms	2 atoms	2 atoms H + 2 atoms Cl
1 mol. wt	1 mol. wt	2 mol. wt
1 mole	1 mole	2 moles
2.0 g	71.0 g	2 × 36.5 g (73.0 g)

These data are very useful in calculating quantitative relationships that exist among substances in a chemical reaction. For example, if we react 2 moles of hydrogen (twice as much as is indicated by the equation) with 2 moles of chlorine, we can expect to obtain 4 moles, or 146 g, of hydrogen chloride as a product. We will study this phase of using equations in more detail in the next chapter.

Let us try another equation. When propane gas is burned in air, the products are carbon dioxide, CO_2, and water, H_2O. The equation and its interpretation are as follows:

$$C_3H_8(g) \quad + \quad 5\ O_2(g) \quad \longrightarrow \quad 3\ CO_2(g) \quad + \quad 4\ H_2O(g)$$

Propane	Oxygen	Carbon dioxide	Water
1 molecule	5 molecules	3 molecules	4 molecules
3 atoms C	10 atoms O	3 atoms C	8 atoms H
8 atoms H		6 atoms O	4 atoms O
1 mol. wt	5 mol. wt	3 mol. wt	4 mol. wt
1 mole	5 moles	3 moles	4 moles
44.0 g	5 × 32.0 g (160.0 g)	3 × 44.0 g (132.0 g)	4 × 18.0 g (72.0 g)

10.5 Types of Chemical Equations

Chemical equations represent chemical changes or reactions. To be of any significance an equation must represent an actual or possible reaction. Part of the problem of writing equations is determining the products formed. We have no sure method of predicting products, nor do we have time to carry out experimentally all the reactions we may wish to consider. Therefore we must use data reported in the writings of other workers, certain rules to aid in our predictions, and the atomic structure and combining capacities of the elements to help us predict the formulas of the products of a chemical reaction. The final proof of the existence of any reaction, of course, is in the actual observation of the reaction in the laboratory (or elsewhere).

Reactions are classified into types to assist in writing equations and to aid in predicting other reactions. Many chemical reactions fit one or another of the four principal reaction types that are discussed in the following paragraphs. Reactions are also classified as oxidation–reduction. Special methods are used to balance complex oxidation–reduction equations (see Chapter 17).

combination or synthesis reaction

1. Combination or synthesis reaction. In a **combination reaction,** two reactants combine to give one product. The general form of the equation is

$$A + B \longrightarrow AB$$

in which A and B are either elements or compounds and AB is a compound. The formula of the compound in many cases can be determined from a knowledge of the oxidation numbers of the reactants in their combined states. Some reactions that fall into this category are the following:

(a) Metal + Oxygen $\longrightarrow$ Metal oxide

$$2\ Mg + O_2 \xrightarrow{\Delta} 2\ MgO$$

$$4\ Al + 3\ O_2 \xrightarrow{\Delta} 2\ Al_2O_3$$

(b) Nonmetal + Oxygen $\longrightarrow$ Nonmetal oxide

$$S(s) + O_2(g) \xrightarrow{\Delta} SO_2(g)$$

$$N_2(g) + O_2(g) \xrightarrow{\Delta} 2\ NO(g)$$

(c) Metal + Nonmetal $\longrightarrow$ Salt

$$2\,Na(s) + Cl_2(g) \longrightarrow 2\,NaCl(s)$$

$$2\,Al(s) + 3\,Br_2(l) \longrightarrow 2\,AlBr_3(s)$$

(d) Metal oxide + Water $\longrightarrow$ Base (metal hydroxide)

$$Na_2O(s) + H_2O(l) \longrightarrow 2\,NaOH(aq)$$

$$CaO(s) + H_2O(l) \longrightarrow Ca(OH)_2(aq)$$

(e) Nonmetal oxide + Water $\longrightarrow$ Oxyacid

$$SO_3(g) + H_2O(l) \longrightarrow H_2SO_4(aq)$$

$$N_2O_5(s) + H_2O(l) \longrightarrow 2\,HNO_3(aq)$$

decomposition reaction

2. **Decomposition reaction.**   In a **decomposition reaction** a single substance is decomposed or broken down to give two or more different substances. The reaction may be considered the reverse of combination. The starting material must be a compound, and the products may be elements or compounds. The general form of the equation is

$$AB \longrightarrow A + B$$

Predicting the products of a decomposition reaction can be difficult and requires an understanding of each individual reaction. Heating oxygen-containing compounds often results in decomposition. Some reactions that fall into this category are the following:

(a) Metal oxides. Some metal oxides decompose to yield the free metal plus oxygen, others give a lower oxide, and some are very stable, resisting decomposition by heating.

$$2\,HgO(s) \xrightarrow{\Delta} 2\,Hg(l) + O_2(g)$$

$$2\,PbO_2(s) \xrightarrow{\Delta} 2\,PbO(s) + O_2(g)$$

(b) Carbonates and bicarbonates decompose to yield CO_2 when heated.

$$CaCO_3(s) \xrightarrow{\Delta} CaO(s) + CO_2(g)$$

$$2\,NaHCO_3(s) \xrightarrow{\Delta} Na_2CO_3(s) + H_2O(g) + CO_2(g)$$

(c) Miscellaneous

$$2\,KClO_3(s) \xrightarrow{\Delta} 2\,KCl(s) + 3\,O_2(g)$$

$$2\,NaNO_3(s) \xrightarrow{\Delta} 2\,NaNO_2(s) + O_2(g)$$

$$2\,H_2O_2(l) \xrightarrow{\Delta} 2\,H_2O(l) + O_2(g)$$

single-displacement reaction

3. **Single-displacement reaction.**   In a **single-displacement reaction,** one element reacts with a compound to take the place of one of the elements of that compound. A different element and a different compound are formed. The

general form of the equation is

$$A + BC \longrightarrow B + AC \qquad \text{or} \qquad A + BC \longrightarrow C + BA$$

Metal   Halogen

If A is a metal, A will replace B to form AC, providing A is a more reactive metal than B. If A is a halogen, it will replace C to form BA, providing A is a more reactive halogen than C.

Brief activity series of selected metals (and hydrogen) and halogens follow. The series are listed in descending order of chemical reactivity, with the most active metals and halogens at the left. From such series it is possible to predict many chemical reactions. Any metal on the list will replace the ions of those metals that appear anywhere to the right of it on the list. For example, zinc metal will replace hydrogen from a hydrochloric acid solution. But copper metal, which is to the right of hydrogen on the list and thus less reactive than hydrogen, will not replace hydrogen from a hydrochloric acid solution.

Activity Series

Metals: K, Ca, Na, Mg, Al, Zn, Fe, Ni, Sn, Pb, H, Cu, Ag, Hg, Au

Halogens: F_2, Cl_2, Br_2, I_2

Some reactions that fall into this category follow.

(a) Metal + Acid $\longrightarrow$ Hydrogen + Salt

$$Zn(s) + 2\ HCl(aq) \longrightarrow H_2(g) + ZnCl_2(aq)$$

$$2\ Al(s) + 3\ H_2SO_4(aq) \longrightarrow 3\ H_2(g) + Al_2(SO_4)_3(aq)$$

(b) Metal + Water $\longrightarrow$ Hydrogen + Metal hydroxide or Metal oxide

$$2\ Na(s) + 2\ H_2O \longrightarrow H_2(g) + 2\ NaOH(aq)$$

$$Ca(s) + 2\ H_2O \longrightarrow H_2(g) + Ca(OH)_2(aq)$$

$$3\ Fe(s) + 4\ H_2O(g) \longrightarrow 4\ H_2(g) + Fe_3O_4(s)$$

            Steam

(c) Metal + Salt $\longrightarrow$ Metal + Salt

$$Fe(s) + CuSO_4(aq) \longrightarrow Cu(s) + FeSO_4(aq)$$

$$Cu(s) + 2\ AgNO_3(aq) \longrightarrow 2\ Ag(s) + Cu(NO_3)_2(aq)$$

(d) Halogen + Halogen Salt $\longrightarrow$ Halogen + Halogen salt

$$Cl_2(g) + 2\ NaBr(aq) \longrightarrow Br_2(l) + 2\ NaCl(aq)$$

$$Cl_2(g) + 2\ KI(aq) \longrightarrow I_2(s) + 2\ KCl(aq)$$

A common chemical reaction is the displacement of hydrogen from water or acids. This reaction illustrates well the relative reactivity of the metals and the use of the activity series.

K, Ca, and Na displace hydrogen from cold water, steam, and acids.
Mg, Al, Zn, and Fe displace hydrogen from steam and acids.
Ni, Sn, and Pb displace hydrogen only from acids.
Cu, Ag, Hg, and Au do not displace hydrogen.

EXAMPLE

10.7

Will a reaction occur between **(a)** nickel metal and hydrochloric acid and **(b)** tin metal and a solution of aluminum chloride? Write balanced equations for the reactions.

(a) Nickel is more reactive than hydrogen so it will displace hydrogen from hydrochloric acid. The products are hydrogen gas and a salt of Ni^{2+} and Cl^- ions.

$$Ni(s) + 2\,HCl(aq) \longrightarrow H_2(g) + NiCl_2(aq)$$

(b) According to the activity series, tin is less reactive than aluminum so no reaction will occur.

$$Sn(s) + AlCl_3(aq) \longrightarrow \text{No reaction}$$

double-displacement or metathesis reaction

4. Double-displacement or metathesis reaction. In a **double-displacement reaction,** two compounds exchange partners with each other to produce two different compounds. The general form of the equation is

$$AB + CD \longrightarrow AD + CB$$

This reaction may be thought of as an exchange of positive and negative groups, in which A combines with D and C combines with B. In writing the formulas of the products, we must take into account the oxidation numbers or charges of the combining groups. Some reactions that fall into this category follow.

(a) Neutralization of an acid and a base

$$\text{Acid} + \text{Base} \longrightarrow \text{Salt} + \text{Water}$$

$$HCl(aq) + NaOH(aq) \longrightarrow NaCl(aq) + H_2O$$

$$H_2SO_4(aq) + Ba(OH)_2(aq) \longrightarrow BaSO_4 \downarrow + 2\,H_2O$$

(b) Formation of an insoluble precipitate

$$BaCl_2(aq) + 2\,AgNO_3(aq) \longrightarrow 2\,AgCl \downarrow + Ba(NO_3)_2(aq)$$

$$FeCl_3(aq) + 3\,NH_4OH(aq) \longrightarrow Fe(OH)_3 \downarrow + 3\,NH_4Cl(aq)$$

(c) Metal oxide + Acid $\longrightarrow$ Salt + Water

$$CuO(s) + 2\,HNO_3(aq) \longrightarrow Cu(NO_3)_2(aq) + H_2O$$

$$CaO(s) + 2\,HCl(aq) \longrightarrow CaCl_2(aq) + H_2O$$

(d) Formation of a gas

$$H_2SO_4(l) + NaCl(s) \longrightarrow NaHSO_4(s) + HCl \uparrow$$

$$2\,HCl(aq) + ZnS(s) \longrightarrow ZnCl_2(aq) + H_2S \uparrow$$

$$2\,HCl(aq) + Na_2CO_3(s) \longrightarrow 2\,NaCl(aq) + H_2O(l) + CO_2 \uparrow$$

Some reactions we attempt may fail because the substances are not reactive, or the proper conditions for reaction may not be present. For example, mercury(II) oxide does not decompose until it is heated; magnesium does not burn in air or oxygen until the temperature is raised to the point at which it begins to react. When silver is placed in a solution of copper(II) sulfate, no reaction takes place; however, when a strip of copper is placed in a solution of silver nitrate, the single-displacement reaction as shown in 3(c) takes place because copper is a more reactive metal than silver. The successful prediction of the products of a reaction is not always easy. The ability to predict products correctly comes with knowledge and experience. Although you may not be able to predict many reactions at this point, as you continue you will find that reactions can be categorized, and that prediction of the products thereby becomes easier, if not always certain.

EXAMPLE

10.8

Write the equation for the reaction between aqueous solutions of hydrobromic acid and potassium hydroxide.

First write the formulas for the reactants. They are HBr and KOH. Then classify the type of reaction that would occur between them. Because the reactants are compounds and one is an acid and the other is a base, the reaction will be of the neutralization type:

Acid + Base $\longrightarrow$ Salt + Water

Now rewrite the equation by putting down the formulas for the known substances:

$$HBr(aq) + KOH(aq) \longrightarrow Salt + H_2O$$

In this reaction, which is a double-displacement type, the H^+ from the acid combines with the OH^- from the base to form water. The salt must be composed of the other two ions, K^+ and Br^-. We determine the formula of the salt to be KBr from the fact that K is a +1 cation and Br is a −1 anion. The final balanced equation is

$$HBr(aq) + KOH(aq) \longrightarrow KBr(aq) + H_2O(l)$$

EXAMPLE

10.9

Complete and balance the equation for the reaction between aqueous solutions of barium chloride and sodium sulfate.

First determine the formulas for the reactants. They are $BaCl_2$ and Na_2SO_4. Then classify these substances as acids, bases, or salts. Both substances are salts. Since both substances are compounds, the reaction looks as though it will be of the double-displacement type. Start writing the equation with the reactants:

$$BaCl_2(aq) + Na_2SO_4(aq) \longrightarrow$$

If the reaction is double-displacement, Ba^{2+} will be written combined with SO_4^{2-} and Na^+ with Cl^- as the products. The balanced equation is

$$BaCl_2(aq) + Na_2SO_4(aq) \longrightarrow BaSO_4 + 2\,NaCl$$

The final step is to determine the nature of the products, which controls whether or not the reaction will take place. If both products are soluble, we may merely have a mixture of all the possible products in solution. But if an insoluble precipitate is formed, the reaction will definitely occur. We know from experience that NaCl is fairly soluble in water, but what about $BaSO_4$? The Solubility Table in Appendix IV can give us this information. From this table we see that $BaSO_4$ is insoluble in water, so it will be a precipitate in the reaction. Thus the reaction will occur, a white precipitate will form, and the equation is

$$BaCl_2(aq) + Na_2SO_4(aq) \longrightarrow BaSO_4 \downarrow\ + 2\,NaCl(aq)$$

There is a great deal yet to learn about which substances react with each other, how they react, and what conditions are necessary to bring about their reaction. It is possible to make accurate predictions concerning the occurrence of proposed reactions. Such predictions require, in addition to appropriate data, a good knowledge of thermodynamics, a subject usually reserved for advanced courses in chemistry and physics. But even without the formal use of thermodynamics, your knowledge of such generalities as the four reaction types just cited, the periodic table, atomic structure, oxidation numbers, and so on, can be put to good use in predicting reactions and in writing equations. Indeed, such applications serve to make chemistry an interesting and fascinating study.

10.6   Heat in Chemical Reactions

Energy changes always accompany chemical reactions. One reason why reactions occur is that the products attain a lower, more stable energy state than the reactants. For the products to attain this more stable state, energy must be liberated and given off to the surroundings as heat (or as heat and work). When a solution of a base is neutralized by the addition of an acid, the liberation of heat energy is signaled by an immediate rise in the temperature of the solution. When an automobile engine burns gasoline, heat is certainly liberated; at the same time, part of the liberated energy does the work of moving the automobile.

exothermic reaction

endothermic reaction

Reactions are either exothermic or endothermic. **Exothermic reactions** liberate heat; **endothermic reactions** absorb heat. In an exothermic reaction heat is a product and may be written on the right side of the equation for the reaction. In an endothermic reaction heat can be regarded as a reactant and is written on the left side of the equation. Examples indicating heat in an exothermic and an endothermic reaction follow.

$$H_2(g) + Cl_2(g) \longrightarrow 2\,HCl(g) + 185\,kJ\ (44.2\,kcal)\quad\text{(exothermic)}$$

$$N_2(g) + O_2(g) + 181\,kJ\ (43.2\,kcal) \longrightarrow 2\,NO(g)\quad\text{(endothermic)}$$

**heat of
reaction**

The quantity of heat produced by a reaction is known as the **heat of reaction.** The units used can be kilojoules or kilocalories. Consider the reaction represented by this equation:

$$C(s) + O_2(g) \longrightarrow CO_2(g) + 393\,kJ\ (94.0\,kcal)$$

When the heat liberated is expressed as part of the equation, the substances are expressed in units of moles. Thus, when 1 mole (12.0 g) of C combines with 1 mole (32.0 g) of O_2, 1 mole (44.0 g) of CO_2 is formed and 393 kJ (94.0 kcal) of heat are liberated. In this reaction, as in many others, the heat energy is more useful than the chemical products.

Aside from relatively small amounts of energy from nuclear processes, the sun is the major provider of energy for life on earth. The sun maintains the temperature necessary for life and also supplies light energy for the endothermic photosynthetic reactions carried on by green plants. In photosynthesis carbon dioxide and water are converted to free oxygen and glucose.

$$6\,CO_2 + 6\,H_2O + 2519\,kJ\ (673\,kcal) \xrightarrow{\text{Light}} C_6H_{12}O_6 + 6\,O_2$$
$$\text{Glucose}$$

Nearly all of the chemical energy used by living organisms is obtained from glucose or compounds derived from glucose. Modern technology depends for energy on fossil fuels—coal, petroleum, and natural gas. The energy is obtained from the combustion (burning) of these fuels, which are converted to carbon

combustion

dioxide and water. **Combustion** is the term for a chemical reaction in which heat and light are given off.

Fossil fuels constitute a huge energy reservoir. Some coal is about 90% carbon. Since 393 kJ are obtained from the combustion of 1 mol (12.0 g) of carbon, the combustion of a single ton of coal yields about 2.68×10^{10} J (6.40×10^9 cal) of energy. At 4.184 J per gram per degree, this energy is enough to heat about 21,000 gallons of water from room temperature (20°C) to the boiling point (100°C).

Natural gas is primarily methane, CH_4. Petroleum is a mixture of hydrocarbons (compounds of carbon and hydrogen). Liquefied petroleum gas (LPG) is a mixture of propane (C_3H_8) and butane (C_4H_{10}). The combustion of these fuels is a major source of energy.

$$CH_4(g) + 2\,O_2(g) \longrightarrow CO_2(g) + 2\,H_2O(g) + 890\,kJ\ (213\,kcal)$$

$$C_3H_8(g) + 5\,O_2(g) \longrightarrow 3\,CO_2(g) + 4\,H_2O(g) + 2200\,kJ\ (526\,kcal)$$

$$2\,C_8H_{18}(l) + 25\,O_2(g) \longrightarrow 16\,CO_2(g) + 18\,H_2O(g) + 10{,}900\,kJ\ (2606\,kcal)$$
Octane in gasoline

Be careful not to confuse an exothermic reaction that merely requires heat (activation energy) to get it started with a truly endothermic process. The combustion of magnesium is highly exothermic, yet magnesium must be heated to a fairly high temperature in air before combustion begins. Once started, however, the combustion reaction goes very vigorously until either the magnesium or the available supply of oxygen is exhausted. The electrolytic decomposition of water to hydrogen and oxygen is highly endothermic. If the electric current is shut off when this process is going on, the reaction stops instantly. The relative energy levels of reactants and products in exothermic and in endothermic processes are presented graphically in Figure 10.1.

In reaction (a) of Figure 10.1, the products are at a lower energy level than the

Figure 10.1   Energy levels in exothermic and endothermic reactions

Figure 10.2 In the endothermic process (a) dissolving 10 g of NH_4Cl in 100 mL of H_2O caused the temperature of the solution to decrease from 24.5°C to 18.1°C. In the exothermic process (b) dissolving 10 mL of concentrated H_2SO_4 in 100 mL of H_2O caused the temperature of the solution to increase from 24.8°C to 47.0°C.

reactants. Energy (heat) is given off, and the reaction is exothermic. In reaction (b) the products are at a higher energy level than the reactants. Energy has therefore been absorbed, and the reaction is endothermic.

Examples of endothermic and exothermic processes that can be demonstrated easily in the laboratory are shown in Figure 10.2. When dissolving ammonium chloride, NH_4Cl, in water, we observe an endothermic process. The temperature changes from 24.5°C to 18.1°C when 10 g of NH_4Cl are added to 100 mL of water. This energy, in the form of heat, is taken from the immediate surroundings, the water, causing the salt solution to become colder. In the second example, we observe a temperature change from 24.8°C to 47.0°C when 10 mL of concentrated sulfuric acid, H_2SO_4, are dissolved in 100 mL of water. This reaction is an exothermic process. In both examples the temperature changes are large enough to be detected by touching the containers.

QUESTIONS

A. *Review the meanings of the new terms intro-duced in this chapter.*

1. Chemical equation
2. Word equation
3. Balanced equation
4. Combination or synthesis reaction
5. Decomposition reaction
6. Single-displacement reaction
7. Double-displacement or metathesis reaction
8. Exothermic reaction
9. Endothermic reaction

10. Heat of reaction
11. Combustion

B. *Study Table 10.1 so that you will be familiar with the most common symbols used in equations.*

C. *Review questions*

1. Balance the following equations:
   (a) $H_2 + O_2 \longrightarrow H_2O$
   (b) $H_2 + Br_2 \longrightarrow HBr$
   (c) $C + Fe_2O_3 \longrightarrow Fe + CO$

(d) $H_2O_2 \longrightarrow H_2O + O_2$

(e) $Ba(ClO_3)_2 \overset{\Delta}{\longrightarrow} BaCl_2 + O_2$

(f) $H_2SO_4 + NaOH \longrightarrow H_2O + Na_2SO_4$

(g) $NH_4I + Cl_2 \longrightarrow NH_4Cl + I_2$

(h) $CrCl_3 + AgNO_3 \longrightarrow Cr(NO_3)_3 + AgCl$

(i) $Al_2(CO_3)_3 \overset{\Delta}{\longrightarrow} Al_2O_3 + CO_2$

(j) $Al + C \overset{\Delta}{\longrightarrow} Al_4C_3$

2. Classify the reactions in Question C.1. as combination, decomposition, single-displacement, or double-displacement.

3. Balance the following equations:

(a) $SO_2 + O_2 \longrightarrow SO_3$

(b) $Al + MnO_2 \overset{\Delta}{\longrightarrow} Mn + Al_2O_3$

(c) $Na + H_2O \longrightarrow NaOH + H_2$

(d) $AgNO_3 + Ni \longrightarrow Ni(NO_3)_2 + Ag$

(e) $Bi_2S_3 + HCl \longrightarrow BiCl_3 + H_2S$

(f) $PbO_2 \overset{\Delta}{\longrightarrow} PbO + O_2$

(g) $LiAlH_4 \overset{\Delta}{\longrightarrow} LiH + Al + H_2$

(h) $KI + Br_2 \longrightarrow KBr + I_2$

(i) $K_3PO_4 + BaCl_2 \longrightarrow KCl + Ba_3(PO_4)_2$

4. Balance the following equations:

(a) $MnO_2 + CO \longrightarrow Mn_2O_3 + CO_2$

(b) $Mg_3N_2 + H_2O \longrightarrow Mg(OH)_2 + NH_3$

(c) $C_3H_5(NO_3)_3 \longrightarrow CO_2 + H_2O + N_2 + O_2$

(d) $FeS_2 + O_2 \longrightarrow Fe_2O_3 + SO_2$

(e) $Cu(NO_3)_2 \longrightarrow CuO + NO_2 + O_2$

(f) $NO_2 + H_2O \longrightarrow HNO_3 + NO$

(g) $Al + H_2SO_4 \longrightarrow Al_2(SO_4)_3 + H_2$

(h) $HCN + O_2 \longrightarrow N_2 + CO_2 + H_2O$

(i) $B_5H_9 + O_2 \longrightarrow B_2O_3 + H_2O$

(j) $NH_3 + O_2 \longrightarrow NO + H_2O$

5. Change the following word equations into formula equations and balance them:

(a) Copper + Sulfur $\overset{\Delta}{\longrightarrow}$ Copper(I) sulfide

(b) Phosphoric acid + Calcium hydroxide →
Calcium phosphate + Water

(c) Silver oxide $\overset{\Delta}{\longrightarrow}$ Silver + Oxygen

(d) Iron(III) chloride + Sodium hydroxide →
Iron(III) hydroxide + Sodium chloride

(e) Nickel(II) phosphate + Sulfuric acid $\longrightarrow$
Nickel(II) sulfate + Phosphoric acid

(f) Zinc carbonate + Hydrochloric acid $\longrightarrow$
Zinc chloride + Water + Carbon dioxide

(g) Silver nitrate + Aluminum chloride $\longrightarrow$
Silver chloride + Aluminum nitrate

6. Change the following word equations into for-

mula equations and balance them:

(a) Water $\longrightarrow$ Hydrogen + Oxygen

(b) Acetic acid + Potassium hydroxide $\longrightarrow$
Potassium acetate + Water

(c) Phosphorus + Iodine $\longrightarrow$
Phosphorus triiodide

(d) Aluminum + Copper(II) sulfate $\longrightarrow$
Copper + Aluminum sulfate

(e) Ammonium sulfate + Barium chloride →
Ammonium chloride + Barium sulfate

(f) Sulfur tetrafluoride + Water $\longrightarrow$
Sulfur dioxide + Hydrogen fluoride

(g) Chromium(III) carbonate $\overset{\Delta}{\longrightarrow}$
Chromium(III) oxide + Carbon dioxide

7. Complete and balance the equations for these combination reactions:

(a) $K + O_2 \longrightarrow$ (c) $CO_2 + H_2O \longrightarrow$

(b) $Al + Cl_2 \longrightarrow$ (d) $CaO + H_2O \longrightarrow$

8. Complete and balance the equations for these decomposition reactions:

(a) $HgO \overset{\Delta}{\longrightarrow}$ (c) $MgCO_3 \overset{\Delta}{\longrightarrow}$

(b) $NaClO_3 \overset{\Delta}{\longrightarrow}$ (d) $PbO_2 \overset{\Delta}{\longrightarrow} PbO +$

9. Complete and balance the equations for these single-displacement reactions:

(a) $Zn + H_2SO_4 \longrightarrow$

(b) $AlI_3 + Cl_2 \longrightarrow$

(c) $Mg + AgNO_3 \longrightarrow$

(d) $Al + CoSO_4 \longrightarrow$

10. Use the activity series to predict which of the following reactions will occur. Complete and balance the equations. Where no reaction will occur, write "no reaction" as the product.

(a) $Ag + H_2SO_4(aq) \longrightarrow$

(b) $Cl_2 + NaBr(aq) \longrightarrow$

(c) $Mg + ZnCl_2(aq) \longrightarrow$

(d) $Pb + AgNO_3(aq) \longrightarrow$

(e) $Cu + FeCl_3(aq) \longrightarrow$

(f) $H_2 + Al_2O_3(s) \overset{\Delta}{\longrightarrow}$

(g) $Al + HBr(aq) \longrightarrow$

(h) $I_2 + HCl(aq) \longrightarrow$

11. Complete and balance the equations for these double-displacement reactions:

(a) $ZnCl_2 + KOH \longrightarrow$

(b) $CuSO_4 + H_2S \longrightarrow$

(c) $Ca(OH)_2 + H_3PO_4 \longrightarrow$

(d) $(NH_4)_3PO_4 + Ni(NO_3)_2 \longrightarrow$

(e) $Ba(OH)_2 + HNO_3 \longrightarrow$

(f) $(NH_4)_2S + HCl \longrightarrow$

12. Complete and balance the equations for these reactions:

(a) $H_2 + I_2 \longrightarrow$

(b) $CaCO_3 \xrightarrow{\Delta}$

(c) $Mg + H_2SO_4 \longrightarrow$

(d) $FeCl_2 + NaOH \longrightarrow$

(e) $SO_2 + H_2O \longrightarrow$

(f) $SO_3 + H_2O \longrightarrow$

(g) $Ca + H_2O \longrightarrow$

(h) $Bi(NO_3)_3 + H_2S \longrightarrow$

13. Complete and balance the equations for the following reactions:

(a) $Ba + O_2 \longrightarrow$

(b) $NaHCO_3 \xrightarrow{\Delta} Na_2CO_3 +$

(c) $Ni + CuSO_4 \longrightarrow$

(d) $MgO + HCl \longrightarrow$

(e) $H_3PO_4 + KOH \longrightarrow$

(f) $C + O_2 \longrightarrow$

(g) $Al(ClO_3)_3 \xrightarrow{\Delta} O_2 +$

(h) $CuBr_2 + Cl_2 \longrightarrow$

(i) $SbCl_3 + (NH_4)_2S \longrightarrow$

(j) $NaNO_3 \xrightarrow{\Delta} NaNO_2 +$

14. What is the purpose of balancing equations?

15. What is represented by the numbers (coefficients) that are placed in front of the formulas in a balanced equation?

16. Interpret the following chemical reactions in terms of the number of moles of each reactant and product:

(a) $MgBr_2 + 2\,AgNO_3 \longrightarrow$
$$Mg(NO_3)_2 + 2\,AgBr$$

(b) $N_2 + 3\,H_2 \longrightarrow 2\,NH_3$

(c) $2\,C_3H_7OH + 9\,O_2 \qquad 6\,CO_2 + 8\,H_2O$

17. Interpret each of the following equations in terms of the relative number of moles of each substance involved, and indicate whether the reaction is exothermic or endothermic:

(a) $2\,Na + Cl_2 \longrightarrow$
$$2\,NaCl + 822\ kJ\ (196.4\ kcal)$$

(b) $PCl_5 + 92.9\ kJ\ (22.2\ kcal) \longrightarrow PCl_3 + Cl_2$

18. Write balanced equations for each of these reactions, including the heat term:

(a) Lime, CaO, is converted to slaked lime, $Ca(OH)_2$, by reaction with water. The reac-

tion liberates 65.3 kJ (15.6 kcal) of heat for each mole of lime reacted.

(b) The industrial production of aluminum metal from aluminum oxide is an endothermic electrolytic process requiring 1630 kJ per mole of Al_2O_3. Oxygen is also a product.

19. Write balanced equations for the combustion of the following hydrocarbons:

(a) Ethane, C_2H_6　　(c) Heptane, C_7H_{16}

(b) Benzene, C_6H_6

20. Which of the following statements are correct?

(a) The coefficients in front of the formulas in a balanced chemical equation give the relative number of moles of the reactants and products in the reaction.

(b) A balanced chemical equation is one that has the same number of moles on each side of the equation.

(c) In a chemical equation, the symbol $\xrightarrow{\Delta}$ indicates that the reaction is exothermic.

(d) A chemical change that absorbs heat energy is said to be endothermic.

(e) In the reaction $H_2 + Cl_2 \longrightarrow 2\,HCl$, 100 molecules of HCl are produced for every 50 molecules of H_2 reacted.

(f) The symbol (aq) after a substance in an equation means that the substance is in a water solution.

(g) The equation $H_2O \longrightarrow H_2 + O_2$ can be balanced by placing a 2 in front of H_2O.

(h) In the equation $3\,H_2 + N_2 \longrightarrow 2\,NH_3$, there are fewer moles of product than there are moles of reactants.

(i) The total number of moles of reactants and products represented by this equation is 5 moles:

$$Mg + 2\,HCl \longrightarrow MgCl_2 + H_2$$

(j) One mole of glucose, $C_6H_{12}O_6$, contains 6 moles of carbon atoms.

(k) The reactants are the substances produced by the chemical reaction.

(l) In a balanced equation each side of the equation contains the same number of atoms of each element.

(m) When a precipitate is formed in a chemical reaction, it can be indicated in the equation with the symbol ↓ or (s) immediately before the formula of the substance precipitated.

(n) When a gas is evolved in a chemical reaction, it can be indicated in the equation with the symbol ↑ or (g) immediately following the formula of the gas.

(o) According to the equation

$$3 H_2 + N_2 \longrightarrow 2 NH_3$$

4 mol of NH_3 will be formed when 6 mol of H_2 and 2 mol of N_2 react.

(p) The products of an exothermic reaction are at a lower energy state than the reactants.

(q) The combustion of hydrocarbons produces carbon dioxide and water as products.

11

Calculations from Chemical Equations

After studying Chapter 11, you should be able to

1. Understand the new terms listed in Question A at the end of the chapter.
2. Write mole ratios for any two substances involved in a chemical reaction.
3. Outline the mole or mole-ratio method for making stoichiometric calculations.
4. Calculate the number of moles of a desired substance obtainable from a given number of moles of a starting substance in a chemical reaction (mole–to–mole calculations).
5. Calculate the mass of a desired substance obtainable from a given number of moles of a starting substance in a chemical reaction and vice versa (mole–to–mass and mass–to–mole calculations).
6. Calculate the mass of a desired substance involved in a chemical reaction from a given mass of a starting substance (mass–to–mass calculations).
7. Deduce the limiting reactant or reagent when given the amounts of starting substances, and then calculate the moles or mass of desired substance obtainable from a given chemical reaction (limiting-reactant calculations).
8. Apply theoretical yield or actual yield to any of the foregoing types of problems, or calculate theoretical and actual yields of a chemical reaction.

This chapter shows the quantitative relationship between reactants and products in chemical reactions and also reviews and correlates such concepts as formula weight, molecular weight, the molecule, the mole, and balanced equations.

11.1 A Short Review

(a) Molecular weight or formula weight. The molecular weight is the sum of the atomic weights of all the atoms in a molecule. The formula weight applies to the mass of any formula unit—atoms, molecules, or ions; it is the atomic weight of an atom, or the sum of the atomic weights in a molecule or an ion.

(b) Relationship between molecule and mole. A molecule is the smallest unit of a molecular substance (for example, Cl_2), and a mole is Avogadro's number, 6.022×10^{23}, of molecules of that substance. A mole of chlorine (Cl_2) has the same number of molecules as a mole of carbon dioxide, a mole of water, or a mole of any other molecular substance. When we relate molecules to molecular weight, 1 mol. wt = 1 mol, or 6.022×10^{23} molecules.

In addition to referring to molecular substances, the term *mole* may refer to any chemical species. It represents a quantity in grams equal to the formula weight (form. wt) and may be applied to atoms, ions, electrons, and formula units of nonmolecular substances.

$$1 \text{ mole} = \begin{cases} 1 \text{ mol. wt} & = 6.022 \times 10^{23} \text{ molecules} \\ 1 \text{ form. wt} & = 6.022 \times 10^{23} \text{ formula units} \\ 1 \text{ atomic wt} & = 6.022 \times 10^{23} \text{ atoms} \\ 1 \text{ ionic wt} & = 6.022 \times 10^{23} \text{ ions} \end{cases}$$

Other useful mole relationships are

$$\text{Number of moles} = \frac{\text{Grams of a substance}}{\text{Molecular weight of the substance}}$$

$$\text{Number of moles} = \frac{\text{Grams of a monatomic element}}{\text{Atomic weight of the element}}$$

$$\text{Number of moles} = \frac{\text{Number of molecules}}{6.022 \times 10^{23} \text{ molecules/mole}}$$

Two other useful equalities can be derived algebraically from each of these mole relationships. What are they?

(c) Balanced equations. When using chemical equations for calculations of mole–mass–volume relationships between reactants and products, the equations must be balanced. Remember that the number in front of a formula in a balanced chemical equation can represent the number of moles of that substance in the chemical reaction.

11.2 Calculations from Chemical Equations: The Mole Method

It is often necessary to calculate the amount of a substance that is produced from, or needed to react with, a given quantity of another substance. The area of

stoichiometry

mole ratio

chemistry that deals with the quantitative relationships among reactants and products is known as **stoichiometry** (*stoy-key-ah-meh-tree*). Although several methods are known, we firmly believe that the *mole* or *mole-ratio* method is generally best for solving problems in stoichiometry. This method is straightforward and, in our opinion, makes it easy to see and understand the relationships of the reacting species.

A **mole ratio** is a ratio between the number of moles of any two species involved in a chemical reaction. For example, in the reaction

$$2\ H_2 + O_2 \longrightarrow 2\ H_2O$$

2 mol   1 mol   2 mol

six mole ratios apply only to this reaction:

$$\frac{2\ \text{mol}\ H_2}{1\ \text{mol}\ O_2} \qquad \frac{2\ \text{mol}\ H_2}{2\ \text{mol}\ H_2O} \qquad \frac{1\ \text{mol}\ O_2}{2\ \text{mol}\ H_2}$$

$$\frac{1\ \text{mol}\ O_2}{2\ \text{mol}\ H_2O} \qquad \frac{2\ \text{mol}\ H_2O}{1\ \text{mol}\ H_2} \qquad \frac{2\ \text{mol}\ H_2O}{1\ \text{mol}\ O_2}$$

The mole ratio is a conversion factor used to convert the number of moles of one substance to the corresponding number of moles of another substance in a chemical reaction. For example, if we want to calculate the number of moles of H_2O that can be obtained from 4.0 mol of O_2, we use the mole ratio 2 mol H_2O/1 mol O_2.

$$4.0\ \cancel{\text{mol}\ O_2} \times \frac{2\ \text{mol}\ H_2O}{1\ \cancel{\text{mol}\ O_2}} = 8.0\ \text{mol}\ H_2O$$

Since stoichiometric problems are encountered throughout the entire field of chemistry, it is profitable to master this general method for their solution. The mole method makes use of three simple basic operations.

1. Convert the quantity of starting substance to moles (if it is not given in moles).
2. Convert the moles of starting substance to moles of desired substance.
3. Convert the moles of desired substance to units specified in the problem.

Like learning to balance chemical equations, learning to make stoichiometric calculations requires practice. A detailed step-by-step description of the general method, together with a variety of worked examples, is given in the following paragraphs. Study this material and apply the method to the problems at the end of this chapter.

Step 1. Use a balanced equation. Write a balanced equation for the chemical reaction in question or check to see that the equation given is balanced.

Step 2. Determine the number of moles of starting substance. Identify the starting substance from the data given in the statement of the problem. When the starting substance is given in moles, use it in that form; if it is not in moles, convert the quantity of the starting substance to moles.

Step 3. Determine the mole ratio of the desired substance to the starting substance. The number of moles of each substance in the balanced equation is indicated by the coefficient in front of each substance. Use these coefficients to set up the mole ratio:

$$\text{Mole ratio} = \frac{\text{Moles of desired substance in the equation}}{\text{Moles of starting substance in the equation}}$$

Step 4. Calculate the number of moles of the desired substance. Multiply the number of moles of starting substance (from Step 2) by the mole ratio (from Step 3) to obtain the number of moles of desired substance:

$$\begin{pmatrix} \text{Moles of desired} \\ \text{substance} \end{pmatrix} = \underbrace{\begin{pmatrix} \text{Moles of starting} \\ \text{substance} \end{pmatrix}}_{\text{From Step 2}} \times \underbrace{\frac{\begin{pmatrix} \text{Moles of desired substance} \\ \text{in the equation} \end{pmatrix}}{\begin{pmatrix} \text{Moles of starting substance} \\ \text{in the equation} \end{pmatrix}}}_{\text{Mole ratio from Step 3}}$$

Note that the units of moles of starting substance cancel out in the numerator and the denominator.

Step 5. Calculate the desired substance in the units specified in the problem. If the answer is to be in moles, the problem is finished in Step 4. If units other than moles are wanted, multiply the moles of the desired substance (from Step 4) by the appropriate factor to convert moles to the units required.

For example, if grams of the desired substance are wanted,

$$\begin{pmatrix} \text{Grams of desired} \\ \text{substance} \end{pmatrix} = \underbrace{\begin{pmatrix} \text{Moles of desired} \\ \text{substance} \end{pmatrix}}_{\text{From Step 4}} \times \frac{\begin{pmatrix} \text{Formula weight of} \\ \text{desired substance} \end{pmatrix}}{\begin{pmatrix} \text{One mole of} \\ \text{desired substance} \end{pmatrix}}$$

Use the conversion factors 6.022×10^{23} atoms/mol or 6.022×10^{23} molecules/mol when the problem asks for the answer in atoms or molecules.

The steps for converting the mass of starting substance A to either mass, atoms, or molecules of desired substance B are summarized below:

$$\text{grams of A} \xrightarrow{\text{Step 2}} \text{moles of A} \xrightarrow{\text{Steps 3 and 4}} \text{moles B} \begin{array}{c} \xrightarrow{\text{Step 5}} \text{grams of B} \\ \\ \xrightarrow{\text{Step 5}} \text{atoms or molecules of B} \end{array}$$

11.3 Mole–Mole Calculations

The object of this type of problem is to calculate the moles of one substance that react with, or are produced from, a given number of moles of another substance. Illustrative problems follow.

PROBLEM

11.1

How many moles of carbon dioxide will be produced by the complete oxidation of 2.5 mol of glucose, $C_6H_{12}O_6$, according to the following reaction?

$$C_6H_{12}O_6 + 6\ O_2 \longrightarrow 6\ CO_2 + 6\ H_2O$$

$$\text{1 mol}\qquad\text{6 mol}\qquad\qquad\text{6 mol}\qquad\text{6 mol}$$

The balanced equation states that 6 mol of CO_2 will be produced from 1 mol of $C_6H_{12}O_6$. Even though we can readily see that 15 mol of CO_2 will be formed from 2.5 mol of $C_6H_{12}O_6$, the mole method of solving the problem is shown here. This method, using mole ratios, will be very helpful in solving later problems.

Step 1. The equation given is balanced.

Step 2. The number of moles of starting substance is 2.5 mol $C_6H_{12}O_6$. The conversion needed is

$$\text{moles } C_6H_{12}O_6 \longrightarrow \text{moles } CO_2$$

Step 3. From the balanced equation, set up the mole ratio between the two substances in question, placing the moles of the substance being sought in the numerator and the moles of the starting substance in the denominator. The number of moles, in each case, is the same as the coefficient in front of the substance in the balanced equation.

$$\text{Mole ratio} = \frac{6\ \text{mol } CO_2}{1\ \text{mol } C_6H_{12}O_6}\quad\text{(From equation)}$$

Step 4. Multiply 2.5 mol of glucose (given in the problem) by this mole ratio:

$$2.5\ \cancel{\text{mol } C_6H_{12}O_6} \times \frac{6\ \text{mol } CO_2}{1\ \cancel{\text{mol } C_6H_{12}O_6}} = 15\ \text{mol } CO_2\quad\text{(Answer)}$$

Again note the use of units. The moles of $C_6H_{12}O_6$ cancel, leaving the answer in units of moles of CO_2.

PROBLEM

11.2

How many moles of ammonia can be produced from 8.00 mol of hydrogen reacting with nitrogen?

Step 1. First we need the balanced equation

$$3\ H_2 + N_2 \longrightarrow 2\ NH_3$$

Step 2. The moles of starting substance are 8.00 mol of hydrogen. The conversion needed is

$$\text{moles } H_2 \longrightarrow \text{moles } NH_3$$

Step 3. The balanced equation states that we get 2 mol of NH_3 for every 3 mol of H_2 that react. Set up the mole ratio of desired substance (NH_3) to starting substance (H_2):

$$\text{Mole ratio} = \frac{2\ \text{mol } NH_3}{3\ \text{mol } H_2}$$

Step 4. Multiplying the 8.00 mol of starting H_2 by this mole ratio, we get

$$8.00\ \cancel{\text{mol } H_2} \times \frac{2\ \text{mol } NH_3}{3\ \cancel{\text{mol } H_2}} = 5.33\ \text{mol } NH_3\quad\text{(Answer)}$$

PROBLEM

11.3

Given the balanced equation

$$K_2Cr_2O_7 + 6 \text{ KI} + 7 \text{ H}_2SO_4 \longrightarrow Cr_2(SO_4)_3 + 4 \text{ K}_2SO_4 + 3 \text{ I}_2 + 7 \text{ H}_2O$$

1 mol	6 mol	

(3 mol under I_2)

calculate **(a)** the number of moles of potassium dichromate ($K_2Cr_2O_7$) that will react with 2.0 mol of potassium iodide (KI); **(b)** the number of moles of iodine (I_2) that will be produced from 2.0 mol of potassium iodide.

After the equation is balanced, we are concerned only with $K_2Cr_2O_7$, KI, and I_2, and we can ignore all the other substances. The equation states that 1 mol of $K_2Cr_2O_7$ will react with 6 mol of KI to produce 3 mol of I_2.

(a) Calculate the number of moles of $K_2Cr_2O_7$.

Step 1. The equation given is balanced.

Step 2. The moles of starting substance are 2.0 mol of KI. The conversion needed is

$$\text{moles KI} \longrightarrow \text{moles } K_2Cr_2O_7$$

Step 3. Set up the mole ratio of desired substance to starting substance:

$$\text{Mole ratio} = \frac{1 \text{ mol } K_2Cr_2O_7}{6 \text{ mol KI}} \quad \text{(From equation)}$$

Step 4. Multiply the moles of starting material by this ratio to obtain the answer:

$$2.0 \text{ mol KI} \times \frac{1 \text{ mol } K_2Cr_2O_7}{6 \text{ mol KI}} = 0.33 \text{ mol } K_2Cr_2O_7 \quad \text{(Answer)}$$

(b) Calculate the number of moles of I_2.

Steps 1 and 2. The equation given is balanced and the moles of starting substance are 2.0 mol KI as in part **(a)**. The conversion needed is

$$\text{moles KI} \longrightarrow \text{moles } I_2$$

Step 3. Set up the mole ratio of desired substance to starting substance:

$$\text{Mole ratio} = \frac{3 \text{ mol } I_2}{6 \text{ mol KI}} \quad \text{(From equation)}$$

Step 4. Multiply the moles of starting material by this ratio to obtain the answer:

$$2.0 \text{ mol KI} \times \frac{3 \text{ mol } I_2}{6 \text{ mol KI}} = 1.0 \text{ mol } I_2 \quad \text{(Answer)}$$

Thus 2.0 mol KI will react with 0.33 mol $K_2Cr_2O_7$ to produce 1.0 mol I_2.

PROBLEM

11.4

How many molecules of water can be produced by reacting 0.010 mol of oxygen with hydrogen?

The sequence of conversions needed in the calculation is

$$\text{moles } O_2 \longrightarrow \text{moles } H_2O \longrightarrow \text{molecules } H_2O$$

Step 1. First we write the balanced equation

$$2\ H_2 +\ O_2 \longrightarrow 2\ H_2O$$
$$\qquad\quad 1\ \text{mol} \qquad\quad 2\ \text{mol}$$

Step 2. The moles of starting substance is 0.010 mol O_2.

Step 3. Set up the mole ratio of desired substance to starting substance:

$$\text{Mole ratio} = \frac{2\ \text{mol } H_2O}{1\ \text{mol } O_2}\quad \text{(From equation)}$$

Step 4. Multiplying the 0.010 mol of oxygen by this ratio, we obtain

$$0.010\ \text{mol } O_2 \times \frac{2\ \text{mol } H_2O}{1\ \text{mol } O_2} = 0.020\ \text{mol } H_2O$$

Step 5. Since the problem asks for molecules instead of moles of H_2O, we must convert moles to molecules. Use the conversion factor 6.022×10^{23} molecules/mole.

$$0.020\ \text{mol } H_2O \times \frac{6.022 \times 10^{23}\ \text{molecules}}{1\ \text{mol}} = 1.2 \times 10^{22}\ \text{molecules } H_2O\ \text{(Answer)}$$

Note that 0.020 mol is still quite a large number of water molecules.

11.4   Mole–Mass and Mass–Mass Calculations

The object of these types of problems is to calculate the mass of one substance that reacts with, or is produced from, a given number of moles or a given mass of another substance in a chemical reaction. The mole ratio is used to convert from moles of starting substance to moles of desired substance.

PROBLEM

11.5

What mass of hydrogen can be produced by reacting 6.0 mol of aluminum with hydrochloric acid?

First calculate the moles of hydrogen produced, using the mole-ratio method, and then calculate the mass of hydrogen by multiplying the moles of hydrogen by its mass per mole. The sequence of conversions in the calculation is

$$\text{moles Al} \longrightarrow \text{moles } H_2 \longrightarrow \text{grams } H_2$$

Step 1. The balanced equation is

$$2\ Al(s) + 6\ HCl(aq) \longrightarrow 2\ AlCl_3(aq) + 3\ H_2(g)$$
$$\quad 2\ \text{mol} \qquad\qquad\qquad\qquad\qquad\quad 3\ \text{mol}$$

Step 2. The moles of starting substance are 6.0 mol of aluminum.

Steps 3 and 4. Calculate moles of H_2 by the mole-ratio method:

$$6.0 \text{ mol Al} \times \frac{3 \text{ mol } H_2}{2 \text{ mol Al}} = 9.0 \text{ mol } H_2$$

Step 5. Convert moles of H_2 to grams $[g = \text{mol} \times (g/\text{mol})]$:

$$9.0 \text{ mol } H_2 \times \frac{2.0 \text{ g } H_2}{1 \text{ mol } H_2} = 18 \text{ g } H_2$$

We see that 18 g of H_2 can be produced by reacting 6.0 mol of Al with HCl. The following setup combines all the above steps into one continuous calculation:

$$6.0 \text{ mol Al} \times \frac{3 \text{ mol } H_2}{2 \text{ mol Al}} \times \frac{2.0 \text{ g } H_2}{1 \text{ mol } H_2} = 18 \text{ g } H_2 \quad \text{(Answer)}$$

PROBLEM

11.6

What mass of carbon dioxide is produced by the complete combustion of 100 g of the hydrocarbon pentane, C_5H_{12}?

The sequence of conversions in the calculation is

$$\text{grams } C_5H_{12} \longrightarrow \text{moles } C_5H_{12} \longrightarrow \text{moles } CO_2 \longrightarrow \text{grams } CO_2$$

Formula weights: C_5H_{12}, 72.0; CO_2, 44.0

Step 1. The balanced equation is

$$C_5H_{12} + 8 \, O_2 \longrightarrow 5 \, CO_2 + 6 \, H_2O$$
$$\text{1 mol} \qquad\qquad\qquad \text{5 mol}$$

Step 2. The starting substance is 100 g of C_5H_{12}. Convert 100 g of C_5H_{12} to moles:

$$100 \text{ g } C_5H_{12} \times \frac{1 \text{ mol } C_5H_{12}}{72.0 \text{ g } C_5H_{12}} = 1.39 \text{ mol } C_5H_{12}$$

Steps 3 and 4. Calculate the moles of CO_2 by the mole-ratio method:

$$1.39 \text{ mol } C_5H_{12} \times \frac{5 \text{ moles } CO_2}{1 \text{ mol } C_5H_{12}} = 6.95 \text{ mol } CO_2$$

Step 5. Convert moles of CO_2 to grams:

$$\text{mol } CO_2 \times \frac{\text{form. wt } CO_2}{1 \text{ mol } CO_2} = \text{grams } CO_2$$

$$6.95 \text{ mol } CO_2 \times \frac{44.0 \text{ g } CO_2}{1 \text{ mol } CO_2} = 306 \text{ g } CO_2 \quad \text{(Answer)}$$

We see that 306 g of CO_2 are produced from the complete combustion of 100 g of C_5H_{12}. The calculation in a continuous setup is

$$\boxed{\begin{array}{c} 100 \text{ g } C_5H_{12} \\ \hline \text{grams } C_5H_{12} \end{array}} \times \boxed{\begin{array}{c} \dfrac{1 \text{ mol } C_5H_{12}}{72.0 \text{ g } C_5H_{12}} \\ \hline \text{moles } C_5H_{12} \end{array}} \times \boxed{\begin{array}{c} \dfrac{5 \text{ mol } CO_2}{1 \text{ mol } C_5H_{12}} \\ \hline \text{moles } CO_2 \end{array}} \times \boxed{\begin{array}{c} \dfrac{44.0 \text{ g } CO_2}{1 \text{ mol } CO_2} \\ \hline \text{grams } CO_2 \end{array}} = 306 \text{ g } CO_2$$

PROBLEM

11.7

How many grams of nitric acid, HNO_3, are required to produce 8.75 g of dinitrogen monoxide, N_2O, according to the following equation?

$$4\ Zn(s) + 10\ HNO_3(aq) \longrightarrow 4\ Zn(NO_3)_2(aq) + N_2O(g) + 5\ H_2O(l)$$
$$\qquad\qquad\quad\ 10\ \text{mol} \qquad\qquad\qquad\qquad\qquad\qquad 1\ \text{mol}$$

In this problem, the amount of product is given, and we are asked to calculate the amount of reactant required to produce that product. The calculation is no different than in Problem 11.6. The starting substance for the calculation is 8.75 g of N_2O. The grams of HNO_3 need to be calculated. We shall do this problem in a continuous calculation setup.

Step 1. The equation for the reaction is balanced.
Step 2. The starting substance is 8.75 g of N_2O. The sequence of conversions needed is

$$\text{grams } N_2O \longrightarrow \text{moles } N_2O \longrightarrow \text{moles } HNO_3 \longrightarrow \text{grams } HNO_3$$

Formula weights: N_2O, 44.0; HNO_3, 63.0

Steps 3–5. The calculation is

$$8.75\ \text{g } N_2O\ \times\ \frac{1\ \text{mol } N_2O}{44.0\ \text{g } N_2O}\ \times\ \frac{10\ \text{mol } HNO_3}{1\ \text{mol } N_2O}\ \times\ \frac{63.0\ \text{g } HNO_3}{1\ \text{mol } HNO_3} = 125\ \text{g } HNO_3$$

$$\text{grams } N_2O \longrightarrow \text{moles } N_2O \longrightarrow \text{moles } HNO_3 \longrightarrow \quad \text{grams } HNO_3$$

Thus, 125 g of HNO_3 are required to produce 8.75 g of N_2O in this reaction.

11.5 **Limiting-Reactant and Yield Calculations**

In many chemical processes the quantities of the reactants used are such that the amount of one reactant is in excess of the amount of a second reactant in the reaction. The amount of the product(s) formed in such a case will depend on the reactant that is not in excess. Thus the reactant that is not in excess is known as the **limiting reactant** (sometimes called the limiting reagent), because it limits the amount of product that can be formed.

limiting reactant

As an example, consider the case in which solutions containing 1.0 mol of sodium hydroxide and 1.5 mol of hydrochloric acid are mixed:

$$NaOH + HCl \longrightarrow NaCl + H_2O$$
$$1\ \text{mol}\quad 1\ \text{mol}\qquad 1\ \text{mol}\quad 1\ \text{mol}$$

According to the equation it is possible to obtain 1.0 mol of NaCl from 1.0 mol of NaOH and 1.5 mol of NaCl from 1.5 mol of HCl. However, we cannot have two different yields of NaCl from the reaction. When 1.0 mol of NaOH and 1.5 mol of HCl are mixed, there is insufficient NaOH to react with all of the HCl. Therefore, HCl is the reactant in excess and NaOH is the limiting reactant. Since the amount of NaCl formed is dependent on the limiting reactant, only 1.0 mol of NaCl will be formed. Because 1.0 mol of NaOH reacts with 1.0 mol of HCl, 0.5 mol of HCl remains unreacted.

$$\left.\begin{array}{l} \text{1.0 mol NaOH} \\ \text{1.5 mol HCl} \end{array}\right\} \longrightarrow \begin{array}{l} \text{1.0 mol NaCl} \\ \text{1.0 mol } H_2O \end{array} + \text{0.5 mol HCl unreacted}$$

Problems giving the amounts of two reactants are generally of the limiting-reactant type. Several methods can be used to identify the limiting reactant in a chemical reaction. In the most direct method, two steps are needed to determine the limiting reactant, the amount of product, and the amount of reactant in excess or unreacted.

1. Calculate the amount of product (moles or grams, as needed) that can be formed from each reactant. The reactant that gives the least amount of product is the limiting reactant. The other reactant is in excess, and some of it will remain at the end of the reaction. The least amount of product is the amount that will be formed by the reaction.
2. Calculate the amount of the reactant in excess that will react with the limiting reactant. Subtract the amount that reacts from the starting quantity of the reactant in excess. This result is the amount of that substance that remains unreacted.

PROBLEM

11.8

How many moles of Fe_3O_4 can be obtained by reacting 16.8 g Fe with 10.0 g H_2O? Which substance is the limiting reactant? Which substance is in excess?

$$3\ Fe(s) + 4\ H_2O(g) \xrightarrow{\Delta} Fe_3O_4(s) + 4\ H_2(g)$$

This is a typical problem in which one of the starting substances will control or limit the yield of product.

Calculate the moles of Fe_3O_4 that can be formed from each reactant:

g reactant $\longrightarrow$ mol reactant $\longrightarrow$ mol Fe_3O_4

Formula weights: Fe, 55.8; H_2O, 18.0

$$16.8\ \text{g Fe} \times \frac{1\ \text{mol Fe}}{55.8\ \text{g Fe}} \times \frac{1\ \text{mol } Fe_3O_4}{3\ \text{mol Fe}} = 0.100\ \text{mol } Fe_3O_4$$

$$10.0\ \text{g } H_2O \times \frac{1\ \text{mol } H_2O}{18.0\ \text{g } H_2O} \times \frac{1\ \text{mol } Fe_3O_4}{4\ \text{mol } H_2O} = 0.139\ \text{mol } Fe_3O_4$$

The limiting reactant is Fe because it produces less Fe_3O_4. H_2O is in excess. The yield of product is 0.100 mol of Fe_3O_4.

PROBLEM

11.9

How many grams of silver bromide, AgBr, can be formed when solutions containing 50.0 g of $MgBr_2$ and 100 g of $AgNO_3$ are mixed together? How many grams of the excess reactant remain unreacted?

First identify the limiting reactant and the reactant in excess.

$$MgBr_2(aq) + 2\ AgNO_3(aq) \longrightarrow 2\ AgBr \downarrow + Mg(NO_3)_2(aq)$$

Formula weights: $MgBr_2$, 184.1; $AgNO_3$, 169.9; AgBr, 187.8

Step 1. Calculate the grams of AgBr that can be formed from each reactant:

$$\text{g reactant} \longrightarrow \text{mol reactant} \longrightarrow \text{mol AgBr} \longrightarrow \text{g AgBr}$$

$$50.0 \text{ g MgBr}_2 \times \frac{1 \text{ mol MgBr}_2}{184.1 \text{ g MgBr}_2} \times \frac{2 \text{ mol AgBr}}{1 \text{ mol MgBr}_2} \times \frac{187.8 \text{ g AgBr}}{1 \text{ mol AgBr}} = 102 \text{ g AgBr}$$

$$100 \text{ g AgNO}_3 \times \frac{1 \text{ mol AgNO}_3}{169.9 \text{ g AgNO}_3} \times \frac{2 \text{ mol AgBr}}{2 \text{ mol AgNO}_3} \times \frac{187.8 \text{ g AgBr}}{1 \text{ mol AgBr}} = 111 \text{ g AgBr}$$

The limiting reactant is $MgBr_2$ because it gives less AgBr. $AgNO_3$ is in excess. The yield is 102 g AgBr. The final mixture will contain 102 g AgBr, $Mg(NO_3)_2$, and some unreacted $AgNO_3$.

Step 2. Calculation of the grams of unreacted $AgNO_3$. Calculate the grams of $AgNO_3$ that will react with 50.0 g of $MgBr_2$:

$$\text{g MgBr}_2 \longrightarrow \text{mol MgBr}_2 \longrightarrow \text{mol AgNO}_3 \longrightarrow \text{g AgNO}_3$$

$$50.0 \text{ g MgBr}_2 \times \frac{1 \text{ mol MgBr}_2}{184.1 \text{ g MgBr}_2} \times \frac{2 \text{ mol AgNO}_3}{1 \text{ mol MgBr}_2} \times \frac{169.9 \text{ g AgNO}_3}{1 \text{ mol AgNO}_3} = 92.3 \text{ g AgNO}_3$$

Thus 92.3 g of $AgNO_3$ react with 50.0 g of $MgBr_2$. The amount of $AgNO_3$ that remains unreacted is

$$100 \text{ g AgNO}_3 - 92.3 \text{ g AgNO}_3 = 7.7 \text{ g AgNO}_3 \text{ unreacted}$$

The quantities of the products that we have been calculating from equations represent the maximum yield (100%) of product according to the reaction represented by the equation. Many reactions, especially those involving organic substances, fail to give a 100% yield of product. The main reasons for this failure are the side reactions that give products other than the main product and the fact that many reactions are reversible. In addition, some product may be lost in handling and transferring from one vessel to another. The **theoretical yield** of a reaction is the calculated amount of product that can be obtained from a given amount of reactant, according to the chemical equation. The **actual yield** is the amount of product that we finally obtain.

The **percentage yield** is the ratio of the actual yield to the theoretical yield multiplied by 100%. Both yields must have the same units.

theoretical yield

actual yield

percentage yield

$$\frac{\text{Actual yield}}{\text{Theoretical yield}} \times 100\% = \text{Percentage yield}$$

For example, if the theoretical yield calculated for a reaction is 14.8 g, and the amount of product obtained is 9.25 g, the percentage yield is

$$\frac{9.25 \text{ g}}{14.8 \text{ g}} \times 100\% = 62.5\%$$

PROBLEM

11.10

Carbon tetrachloride was prepared by reacting 100 g of carbon disulfide and 100 g of chlorine. Calculate the percentage yield if 65.0 g of CCl_4 were obtained from the reaction.

$$CS_2 + 3\,Cl_2 \longrightarrow CCl_4 + S_2Cl_2$$

Formula weights: CS_2, 76.2; Cl_2, 71.0; CCl_4, 154

In this problem we need to determine the limiting reactant in order to calculate the quantity of CCl_4 (theoretical yield) that can be formed. Then we can compare this amount with the actual yield of 65.0 g of CCl_4 to calculate the percentage yield.

Step 1. Calculate the grams of CCl_4 that can be formed from each reactant:

$$\text{g reactant} \longrightarrow \text{mol reactant} \longrightarrow \text{mol } CCl_4 \longrightarrow \text{g } CCl_4$$

$$100\ \text{g } CS_2 \times \frac{1\ \text{mol } CS_2}{76.2\ \text{g } CS_2} \times \frac{1\ \text{mol } CCl_4}{1\ \text{mol } CS_2} \times \frac{154\ \text{g } CCl_4}{1\ \text{mol } CCl_4} = 202\ \text{g } CCl_4$$

$$100\ \text{g } Cl_2 \times \frac{1\ \text{mol } Cl_2}{71.0\ \text{g } Cl_2} \times \frac{1\ \text{mol } CCl_4}{3\ \text{mol } Cl_2} \times \frac{154\ \text{g } CCl_4}{1\ \text{mol } CCl_4} = 72.3\ \text{g } CCl_4$$

The limiting reactant is Cl_2. CS_2 is in excess. The theoretical yield is 72.3 g CCl_4.

Step 2. Calculate the percentage yield. According to the equation, 72.3 g of CCl_4 is the maximum amount or theoretical yield of CCl_4 possible from 100 g of Cl_2. Actual yield is 65.0 g of CCl_4.

$$\text{Percentage yield} = \frac{65.0\ \text{g}}{72.3\ \text{g}} \times 100\% = 89.9\%$$

When solving problems, you will achieve better results if at first you do not try to take shortcuts. Write the data and numbers in a logical, orderly manner. Make certain that the equations are balanced and that the computations are accurate and expressed to the correct number of significant figures. Remember that units are very important; a number without units has little meaning. Finally, an electronic calculator can save you many hours of tedious computations.

QUESTIONS

A. *Review the meanings of the new terms introduced in this chapter.*

1. Stoichiometry
2. Mole ratio
3. Limiting reactant
4. Theoretical yield
5. Actual yield
6. Percentage yield

B. *Review problems*
In some of the following problems, equations have not been balanced.

Mole Review Problems

1. Calculate the number of moles in each of the following quantities:
(a) 25.0 g KNO_3
(b) 10.8 g $Ca(NO_3)_2$
(c) 5.4×10^2 g $(NH_4)_2C_2O_4$
(d) 2.10 kg $NaHCO_3$
(e) 525 mg $ZnCl_2$
(f) 56 millimole $NaOH$

(g) 9.8×10^{24} molecules CO_2

(h) 250 mL ethyl alcohol, C_2H_5OH
($d = 0.789$ g/mL)

*(i) 16.8 mL H_2SO_4 solution ($d = 1.727$ g/mL, 80.0% H_2SO_4 by weight)

2. Calculate the number of grams in each of the following quantities:

(a) 2.55 mol $Fe(OH)_3$

(b) 0.00844 mol $NiSO_4$

(c) 125 kg $CaCO_3$

(d) 0.0600 mol $HC_2H_3O_2$

(e) 10.5 mol NH_3

(f) 0.725 mol Bi_2S_3

(g) 72 millimole HCl

(h) 4.50×10^{21} molecules glucose, $C_6H_{12}O_6$

(i) 500 mL of liquid Br_2 ($d = 3.119$ g/mL)

*(j) 75 mL K_2CrO_4 solution ($d = 1.175$ g/mL, 20.0% K_2CrO_4 by weight)

3. Which contains the larger number of molecules?

(a) 10.0 g H_2O or 10.0 g H_2O_2

(b) 25.0 g HCl or 85.0 g $C_6H_{12}O_6$

Mole-Ratio Problems

4. Given the equation for the combustion of isopropyl alcohol:

$$2 C_3H_7OH + 9 O_2 \longrightarrow 6 CO_2 + 8 H_2O$$

what is the mole ratio of:

(a) CO_2 to C_3H_7OH

(b) C_3H_7OH to O_2

(c) O_2 to CO_2

(d) H_2O to C_3H_7OH

(e) CO_2 to H_2O

(f) H_2O to O_2

5. For the reaction

$$3 CaCl_2 + 2 H_3PO_4 \longrightarrow Ca_3(PO_4)_2 + 6 HCl$$

set up the mole ratio of

(a) $CaCl_2$ to $Ca_3(PO_4)_2$

(b) HCl to H_3PO_4

(c) $CaCl_2$ to H_3PO_4

(d) $Ca_3(PO_4)_2$ to H_3PO_4

(e) HCl to $Ca_3(PO_4)_2$

(f) H_3PO_4 to HCl

Mole–Mass Problems

6. How many moles of Cl_2 can be produced from 5.60 mol HCl?

$$4 HCl + O_2 \longrightarrow 2 Cl_2 + 2 H_2O$$

7. How many grams of sodium hydroxide can be produced from 500 g of calcium hydroxide according to this equation?

$$Ca(OH)_2 + Na_2CO_3 \longrightarrow 2 NaOH + CaCO_3$$

8. Given the equation

$$Al_4C_3 + 12 H_2O \longrightarrow 4 Al(OH)_3 + 3 CH_4$$

(a) How many moles of water are needed to react with 100 g of Al_4C_3?

(b) How many moles of $Al(OH)_3$ will be produced when 0.600 mol of CH_4 is formed?

9. How many grams of zinc phosphate, $Zn_3(PO_4)_2$, are formed when 10.0 g of Zn are reacted with phosphoric acid?

10. Given the equation

$$4 FeS_2 + 11 O_2 \longrightarrow 2 Fe_2O_3 + 8 SO_2$$

(a) How many moles of Fe_2O_3 can be made from 1.00 mol of FeS_2?

(b) How many moles of O_2 are required to react with 4.50 mol of FeS_2?

(c) If the reaction produces 1.55 mol of Fe_2O_3, how many moles of SO_2 are produced?

(d) How many grams of SO_2 can be formed from 0.512 mol of FeS_2?

(e) If the reaction produces 40.6 g of SO_2, how many moles of O_2 were reacted?

(f) How many grams of FeS_2 are needed to produce 221 g of Fe_2O_3?

11. An early method of producing chlorine was by the reaction of pyrolusite, MnO_2, and hydrochloric acid. How many moles of HCl will react with 1.05 mol of MnO_2? (Balance the equation first.)

$$MnO_2(s) + HCl(aq) \longrightarrow$$
$$Cl_2(g) + MnCl_2(aq) + H_2O$$

12. Given the reaction

$$Zn + HCl \longrightarrow ZnCl_2 + H_2$$

180 g of zinc were dropped into a beaker of hydrochloric acid. After the reaction ceased, 35 g of unreacted zinc remained in the beaker.

(a) How many moles of hydrogen gas were produced?

(b) How many grams of HCl were reacted?

13. In a blast furnace, iron(III) oxide reacts with coke (carbon) to produce molten iron and carbon monoxide:

$$Fe_2O_3 + 3\,C \longrightarrow 2\,Fe + 3\,CO$$

How many kilograms of iron would be formed from 125 kg of Fe_2O_3?

14. How many grams of steam and iron must react to produce 375 g of magnetic iron oxide, Fe_3O_4?

$$3\,Fe(s) + 4\,H_2O(g) \longrightarrow Fe_3O_4(s) + 4\,H_2(g)$$

15. Ethane gas, C_2H_6, burns in air (i.e., reacts with the oxygen in air) to form carbon dioxide and water:

$$2\,C_2H_6 + 7\,O_2 \longrightarrow 4\,CO_2 + \overset{\bullet}{6}\,H_2O$$

(a) How many moles of O_2 are needed for the complete combustion of 15.0 mol of ethane?

(b) How many grams of CO_2 are produced for each 8.00 g of H_2O produced?

(c) How many grams of CO_2 will be produced by the combustion of 75.0 g of C_2H_6?

Limiting-Reactant and Percentage-Yield Problems

16. In the following equations, determine which reactant is the limiting reactant and which reactant is in excess. The amounts mixed together are shown below each reactant. Show evidence for your answers.

(a) $KOH + HNO_3 \longrightarrow KNO_3 + H_2O$
    16.0 g   12.0 g
    .29 mole   .19 mole

(b) $2\,NaOH + H_2SO_4 \longrightarrow Na_2SO_4 + 2\,H_2O$
    10.0 g   10.0 g

(c) $2\,Bi(NO_3)_3 + 3\,H_2S \longrightarrow Bi_2S_3 + 6\,HNO_3$
    50.0 g   6.00 g
    .13 moles   .18 moles

(d) $3\,Fe + 4\,H_2O \longrightarrow Fe_3O_4 + 4\,H_2$
    40.0 g   16.0 g

17. Given the equation

$$Fe(s) + CuSO_4(aq) \longrightarrow Cu(s) + FeSO_4(aq)$$

(a) When 2.0 mol of Fe and 3.0 mol of $CuSO_4$ are reacted, what substances will be present when the reaction is over? How many moles of each substance are present?

(b) When 20.0 g of Fe and 40.0 g of $CuSO_4$ are reacted, what substances will be present when the reaction is over? How many grams of each substance are present?

18. The reaction for the combustion of propane, C_3H_8, is

$$C_3H_8 + 5\,O_2 \longrightarrow 3\,CO_2 + 4\,H_2O$$

(a) If 6.0 mol of C_3H_8 and 6.0 mol of O_2 are reacted, how many moles of CO_2 can be produced?

(b) If 4.0 mol of C_3H_8 and 30.0 mol of O_2 are reacted, how many moles of CO_2 can be produced?

(c) If 20.0 mol of C_3H_8 and 4.0 mol of O_2 are reacted, how many moles of CO_2 can be produced?

*(d) If 2.0 mol of C_3H_8 and 20.0 mol of O_2 are placed in a closed container, and they react to completion (until one reactant is completely used up), what compounds are present in the container after the reaction, and how many moles of each compound are present?

(e) If 30.0 g of C_3H_8 and 30.0 g of O_2 are reacted, how many grams of CO_2 can be produced?

(f) If 25.0 g of C_3H_8 and 100.0 g of O_2 are reacted, how many grams of CO_2 can be produced?

(g) If 20.0 g of C_3H_8 and 300 g of O_2 are reacted, how many grams of CO_2 can be produced?

19. Aluminum reacts with bromine to form aluminum bromide:

$$2\,Al + 3\,Br_2 \longrightarrow 2\,AlBr_3$$

If 25.0 g of Al and 100 g of Br_2 are reacted, and 64.2 g of $AlBr_3$ product are recovered, what is the percentage yield for the reaction?

20. Methyl alcohol, CH_3OH, is made by reacting carbon monoxide and hydrogen in the presence of certain metal oxide catalysts. How much alcohol can be obtained by reacting 30.0 g of CO and 10.0 g of H_2? How many grams of excess reactant remain unreacted?

$$CO(g) + 2\,H_2(g) \longrightarrow CH_3OH(l)$$

21. Iron was reacted with a solution containing 400 g of copper(II) sulfate. The reaction was stopped after 1 hour, and 151 g of copper were obtained. Calculate the percentage yield of copper obtained.

$$Fe(s) + CuSO_4(aq) \longrightarrow Cu(s) + FeSO_4(aq)$$

*22. Ethyl alcohol, C_2H_5OH, also called grain alcohol, can be made by the fermentation of sugar, which often comes from starch in grain:

$$C_6H_{12}O_6 \longrightarrow 2\,C_2H_5OH + 2\,CO_2$$

Glucose   Ethyl alcohol

If an 84.6% yield of ethyl alcohol is obtained,
(a) What weight of ethyl alcohol will be produced from 750 g of glucose?
(b) What weight of glucose should be used to produce 475 g of C_2H_5OH?

*23. Carbon disulfide, CS_2, can be made from coke, C, and sulfur dioxide, SO_2:

$$3\,C + 2\,SO_2 \longrightarrow CS_2 + 2\,CO_2$$

If the actual yield of CS_2 is 86.0% of the theoretical yield, what weight of coke is needed to produce 950 g of CS_2?

*24. Acetylene, C_2H_2, can be manufactured by the reaction of water and calcium carbide, CaC_2:

$$CaC_2 + 2\,H_2O \longrightarrow C_2H_2(g) + Ca(OH)_2$$

When 44.5 g of commercial grade (impure) calcium carbide were reacted, 0.540 mol of C_2H_2 was produced. Assuming that all of the CaC_2 was reacted to C_2H_2, what is the percent of CaC_2 in the commercial grade material?

Additional Problems

*25. Both $CaCl_2$ and $MgCl_2$ react with $AgNO_3$ to precipitate AgCl. When solutions containing equal weights of $CaCl_2$ and $MgCl_2$ are reacted, which salt will produce the larger amount of AgCl? Show proof.

*26. An astronaut excretes about 2500 g of water a day. If lithium oxide, Li_2O, is used in the spaceship to absorb this water, how many kilograms of Li_2O must be carried for a 30-day space trip for three astronauts?

$$Li_2O + H_2O \longrightarrow 2\,LiOH$$

*27. Much commercial hydrochloric acid is prepared by the reaction of concentrated sulfuric acid with sodium chloride:

$$H_2SO_4 + 2\,NaCl \longrightarrow Na_2SO_4 + 2\,HCl$$

How many kilograms of concentrated H_2SO_4, 96% H_2SO_4 by weight, are required to produce 25.0 L of concentrated hydrocholoric acid ($d = 1.20$ g/mL, 42.0% HCl by weight)?

*28. Gastric juice contains about 3.0 g of HCl per liter. If a person produces about 2.5 L of gastric juice per day, how many antacid tablets, each containing 400 mg of $Al(OH)_3$, are needed to neutralize all the HCl produced in one day?

$$Al(OH)_3(s) + 3\,HCl(aq) \longrightarrow$$
$$AlCl_3(aq) + 6\,H_2O(l)$$

*29. 12.82 g of a mixture of $KClO_3$ and NaCl are heated strongly. The $KClO_3$ reacts according to the following equation:

$$2\,KClO_3(s) \longrightarrow 2\,KCl(s) + 3\,O_2(g)$$

The NaCl does not undergo any reaction. After the heating, the residue (KCl and NaCl) weighs 9.45 g. Assuming that all the loss of weight represents loss of oxygen gas, calculate the percentage of $KClO_3$ in the original mixture.

30. Phosphine, PH_3, can be prepared by the hydrolysis of calcium phosphide, Ca_3P_2:

$$Ca_3P_2 + 6\,H_2O \longrightarrow 3\,Ca(OH)_2 + 2\,PH_3$$

Based on this equation, which of the following statements are correct?
(a) One mole of Ca_3P_2 produces 2 mol of PH_3.
(b) One gram of Ca_3P_2 produces 2 g of PH_3.
(c) Three moles of $Ca(OH)_2$ are produced for each 2 mol of PH_3 produced.
(d) The mole ratio between phosphine and calcium phosphide is

$$\frac{2\text{ mol } PH_3}{1\text{ mol } Ca_3P_2}$$

(e) When 2.0 mol of Ca_3P_2 and 3.0 mol of H_2O react, 4.0 mol of PH_3 can be formed.
(f) When 2.0 mol of Ca_3P_2 and 15.0 mol of H_2O react, 6.0 mol of $Ca(OH)_2$ can be formed.
(g) When 200 g of Ca_3P_2 and 100 g of H_2O react, Ca_3P_2 is the limiting reactant.
(h) When 200 g of Ca_3P_2 and 100 g of H_2O react, the theoretical yield of PH_3 is 57.4 g.

31. The equation representing the reaction used for the commercial preparation of hydrogen cyanide is

$$2\,CH_4 + 3\,O_2 + 2\,NH_3 \longrightarrow 2\,HCN + 6\,H_2O$$

Based on this equation, which of the following statements are correct?

(a) Three moles of O_2 are required for 2 moles of NH_3.

(b) Twelve moles of HCN are produced for every 16 moles of O_2 that react.

(c) The mole ratio between H_2O and CH_4 is

$$\frac{6 \text{ mol } H_2O}{2 \text{ mol } CH_4}$$

(d) When 12 moles of HCN are produced, 4 moles of H_2O will be formed.

(e) When 10 moles of CH_4, 10 moles of O_2, and 10 moles of NH_3 are mixed and reacted, O_2 is the limiting reactant.

(f) When 3 moles each of CH_4, O_2, and NH_3 are mixed and reacted, 3 moles of HCN will be produced.

12

The Gaseous State of Matter

After studying Chapter 12, you should be able to

1. Understand the new terms listed in Question A at the end of the chapter.
2. State the principal assumptions of the Kinetic-Molecular Theory (KMT).
3. Estimate the relative rates of effusion of two gases of known molecular weight.
4. Sketch and explain the operation of a mercury barometer.
5. Tell what two factors determine gas pressure in a vessel of fixed volume.
6. Work problems involving (a) Boyle's and (b) Charles' gas laws.
7. State what is meant by standard temperature and pressure (STP).
8. Give the equation for the combined gas law that deals with the pressure, volume, and temperature relationships expressed in Boyle's, Charles', and Gay-Lussac's gas laws.
9. Use Dalton's law of partial pressures and the combined gas laws to calculate the dry STP volume of a gas collected over water.
10. State Avogadro's law.
11. Understand the mole–mass–volume relationship of gases.
12. Determine the density of any gas at STP.
13. Determine the molecular weight of a gas from its density at a known temperature and pressure.
14. Solve problems involving the ideal gas equation.
15. Make mole-to-volume, mass-to-volume, and volume-to-volume stoichiometric calculations from balanced chemical equations.
16. State two valid reasons why real gases may deviate from the behavior predicted for an ideal gas.

12.1   General Properties of Gases

In Chapter 3, solids, liquids, and gases are described in a brief outline. In this chapter we shall consider the behavior of gases in greater detail.

Gases are the least compact and most mobile of the three states of matter. A solid has a rigid structure, and its particles remain in essentially fixed positions. When a solid absorbs sufficient heat, it melts and changes into a liquid. Melting occurs because the molecules (or ions) have absorbed enough energy to break out of the rigid crystal lattice structure of the solid. The molecules or ions in the liquid are more energetic than they were in the solid, as shown by their increased mobility. Molecules in the liquid state are *coherent*; that is, they cling to one another. When the liquid absorbs additional heat, the more energetic molecules break away from the liquid surface and go into the gaseous state. Gases represent the most mobile state of matter. Gas molecules move with very high velocities and have high kinetic energy (KE). The average velocity of hydrogen molecules at 0°C is over 1600 meters (1 mile) per second. Because of the high velocities of their molecules, mixtures of gases are uniformly distributed within the container in which they are confined.

A quantity of a substance occupies a much greater volume as a gas than it does as a liquid or a solid. For example, 1 mole of water (18 g) has a volume of 18 mL at 4°C. This same amount of water would occupy about 22,400 mL in the gaseous state—more than a 1200-fold increase in volume. We may assume from this difference in volume that (1) gas molecules are relatively far apart, (2) gases can be greatly compressed, and (3) the volume occupied by a gas is mostly empty space.

12.2   The Kinetic-Molecular Theory

Careful scientific studies of the behavior and properties of gases were begun in the 17th century by Robert Boyle (1627–1691). This work was carried forward by many investigators after Boyle. The accumulated data were used in the second half of the 19th century to formulate a general theory to explain the behavior and properties of gases. This theory is called the **Kinetic-Molecular Theory (KMT).** The KMT has since been extended to cover, in part, the behavior of liquids and solids. It ranks today with the atomic theory as one of the greatest generalizations of modern science.

Kinetic-Molecular Theory (KMT)

The KMT is based on the motion of particles, particularly gas molecules. A gas that behaves exactly as outlined by the theory is known as an **ideal,** or **perfect, gas.** Actually no ideal gases exist, but under certain conditions of temperature and pressure, gases approach ideal behavior, or at least show only small deviations from it. Under extreme conditions, such as very high pressure and low temperature, real gases may deviate greatly from ideal behavior. For example, at low temperature and high pressure, many gases become liquids.

ideal, or perfect, gas

The principal assumptions of the Kinetic-Molecular Theory are

1. Gases consist of tiny (submicroscopic) atoms or molecules.
2. The distance between molecules is large compared with the size of the molecules themselves. The volume occupied by a gas consists mostly of empty space.

3. Gas molecules have no attraction for one another.
4. Gas molecules move in straight lines in all directions, colliding frequently with one another and with the walls of the container.
5. No energy is lost by the collision of a gas molecule with another gas molecule or with the walls of the container. All collisions are perfectly elastic.
6. The average kinetic energy for molecules is the same for all gases at the same temperature, and its value is directly proportional to the Kelvin temperature.

The kinetic energy (KE) of a molecule is one-half its mass times its velocity squared. It is expressed by the equation

$$KE = \frac{1}{2}mv^2$$

where m is the mass and v is the velocity of the molecule.

All gases have the same kinetic energy at the same temperature. Therefore, from the kinetic energy equation we can see that, if we compare the velocities of the molecules of two gases, the lighter molecules will have a greater velocity than the heavier ones. For example, calculations show that the velocity of a hydrogen molecule is four times the velocity of an oxygen molecule.

$$KE \text{ of } H_2 = KE \text{ of } O_2$$

$$\tfrac{1}{2}m_{H_2}v_{H_2}^2 = \tfrac{1}{2}m_{O_2}v_{O_2}^2$$

$$m_{H_2} = 2; \quad m_{O_2} = 32$$

$$\tfrac{1}{2} \times 2 \times v_{H_2}^2 = \tfrac{1}{2} \times 32 \times v_{O_2}^2$$

$$\frac{v_{H_2}^2}{v_{O_2}^2} = \frac{16}{1}$$

Taking the square root of both sides, we have

$$\frac{v_{H_2}}{v_{O_2}} = \frac{4}{1}$$

diffusion

Due to their molecular motion gases have the property of **diffusion,** the ability of two or more gases to mix spontaneously until they form a uniform mixture. The diffusion of gases may be illustrated by use of the apparatus shown in Figure 12.1. Two large flasks, one containing reddish-brown bromine vapors and the other dry air, are connected by a side tube. When the stopcock between the flasks is opened, the bromine and air will diffuse into each other. After standing awhile, both flasks will contain bromine and air.

effusion

If we put a pinhole in a balloon, the gas inside will effuse or flow out of the balloon. **Effusion** is a process by which gas molecules pass through a very small orifice (opening) from a container at higher pressure to one at lower pressure.

Graham's law of effusion

Thomas Graham (1805–1869), a Scottish chemist, observed that the rate of effusion was dependent on the density of a gas. This observation led to **Graham's law of effusion:** The rates of effusion of two gases at the same temperature and

Bromine   Air   Bromine and air   Bromine and air

Figure 12.1   Diffusion of gases: When the stopcock between the two flasks is opened, colored bromine molecules can be seen diffusing into the flask containing air.

pressure are inversely proportional to the square roots of their densities or molecular weights,

$$\frac{\text{Rate of effusion of gas A}}{\text{Rate of effusion of gas B}} = \sqrt{\frac{dB}{dA}} = \sqrt{\frac{\text{mol. wt B}}{\text{mol. wt A}}}$$

A major application of Graham's law occurred during World War II with the separation of the isotopes of uranium-235 (U-235) and uranium-238 (U-238). Naturally occurring uranium consists of 0.7% U-235, 99.3% U-238, and a trace of U-234. However, only U-235 is useful as fuel for nuclear reactors and atomic bombs, so the concentration of U-235 in the mixture of isotopes had to be increased.

Uranium was first changed to uranium hexafluoride, UF_6, a white solid that readily goes into the gaseous state. The gaseous mixture of $^{235}UF_6$ and $^{238}UF_6$ was then allowed to effuse through porous walls. Although the effusion rate of the lighter gas is only slightly faster than that of the heavier one,

$$\frac{\text{Effusion rate } ^{235}UF_6}{\text{Effusion rate } ^{238}UF_6} = \sqrt{\frac{\text{Mol. wt } ^{238}UF_6}{\text{Mol. wt } ^{235}UF_6}} = \sqrt{\frac{352}{349}} = 1.0043$$

the separation and enrichment of U-235 was accomplished by subjecting the gaseous mixture to several thousand stages of effusion.

The properties of an ideal gas are independent of the molecular constitution of the gas. Mixtures of gases also obey the Kinetic-Molecular Theory if the gases in the mixture do not enter into a chemical reaction with one another.

12.3   Measurement of Pressure of Gases

pressure

Pressure is defined as force per unit area. Do gases exert pressure? Yes. When a rubber balloon is inflated with air, it stretches and maintains its larger size because the pressure on the inside is greater than that on the outside. Pressure results from the collisions of gas molecules with the walls of the balloon (see Figure 12.2). When the gas is released, the force or pressure of the air escaping from the small neck propels the balloon in a rapid, irregular flight. If the balloon

Figure 12.2 Pressure resulting from the collisions of gas molecules with the walls of the balloon keeps the balloon inflated.

is inflated until it bursts, the gas escaping all at once causes an explosive noise. This pressure that gases display can be measured; it can also be transformed into useful work. Steam under pressure, used in the steam locomotive, played an important role in the early development of the United States. Compressed steam is used today to generate at least part of the electricity for many cities. Compressed air is used to operate many different kinds of mechanical equipment.

The mass of air surrounding the earth is called the *atmosphere*. It is composed by volume of about 78% nitrogen, 21% oxygen, 1% argon, and other minor constituents (see Table 12.1). The outer boundary of the atmosphere is not known precisely, but more than 99% of the atmosphere is below an altitude of 20 miles (32 km). Thus, the concentration of gas molecules in the atmosphere decreases with altitude, and at about 4 miles the amount of oxygen is insufficient to sustain human life. The gases in the atmosphere exert a pressure known as **atmospheric pressure.** The pressure exerted by a gas depends on the number of molecules of gas present, the temperature, and the volume in which the gas is confined. Gravitational forces hold the atmosphere relatively close to the earth and prevent air molecules from flying off into outer space. Thus, the atmospheric pressure at any point is due to the mass of the atmosphere pressing downward at that point.

atmospheric pressure

The pressure of a gas can be measured with a pressure gauge, a manometer, or a **barometer.** A mercury barometer is commonly used in the laboratory to measure atmospheric pressure. A simple barometer of this type may be prepared by completely filling a long tube with pure, dry mercury and inverting the open end into an open dish of mercury. If the tube is longer than 760 mm, the mercury level will drop to a point at which the column of mercury in the tube is just

barometer

Table 12.1 Average composition of normal dry air

Gas	Percent by volume	Gas	Percent by volume
N_2	78.08	He	0.0005
O_2	20.95	CH_4	0.0002
Ar	0.93	Kr	0.0001
CO_2	0.033	Xe, H_2, and N_2O	Trace
Ne	0.0018		

Figure 12.3   Preparation of a mercury barometer: The full tube of mercury at the left is inverted and placed in a dish of mercury.

supported by the pressure of the atmosphere. If the tube is properly prepared, a vacuum will exist above the mercury column. The mass of mercury, per unit area, is equal to the pressure of the atmosphere. The column of mercury is supported by the pressure of the atmosphere, and the height of the column is a measure of this pressure (see Figure 12.3). The mercury barometer was invented in 1643 by the Italian physicist E. Torricelli (1608–1647), for whom the unit of pressure *torr* was named.

1 atmosphere   Air pressure is measured and expressed in many units. The standard atmospheric pressure, or simply **1 atmosphere,** is the pressure exerted by a column of mercury 760 mm high at a temperature of 0°C. The abbreviation for atmosphere is atm. The normal pressure of the atmosphere at sea level is 1 atm or 760 torr or 760 mm Hg. The SI unit for pressure is the pascal (Pa), where 1 atm = 101,325 Pa or 101.3 kPa. Other units for expressing pressure are inches of mercury, centimeters of mercury, the millibar (mbar), and pounds per square inch (lb/in.^{2} or psi). The meteorologist uses inches of mercury in reporting atmospheric pressure. The values of these units equivalent to 1 atm are summarized in Table 12.2 (1 atm ≡ 760 torr ≡ 760 mm Hg ≡ 76 cm Hg ≡ 101,325 Pa ≡ 1013 mbar ≡ 29.9 in. Hg ≡ 14.7 lb/in.^{2}). (The symbol ≡ means *identical with.*)

Atmospheric pressure varies with altitude. The average pressure at Denver, Colorado, 1.61 km (1 mile) above sea level, is 630 torr (0.83 atm). Atmospheric pressure is 0.5 atm at about 5.5 km (3.4 miles) altitude.

Other liquids besides mercury may be employed for barometers, but they are not as useful as mercury because of the difficulty of maintaining a vacuum above the liquid and because of impractical heights of the liquid column. For example, a pressure of 1 atm will support a column of water about 10,336 mm (33.9 ft) high.

Table 12.2 Pressure units
equivalent to 1 atmosphere

1 atm
760 torr
760 mm Hg
76 cm Hg
101,325 Pa
1013 mbar
29.9 in. Hg
14.7 lb/in.^{2}

Pressure is often measured by reading the heights of mercury columns in millimeters on barometers and manometers. Thus pressure may be recorded as mm Hg. But in many applications the torr is superseding mm Hg as a unit of pressure. In problems dealing with gases it is necessary to make interconversions among the various pressure units. Since atm, torr, and mm Hg are common pressure units, illustrative problems involving all three of these units are used in this text.

1 atm = 760 torr = 760 mm Hg

PROBLEM

12.1

The average atmospheric pressure at Walnut, California, is 740 mm Hg. Calculate this pressure in **(a)** torr and **(b)** atmospheres.

This problem can be solved using conversion factors relating one unit of pressure to another.

(a) To convert mm Hg to torr, use the conversion factor 760 torr/760 mm Hg (1 torr/1 mm Hg):

$$740 \text{ mm Hg} \times \frac{1 \text{ torr}}{1 \text{ mm Hg}} = 740 \text{ torr}$$

(b) To convert mm Hg to atm, use the conversion factor 1 atm/760 mm Hg:

$$740 \text{ mm Hg} \times \frac{1 \text{ atm}}{760 \text{ mm Hg}} = 0.934 \text{ atm}$$

12.4 **Dependence of Pressure on Number of Molecules and Temperature**

Pressure is produced by gas molecules colliding with the walls of a container. At a specific temperature and volume, the number of collisions depends on the number of gas molecules present. The number of collisions can be increased by

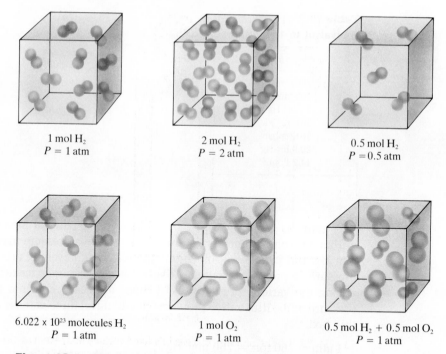

1 mol H_2
$P = 1$ atm

2 mol H_2
$P = 2$ atm

0.5 mol H_2
$P = 0.5$ atm

6.022×10^{23} molecules H_2
$P = 1$ atm

1 mol O_2
$P = 1$ atm

0.5 mol H_2 + 0.5 mol O_2
$P = 1$ atm

Figure 12.4   The pressure exerted by a gas is directly proportional to the number of molecules present. In each case shown, the volume is 22.4 L and the temperature is 0°C.

increasing the number of gas molecules present. If we double the number of molecules, the frequency of collisions and the pressure should double. We find, for an ideal gas, that this doubling is actually what happens: When the temperature and volume are kept constant, the pressure is directly proportional to the number of moles or molecules of gas present as shown in Figure 12.4.

A good example of this molecule–pressure relationship may be observed on an ordinary cylinder of compressed gas that is equipped with a pressure gauge. When the valve is opened, gas escapes from the cylinder. The volume of the cylinder is constant, and the decrease in quantity (moles) of gas is registered by a drop in pressure indicated on the gauge.

The pressure of a gas in a fixed volume also varies with temperature. When the temperature is increased, the kinetic energy of the molecules increases, causing more frequent collisions of the molecules with the walls of the container. This increase in collision frequency results in a pressure increase (see Figure 12.5).

12.5   Boyle's Law: The Relationship of the Volume and Pressure of a Gas

Robert Boyle demonstrated experimentally that, at constant temperature (T), the volume (V) of a fixed mass of a gas is inversely proportional to the pressure (P).

0°C
Volume = 1 liter
0.1 mole gas
$P = 2.24$ atm

100°C
Volume = 1 liter
0.1 mole gas
$P = 3.06$ atm

Figure 12.5 The pressure of a gas in a fixed volume increases with increasing temperature. The increased pressure is due to more frequent collisions of the gas molecules with the walls of the container at the higher temperature.

Boyle's law

This relationship of P and V is known as **Boyle's law.** Mathematically, Boyle's law may be expressed as

$$V \propto \frac{1}{P} \quad \text{(Mass and temperature are constant.)}$$

This equation says that the volume varies ($\propto$) inversely with the pressure, at constant mass and temperature. When the pressure on a gas is increased, its volume will decrease, and vice versa. The inverse relationship of pressure and volume is shown graphically in Figure 12.6.

Boyle demonstrated that, when he doubled the pressure on a specific quantity of a gas, keeping the temperature constant, the volume was reduced to one-half the original volume; when he tripled the pressure on the system, the new volume was one-third the original volume; and so on. His demonstration showed that the product of volume and pressure is constant if the temperature is not changed:

$$PV = \text{Constant} \quad \text{or} \quad PV = k \quad \text{(Mass and temperature are constant.)}$$

Let us demonstrate this law by using a cylinder with a movable piston so that the volume of gas inside the cylinder may be varied by changing the external pressure (see Figure 12.7). We assume that the temperature and the number of gas molecules do not change. Let us start with a volume of 1000 mL and a pressure of 1 atm. When we change the pressure to 2 atm, the gas molecules

Figure 12.6   Graph of pressure versus volume showing the inverse pressure–volume relationship of an ideal gas.

Figure 12.7   The effect of pressure on the volume of a gas

are crowded closer together, and the volume is reduced to 500 mL. When we increase the pressure to 4 atm, the volume becomes 250 mL.

Note that the product of the pressure times the volume in each case is the same number, substantiating Boyle's law. We may then say that

$$P_1V_1 = P_2V_2$$

where P_1V_1 is the product of the pressure times the volume at one set of conditions, and P_2V_2 is the product at another set of conditions. In each case the new volume may be calculated by multiplying the starting volume by a ratio of the two pressures involved. Of course, the ratio of pressures used must reflect the direction in which the volume should change. When the pressure is changed from 1 atm to 2 atm, the ratio to be used is 1 atm/2 atm. Now we can verify the results given in Figure 12.7:

(a) Starting volume, 1000 mL; pressure change, 1 atm ⟶ 2 atm

$$1000 \text{ mL} \times \frac{1 \text{ atm}}{2 \text{ atm}} = 500 \text{ mL}$$

(b) Starting volume, 1000 mL; pressure change, 1 atm ⟶ 4 atm

$$1000 \text{ mL} \times \frac{1 \text{ atm}}{4 \text{ atm}} = 250 \text{ mL}$$

(c) Starting volume, 500 mL; pressure change, 2 atm ⟶ 4 atm

$$500 \text{ mL} \times \frac{2 \text{ atm}}{4 \text{ atm}} = 250 \text{ mL}$$

In summary, a change in the volume of a gas due to a change in pressure can be calculated by multiplying the original volume by a ratio of the two pressures. If the pressure is increased, the ratio should have the smaller pressure in the numerator and the larger pressure in the denominator. If the pressure is decreased, the larger pressure should be in the numerator and the smaller pressure in the denominator.

New volume = Original volume × Ratio of pressures

Examples of problems based on Boyle's law follow. If no mention is made of temperature, assume that it remains constant.

PROBLEM

12.2

What volume will 2.50 L of a gas occupy if the pressure is changed from 760 torr to 630 torr?

First we must determine whether the pressure is being increased or decreased. In this case it is being decreased. This decrease in pressure should result in an increase in volume. Therefore, we need to multiply 2.50 L by a ratio of the pressures that will give us an increase in volume. This ratio is 760 torr/630 torr. The calculation is

$$V = 2.50 \text{ L} \times \frac{760 \text{ torr}}{630 \text{ torr}} = 3.02 \text{ L} \qquad \text{(New volume)}$$

Alternatively an algebraic approach may be used, solving $P_1V_1 = P_2V_2$ for V_2:

$$V_2 = V_1 \times \frac{P_1}{P_2} = 2.50 \text{ L} \times \frac{760 \text{ torr}}{630 \text{ torr}} = 3.02 \text{ L}$$

where $V_1 = 2.50$ L, $P_1 = 760$ torr, and $P_2 = 630$ torr

PROBLEM

12.3

A given mass of hydrogen occupies 40.0 L at 700 torr pressure. What volume will it occupy at 5.00 atm pressure?

Since the units of the two pressures are not the same, they must be made the same; otherwise, the units will not cancel in the final calculation. Because the pressure is increased, the volume should decrease. Therefore, we need to multiply 40.0 L by a ratio of the pressures that will give us a decrease in volume.

Step 1. Convert 700 torr to atmospheres by multiplying by the conversion factor 1 atm/760 torr:

$$700 \text{ torr} \times \frac{1 \text{ atm}}{760 \text{ torr}} = 0.921 \text{ atm}$$

Step 2. Multiply the volume (40.0 L) by a pressure ratio that will give a volume decrease:

$$V = 40.0 \text{ L} \times \frac{0.921 \text{ atm}}{5.00 \text{ atm}} = 7.37 \text{ L} \quad \text{(Answer)}$$

PROBLEM

12.4

A gas occupies a volume of 200 mL at 400 torr pressure. To what pressure must the gas be subjected in order to change the volume to 75.0 mL?

In order to reduce the volume from 200 mL to 75.0 mL, it will be necessary to increase the pressure. In the same way that we calculated volume change affected by a change in pressure, we must multiply the original pressure by a ratio of the two volumes. The volume ratio in this case is 200 mL/75.0 mL. The calculation is

New pressure = Original pressure × Ratio of volumes

$$P = 400 \text{ torr} \times \frac{200 \text{ mL}}{75.0 \text{ mL}} = 1067 \text{ torr} \quad \text{or} \quad 1.07 \times 10^3 \text{ torr} \quad \text{(New pressure)}$$

Algebraically, $P_1V_1 = P_2V_2$ may be solved for P_2:

$$P_2 = P_1 \times \frac{V_1}{V_2} = 400 \text{ torr} \times \frac{200 \text{ mL}}{75.0 \text{ mL}} = 1.07 \times 10^3 \text{ torr}$$

where $P_1 = 400$ torr, $V_1 = 200$ mL, and $V_2 = 75.0$ mL.

In problems of this type, it is good practice to check the answers to see if they are consistent with the given facts. For example, if the data indicate that the pressure is increased, the final volume should be smaller than the initial volume.

12.6   Charles' Law: The Effect of Temperature on the Volume of a Gas

The effect of temperature on the volume of a gas was observed in about 1787 by the French physicist J. A. C. Charles (1746–1823). Charles found that various gases expanded by the same fractional amount when heated through the same temperature interval. Later it was found that, if a given volume of any gas initially at 0°C was cooled by 1°C, the volume decreased by $\frac{1}{273}$; if cooled by 2°C,

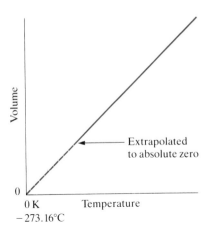

Figure 12.8 Volume–temperature relationship of gases: Extrapolated portion of the graph is shown by the broken line.

by $\frac{2}{273}$; if cooled by 20°C, by $\frac{20}{273}$; and so on. Since each degree of cooling reduced the volume by $\frac{1}{273}$, it was apparent that any quantity of any gas would have zero volume, if it could be cooled to −273°C. Of course no real gas can be cooled to −273°C for the simple reason that it liquefies before that temperature is reached. However, −273°C (more precisely, −273.16°C) is referred to as *absolute zero*; this temperature is the zero point on the Kelvin (absolute) temperature scale. It is the temperature at which the volume of an ideal, or perfect, gas would become zero.

The volume–temperature relationship for gases is shown graphically in Figure 12.8. Experimental data show the graph to be a straight line that, when extrapolated, crosses the temperature axis at −273.16°C, or absolute zero.

Charles' law

In modern form, **Charles' law** states that at constant pressure the volume of a fixed mass of any gas is directly proportional to the absolute temperature. Mathematically, Charles' law may be expressed as

$$V \propto T \qquad (P \text{ is constant})$$

which means that the volume of a gas varies directly with the absolute temperature when the pressure remains constant. In equation form Charles' law may be written as

$$V = kT \qquad \text{or} \qquad \frac{V}{T} = k \qquad (\text{At constant pressure})$$

where k is a constant for a fixed mass of the gas. If the absolute temperature of a gas is doubled, the volume will double. (A capital T is usually used for absolute temperature, K, and a small t for °C.)

To illustrate, let us return to the gas cylinder with the movable or free-floating piston (see Figure 12.9). Assume that the cylinder labeled (a) contains a quantity of gas and the pressure on it is 1 atm. When the gas is heated, the molecules move faster, and their kinetic energy increases. This action should increase the number

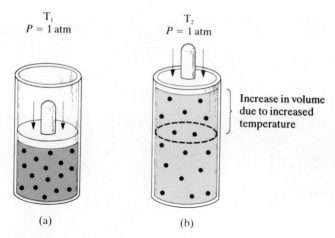

T_1
$P = 1$ atm

T_2
$P = 1$ atm

Increase in volume
due to increased
temperature

(a)   (b)

Figure 12.9   The effect of temperature on the volume of a gas: The gas in cylinder (a) is heated from T_1 to T_2. With the external pressure constant at 1 atm, the free-floating piston rises, resulting in an increased volume, as shown in cylinder (b).

of collisions per unit of time and therefore increase the pressure. However, the increased internal pressure will cause the piston to rise to a level at which the internal and external pressures again equal 1 atm, as we see in cylinder (b). The net result is an increase in volume due to an increase in temperature.

Another equation relating the volume of a gas at two different temperatures is

$$\frac{V_1}{T_1} = \frac{V_2}{T_2} \qquad \text{(Constant } P\text{)}$$

where V_1 and T_1 are one set of conditions and V_2 and T_2 are another set of conditions.

A simple experiment showing the variation of the volume of a gas with temperature is illustrated in Figure 12.10. A flask to which a balloon is attached is immersed in either ice water or hot water. In ice water the volume is reduced, as shown by the collapse of the balloon; in hot water the gas expands and the balloon increases in size.

The calculation of changes in volume due to changes in temperature involves two basic steps: (1) changing the temperatures to K and (2) multiplying the original volume by a ratio of the initial and final temperatures. If the temperature is increased, the higher temperature is placed in the numerator of the ratio and the lower temperature in the denominator. If the temperature is decreased, the lower temperature is placed in the numerator of the ratio and the higher temperature in the denominator.

New volume = Original volume × Ratio of temperatures (K)

Problems based on Charles' law follow.

0°C   25°C   85°C

Figure 12.10 The effect of temperature on the volume of a gas: A volume decrease occurs when a flask to which a balloon is attached is immersed in ice water; the volume increases when the flask is immersed in hot water.

PROBLEM

12.5

Three liters of hydrogen at −20°C are allowed to warm to a room temperature of 27°C. What is the volume at room temperature if the pressure remains constant?

Step 1. Change °C to K:

$$°C + 273 = K$$

$$−20°C + 273 = 253 \ K$$

$$27°C + 273 = 300 \ K$$

Step 2. Since the temperature is increased, the volume should increase. The original volume should be multiplied by the temperature ratio of 300 K/253 K. The calculation is

$$V = 3.00 \ L \times \frac{300 \ \cancel{K}}{253 \ \cancel{K}} = 3.56 \ L \qquad \text{(New volume)}$$

To obtain the answer by algebra, solve $V_1/T_1 = V_2/T_2$ for V_2:

$$V_2 = V_1 \times \frac{T_2}{T_1} = 3.00 \ L \times \frac{300 \ \cancel{K}}{253 \ \cancel{K}} = 3.56 \ L$$

where $V_1 = 3.00 \ L$, $T_1 = 253 \ K$, and $T_2 = 300 \ K$.

PROBLEM

12.6

If 20.0 L of nitrogen are cooled from 100°C to 0°C, what is the new volume?
Since no mention is made of pressure, assume that pressure does not change.

Step 1. Change °C to K:

$$100°C + 273 = 373 \text{ K}$$

$$0°C + 273 = 273 \text{ K}$$

Step 2. The ratio of temperatures to be used is 273 K/373 K, because the final volume should be smaller than the original volume. The calculation is

$$V = 20.0 \text{ L} \times \frac{273 \text{ K}}{373 \text{ K}} 14.6 \text{ L} \quad \text{(New volume)}$$

Three variables—pressure, P; volume, V; and temperature, T—are needed to describe a fixed amount of a gas. Boyle's law, $PV = k$, relates pressure and volume at constant temperature; Charles' law, $V = kT$, relates volume and temperature at constant pressure. A third relationship involving pressure and temperature at constant volume is stated: The pressure of a fixed mass of a gas, at constant volume, is directly proportional to the Kelvin temperature. In equation form the relationship is

$$P = kT \quad \text{(At constant volume)} \qquad \frac{P_1}{T_1} = \frac{P_2}{T_2}$$

This relationship is a modification of Charles' law and is sometimes called Gay-Lussac's law.

We may summarize the effects of changes in pressure, temperature, and quantity of a gas as follows:

1. In the case of a fixed or constant volume,
   (a) when the temperature is increased, the pressure increases.
   (b) when the quantity of a gas is increased, the pressure increases (T remaining constant).
2. In the case of a variable volume,
   (a) when the external pressure is increased, the volume decreases (T remaining constant).
   (b) when the temperature of a gas is increased, the volume increases (P remaining constant).
   (c) when the quantity of a gas is increased, the volume increases (P and T remaining constant).

12.7   Standard Temperature and Pressure

standard
conditions

standard
temperature
and pressure
(STP)

In order to compare volumes of gases, common reference points of temperature and pressure were selected and called **standard conditions** or **standard temperature and pressure** (abbreviated **STP**). Standard temperature is 273 K (0°C), and standard pressure is 1 atm or 760 torr or 760 mm Hg. For purposes of comparison, volumes of gases are usually changed to STP conditions.

> **Standard temperature = 273 K or 0°C**
>
> **Standard pressure = 1 atm or 760 torr or 760 mm Hg**

Combined Gas Laws: Simultaneous Changes in Pressure, Volume, and Temperature

When temperature and pressure change at the same time, the new volume may be calculated by multiplying the initial volume by the correct ratios of both pressure and temperature, as follows:

$$\text{Final volume} = \text{Initial volume} \times \left(\begin{array}{c}\text{Ratio of} \\ \text{pressures}\end{array}\right) \times \left(\begin{array}{c}\text{Ratio of} \\ \text{temperatures}\end{array}\right)$$

This equation combines Boyle's and Charles' laws, and the same considerations for the pressure and the temperature ratios should be used in the calculation. The four possible variations are:

1. Both T and P cause an increase in volume.
2. Both T and P cause a decrease in volume.
3. T causes an increase and P causes a decrease in volume.
4. T causes a decrease and P causes an increase in volume.

The P, V, and T relationships for a given mass of any gas, in fact, may be expressed as a single equation, $PV/T = k$. For problem solving this equation is usually written

$$\frac{P_1 V_1}{T_1} = \frac{P_2 V_2}{T_2}$$

where P_1, V_1, and T_1 are the initial conditions and P_2, V_2, and T_2 are the final conditions.

This equation can be solved for any one of the six variables and is useful in dealing with the pressure–volume–temperature relationships of gases. Note that when T is constant ($T_1 = T_2$), Boyle's law is represented; when P is constant ($P_1 = P_2$), Charles' law is represented; and when V is constant ($V_1 = V_2$), the modified Charles' law, or Gay-Lussac's law, is represented.

PROBLEM

12.7

Given 20.0 L of ammonia gas at 5°C and 730 torr pressure, calculate the volume at 50°C and 800 torr.

In order to get a better look at the data, tabulate the initial and final conditions:

	Initial	*Final*
V	20.0 L	V_2
T	5°C	50°C
P	730 torr	800 torr

Step 1. Change °C to K:

$$5°C + 273 = 278 \text{ K}$$

$$50°C + 273 = 323 \text{ K}$$

Step 2. Set up ratios of T and P:

$$T \text{ ratio} = \frac{323 \text{ K}}{278 \text{ K}} \qquad \text{(Increase in } T \text{ should increase V.)}$$

$$P \text{ ratio} = \frac{730 \text{ torr}}{800 \text{ torr}} \qquad \text{(Increase in } P \text{ should decrease V.)}$$

Step 3. The calculation is

$$V_2 = 20.0 \text{ L} \times \frac{730 \text{ torr}}{800 \text{ torr}} \times \frac{323 \text{ K}}{278 \text{ K}} = 21.2 \text{ L}$$

The algebraic solution is:

Solve $\quad \dfrac{P_1 V_1}{T_1} = \dfrac{P_2 V_2}{T_2} \quad$ for V_2 by multiplying both sides of the equation by T_2/P_2 and rearranging to obtain

$$V_2 = \frac{V_1 \times P_1 \times T_2}{P_2 \times T_1}$$

Tabulate the known values:

$V_1 = 20.0 \text{ L}$ $\qquad\qquad$ $V_2 = ?$

$T_1 = 5°C + 273 = 278 \text{ K}$ $\qquad$ $T_2 = 50°C + 273 = 323 \text{ K}$

$P_1 = 730 \text{ torr}$ $\qquad\qquad$ $P_2 = 800 \text{ torr}$

Substitute these values in the equation and calculate the value of V_2:

$$V_2 = \frac{20.0 \text{ L} \times 730 \text{ torr} \times 323 \text{ K}}{800 \text{ torr} \times 278 \text{ K}} = 21.2 \text{ L}$$

PROBLEM

12.8

To what temperature (°C) must 10.0 L of nitrogen at 25°C and 700 torr be heated in order to have a volume of 15.0 L and a pressure of 760 torr?

This problem is conveniently handled by an algebraic solution:

Solve $\quad \dfrac{P_1 V_1}{T_1} = \dfrac{P_2 V_2}{T_2} \quad$ for T_2 to obtain $\quad T_2 = \dfrac{T_1 \times P_2 \times V_2}{P_1 \times V_1}$

Tabulate the known values:

$P_1 = 700 \text{ torr}$ $\qquad\qquad$ $P_2 = 760 \text{ torr}$

$V_1 = 10.0 \text{ L}$ $\qquad\qquad$ $V_2 = 15.0 \text{ L}$

$T_1 = 25°C + 273 = 298 \text{ K}$ $\qquad$ $T_2 = ?$

Substitute these known values in the equation and calculate T_2:

$$T_2 = \frac{298 \text{ K} \times 760 \text{ torr} \times 15.0 \text{ L}}{700 \text{ torr} \times 10.0 \text{ L}} = 485 \text{ K}$$

Since the problem asks for °C, we must subtract 273 from the K answer:

485 K − 273 = 212°C   (Answer)

PROBLEM

12.9

The volume of a gas-filled balloon is 50.0 L at 20°C and 742 torr. What volume will it occupy at standard temperature and pressure (STP)?

Tabulate the data:

	Initial	Final
V	50.0 L	V_2
T	20°C	273 K
P	742 torr	760 torr

Step 1. STP conditions are 273 K and 760 torr. First change °C to K:

20°C + 273 = 293 K

Step 2. Set up ratios of T and P:

$$T \text{ ratio} = \frac{273 \text{ K}}{293 \text{ K}}$$ [Decrease in T (293 K to 273 K) should decrease V.]

$$P \text{ ratio} = \frac{742 \text{ torr}}{760 \text{ torr}}$$ [Increase in P (742 torr to 760 torr) should decrease V.]

Step 3. The calculation is

$$V_2 = 50.0 \text{ L} \times \frac{273 \text{ K}}{293 \text{ K}} \times \frac{742 \text{ torr}}{760 \text{ torr}} = 45.5 \text{ L}$$

The problem can also be done by solving $\dfrac{P_1 V_1}{T_1} = \dfrac{P_2 V_2}{T_2}$ for V_2 and substituting P, V, and T values in the new equation.

12.9   Dalton's Law of Partial Pressures

Dalton's law of partial pressures

If gases behave according to the Kinetic-Molecular Theory, there should be no difference in the pressure–volume–temperature relationships whether the gas molecules are all the same or different. This similarity in the behavior of gases is the basis for an understanding of **Dalton's law of partial pressures,** which states that the total pressure of a mixture of gases is the sum of the partial pressures exerted by each of the gases in the mixture. Each gas in the mixture exerts a pressure that is independent of the other gases present. These pressures are called *partial pressures*. Thus, if we have a mixture of three gases, A, B, and C,

Oxygen from → generator

← Oxygen plus water vapor

Figure 12.11   Oxygen collected over water

exerting partial pressures of 50 torr, 150 torr, and 400 torr, respectively, the total pressure will be 600 torr:

$$P_{Total} = P_A + P_B + P_C$$

$$P_{Total} = 50 \text{ torr} + 150 \text{ torr} + 400 \text{ torr} = 600 \text{ torr}$$

We can see an application of Dalton's law in the collection of insoluble gases over water. When prepared in the laboratory, oxygen is commonly collected by the downward displacement of water. Thus the oxygen is not pure but is mixed with water vapor (see Figure 12.11). When the water levels are adjusted to the same height inside and outside the bottle, the pressure of the oxygen plus water vapor inside the bottle is equal to the atmospheric pressure:

$$P_{atm} = P_{O_2} + P_{H_2O}$$

$$P_{O_2} = P_{atm} - P_{H_2O}$$

To determine the amount of O_2 or any other gas collected over water, we must subtract the pressure of the water vapor from the total pressure of the gas. The vapor pressure of water at various temperatures is tabulated in Appendix II.

An illustrative problem follows.

PROBLEM

12.10

A 500 mL sample of oxygen, O_2, was collected over water at 23°C and 760 torr pressure. What volume will the dry O_2 occupy at 23°C and 760 torr? The vapor pressure of water at 23°C is 21.2 torr.

To solve this problem we must first find the pressure of the O_2 alone by substracting the pressure of the water vapor present:

$$P_{Total} = 760 \text{ torr} = P_{O_2} + P_{H_2O}$$

$$P_{O_2} = 760 \text{ torr} - 21.2 \text{ torr} = 739 \text{ torr}$$

Thus the pressure of dry O_2 is 739 torr.

The problem is now of the Boyle's law type. It is treated as if we had 500 mL of dry O_2 at 739 torr pressure, which is then changed to 760 torr pressure with the temperature remaining constant. The calculation is

$$V = 500 \text{ mL} \times \frac{739 \text{ torr}}{760 \text{ torr}} = 486 \text{ mL dry } O_2$$

This means that 486 mL of the 500 mL mixture of O_2 and water vapor is pure O_2.

12.10 Avogadro's Law

Gay-Lussac's law of combining volumes of gases

Early in the 19th century, J. L. Gay-Lussac (1778–1850) of France studied the volume relationships of reacting gases. His results, published in 1809, were summarized in a statement known as **Gay-Lussac's law of combining volumes of gases:** *When measured at the same temperature and pressure, the ratios of the volumes of reacting gases are small whole numbers.* Thus, H_2 and O_2 combine to form water vapor in a volume ratio of 2 to 1 (Figure 12.12); H_2 and Cl_2 react to form HCl in a volume ratio of 1 to 1; and H_2 and N_2 react to form NH_3 in a volume ratio of 3 to 1.

Two years later, in 1811, Amedeo Avogadro used the law of combining volumes of gases to make a simple but significant and far-reaching generalization concerning gases. **Avogadro's law** states:

Avogadro's law

> **Equal volumes of different gases at the same temperature and pressure contain the same number of molecules.**

This law was a real breakthrough in understanding the nature of gases: (1) It offered a rational explanation of Gay-Lussac's law of combining volumes of gases and indicated the diatomic nature of such elemental gases as hydrogen, chlorine, and oxygen; (2) it provided a method for determining the molecular weights of gases and for comparing the densities of gases of known molecular weight (see Sections 12.11 and 12.12); and (3) it afforded a firm foundation for the development of the Kinetic-Molecular Theory.

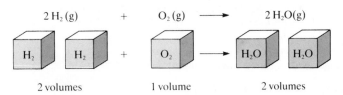

Figure 12.12 Gay-Lussac's law of combining volumes of gases applied to the reaction of hydrogen and oxygen. When measured at the same temperature and pressure. hydrogen and oxygen react in a volume ratio of 2 to 1.

On a volume basis, hydrogen and chlorine react thus:

Hydrogen + Chlorine $\longrightarrow$ Hydrogen chloride

  1 volume   1 volume   2 volumes

By Avogadro's law, equal volumes of hydrogen and chlorine contain the same number of molecules. Therefore, hydrogen molecules react with chlorine molecules in a 1:1 ratio. Since two volumes of hydrogen chloride are produced, one molecule of hydrogen and one molecule of chlorine must produce two molecules of hydrogen chloride. Therefore, each hydrogen molecule and each chlorine molecule must be made up of two atoms. The coefficients of the balanced equation for the reaction give the correct ratios for volumes, molecules, and moles of reactants and products:

$$H_2 \quad + \quad Cl_2 \quad \longrightarrow \quad 2\ HCl$$

  1 volume   1 volume   2 volumes
1 molecule 1 molecule   2 molecules
  1 mol   1 mol   2 mol

By like reasoning, oxygen molecules also must contain at least two atoms because one volume of oxygen reacts with two volumes of hydrogen to produce two volumes of water vapor.

The volume of a gas depends on the temperature, the pressure, and the number of gas molecules. Different gases at the same temperature have the same average kinetic energy. Hence, if two different gases are at the same temperature, occupy equal volumes, and exhibit equal pressures, each gas must contain the same number of molecules. This statement is true because systems with identical PVT properties can be produced only by equal numbers of molecules having the same average kinetic energy.

12.11   Mole–Mass–Volume Relationship of Gases

molar volume of a gas

Because a mole contains 6.022×10^{23} molecules (Avogadro's number), a mole of any gas will have the same volume as a mole of any other gas at the same temperature and pressure. It has been experimentally determined that the volume occupied by a mole of any gas is 22.4 L at standard temperature and pressure. This volume, 22.4 L, is known as the **molar volume of a gas.** The molar volume is a cube about 28.2 cm (11.1 in.) on a side (see Figure 12.13). The molecular weights of several gases, each occupying 22.4 L at STP, are also shown in Figure 12.13.

> **One mole of a gas occupies 22.4 L at STP.**

The molar volume is useful for determining the molecular weight of a gas or of substances that can be easily vaporized. If the mass and the volume of a gas at STP are known, we can calculate its molecular weight. For example, 1 liter of pure oxygen at STP weighs 1.429 g. The molecular weight of oxygen may be

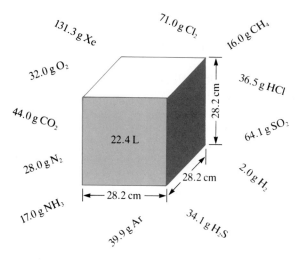

Figure 12.13 One mole of a gas occupies 22.4 L at STP. The weight given for each gas is the weight of one mole.

calculated by multiplying the weight of 1 liter by 22.4 L/mol:

$$\frac{1.429 \text{ g}}{1 \text{ L}} \times \frac{22.4 \text{ L}}{1 \text{ mol}} = 32.0 \text{ g/mol} \quad \text{(mol. wt)}$$

If the mass and volume are at other than standard conditions, we change the volume to STP and then calculate the molecular weight. Note that we do not correct the mass to standard conditions—only the volume.

The molar volume, 22.4 L/mol, is used as a conversion factor to convert grams per liter to grams per mole (mol. wt) and also to convert liters to moles. The two conversion factors are

$$\frac{22.4 \text{ L}}{1 \text{ mol}} \quad \text{and} \quad \frac{1 \text{ mol}}{22.4 \text{ L}}$$

These conversions must be done at STP except under certain special circumstances. Examples follow.

PROBLEM

12.11

If 2.00 L of a gas measured at STP weigh 3.23 g, what is the molecular weight of the gas? The unit of molecular weight is g/mol; the conversion is from

$$\frac{\text{g}}{\text{L}} \longrightarrow \frac{\text{g}}{\text{mol}}$$

The starting amount is $\dfrac{3.23 \text{ g}}{2.00 \text{ L}}$. The conversion factor is $\dfrac{22.4 \text{ L}}{1 \text{ mol}}$.

The calculation is $\dfrac{3.23 \text{ g}}{2.00 \text{ L}} \times \dfrac{22.4 \text{ L}}{1 \text{ mol}} = 36.2 \text{ g/mol} \quad \text{(mol. wt)}$

PROBLEM

12.12

Measured at 40°C and 630 torr, 691 mL of ethyl ether weigh 1.65 g. Calculate the molecular weight of ethyl ether.

In order to use 22.4 L/mol, we must first calculate the volume at STP.

630 torr $\longrightarrow$ 760 torr   (Standard pressure)

40°C (313 K) $\longrightarrow$ 273 K   (Standard temperature)

$$V = 691 \text{ mL} \times \frac{273 \ K}{313 \ K} \times \frac{630 \ \text{torr}}{760 \ \text{torr}} = 500 \text{ mL} = 0.500 \text{ L} \quad \text{(At STP)}$$

The mass of the gas has not been altered by changing the volume to STP, so 0.500 L at STP weighs 1.65 g. The conversion is from g/L to g/mol:

$$\frac{1.65 \text{ g}}{0.500 \ L} \times \frac{22.4 \ L}{\text{mol}} = 73.9 \text{ g/mol} \quad \text{(mol. wt)}$$

12.12   **Density and Specific Gravity of Gases**

The density, d, of a gas is its mass per unit volume, which is generally expressed in grams per liter (g/L) as follows:

$$d = \frac{\text{mass}}{\text{volume}} = \frac{\text{g}}{\text{L}}$$

Because the volume of a gas depends on temperature and pressure, both should be given when stating the density of a gas. The volume of a solid or liquid is hardly affected by changes in pressure and is changed only slightly when the temperature is varied. Increasing the temperature from 0°C to 50°C will reduce the density of a gas by about 18% if the gas is allowed to expand, whereas a 50°C rise in the temperature of water (from 0°C to 50°C) will change its density by less than 0.2%.

The density of a gas at any temperature and pressure can be determined by calculating the weight of gas present in 1 liter. At STP, in particular, the density can be calculated by multiplying the molecular weight of the gas by 1 mol/22.4 L.

$$d \text{ (at STP)} = \text{mol. wt} \times \frac{1 \text{ mol}}{22.4 \text{ L}} \qquad \text{mol. wt} = d \text{ (at STP)} \times \frac{22.4 \text{ L}}{1 \text{ mol}}$$

PROBLEM

12.13

Calculate the density of Cl_2 at STP.

First calculate the molecular weight of Cl_2. It is 71.0 g/mol. Since $d = $ g/L, the conversion is

$$\frac{\text{g}}{\text{mol}} \longrightarrow \frac{\text{g}}{\text{L}}$$

The conversion factor is $\dfrac{1 \text{ mol}}{22.4 \text{ L}}$.

$$d = \frac{71.0 \text{ g}}{1 \text{ mol}} \times \frac{1 \text{ mol}}{22.4 \text{ L}} = 3.17 \text{ g/L}$$

The specific gravity (sp gr) of a gas is the ratio of the mass of any volume of the gas to the mass of an equal volume of some reference gas. Specific gravities of gases are commonly quoted in reference to air. The mass of air at STP is 1.29 g/L, which is the density of air.

The specific gravity of a gas can be calculated by dividing its density by the density of air. Both gases must be at the same temperature and pressure.

$$\text{sp gr} = \frac{\text{Density of a gas}}{\text{Density of air}}$$

The specific gravity of Cl_2, for example, is

$$\text{sp gr of } Cl_2 = \frac{\text{Density of } Cl_2}{\text{Density of air}} = \frac{3.17 \text{ g/L}}{1.29 \text{ g/L}} = 2.46$$

This indicates that Cl_2 is 2.46 times as heavy as air. Table 12.3 lists the densities and specific gravities of some common gases.

Table 12.3   Density and specific gravity of common gases at STP

Gas	Molecular weight	Density (g/L at STP)	Specific gravity (unitless)
H_2	2.0	0.090	0.070
CH_4	16.0	0.714	0.553
NH_3	17.0	0.760	0.589
C_2H_2	26.0	1.16	0.899
HCN	27.0	1.21	0.938
CO	28.0	1.25	0.969
N_2	28.0	1.25	0.969
O_2	32.0	1.43	1.11
H_2S	34.1	1.52	1.18
HCl	36.5	1.63	1.26
F_2	38.0	1.70	1.32
CO_2	44.0	1.96	1.52
C_3H_8	44.0	1.96	1.52
O_3	48.0	2.14	1.66
SO_2	64.1	2.86	2.22
Cl_2	71.0	3.17	2.46

12.13   Ideal Gas Equation

We have used four variables in calculations involving gases: the volume, V; the pressure, P; the absolute temperature, T; and the number of molecules or moles, which is abbreviated n. Combining these variables into a single expression, we obtain

$$V \propto \frac{nT}{P} \quad \text{or} \quad V = \frac{nRT}{P}$$

where R is a proportionality constant known as the *ideal gas constant*. The equation is commonly written as

$$PV = nRT$$

ideal gas equation

and is known as the **ideal gas equation.** This equation states in a single expression what we have considered in our earlier discussions: The volume of a gas varies directly with the number of gas molecules and the absolute temperature and varies inversely with the pressure. The value and units of R depend on the units of P, V, and T. We can calculate one value of R by taking 1 mol of a gas at STP conditions. Solve the equation for R:

$$R = \frac{PV}{nT} = \frac{1 \text{ atm} \times 22.4 \text{ L}}{1 \text{ mol} \times 273 \text{ K}} = 0.0821 \ \frac{\text{L-atm}}{\text{mol-K}}$$

The units of R in this case are liter-atmospheres (L-atm) per mol-K.

The ideal gas equation can be used to calculate any one of the four variables if the other three are known.

When the value of $R = 0.0821$ L-atm/mol-K, P is in atmospheres, n is in moles, V is in liters, and T is in Kelvin.

PROBLEM

12.14

What pressure will be exerted by 0.400 mol of a gas in a 5.00 L container at 17.0°C?

First solve the ideal gas equation for P:

$$PV = nRT \quad \text{or} \quad P = \frac{nRT}{V}$$

Then substitute the data in the problem into the equation and solve (change °C to K):

$$P = \frac{0.400 \ \cancel{\text{mol}} \times 290 \ \cancel{K} \times 0.0821 \ \cancel{\text{L}}\text{-atm}}{5.00 \ \cancel{\text{L}} \times \cancel{\text{mol-K}}} = 1.90 \text{ atm} \quad \text{(Answer)}$$

PROBLEM

12.15

How many moles of oxygen gas are in a 50.0 L tank at 22.0°C if the pressure gauge reads 2000 lb/in.²?

First change the pressure to atmospheres and °C to K. Then solve the ideal gas equation for n (moles), and substitute the data into the equation to complete the calculation.

Step 1. Change pressure to atmospheres and °C to K:

$$\frac{2000 \text{ lb}}{\text{in.}^2} \times \frac{1 \text{ atm}}{14.7 \text{ lb/in.}^2} = 136 \text{ atm}$$

$$22.0°C + 273 = 295 \text{ K}$$

Step 2. Solve for moles using the ideal gas equation:

$$PV = nRT \quad \text{or} \quad n = \frac{PV}{RT}$$

$$n = \frac{136 \text{ atm} \times 50.0 \text{ L}}{(0.0821 \text{ L atm}/\text{mol·K}) \times 295 \text{ K}} = 281 \text{ mol } O_2 \quad \text{(Answer)}$$

The molecular weight of a gaseous substance can be determined using the ideal gas equation. Since mol. wt = g/mol, then mol = g/mol. wt. Using MW for molecular weight, we can substitute g/MW for n (moles) in the ideal gas equation to get

$$PV = \frac{g}{MW} RT \quad \text{or} \quad MW = \frac{gRT}{PV}$$

which will allow us to calculate the molecular weight, MW, for any substance in the gaseous state.

PROBLEM

12.16

Calculate the molecular weight of butane gas if 3.69 g occupy 1.53 L at 20°C and 1 atm pressure.

Change 20°C to 293 K and substitute the data into the equation:

$$MW = \frac{gRT}{PV} = \frac{3.69 \text{ g} \times 293 \text{ K} \times 0.0821 \text{ L atm}}{1 \text{ atm} \times 1.53 \text{ L} \times \text{mol·K}} = 58.0 \text{ g/mol} \quad \text{(Answer)}$$

12.14 Calculations from Chemical Equations Involving Gases

1. Mole–volume (gas) and mass–volume (gas) calculations. Stoichiometric problems involving gas volumes can be solved by the general mole-ratio method outlined in Chapter 11. The factors 1 mol/22.4 L and 22.4 L/1 mol are used for converting volume to moles and moles to volume, respectively. These conversion factors are used under the assumption that the gases are at STP and behave as ideal gases. In practice, gases are measured at other than STP conditions, and the volumes are converted to STP for stoichiometric calculations.

In a balanced equation, the number preceding the formula of a gaseous substance represents the number of moles or molar volumes (22.4 L at STP) of that substance.

The following are examples of typical problems involving gases and chemical equations.

PROBLEM

12.17

What volume of oxygen (at STP) can be formed from 0.500 mol of potassium chlorate?

Step 1. Write the balanced equation:

$$2 \text{ KClO}_3 \longrightarrow 2 \text{ KCl} + 3 \text{ O}_2 \uparrow$$
$$ 2 \text{ mol} 3 \text{ mol}$$

Step 2. The starting amount is 0.500 mol $KClO_3$. The conversion is from

$$\text{mol KClO}_3 \longrightarrow \text{mol O}_2 \longrightarrow \text{L O}_2$$

Step 3. Calculate the moles of O_2, using the mole-ratio method:

$$0.500 \text{ mol KClO}_3 \times \frac{3 \text{ mol O}_2}{2 \text{ mol KClO}_3} = 0.750 \text{ mol O}_2$$

Step 4. Convert moles of O_2 to liters of O_2. The moles of a gas at STP are converted to liters by multiplying by the molar volume, 22.4 L/mol:

$$0.750 \text{ mol O}_2 \times \frac{22.4 \text{ L}}{1 \text{ mol}} = 16.8 \text{ L O}_2 \quad \text{(Answer)}$$

Setting up a continuous calculation, we obtain

$$0.500 \text{ mol KClO}_3 \times \frac{3 \text{ mol O}_2}{2 \text{ mol KClO}_3} \times \frac{22.4 \text{ L}}{1 \text{ mol}} = 16.8 \text{ L O}_2$$

PROBLEM

12.18

How many grams of aluminum must react with sulfuric acid to produce 1.25 L of hydrogen gas at STP?

Step 1. The balanced equation is

$$2 \text{ Al}(s) + 3 \text{ H}_2\text{SO}_4(aq) \longrightarrow \text{Al}_2(\text{SO}_4)_3(aq) + 3 \text{ H}_2(g)$$
$$2 \text{ mol} 3 \text{ mol}$$

Step 2. We first convert liters of H_2 to moles of H_2. Then the familiar stoichiometric calculation from the equation is used. The conversion is:

$$\text{L H}_2 \longrightarrow \text{mol H}_2 \longrightarrow \text{mol Al} \longrightarrow \text{g Al}$$

$$1.25 \text{ L H}_2 \times \frac{1 \text{ mol}}{22.4 \text{ L}} \times \frac{2 \text{ mol Al}}{3 \text{ mol H}_2} \times \frac{27.0 \text{ g Al}}{1 \text{ mol Al}} = 1.00 \text{ g Al} \quad \text{(Answer)}$$

PROBLEM

12.19

What volume of hydrogen, collected at 30°C and 700 torr pressure, will be formed by reacting 50.0 g of aluminum with hydrochloric acid?

$$2 \text{ Al(s)} + 6 \text{ HCl(aq)} \longrightarrow 2 \text{ AlCl}_3\text{(aq)} + 3 \text{ H}_2\text{(g)}$$

2 mol   3 mol

In this problem the conditions are not at STP, so we cannot use the method shown in Problem 12.17. Either we need to calculate the volume at STP from the equation and then convert this volume to the conditions given in the problem, or we can use the ideal gas equation. Let's use the ideal gas equation.

First calculate the moles of H_2 obtained from 50.0 g of Al. Then, using the ideal gas equation, calculate the volume of H_2 at the conditions given in the problem.

Step 1. Moles of H_2: The conversion is

$$\text{grams Al} \longrightarrow \text{moles Al} \longrightarrow \text{moles H}_2$$

$$50.0 \text{ g Al} \times \frac{1 \text{ mol Al}}{27.0 \text{ g Al}} \times \frac{3 \text{ mol H}_2}{2 \text{ mol Al}} = 2.78 \text{ mol H}_2$$

Step 2. Liters of H_2: Solve $PV = nRT$ for V and substitute the data into the equation.
Convert °C to K: 30°C + 273 = 303 K.
Convert torr to atm: 700 torr × 1 atm/760 torr = 0.921 atm.

$$V = \frac{nRT}{P} = \frac{2.78 \text{ mol H}_2 \times 0.0821 \text{ L·atm} \times 303 \text{ K}}{0.921 \text{ atm} \times \text{mol·K}} = 75.1 \text{ L H}_2 \quad \text{(Answer)}$$

Note: The volume at STP is 62.3 L H_2.

---

2. Volume–volume calculations. When all substances in a reaction are in the gaseous state, simplifications in the calculation can be made that are based on Avogadro's law that gases under identical conditions of temperature and pressure contain the same number of molecules and occupy the same volume. Using this same law, we can also state that, under the same conditions of temperature and pressure, the volumes of gases reacting are proportional to the numbers of moles of the gases in the balanced equation. Consider the reaction

$$\text{H}_2\text{(g)} + \text{Cl}_2\text{(g)} \longrightarrow 2 \text{ HCl(g)}$$

1 mol	1 mol	2 mol
22.4 L	22.4 L	2 × 22.4 L
1 volume	1 volume	2 volumes
Y volume	Y volume	2Y volumes

In this reaction 22.4 L of hydrogen will react with 22.4 L of chlorine to give 2 × 22.4 = 44.8 L of hydrogen chloride gas. This statement is true because these volumes are equivalent to the number of reacting moles in the equation. Therefore, Y volumes of H_2 will combine with Y volumes of Cl_2 to give 2 Y volumes of HCl. For example, 100 L of H_2 react with 100 L of Cl_2 to give 200 L of HCl; if the 100 L of H_2 and of Cl_2 are at 50°C, they will give 200 L of HCl at 50°C. When the temperature and pressure before and after a reaction are the same, volumes can be calculated without changing the volumes to STP.

For reacting gases: Volume–volume relationships are the same as mole–mole relationships.

PROBLEM

12.20

What volume of oxygen will react with 150 L of hydrogen to form water vapor? What volume of water vapor will be formed?

Assume that both reactants and products are measured at the same conditions. Calculation by reacting volumes:

2 H$_2$(g)	+ O$_2$(g)	$\longrightarrow$	2 H$_2$O(g)
2 mol	1 mol		2 mol
2 × 22.4 L	22.4 L		2 × 22.4 L
2 volumes	1 volume		2 volumes
150 L	75 L		150 L

Thus, 150 L of H$_2$ will react with 75 L of O$_2$ to produce 150 L of H$_2$O(g). For every two volumes of H$_2$ that react, one volume of O$_2$ and two volumes of H$_2$O(g) are produced.

PROBLEM

12.21

The equation for the preparation of ammonia is

$$3 \text{ H}_2(g) + \text{N}_2(g) \xrightarrow{400°C} 2 \text{ NH}_3(g)$$

Assuming that the reaction goes to completion,

(a) What volume of H$_2$ will react with 50.0 L of N$_2$?
(b) What volume of NH$_3$ will be formed from 50.0 L of N$_2$?
(c) What volume of N$_2$ will react with 100 mL of H$_2$?
(d) What volume of NH$_3$ will be produced from 100 mL of H$_2$?
(e) If 600 mL of H$_2$ and 400 mL of N$_2$ are sealed in a flask and allowed to react, what amounts of H$_2$, N$_2$, and NH$_3$ are in the flask at the end of the reaction?

The answers to parts **(a)–(d)** are shown in the boxes and can be determined from the equation by inspection, using the principle of reacting volumes.

3 H$_2$	+	N$_2$	$\longrightarrow$	2 NH$_3$
3 volumes		1 volume		2 volumes

(a) | 150 L | 50 L

(b) 50 L | 100 L

(c) 100 mL | 33.3 mL

(d) 100 mL | 66.7 mL

(e) Volume ratio from the equation = $\dfrac{3 \text{ volumes H}_2}{1 \text{ volume N}_2}$

Volume ratio used = $\dfrac{600 \text{ mL H}_2}{400 \text{ mL N}_2} = \dfrac{3 \text{ volumes H}_2}{2 \text{ volumes N}_2}$

Comparing these two ratios, we see that an excess of N$_2$ is present in the gas mixture. Therefore, the reactant limiting the amount of NH$_3$ that can be formed is H$_2$:

3 H$_2$	+	N$_2$	$\longrightarrow$	2 NH$_3$
600 mL		200 mL		400 mL

In order to have a 3:1 ratio of volumes reacting, 600 mL of H_2 will react with 200 mL of N_2 to produce 400 mL of NH_3, leaving 200 mL of N_2 unreacted. At the end of the reaction, the flask will contain 400 mL of NH_3 and 200 mL of N_2.

All the gas laws are based on the behavior of an ideal gas—that is, a gas with a behavior that is described exactly by the gas laws for all possible values of P, V, and T. Most real gases actually do behave very nearly as predicted by the gas laws over a fairly wide range of temperatures and pressures. However, when conditions are such that the gas molecules are crowded closely together (high pressure and/or low temperature), they show marked deviations from ideal behavior. Deviations occur because molecules have finite volumes and also have intermolecular attractions, which results in less compressibility at high pressures and greater compressibility at low temperatures than predicted by the gas laws. Many gases become liquids at high pressure and low temperature.

QUESTIONS

A. *Review the meanings of the new terms introduced in this chapter.*

1. Kinetic-Molecular Theory (KMT)
2. Ideal, or perfect, gas
3. Diffusion
4. Effusion
5. Graham's law of effusion
6. Pressure
7. Atmospheric pressure
8. Barometer
9. 1 atmosphere
10. Boyle's law
11. Charles' law
12. Standard conditions
13. Standard temperature and pressure (STP)
14. Dalton's law of partial pressures
15. Gay-Lussac's law of combining volumes of gases
16. Avogadro's law
17. Molar volume of a gas
18. Ideal gas equation

B. *Information useful in answering the following questions will be found in the tables and figures.*

1. What evidence is used to show diffusion in Figure 12.1? If hydrogen, H_2, and oxygen, O_2, were in the two flasks, how could we prove that diffusion had taken place?
2. How does the air pressure inside the balloon shown in Figure 12.2 compare with the air pressure outside the balloon? Explain.
3. According to Table 12.1, what two gases are the major constituents of dry air?
4. How does the pressure represented by 1 torr compare in magnitude to the pressure represented by 1 mm Hg? See Table 12.2.
5. In which container illustrated in Figure 12.5 are the molecules of gas moving faster? Assume both gases to be hydrogen.
6. In Figure 12.6, what gas pressure corresponds to a volume of 4 L?
7. How do the data illustrated in Figure 12.6 substantiate Boyle's law?
8. What effect would you observe in Figure 12.9 if T_2 were lower than T_1?
9. In the diagram shown in Figure 12.11, is the pressure of the oxygen plus water vapor inside the bottle equal to, greater than, or less than the atmospheric pressure outside the bottle? Explain.
10. List five gases in Table 12.3 that are denser than air. Explain the basis for your selections.

C. *Review questions*

1. What are the basic assumptions of the Kinetic-Molecular Theory?
2. Arrange the following gases, all at standard temperature, in order of increasing relative

molecular velocities: H_2, CH_4, Rn, N_2, F_2, He. What is your basis for determining the order?

3. List, in descending order, the average kinetic energies of the molecules in Question C.2.

4. What are the four parameters used to describe the behavior of a gas?

5. What are the characteristics of an ideal gas?

6. Under what condition of temperature, high or low, is a gas least likely to exhibit ideal behavior? Explain.

7. Under what conditions of pressure, high or low, is a gas least likely to exhibit ideal behavior? Explain.

8. Compare, at the same temperature and pressure, equal volumes of H_2 and O_2 as to:
   (a) Number of molecules
   (b) Mass
   (c) Number of moles
   (d) Average kinetic energy of the molecules
   (e) Rate of effusion
   (f) Density

9. How does the Kinetic-Molecular Theory account for the behavior of gases as described by:
   (a) Boyle's law
   (b) Charles' law
   (c) Dalton's law of partial pressures

10. Explain how the reaction

$$N_2(g) + O_2(g) \xrightarrow{\Delta} 2\,NO(g)$$

proves that nitrogen and oxygen are diatomic molecules.

11. What is the reason for referring gases to STP?

12. When constant pressure is maintained, what effect does heating a mole of N_2 gas have on the following?
   (a) Its density
   (b) Its specific gravity
   (c) Its mass
   (d) The average kinetic energy of its molecules
   (e) The average velocity of its molecules   .
   (f) The number of N_2 molecules in the sample

13. Assuming ideal gas behavior, which of the following statements are correct. (Try to answer without referring to your text.)
   (a) The pressure exerted by a gas at constant volume is independent of the temperature of the gas.
   (b) At constant temperature, increasing the pressure exerted on a gas sample will cause a decrease in the volume of the gas sample.

(c) At constant pressure, the volume of a gas is inversely proportional to the absolute temperature.

(d) At constant temperature, doubling the pressure on a gas sample will cause the volume of the gas sample to decrease to one-half its original volume.

(e) Compressing a gas at constant temperature will cause its density and mass to increase.

(f) Equal volumes of CO_2 and CH_4 gases at the same temperature and pressure contain
   (1) The same number of molecules
   (2) The same mass
   (3) The same densities
   (4) The same number of moles
   (5) The same number of atoms

(g) At constant temperature, the average kinetic energy of O_2 molecules at 200 atm pressure is greater than the average kinetic energy of O_2 molecules at 100 atm pressure.

(h) According to Charles' law, the volume of a gas becomes zero at $-273°C$.

(i) One liter of O_2 gas at STP has the same mass as 1 L of O_2 gas at 273°C and 2 atm pressure.

(j) The volume occupied by a gas depends only on its temperature and pressure.

(k) In a mixture containing O_2 molecules and N_2 molecules, the O_2 molecules, on the average, are moving faster than the N_2 molecules.

(l) $PV = k$ is a statement of Charles' law.

(m) If the temperature of a sample of gas is increased from 25°C to 50°C, the volume of the gas will increase by 100%.

(n) One mole of chlorine, Cl_2, at 20°C and 600 torr pressure contains 6.022×10^{23} molecules.

(o) One mole of H_2 plus 1 mole of O_2 in an 11.2 L container exert a pressure of 4 atm at 0°C.

(p) When the pressure on a sample of gas is halved, with the temperature remaining constant, the density of the gas is also halved.

(q) When the temperature of a sample of gas is increased at constant pressure, the density of the gas will decrease.

(r) According to the equation

$$2\,KClO_3(s) \xrightarrow{\Delta} 2\,KCl(s) + 3\,O_2(g),$$

1 mol of $KClO_3$ will produce 67.2 L of O_2 at STP.

(s) $PV = nRT$ is a statement of Avogadro's law.

(t) STP conditions are 1 atm and 0°C.

D. *Review problems*

Pressure Units

1. The barometer reads 715 mm Hg. Calculate the corresponding pressure in
   (a) atmospheres   (d) torrs
   (b) inches of Hg   (e) millibars
   (c) lb/in.^{2} (f) kilopascals

2. Express the following pressures in atmospheres:
   (a) 28 mm Hg   (c) 795 torr
   (b) 6000 cm Hg   (d) 5.00 kPa

Boyle's, Charles', and Gay-Lussac's Laws

3. A gas occupies a volume of 400 mL at 500 mm Hg pressure. What will be its volume, at constant temperature, if the pressure is changed to (a) 760 mm Hg; (b) 250 torr; (c) 2.00 atm?

4. A 500 mL sample of a gas is at a pressure of 640 mm Hg. What must be the pressure, at constant temperature, if the volume is changed to (a) 855 mL and (b) 450 mL?

5. At constant temperature, what pressure would be required to compress 2500 L of hydrogen gas at 1.0 atm pressure into a 25 L tank?

6. Given 6.00 L of N_2 gas at −25°C, what volume will the nitrogen occupy at (a) 0.0°C; (b) 0.0°F; (c) 100 K; (d) 345 K? (Assume constant pressure.)

7. Given a sample of a gas at 27°C, at what temperature would the volume of the gas sample be doubled, the pressure remaining constant?

*8. A gas sample at 22°C and 740 torr pressure is heated until its volume is doubled. What pressure would restore the sample to its original volume?

9. A gas occupies 250 mL at 700 torr and 22°C. When the pressure is changed to 500 torr, what temperature (°C) is needed to maintain the same volume?

10. Hydrogen stored in a metal cylinder has a pressure of 252 atm at 25°C. What will be the pressure in the cylinder when the cylinder is lowered into liquid nitrogen at −196°C?

11. The tires on an automobile were filled with air to 30 psi at 71.0°F. When driving at high speeds, the tires become hot. If the tires have a bursting pressure of 44 psi, at what temperature (°F) will the tires "blow out"?

Combined Gas Laws

12. A gas occupies a volume of 410 mL at 27°C and 740 mm Hg pressure. Calculate the volume the gas would occupy at (a) STP; (b) 250°C and 680 mm Hg pressure.

13. What volume would 5.30 L of H_2 gas at STP occupy at 70°C and 830 torr pressure?

14. What pressure will 800 mL of a gas at STP exert when its volume is 250 mL at 30°C?

15. An expandable balloon contains 1400 L of He at 0.950 atm pressure and 18°C. At an altitude of 22 miles (temperature 2.0°C and pressure 4.0 torr), what will be the volume of the balloon?

16. A gas occupies 22.4 L at 2.50 atm and 27°C. What will be its volume at 1.50 atm and −5.00°C?

17. How many gas molecules are present in 600 mL of N_2O at 40°C and 400 torr pressure? How many atoms are present? What would be the volume of the sample at STP?

Dalton's Law of Partial Pressures

18. What would be the partial pressure of O_2 gas collected over water at 20°C and 720 torr pressure? (Check Appendix II for the vapor pressure of water.)

19. A mixture contains H_2 at 700 torr pressure, N_2 at 200 torr pressure, and O_2 at 300 torr pressure. What is the total pressure of the gases in the system?

20. A sample of methane gas, CH_4, was collected over water at 25.0°C and 720 torr. The volume of the wet gas is 2.50 L. What will be the volume of the methane after the gas is dried?

21. 5.00 L of CO_2 at 500 torr and 3.00 L of CH_4 at 400 torr are put into a 10.0 L container. What is the pressure exerted by the gases in the container?

Mole–Mass–Volume Relationships

22. What volume will 2.5 mol of Cl_2 occupy at STP?

23. A steel cylinder contains 60 mol of H_2 at a pressure of 1500 lb/in.^{2} (a) How many moles of H_2 are in the cylinder when the pressure reads 850 lb/in.^{2}? (b) How many grams of H_2 were initially in the cylinder?

24. How many grams of CO_2 are present in 2500 mL of CO_2 at STP?

25. At STP, 560 mL of a gas have a mass of 1.08 g. What is the molecular weight of the gas?
26. What volume will each of the following occupy at STP?
    (a) 1.0 mol of NO_2
    (b) 17.05 g of NO_2
    (c) 1.20×10^{24} molecules of NO_2
27. How many molecules of ammonia gas are present in a 1.00 L flask of NH_3 at STP?
28. How many moles of chlorine are in one cubic meter (1.00 m^3) of Cl_2 at STP?

Density of Gases
29. A gas has a density at STP of 1.78 g/L. What is its molecular weight?
30. Calculate the density of the following gases at STP:
    (a) Kr (b) He (c) SO_3 (d) C_4H_8
31. Calculate the density of:
    (a) F_2 gas at STP
    (b) F_2 gas at 27°C and 1 atm pressure
*32. At what temperature (°C) will the density of methane, CH_4, be 1.0 g/L at 1.0 atm pressure?

Ideal Gas Equation and Stoichiometry
33. Using the ideal gas equation, $PV = nRT$, calculate:
    (a) The volume of 0.510 mole of H_2 at 47°C and 1.6 atm pressure
    (b) The number of grams in 16.0 L of CH_4 at 27°C and 600 torr pressure
    *(c) The density of CO_2 at 4.00 atm pressure and −20°C
    *(d) The molecular weight of a gas having a density of 2.58 g/L at 27°C and 1 atm pressure
    Hints for (c) and (d): n = moles = g/mol. wt, and d = g/V.
34. What is the molecular weight of a gas if 1.15 g occupy 0.215 L at 0.813 atm and 30°C?
35. At 27°C and 750 torr pressure, what will be the volume of 2.3 mol of Ne?
36. What volume will a mixture of 5.00 mol of H_2 and 0.500 mol of CO_2 occupy at STP?
37. 4.50 mol of a gas occupy 0.250 L at 4.15 atm. What is the Kelvin temperature of the system?
38. How many moles of N_2 gas occupy 5.20 L at 250 K and 0.500 atm?
39. What volume of hydrogen at STP can be produced by reacting 8.30 mol of Al with sulfuric

acid? The equation is

$$2\ Al(s) + 3\ H_2SO_4(aq) \longrightarrow$$
$$Al_2(SO_4)_3(aq) + 3\ H_2(g)$$

40. Given the equation

$$4\ NH_3(g) + 5\ O_2(g) \longrightarrow 4\ NO(g) + 6\ H_2O(g)$$

    (a) How many moles of NH_3 are required to produce 5.5 mol of NO?
    (b) How many moles of NH_3 will react with 7.0 mol of O_2?
    (c) How many liters of NO can be made from 12 L of O_2 and 10 L of NH_3 at STP?
    (d) At constant temperature and pressure, how many liters of NO can be made by the reaction of 800 mL of O_2?
    (e) At constant temperature and pressure, what is the maximum volume, in liters, of NO that can be made from 3.0 L of NH_3 and 3.0 L of O_2?
    (f) How many grams of O_2 must react to produce 60 L of NO measured at STP?
    *(g) How many grams of NH_3 must react to produce a total of 32 L of products, NO plus H_2O, measured at STP?
41. Given the equation

$$4\ FeS_2(s) + 11\ O_2(g) \xrightarrow{\Delta}$$
$$2\ Fe_2O_3(s) + 8\ SO_2(g)$$

    (a) How many liters of O_2, measured at STP, will react with 0.600 kg of FeS_2?
    (b) How many liters of SO_2, measured at STP, will be produced from 0.600 kg of FeS_2?
*42. Acetylene, C_2H_2, and hydrogen fluoride react to give difluoroethane:

$$C_2H_2(g) + 2\ HF(g) \longrightarrow C_2H_4F_2(g)$$

When 1.0 mol of C_2H_2 and 5.0 mol of HF are reacted in a 10.0 L flask, what will be the pressure in the flask at 0°C when the reaction is complete?

Additional Problems
43. What are the relative rates of effusion of N_2 and He?
*44. (a) What are the relative rates of effusion of methane, CH_4, and helium, He?
    (b) If these two gases are simultaneously introduced into opposite ends of a 100 cm tube

and allowed to diffuse toward each other, at what distance from the helium end will molecules of the two gases meet?

*45. A gas has a percent composition by weight of 85.7 % carbon and 14.3% hydrogen. At STP the density of the gas is 2.50 g/L. What is the molecular formula of the gas?

*46. Assume that the reaction

$$2\ CO(g) + O_2(g) \longrightarrow 2\ CO_2(g)$$

goes to completion. When 10 mol of CO and 8.0 mol of O_2 react in a closed 10 L vessel,

(a) How many moles of CO, O_2, and CO_2 are present at the end of the reaction?

(b) What will be the total pressure in the flask at 0°C?

*47. 250 mL of O_2, measured at STP, were obtained by the decomposition of the $KClO_3$ in a 1.20 g mixture of KCl and $KClO_3$:

$$2\ KClO_3(s) \xrightarrow{\Delta} 2\ KCl(s) + 3\ O_2(g),$$

What is the percentage by weight of $KClO_3$ in the mixture?

Water and the Properties of Liquids

1. Understand the new terms listed in Question A at the end of the chapter.
2. Describe a water molecule with respect to Lewis structure, bond angle, and polarity.
3. Make sketches showing hydrogen bonding (a) between water molecules and (b) between hydrogen fluoride molecules.
4. Explain the effect of hydrogen bonding on the physical properties of water.
5. Determine whether a compound will or will not form hydrogen bonds.
6. Explain the process of evaporation from the standpoint of kinetic energy.
7. Relate vapor pressure data or vapor pressure curves of different substances to their relative rates of evaporation and to their relative boiling points.
8. Explain what is happening in the different segments of the time–temperature heating curve of water.
9. Complete and balance equations showing the formation of water (a) from hydrogen and oxygen, (b) by neutralization, and (c) by combustion of hydrogen-containing compounds.
10. Complete and balance equations for (a) the reaction of water with Na, K, and Ca; (b) the reaction of steam with Zn, Al, Fe, and C; and (c) the reaction of water with halogens.
11. Identify metal oxides as basic anhydrides and write balanced equations for their reactions with water.

12. Identify nonmetal oxides as acid anhydrides and write balanced equations for their reactions with water.
13. Deduce the formula of the acid anhydride or the basic anhydride when given the formula of the corresponding acid or base.
14. Identify, name, and write equations for the complete dehydration of hydrates.
15. Distinguish clearly between peroxides and ordinary oxides.
16. Discuss the occurrence of ozone and its effects on humans.
17. Outline the processes needed to prepare a potable water supply from a contaminated river source.
18. Describe how water may be softened by distillation, chemical precipitation, ion exchange, and demineralization. Write chemical equations for these processes where appropriate.

13.1 Occurrence of Water

Water is our most common natural resource; it covers about 70% of the earth's surface. Not only is it found in the oceans and seas, in lakes, rivers, streams, and in glacial ice deposits, it is also always present in the atmosphere and in cloud formations.

About 97% of the earth's water is in the oceans. This *saline* water contains vast amounts of dissolved minerals. More than 70 elements have been detected in the mineral content of seawater. Only four of these—chlorine, sodium, magnesium, and bromine— are now commercially obtained from the sea. The world's *fresh* water comprises the other 3%, of which about two-thirds is locked up in polar ice caps and glaciers. The remaining fresh water is found in groundwater, lakes, and the atmosphere.

Water is an essential constituent of all living matter. It is the most abundant compound in the human body, making up about 70% of total body weight. About 92% of blood plasma is water, about 80% of muscle tissue is water; and about 60% of a red blood cell is water. Water is more important than food in the sense that a person can survive much longer without food than without water.

13.2 Physical Properties of Water

heat of fusion

heat of vaporization

Water is a colorless, odorless, tasteless liquid with a melting point of 0°C and a boiling point of 100°C at 1 atm pressure. Two additional physical properties of matter are introduced with the study of water: heat of fusion and heat of vaporization. **Heat of fusion** is the amount of heat required to change 1 g of a solid into a liquid at its melting point. The heat of fusion of water is 335 J/g (80 cal/g). The temperature of the solid–liquid system does not change during the absorption of this heat. The heat of fusion is the energy needed to break down the crystalline lattice of ice from a solid to a liquid. **Heat of vaporization** is the amount of heat required to change 1 g of liquid to a vapor at its normal boiling

0°C

Figure 13.1   Ice and water in equilibrium at 0°C

point. The value for water is 2.26 kJ/g (540 cal/g). Once again, the temperature does not change during the absorption of this heat. The heat of vaporization is the energy needed to overcome the attractive forces between molecules in changing a substance from the liquid to the gaseous state at its normal boiling point. The values for both the heat of fusion and the heat of vaporization for water are high compared with those for other substances: these high values indicate that strong attractive forces are acting between the molecules.

Ice and water exist together in equilibrium at 0°C, as shown in Figure 13.1. When ice at 0°C melts, it absorbs 335 J/g (80 cal/g) in changing into a liquid; the temperature remains at 0°C. In order to refreeze the water, we have to remove 335 J/g (80 cal/g) from the liquid at 0°C.

In Figure 13.2 both boiling water and steam are shown to have a temperature of 100°C. It takes 418 J (100 cal) to heat 1 g of water from 0°C to 100°C, but water at its boiling point absorbs 2.26 kJ/g (540 cal/g) in changing to steam. Although boiling water and steam are both at the same temperature, steam contains considerably more heat per gram and can cause more severe burns than hot water. In Table 13.1 the physical properties of water are tabulated and compared with those of other hydrogen compounds of Group VIA elements.

The maximum density of water is 1.000 g/mL at 4°C. Water has the unusual property of contracting in volume as it is cooled to 4°C and then expanding when cooled from 4°C to 0°C. Therefore 1 g of water occupies a volume greater than 1 mL at all temperatures except 4°C. Although most liquids contract in volume all the way down to the point at which they solidify, a large increase (about 9%) in volume occurs when water changes from a liquid at 0°C to a solid (ice) at 0°C. The density of ice at 0°C is 0.917 g/mL, which means that ice, being less dense than water, will float in water.

Figure 13.2 Boiling water and steam in equilibrium at 100°C

Table 13.1 Physical properties of water and other hydrogen compounds of Group VIA elements

Formula	Color	Molecular weight	Melting point (°C)	Boiling point 1 atm (°C)	Heat of fusion J/g (cal/g)	Heat of vaporization J/g (cal/g)
H_2O	Colorless	18.0	0.00	100.0	335 (80.0)	2260 (540)
H_2S	Colorless	34.1	−85.5	−60.3	69.9 (16.7)	548 (131)
H_2Se	Colorless	81.0	−65.7	−41.3	31 (7.4)	238 (57.0)
H_2Te	Colorless	129.6	−51	−2.3	—	179 (42.8)

PROBLEM

13.1

How many joules of energy are needed to change 10.0 g of ice at 0°C to water at 20°C?
Ice will absorb 335 J/g (heat of fusion) in going from a solid at 0°C to a liquid at 0°C. The specific heat of water (Section 2.12) is 4.184 J/g. Thus an additional 4.184 J/g are needed to raise the temperature for each 1°C.

Joules needed to melt the ice:

$$10.0 \ \cancel{g} \times \frac{335 \ J}{1 \ \cancel{g}} = 3.35 \times 10^3 \ J \ (801 \ cal)$$

Joules needed to heat the water from 0°C to 20°C:

$$10.0 \; \cancel{g} \times \frac{4.184 \; J}{1 \; \cancel{g} \; \cancel{°C}} \times 20 \; \cancel{°C} = 837 \; J \; (200 \; cal)$$

Thus, $3350 \; J + 837 \; J = 4.19 \times 10^3 \; J$ (1000 cal) are needed.

13.2

How many kilojoules of energy are needed to change 20.0 g of water at 20°C to steam at 100°C?

Kilojoules needed to heat the water from 20°C to 100°C:

$$20.0 \; \cancel{g} \times \frac{4.184 \; J}{1 \; \cancel{g} \cancel{°C}} \times \frac{1 \; kJ}{1000 \; J} \times 80 \; \cancel{°C} = 6.7 \; kJ \; (1.6 \; kcal)$$

Kilojoules needed to change water at 100°C to steam at 100°C:

$$20.0 \; \cancel{g} \times \frac{2.26 \; kJ}{1 \; \cancel{g}} = 45.2 \; kJ \; (10.8 \; kcal)$$

Thus, $6.7 \; kJ + 45.2 \; kJ = 51.9 \; kJ$ (12.4 kcal) are needed.

13.3   Structure of the Water Molecule

A single water molecule consists of two hydrogen atoms and one oxygen atom. Each H atom is attached to the O atom by a single covalent bond. This bond is formed by the overlap of the 1s orbital of hydrogen with an unpaired 2p orbital of oxygen. The average distance between the two nuclei is known as the *bond length*. The O—H bond length in water is 0.096 nm. The water molecule is nonlinear and has a V-shaped structure with an angle of about 105° between the two bonds (see Figure 13.3).

Oxygen is the second most electronegative element. As a result, the two covalent OH bonds in water are polar. If the three atoms in a water molecule were aligned in a linear structure such as H—→O←—H, the two polar bonds

Figure 13.3   Diagrams of a water molecule: (a) electron distribution, (b) bond angle and O—H bond length, (c) molecular orbital structure, and (d) dipole representation

would be acting in equal and opposite directions and the molecule would be nonpolar. However, water is a highly polar molecule and it does not have a linear structure. When atoms are bonded together in a nonlinear fashion, the angle formed by the bonds is called the *bond angle*. In water the HOH bond angle is 105°. The two polar covalent bonds and the bent structure result in a partial negative charge on the oxygen atom and a partial positive charge on each hydrogen atom. The polar nature of water is responsible for many of its properties, including its behavior as a solvent.

13.4   The Hydrogen Bond

Table 13.1 compares the physical properties of H_2O, H_2S, H_2Se, and H_2Te. From this comparison it is apparent that four physical properties of water—melting point, boiling point, heat of fusion, and heat of vaporization—are extremely high and do not fit the trend relative to the molecular weights of the four compounds. If the properties of water followed the progression shown by the other three compounds, we would expect the melting point of water to be below −85°C and the boiling point to be below −60°C.

hydrogen bond

Why does water have these anomalous physical properties? The answer is that liquid water molecules are linked together by hydrogen bonds. A **hydrogen bond** is a chemical bond that is formed between polar molecules that contain hydrogen covalently bonded to a small, highly electronegative atom such as fluorine, oxygen, or nitrogen (F—H, O—H, N—H). The bond is actually the dipole–dipole attraction of polar molecules containing any of these three types of polar bonds.

> **Elements that have significant hydrogen bonding ability are F, O, and N.**

What is a hydrogen bond, or H-bond? Because a hydrogen atom has only one electron, it can form only one covalent bond. When it is attached to a strong electronegative atom such as oxygen, a hydrogen atom will also be attracted to an oxygen atom of another molecule, forming a bond (or bridge) between the two molecules. Water has two types of bonds: covalent bonds that exist between hydrogen and oxygen atoms within a molecule and hydrogen bonds that exist between hydrogen and oxygen atoms in different water molecules.

Hydrogen bonds are *intermolecular* bonds; that is, they are formed between atoms in different molecules. They are somewhat ionic in character because they are formed by electrostatic attraction. Hydrogen bonds are much weaker than the ionic or covalent bonds that unite atoms to atoms to form compounds. Despite their weakness, hydrogen bonds are of great chemical importance.

The oxygen atom in water can form two hydrogen bonds—one through each of the unbonded pairs of electrons. Figure 13.4 shows (a) two water molecules linked by a hydrogen bond and (b) six water molecules linked by hydrogen bonds. A dash (—) is used for the covalent bond and a dotted line (· · · ·) for the hydrogen bond. In water each molecule is linked to others through hydrogen

(a)

⬤ Oxygen

⬤ Hydrogen

—— Covalent bonds

· · · · Hydrogen bonds

(b)

Figure 13.4   Hydrogen bonding: Water in the liquid and solid states exists as aggregates in which the water molecules are linked together by hydrogen bonds.

bonds to form a three-dimensional aggregate of water molecules. This inter-molecular hydrogen bonding effectively gives water the properties of a much larger, heavier molecule, explaining in part its relatively high melting point, boiling point, heat of fusion, and heat of vaporization. As water is heated and energy is absorbed, hydrogen bonds are continually being broken until at 100°C, with the absorption of an additional 2.26 kJ/g (540 cal/g), water separates into individual molecules, going into the gaseous state. Sulfur, selenium, and tellurium are not sufficiently electronegative for their hydrogen compounds to behave like water. As a result, H-bonding in H_2S, H_2Se, and H_2Te is only of small consequence (if any) to their physical properties. For example, the lack of hydrogen bonding is one reason why H_2S is a gas and not a liquid at room temperature.

Fluorine, the most electronegative element, forms the strongest hydrogen bonds. This bonding is strong enough to link hydrogen fluoride molecules together as *dimers*, H_2F_2, or as larger, $(HF)_n$, molecular units. The dimer structure may be represented in this way:

$$H\diagdown_{\textstyle F\cdots\cdot}{}^{.H}\diagup^{\textstyle F}\diagdown_{\text{H-bond}}$$

The existence of salts, such as KHF_2 and NH_4HF_2, verifies the hydrogen fluoride (bifluoride) structure, HF_2^- $(F—H\cdots F)^-$, where one H atom is bonded to two F atoms through one covalent bond and one hydrogen bond.

Hydrogen bonding can occur between two different atoms that are capable of forming H-bonds. Thus we may have an $O \cdots H-N$ or $O-H \cdots N$ linkage in which the hydrogen atom forming the H-bond is between an oxygen and a nitrogen atom. This form of the H-bond exists in certain types of protein molecules and many biologically active substances.

PROBLEM

13.3

Would you expect hydrogen bonding to occur between molecules of the following substances?

(a)
$$H-\underset{\underset{H}{|}}{\overset{\overset{H}{|}}{C}}-\underset{\underset{H}{|}}{\overset{\overset{H}{|}}{C}}-O-H$$
Ethyl alcohol

(b)
$$H-\underset{\underset{H}{|}}{\overset{\overset{H}{|}}{C}}-O-\underset{\underset{H}{|}}{\overset{\overset{H}{|}}{C}}-H$$
Dimethyl ether

(a) Hydrogen bonding should occur in ethyl alcohol because one hydrogen atom is bonded to an oxygen atom.

$$H-\underset{\underset{H}{|}}{\overset{\overset{H}{|}}{C}}-\underset{\underset{H}{|}}{\overset{\overset{H}{|}}{C}}-O-H \cdots O-\underset{\underset{H}{|}}{\overset{\overset{H}{|}}{C}}-\underset{\underset{H}{|}}{\overset{\overset{H}{|}}{C}}-H$$
$\uparrow$
H-bond

(b) There is no hydrogen bonding in dimethyl ether because all the hydrogen atoms are bonded only to carbon atoms.

Both ethyl alcohol and dimethyl ether have the same molecular weight (46.0). Although both compounds have the same molecular formula, C_2H_6O, ethyl alcohol has a much higher boiling point (78.4°C) than dimethyl ether (-23.7°C), because of hydrogen bonding between the alcohol molecules.

13.5 ## Evaporation

When beakers of water, ethyl ether, and ethyl alcohol are allowed to stand uncovered in an open room, the volumes of these liquids gradually decrease. The process by which this change takes place is called *evaporation*.

Attractive forces exist between molecules in the liquid state. Not all of these molecules, however, have the same kinetic energy. Molecules that have greater than average kinetic energy can overcome the attractive forces and break away from the surface of the liquid to become a gas. **Evaporation** or **vaporization** is the escape of molecules from the liquid state to the gaseous or vapor state.

evaporation or vaporization

In evaporation, molecules of higher than average kinetic energy escape from a liquid, leaving it cooler than it was before they escaped. For this reason, evaporation of perspiration is one way the human body cools itself and keeps its temperature constant. When volatile liquids such as ethyl chloride (C_2H_5Cl) are sprayed on the skin, they evaporate rapidly, cooling the area by removing heat.

The numbing effect of the low temperature produced by evaporation of ethyl chloride allows it to be used as a local anesthetic for minor surgery.

Solids such as iodine, camphor, naphthalene (moth balls), and, to a small extent, even ice will go directly from the solid to the gaseous state, bypassing the liquid state. This change is a form of evaporation and is called **sublimation**:

sublimation

$$\text{Liquid} \xrightarrow{\text{Evaporation}} \text{Vapor}$$

$$\text{Solid} \xrightarrow{\text{Sublimation}} \text{Vapor}$$

13.6   Vapor Pressure

When a liquid vaporizes in a closed system as shown in Figure 13.5, part (b), some of the molecules in the vapor or gaseous state strike the surface and return to the liquid state by the process of *condensation*. The rate of condensation increases until it is equal to the rate of vaporization. At this point, the space above the liquid is said to be saturated with vapor, and an equilibrium, or steady state, exists between the liquid and the vapor. The equilibrium equation is

$$\text{Liquid} \underset{\text{Condensation}}{\overset{\text{Vaporization}}{\rightleftharpoons}} \text{Vapor}$$

This equilibrium is dynamic; both processes—vaporization and condensation—are taking place, even though one cannot see or measure a change. The number of molecules leaving the liquid in a given time interval is equal to the number of molecules returning to the liquid.

At equilibrium the molecules in the vapor exert a pressure like any other gas. The pressure exerted by a vapor in equilibrium with its liquid is known as the **vapor pressure** of the liquid. The vapor pressure may be thought of as an internal pressure, a measure of the "escaping" tendency of molecules to go from the liquid to the vapor state. The vapor pressure of a liquid is independent of the amount of liquid and vapor present, but it increases as the temperature rises (see Table 13.2). Figure 13.6 illustrates a liquid–vapor equilibrium and the measurement of vapor pressure.

vapor pressure

(a)   (b)

Figure 13.5 (a) Molecules in an open beaker evaporate from the liquid and disperse into the atmosphere. Under this condition, evaporation will continue until all the liquid is gone. (b) Molecules leaving the liquid are confined to a limited space. With time, the concentration in the vapor phase will increase to a point at which an equilibrium between liquid and vapor is established.

Table 13.2 The vapor pressure of water, ethyl alcohol, and ethyl ether at various temperatures

Temperature (°C)	Vapor pressure (torr)		
	Water	Ethyl alcohol	Ethyl ether[a]
0	4.6	12.2	185.3
10	9.2	23.6	291.7
20	17.5	43.9	442.2
30	31.8	78.8	647.3
40	55.3	135.3	921.3
50	92.5	222.2	1276.8
60	152.9	352.7	1729.0
70	233.7	542.5	2296.0
80	355.1	812.6	2993.6
90	525.8	1187.1	3841.0
100	760.0	1693.3	4859.4
110	1074.6	2361.3	6070.1

[a] Note that the vapor pressure of ethyl ether at temperatures of 40°C and higher exceeds standard pressure, 760 torr, which indicates that the substance has a low boiling point and therefore should be stored in a cool place in a tightly sealed container.

(a) Evacuated flask

(b) Water added at 20°C

(c) Water–vapor equilibrium at 20°C

(d) Water–vapor equilibrium at 30°C

Figure 13.6 Measurement of the vapor pressure of water at 20°C and 30°C. In flask (a) the system is evacuated. The mercury manometer attached to the flask shows equal pressure in both legs. In (b) water has been added to the flask and begins to evaporate, exerting pressure as indicated by the manometer. In (c), when equilibrium is established, the pressure inside the flask remains constant at 17.5 torr. In (d) the temperature is changed to 30°C, and equilibrium is reestablished with the vapor pressure at 31.8 torr.

When equal volumes of water, ethyl ether, and ethyl alcohol are placed in separate beakers and allowed to evaporate at the same temperature, we observe that the ether evaporates faster than the alcohol, which evaporates faster than the water. This order of evaporation is consistent with the fact that ether has a higher vapor pressure at any particular temperature than ethyl alcohol or water. One reason for this higher vapor pressure is that the attraction is less between ether molecules than between alcohol molecules or between water molecules. The vapor pressures of these three compounds at various temperatures are compared in Table 13.2.

volatile

Substances that evaporate readily are said to be **volatile**. A volatile liquid has a relatively high vapor pressure at room temperature. Ethyl ether is a very volatile liquid; water is not too volatile; mercury, which has a vapor pressure of 0.0012 torr at 20°C, is essentially a nonvolatile liquid. Most substances that are normally solids are nonvolatile (solids that sublime are exceptions).

13.7 Boiling Point

The boiling temperature of a liquid is associated with its vapor pressure. We have seen that the vapor pressure increases as the temperature increases. When the internal or vapor pressure of a liquid becomes equal to the external pressure, the liquid boils. (By external pressure we mean the pressure of the atmosphere above the liquid.) The boiling temperature of a pure liquid remains constant as long as the external pressure does not vary.

The boiling point (bp) of water is 100°C. Table 13.2 shows that the vapor pressure of water at 100°C is 760 torr, a figure we have seen many times before. The significant fact here is that the boiling point is the temperature at which the vapor pressure of the water or other liquid is equal to standard, or atmospheric, pressure at sea level. These relationships lead to the following definition: The **boiling point**

boiling point

is the temperature at which the vapor pressure of a liquid is equal to the external pressure above the liquid.

We can readily see that a liquid has an infinite number of boiling points. When we give the boiling point of a liquid, we should also state the pressure. When we express the boiling point without stating the pressure, we mean it to be the

standard or normal boiling point

standard or **normal boiling point** at standard pressure (760 torr). Using Table 13.2 again, we see that the normal boiling point of ethyl ether is between 30°C and 40°C, and for ethyl alcohol it is between 70°C and 80°C, because, for each compound, 760 torr pressure lies within these stated temperature ranges. At the normal boiling point, 1 g of a liquid changing to a vapor (gas) absorbs an amount of energy equal to its heat of vaporization (see Table 13.3).

The boiling point at various pressures may be evaluated by plotting the data of Table 13.2 on the graph in Figure 13.7, where temperature is plotted horizontally along the x-axis and vapor pressure is plotted vertically along the y-axis. The

vapor pressure curves

resulting curves are known as **vapor pressure curves**. Any point on these curves represents a vapor–liquid equilibrium at a particular temperature and pressure. We may find the boiling point at any pressure by tracing a horizontal line from the designated pressure to a point on the vapor pressure curve. From this point

Table 13.3 Physical properties of ethyl chloride, ethyl ether, ethyl alcohol, and water

	Boiling point (°C)	Melting point (°C)	Heat of vaporization J/g (cal/g)	Heat of fusion J/g (cal/g)
Ethyl chloride	13	−139	387 (92.5)	—
Ethyl ether	34.6	−116	351 (83.9)	—
Ethyl alcohol	78.4	−112	855 (204.3)	104 (24.9)
Water	100.0	0	2260 (540)	335 (80)

Figure 13.7 Vapor pressure–temperature curves for ethyl chloride, ethyl ether, ethyl alcohol, and water

we draw a vertical line to obtain the boiling point on the temperature axis. Four such points are shown in Figure 13.7; they represent the normal boiling points of the four compounds at 760 torr pressure.

See if you can verify from the graph that the boiling points of ethyl chloride, ethyl ether, ethyl alcohol, and water at 600 torr pressure are 8.5°C, 28°C, 73°C, and 93°C, respectively. By reversing this process, you can ascertain at what pressure a substance will boil at a specific temperature. The boiling point is one of the most commonly used physical properties for characterizing and identifying substances.

13.8   Freezing Point or Melting Point

As heat is removed from a liquid, the liquid becomes colder and colder, until a temperature is reached at which it begins to solidify. A liquid that is changing into a solid is said to be *freezing*, or *solidifying*. When a solid is heated continuously, a temperature is reached at which the solid begins to liquefy. A solid that is changing into a liquid is said to be *melting*. The temperature at which the solid phase of a substance is in equilibrium with its liquid phase is known as the **freezing point** or **melting point** of that substance. The equilibrium equation is

freezing or melting point

$$\text{Solid} \underset{\text{Freezing}}{\overset{\text{Melting}}{\rightleftharpoons}} \text{Liquid}$$

When a solid is slowly and carefully heated so that a solid–liquid equilibrium is achieved and then maintained, the temperature will remain constant as long as both phases are present. One gram of a solid in changing into a liquid absorbs an amount of energy equal to its *heat of fusion* (see Table 13.3). The melting point is another physical property that is commonly used for characterizing substances.

The most common example of a solid–liquid equilibrium is ice and water (see Figure 13.1). In a well-stirred system of ice and water, the temperature remains at 0°C as long as both phases are present. The melting point changes with pressure but only slightly unless the pressure change is very large.

It has been known for a long time that dissolved substances markedly decrease the freezing point of a liquid. For example, salt–water–ice equilibrium mixtures can be obtained at temperatures as low as −20°C, 20 degrees below the usual freezing point of water.

If a liquid is heated continuously after all the solid has been melted, the temperature will rise until the liquid boils. The temperature will remain constant at the boiling point until all the liquid has boiled away. One gram of a liquid in changing into a gas at the normal boiling point absorbs an amount of energy equal to its *heat of vaporization* (see Table 13.3). The whole process of heating a substance (water) is illustrated graphically by the heating curve shown in Figure 13.8. In the diagram, line *AB* represents the solid being heated, and line *BC* represents the time during which the solid is melting and is in equilibrium with the liquid. Along line *CD* the liquid absorbs heat; finally, at point *D*, it boils and continues to boil at a constant temperature (line *DE*). In the interval *EF* all the water exists as steam and is being further heated or superheated.

13.9   Formation of Water and Chemical Properties of Water

Water is very stable to heat; it decomposes to the extent of only about 1% at temperatures up to 2000°C. Pure water is a nonconductor of electricity. But when

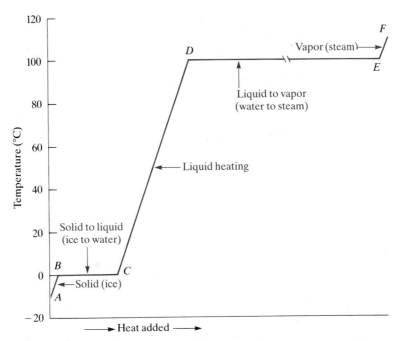

Figure 13.8 Heating curve: The absorption of heat by a substance going from the solid state to the vapor state. Using water as an example, the interval AB represents the ice phase; BC interval, the melting of ice to water; CD interval, the elevation of the temperature of water from 0°C to 100°C; DE interval, the boiling of water to steam; and EF interval, the heating of steam.

a small amount of sulfuric acid or sodium hydroxide is added, the solution is readily decomposed into hydrogen and oxygen by an electric current. Two volumes of hydrogen are produced for each volume of oxygen:

$$2\ H_2O(l)\ \xrightarrow[\text{H}_2\text{SO}_4 \text{ or NaOH}]{\text{Electrical energy}}\ 2\ H_2(g) + O_2(g)$$

Formation. Water is formed when hydrogen burns in air. Pure hydrogen burns very smoothly in air, but mixtures of hydrogen and air or oxygen explode when ignited. The reaction is strongly exothermic.

$$2\ H_2(g) + O_2(g) \longrightarrow 2\ H_2O(g) + 484\ kJ\ (115.6\ kcal)$$

Water is produced by a variety of other reactions, especially by (1) acid–base neutralizations, (2) combustion of hydrogen-containing materials, and (3) metabolic oxidation in living cells:

1. $HCl(aq) + NaOH(aq) \longrightarrow NaCl(aq) + H_2O(l)$

2. $2\ C_2H_2(g) + 5\ O_2(g) \longrightarrow 4\ CO_2(g) + 2\ H_2O(g) + 1212\ kJ\ (289.6\ kcal)$
   Acetylene

$$CH_4 + 2 O_2 \longrightarrow CO_2 + 2 H_2O + 803 \text{ kJ (192 kcal)}$$
Methane

3. $C_6H_{12}O_6 + 6 O_2 \xrightarrow{\text{Enzymes}} 6 CO_2 + 6 H_2O + 2820 \text{ kJ (673 kcal)}$
Glucose

The combustion of acetylene shown in (2) is strongly exothermic and is capable of producing very high temperatures. It is used in oxygen–acetylene torches to cut and weld steel and other metals. Methane is known as natural gas and is commonly used as fuel for heating and cooking. The reaction of glucose with oxygen shown in (3) is the reverse of photosynthesis. It is the overall reaction by which living cells obtain needed energy by metabolizing glucose to carbon dioxide and water.

Reactions of water with metals and nonmetals.   The reactions of metals with water at different temperatures show that these elements vary greatly in their reactivity. Metals such as sodium, potassium, and calcium react with cold water to produce hydrogen and a metal hydroxide. A small piece of sodium added to water melts from the heat produced by the reaction, forming a silvery metal ball, which rapidly flits back and forth on the surface of the water. Caution must be used when experimenting with this reaction, because the hydrogen produced is frequently ignited by the sparking of the sodium, and it will explode, spattering sodium. Potassium reacts even more vigorously than sodium. Calcium sinks in water and liberates a gentle stream of hydrogen. The equations for these reactions are

$$2 Na(s) + 2 H_2O(l) \longrightarrow H_2 \uparrow + 2 NaOH(aq)$$

$$2 K(s) + 2 H_2O(l) \longrightarrow H_2 \uparrow + 2 KOH(aq)$$

$$Ca(s) + 2 H_2O(l) \longrightarrow H_2 \uparrow + Ca(OH)_2(aq)$$

Zinc, aluminum, and iron do not react with cold water but will react with steam at high temperatures, forming hydrogen and a metallic oxide. The equations are

$$Zn(s) + H_2O(steam) \longrightarrow H_2 \uparrow + ZnO(s)$$

$$2 Al(s) + 3 H_2O(steam) \longrightarrow 3 H_2 \uparrow + Al_2O_3(s)$$

$$3 Fe(s) + 4 H_2O(steam) \longrightarrow 4 H_2 \uparrow + Fe_3O_4(s)$$

Copper, silver, and mercury are examples of metals that do not react with cold water or steam to produce hydrogen. We conclude that sodium, potassium, and calcium are chemically more reactive than zinc, aluminum, and iron, which are more reactive than copper, silver, and mercury.

Certain nonmetals react with water under various conditions. For example, fluorine reacts violently with cold water, producing hydrogen fluoride and free oxygen. The reactions of chlorine and bromine are much milder, producing what are commonly known as "chlorine water" and "bromine water," respectively. Chlorine water contains HCl, HOCl, and dissolved Cl_2; the free chlorine gives it a yellow-green color. Bromine water contains HBr, HOBr, and dissolved Br_2; the free bromine gives it a reddish-brown color. Steam passed over hot coke (carbon) produces a mixture of carbon monoxide and hydrogen that is known as "water gas." Since water gas is combustible, it is useful as a fuel. It is also the starting material for the commerical production of several alcohols. The equations for these reactions are

$$2\ F_2(g) + 2\ H_2O(l) \longrightarrow 4\ HF(aq) + O_2(g)$$

$$Cl_2(g) + H_2O(l) \longrightarrow HCl(aq) + HOCl(aq)$$

$$Br_2(l) + H_2O(l) \longrightarrow HBr(aq) + HOBr(aq)$$

$$C(s) + H_2O(g) \xrightarrow{1000°C} CO(g) + H_2(g)$$

basic anhydride

Reactions of water with metal and nonmetal oxides.   Metal oxides that react with water to form bases are known as **basic anhydrides**. Examples are

$$CaO(s) + H_2O \longrightarrow \quad Ca(OH)_2(aq)$$
$$\text{Calcium hydroxide}$$

$$Na_2O(s) + H_2O \longrightarrow \quad 2\ NaOH(aq)$$
$$\text{Sodium hydroxide}$$

Certain metal oxides, such as CuO and Al_2O_3, do not form basic solutions because the oxides are insoluble in water.

acid anhydride

Nonmetal oxides that react with water to form acids are known as **acid anhydrides.** Examples are

$$CO_2(g) + H_2O(l) \rightleftharpoons H_2CO_3(aq)$$
$$\text{Carbonic acid}$$

$$SO_2(g) + H_2O(l) \rightleftharpoons H_2SO_3(aq)$$
$$\text{Sulfurous acid}$$

$$N_2O_5(s) + H_2O(l) \longrightarrow 2\ HNO_3(aq)$$
$$\text{Nitric acid}$$

The word *anhydrous* means "without water." An anhydride is a metal oxide or a nonmetal oxide derived from a base or an oxyacid by the removal of water. To determine the formula of an anhydride, the elements of water, H_2O, are removed from an acid or base formula until all the hydrogen is removed. Sometimes more than one formula unit is needed to remove all the hydrogen as water. The formula of the anhydride then consists of the remaining metal or nonmetal and the remaining oxygen atoms. In calcium hydroxide, removal of water as indicated leaves CaO as the anhydride:

$$Ca \underset{\overline{OH}}{\overset{O\,H}{\cdots}} \xrightarrow{\Delta} CaO + H_2O$$

In sodium hydroxide, H_2O cannot be removed from one formula unit, so two formula units of NaOH must be used, leaving Na_2O as the formula of the anhydride:

$$NaO\boxed{H} \atop Na\ \boxed{OH} \xrightarrow{\Delta} Na_2O + H_2O$$

The removal of water from sulfuric acid, H_2SO_4, gives the acid anhydride SO_3:

$$H_2SO_4 \xrightarrow{\Delta} SO_3 + H_2O$$

The foregoing are examples of typical reactions of water but are by no means a complete list of the known reactions of water.

13.10 Hydrates

hydrate

water of hydration or water of crystallization

When certain salt solutions are allowed to evaporate, some water molecules remain as part of the crystalline salt that is left after evaporation is complete. Solids that contain water molecules as part of their crystalline structure are known as **hydrates.** Water in a hydrate is known as **water of hydration** or **water of crystallization.**

Formulas for hydrates are expressed by first writing the usual anhydrous (without water) formula for the compound and then adding a dot followed by the number of water molecules present. An example is $BaCl_2 \cdot 2\,H_2O$. This formula tells us that each formula unit of this salt contains one barium ion, two chloride ions, and two water molecules. A crystal of the salt contains many of these units in its crystalline lattice.

In naming hydrates, we first name the compound exclusive of the water and then add the term *hydrate*, with the proper prefix representing the number of water molecules in the formula. For example, $BaCl_2 \cdot 2\,H_2O$ is called barium chloride dihydrate. Hydrates are true compounds and follow the Law of Definite Composition. The formula weight of $BaCl_2 \cdot 2\,H_2O$ is 244.3; it contains 56.20% barium, 29.06% chlorine, and 14.74% water.

Water molecules in hydrates are bonded by electrostatic forces between polar water molecules and the positive or negative ions of the compound. These forces are not as strong as covalent or ionic chemical bonds. As a result, water of crystallization can be removed by moderate heating of the compound. A partially dehydrated or completely anhydrous compound may result. When $BaCl_2 \cdot 2\,H_2O$ is heated, it loses its water at about 100°C:

$$BaCl_2 \cdot 2\,H_2O \xrightarrow{100°C} BaCl_2 + 2\,H_2O\uparrow$$

When a solution of copper(II) sulfate ($CuSO_4$) is allowed to evaporate, beautiful blue crystals containing 5 moles of water per mole of $CuSO_4$ are formed. The formula for this hydrate is $CuSO_4 \cdot 5\,H_2O$; it is called copper(II) sulfate pentahydrate, or cupric sulfate pentahydrate. When $CuSO_4 \cdot 5\,H_2O$ is

Table 13.4 Selected hydrates

Hydrate	Name
$CaCl_2 \cdot 2\,H_2O$	Calcium chloride dihydrate
$Ba(OH)_2 \cdot 8\,H_2O$	Barium hydroxide octahydrate
$MgSO_4 \cdot 7\,H_2O$	Magnesium sulfate heptahydrate
$SnCl_2 \cdot 2\,H_2O$	Tin(II) chloride dihydrate
$CoCl_2 \cdot 6\,H_2O$	Cobalt(II) chloride hexahydrate
$Na_2CO_3 \cdot 10\,H_2O$	Sodium carbonate decahydrate
$(NH_4)_2C_2O_4 \cdot H_2O$	Ammonium oxalate monohydrate
$NaC_2H_3O_2 \cdot 3\,H_2O$	Sodium acetate trihydrate
$Na_2B_4O_7 \cdot 10\,H_2O$	Sodium tetraborate decahydrate
$Na_2S_2O_3 \cdot 5\,H_2O$	Sodium thiosulfate pentahydrate

heated, water is lost, and a pale green-white powder, anhydrous $CuSO_4$, is formed:

$$CuSO_4 \cdot 5\,H_2O \xrightarrow{250°C} CuSO_4 + 5\,H_2O \uparrow$$

When water is added to anhydrous copper(II) sulfate, the foregoing reaction is reversed, and the salt turns blue again. Because of this outstanding color change, anhydrous copper(II) sulfate has been used as an indicator to detect small amounts of water. The formation of the hydrate is noticeably exothermic.

The formula for plaster of paris is $(CaSO_4)_2 \cdot H_2O$. When mixed with the proper quantity of water, plaster of paris forms a dihydrate and sets to a hard mass. It is, therefore, useful for making patterns for the reproduction of art objects, molds, and surgical casts. The chemical reaction is

$$(CaSO_4)_2 \cdot H_2O(s) + 3\,H_2O(l) \longrightarrow 2\,CaSO_4 \cdot 2\,H_2O(s)$$

The occurrence of hydrates is commonplace in salts. Table 13.4 lists a number of common hydrates.

13.11 Hygroscopic Substances: Deliquescence; Efflorescence

hygroscopic substances

Many anhydrous salts and other substances readily absorb water from the atmosphere. Such substances are said to be **hygroscopic**. This property can be observed in the following simple experiment: Spread a weighed 10–20 g sample of anhydrous copper(II) sulfate on a watch glass and set it aside so that the salt is exposed to the air. Then weigh the sample periodically for 24 hours, noting the increase in weight and the change in color. Water is absorbed from the atmosphere, forming the blue pentahydrate $CuSO_4 \cdot 5\,H_2O$.

deliquescence

Some compounds continue to absorb water beyond the hydrate stage to form solutions. A substance that absorbs water from the air until it forms a solution is said to be **deliquescent**. A few granules of anhydrous calcium chloride or pellets of sodium hydroxide exposed to the air will appear moist in a few minutes, and within an hour will absorb enough water to form a puddle of solution. Phosphorus pentoxide (P_2O_5) picks up water so rapidly that it cannot be weighed accurately except in an anhydrous atmosphere.

Compounds that absorb water are useful as drying agents (desiccants). Refrigeration systems must be kept dry with such agents or the moisture will freeze and clog the tiny orifices in the mechanism. Bags of drying agents are often enclosed in packages containing iron or steel parts to absorb moisture and prevent rusting. Anhydrous calcium chloride, magnesium sulfate, sodium sulfate, calcium sulfate, silica gel, and phosphorus pentoxide are some of the compounds commonly used for drying liquids and gases that contain small amounts of moisture.

efflorescence

The process by which crystalline materials spontaneously lose water when exposed to the air is known as **efflorescence**. Glauber's sallt ($Na_2SO_4 \cdot 10\ H_2O$), a transparent crystalline salt, loses water when exposed to the air. One can actually observe these well-defined, large crystals crumbling away as they lose water and form a white, noncrystalline-appearing powder. From our discussion of the decomposition of hydrates, we can predict that heat will increase the rate of efflorescence. The rate also depends on the concentration of moisture in the air. A dry atmosphere will allow the process to take place more rapidly.

13.12 Hydrogen Peroxide and Ozone

Although both water and hydrogen peroxide are compounds of hydrogen and oxygen, their properties are very different. A hydrogen peroxide molecule (H_2O_2) is composed of two H atoms and two O atoms. Its composition by weight is 94.1% oxygen and 5.9% hydrogen. Pure hydrogen peroxide is a pale blue liquid that has a melting point of $-0.41°C$, boils at $150°C$, and has a density of $1.44\ g/mL$ at $25°C$. It is miscible with water in all proportions. Water solutions of hydrogen peroxide are slightly acidic. The structure of hydrogen peroxide may be represented as

$$\overset{\displaystyle H}{\underset{\displaystyle H}{:\ddot{O}:\ddot{O}:}} \quad \text{or} \quad \overset{\displaystyle H}{\underset{\displaystyle H}{:\ddot{O}\text{--}\ddot{O}:}}$$

Hydrogen peroxide is a common, useful source of oxygen, because it decomposes easily to give oxygen and water:

$$2\ H_2O_2(l) \longrightarrow 2\ H_2O(l) + O_2(g) + 192\ kJ\ (46.0\ kcal)$$

This decomposition is accelerated by heat and light but can be minimized by storing peroxide solutions in brown bottles, keeping it cold, and adding stabilizers. The decomposition can also be accelerated by catalysts such as manganese dioxide.

The peroxide group, like an oxygen molecule (O_2), contains two oxygen atoms linked by a covalent bond. It has a -2 oxidation number and is written O_2^{2-} or

:Ö:Ö:$^{2-}$; each O atom is considered to have an oxidation number of -1. Metal dioxides also contain two O atoms, but each is bonded individually to the metal ion. Thus, a metal dioxide contains two oxide (:Ö:$^{2-}$) ions.

Some discretion must be used when working with peroxide formulas. From their formulas, BaO_2 and TiO_2 appear to be similar compounds, but BaO_2 is a peroxide consisting of a $+2$ barium ion and a -2 peroxide ion, whereas titanium dioxide is an oxide consisting of a $+4$ titanium ion and two -2 oxide ions. Peroxides can be distinguished from dioxides chemically, because they generally yield H_2O_2 or O_2 when treated with acids or water. Two examples are the reactions of barium peroxide and sodium peroxide:

$$BaO_2(s) + H_2SO_4(aq) \longrightarrow H_2O_2(aq) + BaSO_4(s)$$

$$Na_2O_2(s) + 2\,H_2O(l) \longrightarrow H_2O_2(aq) + 2\,NaOH(aq)$$

A 3% solution of H_2O_2, which is commonly available at drugstores, is used as an antiseptic to cleanse open wounds. Somewhat stronger H_2O_2 solutions are widely used as bleaching agents for cotton, wood, and hair. For some oxidation processes the chemical industry uses a 30% solution. Concentrations of 85% and higher are used for oxidizing fuels in rocket propulsion. These highly concentrated solutions are extremely sensitive to decomposition and are fire hazards if allowed to come into contact with organic materials.

Ozone is another substance containing multiple oxygen linkages. One molecule, O_3, contains three atoms of oxygen:

:Ö::Ö: :O: .O:

Oxygen   Ozone

Ozone can be prepared by passing air or oxygen through an electrical discharge:

$$3\,O_2(g) + 286 \text{ kJ } (68.4 \text{ kcal}) \xrightarrow[\text{discharge}]{\text{Electrical}} 2\,O_3(g)$$

The characteristic pungent odor of ozone is noticeable in the vicinity of electrical machines and power transmission lines. Ozone is formed in the atmosphere during electrical storms and by the photochemical action of ultraviolet radiation on a mixture of nitrogen dioxide and oxygen. Areas with high air pollution are subject to high atmospheric ozone concentrations.

Ozone is not a desirable low-altitude constituent of the atmosphere, because it is known to cause extensive plant damage, cracking of rubber, and the formation of eye-irritating substances. Concentrations of ozone greater than 0.1 part per million (ppm) of air cause coughing, choking, headache, fatigue, and reduced resistance to respiratory infection. Concentrations between 10 and 20 ppm are fatal to humans.

High-energy radiation from the sun also converts oxygen in the upper atmosphere (stratosphere) to ozone, forming a protective ozone layer in the stratosphere:

$$O_2 \xrightarrow{\text{Sunlight}} O + O$$
$$\text{Oxygen atoms}$$

$$O_2 + O \longrightarrow O_3$$

Ultraviolet radiation from the sun is highly damaging to living tissues of plants and animals. The ozone layer, however, shields the earth by absorbing ultraviolet radiation and thus prevents most of this lethal radiation from reaching the earth's surface. The reaction that occurs is the reverse of the preceding one:

$$O_3 \xrightarrow[\text{radiation}]{\text{Ultraviolet}} O_2 + O + \text{Heat}$$

Scientists have become concerned about a growing hazard to the ozone layer. Fluorocarbon propellants, such as the Freons, CCl_3F and CCl_2F_2, which were used in aerosol spray cans and are used in refrigeration and air conditioning units, are stable compounds and remain unchanged in the lower atmosphere. When these fluorocarbons are carried by convection currents to the stratosphere, however, they absorb ultraviolet radiation and produce chlorine atoms (chlorine free radicals) that in turn react with ozone. The following reaction sequence involving free radicals (see Section 16.15) has been proposed to explain the partial destruction of the ozone layer by fluorocarbons.

$$CCl_3F \xrightarrow[\text{radiation}]{\text{Ultraviolet}} \cdot CCl_2F \; + \; Cl\cdot$$

Fluorocarbon   Fluorocarbon   Chlorine free
molecule   free radical   radical (atom)

$$Cl\cdot + O_3 \longrightarrow ClO\cdot + O_2$$
$$ClO\cdot + O \longrightarrow O_2 + Cl\cdot$$

Because a chlorine atom (radical) is regenerated for each ozone molecule that is destroyed, a single fluorocarbon molecule can be responsible for the destruction of many ozone molecules.

With the amount of fluorocarbons in the atmosphere already, scientists predict that up to 15% of the ozone layer could be destroyed by the year 2000. This destruction could result in damaging effects on life and major climate changes due to more heat passing into the lower atmosphere.

allotropy

Many elements exist in two or more molecular or cystalline forms. This phenomenon is known as **allotropy** (from the Greek *allotropia*, meaning "variety"). The individual forms of an element are known as allotropic forms, or allotropes. Oxygen (O_2) and ozone (O_3) are allotropic forms of the element oxygen. Two other common elements that exhibit allotropy are sulfur and carbon. Allotropic forms of sulfur are rhombic and monoclinic sulfur. Diamond and graphite are allotropic forms of carbon.

13.13 Natural Waters

Natural fresh waters are not pure, but contain dissolved minerals, suspended matter, and sometimes harmful bacteria. The water supplies of large cities are usually drawn from rivers or lakes. Such water is generally unsafe to drink without treatment. To make such water potable (that is, safe to drink), it is treated by some or all of the following processes:

1. **Screening.** Removal of relatively large objects, such as trash, fish, and so on.
2. **Flocculation and sedimentation.** Chemicals, usually lime and alum (aluminum sulfate), are added to form a flocculent jellylike precipitate of aluminum hydroxide. This precipitate traps most of the fine suspended matter in the water and carries it to the bottom of the sedimentation basin.
3. **Sand filtration.** Water is drawn from the top of the sedimentation basin and passed downward through fine sand filters. Nearly all the remaining suspended matter and bacteria are removed by the sand filters.
4. **Aeration.** Water is drawn from the bottom of the sand filters and is aerated by spraying. The purpose of this process is to remove objectionable odors and tastes.
5. **Disinfection.** In the final stage chlorine gas is injected into the water to kill harmful bacteria before the water is distributed to the public. Ozone is also used in some countries to disinfect water. In emergencies water may be disinfected by simply boiling for a few minutes.

If the drinking water of children contains an optimum amount of fluoride ion, their teeth will be more resistant to decay. Therefore, in many communities NaF or Na_2SiF_6 is added to the water supply to bring the fluoride ion concentration up to the optimum level of about 1.0 ppm. Excessively high concentrations of fluoride ion can cause mottling of the teeth.

Water that contains dissolved calcium and magnesium salts is called *hard water*. One drawback of hard water is that ordinary soap does not lather well in it; the soap reacts with the calcium and magenesium ions to form an insoluble greasy scum. However, synthetic soaps or detergents, also known as syndets, are available; they have excellent cleansing qualities and do not form precipitates with hard water. Hard water is also undesirable because it causes "boiler scale" to form on the walls of water heaters and steam boilers, which greatly reduces their efficiency.

Four techniques used to "soften" hard water are distillation, chemical precipitation, ion exchange, and demineralization. In distillation the water is boiled, and the steam thus formed is condensed to a liquid again, leaving the minerals behind in the distilling vessel. Figure 13.9 illustrates a simple laboratory distillation apparatus. Commercial stills are available that are capable of producing hundreds of liters of distilled water per hour.

Calcium and magnesium ions are precipitated from hard water by adding sodium carbonate and lime. Insoluble calcium carbonate and magnesium hydroxide are precipitated and are removed by filtration or sedimentation.

In the ion-exchange method, used in many households, hard water is

Figure 13.9   Simple laboratory setup for distillation of liquids

effectively softened as it is passed through a bed or tank of zeolite. Zeolite is a complex sodium aluminum silicate. In this process sodium ions replace objectionable calcium and magnesium ions, and the water is thereby softened:

$$Na_2Zeolite(s) + Ca^{2+}(aq) \longrightarrow CaZeolite(s) + 2\,Na^+(aq)$$

The zeolite is regenerated by back-flushing with concentrated sodium chloride solution, reversing the foregoing reaction.

The sodium ions that are present in water softened either by chemical precipitation or by the zeolite process are not objectionable to most users of soft water.

In demineralization both cations and anions are removed by a two-stage ion-exchange system. Special synthetic organic resins are used in the ion-exchange beds. In the first stage metal cations are replaced by hydrogen ions. In the second stage anions are replaced by hydroxide ions. The hydrogen and hydroxide ions react, and essentially pure, mineral-free water leaves the second stage (see Figure 13.10).

The oceans are an inexhaustible source of water; however, seawater contains about 3.5 lb of salts per 100 lb of water. This 35,000 ppm of dissolved salts makes seawater unfit for agricultural and domestic uses. Water that contains less than 1000 ppm of salts is considered reasonably good for drinking, and potable water is already being obtained from the sea in many parts of the world. Continuous research is being done in an effort to make usable water from the oceans more abundant and economical.

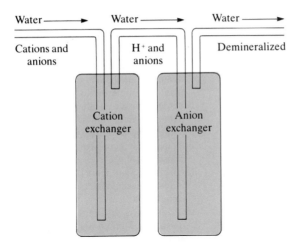

Water ⟶   Water ⟶   Water ⟶

Cations and   H⁺ and   Demineralized
anions   anions

Cation   Anion
exchanger   exchanger

Figure 13.10 Demineralization of water: Water is passed through two beds of synthetic resin. In the cation exchanger metal ions are exchanged for hydrogen ions. In the anion exchanger anions are exchanged for hydroxide ions. The H^+ and OH^- ions react to form water, giving essentially pure, demineralized water.

13.14 Water Pollution

Polluted water was formerly thought of as water that was unclear, had a bad odor or taste, and contained disease-causing bacteria. However, such factors as increased population, industrial requirements for water, atmospheric pollution, toxic waste dumps, and use of pesticides have greatly increased the problems of water pollution.

Many of the newer pollutants are not removed or destroyed by the usual water-treatment processes. For example, among the 66 organic compounds found in the drinking water of a major city on the Mississippi River, 3 are labeled slightly toxic, 17 moderately toxic, 15 very toxic, 1 extremely toxic, and 1 supertoxic. Two are known carcinogens (cancer-producing agents), 11 are suspect, and 3 are metabolized to carcinogens. The United States Public Health Service classifies water pollutants under eight broad categories. These categories are shown in Table 13.5.

Many outbreaks of disease or poisoning such as typhoid, dysentery, and cholera have been attributed directly to drinking water. Rivers and streams are an easy means for municipalities to dispose of their domestic and industrial waste products. Much of this water is used again by people downstream, and then discharged back into the water source. Then another community still farther downstream draws the same water and discharges its own wastes. Thus, along waterways such as the Mississippi and Delaware rivers, water is withdrawn and discharged many times. If this water is not properly treated, harmful pollutants will build up, causing epidemics of various diseases.

Hazardous waste products are unavoidable in the manufacture of many products that we use in everyday life. One common way to dispose of these

Table 13.5 Classification of water pollutants

Type of pollutant	Examples
Oxygen-demanding wastes	Decomposable organic wastes from domestic sewage and industrial wastes of plant and animal origin
Infectious agents	Bacteria, viruses, and other organisms from domestic sewage, animal wastes, and animal process wastes
Plant nutrients	Principally compounds of nitrogen and phosphorus
Organic chemicals	Large numbers of chemicals synthesized by industry, pesticides, chlorinated organic compounds
Other minerals and chemicals	Inorganic chemicals from industrial operations, mining, oil field operations, and agriculture
Radioactive substances	Waste products from mining and processing of radioactive materials, airborne radioactive fallout, increased use of radioactive materials in hospitals and research
Heat from industry	Large quantities of heated water returned to water bodies from power plants and manufacturing facilities after use for cooling
Sediment from land erosion	Solid matter washed into streams and oceans by water runoff

wastes is to place them in toxic waste dumps. What has been found after many years of disposing of wastes in this manner is that toxic substances have seeped into the groundwater deposits. As a result many people have become ill, and water wells have been closed until satisfactory methods of detoxifying this water are found. This problem is serious, because one-half of the U.S. population gets its drinking water from groundwater. To clean up the thousands of industrial dumps and to find and implement new and safe methods of disposing of wastes will be very costly.

The sequence of events that have led to incidents of mercury poisoning is as follows: Mercury and its compounds are used in many industries and in agriculture, primarily as a fungicide in the treatment of seeds. One of the largest uses is in the electrochemical conversion of sodium chloride brines to chlorine and sodium hydroxide, as represented by this equation:

$$2 \text{ NaCl} + 2 \text{ H}_2\text{O} \xrightarrow{\text{Electrolysis}} \text{Cl}_2 + 2 \text{ NaOH} + \text{H}_2$$

Although no mercury is shown in the chemical equation, it is used in the process for electrical contact, and small amounts are discharged along with spent brine solutions. Thus considerable quantities of mercury, in low concentrations, have been discharged into lakes and other surface waters from the effluents of these manufacturing plants. The mercury compounds discharged into the water are converted by bacterial action and other organic compounds to methyl mercury, $(CH_3)_2Hg$, which then accumulates in the bodies of fish. Several major episodes of mercury poisoning that have occurred in the past years were the result of eating mercury-contaminated fish. The best way to control this contaminant is at the source, and much has been done since 1970 to eliminate the discharge of mercury in industrial wastes. In 1976 the Environmental Protection Agency banned the use of all mercury-containing insecticides and fungicides.

Many other major water pollutants have been recognized and steps have been taken to eliminate them. Three that pose serious problems are lead, detergents, and chlorine-containing organic compounds. Lead poisoning, for example, has been responsible for many deaths in past years. The toxic action of lead in the body is the inhibition of the enzyme necessary for the production of hemoglobin in the blood. The usual intake of lead into the body is through food. However, extraordinary amounts of lead can be ingested from water running through lead pipes and by using lead-containing ceramic containers for storage of food and beverages.

It has been clearly demonstrated that waterways rendered so polluted that the water is neither fit for human use nor able to sustain marine life can be successfully restored. However, keeping our lakes and rivers free from pollution is a very costly and complicated process.

QUESTIONS

A. *Review the meanings of the new terms introduced in this chapter.*

1. Heat of fusion
2. Heat of vaporization
3. Hydrogen bond
4. Evaporation
5. Vaporization
6. Sublimation
7. Vapor pressure
8. Volatile
9. Boiling point
10. Standard or normal boiling point
11. Vapor pressure curves
12. Freezing or melting point
13. Basic anhydride
14. Acid anhydride
15. Hydrate
16. Water of hydration
17. Water of crystallization
18. Hygroscopic substances
19. Deliquescence
20. Efflorescence
21. Allotropy

B. *Information useful in answering the following questions will be found in tables and figures.*

1. Compare the potential energy of the two states of water shown in Figure 13.1.
2. In what state (solid, liquid, or gas) would H_2S, H_2Se, and H_2Te be at 0°C? (See Table 13.1.)
3. The two thermometers in Figure 13.2 read 100°C. What is the pressure of the atmosphere?
4. Draw a diagram of a water molecule and point out the areas that are the negative and positive ends of the dipole.
5. If the water molecule were linear, with all three

atoms in a straight line rather than in the shape of a V, as shown in Figure 13.3, what effect would this have on the physical properties of water?

6. Based on Table 13.4, how do we specify 1, 2, 3, 4, 5, 6, 7, and 8 molecules of water in the formulas of hydrates?

7. Would the distillation setup in Figure 13.9 be satisfactory for separating salt and water? Ethyl alcohol and water? Explain.

8. If the liquid in the flask in Figure 13.9 is ethyl alcohol and the atmospheric pressure is 543 torr, what temperature will show on the thermometer? (Use Figure 13.7.)

9. If water were placed in both containers in Figure 13.5, would both have the same vapor pressure at the same temperature? Explain.

10. In Figure 13.5, in which case, (a) or (b), will the atmosphere above the liquid reach a point of saturation?

11. Suppose that a solution of ethyl ether and ethyl alcohol were placed in the closed bottle in Figure 13.5. Use Figure 13.7 for information on the substances.
    (a) Would both substances be present in the vapor?
    (b) If the answer to part (a) is yes, which would have more molecules in the vapor?

12. In Figure 13.6, if 50% more water had been added in part (b), what equilibrium vapor pressure would have been observed in (c)?

13. At approximately what temperature would each of the substances listed in Table 13.3 boil when the pressure is 30 torr? (See Figure 13.7.)

14. Use the graph in Figure 13.7 to find the following:
    (a) The boiling point of water at 500 torr pressure
    (b) The normal boiling point of ethyl alcohol
    (c) The boiling point of ethyl ether at 0.50 atm

15. Consider Figure 13.8.
    (a) Why is line BC horizontal? What is happening in this interval?
    (b) What phases are present in the interval BC?
    (c) When heating is continued after point C, another horizontal line, DE, is reached at a higher temperature. What does this line represent?

C. *Review questions*

1. List six physical properties of water.

2. What condition is necessary for water to have its maximum density? What is its maximum density?

3. Account for the fact that an ice–water mixture remains at 0°C until all the ice is melted, even though heat is applied to it.

4. Which contains less heat, ice at 0°C or water at 0°C? Explain.

5. Why does ice float in water? Would ice float in ethyl alcohol (d = 0.789 g/mL)? Explain.

6. If water molecules were linear instead of bent, would the heat of vaporization be higher or lower? Explain.

7. The heat of vaporization for ethyl ether is 351 J/g (83.9 cal/g) and that for ethyl alcohol is 855 J/g (204 cal/g). Which of these compounds has hydrogen bonding? Explain.

8. Would there be more or less H-bonding if water molecules were linear instead of bent? Explain.

9. Which would show hydrogen bonding, ammonia, NH_3, or methane, CH_4? Explain.

10. In which condition are there fewer hydrogen bonds between molecules: water at 40°C or water at 80°C?

11. Which compound, $H_2NCH_2CH_2NH_2$ or $CH_3CH_2CH_2NH_2$, would you expect to have the higher boiling point? Explain your answer. (Both compounds have similar molecular weights.)

12. The vapor pressure at 20°C is given for the following compounds:

Methyl alcohol	96	torr
Acetic acid	11.7	torr
Benzene	74.7	torr
Bromine	173	torr
Water	17.5	torr
Carbon tetrachloride	91	torr
Mercury	0.0012	torr
Toluene	23	torr

    (a) Arrange these compounds in their order of increasing rate of evaporation.
    (b) Which substance listed would have the highest boiling point, and which would have the lowest?

13. Explain why rubbing alcohol, warmed to body

temperature, still feels cold when applied to your skin.

14. Suggest a method whereby water could be made to boil at 50°C.

15. If a dish of water initially at 20°C is placed in a living room maintained at 20°C, the water temperature will fall below 20°C. Explain.

16. Explain why a higher temperature is obtained in a pressure cooker than in an ordinary cooking pot.

17. What is the relationship between vapor pressure and boiling point?

18. On the basis of the Kinetic-Molecular Theory, explain why vapor pressure increases with temperature.

19. Why does water have such a relatively high boiling point?

20. The boiling point of ammonia, NH_3, is -33.4°C and that of sulfur dioxide, SO_2, is -10.0°C. Which has the higher vapor pressure at -40°C?

21. Explain what is occurring physically when a substance is boiling.

22. Explain why HF (bp = 19.4°C) has a higher boiling point than HCl (bp = -85°C), whereas F_2 (bp = -188°C) has a lower boiling point than Cl_2(bp = -34°C).

23. Can ice be colder than 0°C? Explain.

24. Why does a boiling liquid maintain a constant temperature when heat is continuously being added?

25. At what specific temperature will copper have a vapor pressure of 760 torr?

26. Why does a lake freeze from the top down?

27. What water temperature would you theoretically expect to find at the bottom of a very deep lake? Explain.

28. Write equations to show how the following metals react with water: aluminum, calcium, iron, sodium, zinc. State the conditions for each reaction.

29. Is the formation of hydrogen and oxygen from water an exothermic or an endothermic reaction? How do you know?

30. (a) What is an anhydride?
(b) What type of compound will be an acid anhydride?
(c) What type of compound will be a basic anhydride?

31. (a) Write the formulas for the anhydrides of the following acids:
H_2SO_3, H_2SO_4, HNO_3, $HClO_4$, ClO_4, H_2CO_3, H_3PO_4
(b) Write the formulas for the anhydrides of the following bases:
NaOH, KOH, $Ba(OH)_2$, $Ca(OH)_2$, $Mg(OH)_2$

32. Complete and balance the following equations:
(a) $Ba(OH)_2 \xrightarrow{\Delta}$
(b) $CH_3OH + O_2 \longrightarrow$
Methyl alcohol
(c) $Rb + H_2O \longrightarrow$
(d) $SnCl_2 \cdot 2 H_2O \xrightarrow{\Delta}$
(e) $HNO_3 + NaOH \longrightarrow$
(f) $Li_2O + H_2O \longrightarrow$
(g) $KOH \xrightarrow{\Delta}$
(h) $Ba + H_2O \longrightarrow$
(i) $Cl_2 + H_2O \longrightarrow$
(j) $SO_3 + H_2O \longrightarrow$
(k) $H_2SO_3 + KOH \longrightarrow$
(l) $CO_2 + H_2O \longrightarrow$

33. Is the conversion of oxygen to ozone an exothermic or an endothermic reaction? How do you know?

34. Write formulas for an oxygen atom, an oxygen molecule, an ozone molecule, and a peroxide ion. How many electrons are in a peroxide ion? How many in an oxygen molecule?

35. How does ozone in the stratosphere protect the earth from excessive ultraviolet radiation?

36. Name each of the following hydrates:
(a) $BaBr_2 \cdot 2 H_2O$ (d) $MgNH_4PO_4 \cdot 6 H_2O$
(b) $AlCl_3 \cdot 6 H_2O$ (e) $FeSO_4 \cdot 7 H_2O$
(c) $FePO_4 \cdot 4 H_2O$ (f) $SnCl_4 \cdot 5 H_2O$

37. Explain how anhydrous copper(II) sulfate ($CuSO_4$) can act as an indicator for moisture.

38. Compare the types of bonds in metal dioxides and metal peroxides.

39. Distinguish between deionized water and:
(a) Hard water (c) Distilled water
(b) Soft water

40. How can soap function to make soft water from hard water? What objections are there to using soap for this purpose?

41. What substance is commonly used to destroy bacteria in water?

42. What chemical, other than chlorine or chlorine compounds, can be used to disinfect water for domestic use?

43. Some organic pollutants in water can be oxidized by dissolved molecular oxygen. What harmful effect can result from this depletion of oxygen in the water?

44. Why should you not drink liquids that are stored in ceramic containers, especially unglazed ones?

45. Write the chemical equation showing how magnesium ions are removed by a zeolite water softener.

46. Write an equation to show how hard water containing calcium chloride ($CaCl_2$) is softened by using sodium carbonate (Na_2CO_3).

47. Which of the following statements are correct?
    (a) The process of a substance changing directly from a solid to a gas is called sublimation.
    (b) When water is decomposed, the volume ratio of H_2 to O_2 is $2:1$, but the mass ratio of H_2 to O_2 is $1:8$.
    (c) Hydrogen sulfide is a larger molecule than water.
    (d) The changing of ice into water is an exothermic process.
    (e) Water and hydrogen fluoride are both nonpolar molecules.
    (f) Hydrogen bonding is stronger in H_2O than in H_2S because oxygen is more electronegative than sulfur.
    (g) $H_2O_2 \longrightarrow 2\ H_2O + O_2$ represents a balanced equation for the decomposition of hydrogen peroxide.
    (h) Steam at 100°C can cause more severe burns than liquid water at 100°C.
    (i) The density of water is independent of temperature.
    (j) Liquid A boils at a lower temperature than liquid B. This fact indicates that liquid A has a lower vapor pressure than liquid B at any particular temperature.
    (k) Water boils at a higher temperature in the mountains than at sea level.
    (l) No matter how much heat you put under an open pot of pure water on a stove, you cannot heat the water above its boiling point.
    (m) The vapor pressure of a liquid at its boiling point is equal to the prevailing atmospheric pressure.
    (n) The normal boiling temperature of water is 273°C.
    (o) The pressure exerted by a vapor in equilibrium with its liquid is known as the vapor pressure of the liquid.
    (p) Sodium, potassium, and calcium each react with water to form hydrogen gas and a metal hydroxide.
    (q) Calcium oxide reacts with water to form calcium hydroxide and hydrogen gas.
    (r) Carbon dioxide is the hydride of carbonic acid.
    (s) Water in a hydrate is known as water of hydration or water of crystallization.
    (t) A substance that spontaneously loses its water of hydration when exposed to the air is said to be efflorescent.
    (u) A substance that absorbs water from the air until it forms a solution is deliquescent.
    (v) Distillation is effective for softening water because the minerals boil away, leaving soft water behind.
    (w) The original source of mercury-contaminated fish is industrial pollution.
    (x) Disposal of toxic industrial wastes in toxic waste dumps has been found to be a very satisfactory long-term solution to the problem of what to do with these wastes.
    (y) The amount of heat needed to change 1 mole of ice at 0°C to a liquid at 0°C is 6.02 kJ (1.44 kcal).
    (z) $BaCl_2 \cdot 2\ H_2O$ has a higher percentage of water than does $CaCl_2 \cdot 2\ H_2O$.

D. *Review questions*

1. How many moles of compound are in 100 g of each of these hydrates?
   (a) $CoCl_2 \cdot 6\ H_2O$ (b) $FeI_2 \cdot 4\ H_2O$

2. How many moles of water can be obtained from 100 g of each of these hydrates?
   (a) $CoCl_2 \cdot 6\ H_2O$ (b) $FeI_2 \cdot 4 H_2O$

3. When a person purchases epsom salts, $MgSO_4 \cdot 7\ H_2O$, what percentage of the compound is water?

4. Calculate the percentage weight of water in the hydrate $Al_2(SO_4)_3 \cdot 18\ H_2O$.

5. Sugar of lead, a hydrate of lead acetate,

$Pb(C_2H_3O_2)_2$, contains 14.2% H_2O. What is the formula for the hydrate?

6. A 25.0 g sample of a hydrate of $FePO_4$ was heated until no more water was driven off. The anhydrous sample weighed 16.9 g. What is the formula of the hydrate?

7. How many joules are needed to change 120 g of water at 20°C to steam at 100°C?

8. How many joules of energy must be removed from 126 g of water at 24°C to form ice at 0°C?

9. How many calories are required to change 225 g of ice at 0°C to steam at 100°C?

10. The molar heat of vaporization is the number of joules required to change 1 mole of a substance from liquid to vapor at its boiling point. What is the molar heat of vaporization of water?

*11. Suppose 100 g of ice at 0°C are added to 300 g of water at 25°C. Is this sufficient ice to lower the temperature of the system to 0°C and still have ice remaining? Show evidence for your answer.

*12. Suppose 35.0 g of steam at 100°C are added to 300 g of water at 25°C. Is there sufficient steam to heat all the water to 100°C and still have steam remaining? Show evidence for your answer.

13. How many joules of energy would be liberated by condensing 50.0 mol of steam and allowing the liquid to cool to 30.0°C?

14. How many kilojoules of energy are needed to convert 100 g of ice at −10.0°C to water at 20.0°C. (The specific heat of ice at −10.0°C is 2.01 J/g°C.)

15. What weight of water must be decomposed to produce 25.0 L of oxygen at STP?

16. Compare the volume occupied by 1.00 mol of liquid water at 0°C and 1.00 mol of water vapor at STP.

17. (a) How many moles of oxygen can be obtained by the decomposition of 12.0 mol of hydrogen peroxide?
    (b) What volume will this much oxygen occupy at 35°C and 710 torr pressure?

18. What volume of oxygen at STP can be obtained by decomposing 625 g of 3.0% hydrogen peroxide?

19. How many grams of water will react with each of the following?
    (a) 1.00 mol K   (d) 1.00 mol SO_3
    (b) 1.00 mol Ca   (e) 1.00 g MgO
    (c) 1.00 g Na   (f) 1.00 g N_2O_5

20. Suppose 1.00 mol of water evaporates in 1.00 day. How many water molecules, on the average, leave the liquid each second?

*21. A quantity of sulfuric acid is added to 100 mL of water. The final volume of the solution is 122 mL and it has a density of 1.26 g/mL. What weight of acid was added? Assume the density of the water is 1.00 g/mL.

22. A mixture of 80.0 mL of hydrogen and 60.0 mL of oxygen is ignited by a spark to form water.
    (a) Does any gas remain unreacted? Which one, H_2 or O_2?
    (b) What volume of which gas (if any) remains unreacted? (Assume the same conditions before and after the reaction.)

14

Solutions

After studying
Chapter 14,
you should be
able to

1. Understand the new terms listed in Question A at the end of the chapter.
2. Describe the different types of solutions that are possible, based on the three states of matter.
3. List the general properties of solutions.
4. Outline the solubility rules for common salts and hydroxides.
5. Describe and illustrate the process by which an ionic substance like sodium chloride dissolves in water.
6. Tell how temperature changes affect the solubilities of solids and gases in liquids.
7. Tell how changes of pressure and temperature affect the solubility of a gas in a liquid.
8. Identify and discuss the variables that affect the rate at which a solid dissolves in a liquid.
9. Determine by using a solubility graph or table whether a given solution is unsaturated, saturated, or supersaturated at a given temperature.
10. Calculate the weight-percent or volume-percent composition of a solution from appropriate data.
11. Calculate the amount of solute in a given quantity of a solution when given the weight-percent or volume-percent composition.

12. Calculate the molarity of a solution when given the volume of solution and the grams or moles of solute.
13. Calculate the weight of a substance needed to prepare a solution of specified volume and molarity.
14. Determine the resulting molarity when a given volume of a solution of known molarity is mixed with a specified volume of water or is mixed with a solution of different molarity.
15. Apply stoichiometric principles to chemical reactions in which the amounts of reactants are given in units of volume and molarity.
16. Understand the concepts of equivalent weight and normality and do calculations involving these concepts.
17. Relate the effect of a solute on the vapor pressure of a solvent to the freezing point and the boiling point of a solution.
18. Calculate the boiling point or freezing point of a solution from appropriate concentration data.
19. Calculate molality and molecular weight of a solute from boiling point or freezing point and weight concentration data.
20. Explain the phenomenon of osmosis.
21. Predict the direction of net solvent flow between solutions of known concentrations separated by a semipermeable membrane.

14.1 Components of a Solution

solution

solute

solvent

The term **solution** is used in chemistry to describe a system in which one or more substances are homogeneously mixed or dissolved in another substance. A simple solution has two components, a solute and a solvent. The **solute** is the component that is dissolved or the least abundant component in the solution. The **solvent** is the dissolving agent or the most abundant component in the solution. For example, when salt is dissolved in water to form a solution, salt is the solute and water is the solvent. Complex solutions containing more than one solute and/or more than one solvent are common.

14.2 Types of Solution

From the three states of matter—solid, liquid, and gas—it is possible to have nine different types of solutions: solid dissolved in solid, solid dissolved in liquid, solid dissolved in gas, liquid dissolved in liquid, and so on. Of these, the most common solutions are solid dissolved in liquid, liquid dissolved in liquid, gas dissolved in liquid, and gas dissolved in gas.

14.3 General Properties of Solutions

A true solution is one in which the particles of dissolved solute are molecular or ionic in size, generally in the range of 0.1 to 1 nm (10^{-8} to 10^{-7} cm). The properties of a true solution are as follows:

1. It is a homogeneous mixture of two or more components—solute and solvent.
2. It has a variable composition; that is, the ratio of solute to solvent may be varied.

3. The dissolved solute is molecular or ionic in size.
4. It may be either colored or colorless but is usually transparent.
5. The solute remains uniformly distributed throughout the solution and will not settle out with time.
6. The solute generally can be separated from the solvent by purely physical means (for example, by evaporation).

These properties are illustrated by water solutions of sugar and of potassium permanganate. Suppose that we prepare two sugar solutions, the first containing 10 g of sugar added to 100 mL of water and the second containing 20 g of sugar added to 100 mL of water. Each solution is stirred until all the solute dissolves, demonstrating that we can vary the composition of a solution. Every portion of the solution has the same sweet taste because the sugar molecules are uniformly distributed throughout. If confined so that no solvent is lost, the solution will taste and appear the same a week or a month later. The properties of the solution are unaltered after the solution is passed through filter paper. But by carefully evaporating the water, we can recover the sugar from the solution.

To observe the dissolving of potassium permanganate ($KMnO_4$) we affix a few crystals of $KMnO_4$ to paraffin wax or rubber cement at the end of a glass rod and submerge the entire rod, with the wax–permanganate end up, in a cylinder of water. Almost at once the beautiful purple color of dissolved permanganate ions (MnO_4^-) appears at the top of the rod and streams to the bottom of the cylinder as the crystals dissolve. The purple color at first is mostly at the bottom of the cylinder because potassium permanganate is denser than water. But after a while the purple color disperses until it is evenly distributed throughout the solution. This dispersal demonstrates that molecules and ions move about freely and spontaneously (diffuse) in a liquid or solution.

Once formed, a solution is permanent; the solute particles do not settle out. Solution permanency is explained in terms of the Kinetic-Molecular Theory (see Section 12.2). According to the KMT both the solute and solvent particles (molecules and/or ions) are in constant random thermal motion. This motion is energetic enough to prevent the solute particles from settling out under the influence of gravity. This same ceaseless, random thermal motion is also responsible for diffusion in gases as well as in liquids.

14.4   Solubility

solubility

The term **solubility** describes the amount of one substance (solute) that will dissolve in a specified amount of another substance (solvent) under stated conditions. For example, 36.0 g of sodium chloride (NaCl) will dissolve in 100 g of water at 20°C. We say, then, that the solubility of NaCl in water is 36.0 g per 100 g of water at 20°C.

Solubility is often used in a relative way. We say that a substance is very soluble, moderately soluble, slightly soluble, or insoluble. Although these terms do not accurately indicate how much solute will dissolve, they are frequently used to describe the solubility of a substance qualitatively.

Two other terms often used to describe solubility are miscible and immiscible.

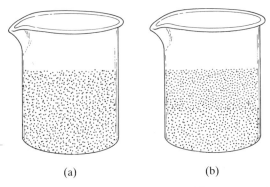

(a)   (b)

Figure 14.1 Miscible and immiscible systems: (a) miscible, H_2O and CH_3OH; (b) immiscible, H_2O and CCl_4. In a miscible system a solution is formed consisting of a single phase with the solute and solvent uniformly dispersed. An immiscible system is heterogeneous and, in the case of two liquids, forms two liquid layers.

miscible

immiscible

Liquids that are capable of mixing and forming a solution are **miscible**; those that do not form solutions or are generally insoluble in each other are **immiscible.** Methyl alcohol and water are miscible in each other in all proportions. Carbon tetrachloride and water are immiscible, forming two separate layers when they are mixed. Miscible and immiscible systems are illustrated in Figure 14.1. Certain liquids such as 1-butanol and water are *partially* miscible. This means that a limited amount of 1-butanol will dissolve in water; and, conversely, a limited amount of water will dissolve in 1-butanol. This solubility behavior can be easily observed if 100 mL of 1-butanol are slowly added and stirred into 100 mL of water. A homogeneous solution forms at first; but as more butanol is added, the solution separates into two phases (layers). The top layer is 1-butanol saturated with water; the bottom layer is water saturated with 1-butanol.

The general rules for the solubility of common salts and hydroxides are given in Table 14.1. The solubilities of over 200 compounds are given in the Solubility Table in Appendix IV. Solubility data for thousands of compounds can be found by consulting standard reference sources.*

concentration of a solution

The quantitative expression of the amount of dissolved solute in a particular quantity of solvent is known as the **concentration of a solution.** Several methods of expressing concentration will be described in Section 14.8.

14.5 Factors Related to Solubility

Predicting solubilities is complex and difficult. Many variables—such as size of ions, charge on ions, interaction between ions, interaction between solute and solvent, and temperature—bear upon the problem. Because of the factors

---

* Two commonly used handbooks are *Lange's Handbook of Chemistry*, 13th ed. (New York: McGraw-Hill, 1985), and *Handbook of Chemistry and Physics*, 68th ed. (Cleveland: Chemical Rubber Co., 1987).

Table 14.1 General solubility rules for common salts and hydroxides[a]

Class	Solubility in cold water[b]
Nitrates	Most nitrates are soluble.
Acetates	Most acetates are soluble.
Chlorides Bromides Iodides	Most chlorides, bromides, and iodides are soluble except those of Ag, Hg(I), and Pb(II); $PbCl_2$ and $PbBr_2$ are slightly soluble in hot water.
Sulfates	Most sulfates are soluble except those of Ba, Sr, and Pb; Ca and Ag sulfates are slightly soluble.
Carbonates Phosphates	Most carbonates and phosphates are insoluble except those of Na, K, and NH_4^+. Many bicarbonates and acid phosphates are soluble.
Hydroxides	Most hydroxides are insoluble except those of the alkali metals and NH_4OH; $Ba(OH)_2$ and $Ca(OH)_2$ are slightly soluble.
Sodium salts Potassium salts Ammonium salts	Most common salts of these ions are soluble.
Sulfides	Most sulfides are insoluble except those of the alkali metals, ammonium, and the alkaline earth metals (Ca, Mg, Ba).

[a] When we say a substance is soluble, we mean that the substance is reasonably soluble. All substances have some solubility in water, although the amount of solubility may be very small; the solubility of silver iodide, for example, is about 1×10^{-8} mol AgI/liter H_2O.
[b] These rules have exceptions.

involved, the general rules of solubility given in Table 14.1 have many exceptions. However, the rules are very useful, because they do apply to many of the more common compounds that we encounter in the study of chemistry. Keep in mind that these are rules, not laws, and are therefore subject to exceptions. Fortunately the solubility of a solute is relatively easy to determine experimentally. Factors related to solubility are discussed in the following paragraphs.

1. The nature of the solute and solvent. The old adage "like dissolves like" has merit, in a general way. Polar or ionic substances tend to be more miscible, or soluble, with other polar substances. Nonpolar substances tend to be miscible with other nonpolar substances and less miscible with polar substances. Thus, mineral acids, bases, and salts, which are polar, tend to be much more soluble in water, which is polar, than in solvents such as ether, carbon tetrachloride, or benzene, which are essentially nonpolar. Sodium chloride, an ionic substance, is soluble in water, slightly soluble in ethyl alcohol (less polar than water), and insoluble in ether and benzene. Pentane (C_5H_{12}), a nonpolar substance, is only slightly soluble in water but is very soluble in benzene and ether.

At the molecular level the formation of a solution from two nonpolar substances, such as carbon tetrachloride and benzene, can be visualized as a process of simple mixing. The nonpolar molecules, having little tendency to either attract or repel one another, easily intermingle to form a homogeneous mixture.

Solution formation between polar substances is much more complex. For example, the process by which sodium chloride dissolves in water is illustrated in Figure 14.2. Water molecules are very polar and are attracted to other polar molecules or ions. When salt crystals (NaCl) are put into water, polar water molecules become attracted to the sodium and chloride ions on the crystal surfaces and weaken the attraction between Na^+ and Cl^- ions. The positive end of the water dipole is attracted to the Cl^- ions, and the negative end of the water dipole to the Na^+ ions. The weaker attraction permits the ions to move apart,

= Water   = Na^+ = Cl^-

Figure 14.2 Dissolution of sodium chloride in water: Polar water molecules are attracted to Na^+ and Cl^- ions in the salt crystal, weakening the attraction between the ions. As the attraction between the ions weakens, the ions move apart and become surrounded by water dipoles. The hydrated ions slowly diffuse away from the crystal to become dissolved in solution.

making room for more water dipoles. Thus, the surface ions are surrounded by water molecules, becoming hydrated ions, $Na^+(aq)$ and $Cl^-(aq)$, and slowly diffuse away from the crystals and dissolve in solution.

$$NaCl(crystal) \xrightarrow{H_2O} Na^+(aq) + Cl^-(aq)$$

Examination of the data in Table 14.2 reveals some of the complex questions relating to solubility. For example: Why are lithium halides, except for lithium fluoride (LiF), more soluble than sodium and potassium halides? Why are the solubilities of LiF and sodium fluoride (NaF) so low in comparison with those of the other salts? Why doesn't the solubility of LiF, NaF, and NaCl increase proportionately with temperature, as do the solubilities of the other salts? Sodium chloride is appreciably soluble in water but is insoluble in concentrated hydrochloric acid (HCl) solution. On the other hand, LiF and NaF are not very soluble in water but are quite soluble in hydrofluoric acid (HF) solution—why? These questions will not be answered directly here, but it is hoped that your curiosity will be aroused to the point that you will do some reading and research on the properties of solutions.

2. The effect of temperature on solubility.   Temperature has major effects on the solubility of most substances, and most solutes have a limited solubility in a specific solvent at a fixed temperature. For most solids dissolved in a liquid, an increase in temperature results in increased solubility (see Figure 14.3). However, no completely valid general rule governs the solubility of solids in liquids with change in temperature. Some solids increase in solubility only

Table 14.2   Solubility of alkali metal halides in water

Salt	Solubility (g salt/100 g H_2O)	
	0°C	*100°C*
LiF	0.12	0.14 (at 35°C)
LiCl	67	127.5
LiBr	143	266
LiI	151	481
NaF	4	5
NaCl	35.7	39.8
NaBr	79.5	121
NaI	158.7	302
KF	92.3 (at 18°C)	Very soluble
KCl	27.6	57.6
KBr	53.5	104
KI	127.5	208

slightly with increasing temperature (see NaCl in Figure 14.3); other solids decrease in solubility with increasing temperature (see Li_2SO_4 in Figure 14.3).

On the other hand, the solubility of a gas in a liquid always decreases with increasing temperature (see HCl and SO_2 in Figure 14.3). The tiny bubbles that are formed when water is heated are due to the decreased solubility of air at higher temperatures. The decreased solubility of gases at higher temperatures is explained in terms of the KMT by assuming that, in order to dissolve, the gas molecules must form "bonds" of some sort with the molecules of the liquid. An increase in temperature decreases the solubility of the gas because it increases the kinetic energy (speed) of the gas molecules and thereby decreases their ability to form "bonds" with the liquid molecules.

3. The effect of pressure on solubility. Small changes in pressure have little effect on the solubility of solids in liquids or liquids in liquids but have a marked effect on the solubility of gases in liquids. The solubility of a gas in a liquid is directly proportional to the pressure of that gas above the solution. Thus, the amount of a gas that is dissolved in solution will double if the pressure of that gas over the solution is doubled. For example, carbonated beverages contain dissolved carbon dioxide at pressures greater than atmospheric pressure. When a bottle of carbonated soda is opened, the pressure is immediately reduced to the atmospheric pressure, and the excess dissolved carbon dioxide bubbles out of the solution.

Figure 14.3 Solubility of various compounds in water

14.6 Rate of Dissolving Solids

The rate at which a solid dissolves is governed by (1) the size of the solute particles, (2) the temperature, (3) the concentration of the solution, and (4) agitation or stirring.

1. Particle size. A solid can dissolve only at the surface that is in contact with the solvent. Because the surface-to-volume ratio increases as size decreases, smaller crystals dissolve faster than large ones. For example, if a salt crystal 1 cm on a side (6 cm^2 surface area) is divided into 1000 cubes, each 0.1 cm on a side, the total surface of the smaller cubes is 60 cm^2—a tenfold increase in surface area (see Figure 14.4).

2. Temperature. In most cases the rate of dissolving of a solid increases with temperature. This increase is due to kinetic effects: The solvent molecules move more rapidly at higher temperatures and strike the solid surfaces more often and harder, causing the rate of dissolving to increase.

3. Concentration of the solution. When the solute and solvent are first mixed, the rate of dissolving is at its maximum. As the concentration of the solution increases and the solution becomes more nearly saturated with the solute, the rate of dissolving decreases greatly. The rate of dissolving is pictured graphically in Figure 14.5. Note that about 17 g dissolve in the first 5 minute interval, but only about 1 g dissolves in the fourth 5 minute interval. Although different solutes show different rates, the rate of dissolving always becomes very slow as the concentration approaches the saturation point.

4. Agitation or stirring. The effect of agitation or stirring is kinetic. When a solid is first put into water, the only solvent with which it comes in contact is in

0.1 cm cube
Surface of this single
cube is 0.06 cm²
Total surface area of
the 1000 smaller cubes is
1000 × 0.06 cm² = 60 cm²

1 cm

1 cm

Surface area of
this cube is
6 × 1 cm² = 6 cm²

Figure 14.4 Surface area of crystals: A crystal 1 cm on a side has a surface area of 6 cm². Subdivided into 1000 smaller crystals, each 0.1 cm on a side, the total surface area is increased to 60 cm².

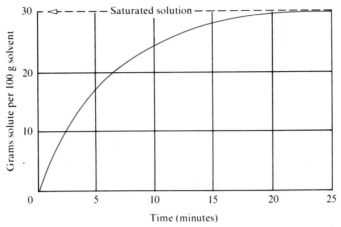

Figure 14.5 Rate of dissolution of a solid solute in a solvent: The rate is maximum at the beginning and decreases as the concentration approaches saturation.

the immediate vicinity. As the solid dissolves, the amount of dissolved solute around the solid becomes more and more concentrated, and the rate of dissolving slows down. If the mixture is not stirred, the dissolved solute diffuses very slowly through the solution; weeks may pass before the solid is entirely dissolved. Stirring distributes the dissolved solute rapidly through the solution, and more solvent is brought into contact with the solid, causing it to dissolve more rapidly.

14.7 Solutions: A Reaction Medium

Many solids must be put into solution in order to undergo appreciable chemical reaction. We can write the equation for the double-displacement reaction between sodium chloride and silver nitrate:

$$NaCl + AgNO_3 \longrightarrow AgCl + NaNO_3$$

But suppose we mix solid NaCl and solid $AgNO_3$ and look for a chemical change. If any reaction occurs, it is slow and virtually undetectable. In fact, the crystalline structures of NaCl and $AgNO_3$ are so different that we could separate them by tediously picking out each kind of crystal from the mixture. But if we dissolve the sodium chloride and silver nitrate separately in water and mix the two solutions, we observe the immediate formation of a white, curdy precipitate of silver chloride.

Molecules or ions must come into intimate contact or collide with one another in order to react. In the foregoing example, the two solids did not react because the ions were securely locked within their crystal structures. But when the sodium chloride and silver nitrate are dissolved, their crystal lattices are broken down and the ions become mobile. When the two solutions are mixed, the mobile Ag^+ and Cl^- ions come into contact and react to form insoluble AgCl, which precipitates out of solution. The soluble Na^+ and NO_3^- ions remain mobile in solution but form the crystalline salt $NaNO_3$ when the water is evaporated:

$$NaCl(aq) + AgNO_3(aq) \longrightarrow AgCl\downarrow + NaNO_3(aq)$$

$$(Na^+ + Cl^-) + (Ag^+ + NO_3^-) \xrightarrow{H_2O} AgCl\downarrow + (Na^+ + NO_3^-)$$

| Sodium chloride solution | Silver nitrate solution | Silver chloride | Sodium nitrate in solution |

The mixture of the two solutions provides a medium or space in which the Ag^+ and Cl^- ions can react. (See Chapter 15 for further discussion of ionic reactions.)

Solutions also function as diluents (diluting agents) in reactions in which the undiluted reactants would combine with each other too violently. Moreover, a solution of known concentration provides a convenient method for delivering specific amounts of reactants.

14.8 Concentration of Solutions

The concentration of a solution expresses the amount of solute dissolved in a given quantity of solvent or solution. Because reactions are often conducted in solution, it is important to understand the methods of expressing concentration and to know how to prepare solutions of particular concentrations.

Dilute and concentrated solutions. When we say that a solution is *dilute* or *concentrated*, we are expressing, in a relative way, the amount of solute present. One gram of salt and 2 g of salt in solution are both dilute solutions when compared with the same volume of a solution containing 20 g of salt. Ordinary concentrated hydrochloric acid (HCl) contains 12 moles of HCl per liter of solution. In some laboratories the dilute acid is made by mixing equal volumes of water and the concentrated acid. In other laboratories the concen-

dilute solution

trated acid is diluted with two or three volumes of water, depending on its use. The term **dilute solution**, then, describes a solution that contains a relatively small amount of dissolved solute. Conversely, a **concentrated solution** contains a

concentrated solution

relatively large amount of dissolved solute.

Saturated, unsaturated, and supersaturated solutions. At a specific temperature there is a limit to the amount of solute that will dissolve in a given amount of solvent. When this limit is reached, the resulting solution is said to be *saturated*. For example, when we put 40.0 g of KCl into 100 g of H_2O at 20°C, we find that 34.0 g of KCl dissolve and 6.0 g of KCl remain undissolved. The solution formed is a saturated solution of KCl.

Two processes are occurring simultaneously in a saturated solution. The solid is dissolving into solution, and at the same time the dissolved solute is crystallizing out of solution. This may be expressed as

Solute (undissolved) $\rightleftharpoons$ Solute (dissolved)

When these two opposing processes are occurring at the same rate, the amount of

saturated
solution

solute in solution is constant, and a condition of equilibrium is established between dissolved and undissolved solute. A **saturated solution** contains dissolved solute in equilibrium with undissolved solute.

It is important to state the temperature of a saturated solution, because a solution that is saturated at one temperature may not be saturated at another. If the temperature of a saturated solution is changed, the equilibrium is disturbed, and the amount of dissolved solute will change to reestablish equilibrium.

A saturated solution may be either dilute or concentrated, depending on the solubility of the solute. A saturated solution can be conveniently prepared by dissolving a little more than the saturated amount of solute at a temperature somewhat higher than room temperature. Then the amount of solute in solution will be in excess of its solubility at room temperature; and, when the solution cools, the excess solute will crystallize, leaving the solution saturated. (In this case, the solute must be more soluble at higher temperatures and must not form a supersaturated solution.) Examples expressing the solubility of saturated solutions at two different temperatures are given in Table 14.3.

unsaturated
solution

An **unsaturated solution** contains less solute per unit of volume than does its corresponding saturated solution. In other words, additional solute can be dissolved in an unsaturated solution without altering any other conditions. Consider a solution made by adding 40 g of KCl to 100 g of H_2O at 20°C (see Table 14.3). The solution formed will be saturated and will contain about 6 g of undissolved salt, because the maximum amount of KCl that can dissolve in 100 g of H_2O at 20°C is 34 g. If the solution is now heated and maintained at 50°C, all the salt will dissolve and, in fact, even more can be dissolved. Thus the solution at 50°C is unsaturated.

supersaturated
solution

In some circumstances, solutions can be prepared that contain more solute than that needed for a saturated solution at a particular temperature. Such solutions are said to be **supersaturated**. However, we must qualify this definition by noting that a supersaturated solution is unstable. Disturbances such as jarring, stirring, scratching the walls of the container, or dropping in a "seed" crystal cause the supersaturation to break. When a supersaturated solution is disturbed, the excess solute crystallizes out rapidly, returning the solution to a saturated state.

Table 14.3 Saturated solutions at 20°C and 50°C

| Solute | Solubility (g solute/100 g H_2O) | |
	20°C	*50°C*
NaCl	36.0	37.0
KCl	34.0	42.6
NaNO$_3$	88.0	114.0
KClO$_3$	7.4	19.3
AgNO$_3$	222.0	455.0
$C_{12}H_{22}O_{11}$	203.9	260.4

Supersaturated solutions are not easy to prepare but may be made from certain substances by dissolving, in warm solvent, an amount of solute greater than that needed for a saturated solution at room temperature. The warm solution is then allowed to cool very slowly. With the proper solute and careful work, a supersaturated solution will result. Two substances commonly used to demonstrate this property are sodium thiosulfate pentahydrate, $Na_2S_2O_3 \cdot 5\ H_2O$, and sodium sulfate, Na_2SO_4 (from a saturated solution at 30°C).

PROBLEM
14.1

Will a solution made by adding 2.5 g of $CuSO_4$ to 10 g of H_2O be saturated or unsaturated at 20°C?

To answer this question we first need to know the solubility of $CuSO_4$ at 20°C. From Figure 14.3 we see that the solubility of $CuSO_4$ at 20°C is about 21 g per 100 g of H_2O. This amount is equivalent to 2.1 g of $CuSO_4$ per 10 g of H_2O.

Since 2.5 g per 10 g of H_2O is greater than 2.1 g per 10 g of H_2O, the solution will be saturated and 0.4 g of $CuSO_4$ will be undissolved.

Weight-percent solution.   This method expresses concentration as the percentage of solute in a given mass of solution. It says that for a given mass of solution a certain percentage of that mass is solute. Suppose that we take a bottle from the reagent shelf that reads "Sodium hydroxide, NaOH, 10%." This statement means that for every 100 g of this solution, 10 g will be NaOH and 90 g will be water. (Note that this amount of solution is 100 g and not 100 mL.) We could also make this same concentration of solution by dissolving 2.0 g of NaOH in 18 g of water. Weight-percent concentrations are most generally used for solids dissolved in liquids.

$$\text{Weight percent} = \frac{\text{g solute}}{\text{g solute} + \text{g solvent}} \times 100\% = \frac{\text{g solute}}{\text{g solution}} \times 100\%$$

PROBLEM
14.2

What is the weight percent of sodium hydroxide in a solution that is made by dissolving 8.00 g of NaOH in 50.0 g of H_2O?

Grams of solute (NaOH) = 8.00 g

Grams of solvent (H_2O) = 50.0 g

$$\frac{8.00\ \text{g NaOH}}{8.00\ \text{g NaOH} + 50.0\ \text{g H}_2\text{O}} \times 100\% = 13.8\%\ \text{NaOH solution}$$

PROBLEM
14.3

What weights of potassium chloride (KCl) and water are needed to make 250 g of 5.00% solution?

The percentage expresses the weight of the solute.

250 g = Total weight of solution

5.00% of 250 g = 0.0500 × 250 g = 12.5 g KCl (solute)

Weight of solution (H_2O + KCl) − Weight of solute (KCl) = Weight of H_2O needed

250 g − 12.5 g = 237.5 g H_2O

Dissolving 12.5 g of KCl in 237.5 g of H_2O gives a 5.00% KCl solution.

PROBLEM

14.4

A 34.0% sulfuric acid solution has a density of 1.25 g/mL. How many grams of H_2SO_4 are contained in 1.00 L of this solution?

Since H_2SO_4 is the solute, we first solve the weight-percent equation for grams of solute:

$$\text{Weight percent} = \frac{\text{g solute}}{\text{g solution}} \times 100\%$$

$$\text{g solute} = \frac{\text{Weight percent} \times \text{g solution}}{100\%}$$

The weight percent is given in the problem. We need to determine the grams of solution. The weight of the solution can be calculated from the density data.

Convert density (g/mL) to grams:

1.00 L = 1000 mL

$$\frac{1.25 \text{ g}}{\text{mL}} \times 1000 \text{ mL} = 1250 \text{ g} \quad \text{(g of solution)}$$

Now we have all the figures to calculate the grams of solute.

$$\text{g solute} = \frac{34.0\% \times 1250 \text{ g}}{100\%} = 425 \text{ g } H_2SO_4$$

1.00 L of 34.0% H_2SO_4 solution contains 425 g of H_2SO_4.

The student should note that the concentration expressed as weight percent is independent of the formula of the solute.

Weight/volume percent (w/v). This method expresses concentration as grams of solute per 100 mL of solution. With this system, a 10.0% (w/v) glucose solution is made by dissolving 10.0 g of glucose in water, diluting to 100 mL, and mixing. The 10.0% (w/v) solution could also be made by diluting 20.0 g to 200 mL, 50.0 g to 500 mL, and so on. Of course, any other appropriate dilution ratio may be used.

$$\text{Weight/volume percent} = \frac{\text{g solute}}{\text{mL solution}} \times 100\%$$

Volume percent. Solutions that are formulated from two liquids are often expressed as *volume percent* with respect to the solute. The volume percent is the volume of a liquid in 100 mL of solution. The label on a bottle of ordinary rubbing alcohol reads "Isopropyl alcohol, 70% by volume." Such a solution could be made by mixing 70 mL of alcohol with water to make a total volume of 100 mL. We cannot use 30 mL of water because the two volumes are not necessarily additive.

$$\text{Volume percent} = \frac{\text{Volume of liquid in question}}{\text{Total volume of solution}} \times 100\%$$

Molarity. Weight-percent solutions do not equate or express the number of formula or molecular weights of the solute in solution. For example, 1000 g of 10% NaOH solution contain 100 g of NaOH; 1000 g of 10% KOH solution contain 100 g of KOH. In terms of moles of NaOH and KOH, these solutions contain

$$\text{Moles NaOH} = 100 \text{ g NaOH} \times \frac{1 \text{ mol NaOH}}{40.0 \text{ g NaOH}} = 2.50 \text{ mol NaOH}$$

$$\text{Moles KOH} = 100 \text{ g KOH} \times \frac{1 \text{ mol KOH}}{56.1 \text{ g KOH}} = 1.78 \text{ mol KOH}$$

From these figures we see that the two 10% solutions do not contain the same number of moles of NaOH and KOH. Yet one mole of each of these bases will neutralize the same amount of acid. As a result we find that a 10% NaOH solution has more reactive alkali than a 10% KOH solution.

We need a method of expressing concentration that will easily indicate how many moles or formula weights of solute are present per unit volume of solution. For this purpose the molar method of expressing concentration is used.

**1 molar
solution**

A **1 molar solution** contains 1 mole, or 1 molecular weight, or 1 formula weight of solute per liter of solution. For example, to make a 1 molar solution of sodium hydroxide (NaOH), we dissolve 40.0 g of NaOH (1 mole) in water and dilute the solution with more water to a volume of 1 liter. The solution contains 1 mole of the solute in 1 liter of solution and is said to be 1 molar (1 *M*) in concentration. Figure 14.6 illustrates the preparation of a 1 molar solution. Note that the volume of the solute and the solvent together is 1 liter.

molarity

The concentration of a solution can, of course, be varied by using more or less solute or solvent; but in any case the **molarity** of a solution is the number of moles of solute per liter of solution. A capital *M* is the abbreviation for molarity. The units of molarity are moles per liter. The expression "2.0 *M* NaOH" means a 2.0 molar solution of NaOH (2.0 mol, or 80 g, of NaOH dissolved in 1 liter of solution).

$$\text{Molarity} = M = \frac{\text{Number of moles of solute}}{\text{Liter of solution}} = \frac{\text{moles}}{\text{liter}}$$

Flasks that are calibrated to contain specific volumes at a particular temperature are used to prepare solutions of a desired concentration. These *volumetric*

(a) Weigh 1 mole of solute

(b) Transfer weighed solute to a 1 liter volumetric flask

(c) Dissolve in solvent

(d) Add solvent to the 1 liter mark and mix thoroughly

Figure 14.6 Preparation of a 1 molar solution

flasks have a calibration mark on the neck to indicate accurately the measured volume. Molarity is based on a specific volume of solution and therefore will vary slightly with temperature because volume varies with temperature (1000 mL of H_2O at 20°C = 1001 mL at 25°C).

Suppose we want to make 500 mL of 1 M solution. This solution can be prepared by weighing 0.5 mol of the solute and diluting with water in a 500 mL (0.5 L) volumetric flask. The molarity will be

$$M = \frac{0.5 \text{ mol solute}}{0.5 \text{ L solution}} = 1 \text{ molar}$$

Thus you can see that it is not necessary to have a liter of solution to express molarity. All we need to know is the number of moles of dissolved solute and the volume of solution. Thus 0.001 mol of NaOH in 10 mL of solution is 0.1 M:

$$\frac{0.001 \text{ mol}}{10 \text{ mL}} \times \frac{1000 \text{ mL}}{1 \text{ L}} = 0.1 \text{ M}$$

When we stop to think that a balance is not calibrated in moles but in grams, we need to incorporate grams into the molarity formula. We do so by using the relationship

$$\text{Moles} = \frac{\text{Grams of solute}}{\text{Formula weight}}$$

Substituting this relationship into our expression for molarity, we get

$$M = \frac{\text{mol}}{\text{L}} = \frac{\text{g solute}}{\text{form. wt solute} \times \text{L solution}} = \frac{\text{g}}{\text{form. wt} \times \text{L}}$$

We can now weigh any amount of a solute that has a known formula, dilute it to any volume, and calculate the molarity of the solution using this formula.

The molarities of the concentrated acids commonly used in the laboratory are

$$\text{HCl} \quad 12 \text{ M} \qquad \text{HC}_2\text{H}_3\text{O}_2 \quad 17 \text{ M} \qquad \text{HNO}_3 \quad 16 \text{ M} \qquad \text{H}_2\text{SO}_4 \quad 18 \text{ M}$$

PROBLEM

14.5

What is the molarity of a solution containing 1.4 mol of acetic acid ($HC_2H_3O_2$) in 250 mL of solution?

Substitute the data, 1.4 mol and 250 mL (0.250 L), directly into the equation for molarity:

$$M = \frac{\text{mol}}{\text{L}} = \frac{1.4 \text{ mol}}{0.250 \text{ L}} = \frac{5.6 \text{ mol}}{1 \text{ L}} = 5.6 \text{ M} \quad \text{(Answer)}$$

By the unit conversion method, we note that the concentration given in the problem statement is 1.4 mol per 250 mL (mol/mL). Since molarity = mol/L, the needed conversion is

$$\frac{\text{mol}}{\text{mL}} \longrightarrow \frac{\text{mol}}{\text{L}} = M$$

$$\frac{1.4 \text{ mol}}{250 \text{ mL}} \times \frac{1000 \text{ mL}}{1 \text{ L}} = \frac{5.6 \text{ mol}}{1 \text{ L}} = 5.6 \text{ M} \quad \text{(Answer)}$$

PROBLEM

14.6

What is the molarity of a solution made by dissolving 2.00 g of potassium chlorate ($KClO_3$) in enough water to make 150 mL of solution?

This problem can be solved using the unit conversion method. The steps in the conversions must lead to units of moles/liter.

$$\frac{\text{g KClO}_3}{\text{mL}} \longrightarrow \frac{\text{g KClO}_3}{\text{L}} \longrightarrow \frac{\text{mol KClO}_3}{\text{L}} = M$$

The data are

$$g = 2.00 \text{ g} \qquad \text{form. wt KClO}_3 = 122.6 \text{ g/mol} \qquad \text{volume} = 150 \text{ mL}$$

$$\frac{2.00 \text{ g KClO}_3}{150 \text{ mL}} \times \frac{1000 \text{ mL}}{1 \text{ L}} \times \frac{1 \text{ mol KClO}_3}{122.6 \text{ g KClO}_3} = \frac{0.109 \text{ mol}}{1 \text{ L}} = 0.109 \text{ M}$$

PROBLEM

14.7

How many grams of potassium hydroxide are required to prepare 600 mL of 0.450 M KOH solution?

The conversion is

milliliters $\longrightarrow$ liters $\longrightarrow$ moles $\longrightarrow$ grams

The data are

$$\text{volume = 600 mL} \qquad M = \frac{0.450 \text{ mol}}{L} \qquad \text{form. wt KOH} = \frac{56.1 \text{ g KOH}}{\text{mol}}$$

The calculation is

$$600 \text{ mL} \times \frac{1 \text{ L}}{1000 \text{ mL}} \times \frac{0.450 \text{ mol}}{L} \times \frac{56.1 \text{ g KOH}}{\text{mol}} = 15.1 \text{ g KOH}$$

PROBLEM

14.8

How many milliliters of 2.00 M HCl will react with 28.0 g of NaOH?

Step 1. Write and balance the equation for the reaction:

$$HCl(aq) + NaOH(aq) \longrightarrow NaCl(aq) + H_2O(aq)$$

The equation states that 1 mol of HCl reacts with 1 mol of NaOH.

Step 2. Find the number of moles of NaOH in 28.0 g of NaOH:

g NaOH $\longrightarrow$ mol NaOH

$$28.0 \text{ g NaOH} \times \frac{1 \text{ mol}}{40.0 \text{ g}} = 0.700 \text{ mol NaOH}$$

$$28.0 \text{ g NaOH} = 0.700 \text{ mol NaOH}$$

Step 3. Solve for moles and volume of HCl needed. From steps 1 and 2 we see that 0.700 mol of HCl will react with 0.700 mol of NaOH, because the ratio of moles reacting is 1:1. We know that 2.00 M HCl contains 2.00 mol of HCl per liter; therefore, the volume that contains 0.700 mol of HCl will be less than 1 L.

mol NaOH $\longrightarrow$ mol HCl $\longrightarrow$ L HCl $\longrightarrow$ mL HCl

$$0.700 \text{ mol NaOH} \times \frac{1 \text{ mol HCl}}{1 \text{ mol NaOH}} \times \frac{1 \text{ L HCl}}{2.00 \text{ mol HCl}} = 0.350 \text{ L HCl}$$

$$0.350 \text{ L HCl} \times \frac{1000 \text{ mL}}{1 \text{ L}} = 350 \text{ mL HCl}$$

Therefore, 350 mL of 2.00 M HCl contain 0.700 mol of HCl and will react with 0.700 mol, or 28.0 g, of NaOH.

PROBLEM

14.9

What volume of 0.250 M solution can be prepared from 16.0 g of potassium carbonate (K_2CO_3)?

We are starting with 16.0 g of K_2CO_3 and need to find the volume of 0.250 M solution that can be prepared from this K_2CO_3.

The conversion therefore is

$$g\ K_2CO_3 \longrightarrow mol\ K_2CO_3 \longrightarrow L\ solution$$

The data are

$$16.0\ g\ K_2CO_3 \qquad M = \frac{0.250\ mol}{1\ L} \qquad form.\ wt\ K_2CO_3 = \frac{138.2\ g\ K_2CO_3}{1\ mol}$$

$$16.0\ \cancel{g\ K_2CO_3} \times \frac{1\ \cancel{mol\ K_2CO_3}}{138.2\ \cancel{g\ K_2CO_3}} \times \frac{1\ L}{0.250\ \cancel{mol\ K_2CO_3}} = 0.463\ L\ (463\ mL)$$

Thus, a 0.250 M solution can be made by dissolving 16.0 g of K_2CO_3 in water and diluting to 463 mL.

PROBLEM

14.10

Calculate the number of moles of nitric acid in 325 mL of 16 M HNO_3 solution.

Use the equation   moles = liters × M

Substitute the data given in the problem and solve:

$$moles = 0.325\ \cancel{L} \times \frac{16\ mol\ HNO_3}{1\ \cancel{L}} = 5.2\ mol\ HNO_3 \quad (Answer)$$

Dilution problems. Chemists often find it necessary to dilute solutions from one concentration to another by adding more solvent to the solution. If a solution is diluted by adding pure solvent, the volume of the solution increases, but the number of moles of solute in the solution remains the same. Thus, the moles/liter (molarity) of the solution decreases. It is important to read a problem carefully to distinguish between (1) how much solvent must be added to dilute a solution to a particular concentration and (2) to what volume a solution must be diluted to prepare a solution of a particular concentration.

PROBLEM

14.11

Calculate the molarity of a sodium hydroxide solution that is prepared by mixing 100 mL of 0.20 M NaOH with 150 mL of water.

This problem is a dilution problem. If we double the volume of a solution by adding water, we cut the concentration in half. Therefore, the concentration of the above solution should be less than 0.10 M. In the dilution, the moles of NaOH remain constant; the molarity and volume change. The final volume is (100 mL + 150 mL) or 250 mL.

To solve this problem, (1) calculate the moles of NaOH in the original solution, and (2) divide the moles of NaOH by the final volume of the solution to obtain the new molarity.

Step 1. Calculate the moles of NaOH in the original solution:

$$M = \frac{mol}{L} \qquad mol = L \times M$$

$$0.100\,\cancel{L} \times \frac{0.20\ mol\ NaOH}{1\,\cancel{L}} = 0.020\ mol\ NaOH$$

Step 2. Solve for the new molarity, taking into account that the total volume of the solution after dilution is 250 mL (0.250 L):

$$M = \frac{0.020\ mol\ NaOH}{0.250\ L} = 0.080\ M\ NaOH \quad (Answer)$$

Alternate solution.   When the moles of solute in a solution before and after dilution are the same, then the moles before and after dilution may be set equal to each other.

$$mol_1 = mol_2$$

where mol_1 = moles before dilution, and mol_2 = moles after dilution. Then

$$mol_1 = L_1 \times M_1 \qquad mol_2 = L_2 \times M_2$$

$$L_1 \times M_1 = L_2 \times M_2$$

When both volumes are in the same units, a more general statement can be made:

$$V_1 \times M_1 = V_2 \times M_2$$

For this problem

$$V_1 = 100\ mL \qquad M_1 = 0.20\ M$$

$$V_2 = 250\ mL \qquad M_2 = M_2 \quad (Unknown)$$

Then

$$100\ mL \times 0.20\ M = 250\ mL \times M_2$$

Solving for M_2, we get

$$M_2 = \frac{100\ \cancel{mL} \times 0.20\ M}{250\ \cancel{mL}} = 0.080\ M\ NaOH$$

PROBLEM

14.12

How many grams of silver chloride, AgCl, will be precipitated by adding sufficient silver nitrate, $AgNO_3$, to react with 1500 mL of 0.400 M $BaCl_2$ (barium chloride) solution?

$$2\ AgNO_3(aq) + BaCl_2(aq) \longrightarrow 2\ AgCl\downarrow + Ba(NO_3)_2(aq)$$

1 mol   2 mol

This problem is a stoichiometry problem. The fact that $BaCl_2$ is in solution means that we need to consider the volume and concentration of the solution in order to know the number of moles of $BaCl_2$ reacting.

Step 1. Determine the number of moles of $BaCl_2$ in 1500 mL of 0.400 M solution:

$$M = \frac{\text{mol}}{\text{L}} \qquad \text{mol} = \text{L} \times \text{M} \qquad 1500 \text{ mL} = 1.500 \text{ L}$$

$$1.500 \,\cancel{L} \times \frac{0.400 \text{ mol } BaCl_2}{\cancel{L}} = 0.600 \text{ mol } BaCl_2$$

Step 2. Calculate the moles and grams of AgCl formed by the mole-ratio method:

$$\text{mol } BaCl_2 \longrightarrow \text{mol AgCl} \longrightarrow \text{g AgCl}$$

$$0.600 \;\cancel{\text{mol } BaCl_2} \times \frac{2 \;\cancel{\text{mol AgCl}}}{1 \;\cancel{\text{mol } BaCl_2}} \times \frac{143.3 \text{ g AgCl}}{\cancel{\text{mol AgCl}}} = 172 \text{ g AgCl}$$

---

normality

1 normal solution

Normality. Normality is another way of expressing the concentration of a solution. It is based on an alternate chemical unit of mass called the *equivalent weight*. The **normality** of a solution is the concentration expressed as the number of equivalent weights (equivalents, abbreviated equiv) of solute per liter of solution. A **1 normal (1 N) solution** contains 1 equivalent weight of solute per liter of solution. Normality is widely used in analytical chemistry because it simplifies many of the calculations involving solution concentration.

$$\text{Normality} = N = \frac{\text{Number of equivalents of solute}}{1 \text{ liter of solution}} = \frac{\text{equivalents}}{\text{liter}}$$

where

$$\text{Number of equivalents of solute} = \frac{\text{Grams of solute}}{\text{Equivalent weight of solute}}$$

Every substance may be assigned an equivalent weight. The equivalent weight may be equal either to the formula weight of the substance or to an integral fraction of the formula weight (that is, the formula weight divided by 2, 3, 4, and so on). To gain an understanding of the meaning of equivalent weight, let us start by considering these two reactions:

$$HCl(aq) + NaOH(aq) \longrightarrow NaCl(aq) + H_2O$$

1 mol   1 mol
(36.5 g)   (40.0 g)

$$H_2SO_4(aq) + 2 \text{ NaOH}(aq) \longrightarrow Na_2SO_4(aq) + 2 \text{ H}_2O$$

1 mol   2 mol
(98.1 g)   (80.0 g)

We note first that 1 mol of hydrochloric acid (HCl) reacts with 1 mol of sodium hydroxide (NaOH) and 1 mol of sulfuric acid (H_2SO_4) reacts with 2 mol of NaOH. If we make 1 molar solutions of these substances, 1 L of 1 M HCl will react with

1 L of 1 M NaOH, and 1 L of 1 M H_2SO_4 will react with 2 L of 1 M NaOH. From this reaction, we can see that H_2SO_4 has twice the chemical capacity of HCl when reacting with NaOH. We can, however, adjust these acid solutions to be equivalent in reactivity by dissolving only 0.5 mol of H_2SO_4 per liter of solution. By doing so, we find that we are required to use 49.0 g of H_2SO_4 per liter (instead of 98.1 g of H_2SO_4 per liter) to make a solution that is equivalent to one made from 36.5 g of HCl per liter. These weights, 49.0 g of H_2SO_4 and 36.5 g of HCl, are chemically equivalent and are known as the equivalent weights of these substances, because each will react with the same amount of NaOH (40.0 g). The equivalent weight of HCl is equal to its formula weight, but that of H_2SO_4 is one-half its formula weight. Table 14.4 summarizes these relationships.

Thus, 1 L of solution containing 36.5 g of HCl would be 1 N, and 1 L of solution containing 49.0 g of H_2SO_4 would also be 1 N. A solution containing 98.1 g of H_2SO_4 (1 mol) per liter would be 2 N when reacting with NaOH in the given equation.

equivalent weight The **equivalent weight** is the weight of a substance that will react with, combine with, contain, replace, or in any other way be equivalent to 1 mole of hydrogen atoms or hydrogen ions.

Normality and molarity can be interconverted in the following manner:

$$N = \frac{\text{equiv}}{L} \qquad M = \frac{\text{mol}}{L}$$

$$N = M \times \frac{\text{equiv}}{\text{mol}} = \frac{\cancel{\text{mol}}}{L} \times \frac{\text{equiv}}{\cancel{\text{mol}}} = \frac{\text{equiv}}{L}$$

$$M = N \times \frac{\text{mol}}{\text{equiv}} = \frac{\cancel{\text{equiv}}}{L} \times \frac{\text{mol}}{\cancel{\text{equiv}}} = \frac{\text{mol}}{L}$$

Thus a 2.0 N H_2SO_4 solution is 1.0 M.

One application of normality and equivalents is in acid–base neutralization reactions. The equivalent weight of an acid is that mass of the acid that will furnish 1 mole of H^+ ions. The equivalent weight of a base is that mass of base

Table 14.4 **Comparison of molar and normal solutions of HCl and H_2SO_4 reacting with NaOH**

	Formula weight	Concentration	Volumes that react	Equivalent weight	Concentration	Volumes that react
HCl	36.5	1 M	1 liter	36.5	1 N	1 liter
NaOH	40.0	1 M	1 liter	40.0	1 N	1 liter
H_2SO_4	98.1	1 M	1 liter	49.0	1 N	1 liter
NaOH	40.0	1 M	2 liters	40.0	1 N	1 liter

that will furnish 1 mole of OH$^-$ ions. Using concentrations in normality, one equivalent of acid (A) will react with one equivalent of base (B).

$$N_A = \frac{equiv_A}{L_A} \quad \text{and} \quad N_B = \frac{equiv_B}{L_B}$$

$$equiv_A = L_A \times N_A \quad \text{and} \quad equiv_B = L_B \times N_B$$

Since $equiv_A = equiv_B$,

$$L_A \times N_A = L_B \times N_B$$

When both volumes are in the same units, we can write a more general equation:

$$V_A N_A = V_B N_B$$

which states that the volume of the acid times the normality of the acid equals the volume of the base times the normality of the base.

PROBLEM

14.13

(a) What is the normality of an H_2SO_4 solution if 25.00 mL of the solution require 22.48 mL of 0.2018 N NaOH for complete neutralization? (b) What is the molarity of the H_2SO_4 solution?

(a) Solve for N_A by substituting the data into

$$V_A N_A = V_B N_B$$

$$25.00 \text{ mL} \times N_A = 22.48 \text{ mL} \times 0.2018 \text{ N}$$

$$N_A = \frac{22.48 \text{ mL} \times 0.2018 \text{ N}}{25.00 \text{ mL}} = 0.1815 \text{ N } H_2SO_4$$

(b) When H_2SO_4 is completely neutralized it furnishes 2 equivalents of H$^+$ ions per mole of H_2SO_4. The conversion from N to M is

$$\frac{equiv}{L} \longrightarrow \frac{mol}{L} \qquad H_2SO_4 = 0.1815 \text{ N}$$

$$\frac{0.1815 \text{ equiv}}{1 \text{ L}} \times \frac{1 \text{ mol}}{2 \text{ equiv}} = 0.09075 \text{ mol/L}$$

The H_2SO_4 solution is 0.09075 M.

The equivalent weight of a substance may be variable; its value is dependent on the reaction that the substance is undergoing. Consider the reactions represented by these equations:

$$NaOH + H_2SO_4 \longrightarrow NaHSO_4 + H_2O$$

$$2\,NaOH + H_2SO_4 \longrightarrow Na_2SO_4 + 2\,H_2O$$

In the first reaction 1 mol of sulfuric acid furnishes 1 mol of hydrogen. Therefore the equivalent weight of sulfuric acid is the formula weight, namely 98.1 g. But in the second reaction 1 mol of H_2SO_4 furnishes 2 mol of hydrogen. Therefore, the equivalent weight of the sulfuric acid is one-half the formula weight, or 49.0 g.

14.9 Colligative Properties of Solutions

Two solutions, one containing 1 mol (60.0 g) of urea (NH_2CONH_2) and the other containing 1 mol (342 g) of sucrose ($C_{12}H_{22}O_{11}$) in 1 kg of water, both have a freezing point of $-1.86°C$, not $0°C$ as for pure water. Urea and sucrose are distinctly different substances, yet they lower the freezing point of the water by the same amount. The only thing apparently common to these two solutions is that each contains 1 mol (6.022×10^{23} molecules) of solute and 1 kg of solvent. In fact, if we dissolve one mole of any nonionizable solute in 1 kg of water, the freezing point of the resulting solution will be $-1.86°C$.

These results lead us to conclude that the freezing point depression for a solution containing 6.022×10^{23} solute molecules (particles) and 1 kg of water is a constant, namely, $1.86°C$. Freezing point depression is a general property of solutions. Furthermore the amount by which the freezing point is depressed is the same for all solutions made with a given solvent; that is, each solvent shows a characteristic *freezing point depression constant*. Freezing point depression constants (K_f) for several solvents are given in Table 14.5.

The solution formed by the addition of a nonvolatile solute to a solvent has a lower freezing point, a higher boiling point, and a lower vapor pressure than that of the pure solvent. All these effects are related and are known as colligative properties. The **colligative properties** are properties that depend only upon the number of solute particles in a solution and not on the nature of those particles. Freezing point depression, boiling point elevation, vapor pressure lowering, and osmotic pressure are colligative properties of solutions.

colligative properties

The colligative properties of a solution can be considered in terms of vapor pressure. The vapor pressure of a pure liquid depends on the tendency of molecules to escape from its surface. Thus, if 10% of the molecules in a solution are nonvolatile solute molecules, the vapor pressure of the solution is 10% lower than that of the pure solvent. The vapor pressure is lower because the surface of

Table 14.5 Freezing point depression and boiling point elevation constants of selected solvents

Solvent	Freezing point of pure solvent (°C)	Freezing point depression constant, K_f $\left(\dfrac{°C, kg\ solvent}{mol\ solute}\right)$	Boiling point of pure solvent (°C)	Boiling point elevation constant, K_b $\left(\dfrac{°C, kg\ solvent}{mol\ solute}\right)$
Water	0.00	1.86	100.0	0.512
Acetic acid	16.6	3.90	118.5	3.07
Benzene	5.5	5.1	80.1	2.53
Camphor	178	40	208.2	5.95

the solution contains 10% nonvolatile molecules and 90% of the volatile solvent molecules. A liquid boils when its vapor pressure equals the pressure of the atmosphere. Thus, we can see that the solution just described as having a lower vapor pressure will have a higher boiling point than the pure solvent. The solution with a lowered vapor pressure does not boil until it has been heated above the boiling point of the solvent (see Figure 14.7). Each solvent has its own characteristic boiling point elevation constant (see Table 14.5). The boiling point elevation constant is based on a solution that contains 1 mole of solute particles per kilogram of solvent. For example, the boiling point elevation constant for a solution containing 1 mole of solute particles per kilogram of water is 0.512°C, which means that this water solution will boil at 100.512°C.

The freezing behavior of a solution can also be considered in terms of lowered vapor pressure. Figure 14.7 shows the vapor pressure relationships of ice, water, and a solution containing 1 mole of solute per kilogram of water. The freezing point of water is at the intersection of the water and ice vapor pressure curves—that is, at the point where water and ice have the same vapor pressure. Because the vapor pressure of water is lowered by the solute, the vapor pressure curve of the solution does not intersect the vapor pressure curve of ice until the solution has been cooled below the freezing point of pure water. Thus it is necessary to cool the solution below 0°C in order to freeze out ice.

The foregoing discussion dealing with freezing point depressions is restricted to *un-ionized* substances. The discussion of boiling point elevations is restricted to *nonvolatile* and *un-ionized* substances. The colligative properties of ionized substances (Electrolytes, Chapter 15) are not under consideration at this point.

Some practical applications involving colligative properties are (1) use of salt–ice mixtures to provide low freezing temperatures for homemade ice cream, (2) use of sodium chloride or calcium chloride to melt ice from streets, and (3)

Figure 14.7   Vapor pressure curves of pure water and water solutions, showing (a) freezing point depression and (b) boiling point elevation effects. (Concentration: 1 mole of a nonionizable solute per kilogram of water.)

use of ethylene glycol and water mixtures as antifreeze in automobile radiators (ethylene glycol also raises the boiling point of radiator fluid and thus allows the engine to operate at a higher temperature).

Both the freezing point depression and the boiling point elevation are directly proportional to the number of moles of solute per kilogram of solvent. When we deal with the colligative properties of solutions, another concentration expression, *molality*, is used. The **molality** (m) of a solute is the number of moles of solute per kilogram of solvent:

molality

$$m = \frac{\text{mol solute}}{\text{kg solvent}}$$

Note that a lowercase m is used for molality concentrations and a capital M for molarity. The difference between molality and molarity is that molality refers to moles of solute *per kilogram of solvent*, whereas molarity refers to moles of solute *per liter of solution*. For un-ionized substances, the colligative properties of a solution are directly proportional to its molality.

Molality is independent of volume. It is a mass-to-mass relationship of solute to solvent and allows for experiments, such as freezing point depression and boiling point elevation, to be conducted at variable temperatures.

The following equations are used in calculations involving colligative properties and molality:

$$\Delta t_f = mK_f \qquad \Delta t_b = mK_b \qquad m = \frac{\text{mol solute}}{\text{kg solvent}}$$

m = molality; mol solute/kg solvent
Δt_f = freezing point depression; °C
Δt_b = boiling point elevation; °C
K_f = freezing point depression constant; °C, kg solvent/mol solute
K_b = boiling point elevation constant; °C, kg solvent/mol solute

PROBLEM

14.14

What is the molality (m) of a solution prepared by dissolving 2.70 g of CH_3OH in 25.0 g of H_2O?

Since $\quad m = \dfrac{\text{mol solute}}{\text{kg solvent}} \quad$ the conversion is

$$\frac{2.70 \text{ g } CH_3OH}{25.0 \text{ g } H_2O} \longrightarrow \frac{\text{mol } CH_3OH}{25.0 \text{ g } H_2O} \longrightarrow \frac{\text{mol } CH_3OH}{1 \text{ kg } H_2O}$$

The molecular weight of CH_3OH is (12.0 + 4.0 + 16.0) or 32.0 g/mol.

$$\frac{2.70 \text{ g } CH_3OH}{25.0 \text{ g } H_2O} \times \frac{1 \text{ mol } CH_3OH}{32.0 \text{ g } CH_3OH} \times \frac{1000 \text{ g } H_2O}{1 \text{ kg } H_2O} = \frac{3.38 \text{ mol } CH_3OH}{1 \text{ kg } H_2O}$$

The molality is 3.38 m.

PROBLEM

14.15

A solution is made by dissolving 100 g of ethylene glycol ($C_2H_6O_2$) in 200 g of water. What is the freezing point of this solution?

To calculate the freezing point of the solution, we first need to calculate Δt_f, the change in freezing point. Use the equation

$$\Delta t_f = mK_f = \frac{\text{mol solute}}{\text{kg solvent}} \times K_f$$

K_f (for water): $\dfrac{1.86°C \text{ kg solvent}}{\text{mol solute}}$ (from Table 14.5)

mol solute: $100 \text{ g } C_2H_6O_2 \times \dfrac{1 \text{ mol } C_2H_6O_2}{62.0 \text{ g } C_2H_6O_2} = 1.61 \text{ mol } C_2H_6O_2$

kg solvent: $200 \text{ g } H_2O \times \dfrac{1 \text{ kg}}{1000 \text{ g}} = 0.200 \text{ kg } H_2O$

$$\Delta t_f = \frac{1.61 \text{ mol } C_2H_6O_2}{0.200 \text{ kg } H_2O} \times \frac{1.86°C \text{ kg } H_2O}{1 \text{ mol } C_2H_6O_2} = 15.0°C$$

The freezing point depression, 15.0°C, must be subtracted from 0°C, the freezing point of the pure solvent:

$$\text{Freezing point of solution} = \text{Freezing point of solvent} - \Delta t_f$$
$$= 0.0°C - 15.0°C = -15.0°C$$

Therefore, the freezing point of the solution is −15.0°C.

The calculation can also be done using the equation

$$\Delta t_f = mK_f = \frac{\text{g solute}}{\text{mol. wt solute}} \times \frac{1}{\text{kg solvent}}$$

PROBLEM

14.16

A solution made by dissolving 4.71 g of a compound of unknown molecular weight in 100.0 g of water has a freezing point of −1.46°C. What is the molecular weight of the compound?

First substitute the data in $\Delta t_f = mK_f$ and solve for m:

$\Delta t_f = +1.46$ since the solvent, water, freezes at 0°C.

$$K_f = \frac{1.86°C \times \text{kg } H_2O}{\text{mol solute}}$$

$$1.46°C = mK_f = m \times \frac{1.86°C \times \text{kg } H_2O}{\text{mol solute}}$$

$$m = \frac{1.46°C \times \text{mol solute}}{1.86°C \times \text{kg } H_2O} = \frac{0.785 \text{ mol solute}}{\text{kg } H_2O}$$

Now convert the data, 4.71 g solute/100.0 g H_2O, to g/mol.

$$\frac{4.71 \text{ g solute}}{100.0 \text{ g } H_2O} \times \frac{1000 \text{ g } H_2O}{1 \text{ kg } H_2O} \times \frac{1 \text{ kg } H_2O}{0.785 \text{ mol solute}} = 60.0 \text{ g/mol}$$

The molecular weight of the compound is 60.0 g/mol.

14.10 Osmosis and Osmotic Pressure

semipermeable membrane

osmosis

When red blood cells are put into distilled water, they gradually swell and, in time, may burst. If red blood cells are put in a 5% urea (or a 5% salt) solution, they gradually shrink and take on a wrinkled appearance. The cells behave in this fashion because they are enclosed in semipermeable membranes. A **semipermeable membrane** allows the passage of water (solvent) molecules through it in either direction but prevents the passage of solute molecules or ions. When two solutions of different concentrations (or water and a water solution) are separated by a semipermeable membrane, water diffuses through the membrane from the solution of lower concentration into the solution of higher concentration. The diffusion of water, either from a dilute solution or from pure water, through a semipermeable membrane into a solution of higher concentration is called **osmosis.**

All solutions exhibit *osmotic pressure.* Osmotic pressure is another colligative property; it is dependent only on the concentration of the solute particles and is independent of their nature. The osmotic pressure of a solution can be measured by determining the amount of counterpressure needed to prevent osmosis; this pressure can be very large. The osmotic pressure of a solution containing 1 mol of solute particles in 1 kg of water is about 22.4 atm, which is about the same as the pressure exerted by 1 mol of a gas confined in a volume of 1 L at 0°C.

Osmosis has a role in many biological processes, and semipermeable membranes occur commonly in living organisms. For example, the roots of plants are covered with tiny structures called root hairs; soil water enters the plant by osmosis, passing through the semipermeable membranes covering the root hairs. Artificial or synthetic membranes can also be made. Cellophane that has been treated to remove the waterproof coating is a good semipermeable membrane.

Osmosis can be demonstrated with the simple laboratory setup shown in Figure 14.8. As a result of osmotic pressure, water passes through the cellophane membrane into the thistle tube, causing the solution level to rise. In osmosis the net transfer of water is always from a less concentrated to a more concentrated solution; that is, the effect is toward equalization of the concentration on both sides of the membrane. It should also be noted that the effective movement of water in osmosis is always from the region of *higher water concentration* to the region of *lower water concentration.*

Osmosis can be explained by assuming that a semipermeable membrane has passages that permit water molecules—but no other molecules or ions—to pass in either direction. Both sides of the membrane are constantly being struck by

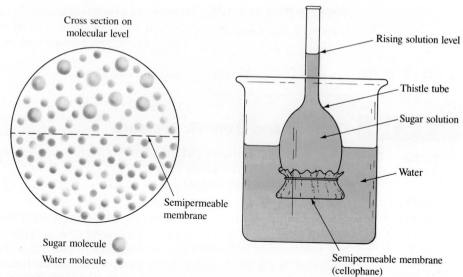

Figure 14.8 Laboratory demonstration of osmosis: As a result of osmosis, water passes through the membrane causing the solution to rise in the thistle tube.

water molecules in random motion. The number of water molecules crossing the membrane is proportional to the number of water molecule–membrane impacts per unit of time. Because the solute molecules or ions reduce the concentration of water, there are more water molecules, and more water molecule impacts, on the side with the lower solute concentration (more dilute solution). The greater number of water molecule–membrane impacts on the dilute side thus causes a net transfer of water to the more concentrated solution. Again note that the overall process involves the net transfer, by diffusion through the membrane, of water molecules from a region of higher water concentration (dilute solution) to one of lower water concentration (more concentrated solution).

This explanation is a simplified picture of osmosis. No one has ever seen the hypothetical passages that allow water molecules, and no other kinds of molecules or ions, to pass through them. Alternative explanations have been proposed. Our discussion has been confined to water solutions, but osmotic pressure is a general colligative property and osmosis is known to occur in nonaqueous systems.

physiological saline solution   A 0.90% (0.15 M) sodium chloride solution is known as a **physiological saline solution** because it is *isotonic* with blood plasma; that is, it has the same osmotic pressure as blood plasma. Because each mole of NaCl yields about 2 moles of ions when in solution, the solute particle concentration in physiological saline solution is nearly 0.30 M. Five percent glucose solution (0.28 molar) is also approximately isotonic with blood plasma. Blood cells neither swell nor shrink in an isotonic solution. The cells described in the first paragraph of this section swelled in water because the water was *hypotonic* to cell plasma. The cells shrank in 5% urea solution because the urea solution was *hypertonic* to the cell plasma. In order to prevent possible injury to blood cells by osmosis, fluids for intravenous use are usually made up at approximately isotonic concentration.

QUESTIONS

A. *Review the meanings of the new terms introduced in this chapter.*

1. Solution
2. Solute
3. Solvent
4. Solubility
5. Miscible
6. Immiscible
7. Concentration of a solution
8. Dilute solution
9. Concentrated solution
10. Saturated solution
11. Unsaturated solution
12. Supersaturated solution
13. 1 molar solution
14. Molarity
15. Normality
16. 1 normal solution
17. Equivalent weight
18. Colligative properties
19. Molality
20. Semipermeable membrane
21. Osmosis
22. Physiological saline solution

B. *Information useful in answering the following questions will be found in the tables and figures.*

1. Make a sketch indicating the orientation of water molecules (a) about a single sodium ion and (b) about a single chloride ion in solution.
2. Which of the substances listed below are reasonably soluble and which are insoluble in water?
   (a) KOH (f) PbI_2
   (b) $NiCl_2$ (g) $MgCO_3$
   (c) ZnS (h) $CaCl_2$
   (d) $AgC_2H_3O_2$ (i) $Fe(NO_3)_3$
   (e) Na_2CrO_4 (j) $BaSO_4$
3. Estimate the number of grams of sodium fluoride that would dissolve in 100 g of water at 50°C.
4. What is the solubility at 25°C of each of the substances listed below? (See Figure 14.3.)
   (a) Potassium chloride   (c) Potassium nitrate
   (b) Potassium chlorate

5. What is different in the solubility trend of the potassium halides compared with that of the lithium halides and the sodium halides? (See Table 14.2.)
6. What is the solubility, in grams of solute per 100 g of H_2O, of (a) $KClO_3$ at 60°C, (b) HCl at 20°C, (c) Li_2SO_4 at 80°C, and (d) KNO_3 at 0°C? (See Figure 14.3.)
7. Which substance, KNO_3 or NH_4Cl, shows the greater increase in solubility with increased temperature? (See Figure 14.3.)
8. Does a 2 m solution in benzene or a 1 m solution in camphor show the greater freezing point depression? (See Table 14.5.)
9. What would be the total surface area if the 1 cm cube in Figure 14.4 were cut into cubes 0.01 cm on a side?
10. At which temperatures—10°C, 20°C, 30°C, 40°C, or 50°C—would you expect a solution made from 63 g of ammonium chloride and 150 g of water to be unsaturated? (See Figure 14.3.)
11. Explain why the rate of dissolving decreases as shown in Figure 14.5.
12. Would the volumetric flasks in Figure 14.6 be satisfactory for preparing normal solutions? Explain.
13. Assume that the thistle tube in Figure 14.8 contains 1.0 M sugar solution and that the water in the beaker has just been replaced by a 2.0 M solution of urea. Would the solution level in the thistle tube continue to rise, remain constant, or fall? Explain.

C. *Review questions*

1. Name and distinguish between the two components of a solution.
2. Is it always apparent in a solution which component is the solute, for example, in a solution of a liquid in a liquid?
3. Explain why the solute does not settle out of a solution.
4. Is it possible to have one solid dissolved in another? Explain.

5. An aqueous solution of KCl is colorless, KMnO$_4$ is purple, and K$_2$Cr$_2$O$_7$ is orange. What color would you expect of an aqueous solution of Na$_2$Cr$_2$O$_7$? Explain.

6. Explain why carbon tetrachloride will dissolve benzene but will not dissolve sodium chloride.

7. Some drinks like tea are consumed either hot or cold, whereas others like Coca Cola are drunk only cold. Why?

8. Why is air considered to be a solution?

9. In which will a teaspoonful of sugar dissolve more rapidly, 200 mL of iced tea or 200 mL of hot coffee? Explain in terms of the KMT.

10. What is the effect of pressure on the solubility of gases in liquids? Solids in liquids?

11. Why do smaller particles dissolve faster than large ones?

12. In a saturated solution containing undissolved solute, solute is continuously dissolving, but the concentration of the solution remains unchanged. Explain.

13. Explain why there is no apparent reaction when crystals of AgNO$_3$ and NaCl are mixed, but a reaction is apparent immediately when solutions of AgNO$_3$ and NaCl are mixed.

14. What do we mean when we say that concentrated nitric acid (HNO$_3$) is 16 molar?

15. Will 1 liter of 1 molar NaCl contain more chloride ions than 0.5 liter of 1 molar MgCl$_2$? Explain.

16. What disadvantages are there in expressing the concentration of solutions as dilute or concentrated?

17. Explain how concentrated H$_2$SO$_4$ can be both 18 molar and 36 normal in concentration.

18. Describe how you would prepare 750 mL of 5 M NaCl solution.

19. Arrange the following bases (in descending order) according to the volume of each that will react with 1 liter of 1 M HCl: (a) 1 M NaOH, (b) 1.5 M Ca(OH)$_2$, (c) 2 M KOH, and (d) 0.6 M Ba(OH)$_2$.

20. Explain in terms of vapor pressure why the boiling point of a solution containing a nonvolatile solute is higher than that of the pure solvent.

21. Explain why the freezing point of a solution is lower than the freezing point of the pure solvent.

22. Which would be colder, a glass of water and crushed ice or a glass of Seven-Up and crushed ice? Explain.

23. When water and ice are mixed, the temperature of the mixture is 0°C. But, if methyl alcohol and ice are mixed, a temperature of -10°C is readily attained. Explain why the two mixtures show such different temperature behavior.

24. Which would be more effective in lowering the freezing point of 500 g of water?
    (a) 100 g of sucrose (C$_{12}$H$_{22}$O$_{11}$) or 100 g of ethyl alcohol (C$_2$H$_5$OH)
    (b) 100 g of sucrose or 20.0 g of ethyl alcohol
    (c) 20.0 g of ethyl alcohol or 20.0 g of methyl alcohol (CH$_3$OH)

25. Is the molarity of a 5 molal aqueous solution of NaCl greater or less than 5 molar? Explain.

26. Express, in terms of its molarity, the normality of an H$_2$SO$_4$ solution used to titrate NaOH solutions. (Assume both hydrogens react.)

27. Explain in terms of the KMT how a semipermeable membrane functions when placed between pure water and a 10% sugar solution.

28. Which has the higher osmotic pressure, a solution containing 100 g of urea (NH$_2$CONH$_2$) in 1 kg of H$_2$O or a solution containing 150 g of glucose (C$_6$H$_{12}$O$_6$) in 1 kg of H$_2$O?

29. Explain why a lettuce leaf in contact with salad dressing containing salt and vinegar soon becomes wilted and limp whereas another lettuce leaf in contact with plain water remains crisp.

30. A group of shipwreck survivors floated for several days on a life raft before being rescued. Those who had drunk some seawater were found to be suffering the most from dehydration. Explain.

31. Which of the following statements are correct?
    (a) A solution is a homogeneous mixture.
    (b) It is possible for the same substance to be the solvent in one solution and the solute in another.
    (c) A solute can be removed from a solution by filtration.
    (d) Saturated solutions are always concentrated solutions.
    (e) If a solution of sugar in water is allowed to stand undisturbed for a long time, the sugar will gradually settle to the bottom of the container.
    (f) It is not possible to prepare an aqueous 1.0 M AgCl solution.
    (g) Gases are generally more soluble in hot water than in cold water.

(h) It is impossible to prepare a two-phase liquid mixture from two liquids that are miscible with each other in all proportions.

(i) A solution that is 10% NaCl by weight always contains 10 g of NaCl.

(j) Small changes in pressure have little effect on the solubility of solids in liquids but a marked effect on the solubility of gases in liquids.

(k) How fast a solute dissolves depends mainly on the size of the solute particles, the temperature of the solvent, and the degree of agitation or stirring taking place.

(l) In order to have a 1 M solution you must have 1 mol of solute dissolved in sufficient solvent to give 1 L of solution.

(m) Dissolving 1 mol of NaCl in 1 L of water will give a 1 M solution.

(n) One mole of solute in 1 L of solution has the same concentration as 0.1 mol of solute in 100 mL of solution.

(o) When 100 mL of 0.200 M HCl is diluted to 200 mL volume by the addition of water, the resulting solution is 0.100 M and contains one-half the number of moles of HCl as were in the original solution.

(p) Fifty milliliters of 0.1 M H_2SO_4 will neutralize the same volume of 0.1 M NaOH as 100 mL of 0.1 M HCl.

(q) Fifty milliliters of 0.1 N H_2SO_4 will neutralize the same volume of 0.1 M NaOH as 100 mL of 0.1 M HCl.

(r) The molarity of a solution will vary slightly with temperature.

(s) The equivalent weight of $Ca(OH)_2$ is one-half its formula weight.

(t) Gram for gram methyl alcohol, CH_3OH, is more effective than ethyl alcohol, C_2H_5OH, in lowering the freezing point of water.

(u) An aqueous solution that freezes below 0°C will have a normal boiling point below 100°C.

(v) The colligative properties of a solution depend on the number of solute particles dissolved in solution.

(w) A solution of 1.00 mol of a nonionizable solute and 1000 g of water will freeze at −1.86°C and will boil at 99.5°C at atmospheric pressure.

(x) Water will diffuse from a 0.1 M sugar solution to a 0.2 M sugar solution when these two solutions are separated by a semipermeable membrane.

(y) An isotonic salt solution has the same osmotic pressure as blood plasma.

(z) Red blood cells will neither swell nor shrink when placed into an isotonic salt solution.

D. *Review problems*

Percent Solutions

1. Calculate the weight percent of the following solutions:
   (a) 25.0 g NaBr + 100 g H_2O
   (b) 1.20 g K_2SO_4 + 10.0 g H_2O
   (c) 40.0 g $Mg(NO_3)_2$ + 500 g H_2O

2. How many grams of a solution that is 12.5% by weight $AgNO_3$ would contain the following?
   (a) 30.0 g of $AgNO_3$ (b) 0.400 mol of $AgNO_3$

3. Calculate the weight percent of the following solutions:
   (a) 60.0 g NaCl + 200.0 g H_2O
   (b) 0.25 mol $HC_2H_3O_2$ + 3.0 mol H_2O
   (c) 1.0 molal solution of $C_6H_{12}O_6$ in water

4. How much solute is present in each of the following?
   (a) 65 g of 5.0% KCl solution
   (b) 250 g of 15.0% K_2CrO_4 solution
   *(c) A solution that contains 100.0 g of water and is 6.0% by weight sodium bicarbonate, $NaHCO_3$

5. What weight of 5.50% solution can be prepared from 25.0 g of KCl?

6. Physiological saline (NaCl) solutions used in intravenous injections have a concentration of 0.90% NaCl by weight.
   (a) How many grams of NaCl are needed to prepare 500 g of this solution?
   *(b) How much water must evaporate from this solution to give a solution that is 9.0% NaCl by weight?

7. A solution is made from 50.0 g of KNO_3 and 175 g of H_2O. How many grams of water must evaporate to give a saturated solution of KNO_3 in water at 20°C? (See Figure 14.3.)

8. What is the weight/volume percent of these solutions?
   (a) 22.0 g of CH_3OH dissolved in C_2H_5OH to make 100 mL of solution

(b) 4.20 g of NaCl dissolved in H_2O to make 12.5 mL of solution

9. What is the volume percent of these solutions?
   (a) 10.0 mL of CH_3OH dissolved in water to a volume of 40.0 mL
   (b) 2.0 mL of CCl_4 dissolved in benzene to a volume of 9.0 mL

10. What volume of 70% rubbing alcohol can you prepare if you have only 150 mL of pure isopropyl alcohol on hand?

11. At 20°C an aqueous solution of HNO_3 that is 35.0% HNO_3 by weight has a density of 1.21 g/mL.
    (a) How many grams of HNO_3 are present in 1.00 L of this solution?
    (b) What volume of this solution will contain 500 g of HNO_3?

Molarity Problems

12. Calculate the molarity of the following solutions:
    (a) 0.10 mol of solute in 250 mL of solution
    (b) 2.5 mol of NaCl in 0.650 L of solution
    (c) 0.025 mol of HCl in 10 mL of solution
    (d) 0.35 mol $BaCl_2 \cdot 2\,H_2O$ in 593 mL of solution

13. Calculate the molarity of the following solutions:
    (a) 53.0 g of Na_2CrO_4 in 1.00 L of solution
    (b) 260 g of $C_6H_{12}O_6$ in 800 mL of solution
    (c) 1.50 g of $Al_2(SO_4)_3$ in 2.00 L of solution
    (d) 0.0282 g of $Ca(NO_3)_2$ in 1.00 mL of solution

14. Calculate the number of moles of solute in each of the following solutions:
    (a) 40.0 L of 1.0 M LiCl solution
    (b) 25.0 mL of 3.00 M H_2SO_4
    (c) 349 mL of 0.0010 M NaOH
    (d) 5000 mL of 3.1 M $CoCl_2$

15. Calculate the grams of solute in each of the following solutions:
    (a) 150 L of 1.0 M NaCl
    (b) 0.035 L of 10.0 M HCl
    (c) 260 mL of 18 M H_2SO_4
    (d) 8.00 mL of 8.00 M $Na_2C_2O_4$

16. How many milliliters of 0.256 M KCl solution will contain the following?
    (a) 0.430 mol of KCl
    (b) 10.0 mol of KCl
    (c) 20.0 g of KCl
    *(d) 71.0 g of chloride ion, Cl^-

*17. What is the molarity of a nitric acid solution if the solution is 35.0% HNO_3 by weight and has a density of 1.21 g/mL?

Dilution Problems

18. What will be the molarity of the resulting solutions made by mixing the following? (Assume volumes are additive.)
    (a) 200 mL 12 M HCl + 200 mL H_2O
    (b) 60.0 mL 0.60 M $ZnSO_4$ + 500 mL H_2O
    (c) 100 mL 1.0 M HCl + 150 mL 2.0 M HCl

19. Calculate the volume of concentrated reagent required to prepare the diluted solutions indicated:
    (a) 12 M HCl to prepare 400 mL of 6.0 M HCl
    (b) 15 M NH_3 to prepare 50 mL of 6.0 M NH_3
    (c) 16 M HNO_3 to prepare 100 mL of 2.5 M HNO_3
    (d) 18 M H_2SO_4 to prepare 250 mL of 10.0 N H_2SO_4

20. To what volume must a solution of 80.0 g of H_2SO_4 in 500 mL of solution be diluted to give a 0.10 M solution?

21. What will be the molarity of each of the solutions made by mixing 250 mL of 0.75 M H_2SO_4 with (a) 150 mL of H_2O, (b) 250 mL of 0.70 M H_2SO_4, and (c) 400 mL of 2.50 M H_2SO_4?

22. How many milliliters of water must be added to 300 mL of 1.40 M HCl to make a solution that is 0.500 M HCl?

23. A 10.0 mL sample of 16 M HNO_3 solution is diluted to 500 mL. What is the molarity of the final solution?

24. Given a 5.00 M KOH solution, how would you prepare 250 mL of 0.625 M KOH?

Stoichiometry Problems

25. $BaCl_2(aq) + K_2CrO_4(aq) \longrightarrow$

    $$BaCrO_4(s) + 2\,KCl(aq)$$
    Using the above equation, calculate:
    (a) The grams of $BaCrO_4$ that can be obtained from 100 mL of 0.300 M $BaCl_2$
    (b) The volume of 1.0 M $BaCl_2$ solution needed to react with 50.0 mL of 0.300 M K_2CrO_4

26. $3\,MgCl_2(aq) + 2\,Na_3PO_4(aq) \longrightarrow$

    $$Mg_3(PO_4)_2(s) + 6\,NaCl(aq)$$
    Using the above equation, calculate:
    (a) The milliliters of 0.250 M Na_3PO_4 that will react with 50.0 mL of 0.250 M $MgCl_2$.
    (b) The grams of $Mg_3(PO_4)_2$ that will be formed from 50.0 mL of 0.250 M $MgCl_2$.

Handwritten at top: $c.\left(\dfrac{3 ml}{L}\right)\left(\dfrac{2 eq}{m\overline{lo}}\right) = 6 N$

27. (a) How many moles of hydrogen will be liberated from 200 mL of 3.00 M HCl reacting with an excess of magnesium?

$$Mg(s) + 2\ HCl(aq) \longrightarrow MgCl_2(aq) + H_2(g)$$

(b) How many liters of hydrogen gas, H_2, measured at 27°C and 720 torr, will be obtained? [*Hint*: Use the ideal gas equation.]

*28. What is the molarity of an HCl solution, 150 mL of which, when treated with excess magnesium, liberates 3.50 L of H_2 gas measured at STP?

29. Given the balanced equation

$$6\ FeCl_2 + K_2Cr_2O_7 + 14\ HCl \longrightarrow$$
$$6\ FeCl_3 + 2\ CrCl_3 + 2\ KCl + 7\ H_2O$$

(a) How many moles of KCl will be produced from 2.0 mol of $FeCl_2$?

(b) How many moles of $CrCl_3$ will be produced from 1.0 mol of $FeCl_2$?

(c) How many moles of $FeCl_2$ will react with 0.050 mol of $K_2Cr_2O_7$?

(d) How many milliliters of 0.060 M $K_2Cr_2O_7$ will react with 0.025 mol of $FeCl_2$?

(e) How many milliliters of 6.0 M HCl will react with 15.0 mL of 6.0 M $FeCl_2$?

30. $2\ KMnO_4 + 16\ HCl \longrightarrow$
$$2\ MnCl_2 + 5\ Cl_2 + 8\ H_2O + 2\ KCl$$

Calculate the following using the above equation:

(a) The moles of Cl_2 produced from 0.50 mol of $KMnO_4$

(b) The moles of HCl required to react with 1.0 L of 2.0 M $KMnO_4$

(c) The milliliters of 6.0 M HCl required to react with 200 mL of 0.50 M $KMnO_4$

(d) The liters of Cl_2 gas at STP produced by the reaction of 75.0 mL of 6.0 M HCl

Equivalent Weight and Normality Problems

31. Calculate the equivalent weight of the acid and base in each of the following reactions:

(a) $HCl + NaOH \longrightarrow NaCl + H_2O$

(b) $2\ HCl + Ba(OH)_2 \longrightarrow BaCl_2 + 2\ H_2O$

(c) $H_2SO_4 + Ca(OH)_2 \longrightarrow CaSO_4 + 2\ H_2O$

(d) $H_2SO_4 + KOH \longrightarrow KHSO_4 + H_2O$

(e) $H_3PO_4 + 2\ LiOH \longrightarrow Li_2HPO_4 + 2\ H_2O$

32. What is the normality of the following solutions? Assume complete neutralization.

(a) 4.0 M HCl   (b) 0.243 M HNO_3

(c) 3.0 M H_2SO_4 (d) 1.85 M H_3PO_4
(e) 0.250 M $HC_2H_3O_2$

33. What is the normality of an H_2SO_4 solution if 36.26 mL are required to neutralize 2.50 g of $Ca(OH)_2$?

34. Which will be more effective in neutralizing stomach acid, HCl—a tablet containing 12.0 g of $Mg(OH)_2$ or a tablet containing 10.0 g of $Al(OH)_3$? Show evidence for your answer.

35. What volume of 0.2550 N NaOH is required to neutralize

(a) 20.22 mL of 0.1254 N HCl
(b) 14.86 mL of 0.1246 N H_2SO_4
(c) 18.00 mL of 0.1430 M H_2SO_4

Molality and Colligative Properties Problems

36. Calculate the molality of these solutions:

(a) 14.0 g of CH_3OH in 100 g of H_2O
(b) 2.50 mol of benzene (C_6H_6) in 250 g of CCl_4
(c) 1.0 g of $C_6H_{12}O_6$ in 1.0 g of H_2O

37. Which would be more effective as an antifreeze in an automobile radiator? (a) 10 kg of methyl alcohol, CH_3OH, or 10 kg of ethyl alcohol, C_2H_5OH (b) 10 m solution of methyl alcohol or 10 m solution of ethyl alcohol

38. Automobile battery acid is 38% H_2SO_4 and has a density of 1.29 g/mL. Calculate the molality and the molarity of this solution.

39. A sugar solution made to feed hummingbirds contains 1.00 lb of sugar to 4.00 lb of water. Can this solution be put outside, without freezing, where the temperature falls to 20.0°F at night? Show evidence for your answer.

*40. What would be (a) the boiling point and (b) the molality of an aqueous sugar ($C_{12}H_{22}O_{11}$) solution that freezes at −5.4°C?

41. (a) What is the molality of a solution containing 100.0 g of ethylene glycol, $C_2H_6O_2$, in 150.0 g of water?

(b) What is the boiling point of this solution?
(c) What is the freezing point of this solution?

42. What are (a) the molality, (b) the freezing point, and (c) the boiling point of a solution containing 2.68 g of naphthalene, $C_{10}H_8$, in 38.4 g of benzene (C_6H_6)?

*43. The freezing point of a solution of 8.00 g of an unknown compound dissolved in 60.0 g of acetic acid is 13.2°C. Calculate the molecular weight of the compound.

44. What is the molecular weight of a compound if

Handwritten at bottom: 4M HCl

$\left(\dfrac{4\ moles}{L}\right)\left(\dfrac{1\ eq}{1\ mole}\right) = 4\ N$

4.80 g of the compound dissolved in 22.0 g of H_2O gives a solution that freezes at $-2.50°C$?

45. A solution of 6.20 g of $C_2H_6O_2$ in water has a freezing point of $-0.372°C$. How many grams of H_2O are in the solution?

46. What (a) weight and (b) volume of ethylene glycol ($C_2H_6O_2$, density = 1.11 g/mL) should be added to 12.0 L of water in an automobile radiator to protect it from freezing at $-20.0°C$? (c) To what temperature Fahrenheit will the radiator be protected?

Additional Problems

47. How many grams of solution, 10% NaOH by weight, are required to neutralize 150 mL of a 1.0 M HCl solution?

*48. How many grams of solution, 10% NaOH by weight, are required to neutralize 250 g of a 1.0 molal solution of HCl?

*49. A sugar syrup solution contains 15.0% sugar, $C_{12}H_{22}O_{11}$, by weight and has a density of 1.06 g/mL.
   (a) How many grams of sugar are in 1.0 L of this syrup?
   (b) What is the molarity of this solution?
   (c) What is the molality of this solution?

*50. A solution of 3.84 g of C_4H_2N (empirical formula) in 250 g of benzene depresses the freezing point of benzene $0.614°C$. What is the molecular formula of the compound?

15

Ionization: Acids, Bases, Salts; Colloids

After studying Chapter 15, you should be able to

1. Understand the new terms listed in Question A at the end of the chapter.
2. State the general characteristics of acids and bases.
3. Define an acid and a base in terms of Arrhenius, Brønsted–Lowry, and Lewis theories.
4. Identify conjugate acid–base pairs in a reaction.
5. When given the reactants, complete and balance equations for the reactions of acids with bases, metals, metal oxides, and carbonates.
6. When given the reactants, complete and balance equations for the reaction of an amphoteric hydroxide with either a strong acid or a strong base.
7. Write balanced equations for the reaction of sodium hydroxide or potassium hydroxide with zinc and with aluminum.
8. Classify common compounds as electrolytes or nonelectrolytes.
9. Distinguish between strong and weak electrolytes.
10. Understand the process of dissociation and ionization.
11. Write equations for the dissociation or ionization of acids, bases, and salts in water.
12. Describe and write equations for the ionization of water.

13. Understand pH as an expression of hydrogen ion or hydronium ion concentration.
14. Given pH as an integer, give the H^+ molarity and vice versa.
15. Use the simplified log scale given in the chapter to estimate pH values from corresponding H^+ molarities.
16. Understand the process of acid–base neutralization.
17. Calculate the molarity, normality, or volume of an acid or base solution from appropriate titration data.
18. Write balanced un-ionized, total ionic, and net ionic equations for neutralization reactions.
19. Discuss colloids and describe methods for their preparation.
20. Describe the characteristics that distinguish true solutions, colloidal dispersions, and mechanical suspensions.
21. Explain (a) how colloidal dispersion can be stabilized and (b) how they can be precipitated.

15.1   Acids and Bases

The word *acid* is derived from the Latin *acidus*, meaning "sour" or "tart," and is also related to the Latin word *acetum*, meaning "vinegar." Vinegar has been known since antiquity as the product of the fermentation of wine and apple cider. The sour constituent of vinegar is acetic acid $(HC_2H_3O_2)$.

Some of the characteristic properties commonly associated with acids are the following: Water solutions of acids taste sour and change the color of litmus, a vegetable dye, from blue to red. Water solutions of nearly all acids react with (1) metals such as zinc and magnesium to produce hydrogen gas, (2) bases to produce water and a salt, and (3) carbonates to produce carbon dioxide. These properties are due to the hydrogen ions, H^+, released by acids in a water solution.

Classically, a *base* is a substance capable of liberating hydroxide ions, OH^-, in water solution. Hydroxides of the alkali metals (Group IA) and alkaline earth metals (Group IIA), such as LiOH, NaOH, KOH, $Ca(OH)_2$, and $Ba(OH)_2$, are the most common inorganic bases. Water solutions of bases are called *alkaline solutions* or *basic solutions*. They have a bitter or caustic taste, a slippery, soapy feeling, the ability to change litmus from red to blue, and the ability to interact with acids to form a salt and water.

Several theories have been proposed to answer the question "What is an acid and a base?" One of the earliest, most significant of these theories was advanced in a doctoral thesis in 1884 by Svante Arrhenius (1859–1927), a Swedish scientist, who stated that an acid is a hydrogen-containing substance that dissociates to produce hydrogen ions, and that a base is a hydroxide-containing substance that dissociates to produce hydroxide ions in aqueous solutions. Arrhenius postulated that the hydrogen ions were produced by the dissociation of acids in water, and that the hydroxide ions were produced by the dissociation of bases in water:

$$HA \longrightarrow H^+ + A^-$$
Acid

$$MOH \longrightarrow M^+ + OH^-$$
Base

Thus, an acid solution contains an excess of hydrogen ions and a base solution an excess of hydroxide ions.

In 1923 the Brønsted–Lowry proton transfer theory was introduced by J. N. Brønsted (1897–1947), a Danish chemist, and T. M. Lowry (1847–1936), an English chemist. This theory states that an acid is a proton donor and a base is a proton acceptor.

Consider the reaction of hydrogen chloride gas with water to form hydrochloric acid:

$$HCl(g) + H_2O(l) \longrightarrow H_3O^+(aq) + Cl^-(aq) \tag{1}$$

In the course of the reaction, HCl donates, or gives up, a proton to form a Cl^- ion, and H_2O accepts a proton to form the H_3O^+ ion. Thus, HCl is an acid and H_2O is a base, according to the Brønsted–Lowry theory.

A hydrogen ion, H^+, is nothing more than a bare proton and does not exist by itself in an aqueous solution. In water a proton combines with a polar water molecule to form a hydrated hydrogen ion, H_3O^+ [that is, $H(H_2O)^+$], commonly called a **hydronium ion**. The proton is attracted to a polar water molecule, forming a coordinate-covalent bond with one of the two pairs of unshared electrons:

hydronium ion

$$H^+ + H{:}\overset{..}{\underset{..}{O}}{:} \longrightarrow \left[H{:}\overset{..}{\underset{..}{O}}{:}H \right]^+$$
$$\qquad\quad \overset{}{H} \qquad\qquad\quad \overset{}{H}$$

Hydronium ion

Note the electron structure of the hydronium ion. For simplicity of expression in equations, we often use H^+ instead of H_3O^+, with the explicit understanding that H^+ is always hydrated in solution.

Whereas the Arrhenius theory is restricted to aqueous solutions, the Brønsted–Lowry approach has applications in all media and has become the more important theory when the chemistry of substances in solutions other than water is studied. Ammonium chloride (NH_4Cl) is a salt, yet its water solution has an acidic reaction. From this test we must conclude that NH_4Cl has acidic properties. The Brønsted–Lowry explanation shows that the ammonium ion, NH_4^+, is a proton donor, and water is the proton acceptor:

$$NH_4^+ \longrightarrow NH_3 + H^+ \tag{2}$$
Acid $\qquad$ Base $\quad$ Acid

$$NH_4^+ + H_2O \longrightarrow H_3O^+ + NH_3 \tag{3}$$
Acid $\quad$ Base $\qquad$ Acid $\quad$ Base

> **A Brønsted–Lowry acid is a proton (H$^+$) donor.**
> **A Brønsted–Lowry base is a proton (H$^+$) acceptor.**

The Brønsted–Lowry theory also applies to certain cases where no solution is involved. For example, in the reaction of hydrogen chloride and ammonia gases, HCl is the proton donor and NH$_3$ is the base. [Remember that (g) after a formula in equations indicates a gas.]

$$HCl(g) + NH_3(g) \longrightarrow NH_4^+ + Cl^- \tag{4}$$
$$\text{Acid} \qquad \text{Base} \qquad\quad \text{Acid} \quad \text{Base}$$

When a Brønsted–Lowry acid donates a proton, it forms the conjugate base of that acid. When a base accepts a proton, it forms the conjugate acid of that base.

In equations (1), (3), and (4), a conjugate acid and base are produced as products. The formulas of a conjugate acid–base pair differ by one proton (H$^+$). In equation (1) the conjugate acid–base pairs are HCl–Cl$^-$ and H$_3$O$^+$–H$_2$O. Cl$^-$ is the conjugate base of HCl, and HCl is the conjugate acid of Cl$^-$. H$_2$O is the conjugate base of H$_3$O$^+$, and H$_3$O$^+$ is the conjugate acid of H$_2$O.

$$\overbrace{HCl(g) + H_2O(l) \longrightarrow \underbrace{Cl^-(aq) + H_3O^+(aq)}}$$

Conjugate acid–base pair

Conjugate acid–base pair

In equation (3) the conjugate acid–base pairs are NH$_4^+$–NH$_3$ and H$_3$O$^+$–H$_2$O; in equation (4) they are HCl–Cl$^-$ and NH$_4^+$–NH$_3$.

PROBLEM

15.1

Write the formula for **(a)** the conjugate base of H$_2$O and of HNO$_3$, and **(b)** the conjugate acid of SO$_4^{2-}$ and of C$_2$H$_3$O$_2^-$. The difference between an acid or a base and its conjugate is one proton, H$^+$.

(a) To write the conjugate base of an acid, remove one proton from the acid formula. Thus,

$$H_2O \xrightarrow{-H^+} OH^- \quad \text{(Conjugate base)}$$

$$HNO_3 \xrightarrow{-H^+} NO_3^- \quad \text{(Conjugate base)}$$

Note that, by removing an H$^+$, the conjugate base becomes more negative than the acid by one minus charge.

(b) To write the conjugate acid of a base, add one proton to the formula of the base. Thus,

$$SO_4^{2-} \xrightarrow{+H^+} HSO_4^- \quad \text{(Conjugate acid)}$$

$$C_2H_3O_2^- \xrightarrow{+H^+} HC_2H_3O_2 \quad \text{(Conjugate acid)}$$

In each case the conjugate acid becomes more positive than the base by one positive charge due to the addition of H$^+$.

Table 15.1 Summary of acid–base definitions according to Arrhenius, Brønsted–Lowry, and G. N. Lewis theories

Theory	Acid	Base
Arrhenius	A hydrogen-containing substance that produces hydrogen ions in aqueous solution	A hydroxide-containing substance that produces hydroxide ions in aqueous solution
Brønsted–Lowry	A proton (H^+) donor	A proton (H^+) acceptor
Lewis	Any species that will bond to an unshared pair of electrons (electron-pair acceptor)	Any species that has an unshared pair of electrons (electron-pair donor)

A more general concept of acids and bases was introduced by Gilbert N. Lewis. The Lewis theory deals with the way in which a substance with an unshared pair of electrons reacts in an acid–base type of reaction. According to this theory a base is any substance that has an unshared pair of electrons (electron-pair donor), and an acid is any substance that will attach itself to or accept a pair of electrons. In the reaction

$$H^+ \; + \; :\!\overset{\overset{\displaystyle H}{..}}{\underset{\underset{\displaystyle H}{..}}{N}}\!:\!H \longrightarrow H\!:\!\overset{\overset{\displaystyle H}{..}}{\underset{\underset{\displaystyle H}{..}}{N}}\!:\!H^+$$

Acid   Base

H^+ is a Lewis acid and $:NH_3$ is a Lewis base. According to the Lewis theory, substances other than proton donors (for example, BF_3) behave as acids:

$$\overset{\overset{\displaystyle F}{}}{\underset{\underset{\displaystyle F}{}}{F\!:\!B}} \; + \; :\!\overset{\overset{\displaystyle H}{..}}{\underset{\underset{\displaystyle H}{..}}{N}}\!:\!H \longrightarrow \overset{\overset{\displaystyle F\;\;H}{}}{\underset{\underset{\displaystyle F\;\;H}{}}{F\!:\!B\!:\!N}}\!:\!H$$

Acid   Base

The Lewis and Brønsted–Lowry bases are identical because, to accept a proton, a base must have an unshared pair of electrons.

The three theories are summarized in Table 15.1. These theories explain how acid–base reactions occur. We will generally use the theory that best explains the reaction that is under consideration. Most of our examples will refer to aqueous solutions. It is important to realize that in an aqueous acidic solution the H^+ ion concentration is always greater than the OH^- ion concentration. And, vice versa, in an aqueous basic solution the OH^- ion concentration is always greater than the H^+ ion concentration. When the H^+ and OH^- ion concentrations in a solution are equal, the solution is neutral; that is, it is neither acidic nor basic.

15.2 Reactions of Acids

In aqueous solutions the H^+ or H_3O^+ ions are responsible for the characteristic reactions of acids. All the following reactions are in an aqueous medium.

(a) Reaction with metals. Acids react with metals that lie above hydrogen in the activity series of elements to produce hydrogen and a salt (see Section 17.5).

Acid + Metal $\longrightarrow$ Hydrogen + Salt

$2\ HCl(aq) + Ca(s) \longrightarrow H_2(g) + CaCl_2(aq)$

$H_2SO_4(aq) + Mg(s) \longrightarrow H_2(g) + MgSO_4(aq)$

$6\ HC_2H_3O_2(aq) + 2\ Al(s) \longrightarrow 3\ H_2(g) + 2\ Al(C_2H_3O_2)_3(aq)$

Acids such as nitric acid (HNO_3) are oxidizing substances (see Chapter 17) and react with metals to produce water instead of hydrogen. For example,

$3\ Zn(s) + 8\ HNO_3(dilute) \longrightarrow 3\ Zn(NO_3)_2(aq) + 2\ NO(g) + 4\ H_2O$

(b) Reaction with bases. The interaction of an acid and a base is called a *neutralization reaction*. In aqueous solutions, the products of this reaction are a salt and water.

Acid + Base $\longrightarrow$ Salt + Water

$HBr(aq) + KOH(aq) \longrightarrow KBr(aq) + H_2O$

$2\ HNO_3(aq) + Ca(OH)_2(aq) \longrightarrow Ca(NO_3)_2(aq) + 2\ H_2O$

$2\ H_3PO_4(aq) + 3\ Ba(OH)_2(aq) \longrightarrow Ba_3(PO_4)_2(s) + 6\ H_2O$

(c) Reaction with metal oxides. This reaction is closely related to that of an acid with a base. With an aqueous acid, the products are a salt and water.

Acid + Metal oxide $\longrightarrow$ Salt + Water

$2\ HCl(aq) + Na_2O(s) \longrightarrow 2\ NaCl(aq) + H_2O$

$H_2SO_4(aq) + MgO(s) \longrightarrow MgSO_4(aq) + H_2O$

$6\ HCl(aq) + Fe_2O_3(s) \longrightarrow 2\ FeCl_3(aq) + 3\ H_2O$

(d) Reaction with carbonates. Many acids react with carbonates to produce carbon dioxide, water, and a salt. Carbonic acid (H_2CO_3) is not the product, because it is unstable and decomposes into water and carbon dioxide.

Acid + Carbonate $\longrightarrow$ Salt + Water + Carbon dioxide

$2\ HCl(aq) + Na_2CO_3(aq) \longrightarrow 2\ NaCl(aq) + H_2O + CO_2(g)$

$H_2SO_4(aq) + MgCO_3(s) \longrightarrow MgSO_4(aq) + H_2O + CO_2(g)$

15.3 Reactions of Bases

The OH^- ions are responsible for the characteristic reactions of bases. All the following reactions are in an aqueous medium.

(a) Reaction with acids. Bases react with acids to produce a salt and water. See reaction of acids with bases in Section 15.2(b).

(b) Amphoteric hydroxides. Hydroxides of certain metals, such as zinc, aluminum, and chromium, are **amphoteric;** that is, they are capable of reacting as either an acid or a base. When treated with a strong acid, they behave like bases; when reacted with a strong base, they behave like acids.

*(margin: amphoteric)*

$$Zn(OH)_2(s) + 2\ HCl(aq) \longrightarrow ZnCl_2(aq) + 2\ H_2O$$

$$Zn(OH)_2(s) + 2\ NaOH(aq) \longrightarrow Na_2Zn(OH)_4(aq)$$

(c) Reaction of NaOH and KOH with certain metals. Some amphoteric metals react directly with the strong bases sodium hydroxide and potassium hydroxide to produce hydrogen.

$$\text{Base} + \text{Metal} + \text{Water} \longrightarrow \text{Salt} + \text{Hydrogen}$$

$$2\ NaOH(aq) + Zn(s) + 2\ H_2O \longrightarrow Na_2Zn(OH)_4(aq) + H_2(g)$$

$$2\ KOH(aq) + 2\ Al(s) + 6\ H_2O \longrightarrow 2\ KAl(OH)_4(aq) + 3\ H_2(g)$$

(d) Reaction with salts. Bases will react with many salts in solution due to the formation of insoluble metal hydroxides.

$$\text{Base} + \text{Salt} \longrightarrow \text{Metal hydroxide}(s) + \text{Salt}$$

$$2\ NaOH(aq) + MnCl_2(aq) \longrightarrow Mn(OH)_2(s) + 2\ NaCl(aq)$$

$$3\ Ca(OH)_2(aq) + 2\ FeCl_3(aq) \longrightarrow 2\ Fe(OH)_3(s) + 3\ CaCl_2(aq)$$

$$2\ KOH(aq) + CuSO_4(aq) \longrightarrow Cu(OH)_2(s) + K_2SO_4(aq)$$

15.4 Salts

Salts are very abundant in nature. Most of the rocks and minerals of the earth's mantle are salts of one kind or another. Huge quantities of dissolved salts also exist in the oceans. Salts may be considered to be compounds that have been derived from acids and bases. They consist of positive metal or ammonium ions (H^+ excluded) combined with negative nonmetal ions (OH^- and O^{2-} excluded). The positive ion is the base counterpart and the nonmetal ion is the acid counterpart:

Base
NaOH

Acid
HCl

↓
NaCl
Salt

Salts are usually crystalline and have high melting and boiling points.

From a single acid such as hydrochloric acid (HCl), we can produce many chloride salts by replacing the hydrogen with metal ions (for example, NaCl, KCl, RbCl, $CaCl_2$, $NiCl_2$). Hence, the number of known salts greatly exceeds the number of known acids and bases. Salts are ionic compounds. If the hydrogen atoms of a binary acid are replaced by a nonmetal, the resulting compound has covalent bonding and is therefore not considered to be a salt (for example, PCl_3, S_2Cl_2, Cl_2O, NCl_3, ICl).

A review of Chapter 8 on the nomenclature of acids, bases, and salts may be beneficial at this point.

15.5 **Electrolytes and Nonelectrolytes**

Some of the most convincing evidence as to the nature of chemical bonding within a substance is the ability (or lack of ability) of a water solution of the substance to conduct electricity.

We can show that solutions of certain substances are conductors of electricity by using a simple conductivity apparatus consisting of a pair of electrodes connected to a voltage source through a light bulb and switch (see Figure 15.1). If the medium between the electrodes is a conductor of electricity, the light bulb will glow when the switch is closed. When chemically pure water is placed in the beaker and the switch is closed, the light does not glow, indicating that water is a virtual nonconductor. When we dissolve a small amount of sugar in the water and test the solution, the light still does not glow, showing that a sugar solution is also a nonconductor. But, when a small amount of salt, NaCl, is

Metal electrodes

To source of electric current

Figure 15.1   A simple conductivity apparatus for testing electrolytes and nonelectrolytes in solution: If the solution contains an electrolyte, the light will glow when the switch is closed.

Table 15.2 Representative electrolytes and nonelectrolytes

Electrolytes	Nonelectrolytes
H_2SO_4	$C_{12}H_{22}O_{11}$ (sugar)
HCl	C_2H_5OH (ethyl alcohol)
HNO_3	$C_2H_4(OH)_2$ (ethylene glycol)
NaOH	$C_3H_5(OH)_3$ (glycerol)
$HC_2H_3O_2$	CH_3OH (methyl alcohol)
NH_4OH	$CO(NH_2)_2$ (urea)
K_2SO_4	O_2
$NaNO_3$	H_2O

dissolved in water and this solution is tested, the light glows brightly. Thus, the salt solution conducts electricity. A fundamental difference exists between the chemical bonding of sugar and that of salt. Sugar is a covalently bonded (molecular) substance; salt is a substance with ionic bonds.

electrolyte

nonelectrolyte

Substances whose aqueous solutions are conductors of electricity are called **electrolytes.** Substances whose solutions are nonconductors are known as **nonelectrolytes.** The classes of compounds that are electrolytes are acids, bases, and salts. Solutions of certain oxides also are conductors because the oxides form an acid or a base when dissolved in water. One major difference between electrolytes and nonelectrolytes is that electrolytes are capable of producing ions in solution, whereas nonelectrolytes do not have this property. Solutions that contain a sufficient number of ions will conduct an electric current. Although pure water is essentially a nonconductor, many city water supplies contain enough dissolved ionic matter to cause the light to glow dimly when the water is tested in a conductivity apparatus. Table 15.2 lists some common electrolytes and nonelectrolytes.

Acids, bases, and salts are electrolytes.

15.6 Dissociation and Ionization of Electrolytes

Arrhenius received the 1903 Nobel prize in chemistry for his work on electrolytes. He stated that a solution conducts electricity because the solute dissociates immediately upon dissolving into electrically charged particles called *ions.* The movement of these ions toward oppositely charged electrodes causes the solution to be a conductor. According to his theory, solutions that are relatively poor conductors contain electrolytes that are only partly dissociated. Arrhenius also believed that ions exist in solution whether or not an electric current is present. In other words, the electric current does not cause the formation of ions. Positive ions, attracted to the cathode, are cations; negative ions, attracted to the anode, are anions.

We have seen that sodium chloride crystals consist of sodium and chloride ions held together by ionic bonds. When placed in water, the sodium and chloride ions are attracted by the polar water molecules, which surround each ion as it dissolves. In water, the salt dissociates, forming hydrated sodium and chloride ions (see Figure 15.2). The sodium and chloride ions in solution are bonded to a specific number of water dipoles and have less attraction for each other than they had in the crystalline state. The equation representing this dissociation is

$$NaCl(s) + (x + y)\, H_2O \longrightarrow Na^+(H_2O)_x + Cl^-(H_2O)_y$$

A simplified dissociation equation in which the water is omitted but understood to be present is

$$NaCl \longrightarrow Na^+ + Cl^-$$

It is important to remember that sodium chloride exists in an aqueous solution as hydrated ions and not as NaCl units, even though the formula NaCl or $Na^+ + Cl^-$ is often used in equations.

The chemical reactions of salts in solution are the reactions of their ions. For example, when sodium chloride and silver nitrate react and form a precipitate of silver chloride, only the Ag^+ and Cl^+ ions participate in the reaction. The Na^+ and NO_3^- remain as ions in solution.

$$Ag^+ + Cl^- \longrightarrow AgCl \downarrow$$

In many cases the number of molecules of water associated with a particular ion is known. For example, the blue color of the copper(II) ion is due to the hydrated ion $Cu(H_2O)_4^{2+}$. The hydration of ions can be demonstrated in a striking way with cobalt(II) chloride. When cobalt(II) chloride hexahydrate is dissolved in water, a pink solution forms due to the $Co(H_2O)_6^{2+}$ ions. If concentrated hydrochloric acid is added to this pink solution, the color gradually changes to blue. If water is then added to the blue solution, the color changes to pink again.

Figure 15.2 Hydrated sodium and chloride ions: When sodium chloride dissolves in water, each Na^+ and Cl^- ion becomes surrounded by water molecules. The negative end of the water dipole is attracted to the Na^+ ion, and the positive end is attracted to the Cl^- ion.

These color changes are due to the exchange of water molecules and chloride ions on the cobalt ion. The $CoCl_4^{2-}$ ion is blue. Thus, the hydration of the cobalt ion is a reversible or equilibrium reaction (see Chapter 16). The equilibrium equation representing these changes is

$$Co(H_2O)_6^{2+} + 4\ Cl^- \rightleftharpoons CoCl_4^{2-} + 6\ H_2O$$
$$\quad\text{Pink}\qquad\qquad\qquad\text{Blue}$$

Ionization is the formation of ions; it may occur as a result of chemical reaction of certain substances with water. Glacial acetic acid (100% $HC_2H_3O_2$) is a liquid that behaves as a nonelectrolyte when tested by the method described in Section 15.5. But a water solution of acetic acid conducts an electric current (as indicated by the dull-glowing light of the conductivity apparatus). The equation for the reaction with water, which forms hydronium and acetate ions, is

$$HC_2H_3O_2 + H_2O \rightleftharpoons H_3O^+ + C_2H_3O_2^-$$
$$\quad\text{Acid}\qquad\text{Base}\qquad\text{Acid}\qquad\text{Base}$$

or, in the simplified equation,

$$HC_2H_3O_2 \rightleftharpoons H^+ + C_2H_3O_2^-$$

In this ionization reaction, water serves not only as a solvent but also as a base according to the Brønsted–Lowry theory.

Hydrogen chloride is predominantly covalently bonded, but when dissolved in water it reacts to form hydronium and chloride ions:

$$HCl(g) + H_2O \longrightarrow H_3O^+ + Cl^-$$

When a hydrogen chloride solution is tested for conductivity, the light glows brilliantly, indicating many ions in the solution.

Ionization occurs in each of the foregoing two reactions with water, producing ions in solution. The necessity for water in the ionization process can be demonstrated by dissolving hydrogen chloride in a nonpolar solvent, such as benzene, and testing the solution for conductivity. The solution fails to conduct electricity, indicating that no ions are produced.

The terms *dissociation* and *ionization* are often used interchangeably to describe processes taking place in water. But, strictly speaking, the two are

dissociation   different. In the **dissociation** of a salt, the salt already exists as ions; when it dissolves in water, the ions separate, or dissociate, and increase in mobility. In the

ionization   **ionization** process, ions are produced by the reaction of a compound with water.

15.7   Strong and Weak Electrolytes

Electrolytes are classified as strong or weak depending on the degree, or extent,

strong   of dissociation or ionization. **Strong electrolytes** are essentially 100% ionized in
electrolyte   solution; **weak electrolytes** are much less ionized (based on comparing 0.1 M solutions). Most electrolytes are either strong or weak, with a few classified as moderately strong or weak. Most salts are strong electrolytes. Acids and bases

weak   that are strong electrolytes (highly ionized) are called *strong acids* and *strong*
electrolyte

bases. Acids and bases that are weak electrolytes (slightly ionized) are called *weak acids* and *weak bases.*

For equivalent concentrations, solutions of strong electrolytes contain many more ions than do solutions of weak electrolytes. As a result, solutions of strong electrolytes are better conductors of electricity. Consider the two solutions, 1 M HCl and 1 M $HC_2H_3O_2$. Hydrochloric acid is almost 100% ionized; acetic acid is about 1% ionized. Thus HCl is a strong acid, and $HC_2H_3O_2$ is a weak acid. Hydrochloric acid has about 100 times as many hydronium ions in solution as acetic acid, making the HCl solution much more acidic.

One can distinguish between strong and weak electrolytes experimentally using the apparatus described in Section 15.5. A 1 M HCl solution causes the light to glow brilliantly, but a 1 M $HC_2H_3O_2$ solution causes only a dim glow. In a similar fashion the strong base sodium hydroxide (NaOH) may be distinguished from the weak base ammonium hydroxide (NH_4OH). The ionization of a weak electrolyte in water is represented by an equilibrium equation showing that both the un-ionized and ionized forms are present in solution. In the equilibrium equation of $HC_2H_3O_2$ and its ions, we say that the equilibrium lies "far to the left" because relatively few hydrogen and acetate ions are present in solution:

$$HC_2H_3O_2(aq) \rightleftharpoons H^+ + C_2H_3O_2^-$$

We have previously used a double arrow in an equation to represent reversible processes in the equilibrium between dissolved and undissolved solute in a saturated solution. A double arrow ($\rightleftharpoons$) is also used in the ionization equation of soluble weak electrolytes to indicate that the solution contains a considerable amount of the un-ionized compound in equilibrium with its ions in solution. (See Section 16.1 for a discussion of reversible reactions.) A single arrow is used to indicate that the electrolyte is essentially all in the ionic form in the solution. For example, nitric acid is a strong acid; nitrous acid is a weak acid. Their ionization equations in water may be indicated as

$$HNO_3(aq) \xrightarrow{H_2O} H^+ + NO_3^-$$
$$HNO_2(aq) \xleftrightharpoons{H_2O} H^+ + NO_2^-$$

Practically all soluble salts; acids such as sulfuric, nitric, and hydrochloric acids; and bases such as sodium, potassium, calcium, and barium hydroxides are strong electrolytes. Weak electrolytes include numerous other acids and bases such as acetic acid, nitrous acid, carbonic acid, and ammonium hydroxide. The terms *strong acid, strong base, weak acid,* and *weak base* refer to whether an acid or base is a strong or weak electrolyte. A brief list of strong and weak electrolytes is given in Table 15.3.

Electrolytes yield two or more ions per formula unit upon dissociation, the actual number being dependent on the compound. Dissociation is complete or nearly complete for nearly all soluble salts and for certain other strong electrolytes such as those given in Table 15.3. The following are dissociation equations for several strong electrolytes. In all cases the ions are actually hydrated.

Table 15.3 Selected list of strong and weak electrolytes

Strong electrolytes	Weak electrolytes
Most soluble salts	$HC_2H_3O_2$
H_2SO_4	H_2CO_3
HNO_3	HNO_2
HCl	H_2SO_3
HBr	H_2S
$HClO_4$	$H_2C_2O_4$
NaOH	H_3BO_3
KOH	HClO
$Ca(OH)_2$	NH_4OH
$Ba(OH)_2$	HF

$$NaOH \xrightarrow{H_2O} Na^+ + OH^- \qquad \text{2 ions in solution per formula unit}$$

$$Na_2SO_4 \xrightarrow{H_2O} 2\,Na^+ + SO_4^{2-} \qquad \text{3 ions in solution per formula unit}$$

$$AlCl_3 \xrightarrow{H_2O} Al^{3+} + 3\,Cl^- \qquad \text{4 ions in solution per formula unit}$$

$$Fe_2(SO_4)_3 \xrightarrow{H_2O} 2\,Fe^{3+} + 3\,SO_4^{2-} \qquad \text{5 ions in solution per formula unit}$$

One mole of NaCl will give 1 mol of Na^+ ions and 1 mol of Cl^- ions in solution, assuming complete dissociation of the salt. One mole of $CaCl_2$ will give 1 mol of Ca^{2+} ions and 2 mol of Cl^- ions in solution.

$$NaCl \xrightarrow{H_2O} Na^+ + Cl^-$$
$$\text{1 mol} \qquad\quad \text{1 mol} \quad \text{1 mol}$$

$$CaCl_2 \xrightarrow{H_2O} Ca^{2+} + 2\,Cl^-$$
$$\text{1 mol} \qquad\quad \text{1 mol} \quad \text{2 mol}$$

PROBLEM

15.2

What is the molarity of each ion in a solution of (a) 2.0 M NaCl, and (b) 0.40 M K_2SO_4? (Assume complete dissociation.)

(a) According to the dissociation equation,

$$NaCl \xrightarrow{H_2O} Na^+ + Cl^-$$
$$\text{1 mol} \qquad\quad \text{1 mol} \quad \text{1 mol}$$

the concentration of Na^+ is equal to that of NaCl (1 mol NaCl $\longrightarrow$ 1 mol Na^+) and the concentration of Cl^- is also equal to that of NaCl. Therefore, the concentrations of the ions in 2.0 M NaCl are 2.0 M Na^+ and 2.0 M Cl^-.

(b) According to the dissociation equation,

$$K_2SO_4 \xrightarrow{H_2O} 2\,K^+ + SO_4^{2-}$$
$$\text{1 mol} \qquad\quad \text{2 mol} \quad \text{1 mol}$$

The concentration of K^+ is twice that of K_2SO_4 and the concentration of SO_4^{2-} is equal to that of K_2SO_4. Therefore, the concentrations of the ions in 0.40 M K_2SO_4 are 0.80 M K^+ and 0.40 M SO_4^{2-}.

Colligative properties of electrolyte solutions.   We have learned that, when 1 mol of sucrose, a nonelectrolyte, is dissolved in 1000 g of water, the solution freezes at $-1.86°C$. When 1 mol of NaCl is dissolved in 1000 g of water, the freezing point of the solution is not $-1.86°C$, as might be expected, but is closer to $-3.72°C$ (-1.86×2). The reason for the lower freezing point is that 1 mol of NaCl in solution produces 2 mol of particles ($2 \times 6.022 \times 10^{23}$ ions) in solution. Thus, the freezing point depression produced by 1 mol of NaCl is essentially equivalent to that produced by 2 mol of a nonelectrolyte. An electrolyte such as $CaCl_2$, which yields three ions in water, gives a freezing point depression of about three times that of a nonelectrolyte. These freezing point data provide additional evidence that electrolytes dissociate when dissolved in water. The other colligative properties are similarly affected by substances that yield ions in aqueous solutions.

15.8   Ionization of Water

The more we study chemistry, the more intriguing the little molecule of water becomes. Two equations commonly used to show how water ionizes are

$$H_2O + H_2O \rightleftharpoons H_3O^+ + OH^-$$
Acid   Base   Acid   Base

and

$$H_2O \rightleftharpoons H^+ + OH^-$$

The first equation represents the Brønsted–Lowry concept, with water reacting as both an acid and a base, forming a hydronium ion and a hydroxide ion. The second equation is a simplified version, indicating that water ionizes to give a hydrogen and a hydroxide ion. Actually, the proton, H^+, is hydrated and exists as a hydronium ion. In either case equal molar amounts of acid and base are produced so that water is neutral, having neither H^+ nor OH^- ions in excess. The ionization of water at 25°C produces an H^+ ion concentration of 1.0×10^{-7} mole per liter and an OH^- ion concentration of 1.0×10^{-7} mole per liter. These concentrations are usually expressed as

$$[H^+] \text{ or } [H_3O^+] = 1.0 \times 10^{-7} \text{ mol/L}$$

$$[OH^-] = 1.0 \times 10^{-7} \text{ mol/L}$$

These figures mean that about two out of every billion water molecules are ionized. This amount of ionization, small as it is, is a significant factor in the behavior of water in many chemical reactions.

The square brackets, [ ], indicate that the concentration is in moles per liter. Thus [H$^+$] means the concentration of H$^+$ in moles per liter.

Introduction to pH

The acidity of an aqueous solution depends on the concentration of hydrogen or hydronium ions. The acidity of solutions involved in a chemical reaction is often critically important, especially for biochemical reactions. The pH scale of acidity was devised to fill the need for a simple, convenient numerical way to state the acidity of a solution. Values on the pH scale are obtained by mathematical conversion of H$^+$ ion concentrations to pH by these expressions:

pH

$$pH = \log \frac{1}{[H^+]} \quad \text{or} \quad pH = -\log[H^+]$$

where [H$^+$] = H$^+$ or H$_3$O$^+$ ion concentration in moles per liter. The **pH** is defined as the logarithm (log) of the reciprocal of the H$^+$ or H$_3$O$^+$ ion concentration in moles per liter. The scale itself is based on the H$^+$ concentration in water at 25°C. At this temperature, water has an H$^+$ concentration of 1×10^{-7} mole per liter and is calculated to have a pH of 7.

$$pH = \log \frac{1}{[H^+]} = \log \frac{1}{(1 \times 10^{-7})} = \log(1 \times 10^7) = 7$$

By an alternate and mathematically equivalent definition, pH is the negative logarithm of the H$^+$ or H$_3$O$^+$ concentration in moles per liter:

$$pH = -\log[H^+] = -\log(1 \times 10^{-7}) = -(-7) = 7$$

The pH of pure water at 25°C is 7 and is said to be neutral; that is, it is neither acidic nor basic, because the concentrations of H$^+$ and OH$^-$ are equal. Solutions that contain more H$^+$ ions than OH$^-$ ions have pH values less than 7, and solutions that contain less H$^+$ ions than OH$^-$ ions have values greater than 7.

pH < 7.00 Acidic solution
pH = 7.00 Neutral solution
pH > 7.00 Basic solution

When [H$^+$] = 1×10^{-5} mol/L, pH = 5 (acidic)

When [H$^+$] = 1×10^{-9} mol/L, pH = 9 (basic)

Instead of saying that the hydrogen ion concentration in the solution is 1×10^{-5} mole per liter, it is customary to say that the pH of the solution is 5. The smaller the pH value, the more acidic the solution (see Figure 15.3).

At a given molarity a strong acid is more acidic (has a higher H$^+$ concentration) than a weak acid. For example, in a 0.100 M concentration, the pH of HCl is

Figure 15.3   The pH scale of acidity and basicity

1.00 and that of $HC_2H_3O_2$ is 2.87. As a weak acid is made more dilute, greater percentages of its molecules ionize, and the pH tends to approach that of a strong acid at comparable dilutions. This behavior is illustrated by the following comparative data for hydrochloric acid (100% ionized) and acetic acid.

HCl *solution*			$HC_2H_3O_2$ *solution*		
M	pH	% *ionized*	*M*	pH	% *ionized*
0.100	1.00	100	0.100	2.87	1.35
0.0100	2.00	100	0.0100	3.37	4.27
0.00100	3.00	100	0.00100	3.90	12.6

The pH scale, along with its interpretation, is given in Table 15.4, and Table 15.5 lists the pH of some common solutions. Note that a change of only 1 pH unit means a tenfold increase or decrease in H^+ ion concentration. A simplified method of determining pH from $[H^+]$ follows:

Table 15.4   The pH scale for expressing acidity

$[H^+]$ *(mol L)*	pH	
1×10^{-14}	14	
1×10^{-13}	13	
1×10^{-12}	12	Increasing
1×10^{-11}	11	basicity
1×10^{-10}	10	
1×10^{-9}	9	
1×10^{-8}	8	
1×10^{-7}	7	Neutral
1×10^{-6}	6	
1×10^{-5}	5	
1×10^{-4}	4	
1×10^{-3}	3	Increasing
1×10^{-2}	2	acidity
1×10^{-1}	1	
1×10^{0}	0	

Table 15.5   The pH of some common solutions

Solution	pH
Gastric juice	1.0
0.1 M HCl	1.0
Lemon juice	2.3
Vinegar	2.8
0.1 M $HC_2H_3O_2$	2.9
Orange juice	3.7
Tomato juice	4.1
Coffee, black	5.0
Urine	6.0
Milk	6.6
Pure water (25°C)	7.0
Blood	7.4
Household ammonia	11.0
1 M NaOH	14.0

Figure 15.4 Simplified logarithm scale: For example, the logarithm (log) of 5 is 0.70; the logarithm of 7.5 is 0.88.

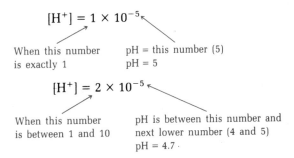

$[H^+] = 1 \times 10^{-5}$

When this number   pH = this number (5)
is exactly 1   pH = 5

$[H^+] = 2 \times 10^{-5}$

When this number   pH is between this number and
is between 1 and 10   next lower number (4 and 5)
                        pH = 4.7

Calculation of the pH value corresponding to any H^+ ion concentration requires the use of logarithms. Logarithms are exponents. The logarithm (log) of a number is simply the power to which 10 must be raised to give that number. Thus the log of 100 is 2, and the log of 1000 is 3 ($100 = 10^2$, $1000 = 10^3$). The log of 500 is 2.70, but you cannot readily determine this value without a log table or a calculator with log capability. However, even though you may not be familiar with logarithms, the simplified log scale of Figure 15.4 can be used to estimate the logarithms of various numbers. For example, let us use this log scale to calculate the pH of a solution with $[H^+] = 2 \times 10^{-5}$:

$[H^+] = ② \times 10^{-⑤}$

pH = This number (5) minus the log of this number (2) (which must be between 1 and 10)

pH $= 5 - \log 2$

$\log 2 = 0.30$ (from the log scale)

pH $= 5 - 0.30 = 4.7$ (Answer)

PROBLEM

15.3

What is the pH of a solution with an $[H^+]$ of **(a)** 1×10^{-11} and **(b)** 6×10^{-4}?

(a) $[H^+] = 1 \times 10^{-11}$
pH = 11

Figure 15.5   pH test for determining the approximate acidity of solutions. (*Courtesy Micro Essential Laboratory, Inc.*)

(b) $[H^+] = 6 \times 10^{-4}$

$pH = 4 - \log 6$

$\log 6 = 0.78$ (from Figure 15.4)

$pH = 4 - 0.78 = 3.22$ (Answer)

The measurement and control of pH is extremely important in many fields of science and technology. The proper soil pH is necessary to grow certain types of plants successfully. The pH of certain foods is too acid for some diets. Many biological processes are delicately controlled pH systems. The pH of human blood is regulated to very close tolerances through the uptake or release of H^+ by mineral ions such as HCO_3^-, HPO_4^{2-}, and $H_2PO_4^-$. Changes in the pH of the blood by as little as 0.4 pH unit may result in death.

Compounds with colors that change at particular pH values are used as indicators in acid–base reactions. For example, phenolphthalein, an organic compound, is colorless in acid solution and changes to pink at a pH of 8.3. When a solution of sodium hydroxide is added to a hydrochloric acid solution containing phenolphthalein, the change in color (from colorless to pink) indicates that all the acid is neutralized. Commercially available pH test paper, such as shown in Figure 15.5, contains chemical indicators. The indicator in the paper takes on different colors when wetted with solutions of different pH. Thus the pH of a solution can be estimated by placing a drop on the test paper and comparing the color of the test paper with a color chart calibrated at different pH values. Electronic pH meters of the type shown in Figure 15.6 are used for making rapid and precise pH determinations.

15.10   Neutralization

neutralization

The reaction of an acid and a base to form a salt and water is known as **neutralization.** We have seen this reaction before; but now, in the light of what

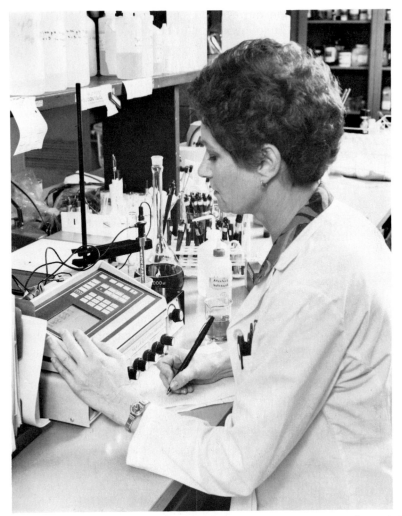

Figure 15.6 An electronic pH meter: Accurate measurements may be made by meters of this type. (*Courtesy Beckman Instruments, Inc. Zeromatic is a registered trademark.*)

we have learned about ions and ionization, let us reexamine the process of neutralization.

Consider the reaction that occurs when solutions of sodium hydroxide and hydrochloric acid are mixed. The ions present initially are Na^+ and OH^- from the base and H^+ and Cl^- from the acid. The products, sodium chloride and water, exist as Na^+ and Cl^- ions and H_2O molecules. A chemical equation representing this reaction is

$$HCl(aq) + NaOH(aq) \longrightarrow NaCl(aq) + H_2O \tag{5}$$

This equation, however, does not show that HCl, NaOH, and NaCl exist as ions in solution. The following total ionic equation gives a better representation of the reaction:

$$(H^+ + Cl^-) + (Na^+ + OH^-) \longrightarrow Na^+ + Cl^- + H_2O \tag{6}$$

spectator ions

Equation (6) shows that the Na^+ and Cl^- ions did not react. These ions are called **spectator ions** because they were present but did not take part in the reaction. The only reaction that occurred was that between the H^+ and OH^- ions. Therefore, the equation for the neutralization can be written as this net ionic equation:

$$\underset{\text{Acid}}{H^+} + \underset{\text{Base}}{OH^-} \longrightarrow \underset{\text{Water}}{H_2O} \tag{7}$$

This simple net ionic equation (7) represents not only the reaction of sodium hydroxide and hydrochloric acid but also the reaction of any acid with any base in an aqueous solution. The driving force of a neutralization reaction is the ability of an H^+ ion and an OH^- ion to react and form a molecule of un-ionized water.

titration

The amount of acid, base, or other species in a sample may be determined by titration. **Titration** is the process of measuring the volume of one reagent that is required to react with a measured weight or volume of another reagent. Let us consider the titration of an acid with a base. A measured volume of acid of unknown concentration is placed in a flask, and a few drops of an indicator solution are added. Base solution of known concentration is slowly added from a buret to the acid until the indicator changes color (see Figure 15.7). The indicator selected is one that changes color when the stoichiometric quantity (according to the equation) of base has been added to the acid. At this point, known as the end

Figure 15.7 Graduated burets are used in titrations for neutralization of acids and bases as well as for many other volumetric determinations.

point of the titration, the titration is complete, and the volume of base used to neutralize the acid is read from the buret. The concentration or amount of acid in solution can be calculated from the titration data and the chemical equation for the reaction. Illustrative problems follow.

PROBLEM

15.4

Suppose that 42.00 mL of 0.150 *M* NaOH solution are required to titrate 50.00 mL of hydrochloric acid solution. What is the molarity of the acid solution?

The equation for the reaction is

$$NaOH(aq) + HCl(aq) \longrightarrow NaCl(aq) + H_2O(l)$$

In this neutralization NaOH and HCl react in a 1:1 mole ratio. Therefore, the moles of HCl in solution are equal to the moles of NaOH required to react with it. First we calculate the moles of NaOH used, and from this value we determine the moles of HCl.

Data: 42.00 mL of 0.150 *M* NaOH   50.00 mL of HCl
Molarity of acid = *M*   (Unknown)

Moles of NaOH:

$$M = mol/L \quad 42.00 \text{ mL} = 0.04200 \text{ L}$$

$$0.04200 \, \cancel{L} \times \frac{0.150 \text{ mol NaOH}}{1 \, \cancel{L}} = 0.00630 \text{ mol NaOH}$$

Since NaOH and HCl react in a 1:1 mole ratio, 0.00630 mol of HCl was present in the 50.00 mL of HCl solution. Therefore the molarity of the HCl is

$$M = \frac{mol}{L} = \frac{0.00630 \text{ mol HCl}}{0.05000 \text{ L}} = 0.126 \text{ M HCl} \quad \text{(Answer)}$$

PROBLEM

15.5

Suppose that 42.00 mL of 0.150 *M* NaOH solution are required to titrate 50.00 mL of sulfuric acid (H_2SO_4) solution. What is the molarity of the acid solution?

The equation for the reaction is

$$2 NaOH(aq) + H_2SO_4(aq) \longrightarrow Na_2SO_4(aq) + 2 H_2O(l)$$

The same amount of base (0.00630 mol of NaOH) is used in this titration as in Problem 15.4, but the mole ratio of acid to base in the reaction is 1:2. The moles of H_2SO_4 reacted can be calculated by using the mole-ratio method.

Data: 42.00 mL of 0.150 *M* NaOH = 0.00630 mol NaOH

$$0.00630 \, \cancel{\text{mol NaOH}} \times \frac{1 \text{ mol } H_2SO_4}{2 \, \cancel{\text{mol NaOH}}} = 0.00315 \text{ mol } H_2SO_4$$

Therefore 0.00315 mol of H_2SO_4 was present in 50.00 mL of H_2SO_4 solution. The molarity of the H_2SO_4 is

$$M = \frac{mol}{L} = \frac{0.00315 \text{ mol } H_2SO_4}{0.05000 \text{ L}} = 0.0630 \text{ M } H_2SO_4 \quad \text{(Answer)}$$

PROBLEM

15.6

A 25.00 mL sample of H_2SO_4 solution required 14.26 mL of 0.2240 N NaOH for complete neutralization. What are the normality and the molarity of sulfuric acid?

The equation for the reaction is

$$2\,NaOH(aq) + H_2SO_4(aq) \longrightarrow Na_2SO_4(aq) + 2\,H_2O(l)$$

The normality of the acid can be calculated from

$$V_A N_A = V_B N_B$$

Substitute the data in the problem and solve for N_A:

$$25.00\ mL \times N_A = 14.26\ mL \times 0.2240\ N$$

$$N_A = \frac{14.26\ mL \times 0.2240\ N}{25.00\ mL} = 0.1278\ N\ H_2SO_4$$

The normality of the acid is 0.1278 N.

Because H_2SO_4 furnishes 2 equivalents of H^+ per mole, the conversion to molarity is

$$\frac{equiv}{L} \times \frac{mol}{equiv}$$

$$\frac{0.1278\ \text{equiv } H_2SO_4}{1\ L} \times \frac{1\ mol\ H_2SO_4}{2\ \text{equiv } H_2SO_4} = 0.06390\ mol/L$$

The H_2SO_4 solution is 0.06390 M.

This problem can also be solved by first calculating the molarity of the H_2SO_4 as in Problem 15.5, and then converting the molarity to normality.

15.11   ## Writing Ionic Equations

un-ionized
equation

total ionic
equation

net ionic
equation

In Section 15.10 we wrote the reaction of hydrochloric acid and sodium hydroxide in three different equations. Equation (5) was the un-ionized equation; equation (6) was the total ionic equation; and equation (7) was the net ionic equation. In the **un-ionized equation,** compounds are written in their molecular, or normal, formula expressions. In the **total ionic equation,** compounds are written to show the form in which they are predominantly present: strong electrolytes as ions in solution; and nonelectrolytes, weak electrolytes, precipitates, and gases in their molecular (or un-ionized) forms. In the **net ionic equation,** only those molecules or ions that have changed are included in the equation; ions or molecules that do not change (spectators) are omitted.

Up to this point, when balancing an equation we have been concerned only with the atoms of the individual elements. Because ions are electrically charged, ionic equations often end up with a net electrical charge. A balanced equation must have the same net charge on each side, whether that charge is positive, negative, or zero. Therefore, when balancing an ionic equation, we must make sure that both the same number of each kind of atom and the same net electrical charge are present on each side.

Following is a list of rules for writing ionic equations:

1. Strong electrolytes in solution are written in their ionic form.
2. Weak electrolytes are written in their molecular (un-ionized) form.
3. Nonelectrolytes are written in their molecular form.
4. Insoluble substances, precipitates, and gases are written in their molecular forms.
5. The net ionic equation should include only those substances that have undergone a chemical change. Spectator ions are omitted from the net ionic equation.
6. Equations must be balanced, both in atoms and in electrical charge.

Study the examples below. Note that all reactions are in solution.

(a) $HNO_3(aq) + KOH(aq) \longrightarrow KNO_3(aq) + H_2O$ Un-ionized equation
$(H^+ + NO_3^-) + (K^+ + OH^-) \longrightarrow (K^+ + NO_3^-) + H_2O$ Total ionic equation
$H^+ + OH^- \longrightarrow H_2O$ Net ionic equation

HNO_3, KOH, and KNO_3 are soluble, strong electrolytes. K^+ and NO_3^- are spectator ions, have not changed, and are not included in the net ionic equation. Water is a nonelectrolyte and is written in the molecular form.

(b) $2\ AgNO_3(aq) + BaCl_2(aq) \longrightarrow 2\ AgCl \downarrow + Ba(NO_3)_2(aq)$
$(2\ Ag^+ + 2\ NO_3^-) + (Ba^{2+} + 2\ Cl^-) \longrightarrow 2\ AgCl \downarrow + (Ba^{2+} + 2\ NO_3^-)$
$Ag^+ + Cl^- \longrightarrow AgCl \downarrow$ Net ionic equation

Although silver chloride (AgCl) is an ionic salt, it is written in the un-ionized form on the right side of the ionic equations because most of the Ag^+ and Cl^- ions are no longer in solution but have formed a precipitate of AgCl. Ba^{2+} and NO_3^- are spectator ions.

(c) $Na_2CO_3(aq) + H_2SO_4(aq) \longrightarrow Na_2SO_4(aq) + H_2O + CO_2 \uparrow$
$(2\ Na^+ + CO_3^{2-}) + (2\ H^+ + SO_4^{2-}) \longrightarrow (2\ Na^+ + SO_4^{2-}) + H_2O + CO_2 \uparrow$
$CO_3^{2-} + 2\ H^+ \longrightarrow H_2O + CO_2 \uparrow$ Net ionic equation

Carbon dioxide (CO_2) is a gas and evolves from the solution; Na^+ and SO_4^{2-} are spectator ions.

(d) $HC_2H_3O_2(aq) + NaOH(aq) \longrightarrow NaC_2H_3O_2(aq) + H_2O$
$HC_2H_3O_2 + (Na^+ + OH^-) \longrightarrow (Na^+ + C_2H_3O_2^-) + H_2O$
$HC_2H_3O_2 + OH^- \longrightarrow C_2H_3O_2^- + H_2O$ Net ionic equation

Acetic acid ($HC_2H_3O_2$), a weak acid, is written in the molecular form, but sodium acetate ($NaC_2H_3O_2$), a soluble salt, is written in the ionic form. The Na^+ ion is the only spectator ion in this reaction. Both sides of the net ionic equation have a -1 electrical charge.

(e) $Mg(s) + 2\ HCl(aq) \longrightarrow MgCl_2(aq) + H_2 \uparrow$
$Mg + (2\ H^+ + 2\ Cl^-) \longrightarrow (Mg^{2+} + 2\ Cl^-) + H_2 \uparrow$
$Mg + 2\ H^+ \longrightarrow Mg^{2+} + H_2 \uparrow$ Net ionic equation

The net electrical charge on both sides of the equation is $+2$.

(f) $H_2SO_4(aq) + Ba(OH)_2(aq) \longrightarrow BaSO_4 \downarrow + 2\ H_2O$

$(2\ H^+ + SO_4^{2-}) + (Ba^{2+} + 2\ OH^-) \longrightarrow BaSO_4 \downarrow + 2\ H_2O$

$2\ H^+ + SO_4^{2-} + Ba^{2+} + 2\ OH^- \longrightarrow BaSO_4 \downarrow + 2\ H_2O$ Net ionic equation

Barium sulfate ($BaSO_4$) is a highly insoluble salt. If we conduct this reaction using the conductivity apparatus described in Section 15.5, the light glows brightly at first but goes out when the reaction is complete, because almost no ions are left in solution. The $BaSO_4$ precipitates out of solution, and water is a nonconductor of electricity.

15.12 Colloids: An Introduction

When we add sugar to a flask of water and shake it, the sugar dissolves and forms a clear homogeneous *solution*. When we do the same experiment with very fine sand and water, the sand particles form a *suspension*, which settles when the shaking stops. When we repeat the experiment again using ordinary corn starch, we find that the starch does not dissolve in cold water; but if the mixture is heated and stirred, the starch forms a cloudy, opalescent *dispersion*. This dispersion does not appear to be clear and homogeneous like the sugar solution. Yet it is not obviously heterogeneous and does not settle like the sand suspension. In short, its properties are intermediate between those of the sugar solution and those of the sand suspension. The starch dispersion is actually a colloid. The name *colloid* is derived from the Greek *kolla*, meaning *glue*, and was coined by the English scientist Thomas Graham in 1861. Graham classified solutes as crystalloids if they diffused through a parchment membrane and as colloids if they did not diffuse through the membrane.

colloid   As it is now used, the word **colloid** means a dispersion in which the dispersed particles are larger than the solute ions or molecules of a true solution and smaller than the particles of a mechanical suspension. The term does not imply a gluelike quality, although most glues are colloidal materials. The size of colloidal particles ranges from a lower limit of about 1 nm (10^{-7} cm) to an upper limit of about 1000 nm (10^{-4} cm).

The fundamental difference between a colloidal dispersion and a true solution is the size, not the nature, of the particles. The solute particles in a solution are usually single ions or molecules that may be hydrated to varying degrees. Colloidal particles are usually aggregations of ions or molecules. However, the molecules of some polymers such as proteins are large enough to be classified as colloidal particles when in solution. To appreciate fully the differences in relative sizes, the volumes, not just the linear dimensions, of colloidal particles and solute particles must be compared. The difference in volumes can be approximated by assuming that the particles are spheres. A large colloidal particle has a diameter of about 500 nm, whereas a fair-sized ion or molecule has a diameter of about 0.5 nm. Thus, the diameter of the collodial particle is about 1000 times that of the solute particle. Because the volumes of spheres are proportional to the cubes of their diameters, we can calculate that the volume of

Table 15.6 Types of colloidal dispersions

Type	Name	Examples
Gas in liquid	Foam	Whipped cream, soap suds
Gas in solid	Solid foam	Styrofoam, foam rubber, pumice
Liquid in gas	Liquid aerosol	Fog, clouds
Liquid in liquid	Emulsion	Milk, vinegar in oil salad dressing, mayonnaise
Liquid in solid	Solid emulsion	Cheese, opals, jellies
Solid in gas	Solid aerosol	Smoke, dust in air
Solid in liquid	Sol	India ink, gold sol
Solid in solid	Solid sol	Tire rubber, certain gems (for example, rubies)

a colloidal particle can be up to a billion ($10^3 \times 10^3 \times 10^3 = 10^9$) times greater than that of a solution particle.

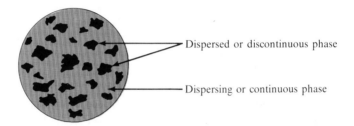

Colloids are mixtures in which one component, the *dispersed phase*, exists as discrete particles in the other component, the *dispersing phase* or *dispersing medium*. The components of a colloidal dispersion are also sometimes called the *discontinuous phase* and the *continuous phase*. Each component, or phase, can exist as a solid, a liquid, or a gas. The components cannot be mutually soluble, nor can both phases of the dispersion be gases, because such conditions would result in an ordinary solution. Hence only eight types of colloidal dispersions, based on the possible physical states of the phases, are known. The eight types, with specific examples, are listed in Table 15.6.

15.13 Preparation of Colloids

Colloidal dispersions can be prepared by two methods: (1) *dispersion*, the breaking down of larger particles to colloidal size, and (2) *condensation*, the formation of colloidal particles from solutions.

Homogenized milk is a good example of a colloid prepared by dispersion. Milk, as drawn from the cow, is an unstable emulsion of fat in water. The fat globules are so large that they rise and form a cream layer in a few hours. To avoid separation of the cream, the milk is homogenized by pumping it through very small holes, or orifices, at high pressure. The violent shearing action of this treatment breaks the fat globules into particles well within the colloidal size range. The butterfat in homogenized milk remains dispersed indefinitely. Colloid mills, which reduce particles to colloidal size by grinding or shearing, are used in preparing many commercial products such as paints, cosmetics, and salad dressings.

The preparation of colloids by condensation frequently involves a precipitation reaction in a dilute solution. For example, a good colloidal sulfur sol can be made by bubbling hydrogen sulfide into a solution of sulfur dioxide. Solid sulfur is formed and dispersed as a colloid:

$$SO_2 + 2\,H_2S \longrightarrow \underset{\substack{\text{Colloidal} \\ \text{sulfur}}}{3\,S} + 2\,H_2O$$

A colloidal dispersion is also easily made by adding iron(III) chloride solution to boiling water. The reddish-brown colloidal dispersion that is formed probably consists of iron(III) hydroxide and hydrated iron(III) oxide:

$$FeCl_3 + 3\,HOH \longrightarrow Fe(OH)_3 + 3\,HCl$$

$$Fe(OH)_3 \xrightarrow{H_2O} Fe_2O_3 \cdot x\,H_2O$$

A great many products for home use (insecticides, insect repellents, and deodorants, to name a few) are packaged as aerosols. The active ingredient, either a liquid or a solid, is dissolved in a liquefied gas and sealed under pressure in a container fitted with a release valve. When this valve is opened, the pressurized solution is ejected. The liquefied gas vaporizes, and the active ingredient is converted to a colloidal aerosol almost instantaneously.

15.14   Properties of Colloids

In 1827 Robert Brown (1773–1858), while observing a strongly illuminated aqueous suspension of pollen under a high-powered microscope, noted that the pollen grains appeared to have a trembling, erratic motion. He determined later that this erratic motion was not confined to pollen but was characteristic of colloidal particles in general. The random motion of colloidal particles, first reported by Brown, is called **Brownian movement.** It is readily observed in cigarette smoke. The smoke is confined in a small transparent chamber and is illuminated with a strong beam of light at right angles to the optical axis of the microscope. The smoke particles appear as tiny randomly moving lights, because the light is reflected from their surfaces. This motion is due to the continual bombardment of the smoke particles by air molecules. Since Brownian movement can be seen when colloidal particles are dispersed in either a gaseous or a liquid medium, it affords nearly direct visual proof that matter at the molecular level actually is moving randomly, as postulated by the Kinetic-Molecular Theory.

Brownian movement

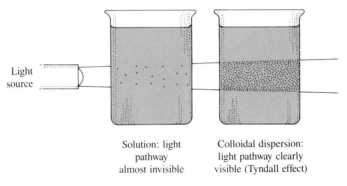

Solution: light pathway almost invisible

Colloidal dispersion: light pathway clearly visible (Tyndall effect)

Figure 15.8   The Tyndall effect

When an intense beam of light is passed through an ordinary solution and is viewed at an angle, the beam passing through the solution is hardly visible. A beam of light, however, is clearly visible and sharply outlined when it is passed through a colloidal dispersion (see Figure 15.8). This phenomenon is known as the **Tyndall effect.** It was first described by Michael Faraday in 1857 and later amplified by John Tyndall. The Tyndall effect, like the Brownian movement, can be observed in nearly all colloidal dispersions. It occurs because the colloidal particles are large enough to scatter the rays of visible light. The ions or molecules of true solutions are too small to scatter light and, therefore, do not exhibit a noticeable Tyndall effect.

Tyndall effect

Another important characteristic of colloids is that the particles have relatively huge surface areas. We saw in Section 14.6 that the surface area is increased tenfold when a 1 cm cube is divided into 1000 cubes with sides of 0.1 cm. When a 1 cm cube is divided into colloidal-size cubes measuring 10^{-6} cm, the combined surface area of all the particles becomes a million times greater than that of the original cube.

Colloidal particles become electrically charged when they adsorb ions on their surfaces. This property is directly related to the large surface area presented by the many tiny particles. Adsorption occurs because the atoms or ions at the surface of a particle are not completely surrounded by other atoms or ions as are those in the interior. Consequently these surface atoms or ions attract and adsorb ions or polar molecules from the dispersion medium onto the surfaces of the colloidal particles. The particles in a given dispersion tend to adsorb only ions having one kind of charge. For example, cations are primarily adsorbed on iron(III) hydroxide sol, resulting in positively charged colloidal particles. On the other hand, the particles of an arsenic(III) sulfide (As_2S_3) sol primarily adsorb anions, resulting in negatively charged colloidal particles. The properties of true solutions, colloidal dispersions, and mechanical suspensions are summarized and compared in Table 15.7.

Adsorption should not be confused with *absorption*. Adsorption refers to the adhesion of molecules or ions to a surface, whereas absorption refers to the taking in of one material by another material.

Table 15.7 Comparison of the properties of true solutions, colloidal dispersions, and suspensions

	Particle size (nm)	Ability to pass through filter paper	Ability to pass through parch-ment	Exhibits Tyndall effect	Exhibits Brownian move-ment	Settles out on standing	Appearance
True solution	<1	Yes	Yes	No	No	No	Transparent, homogeneous
Colloidal dispersion	1–1000	Yes	No	Yes	Yes	Generally does not	Usually not transparent, but may appear to be homogeneous
Suspension	>1000	No	No	—	No	Yes	Not transparent, heterogeneous

15.15 Stability of Colloids

The stability of different dispersions varies with the properties of the dispersed and dispersing phases. We have noted that nonhomogenized milk is a colloid, yet it will separate after standing for a few hours. However, the particles of a good colloidal dispersion will remain in suspension indefinitely. As a case in point, a ruby-red gold sol has been kept in the British Museum for more than a century without noticeable settling. (This specimen is kept for historical interest; it was prepared by Michael Faraday.) The particles of a specific colloid remain dispersed for two reasons: (1) They are bombarded by the molecules of the dispersing phase, which keeps the particles in motion (Brownian movement) so that gravity does not cause them to settle out; (2) since the colloidal particles have the same kind of electrical charge, they repel each other. This mutual repulsion prevents the dispersed particles from coalescing to larger particles, which would settle out of suspension.

In certain types of colloids, the presence of a material known as a protective colloid is necessary for stability. Egg yolk, for example, acts as a stabilizer, or protective colloid, in mayonnaise. The yolk adsorbs on the surfaces of the oil particles and prevents them from coalescing.

15.16 Applications of Colloidal Properties

Activated charcoal has an enormous surface area, approximately 1 million square centimeters per gram in some samples. Hence, charcoal is very effective in selectively adsorbing the polar molecules of some poisonous gases and is used in gas masks. Charcoal can be used to adsorb impurities from liquids as well as from gases, and large amounts are used to remove substances that have objectionable tastes and odors from water supplies. In sugar refineries activated charcoal is used to adsorb colored impurities from the raw sugar solutions.

The Cottrell process is widely used for dust and smoke control in many urban and industrial areas. This process, devised by an American, Frederick Cottrell (1877–1948), takes advantage of the fact that the particulate matter in dust and smoke is electrically charged. Air to be cleaned of dust or smoke is passed between electrode plates charged with a high voltage. Positively charged particles are attracted to, neutralized, and thereby precipitated at the negative electrodes. Negatively charged particles are removed in the same fashion at the positive electrodes. Large Cottrell units are fitted with devices for automatic removal of precipitated material. In some installations, particularly at cement mills and smelters, the value of the dust collected may be sufficient to pay for the precipitation equipment. Small units, designed for removing dust and pollen from air in the home, are now on the market. Unfortunately, Cottrell units remove only particulate matter; they cannot remove gaseous pollutants such as carbon monoxide, sulfur dioxide, and nitrogen oxides.

Thomas Graham found that a parchment membrane would allow the passage of true solutions but would prevent the passage of colloidal dispersions. Dissolved solutes can be removed from colloidal dispersions through the use of **dialysis** such a membrane by a process called **dialysis.** The membrane itself is called a *dialyzing membrane.* Many animal membranes can act as dialyzing membranes. Artificial membranes are made from such materials as parchment paper, collodion, or certain kinds of cellophane. Dialysis can be demonstrated by putting a colloidal starch dispersion and some copper(II) sulfate solution in a parchment paper bag and suspending it in running water. In a few hours the blue color of the copper(II) sulfate has disappeared, and only the starch dispersion remains in the bag.

An interesting application of dialysis has been the development of artificial kidneys. These devices are dialyzing units that are able to act as kidneys by removing soluble waste products from the blood. The blood of a patient suffering from partial kidney failure is passed through the artificial kidney machine for several hours. During passage through the machine, the soluble waste products are removed by dialysis.

QUESTIONS

A. *Review the meanings of the new terms introduced in this chapter.*

1. Hydronium ion
2. Amphoteric
3. Electrolyte
4. Nonelectrolyte
5. Dissociation
6. Ionization
7. Strong electrolyte
8. Weak electrolyte
9. pH
10. Neutralization
11. Spectator ions
12. Titration
13. Un-ionized equation
14. Total ionic equation
15. Net ionic equation
16. Colloid
17. Brownian movement
18. Tyndall effect
19. Dialysis

B. *Information useful in answering the following questions will be found in the tables and figures.*

1. Since a hydrogen ion and a proton are identical, what differences exist between the Arrhenius and Brønsted–Lowry definitions of an acid? (See Table 15.1.)
2. According to Figure 15.1, what type of substance must be in solution in order for the bulb to light?
3. Which of the following classes of compounds are electrolytes: acids, alcohols, bases, salts? (See Table 15.2.)
4. What two differences are apparent in the

arrangement of water molecules about the hydrated sodium and chloride ions as depicted in Figure 15.2?

5. The pH of a solution with a hydrogen ion concentration of 0.003 M is between what two whole numbers? (See Table 15.4.)

6. Which is the more acidic, tomato juice or blood? (See Table 15.5.)

C. *Review questions*

1. Using each of the three acid–base theories (Arrhenius, Brønsted–Lowry, and Lewis), define an acid and a base.

2. For each of the acid–base theories referred to in Question 1, write an equation illustrating the neutralization of an acid with a base.

3. Identify the conjugate acid–base pairs in the following equations:
   (a) $HCl + NH_3 \longrightarrow NH_4^+ + Cl^-$
   (b) $HCO_3^- + OH^- \rightleftharpoons CO_3^{2-} + H_2O$
   (c) $HCO_3^- + H_3O^+ \rightleftharpoons H_2CO_3 + H_2O$
   (d) $HC_2H_3O_2 + H_2O \rightleftharpoons H_3O^+ + C_2H_3O_2^-$
   (e) $HC_2H_3O_2 + H_2SO_4 \rightleftharpoons$
   $$H_2C_2H_3O_2^+ + HSO_4^-$$
   (f) The two-step ionization of sulfuric acid,
   $$H_2SO_4 + H_2O \longrightarrow H_3O^+ + HSO_4^-$$
   $$HSO_4^- + H_2O \rightleftharpoons H_3O^+ + SO_4^{2-}$$
   (g) $HClO_4 + H_2O \longrightarrow H_3O^+ + ClO_4^-$
   (h) $CH_3O^- + H_3O^+ \longrightarrow CH_3OH + H_2O$

4. Write the Lewis structure for (a) bromide ion, (b) hydroxide ion, and (c) cyanide ion. Why are these ions considered to be bases according to the Brønsted–Lowry and Lewis acid–base theories?

5. Complete and balance the following equations:
   (a) $Mg(s) + HCl(aq) \longrightarrow$
   (b) $BaO(s) + HBr(aq) \longrightarrow$
   (c) $Al(s) + H_2SO_4(aq) \longrightarrow$
   (d) $Na_2CO_3(aq) + HCl(aq) \longrightarrow$
   (e) $Fe_2O_3(s) + HBr(aq) \longrightarrow$
   (f) $Ca(OH)_2(aq) + H_2CO_3(aq) \longrightarrow$
   (g) $NaOH(aq) + HBr(aq) \longrightarrow$
   (h) $KOH(aq) + HCl(aq) \longrightarrow$
   (i) $Ca(OH)_2(aq) + HI(aq) \longrightarrow$
   (j) $Al(OH)_3(s) + HBr(aq) \longrightarrow$
   (k) $Na_2O(s) + HClO_4(aq) \longrightarrow$
   (l) $LiOH(aq) + FeCl_3(aq) \longrightarrow$
   (m) $NH_4OH(aq) + FeCl_2(aq) \longrightarrow$

6. Into what three classes of compounds do electrolytes generally fall?

7. Which of the following compounds are electrolytes? Consider each substance to be mixed with water.
   (a) HCl
   (b) CO_2
   (c) $CaCl_2$
   (d) $C_{12}H_{22}O_{11}$ (sugar)
   (e) C_3H_7OH (rubbing alcohol)
   (f) CCl_4 (insoluble)
   (g) $NaHCO_3$ (baking soda)
   (h) N_2 (insoluble gas)
   (i) $AgNO_3$
   (j) HCOOH (formic acid)
   (k) RbOH
   (l) K_2CrO_4

8. Name each compound listed in Table 15.3.

9. A solution of HCl in water conducts an electric current, but a solution of HCl in benzene does not. Explain this behavior in terms of ionization and chemical bonding.

10. How do salts exist in their crystalline structure? What occurs when they are dissolved in water?

11. An aqueous methyl alcohol, CH_3OH, solution does not conduct an electric current, but a solution of sodium hydroxide, NaOH, does. What does this information tell us about the OH group in the alcohol?

12. Why does molten sodium chloride conduct electricity?

13. Explain the difference between dissociation of ionic compounds and ionization of molecular compounds.

14. Distinguish between strong and weak electrolytes.

15. Explain why ions are hydrated in aqueous solutions.

16. Indicate, by simple equations, how the following substances dissociate or ionize in water:
   (a) $Cu(NO_3)_2$ (e) NH_2Br
   (b) $HC_2H_3O_2$ (f) K_2SO_4
   (c) HNO_2 (g) $NaClO_3$
   (d) LiOH   (h) K_3PO_4

17. What is the main distinction between water solutions of strong and weak electrolytes?

18. What are the relative concentrations of $H^+(aq)$ and $OH^-(aq)$ in (a) a neutral solution, (b) an acid solution, and (c) a basic solution?

19. Write the net ionic equation for the reaction of an acid with a base in an aqueous solution.

20. The solubility of hydrogen chloride gas in water, a polar solvent, is much greater than its solubility in benzene, a nonpolar solvent. How can you account for this difference?

21. Pure water, containing both acid and base ions, is neutral. Why?

22. Rewrite the following unbalanced equations, changing them into balanced net ionic equations. All reactions are in water solution.
    (a) $K_2SO_4(aq) + Ba(NO_3)_2(aq) \longrightarrow$
    $$KNO_3(aq) + BaSO_4(s)$$
    (b) $CaCO_3(s) + HCl(aq) \longrightarrow$
    $$CaCl_2(aq) + CO_2(g) + H_2O$$
    (c) $Mg(s) + HC_2H_3O_2(aq) \longrightarrow$
    $$Mg(C_2H_3O_2)_2(aq) + H_2(g)$$
    (d) $H_2S(g) + CdCl_2(aq) \longrightarrow CdS(s) + HCl(aq)$
    (e) $Zn(s) + H_2SO_4(aq) \longrightarrow ZnSO_4(aq) + H_2(g)$
    (f) $AlCl_3(aq) + Na_3PO_4(aq) \longrightarrow$
    $$AlPO_4(s) + NaCl(aq)$$

23. In each of the following pairs, which solution is more acidic? (All are water solutions.)
    (a) 1 M HCl or 1 M H_2SO_4
    (b) 1 M HCl or 1 M $HC_2H_3O_2$
    (c) 1 M HCl or 2 M HCl
    (d) 1 N H_2SO_4 or 1 M H_2SO_4

24. How does a hydronium ion differ from a hydrogen ion?

25. Arrange, in decreasing order of freezing points, 1 molal aqueous solutions of HCl, $HC_2H_3O_2$, $C_{12}H_{22}O_{11}$ (sucrose), and $CaCl_2$. (List the one with the highest freezing point first.)

26. At 100°C the H^+ concentration in water is about 1×10^{-6} mol/L, about 10 times that of water at 25°C. At which of these temperatures is (a) the pH of water the greater, (b) the hydrogen ion (hydronium ion) concentration the higher, and (c) the water neutral?

27. What is the relative difference in H^+ concentration in solutions that differ by 1 pH unit?

28. A 1 molal solution of acetic acid in water freezes at a lower temperature than a 1 molal solution of ethyl alcohol, C_2H_5OH, in water. Explain.

29. At the same cost per pound, which alcohol, CH_3OH or C_2H_5OH, would be more economical to purchase as an antifreeze for your car?

30. Based on the physical states of the dispersed phases, what type of colloidal dispersion cannot exist? Explain.

31. Give brief descriptions of the two general methods for preparing colloidal dispersions.

32. What are the principal reasons that colloidal particles, once dispersed, do not settle out?

33. How does homogenized milk differ physically from nonhomogenized milk?

34. Ozone is a serious air pollutant in some areas. Would a small Cottrell precipitation unit be of value in reducing the ozone concentration in a home in such an area? Explain.

35. Would activated charcoal be more efficient at 0°C or at 100°C in absorbing gaseous hydrogen sulfide? Explain.

36. Which of the following statements are correct?
    (a) The Arrhenius theory of acids and bases is restricted to aqueous solutions.
    (b) The Brønsted–Lowry theory of acids and bases is restricted to solutions other than aqueous solutions.
    (c) All substances that are acids according to the Brønsted–Lowry theory will also be acids by the Lewis theory.
    (d) All substances that are acids according to the Lewis theory will also be acids by the Brønsted–Lowry theory.
    (e) An electron-pair donor is a Lewis acid.
    (f) All Arrhenius acid–base neutralization reactions can be represented by a single net ionic equation.
    (g) When an ionic compound dissolves in water, the ions separate; this process is called ionization.
    (h) In the autoionization of water

    $$2\,H_2O \rightleftharpoons H_3O^+ + OH^-$$

    the H_3O^+ and the OH^- constitute a conjugate acid–base pair.
    (i) In the reaction in part (h), H_2O is both the acid and the base.
    (j) Most common Na, K, and NH_4^+ salts are soluble in water.
    (k) A solution of pH 3 is 100 times more acidic than a solution of pH 5.
    (l) In general, ionic substances when placed in water will give a solution capable of conducting an electric current.
    (m) The terms *dissociation* and *ionization* are synonymous.

(n) A saturated solution may become unsaturated by raising the temperature of the solution.

(o) The terms *strong acid*, *strong base*, *weak acid*, and *weak base* refer to whether an acid or base solution is concentrated or dilute.

(p) pH is defined as the negative logarithm of the molar concentration of H^+ ions (or H_3O^+ ions).

(q) All reactions may be represented by net ionic equations.

(r) One mole of $CaCl_2$ contains more anions than cations.

(s) It is possible to boil seawater at a lower temperature than that required to boil pure water (both at the same pressure).

(t) It is possible to have a neutral aqueous solution whose pH is not 7.

(u) The size of colloidal particles ranges from 1 mm to 1000 mm.

(v) The Tyndall effect is observable in both colloidal and true solutions.

D. *Review problems*

1. Calculate the molarity of the ions present in each of the following salt solutions. Assume each salt to be 100% dissociated.
   (a) 0.015 M NaCl
   (b) 4.25 M NaKSO$_4$
   (c) 0.75 M ZnBr$_2$
   (d) 1.65 M Al$_2$(SO$_4$)$_3$
   (e) 0.20 M CaCl$_2$
   (f) 22.0 g KI in 500 mL of solution
   (g) 900 g (NH$_4$)$_2$SO$_4$ in 20.0 L of solution
   (h) 0.0120 g Mg(ClO$_3$)$_2$ in 1.00 mL of solution

2. In Problem 1, how many grams of each ion would be present in 100 mL of each solution?

3. What is the concentration of Ca^{2+} ions in a solution of CaI$_2$ having an I^- ion concentration of 0.520 M?

4. What is the molar concentration of all ions present in a solution prepared by mixing the following?
   (a) 30.0 mL of 1.0 M NaCl and 40.0 mL of 1.0 M NaCl
   (b) 30.0 mL of 1.0 M HCl and 30.0 mL of 1.0 M NaOH
   (c) 100.0 mL of 2.0 M KCl and 100.0 mL of 1.0 M CaCl$_2$

*(d) 100.0 mL of 0.40 M KOH and 100.0 mL of 0.80 M HCl
(e) 35.0 mL of 0.20 M Ba(OH)$_2$ and 35.0 mL of 0.20 M H$_2$SO$_4$
(f) 1.00 L of 1.0 M AgNO$_3$ and 500 mL of 2.0 M NaCl.
(Neglect the concentration of H^+ and OH^- from water. Also, assume volumes of solutions are additive.)

5. How many milliliters of 0.40 M HCl can be made by diluting 100 mL of 12 M HCl with water?

6. Given the data for the following six titrations, calculate the molarity of the HCl in titrations (a), (b), and (c), and the molarity of the NaOH in titrations (d), (e), and (f).

	mL HCl	Molarity HCl	mL NaOH	Molarity NaOH
(a)	40.13	M HCl	37.70	0.728
(b)	19.00	M HCl	33.66	0.306
(c)	27.25	M HCl	18.00	0.555
(d)	37.19	0.126	31.91	M NaOH
(e)	48.04	0.482	24.02	M NaOH
(f)	13.13	1.425	39.39	M NaOH

7. If 29.26 mL of 0.430 M HCl neutralize 20.40 mL of Ba(OH)$_2$ solution, what is the molarity of the Ba(OH)$_2$ solution? The reaction is

$$Ba(OH)_2(aq) + 2\ HCl(aq) \longrightarrow$$
$$BaCl_2(aq) + 2\ H_2O$$

8. What volume (in milliliters) of 0.245 M HCl will neutralize (a) 50.0 mL of 0.100 M Ca(OH)$_2$ and (b) 10.0 g of Al(OH)$_3$? The equations are
   (a) $2\ HCl(aq) + Ca(OH)_2(aq) \longrightarrow$
   $$CaCl_2(aq) + 2\ H_2O$$
   (b) $3\ HCl(aq) + Al(OH)_3(s) \longrightarrow$
   $$AlCl_3(aq) + 3\ H_2O$$

9. A sample of pure sodium carbonate weighing 0.452 g was dissolved in water and neutralized with 42.4 mL of hydrochloric acid. Calculate the molarity of the acid:

$$Na_2CO_3(aq) + 2\ HCl(aq) \longrightarrow$$
$$2\ NaCl(aq) + CO_2(g) + H_2O$$

10. What volume (mL) of 0.1234 M HCl is needed to neutralize 2.00 g of Ca(OH)$_2$?

11. How many grams of KOH are required to neutralize 50.00 mL of 0.240 M HNO_3?

*12. A 0.200 g sample of impure NaOH requires 18.25 mL of 0.2406 M HCl for neutralization. What is the weight percent of NaOH in the sample?

*13. A batch of sodium hydroxide was found to contain sodium chloride as an impurity. To determine the amount of impurity, a 1.00 g sample was analyzed and found to require 49.90 mL of 0.466 M HCl for neutralization. What is the percentage of NaCl in the sample?

*14. What volume of H_2 gas, measured at 27°C and 700 torr pressure, can be obtained by reacting 5.00 g of zinc metal with (a) 100 mL of 0.350 M HCl and (b) 200 mL of 0.350 M HCl? The equation is

$$Zn(s) + 2\,HCl(aq) \longrightarrow ZnCl_2(aq) + H_2(g)$$

15. Calculate the pH of solutions having the following H^+ ion concentrations:
   (a) 0.01 M   (d) 1×10^{-7} M
   (b) 1.0 M   (e) 0.50 M
   (c) 6.5×10^{-9} M   (f) 0.00010 M

16. Calculate the pH of the following:
   (a) Orange juice, 3.7×10^{-4} M H^+
   (b) Vinegar, 2.8×10^{-3} M H^+
   (c) Black coffee, 5.0×10^{-5} M H^+
   (d) Limewater, 3.4×10^{-11} M H^+

17. Two drops (0.1 mL) of 1.0 M HCl are added to water to make 1.0 L of solution. What is the pH of this solution if the HCl is 100% ionized?

18. What volume of concentrated (18.0 M) sulfuric acid must be used to prepare 50.0 L of 5.00 M solution?

19. Three (3.0) grams of NaOH are added to 500 mL of 0.10 M HCl. Will the resulting solution be acidic or basic? Show evidence for your answer.

20. A 10.00 mL sample of base solution requires 28.92 mL of 0.1240 N H_2SO_4 for neutralization. What is the normality of the base?

21. How many milliliters of 0.325 N HNO_3 are required to neutralize 32.8 mL of 0.225 N NaOH?

22. How many milliliters of 0.325 N H_2SO_4 are required to neutralize 32.8 mL of 0.225 N NaOH?

23. What is the normality and the molarity of a 25.00 mL sample of H_3PO_4 solution that requires 22.68 mL of 0.5000 N NaOH for complete neutralization?

24. What is (a) the weight-percent, (b) the molarity, and (c) the molality of 125 mL of an aqueous solution containing 29.4 g $CaCl_2$ and having a density of 1.178 g/mL?

16

Chemical Equilibrium

After studying Chapter 16, you should be able to

1. Understand the new terms listed in Question A at the end of the chapter.
2. Describe a reversible reaction.
3. Explain why the rate of the forward reaction decreases and the rate of the reverse reaction increases as a chemical reaction approaches equilibrium.
4. State and understand the qualitative effect of Le Châtelier's principle.
5. Predict how the rate of a chemical reaction is affected by (a) changes in concentration of reactants, (b) changes in pressure on gaseous reactants, (c) changes in temperature, and (d) the presence of a catalyst.
6. Write the equilibrium constant expression for a chemical reaction from a balanced equation.
7. Explain the meaning of the numerical value of an equilibrium constant relative to the amounts of reactants and products in equilibrium.
8. Calculate the equilibrium constant, K_{eq}, when given the concentration of reactants and products in equilibrium.
9. Calculate the concentration of one substance in an equilibrium when given the equilibrium constant and the concentrations of all the other substances.
10. Calculate the ionization constant for a weak acid from appropriate data.
11. Calculate the concentrations of all the chemical species in a solution of a weak acid when given the percent ionization or the ionization constant.
12. Compare the relative strengths of acids by using their ionization constants.
13. Use the ion product constant for water, K_w, to calculate $[H^+]$, $[OH^-]$, pH, and pOH when given any one of these quantities.

14. Calculate the solubility product constant, K_{sp}, of a slightly soluble salt when given its solubility, or vice versa.
15. Compare the relative solubilities of salts when given their solubility products.
16. Discuss the common ion effect on a system in equilibrium.
17. Explain hydrolysis and why some salts form acidic or basic aqueous solutions.
18. Explain how a buffer solution is able to counteract the addition of small amounts of either H^+ or OH^- ions.
19. Draw the relative energy diagram of a reaction in terms of activation energy, exothermic or endothermic reaction, and the effect of a catalyst.

16.1 Reversible Reactions

In the preceding chapters we have treated chemical reactions mainly as reactants going to products. However, many reactions do not go to completion. Some reactions do not go to completion because they are reversible; that is, when the products are formed, they react to produce the starting reactants.

We have encountered reversible systems before. One is the vaporization of a liquid by heating and its subsequent condensation by cooling:

$$\text{Liquid} + \text{Heat} \longrightarrow \text{Vapor}$$

$$\text{Vapor} + \text{Cooling} \longrightarrow \text{Liquid} \quad \text{(removal of heat energy)}$$

The interconversion of nitrogen dioxide (NO_2) and dinitrogen tetroxide (N_2O_4) offers visible evidence of the reversibility of a reaction. NO_2 is a reddish-brown gas that changes, with cooling, to N_2O_4, a yellow liquid that boils at 21.2°C, and then to a colorless solid (N_2O_4) that melts at −11.2°C. The reaction is reversible by heating N_2O_4:

$$2\ NO_2(g) \xrightarrow{\text{Cooling}} N_2O_4(l)$$
$$N_2O_4(l) \xrightarrow{\text{Heating}} 2\ NO_2(g)$$

These two reactions may be represented by a single equation with a double arrow, $\rightleftarrows$, to indicate that the reactions are taking place in both directions at the same time:

$$2\ NO_2(g) \rightleftharpoons N_2O_4(l)$$

This reversible reaction can be demonstrated by sealing samples of NO_2 in two tubes and placing one tube in warm water and the other in ice water (see Figure 16.1). Heating promotes disorder or randomness in a system, so we would expect more NO_2, a gas, to be present at higher temperatures.

reversible chemical reaction

A **reversible chemical reaction** is one in which the products formed react to produce the original reactants. Both the forward and reverse reactions occur simultaneously. The forward reaction is called *the reaction to the right*, and the

Figure 16.1 Reversible reaction of nitrogen dioxide (NO_2) and dinitrogen tetroxide (N_2O_4): More of the reddish-brown NO_2 molecules are visible in the tube that is heated than in the tube that is cooled.

0°C   80°C

$$N_2O_4 \underset{\text{Cooling}}{\overset{\text{Heating}}{\rightleftarrows}} 2\,NO_2$$

reverse reaction is called *the reaction to the left*. A double arrow is used in the equation to indicate that the reaction is reversible.

16.2   Rates of Reaction

chemical kinetics

Every reaction has a rate, or speed, at which it proceeds. Some are fast and some are extremely slow. The study of reaction rates and reaction mechanisms is known as **chemical kinetics.**

The rate of a reaction is variable and depends on the concentration of the reacting species, the temperature, the presence or absence of catalytic agents, and the nature of the reactants. Consider the hypothetical reaction

$A + B \longrightarrow C + D$ (forward reaction)

$C + D \longrightarrow A + B$ (reverse reaction)

in which a collision between A and B is necessary for a reaction to occur. The rate at which A and B react depends on the concentration or the number of A and B molecules present; it will be fastest, for a fixed set of conditions, when they are first mixed. As the reaction proceeds, the number of A and B molecules available for reaction decreases, and the rate of reaction slows down. If the reaction is reversible, the speed of the reverse reaction is zero at first and gradually increases as the concentrations of C and D increase. As the number of A and B molecules decreases, the forward rate slows down because A and B cannot find one another as often in order to accomplish a reaction. To counteract this diminishing rate of reaction, an excess of one reagent is often used to keep the reaction from becoming impractically slow. Collisions between molecules may be likened to the scooters or "dodge'ems" at amusement parks. When many cars are on the floor, collisions occur frequently; but if only a few cars are present, collisions can usually be avoided.

16.3   Chemical Equilibrium

equilibrium

Any system at **equilibrium** represents a dynamic state in which two or more opposing processes are taking place at the same time and at the same rate. A

chemical equilibrium

chemical equilibrium is a dynamic system in which two or more opposing chemical reactions are going on at the same time and at the same rate. When the rate of the forward reaction is exactly equal to the rate of the reverse reaction, a condition of **chemical equilibrium** exists (see Figure 16.2). The concentrations of the products and the reactants are not changing, and the system appears to be at a standstill because the products are reacting at the same rate at which they are being formed.

> **Chemical equilibrium:**
> **Rate of forward reaction = Rate of reverse reaction**

A saturated salt solution is in a condition of equilibrium:

$$NaCl(s) \rightleftharpoons Na^+(aq) + Cl^-(aq)$$

At equilibrium, salt crystals are continuously dissolving, and Na^+ and Cl^- ions are continuously crystallizing. Both processes are occurring at the same rate.

The ionization of weak electrolytes is another common chemical equilibrium system:

$$HC_2H_3O_2(aq) + H_2O(l) \rightleftharpoons H_3O^+(aq) + C_2H_3O_2^-(aq)$$

In this reaction, the equilibrium is established in a 1 M solution when the forward reaction has gone about 1%; that is, when only 1% of the acetic acid molecules in solution have ionized. Therefore, only a relatively few ions are

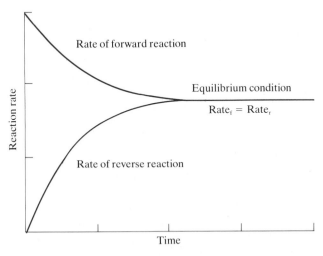

Figure 16.2 The graph illustrates that the rates of the forward and reverse reactions become equal at some point in time. The forward reaction rate decreases as a result of decreasing amounts of reactants. The reverse reaction rate starts at zero and increases as the amount of product increases. When the two rates become equal, a state of chemical equilibrium has been reached.

present, and the acid behaves as a weak electrolyte. In any acid–base equilibrium system, the position of equilibrium is toward the weaker conjugate acid and base. In the ionization of acetic acid, $HC_2H_3O_2$ is a weaker acid than H_3O^+, and H_2O is a weaker base than $C_2H_3O_2^-$.

The reactions represented by

$$H_2(g) + I_2(g) \rightleftharpoons 2\,HI(g)$$

$K_e = \dfrac{[HI]^2}{[H_2][I_2]}$

provide another example of a chemical equilibrium. Theoretically, 1.00 mol of hydrogen should react with 1.00 mol of iodine to yield 2.00 mol of hydrogen iodide. Actually, when 1.00 mol of H_2 and 1.00 mol of I_2 are reacted at 700 K, only 1.58 mol of HI are present when equilibrium is attained. Since 1.58 is 79% of the theoretical yield of 2.00 mol of HI, the forward reaction is only 79% complete at equilibrium. The equilibrium mixture will also contain 0.21 mol each of unreacted H_2 and I_2 (1.00 mol − 0.79 mol = 0.21 mol).

$$\begin{array}{ccc} H_2 & + & I_2 \xrightarrow{\;700\text{ K}\;} 2\,HI \\ 1.00 & & 1.00 \qquad\qquad 2.00 \\ \text{mol} & & \text{mol} \qquad\qquad \text{mol} \end{array}$$
(This equation would represent the condition if the reaction were 100% complete; 2.00 mol of HI would be formed and no H_2 and I_2 would be left unreacted.)

$$\begin{array}{ccc} H_2 & + & I_2 \xrightleftharpoons{\;700\text{ K}\;} 2\,HI \\ 0.21 & & 0.21 \qquad\qquad 1.58 \\ \text{mol} & & \text{mol} \qquad\qquad \text{mol} \end{array}$$
(This equation represents the actual equilibrium attained starting with 1.00 mol each of H_2 and I_2. It shows that the forward reaction is only 79% complete.)

16.4   Le Châtelier's Principle

Le Châtelier's principle

In 1888 the French chemist Henri Le Châtelier (1850–1936) set forth a simple, far-reaching generalization on the behavior of equilibrium systems. This generalization, known as **Le Châtelier's principle,** states: If a stress is applied to a system in equilibrium, the system will respond in such a way as to relieve that stress and restore equilibrium under a new set of conditions. The application of Le Châtelier's principle helps us to predict the effect of changing conditions in chemical reactions. We will examine the effect of changes in concentration, temperature, and pressure.

16.5   Effect of Concentration on Reaction Rate and Equilibrium

The way in which the rate of a chemical reaction depends on the concentration of the reactants must be determined experimentally. Many simple, one-step reactions result from a collision between two molecules or ions. The rate of such one-step reactions can be altered by changing the concentration of the reactants or products. An increase in concentration of the reactants provides more individual reacting species for collisions and results in an increase in the rate of reaction.

An equilibrium is disturbed when the concentration of one or more of its components is changed. As a result the concentration of all the species will change, and a new equilibrium mixture will be established. Consider the hypothetical equilibrium represented by the equation

$$A + B \rightleftharpoons C + D$$

where A and B react in one step to form C and D. When the concentration of B is increased, the following occurs:

1. The rate of the reaction to the right (forward) increases. This rate is proportional to the concentration of A times the concentration of B.
2. The rate to the right becomes greater than the rate to the left.
3. Reactants A and B are used faster than they are produced; C and D are produced faster than they are used.
4. After a period of time, rates to the right and left become equal, and the system is again in equilibrium.
5. In the new equilibrium the concentration of A is less and the concentrations of B, C, and D are greater than in the original equilibrium.

Conclusion: The equilibrium has shifted to the right.

Applying this change in concentration to the equilibrium mixture of 1.00 mol of hydrogen and 1.00 mol of iodine from Section 16.3, we find that, when an additional 0.20 mol of I_2 is added, the yield of HI (based on H_2) is 85% (1.70 mol) instead of 79%. A comparision of the two systems, after the new equilibrium mixture is reached, follows.

Original equilibrium	*New equilibrium*
1.00 mol H_2 + 1.00 mol I_2	1.00 mol H_2 + 1.20 mol I_2
Yield: 79% HI	Yield: 85% HI (based on H_2)
Equilibrium mixture contains:	Equilibrium mixture contains:
1.58 mol HI	1.70 mol HI
0.21 mol H_2	0.15 mol H_2
0.21 mol I_2	0.35 mol I_2

Analyzing this new system, we see that, when the 0.20 mol I_2 was added, the equilibrium shifted to the right in order to counteract the increase in I_2 concentration. Some of the H_2 reacted with added I_2 and produced more HI, until an equilibrium mixture was established again. When I_2 was added, the concentration of I_2 increased, the concentration of H_2 decreased, and the concentration of HI increased. What do you think would be the effects of adding (a) more H_2 or (b) more HI?

The equation

$$Fe^{3+}(aq) + SCN^-(aq) \rightleftharpoons Fe(SCN)^{2+}(aq)$$

Pale yellow   Colorless   Red

represents an equilibrium that is used in certain analytical procedures as an indicator because of the readily visible, intense red color of the complex $Fe(SCN)^{2+}$ ion. A very dilute solution of iron(III), Fe^{3+}, and thiocyanate, SCN^-, is light red. When the concentration of either Fe^{3+} or SCN^- is increased, the equilibrium shift to the right is observed by an increase in the intensity of the color, resulting from the formation of additional $Fe(SCN)^{2+}$.

If either Fe^{3+} or SCN^- is removed from solution, the equilibrium will shift to the left, and the solution will become lighter in color. When Ag^+ is added to the solution, a white precipitate of silver thiocyanate (AgSCN) is formed, thus removing SCN^- ion from the equilibrium.

$$Ag^+(aq) + SCN^-(aq) \rightleftharpoons AgSCN(s)$$

The system accordingly responds to counteract the change in SCN^- concentration by shifting the equilibrium to the left. This shift is evident by a decrease in the intensity of the red color due to a decreased concentration of $Fe(SCN)^{2+}$.

Let us now consider the effect of changing the concentrations in the equilibrium mixture of chlorine water. The equilibrium equation is

$$Cl_2(aq) + 2\,H_2O \rightleftharpoons HOCl(aq) + H_3O^+(aq) + Cl^-(aq)$$

The variation in concentrations and the equilibrium shifts are tabulated in the following table. An X in the second or third column indicates the reagent that is increased or decreased. The fourth column indicates the direction of the equilibrium shift.

	Concentration		
Reagent	**Increase**	**Decrease**	**Equilibrium shift**
Cl_2	—	X	Left
H_2O	X	—	Right
HOCl	X	—	Left
H_3O^+	—	X	Right
Cl^-	X	—	Left

Consider the equilibrium in a 0.100 M acetic acid solution:

$$HC_2H_3O_2 + H_2O \rightleftharpoons H_3O^+ + C_2H_3O_2^-$$

In this solution the concentration of the hydronium ion (H_3O^+), which is a measure of the acidity, is 1.34×10^{-3} mol/L, corresponding to a pH of 2.87. What will happen to the acidity when 0.100 mol of sodium acetate ($NaC_2H_3O_2$) is added to 1 L of 0.100 M $HC_2H_3O_2$? When $NaC_2H_3O_2$ dissolves, it dissociates into sodium ions (Na^+) and acetate ions ($C_2H_3O_2^-$). The acetate ion from the salt is a common ion to the acetic acid equilibrium system and increases the total acetate ion concentration in the solution. As a result the equilibrium shifts to the left, decreasing the hydronium ion concentration and lowering the acidity of the solution. Evidence of this decrease in acidity is shown by the fact that the pH of a solution that is 0.100 M in $HC_2H_3O_2$ and 0.100 M in $NaC_2H_3O_2$ is 4.74. The pH of several different solutions of $HC_2H_3O_2$ and $NaC_2H_3O_2$ is shown in the table that follows. Each time the acetate ion is increased, the pH increases, indicating a further shift in the equilibrium toward un-ionized acetic acid.

Solution	pH
1 L 0.100 M $HC_2H_3O_2$	2.87
1 L 0.100 M $HC_2H_3O_2$ + 0.100 mol $NaC_2H_3O_2$	4.74
1 L 0.100 M $HC_2H_3O_2$ + 0.200 mol $NaC_2H_3O_2$	5.05
1 L 0.100 M $HC_2H_3O_2$ + 0.300 mol $NaC_2H_3O_2$	5.23

learn

In summary, we can say that, when the concentration of a reagent on the left side of an equation is increased, the equilibrium shifts to the right. When the concentration of a reagent on the right side of an equation is increased, the equilibrium shifts to the left. In accordance with Le Châtelier's principle, the equilibrium always shifts in the direction that tends to reduce the concentration of the added reactant.

16.6   Effect of Pressure on Reaction Rate and Equilibrium

Changes in pressure significantly affect the reaction rate only when one or more of the reactants or products is a gas. In these cases the effect of increasing the pressure of the reacting gases is equivalent to increasing their concentrations. In the reaction

$$CaCO_3(s) \xrightarrow{\Delta} CaO(s) + CO_2(g)$$

calcium carbonate decomposes into calcium oxide and carbon dioxide when heated above 825°C. Increasing the pressure of the equilibrium system by adding CO_2 or by decreasing the volume speeds up the reverse reaction and causes the equilibrium to shift to the left. The increased pressure gives the same effect as that caused by increasing the concentration of CO_2, the only gaseous substance in the reaction.

We have seen that, when the pressure on a gas is increased, its volume is decreased. In a system composed entirely of gases, an increase in pressure will cause the reaction and the equilibrium to shift to the side that contains the smaller volume or smaller number of moles. This shift occurs because the increase in pressure is partially relieved by the system's shifting its equilibrium toward the side in which the substances occupy the smaller volume.

Prior to World War I, Fritz Haber (1868–1934) in Germany invented the first major process for the fixation of nitrogen. In the Haber process nitrogen and hydrogen are reacted together in the presence of a catalyst at moderately high temperature and pressure to produce ammonia. The catalyst consists of iron and iron oxide with small amounts of potassium and aluminum oxides. For this process, Haber received the Nobel prize in chemistry in 1918.

$$N_2(g) \;+\; 3\,H_2(g) \rightleftharpoons 2\,NH_3(g) + 92.5 \text{ kJ } (22.1 \text{ kcal}) \quad \text{(at 25°C)}$$

1 mol	3 mol	2 mol
1 volume	3 volume	2 volumes

Table 16.1   The effect of pressure on the conversion of H_2 and N_2 to NH_3 at 450°C. The starting ratio of H_2 to N_2 is 3 moles to 1 mole.

Pressure (atm)	Yield of NH_3(%)	Pressure (atm)	Yield of NH_3(%)
10	2.04	300	35.5
30	5.8	600	53.4
50	9.17	1000	69.4
100	16.4		

The left side of the equation in the Haber process represents four volumes of gas combining to give two volumes of gas on the right side of the equation. An increase in the total pressure on the system shifts the equilibrium to the right. This increase in pressure results in a higher concentration of both reactants and products. The equilibrium shifts to the right when the pressure is increased, because fewer moles of NH_3 than moles of N_2 and H_2 are in the equilibrium reaction.

Ideal conditions for the Haber process are 200°C and 1000 atm pressure. However, at 200°C the rate of reaction is very slow, and at 1000 atm extraordinarily heavy equipment is required. As a compromise the reaction is run at 400–600°C and 200–350 atm pressure, which gives a reasonable yield at a reasonable rate. The effect of pressure on the yield of ammonia at one particular temperature is shown in Table 16.1.

When the total number of gaseous molecules on both sides of an equation is the same, a change in pressure does not cause an equilibrium shift. The following reaction is an example.

$$N_2(g) \quad + \quad O_2(g) \quad \rightleftharpoons \quad 2\,NO(g)$$

1 mol	1 mol	2 mol
1 volume	1 volume	2 volumes
6.022×10^{23}	6.022×10^{23}	$2 \times 6.022 \times 10^{23}$
molecules	molecules	molecules

When the pressure on this system is increased, the rate of both the forward and the reverse reactions will increase because of the higher concentrations of N_2, O_2, and NO. But the equilibrium will not shift, because the increase in concentration of molecules is the same on both sides of the equation and the decrease in volume is the same on both sides of the equation.

PROBLEM

16.1

What effect would an increase in pressure have on the position of equilibrium in the following reactions?

(a) $2\,SO_2(g) + O_2(g) \rightleftharpoons 2\,SO_3(g)$
(b) $H_2(g) + Cl_2(g) \rightleftharpoons 2\,HCl(g)$
(c) $N_2O_4(l) \rightleftharpoons 2\,NO_2(g)$

(a) The equilibrium will shift to the right because the substance on the right has a smaller volume than those on the left.

(b) The equilibrium position will be unaffected because the volumes (or moles) of gases on both sides of the equation are the same.

(c) The equilibrium will shift to the left because $N_2O_4(l)$ occupies a much smaller volume than does $2\ NO_2(g)$.

16.7 Effect of Temperature on Reaction Rate and Equilibrium

An increase in temperature generally increases the rate of reaction. Molecules at elevated temperatures are more energetic and have more kinetic energy; thus, their collisions are more likely to result in a reaction. However, we cannot assume that the rate of a desired reaction will increase indefinitely as the temperature is raised. High temperatures may cause the destruction or decomposition of the reactants and products or may initiate reactions other than the one desired. For example, when calcium oxalate (CaC_2O_4) is heated to 500°C, it decomposes into calcium carbonate and carbon monoxide:

$$CaC_2O_4(s) \xrightarrow{500°C} CaCO_3(s) + CO(g)$$

If calcium oxalate is heated to 850°C, the products are calcium oxide, carbon monoxide, and carbon dioxide:

$$CaC_2O_4(s) \xrightarrow{850°C} CaO(s) + CO(g) + CO_2(g)$$

When heat is applied to a system in equilibrium, the reaction that absorbs heat is favored. When the process, as written, is endothermic, the forward reaction is increased. When the reaction is exothermic, the reverse reaction is favored. In this sense heat may be treated as a reactant in endothermic reactions or as a product in exothermic reactions. Therefore, temperature is analogous to concentration when applying Le Châtelier's principle to heat effects on a chemical reaction.

Hot coke (C) is a very reactive element. In the reaction

$$C(s) + CO_2(g) + heat \rightleftharpoons 2\ CO(g)$$

very little, if any, CO is formed at room temperature. At 1000°C the equilibrium mixture contains about an equal number of moles of CO and CO_2. At higher temperatures the equilibrium shifts to the right, increasing the yield of CO. The reaction is endothermic, and, as can be seen, the equilibrium is shifted to the right at higher temperatures.

Phosphorus trichloride reacts with dry chlorine gas to form phosphorus pentachloride. The reaction is exothermic:

$$PCl_3(l) + Cl_2(g) \rightleftharpoons PCl_5(s) + 88\ kJ\ (21\ kcal)$$

Heat must continuously be removed during the reaction to obtain a good yield of the product. According to Le Châtelier's principle, heat will cause the product, PCl_5, to decompose, re-forming PCl_3 and Cl_2. The equilibrium mixture at 200°C contains 52% PCl_5, and at 300°C it contains 3% PCl_5, verifying that heat causes the equilibrium to shift to the left.

When the temperature of a system is raised, the rate of reaction increases because of increased kinetic energy and more frequent collisions of the reacting species. In a reversible reaction the rate of both the forward and the reverse reactions is increased by an increase in temperature; however, the reaction that absorbs heat increases to a greater extent, and the equilibrium shifts to favor that reaction. The following examples illustrate these effects:

$$4\,HCl(g) + O_2(g) \rightleftharpoons 2\,H_2O(g) + 2\,Cl_2(g) + 95.4\ kJ\ (28.4\ kcal) \tag{1}$$

$$H_2(g) + Cl_2(g) \rightleftharpoons 2\,HCl(g) + 185\ kJ\ (44.2\ kcal) \tag{2}$$

$$CH_4(g) + 2\,O_2(g) \rightleftharpoons CO_2(g) + 2\,H_2O(g) + 890\ kJ\ (212.8\ kcal) \tag{3}$$

$$N_2O_4(l) + 58.6\ kJ\ (14.0\ kcal) \rightleftharpoons 2\,NO_2(g) \tag{4}$$

$$2\,CO_2(g) + 566\ kJ\ (135.2\ kcal) \rightleftharpoons 2\,CO(g) + O_2(g) \tag{5}$$

$$H_2(g) + I_2(g) + 51.9\ kJ\ (12.4\ kcal) \rightleftharpoons 2\,HI(g) \tag{6}$$

Reactions (1), (2), and (3) are exothermic; an increase in temperature will cause the equilibrium to shift to the left. Reactions (4), (5), and (6) are endothermic; an increase in temperature will cause the equilibrium to shift to the right.

16.8   Effect of Catalysts on Reaction Rate and Equilibrium

catalyst

A **catalyst** is a substance that influences the rate of a reaction and can be recovered essentially unchanged at the end of the reaction. A catalyst does not shift the equilibrium of a reaction; it affects only the speed at which the equilibrium is reached. If a catalyst does not affect the equilibrium, then it follows that it must affect the rate of both the forward and the reverse reactions equally.

The reaction between phosphorus trichloride (PCl_3) and sulfur is highly exothermic, but it is so slow that very little product, thiophosphoryl chloride ($PSCl_3$), is obtained, even after prolonged heating. When a catalyst, such as aluminum chloride ($AlCl_3$), is added, the reaction is complete in a few seconds:

$$PCl_3(l) + S(s) \xrightarrow{\ AlCl_3\ } PSCl_3(l)$$

In the laboratory preparation of oxygen, manganese dioxide is used as a catalyst to increase the rates of decomposition of both potassium chlorate and hydrogen peroxide.

$$2\,KClO_3(s) \xrightarrow[\Delta]{\ MnO_2\ } 2\,KCl(s) + 3\,O_2(g)$$

$$2\,H_2O_2(aq) \xrightarrow{\ MnO_2\ } 2\,H_2O(l) + O_2(g)$$

Catalysts are extremely important to industrial chemistry. Hundreds of chemical reactions that are otherwise too slow to be of practical value have been put to commercial use once a suitable catalyst was found. But in the area of biochemistry, catalysts are of supreme importance because nearly all chemical reactions in all forms of life are completely dependent on biochemical catalysts known as *enzymes*.

16.9 Equilibrium Constants

In a reversible chemical reaction at equilibrium, the concentrations of the reactants and products are constant; that is, they are not changing. The rates of the forward and reverse reactions are constant, and an equilibrium constant expression can be written relating the products to the reactants. For the general reaction

$$a\,A + b\,B \rightleftharpoons c\,C + d\,D$$

at constant temperature, the following equilibrium constant expression can be written:

$$K_{eq} = \frac{[C]^c[D]^d}{[A]^a[B]^b}$$

equilibrium constant, K_{eq}

where K_{eq} is constant at a particular temperature and is known as the **equilibrium constant**. The quantities in brackets are the concentrations of each substance in moles per liter. The superscript letters a, b, c, and d are the coefficients of the substances in the balanced equation. The units for K_{eq} are not the same for every equilibrium reaction; however, the units are generally omitted. Observe that the concentration of each substance is raised to a power that is the same as the substance's numerical coefficient in the balanced equation. The convention is to place the concentrations of the products (the substances on the right side of the equation as written) in the numerator and the concentrations of the reactants in the denominator.

PROBLEM

16.2

Write equilibrium constant expressions for

(a) $3\,H_2(g) + N_2(g) \rightleftharpoons 2\,NH_3(g)$
(b) $CO(g) + 2\,H_2(g) \rightleftharpoons CH_3OH(g)$

(a) The only product, NH_3, has a coefficient of 2. Therefore the numerator of the equilibrium constant will be $[NH_3]^2$. Two reactants are present, H_2 with a coefficient of 3 and N_2 with a coefficient of 1. Therefore the denominator will be $[H_2]^3[N_2]$. The equilibrium constant expression is

$$K_{eq} = \frac{[NH_3]^2}{[H_2]^3[N_2]}$$

(b) For this equation the numerator is [CH$_3$OH] and the denominator is [CO][H$_2$]^2. The equilibrium constant expression is

$$K_{eq} = \frac{[CH_3OH]}{[CO][H_2]^2}$$

The magnitude of an equilibrium constant indicates the extent to which the forward and reverse reactions take place. When K_{eq} is greater than 1, the amount of the products at equilibrium is greater than the amount of the reactants. When K_{eq} is less than 1, the amount of reactants at equilibrium is greater than the amount of the products. A very large value for K_{eq} indicates that the forward reaction goes essentially to completion. A very small K_{eq} means that the reverse reaction goes nearly to completion and that the equilibrium is far to the left (toward the reactants). Two examples follow:

$$H_2(g) + I_2(g) \rightleftharpoons 2\ HI(g) \qquad K_{eq} = 54.8 \text{ at } 425°C$$

This K_{eq} indicates that considerably more product than reactants is present at equilibrium.

$$COCl_2(g) \rightleftharpoons CO(g) + Cl_2(g) \qquad K_{eq} = 7.6 \times 10^{-4} \text{ at } 400°C$$

This K_{eq} indicates that COCl$_2$ is stable and that very little decomposition to CO and Cl$_2$ occurs at 400°C. The equilibrium is far to the left.

When the molar concentrations of all the species in an equilibrium reaction are known, the K_{eq} can be calculated by substituting the concentrations into the equilibrium constant expression.

PROBLEM

16.3

Calculate the K_{eq} for the following reaction based on concentrations of: PCl$_5$ = 0.030 mol/L; PCl$_3$ = 0.97 mol/L; Cl$_2$ = 0.97 mol/L at 300°C.

$$PCl_5(g) \rightleftharpoons PCl_3(g) + Cl_2(g)$$

First write the K_{eq} expression; then substitute the respective concentrations into this equation and solve:

$$K_{eq} = \frac{[PCl_3][Cl_2]}{[PCl_5]} = \frac{[0.97][0.97]}{[0.030]} = 31$$

This K_{eq} is considered to be a fairly large value, indicating that at 300°C the decomposition of PCl$_5$ proceeds far to the right.

16.10 **Ionization Constants**

As a first application of an equilibrium constant, let us consider the constant for acetic acid in solution. Because it is a weak acid, an equilibrium is established between molecular HC$_2$H$_3$O$_2$ and its ions in solution. The constant is called the

acid ionization constant, K_a   **acid ionization constant, K_a**, a special type of equilibrium constant. The concentration of water in the solution is large compared to the other concentrations and does not change appreciably, so we may use the following simplified equation to set up the constant:

$$HC_2H_3O_2 \rightleftharpoons H^+ + C_2H_3O_2^-$$

The ionization constant expression is the concentration of the products divided by the concentration of the reactants:

$$K_a = \frac{[H^+][C_2H_3O_2^-]}{[HC_2H_3O_2]}$$

It states that the ionization constant, K_a, is equal to the product of the hydrogen ion $[H^+]$ concentration and the acetate ion $[C_2H_3O_2^-]$ concentration divided by the concentration of the un-ionized acetic acid $[HC_2H_3O_2]$.

At 25°C, a 0.1 M $HC_2H_3O_2$ solution is 1.34% ionized and has a hydrogen ion concentration of 1.34×10^{-3} mol/L. From this information we can calculate the ionization constant for acetic acid.

A 0.10 M solution initially contains 0.10 mol of acetic acid per liter. Of this 0.10 mol, only 1.34%, or 1.34×10^{-3} mol, is ionized, which gives an H^+ ion concentration of 1.34×10^{-3} mol/L. Because each molecule of acid that ionizes yields one H^+ and one $C_2H_3O_2^-$, the concentration of $C_2H_3O_2^-$ ions is also 1.34×10^{-3} mol/L. This ionization leaves $0.10 - 0.00134 = 0.09866$ mol/L of un-ionized acetic acid.

	Initial concentration (mol/L)	*Equilibrium concentration (mol/L)*
$[HC_2H_3O_2]$	0.10	0.09866
$[H^+]$	0	0.00134
$[C_2H_3O_2^-]$	0	0.00134

Substituting these concentrations in the equilibrium expression, we obtain the value for K_a:

$$K_a = \frac{[H^+][C_2H_3O_2^-]}{[HC_2H_3O_2]} = \frac{[1.34 \times 10^{-3}][1.34 \times 10^{-3}]}{[0.09866]} = 1.8 \times 10^{-5}$$

The K_a for acetic acid, 1.8×10^{-5}, is small and indicates that the position of the equilibrium is far toward the un-ionized acetic acid. In fact, a 0.10 M acetic acid solution is 98.66% un-ionized.

Once the K_a for acetic acid is established, it can be used to describe other systems containing H^+, $C_2H_3O_2^-$, and $HC_2H_3O_2$ in equilibrium at 25°C. The ionization constants for several other weak acids are listed in Table 16.2.

PROBLEM

16.4

What is the H^+ ion concentration in a 0.50 M $HC_2H_3O_2$ solution? The ionization constant, K_a, for $HC_2H_3O_2$ is 1.8×10^{-5}.

Table 16.2 Ionization constants (K_a) of weak acids at 25°C

Acid	Formula	K_a
Acetic	$HC_2H_3O_2$	1.8×10^{-5}
Benzoic	$HC_7H_5O_2$	6.3×10^{-5}
Carbolic (phenol)	HC_6H_5O	1.3×10^{-10}
Cyanic	HCNO	2.0×10^{-4}
Formic	$HCHO_2$	1.8×10^{-4}
Hydrocyanic	HCN	4.0×10^{-10}
Hypochlorous	HClO	3.5×10^{-8}
Nitrous	HNO_2	4.5×10^{-4}
Hydrofluoric	HF	6.5×10^{-4}

To solve this problem, first write the equilibrium equation and the K_a expression:

$$HC_2H_3O_2 \rightleftharpoons H^+ + C_2H_3O_2^- \qquad K_a = \frac{[H^+][C_2H_3O_2^-]}{[HC_2H_3O_2]} = 1.8 \times 10^{-5}$$

We know that the initial concentration of $HC_2H_3O_2$ is 0.50 M. We also know from the ionization equation that one $C_2H_3O_2^-$ is produced for every H^+ produced; that is, the $[H^+]$ and the $[C_2H_3O_2^-]$ are equal. To solve, let $Y = [H^+]$, which also equals the $[C_2H_3O_2^-]$. The un-ionized $[HC_2H_3O_2]$ remaining will then be $0.50 - Y$, the starting concentration minus the amount that ionized.

$$[H^+] = [C_2H_3O_2^-] = Y \qquad [HC_2H_3O_2] = 0.50 - Y$$

Substituting these values into the K_a expression, we obtain

$$K_a = \frac{(Y)(Y)}{0.50 - Y} = \frac{Y^2}{0.50 - Y} = 1.8 \times 10^{-5}$$

An exact solution of this equation for Y requires the use of a mathematical equation known as the quadratic equation. However, an approximate solution is obtained if we assume that Y is small and can be neglected compared with 0.50. Then $0.50 - Y$ will be equal to approximately 0.50. The equation now becomes

$$\frac{Y^2}{0.50} = 1.8 \times 10^{-5}$$

$$Y^2 = 0.50 \times 1.8 \times 10^{-5} = 0.90 \times 10^{-5} = 9.0 \times 10^{-6}$$

Taking the square root of both sides of the equation, we obtain

$$Y = \sqrt{9.0 \times 10^{-6}} = 3.0 \times 10^{-3} \text{ mol/L}$$

Thus, $[H^+]$ is approximately 3.0×10^{-3} mol/L in a 0.50 M $HC_2H_3O_2$ solution. The exact solution to this problem, using the quadratic equation, gives a value of 2.99×10^{-3} mol/L for $[H^+]$, showing that we were justified in neglecting Y compared with 0.50.

PROBLEM

16.5

Calculate the percent ionization in a 0.50 M $HC_2H_3O_2$ solution.

The percent ionization of a weak acid, $HA(aq) \rightleftharpoons H^+ + A^-$, is found by dividing the concentration of the H^+ or A^- ions at equilibrium by the initial concentration of HA. For acetic acid

$$\frac{\text{Concentration of } [H^+] \text{ or } [C_2H_3O_2^-]}{\text{Initial concentration of } [HC_2H_3O_2]} \times 100\% = \text{Percent ionized}$$

To solve this problem we first need to calculate $[H^+]$. This calculation has already been done in Problem 16.4 for a 0.50 M solution.

$[H^+] = 3.0 \times 10^{-3}$ mol/L in a 0.50 M solution   (from Problem 16.4)

This $[H^+]$ represents a fractional amount of the initial 0.50 M $HC_2H_3O_2$. Therefore

$$\frac{3.0 \times 10^{-3} \text{ mol/L}}{0.50 \text{ mol/L}} \times 100\% = 0.60\% \text{ ionized}$$

A 0.50 M $HC_2H_3O_2$ solution is 0.60% ionized.

16.11   **Ion Product Constant for Water**

We have seen that water ionizes to a slight degree. This ionization is represented by these equilibrium equations:

$$H_2O + H_2O \rightleftharpoons H_3O^+ + OH^- \tag{7}$$

$$H_2O \rightleftharpoons H^+ + OH^- \tag{8}$$

Equation (7) is the more accurate representation of the equilibrium, since free protons (H^+) do not exist in water. Equation (8) is a simplified and often-used representation of the water equilibrium. The actual concentration of H^+ produced in pure water is very minute and amounts to only 1.00×10^{-7} mol/L at 25°C. In pure water

$$[H^+] = [OH^-] = 1.00 \times 10^{-7} \text{ mol/L}$$

since both ions are produced in equal molar amounts, as shown in equation (8).

The $H_2O \rightleftharpoons H^+ + OH^-$ equilibrium exists in water and in all water solutions. A special equilibrium constant called the **ion product constant for water,** K_w, applies to this equilibrium. The constant K_w is defined as the product of the H^+ ion concentration and the OH^- ion concentration, each in moles per liter:

ion product constant for water, K_w

$$K_w = [H^+][OH^-]$$

The numerical value of K_w is 1.00×10^{-14}, since for pure water at 25°C,

$$K_w = [H^+][OH^-] = [1.00 \times 10^{-7}][1.00 \times 10^{-7}] = 1.00 \times 10^{-14}$$

Table 16.3 Relationship of H^+ and OH^- concentrations in water solutions

$[H^+]$	$[OH^-]$	K_w	pH	pOH
1.00×10^{-2}	1.00×10^{-12}	1.00×10^{-14}	2.00	12.0
1.00×10^{-4}	1.00×10^{-10}	1.00×10^{-14}	4.00	10.0
2.00×10^{-6}	5.00×10^{-9}	1.00×10^{-14}	5.70	8.30
1.00×10^{-7}	1.00×10^{-7}	1.00×10^{-14}	7.00	7.00
1.00×10^{-9}	1.00×10^{-5}	1.00×10^{-14}	9.00	5.00

The value of K_w for all water solutions at 25°C is the constant 1.00×10^{-14}. It is important to realize that, as the concentration of one of these ions, H^+ or OH^-, increases, the other decreases. However, the product of $[H^+]$ and $[OH^-]$ always equals the constant 1.00×10^{-14}. This relationship can be seen in the examples shown in Table 16.3. If the concentration of one ion is known, the concentration of the other can be calculated from the K_w expression.

$$K_w = [H^+][OH^-] \qquad [H^+] = \frac{K_w}{[OH^-]} \qquad [OH^-] = \frac{K_w}{[H^+]}$$

PROBLEM

16.6

What is the concentration of **(a)** H^+ and **(b)** OH^- in a 0.001 M HCl solution? Assume that HCl is 100% ionized.

(a) Since all the HCl is ionized, H^+ = 0.001 mol/L

$$HCl \longrightarrow H^+ + Cl^-$$
0.001 M 0.001 M 0.001 M

$[H^+] = 1 \times 10^{-3}$ mol/L   (Answer)

(b) To calculate the $[OH^-]$ in this solution, use the following equation and substitute the values for K_w and $[H^+]$:

$$[OH^-] = \frac{K_w}{[H^+]}$$

$$[OH^-] = \frac{1.00 \times 10^{-14}}{1 \times 10^{-3}} = 1 \times 10^{-11} \text{ mol/L} \quad \text{(Answer)}$$

PROBLEM

16.7

What is the pH of a 0.010 M NaOH solution? Assume that NaOH is 100% ionized. Since all the NaOH is ionized, OH^- = 0.010 mol/L or 1.0×10^{-2} mol/L:

$$NaOH \longrightarrow Na^+ + OH^-$$
0.010 M 0.010 M 0.010 M

To find the pH of the solution, we first calculate the H^+ concentration. Use the following equation and substitute the values for K_w and $[OH^-]$:

$$[H^+] = \frac{K_w}{[OH^-]} = \frac{1.00 \times 10^{-14}}{1.0 \times 10^{-2}} = 1.0 \times 10^{-12} \text{ mol/L}$$

$$pH = -\log[H^+] = -\log(1 \times 10^{-12}) = 12 \quad \text{(Answer)}$$

Just as pH is used to express the acidity of a solution, pOH is used to express the basicity of an aqueous solution. The pOH is related to the OH^- ion concentration in the same way that the pH is related to the H^+ ion concentration:

$$pOH = \log\frac{1}{[OH^-]} \quad \text{or} \quad pOH = -\log[OH^-]$$

Thus, a solution in which $[OH^-] = 1.0 \times 10^{-2}$, as in Problem 16.7, will have pOH = 2.0.

In pure water, where $[H^+] = 1 \times 10^{-7}$ and $[OH^-] = 1 \times 10^{-7}$, the pH is 7, and the pOH is 7. The sum of the pH and pOH is always 14.

$$pH + pOH = 14$$

In Problem 16.7 the pH can also be found by first calculating the pOH (2) from the OH^- ion concentration and then subtracting from 14:

$$pH = 14 - pOH = 14 - 2 = 12$$

This relationship holds for all aqueous solutions, as can be seen in Table 16.3.

16.12 Solubility Product Constant

solubility product constant, K_{sp}

The **solubility product constant,** abbreviated K_{sp}, is another application of the equilibrium constant. It is the equilibrium constant of a slightly soluble salt. The following example illustrates how K_{sp} is evaluated.

The solubility of silver chloride (AgCl) in water is 1.3×10^{-5} mol/L at 25°C. The equation for the equilibrium between AgCl and its ions in solution is

$$AgCl(s) \rightleftharpoons Ag^+ + Cl^-$$

The equilibrium constant expression is

$$K_{eq} = \frac{[Ag^+][Cl^-]}{[AgCl(s)]}$$

The amount of solid AgCl does not affect the equilibrium system provided that some is present. In other words, the concentration of solid silver chloride is constant whether 1 mg or 10 g of the salt are present. Therefore, the product obtained by multiplying the two constants K_{eq} and $[AgCl(s)]$ is also a constant. This constant is the solubility product constant, K_{sp}.

$$K_{eq} \times [AgCl(s)] = [Ag^+][Cl^-] = K_{sp}$$

$$K_{sp} = [Ag^+][Cl^-]$$

The K_{sp} is equal to the product of the Ag^+ ion and the Cl^- ion concentrations, each in moles per liter. When 1.3×10^{-5} mol/L of AgCl dissolves, it produces 1.3×10^{-5} mol/L each of Ag^+ and Cl^-. From these concentrations the K_{sp} can be evaluated.

$$[Ag^+] = 1.3 \times 10^{-5} \text{ mol/L} \qquad [Cl^-] = 1.3 \times 10^{-5} \text{ mol/L}$$

$$K_{sp} = [Ag^+][Cl^-] = [1.3 \times 10^{-5}][1.3 \times 10^{-5}] = 1.7 \times 10^{-10}$$

Once the K_{sp} value for AgCl is established, it can be used to describe other systems containing Ag^+ and Cl^-.

The K_{sp} expression does not have a denominator. It consists only of the concentrations (mol/L) of the ions in solution. As in other equilibria expressions, each of these concentrations is raised to a power that is the same number as its coefficient in the balanced equation. The equilibrium equations and the K_{sp} expressions for several other substances follow.

$$AgBr(s) \rightleftharpoons Ag^+ + Br^- \qquad\qquad K_{sp} = [Ag^+][Br^-]$$

$$BaSO_4(s) \rightleftharpoons Ba^{2+} + SO_4^{2-} \qquad K_{sp} = [Ba^{2+}][SO_4^{2-}]$$

$$Ag_2CrO_4(s) \rightleftharpoons 2\,Ag^+ + CrO_4^{2-} \qquad K_{sp} = [Ag^+]^2[CrO_4^{2-}]$$

$$CuS(s) \rightleftharpoons Cu^{2+} + S^{2-} \qquad\qquad K_{sp} = [Cu^{2+}][S^{2-}]$$

$$Mn(OH)_2(s) \rightleftharpoons Mn^{2+} + 2\,OH^- \qquad K_{sp} = [Mn^{2+}][OH^-]^2$$

$$Fe(OH)_3(s) \rightleftharpoons Fe^{3+} + 3\,OH^- \qquad K_{sp} = [Fe^{3+}][OH^-]^3$$

Table 16.4 lists K_{sp} values for these and several other substances.

When the product of the molar concentration of the ions in solution, each raised to its proper power, is greater than the K_{sp} for that substance, precipitation should occur. If the ion product is less than the K_{sp} value, no precipitation will occur.

Table 16.4 Solubility product constant (K_{sp}) at 25°C

Compound	K_{sp}
AgCl	1.7×10^{-10}
AgBr	5×10^{-13}
AgI	8.5×10^{-17}
$AgC_2H_3O_2$	2×10^{-3}
Ag_2CrO_4	1.9×10^{-12}
$BaCrO_4$	8.5×10^{-11}
$BaSO_4$	1.5×10^{-9}
CaF_2	3.9×10^{-11}
CuS	9×10^{-45}
$Fe(OH)_3$	6×10^{-38}
PbS	7×10^{-29}
$PbSO_4$	1.3×10^{-8}
$Mn(OH)_2$	2.0×10^{-13}

PROBLEM

16.8

Write K_{sp} expressions for AgI and PbI$_2$, both of which are slightly soluble salts.
First write the equilibrium equations:

$$AgI(s) \rightleftharpoons Ag^+ + I^-$$

$$PbI_2(s) \rightleftharpoons Pb^{2+} + 2\,I^-$$

Since the concentration of the solid crystals is constant, the K_{sp} equals the product of the molar concentrations of the ions in solution. In the case of PbI$_2$, the [I$^-$] must be squared.

$$K_{sp} = [Ag^+][I^-]$$

$$K_{sp} = [Pb^{2+}][I^-]^2$$

PROBLEM

16.9

The K_{sp} value for lead sulfate is 1.3×10^{-8}. Calculate the solubility of PbSO$_4$ in grams per liter.
First write the equilibrium equation and the K_{sp} expression:

$$PbSO_4 \rightleftharpoons Pb^{2+} + SO_4^{2-}$$

$$K_{sp} = [Pb^{2+}][SO_4^{2-}] = 1.3 \times 10^{-8}$$

Since the lead sulfate that is in solution is completely dissociated, the concentration of [Pb^{2+}] or [SO$_4^{2-}$] is equal to the solubility of PbSO$_4$ in moles per liter.
Let

$$Y = [Pb^{2+}] = [SO_4^{2-}]$$

Substitute Y into the K_{sp} equation and solve.

$$[Pb^{2+}][SO_4^{2-}] = [Y][Y] = 1.3 \times 10^{-8}$$

$$Y^2 = 1.3 \times 10^{-8}$$

$$Y = 1.1 \times 10^{-4}\,\text{mol/L}$$

The solubility of PbSO$_4$, therefore, is 1.1×10^{-4} mol/L. Now convert mol/L to g/L:

1 mol of PbSO$_4$ weighs $(207.2 + 32.1 + 64.0)$ or 303.3 g.

$$\frac{1.1 \times 10^{-4}\,\cancel{\text{mol}}}{L} \times \frac{303.3\,\text{g}}{\cancel{\text{mol}}} = 3.3 \times 10^{-2}\,\text{g/L}$$

The solubility of PbSO$_4$ is 3.3×10^{-2} g/L.

PROBLEM

16.10

The solubility of Mg(OH)$_2$ is 1.21×10^{-4} mol/L. Calculate the K_{sp} for Mg(OH)$_2$.
First write the equilibrium equation and the K_{sp} expression:

$$Mg(OH)_2(s) \rightleftharpoons Mg^{2+} + 2\,OH^- \qquad K_{sp} = [Mg^{2+}][OH^-]^2$$

For every mole of $Mg(OH)_2$ that dissolves, 1 mole of Mg^{2+} and 2 moles of OH^- are produced in solution. Therefore, the molar concentrations in solution are

$$[Mg^{2+}] = 1.21 \times 10^{-4} \qquad \text{and} \qquad [OH^-] = 2 \times 1.21 \times 10^{-4} = 2.42 \times 10^{-4}$$

Substituting these values into the K_{sp} expression, we have

$$K_{sp} = [Mg^{2+}][OH^-]^2 = [1.21 \times 10^{-4}][2.42 \times 10^{-4}]^2$$

$$K_{sp} = 7.09 \times 10^{-12}$$

An ion added to a solution that already contains that ion is called a common ion. When a common ion is added to an equilibrium solution of a weak electrolyte or a slightly soluble salt, the equilibrium shifts according to Le Châtelier's principle. For example, when silver nitrate, $AgNO_3$, is added to a saturated solution of silver chloride [$AgCl(s) \rightleftharpoons Ag^+ + Cl^-$], the equilibrium shifts to the left due to the increase in the Ag^+ concentration. As a result, the Cl^- concentration and the solubility of AgCl decrease. AgCl and $AgNO_3$ have the common ion Ag^+. The effect of the common ion causing the equilibrium to shift is known as the **common ion effect.**

common ion effect

PROBLEM

16.11

Silver nitrate, $AgNO_3$, is added to saturated AgCl solution until the Ag^+ concentration is 0.10 M. What will be the Cl^- concentration remaining in solution?

This problem is an example of the common ion effect. The addition of $AgNO_3$ puts more Ag^+ in solution; the Ag^+ combines with Cl^- and causes the equilibrium to shift to the left, reducing the Cl^- concentration in solution.

We use the K_{sp} to calculate the Cl^- ion concentration remaining in solution. The K_{sp} is constant at a particular temperature and remains the same no matter how we change the concentration of the species involved.

$$K_{sp} = [Ag^+][Cl^-] = 1.7 \times 10^{-10} \qquad [Ag^+] = 0.10 \text{ mol/L}$$

We then substitute the concentration of Ag^+ ion into the K_{sp} expression and calculate the Cl^- concentration:

$$[0.10][Cl^-] = 1.7 \times 10^{-10}$$

$$[Cl^-] = \frac{1.7 \times 10^{-10}}{0.10} = 1.7 \times 10^{-9} \text{ mol/L}$$

This calculation shows a 10,000-fold reduction of Cl^- ions in solution. It illustrates that Cl^- ions may be quantitatively removed from solution with an excess of Ag^+ ions.

16.13   **Hydrolysis**

hydrolysis

Hydrolysis is the term used for the general reaction in which a water molecule is split. When sodium acetate is dissolved in water, the resulting solution is basic.

Table 16.5 Ionic composition of salts and the nature of the aqueous solutions they form

Type of salt	Nature of aqueous solution	Examples
Weak base–strong acid	Acidic	NH_4Cl, NH_4NO_3
Strong base–weak acid	Basic	$NaC_2H_3O_2$, K_2CO_3
Weak base–weak acid	Depends on the salt	$NH_4C_2H_3O_2$, NH_4NO_2
Strong base–strong acid	Neutral	NaCl, KBr

The salt first dissociates into Na^+ and $C_2H_3O_2^-$ ions. The acetate ion then hydrolyzes (reacts with water) according to the following equation:

$$C_2H_3O_2^-(aq) + H_2O(l) \rightleftharpoons HC_2H_3O_2(aq) + OH^-(aq)$$

In the reaction the water molecule is split, with the H^+ combining with $C_2H_3O_2^-$ to give the weak acid $HC_2H_3O_2$ and the OH^- going into solution, making the solution more basic. A 0.1 M $NaC_2H_3O_2$ solution has a pH of 8.9.

Salts that contain an ion of a weak acid or a weak base undergo hydrolysis. For example, a 0.10 M NH_4Cl solution has a pH of 5.1, and 0.10 M NaCN solution has a pH of 11.1. The hydrolysis reactions that cause these solutions to become acidic or basic are

$$NH_4^+(aq) + H_2O(l) \rightleftharpoons NH_4OH(aq) + H^+(aq)$$

$$CN^-(aq) + H_2O(l) \rightleftharpoons HCN(aq) + OH^-(aq)$$

The ions of a salt derived from a strong acid and a strong base, such as NaCl, do not undergo hydrolysis and thus form neutral solutions. Table 16.5 lists the ionic composition of various salts and the nature of the aqueous solutions they form.

16.14 Buffer Solutions: The Control of pH

The control of pH within narrow limits is critically important in many chemical applications and vitally important in many biological systems. For example, human blood must be maintained between pH 7.35 and 7.45 for the efficient transport of oxygen from the lungs to the cells. This narrow pH range is maintained by buffer systems in the blood.

buffer solution A **buffer solution** resists changes in pH when diluted or when small amounts of acid or base are added. Two common types of buffer solutions are (1) a weak acid mixed with a salt of that weak acid and (2) a weak base mixed with a salt of that weak base.

The action of a buffer system can be understood by considering a solution of acetic acid and sodium acetate. The weak acid, $HC_2H_3O_2$, is mostly un-ionized and is in equilibrium with its ions in solution. The salt, $NaC_2H_3O_2$, is completely ionized.

$$HC_2H_3O_2(aq) \rightleftharpoons H^+(aq) + C_2H_3O_2^-(aq)$$

$$NaC_2H_3O_2(aq) \longrightarrow Na^+(aq) + C_2H_3O_2^-(aq)$$

Table 16.6 Changes in pH caused by the addition of
HCl and NaOH to pure water and to an acetic
acid–sodium acetate buffer solution

Solution	pH	Change in pH
H$_2$O (1000 mL)	7	—
H$_2$O + 0.010 mol HCl	2	5
H$_2$O + 0.010 mol NaOH	12	5
Buffer solution (1000 mL)		
0.10 M HC$_2$H$_3$O$_2$ + 0.10 M NaC$_2$H$_3$O$_2$	4.74	—
Buffer + 0.010 mol HCl	4.66	0.08
Buffer + 0.010 mol NaOH	4.83	0.09

Because the salt is completely ionized, the solution contains a much higher concentration of acetate ions than would be present if only acetic acid were in solution. The acetate ion represses the ionization of acetic acid and also reacts with water, causing the solution to have a higher pH (be more basic) than an acetic acid solution (see Section 16.5). Thus, a 0.1 M acetic acid solution has a pH of 2.87, but a solution that is 0.1 M in acetic acid and 0.1 M in sodium acetate has a pH of 4.74. This difference in pH is the result of the common ion effect.

A buffer solution has a built-in mechanism that counteracts the effect of adding acid or base. Consider the effect of adding HCl or NaOH to an acetic acid–sodium acetate buffer. When a small amount of HCl is added, the acetate ions of the buffer combine with the H$^+$ ions from HCl to form un-ionized acetic acid, thus neutralizing the added acid and maintaining the approximate pH of the solution. When NaOH is added, the OH$^-$ ions react with acetic acid to neutralize the added base and thus maintain the approximate pH. The equations for these reactions are

$$H^+(aq) + C_2H_3O_2^-(aq) \rightleftharpoons HC_2H_3O_2(aq)$$

$$OH^-(aq) + HC_2H_3O_2(aq) \rightleftharpoons H_2O(l) + C_2H_3O_2^-(aq)$$

Data comparing the changes in pH caused by adding HCl and NaOH to pure water and to an acetic acid–sodium acetate buffer solution are shown in Table 16.6.

The human body has a number of buffer systems. One of these, the bicarbonate–carbonic acid buffer, HCO$_3^-$–H$_2$CO$_3$, maintains the blood plasma at a pH of 7.4. The phosphate system, HPO$_4^{2-}$–H$_2$PO$_4^-$ is an important buffer in red blood cells as well as in other places in the body.

16.15   Mechanism of Reactions

**mechanism
of a reaction**

How a reaction occurs—that is, the manner in which it proceeds—is known as the **mechanism of the reaction.** The mechanism is the path, or route, the atoms and molecules take to arrive at the products. Our aim here is not to study the

Figure 16.3 Mechanism of the reaction between hydrogen and iodine: H_2 and I_2 molecules of sufficient energy unite, forming the intermediate activated complex that decomposes to the product, hydrogen iodide.

mechanisms themselves but to show that chemical reactions occur by specific routes.

When hydrogen and iodine are mixed at room temperature, we observe no appreciable reaction. In this case, the reaction takes place as a result of collisions between H_2 and I_2 molecules, but at room temperature the collisions do not result in reaction because the molecules lack sufficient energy to react. We say that an energy barrier to reaction exists. If heat is added, the kinetic energy of the molecules increases. When molecules of H_2 and I_2 with sufficient energy collide, **activated** an intermediate product, known as the **activated complex,** is formed. The **complex** amount of energy needed to form the activated complex is known as the **activation energy.** The activated complex, H_2I_2, is in a metastable form and has **activation** an energy level higher than that of the reactants or the product. It can decompose **energy** to form either the reactants or the product. Three steps constitute the mechanism of the reaction: (1) collision of an H_2 and an I_2 molecule; (2) formation of the activated complex, H_2I_2; and (3) decomposition to the product, HI. The various steps in the formation of HI are shown in Figure 16.3. Figure 16.4 illustrates the energy relationships in this reaction.

The reaction of hydrogen and chlorine proceeds by a different mechanism. When H_2 and Cl_2 are mixed and kept in the dark, essentially no product is formed. But, if the mixture is exposed to sunlight or ultraviolet radiation, it reacts very rapidly. The overall reaction is

$$H_2(g) + Cl_2(g) \longrightarrow 2\ HCl(g)$$

free radical This reaction proceeds by what is known as a *free radical mechanism.* A **free radical** is a neutral atom or group of atoms containing one or more unpaired electrons. Both atomic chlorine ($:\overset{..}{\underset{..}{Cl}}\cdot$) and atomic hydrogen ($H\cdot$) have an unpaired electron and are free radicals. The reaction occurs in three steps:

Step 1. *Initiation*

$$:\overset{..}{\underset{..}{Cl}}:\overset{..}{\underset{..}{Cl}}: + h\nu \longrightarrow \quad :\overset{..}{\underset{..}{Cl}}\cdot + :\overset{..}{\underset{..}{Cl}}\cdot$$

Chlorine free radicals

Figure 16.4 Relative energy diagram for the reaction between hydrogen and iodine,

$$H_2 + I_2 \longrightarrow [H_2I_2] \longrightarrow 2\,HI$$

Energy equal to the activation energy is put into the system to form the activated complex, H_2I_2. When this complex decomposes, the product is formed and energy is liberated. In this case, the product is at a higher energy level than the reactants, indicating that the reaction is endothermic and that energy is absorbed during the reaction. The dotted line represents the effect that a catalyst would have on the reaction. The catalyst lowers the activation energy, thereby increasing the rate of the reaction.

In this step a chlorine molecule absorbs energy in the form of a photon, $h\nu$, of light or ultraviolet radiation. The energized chlorine molecule then splits into two chlorine free radicals.

Step 2. *Propagation*

$$:\!\overset{..}{\underset{..}{Cl}}\!\cdot + H\!:\!H \longrightarrow HCl + \quad H\cdot$$
Hydrogen
free radical

$$H\cdot + :\!\overset{..}{\underset{..}{Cl}}\!:\!\overset{..}{\underset{..}{Cl}}\!: \longrightarrow HCl + :\!\overset{..}{\underset{..}{Cl}}\!\cdot$$

This step begins when a chlorine free radical reacts with a hydrogen molecule to produce a molecule of hydrogen chloride and a hydrogen free radical. The hydrogen radical then reacts with another chlorine molecule to form hydrogen chloride and another chlorine free radical. This chlorine radical can repeat the process by reacting with another hydrogen molecule, and the reaction continues to propagate itself in this manner until one or both of the reactants are used up. Almost all of the product is formed in this step.

Step 3. *Termination*

$$:\ddot{Cl}\cdot + :\ddot{Cl}\cdot \longrightarrow Cl_2$$

$$H\cdot + H\cdot \longrightarrow H_2$$

$$H\cdot + :\ddot{Cl}\cdot \longrightarrow HCl$$

Hydrogen and chlorine free radicals can react in any of the three ways shown. Unless further activation occurs, the formation of hydrogen chloride will terminate when the radicals form molecules. In an exothermic reaction such as that between hydrogen and chlorine, usually enough heat and light energy is available to maintain the supply of free radicals, and the reaction will continue until at least one reactant is exhausted.

QUESTIONS

A. *Review the meanings of the new terms introduced in this chapter.*

1. Reversible chemical reaction
2. Chemical kinetics
3. Equilibrium
4. Chemical equilibrium
5. Le Châtelier's principle
6. Catalyst
7. Equilibrium constant, K_{eq}
8. Acid ionization constant, K_a
9. Ion product constant for water, K_w
10. Solubility product constant, K_{sp}
11. Common ion effect
12. Hydrolysis
13. Buffer solution
14. Mechanism of a reaction
15. Activated complex
16. Activation energy
17. Free radical

B. *Information useful in answering the following questions will be found in the tables and figures.*

1. How would you expect the two tubes in Figure 16.1 to appear if both are at 25°C?
2. Is the reaction $N_2O_4 \rightleftharpoons 2 NO_2$ (Figure 16.1) exothermic or endothermic?
3. At equilibrium how do the forward and reverse reaction rates compare? (See Figure 16.2.)
4. Would the reaction of 30 mol of H_2 and 10 mol of N_2 produce a greater yield of NH_3 carried out in a 1 L or a 2 L vessel? (See Table 16.1.)

5. Of the acids listed in Table 16.2, which ones are stronger than acetic acid and which are weaker?
6. For each of the solutions in Table 16.3, what is the sum of the pH plus the pOH? What would be the pOH of a solution whose pH was −1?
7. Tabulate the relative order of molar solubilities of AgCl, AgBr, AgI, $AgC_2H_3O_2$, $PbSO_4$, $BaSO_4$, $BaCrO_4$, and PbS. (Use Table 16.4.) List the most soluble first.
8. Which compound in each of the following pairs has the greater molar solubility? (See Table 16.4.)
   (a) $Mn(OH)_2$ or Ag_2CrO_4
   (b) $BaCrO_4$ or Ag_2CrO_4
9. Using Table 16.6, explain how the acetic acid–sodium acetate buffer system maintains its pH when 0.010 mol of HCl is added to 1 L of the buffer solution.
10. How would Figure 16.4 be altered if the reaction were exothermic?

C. *Review questions*

1. Express the following reversible systems in equation form:
   (a) A mixture of ice and liquid water at 10°C
   (b) Liquid water and vapor at 100°C in a pressure cooker
   (c) Crystals of Na_2SO_4 in a saturated aqueous solution of Na_2SO_4
   (d) A closed system containing boiling sulfur dioxide, SO_2

2. Explain why a precipitate of NaCl forms when hydrogen chloride gas is passed into a saturated aqueous solution of NaCl.

3. Why does the rate of a reaction usually increase when the concentration of one of the reactants is increased?

4. Consider the following system at equilibrium:

$$4 NH_3(g) + 3 O_2(g) \rightleftharpoons$$
$$2 N_2(g) + 6 H_2O(g) + 1531 kJ$$

   (a) A mixture of ice and liquid water at 10°C
   (b) If the system's state of equilibrium is disturbed by the addition of O_2, in which direction, left or right, must reaction occur to reestablish equilibrium? After the new equilibrium has been established, how will the final molar concentrations of NH_3, O_2, N_2, and H_2O compare (increase or decrease) with their concentrations before the addition of the O_2?
   (c) If the system's state of equilibrium is disturbed by the addition of heat, in which direction will reaction occur, left or right, to reestablish equilibrium?

5. Consider the following system at equilibrium:

$$N_2(g) + 3 H_2(g) \rightleftharpoons 2 NH_3(g) + 92.5 kJ$$

   Complete the following table. Indicate changes in moles by entering I, D, N, or ? in the table. (I = increase, D = decrease, N = no change, ? = insufficient information to determine.)

6. If pure hydrogen iodide, HI, is placed in a vessel at 700 K, will it decompose? Explain.

7. For each of the equations that follow, tell in which direction, left or right, the equilibrium will shift when the following changes are made: The temperature is increased; the pressure is increased by decreasing the volume of the reaction vessel; a catalyst is added.
   (a) $3 O_2(g) + 271 kJ \rightleftharpoons 2 O_3(g)$
   (b) $CH_4(g) + Cl_2(g) \rightleftharpoons$
   $$CH_3Cl(g) + HCl(g) + 110 kJ$$
   (c) $2 NO(g) + 2 H_2(g) \rightleftharpoons$
   $$N_2(g) + 2 H_2O(g) + 665 kJ$$
   (d) $2 SO_3(g) + 197 kJ \rightleftharpoons 2 SO_2(g) + O_2(g)$
   (e) $4 NH_3(g) + 3 O_2(g) \rightleftharpoons$
   $$2 N_2(g) + 6 H_2O(g) + 1531 kJ$$

8. Explain why an increase in temperature causes the rate of reaction to increase.

9. Give a word description of how equilibrium is reached when the substances A and B are first mixed and react as

$$A + B \rightleftharpoons C + D$$

10. With dilution, aqueous solutions of acetic acid, $HC_2H_3O_2$, show increased ionization. For example, a 1.0 M solution of acetic acid is 0.42% ionized, whereas a 0.10 M solution is 1.34% ionized. Explain this behavior using the ionization equation and equilibrium principles.

11. A 1.0 M solution of acetic acid ionizes less and has a higher concentration of H^+ ions than a

Change or stress imposed on the system at equilibrium	Direction of reaction, left or right, to reestablish equilibrium	Change in number of moles		
		N_2	H_2	NH_3
(a) Add N_2				
(b) Remove H_2				
(c) Decrease volume of reaction vessel				
(d) Increase volume of reaction vessel				
(e) Increase temperature				
(f) Add catalyst				
(g) Add both H_2 and NH_3				

0.10 M acetic acid solution. Explain this behavior. (See Question 10 for data.)

12. Write the equilibrium constant expression for each of the following reactions:
    (a) $4 HCl(g) + O_2(g) \rightleftharpoons 2 Cl_2(g) + 2 H_2O(g)$
    (b) $N_2(g) + 3 H_2(g) \rightleftharpoons 2 NH_3(g)$
    (c) $PCl_5(g) \rightleftharpoons PCl_3(g) + Cl_2(g)$
    (d) $HClO_2(aq) \rightleftharpoons H^+(aq) + ClO_2^-(aq)$
    (e) $NH_4OH(aq) \rightleftharpoons NH_4^+(aq) + OH^-(aq)$
    (f) $4 NH_3(g) + 5 O_2(g) \rightleftharpoons$
    $$4 NO(g) + 6 H_2O(g)$$

13. What would cause two separate samples of pure water to have slightly different pH values?

14. Why are the pH and pOH equal in pure water?

15. What effect will increasing the H^+ ion concentration of a solution have on (a) pH, (b) pOH, (c) $[OH^-]$, and (d) K_w?

16. Write the solubility product constant expression (K_{sp}) for each of the following substances:
    (a) CuS   (e) $Fe(OH)_3$
    (b) $BaSO_4$ (f) Sb_2S_5
    (c) $PbBr_2$ (g) CaF_2
    (d) Ag_3AsO_4 (h) $Ba_3(PO_4)_2$

17. Explain why silver acetate, $AgC_2H_3O_2$, is more soluble in nitric acid than in water. [*Hint*: Write the equilibrium equation first and then consider the effect of the acid on the acetate ion.] What would happen if hydrochloric acid, HCl, were used in place of nitric acid?

18. Decide whether each of the following salts forms an acidic, a basic, or a neutral aqueous solution:
    (a) KCl   (d) $(NH_4)_2SO_4$ (g) $NaNO_2$
    (b) Na_2CO_3 (e) $Ca(CN)_2$ (h) NaF
    (c) K_2SO_4 (f) $BaBr_2$

19. Dissolution of sodium acetate, $NaC_2H_3O_2$, in pure water gives a basic solution. Why? [*Hint*: A small amount of $HC_2H_3O_2$ is formed.]

20. Write hydrolysis equations for aqueous solutions of these salts:
    (a) KNO_2 (c) NH_4NO_3
    (b) $Mg(C_2H_3O_2)_2$ (d) Na_2SO_3

21. Write hydrolysis equations for the following ions:
    (a) HCO_3^- (b) NH_4^+ (c) OCl^- (d) ClO_2^-

22. Describe why the pH of a buffer solution remains almost constant when a small amount of acid or base is added to it.

23. One of the important pH-regulating systems in the blood consists of a carbonic acid–sodium bicarbonate buffer.

$$H_2CO_3(aq) \rightleftharpoons H^+(aq) + HCO_3^-(aq)$$

$$NaHCO_3(aq) \longrightarrow Na^+(aq) + HCO_3^-(aq)$$

Explain how this buffer resists changes in pH when (a) excess acid and (b) excess base get into the bloodstream.

24. Which of the following statements are correct?
    (a) In a reaction at equilibrium the concentrations of reactants and products are equal.
    (b) A catalyst increases the concentrations of products present at equilibrium.
    (c) Enzymes are the catalysts in living systems.
    (d) A catalyst lowers the activation energy of a reaction by equal amounts for both the forward and the reverse reactions.
    (e) If an increase in temperature causes an increase in the concentration of products present at equilibrium, then the reaction is exothermic.
    (f) The magnitude of an equilibrium constant is independent of the reaction temperature.
    (g) A large equilibrium constant for a reaction indicates that the reaction, at equilibrium, favors products over reactants.
    (h) The amount of product obtained at equilibrium is proportional to how fast equilibrium is attained.
    (i) The study of reaction rates and reaction mechanisms is known as chemical kinetics.
    (j) For the reaction

    $$CaCO_3(s) \overset{\Delta}{\rightleftharpoons} CaO(s) + CO_2(g)$$

    increasing the pressure of CO_2 present at equilibrium will cause the reaction to shift left.
    (k) The larger the value of the equilibrium constant, the greater the proportion of products present at equilibrium.
    (l) At chemical equilibrium the rate of the reverse reaction is equal to the rate of the forward reaction.

    Statements (m)–(s) pertain to the equilibrium system

    $$2 NO(g) + O_2(g) \rightleftharpoons 2 NO_2(g) + Heat$$

    (m) The reaction as shown is endothermic.
    (n) Increasing the temperature will cause the equilibrium to shift left.

(o) Increasing the temperature will increase the magnitude of the equilibrium constant, K_{eq}.

(p) Decreasing the volume of the reaction vessel will shift the equilibrium to the right and decrease the concentrations of the reactants.

(q) Removal of some of the O_2 will cause an increase in the concentration of NO.

(r) High temperatures and pressures favor increased yields of NO_2.

(s) The equilibrium constant expression for the reaction is

$$K_{eq} = \frac{[NO_2]^2}{[NO]^2[O_2]}$$

(t) A solution with an H^+ ion concentration of 1×10^{-5} mol/L has a pOH of 9.

(u) An aqueous solution that has an OH^- ion concentration of 1×10^{-4} mol/L has an H^+ ion concentration of 1×10^{-10} mol/L.

(v) $K_w = [H^+][OH^-] = 1.00 \times 10^{-14}$, and pH + pOH = 14.

(w) An aqueous solution of KNO_2 will be acidic.

(x) A solution of pOH 10 is basic.

(y) The pH increases as the $[H^+]$ increases.

(z) The pH of 0.050 M $Ca(OH)_2$ is 13.

D. *Review problems*

Equilibrium Constants

1. What is the maximum amount (moles) of HI that can be obtained from a reaction mixture containing 2.30 mol of I_2 and 2.10 mol of H_2?

2. (a) How many moles of hydrogen iodide, HI, will be produced when 2.00 mol of H_2 and 2.00 mol of I_2 are reacted at 700 K? (Reaction is 79% complete.)

   (b) Addition of 0.27 mol of I_2 to the system increases the yield of HI to 85%. How many moles of H_2, I_2, and HI are now present?

   (c) From the data in part (a), calculate K_{eq} for the reaction at 700 K.

* 3. 6.00 g of hydrogen, H_2, and 200 g of iodine, I_2, are reacted at 500 K. After equilibrium is reached, analysis shows that the flask contains 64.0 g of HI. How many moles of H_2, I_2, and HI are present in this equilibrium mixture?

4. What is the equilibrium constant of the reaction shown if a 20 L flask contains 0.10 mol of PCl_3,

1.50 mol of Cl_2, and 0.22 mol of PCl_5?

$$PCl_3(g) + Cl_2(g) \rightleftharpoons PCl_5$$

5. If the rate of a reaction doubles for every 10° rise in temperature, how much faster will the reaction go at 100°C than at 30°C?

Ionization Constants

6. Calculate the ionization constant for each of the following monoprotic acids. Each acid ionizes as follows: HA $\rightleftharpoons$ $H^+ + A$

Acid	Acid concentration	$[H^+]$
Hypochlorous, HClO	0.10 M	5.9×10^{-5} mol/L
Propanoic, $HC_3H_5O_2$	0.15 M	1.4×10^{-3} mol/L
Hydrocyanic, HCN	0.20 M	8.9×10^{-6} mol/L

7. Calculate (a) the H^+ ion concentration, (b) the pH, and (c) the percent ionization of a 0.25 M solution of $HC_2H_3O_2$. ($K_a = 1.8 \times 10^{-5}$)

8. A 1.0 M solution of a weak acid, HA, is 0.52% ionized. Calculate the ionization constant, K_a, for the acid.

9. A 0.15 M solution of a weak acid, HA, has a pH of 5. Calculate the ionization constant, K_a, for the acid.

10. Calculate the percent ionization and pH of solutions of $HC_2H_3O_2$ having the following molarities: (a) 1.0 M, (b) 0.10 M, and (c) 0.010 M. ($K_a = 1.8 \times 10^{-5}$.)

11. A 0.37 M solution of a weak acid, HA, has a pH of 3.7. What is the K_a for this acid?

12. A 0.23 M solution of a weak acid, HA, has a pH of 2.89. What is the K_a for this acid?

13. A common laboratory reagent is 6.0 M HCl. Calculate the $[H^+]$, $[OH^-]$, pH, and pOH of this solution.

14. Calculate the pH and the pOH of the following solutions:

   (a) 0.00010 M HCl

   (b) 0.010 M NaOH

   (c) 0.0025 M NaOH

   (d) 0.10 M HClO ($K_a = 3.5 \times 10^{-8}$)

   *(e) Saturated $Fe(OH)_2$ solution ($K_{sp} = 8.0 \times 10^{-16}$)

15. Calculate the $[OH^-]$ in each of these solutions:
    (a) $[H^+] = 1.0 \times 10^{-4}$
    (b) $[H^+] = 2.8 \times 10^{-6}$
    (c) $[H^+] = 4.0 \times 10^{-9}$
16. Calculate the $[H^+]$ in each of these solutions:
    (a) $[OH^-] = 6.0 \times 10^{-7}$
    (b) $[OH^-] = 1 \times 10^{-8}$
    (c) $[OH^-] = 4.5 \times 10^{-6}$

Solubility Product Constant
17. Given the following solubility data, calculate the solubility product constant for each substance.
    (a) $BaSO_4$, 3.9×10^{-5} mol/L
    (b) Ag_2CrO_4, 7.8×10^{-5} mol/L
    (c) ZnS, 3.5×10^{-12} mol/L
    (d) $Pb(IO_3)_2$, 4.0×10^{-5} mol/L
    (e) Bi_2S_3, 4.9×10^{-15} mol/L
    (f) $AgCl$, 0.0019 g/L
    (g) $CaSO_4$, 0.67 g/L
    (h) $Zn(OH)_2$, 2.33×10^{-4} g/L
    (i) Ag_3PO_4, 6.73×10^{-3} g/L
18. Calculate the molar solubility for each of the following substances:
    (a) $BaCO_3$, $K_{sp} = 2.0 \times 10^{-9}$
    (b) $AlPO_4$, $K_{sp} = 5.8 \times 10^{-19}$
    (c) Ag_2SO_4, $K_{sp} = 1.5 \times 10^{-5}$
    (d) $Mg(OH)_2$, $K_{sp} = 7.1 \times 10^{-12}$
19. Calculate, for each of the substances in Question 18, the solubility in grams per 100 mL of water.
20. The K_{sp} of CaF_2 is 3.9×10^{-11}. Calculate (a) the molar concentrations of Ca^{2+} and F^- in a saturated solution, and (b) the grams of CaF_2 that will dissolve in 500 mL of water.
*21. The following pairs of solutions are mixed. Show by calculation whether or not a precipitate will form.
    (a) 100 mL of 0.010 M Na_2SO_4 and 100 mL of 0.001 M $Pb(NO_3)_2$
    (b) 50.0 mL of 1.0×10^{-4} M $AgNO_3$ and 100 mL of 1.0×10^{-4} M NaCl
    (c) 1.0 g of $Ca(NO_3)_2$ in 150 mL of H_2O and 250 mL of 0.01 M NaOH
    $K_{sp} = 1.3 \times 10^{-8}$ for $PbSO_4$
    $K_{sp} = 1.7 \times 10^{-10}$ for $AgCl$
    $K_{sp} = 1.3 \times 10^{-6}$ for $Ca(OH)_2$

22. $BaCl_2$ is added to a saturated $BaSO_4$ solution until the Ba^{2+} concentration is 0.050 M. (a) What concentration of SO_4^{2-} remains in solution? (b) How many grams of $BaSO_4$ remain dissolved in 100 mL of the solution? ($K_{sp} = 1.5 \times 10^{-9}$ for $BaSO_4$.)
23. The concentration of a solution is 0.10 M Ba^{2+} and 0.10 M Sr^{2+}. Which sulfate, $BaSO_4$ or $SrSO_4$, will precipitate first when a dilute solution of H_2SO_4 is added dropwise to the solution? Show evidence for your answer.
    ($K_{sp} = 1.5 \times 10^{-9}$ for $BaSO_4$ and $K_{sp} = 3.5 \times 10^{-7}$ for $SrSO_4$.)
24. How many moles of $AgBr$ will dissolve in 1.0 L of (a) 0.10 M NaBr and (b) 0.10 M $MgBr_2$?
    ($K_{sp} = 5.0 \times 10^{-13}$ for $AgBr$.)
25. The K_{sp} for $PbCl_2$ is 2.0×10^{-5}. Will a precipitate form when 0.050 mol of $Pb(NO_3)_2$ and 0.010 mol of NaCl are dissolved in 1.0 L of H_2O? Show evidence for your answer.

Buffer Solutions
26. Calculate the H^+ ion concentration and the pH of buffer solutions that are 0.20 M in $HC_2H_3O_2$ and contain sufficient sodium acetate to make the $C_2H_3O_2^-$ ion concentration equal to (a) 0.10 M and (b) 0.20 M.
    $K_a = 1.8 \times 10^{-5}$ for $HC_2H_3O_2$
27. (a) When 1.0 mL of 1.0 M HCl is added to 50 mL of 1.0 M NaCl, the H^+ ion concentration changes from 1×10^{-7} M to 2.0×10^{-2} M.
    (b) When 1.0 mL of 1.0 M HCl is added to 50 mL of a buffer solution that is 1.0 M in $HC_2H_3O_2$ and 1.0 M in $NaC_2H_3O_2$, the H^+ ion concentration changes from 1.8×10^{-5} M to 1.9×10^{-5} M.
    Calculate the initial pH and the pH change in each solution. (Log 1.8 = 0.26; log 1.9 = 0.28; log 2.0 = 0.30)

17

Oxidation–Reduction

After studying
Chapter 17,
you should be
able to

1. Understand the new terms listed in Question A at the end of the chapter.
2. Assign oxidation numbers to all the elements in a given compound or ion.
3. Determine which element is being oxidized and which element is being reduced in an oxidation–reduction reaction.
4. Identify the oxidizing agent and the reducing agent in an oxidation–reduction reaction.
5. Balance oxidation–reduction equations in molecular and ionic form.
6. Outline the general principles concerning the activity series of the metals.
7. Use the activity series to determine whether a proposed single-displacement reaction will occur.
8. Distinguish between an electrolytic and a voltaic cell.
9. Draw a voltaic cell that will produce electric current from an oxidation–reduction reaction involving two metals and their salts.
10. Identify the anode reaction and the cathode reaction in a given electrolytic or voltaic cell.
11. Write equations for the overall chemical reaction and for the oxidation and reduction reactions involved in the discharging or charging of a lead storage battery.
12. Explain how the charge condition of a lead storage battery can be estimated with the aid of a hydrometer.

17.1 Oxidation Number

The oxidation number of an atom (sometimes called its oxidation state) can be considered to represent the number of electrons lost, gained, or unequally shared by the atom. Oxidation numbers can be zero, positive, or negative. When the oxidation number of an atom is zero, the atom has the same number of electrons assigned to it as there are in the free neutral atom. When the oxidation number is positive, the atom has fewer electrons assigned to it than there are in the neutral atom. When the oxidation number is negative, the atom has more electrons assigned to it than there are in the neutral atom.

The oxidation number of an atom that has lost or gained electrons to form an ion is the same as the plus or minus charge of the ion. In the ionic compound NaCl, the oxidation numbers are clearly established to be $+1$ for the Na^+ ion and -1 for the Cl^- ion. The Na^+ ion has one less electron than the neutral Na atom; and the Cl^- ion has one more electron than the neutral Cl atom. In $MgCl_2$ two electrons have transferred from the Mg atom to the Cl atoms; thus, the oxidation number of Mg is $+2$.

In covalently bonded substances, where electrons are shared between two atoms, oxidation numbers are assigned by a somewhat arbitrary system based on relative electronegativities. For symmetrical covalent molecules, such as H_2 and Cl_2, each atom is assigned an oxidation number of zero because the bonding pair of electrons is shared equally between two like atoms, neither of which is more electronegative than the other.

$$H:H \qquad :\overset{..}{\underset{..}{Cl}}:\overset{..}{\underset{..}{Cl}}:$$

When the covalent bond is between two unlike atoms, the bonding electrons are shared unequally because the more electronegative element has a greater attraction for them. In this case the oxidation numbers are determined by assigning both electrons to the more electronegative element.

Thus in compounds with covalent bonds, such as NH_3 and H_2O,

the pairs of electrons are unequally shared between the atoms and are attracted toward the more electronegative elements, N and O. This unequal sharing causes the N and O atoms to be relatively negative with respect to the H atoms. At the same time it causes the H atoms to be relatively positive with respect to the N and O atoms. In H_2O both pairs of shared electrons are assigned to the O atom, giving it two electrons more than the neutral O atom. At the same time, each H atom is assigned one electron less than the neutral H atom. Therefore, the O atom is assigned an oxidation number of -2, and each H atom is assigned an oxidation number of $+1$. In NH_3 the three pairs of shared electrons are assigned to the N atom, giving it three electrons more than the neutral N atom. At the same time,

Table 17.1   Arbitrary rules for assigning oxidation numbers

1. All elements in their free state (uncombined with other elements) have an oxidation number of zero (for example, Na, Cu, Mg, H_2, O_2, Cl_2, N_2).
2. H is +1, except in metal hydrides, where it is −1 (for example, NaH, CaH_2).
3. O is −2, except in peroxides, where it is −1, and in OF_2, where it is +2.
4. The metallic element in an ionic compound has a positive oxidation number.
5. In covalent compounds the negative oxidation number is assigned to the most electronegative atom.
6. The algebraic sum of the oxidation numbers of the elements in a compound is zero.
7. The algebraic sum of the oxidation numbers of the elements in a polyatomic ion is equal to the charge of the ion.

Table 17.2   Oxidation numbers of atoms in selected compounds

Ion or compound	Oxidation number		
H_2O	H, +1;	O, −2	
SO_2	S, +4;	O, −2	
CH_4	C, −4;	H, +1	
CO_2	C, +4;	O, −2	
$KMnO_4$	K, +1;	Mn, +7;	O, −2
Na_3PO_4	Na, +1;	P, +5;	O, −2
$Al_2(SO_4)_3$	Al, +3;	S, +6;	O, −2
NO	N, +2;	O, −2	
BCl_3	B, +3;	Cl, −1	
SO_4^{2-}	S, +6;	O, −2	
NO_3^-	N, +5;	O, −2	
CO_3^{2-}	C, +4;	O, −2	

each H atom has one electron less than the neutral atom. Therefore, the N atom is assigned an oxidation number of −3, and each H atom is assigned an oxidation number of +1.

The assignment of correct oxidation numbers to elements is essential for balancing oxidation–reduction equations. Review Sections 8.1, 8.2, and 8.4, regarding oxidation numbers, oxidation number tables, and the determination of oxidation numbers from formulas. Table 7.3 lists relative electronegativities of the elements. Rules for assigning oxidation numbers are given in Section 8.1 and are summarized in Table 17.1. Examples showing oxidation numbers in compounds and ions are given in Table 17.2.

PROBLEM

17.1

Determine the oxidation number of each element in **(a)** KNO_3 and **(b)** SO_4^{2-}.

(a) K is a Group IA metal; therefore it has an oxidation number of +1. The oxidation number of each O atom is −2 (Table 17.1, Rule 3). Using these values and the fact that the sum of the oxidation numbers of all the atoms in a compound is zero, we can determine the oxidation number of N:

$$KNO_3$$
$$+1 + N + 3(-2) = 0$$
$$N = +6 - 1 = +5$$

The oxidation numbers are K, +1; N, +5; O, −2.

(b) SO_4^{2-} is an ion; therefore, the sum of oxidation numbers of the S and the O atoms must be −2, the charge of the ion. The oxidation number of each O atom is −2 (Table 17.1, Rule 3). Then

$$SO_4^{2-}$$
$$S + 4(-2) = -2$$
$$S = -2 + 8 = +6$$

The oxidation numbers are S, +6; O, −2.

17.2   Oxidation–Reduction

**oxidation–
reduction**

redox

oxidation

reduction

Oxidation–reduction, also known as **redox,** is a chemical process in which the oxidation number of an element is changed. The process may involve the complete transfer of electrons to form ionic bonds or only a partial transfer or shift of electrons to form covalent bonds.

   Oxidation occurs whenever the oxidation number of an element increases as a result of losing electrons. Conversely, **reduction** occurs whenever the oxidation number of an element decreases as a result of gaining electrons. For example, a change in oxidation number from +2 to +3 or from −1 to 0 is oxidation; a change from +5 to +2 or from −2 to −4 is reduction (see Figure 17.1). Oxidation and reduction occur simultaneously in a chemical reaction; one cannot take place without the other.

   Many combination, decomposition, and single-displacement reactions involve oxidation–reduction. Let us examine the combustion of hydrogen and

Figure 17.1   Oxidation and reduction: Oxidation results in an increase in the oxidation number, and reduction results in a decrease in the oxidation number.

oxygen from this point of view:

$$2 H_2 + O_2 \longrightarrow 2 H_2O$$

Both reactants, hydrogen and oxygen, are elements in the free state and have an oxidation number of zero. In the product, water, hydrogen has been oxidized to $+1$ and oxygen reduced to -2. The substance that causes an increase in the oxidation state of another substance is called an **oxidizing agent.** The substance that causes a decrease in the oxidation state of another substance is called a **reducing agent.** In this reaction the oxidizing agent is free oxygen, and the reducing agent is free hydrogen. In the reaction

oxidizing agent

reducing agent

$$Zn(s) + H_2SO_4(aq) \longrightarrow ZnSO_4(aq) + H_2 \uparrow$$

metallic zinc is oxidized, and hydrogen ions are reduced. Zinc is the reducing agent, and hydrogen ions are the oxidizing agent. Electrons are transferred from the zinc metal to the hydrogen ions. The reaction is better expressed as

$$Zn^0 + 2 H^+ + SO_4^{2-} \longrightarrow Zn^{2+} + SO_4^{2-} + H_2^0 \uparrow$$

Oxidation:	**Increase in oxidation number**
	Loss of electrons
Reduction:	**Decrease in oxidation number**
	Gain of electrons

The oxidizing agent is reduced and gains electrons. The reducing agent is oxidized and loses electrons. The loss and gain of electrons is characteristic of all redox reactions.

17.3 Balancing Oxidation–Reduction Equations

Many simple redox equations can be balanced readily by inspection or by trial and error.

$$Na + Cl_2 \longrightarrow NaCl \qquad \text{(unbalanced)}$$

$$2 Na + Cl_2 \longrightarrow 2 NaCl \qquad \text{(unbalanced)}$$

Balancing this equation is certainly not complicated. But as we study more complex reactions and equations, such as

$$P + HNO_3 + H_2O \longrightarrow NO + H_3PO_4 \qquad \text{(unbalanced)}$$

$$3 P + 5 HNO_3 + 2 H_2O \longrightarrow 5 NO + 3 H_3PO_4 \qquad \text{(balanced)}$$

the trial-and-error method of finding the proper numbers to balance the equation would take an unnecessarily long time.

One systematic method for balancing oxidation–reduction equations is based on the transfer of electrons between the oxidizing and reducing agents. Consider the first equation again.

$$Na^0 + Cl_2^0 \longrightarrow Na^+Cl^- \quad \text{(unbalanced)}$$

In this reaction sodium metal loses one electron per atom when it changes to a sodium ion. At the same time chlorine gains one electron per atom. Because chlorine is diatomic, two electrons per molecule are needed to form a chloride ion from each atom. These electrons are furnished by two sodium atoms. Stepwise, the reaction may be written as two half-reactions, the oxidation half-reaction and the reduction half-reaction:

Oxidation half-reaction	$2\,Na^0 \longrightarrow 2\,Na^+ + 2\,e^-$
Reducton half-reaction	$Cl_2^0 + 2\,e^- \longrightarrow 2\,Cl^-$
	$2\,Na^0 + Cl_2^0 \longrightarrow 2\,Na^+Cl^-$

When the two half-reactions, each containing the same number of electrons, are added together algebraically, the electrons cancel out. In this reaction there are no excess electrons; the two electrons lost by the two sodium atoms are utilized by chlorine. In all redox reactions the loss of electrons by the reducing agent must equal the gain of electrons by the oxidizing agent. Sodium is oxidized; chlorine is reduced. Chlorine is the oxidizing agent; sodium is the reducing agent.

The following examples illustrate a systematic method of balancing more complicated redox equations by the oxidation-number method.

PROBLEM

17.2

Balance the equation

$$Sn + HNO_3 \longrightarrow SnO_2 + NO_2 + H_2O \quad \text{(unbalanced)}$$

Step 1. Assign oxidation numbers to each element to identify the elements that are being oxidized and those that are being reduced. Write the oxidation numbers below each element in order to avoid confusing them with the charge on an ion or radical.

$$Sn + HNO_3 \longrightarrow SnO_2 + NO_2 + H_2O$$
$$0 \quad +1+5-2 \quad\quad +4-2 \quad +4-2 \quad +1-2$$

Note that the oxidation numbers of Sn and N have changed.

Step 2. Now write two new equations, using only the elements that change in oxidation number. Then add electrons to bring the equations into electrical balance. One equation represents the oxidation step; the other represents the reduction step. The oxidation step produces electrons; the reduction step uses electrons.

Oxidation	$Sn^0 \longrightarrow Sn^{4+} + 4\,e^-$	Sn^0 loses 4 electrons.
Reduction	$N^{5+} + 1\,e^- \longrightarrow N^{4+}$	N^{5+} gains 1 electron.

Step 3. Now multiply the two equations by the smallest integral numbers that will make the loss of electrons by the oxidation step equal to the number of electrons gained in the reduction step. In this reaction the oxidation step is multiplied by 1 and

the reduction step by 4. The equations become

> Oxidation $Sn^0 \longrightarrow Sn^{4+} + 4\,e^-$ Sn^0 loses 4 electrons.
>
> Reduction $4\,N^{5+} + 4\,e^- \longrightarrow 4\,N^{4+}$ $4\,N^{5+}$ gain 4 electrons.

We have now established the ratio of the oxidizing to the reducing agent as being four atoms of N to one atom of Sn.

Step 4. Now transfer the coefficient that appears in front of each substance in the balanced oxidation–reduction equations to the corresponding substance in the original equation. We need to use 1 Sn, 1 SnO_2, 4 HNO_3, and 4 NO_2:

$$Sn + 4\,HNO_3 \longrightarrow SnO_2 + 4\,NO_2 + H_2O \qquad \text{(unbalanced)}$$

Step 5. In the usual manner, balance the remaining elements that are not oxidized or reduced to give the final balanced equation:

$$Sn + 4\,HNO_3 \longrightarrow SnO_2 + 4\,NO_2 + 2\,H_2O \qquad \text{(balanced)}$$

In balancing the final elements, we must not change the ratio of the elements that were oxidized and reduced. We should make a final check to ensure that both sides of the equation have the same number of atoms of each element. The final balanced equation contains 1 atom of Sn, 4 atoms of N, 4 atoms of H, and 12 atoms of O on each side.

Because each new equation may present a slightly different problem and because proficiency in balancing equations requires practice, we will work through a few more problems.

PROBLEM

17.3

Balance the equation

$$I_2 + Cl_2 + H_2O \longrightarrow HIO_3 + HCl \qquad \text{(unbalanced)}$$

Step 1. Assign oxidation numbers:

$$\underset{0}{I_2} + \underset{0}{Cl_2} + \underset{+1\ -2}{H_2O} \longrightarrow \underset{+1\ +5\ -2}{H\,I\,O_3} + \underset{+1\ -1}{HCl}$$

The oxidation numbers of I_2 and Cl_2 have changed: I_2 from 0 to +5 and Cl_2 from 0 to −1.

Step 2. Write oxidation and reduction steps. Balance the number of atoms and then balance the electrical charge using electrons.

> Oxidation $I_2 \longrightarrow 2\,I^{5+} + 10\,e^-$ I_2 loses 10 electrons.
>
> Reduction $Cl_2 + 2\,e^- \longrightarrow 2\,Cl^-$ Cl_2 gains 2 electrons.

Step 3. Adjust loss and gain of electrons so that they are equal. Multiply the oxidation step by 1 and the reduction step by 5:

> Oxidation $I_2 \longrightarrow 2\,I^{5+} + 10\,e^-$ I_2 loses 10 electrons.
>
> Reduction $5\,Cl_2 + 10\,e^- \longrightarrow 10\,Cl^-$ $5\,Cl_2$ gain 10 electrons.

Step 4. Transfer the coefficients from the balanced redox equations into the original equation. We need to use 1 I_2, 2 HIO_3, 5 Cl_2, and 10 HCl.

$$I_2 + 5\ Cl_2 + H_2O \longrightarrow 2\ HIO_3 + 10\ HCl \qquad \text{(unbalanced)}$$

Step 5. Balance the remaining elements, H and O:

$$I_2 + 5\ Cl_2 + 6\ H_2O \longrightarrow 2\ HIO_3 + 10\ HCl \qquad \text{(balanced)}$$

Check: The final balanced equation contains 2 atoms of I, 10 atoms of Cl, 12 atoms of H, and 6 atoms of O on each side.

PROBLEM

17.4

Balance the equation

$$K_2Cr_2O_7 + FeCl_2 + HCl \longrightarrow CrCl_3 + KCl + FeCl_3 + H_2O \qquad \text{(unbalanced)}$$

Step 1. Assign oxidation numbers (Cr and Fe have changed):

$$K_2Cr_2O_7 + FeCl_2 + HCl \longrightarrow CrCl_3 + KCl + FeCl_3 + H_2O$$
$$+1+6-2 \quad +2-1 \quad +1-1 \qquad +3-1 \quad +1-1 \quad +3-1 \quad +1-2$$

Step 2. Write the oxidation and reduction steps. Balance the number of atoms and then balance the electrical charge using electrons.

Oxidation $Fe^{2+} \longrightarrow Fe^{3+} + 1\ e^-$ Fe^{2+} loses 1 electron.

Reduction $2\ Cr^{6+} + 6\ e^- \longrightarrow 2\ Cr^{3+}$ $2\ Cr^{6+}$ gain 6 electrons.

Step 3. Balance the loss and gain of electrons. Multiply the oxidation step by 6 and the reduction step by 1 to equalize the transfer of electrons:

Oxidation $6\ Fe^{2+} \longrightarrow 6\ Fe^3 + 6\ e^-$ $6\ Fe^{2+}$ lose 6 electrons.

Reduction $2\ Cr^{6+} + 6\ e^- \longrightarrow 2\ Cr^{3+}$ $2\ Cr^{6+}$ gain 6 electrons.

Step 4. Transfer the coefficients from the balanced redox equations into the original equation. (Note that one formula unit of $K_2Cr_2O_7$ contains two Cr atoms.) We need to use 1 $K_2Cr_2O_7$, 2 $CrCl_3$, 6 $FeCl_2$, and 6 $FeCl_3$.

$$K_2Cr_2O_7 + 6\ FeCl_2 + HCl \longrightarrow$$
$$2\ CrCl_3 + KCl + 6\ FeCl_3 + H_2O \qquad \text{(unbalanced)}$$

Step 5. Balance the remaining elements in this order: K, Cl, H, O.

$$K_2Cr_2O_7 + 6\ FeCl_2 + 14\ HCl \longrightarrow$$
$$2\ CrCl_3 + 2\ KCl + 6\ FeCl_3 + 7\ H_2O \qquad \text{(balanced)}$$

Check: The final balanced equation contains 2 K atoms, 2 Cr atoms, 7 O atoms, 6 Fe atoms, 26 Cl atoms, and 14 H atoms on each side.

17.4   Balancing Ionic Redox Equations

The main difference between balancing ionic and balancing molecular redox equations is in the handling of ions. In addition to having the same number of each kind of element on both sides of the final equation, the net charges must also be equal. In assigning oxidation numbers we must be careful to consider the charge on the ions. In many respects, balancing ionic equations is much simpler than balancing molecular equations.

Several methods can be used to balance ionic redox equations. These methods include, with slight modification, the oxidation-number method just shown for molecular equations. But the most popular is probably the ion–electron method, which is explained in the following paragraphs.

The ion–electron method uses ionic charges and electrons to balance ionic redox equations. Oxidation numbers are not formally used, but it is necessary to determine what is being oxidized and what is being reduced. The method is as follows:

1. Write the two half-reactions that contain the elements being oxidized and reduced.
2. Balance the elements other than oxygen and hydrogen.
3. Balance oxygen and hydrogen: **(a)** acidic solutions; **(b)** basic solutions.
    (a) For reactions that occur in acidic solution, use H^+ and H_2O to balance oxygen and hydrogen. For each oxygen needed, use one H_2O. Then add H^+ as needed to balance the hydrogen atoms.
    (b) Balancing equations that occur in alkaline solutions is a bit more complicated. For reactions that occur in alkaline solutions, first balance as though the reaction were in an acidic solution, using Steps 1, 2, and 3(a). Then add as many OH^- ions to each side of the equation as there are H^+ ions in the equation. Now combine the H^+ and OH^- ions into water (for example, $4\,H^+$ and $4\,OH^-$ give $4\,H_2O$). Rewrite the equation, canceling equal numbers of water molecules that appear on opposite sides of the equation. Now proceed to Step 4 for electrical balance.
4. Add electrons (e^-) to each half-reation to bring them into electrical balance.
5. Since the loss and gain of electrons must be equal, multiply each half-reaction by the appropriate number to make the number of electrons the same in each half-reaction.
6. Add the two half-reactions together, canceling electrons and any other identical substances that appear on opposite sides of the equation.

PROBLEM

17.5

Balance this equation using the ion–electron method:

$$MnO_4^- + S^{2-} \longrightarrow Mn^{2+} + S^0 \quad \text{(Acidic solution)}$$

Step 1. Write two half-reactions, one containing the element being oxidized and the other, the element being reduced:

Oxidation $S^{2-} \longrightarrow S^0$

Reduction $MnO_4^- \longrightarrow Mn^{2+}$

Step 2. Balance elements other than oxygen and hydrogen (accomplished in Step 1 in this example—1 S and 1 Mn on each side).

Step 3. Balance O and H. The oxidation requires neither O nor H, but the reduction equation needs 4 H_2O on the right and 8 H^+ on the left [Step 3(a)].

$$S^{2-} \longrightarrow S^0$$

$$8\,H^+ + MnO_4^- \longrightarrow Mn^{2+} + 4\,H_2O$$

Step 4. Balance electrically with electrons:

$$S^{2-} \longrightarrow S^0 + 2\,e^- \qquad \text{Net charge} = -2 \text{ on each side.}$$

$$5\,e^- + 8\,H^+ + MnO_4^- \longrightarrow Mn^{2+} + 4\,H_2O \qquad \text{Net charge} = +2 \text{ on each side.}$$

Step 5. Equalize loss and gain of electrons. In this case multiply the oxidation equation by 5 and the reduction equation by 2:

$$5\,S^{2-} \longrightarrow 5\,S^0 + 10\,e^-$$

$$10\,e^- + 16\,H^+ + 2\,MnO_4^- \longrightarrow 2\,Mn^{2+} + 8\,H_2O$$

Step 6. Add the two half-reactions together, cancelling the 10 e^- from each side, to obtain the balanced equation:

$$5\,S^{2-} \rightarrow 5\,S^0 + \cancel{10\,e^-}$$
$$\underline{\cancel{10\,e^-} + 16\,H^+ + 2\,MnO_4^- \rightarrow 2\,Mn^{2+} + 8\,H_2O}$$
$$16\,H^+ + 2\,MnO_4^- + 5\,S^{2-} \rightarrow 2\,Mn^{2+} + 5\,S^0 + 8\,H_2O \qquad \text{(balanced)}$$

Check: Both sides of the equation have a charge of +4 and contain the same number of atoms of each element.

PROBLEM

17.6

Balance the following equation:

$$CrO_4^{2-} + Fe(OH)_2 \longrightarrow Cr(OH)_3 + Fe(OH)_3 \qquad \text{(Basic solution)}$$

Step 1. Write the two half-reactions:

Oxidation $\qquad Fe(OH)_2 \longrightarrow Fe(OH)_3$

Reduction $\qquad CrO_4^{2-} \longrightarrow Cr(OH)_3$

Step 2. Balance elements other than O and H (accomplished in Step 1).

Step 3. Balance O and H as though the solution were acidic [Step 3(a)]. Use H_2O and H^+. To balance O and H in the oxidation equation, add 1 H_2O on the left and 1 H^+ on the right side of the equation:

$$Fe(OH)_2 + H_2O \longrightarrow Fe(OH)_3 + H^+$$

Add 1 OH^- to each side:

$$Fe(OH)_2 + H_2O + OH^- \longrightarrow Fe(OH)_3 + H^+ + OH^-$$

Combine H^+ and OH^- as H_2O and rewrite, canceling H_2O on each side [Step 3(b)]:

$$Fe(OH)_2 + \cancel{H_2O} + OH^- \longrightarrow Fe(OH)_3 + \cancel{H_2O}$$

$$Fe(OH)_2 + OH^- \longrightarrow Fe(OH)_3$$

To balance O and H in the reduction equation, add 1 H_2O on the right and 5 H^+ on the left:

$$CrO_4^{2-} + 5\ H^+ \longrightarrow Cr(OH)_3 + H_2O$$

Add 5 OH^- to each side:

$$CrO_4^{2-} + 5\ H^+ + 5\ OH^- \longrightarrow Cr(OH)_3 + H_2O + 5\ OH^-$$

Combine 5 H^+ and 5 OH^- as 5 H_2O:

$$CrO_4^{2-} + 5\ H_2O \longrightarrow Cr(OH)_3 + H_2O + 5\ OH^-$$

Rewrite, cancelling 1 H_2O from each side:

$$CrO_4^{2-} + 4\ H_2O \longrightarrow Cr(OH)_3 + 5\ OH^-$$

Step 4. Balance electrically with electrons:

$$Fe(OH)_2 + OH^- \longrightarrow Fe(OH)_3 + e^-$$ (Balanced oxidation equation)

$$CrO_4^{2-} + 4\ H_2O + 3\ e^- \longrightarrow Cr(OH)_3 + 5\ OH^-$$ (Balanced reduction equation)

Step 5. Equalize the loss and gain of electrons. Multiply the oxidation reaction by 3:

$$3\ Fe(OH)_2 + 3\ OH^- \longrightarrow 3\ Fe(OH)_3 + 3\ e^-$$

$$CrO_4^{2-} + 4\ H_2O + 3\ e^- \longrightarrow Cr(OH)_3 + 5\ OH^-$$

Step 6. Add the two half-reactions together, cancelling the 3 e^- and 3 OH^- from each side of the equation.

$$3\ Fe(OH)_2 + 3\ OH^- \longrightarrow 3\ Fe(OH)_3 + \cancel{3\ e^-}$$
$$\underline{CrO_4^{2-} + 4\ H_2O + \cancel{3\ e^-} \longrightarrow Cr(OH)_3 + 5\ OH^-}$$
$$CrO_4^{2-} + 3\ Fe(OH)_2 + 4\ H_2O \longrightarrow Cr(OH)_3 + 3\ Fe(OH)_3 + 2\ OH^-$$ (balanced)

Check: Each side of the equation has a charge of -2 and contains the same number of atoms of each element.

Ionic equations can also be balanced by using the electron-transfer method shown in Section 17.3. Steps 1, 2, 3, and 4 are the same. In Step 5 the electrical charges are balanced with H^+ in acidic solutions and with OH^- in basic solutions. H_2O is then used to complete the balancing of the equation. Let us use the same equation as in Problem 17.6 as an example of this method.

PROBLEM

17.7

Balance the following equation using the electron-transfer method:

$$CrO_4^{2-} + Fe(OH)_2 \longrightarrow Cr(OH)_3 + Fe(OH)_3 \quad \text{(Basic solution)}$$

Steps 1 and 2. Assign oxidation numbers and balance the charges with electrons:

Reduction $\quad Cr^{6+} + 3\,e^- \longrightarrow Cr^{3+} \qquad Cr^{6+}$ gains 3 e$^-$.

Oxidation $\quad Fe^{2+} \longrightarrow Fe^{3+} + e^- \qquad Fe^{2+}$ loses 1 e$^-$.

Step 3. Equalize the loss and gain of electrons. Multiply the oxidation step by 3:

$$3\,Fe^{2+} \longrightarrow 3\,Fe^{3+} + 3\,e^+ \qquad 3\,Fe^{2+} \text{ lose 3 e}^-.$$

$$Cr^{6+} + 3\,e^- \longrightarrow Cr^{3+} \qquad Cr^{6+} \text{ gains 3 e}^-.$$

Step 4. Transfer coefficients back to the original equation:

$$CrO_4^{2-} + 3\,Fe(OH)_2 \longrightarrow Cr(OH)_3 + 3\,Fe(OH)_3$$

Step 5. Balance electrically. Because the solution is basic, use OH$^-$ to balance charges. The charge on the left side is -2, and on the right side is 0. Add 2 OH$^-$ ions to the right side of the equations:

$$CrO_4^{2-} + 3\,Fe(OH)_2 \longrightarrow Cr(OH)_3 + 3\,Fe(OH)_3 + 2\,OH^-$$

Adding 4 H$_2$O to the left side balances the equation:

$$CrO_4^{2-} + 3\,Fe(OH)_2 + 4\,H_2O \longrightarrow Cr(OH)_3 + 3\,Fe(OH)_3 + 2\,OH^- \quad \text{(balanced)}$$

Check: Each side of the equation has a charge of -2 and contains the same number of atoms of each element.

17.5 Activity Series of Metals

Knowledge of the relative chemical reactivities of the elements helps us to predict the course of many chemical reactions.

Calcium reacts with cold water to produce hydrogen, and magnesium reacts with steam to produce hydrogen. Therefore, calcium is considered to be a more reactive metal than magnesium.

$$Ca(s) + 2\,H_2O(l) \longrightarrow Ca(OH)_2(aq) + H_2(g)$$

$$Mg(s) + \underset{\text{Steam}}{H_2O(g)} \longrightarrow MgO(s) + H_2(g)$$

The difference in their activity is attributed to the fact that calcium loses its two valence electrons more easily than does magnesium and is therefore more reactive and/or more readily oxidized than magnesium.

When a strip of copper is placed in a solution of silver nitrate ($AgNO_3$), free silver begins to plate out on the copper. After the reaction has continued for some time, we can observe a blue color in the solution, indicating the presence of copper(II) ions. If a strip of silver is placed in a solution of copper(II) nitrate, $Cu(NO_3)_2$, no reaction is visible. The equations are

$$Cu^0 + 2\ AgNO_3(aq) \longrightarrow 2\ Ag^0 + Cu(NO_3)_2(aq)$$

$$Cu^0 + 2\ Ag^+ \longrightarrow 2\ Ag^0 + Cu^{2+} \qquad \text{Net ionic equation}$$

$$Cu^0 \longrightarrow Cu^{2+} + 2\ e^- \qquad\qquad \text{Oxidation of } Cu^0$$

$$Ag^+ + e^- \longrightarrow Ag^0 \qquad\qquad \text{Reduction of } Ag^+$$

$$Ag^0 + Cu(NO_3)_2(aq) \longrightarrow \text{No reaction}$$

In the reaction between Cu and $AgNO_3$, electrons are transferred from Cu^0 atoms to Ag^+ ions in solution. Copper has a greater tendency than silver to lose electrons, so an electrochemical force is exerted upon silver ions to accept electrons from copper atoms. When a Ag^+ ion accepts an electron, it is reduced to a Ag^0 atom and is no longer soluble in solution. At the same time, Cu^0 is oxidized and goes into solution as Cu^{2+} ions. From this reaction we can conclude that copper is more reactive than silver.

Metals such as sodium, magnesium, zinc, and iron, which react with solutions of acids to liberate hydrogen, are more reactive than hydrogen. Metals such as copper, silver, and mercury, which do not react with solutions of acids to liberate hydrogen, are less reactive than hydrogen. By studying a series of reactions such as those given above, we can list metals according to their chemical activity, placing the most active at the top and the least active at the bottom. This list is called the **activity series of metals.** Table 17.3 shows some of the common metals in the series. The arrangement corresponds to the ease with which the elements listed are oxidized (lose electrons), with the most easily oxidizable element listed first. More extensive tables are available in chemistry reference books.

activity series of metals

The general principles governing the arrangement and use of the activity series are as follows:

1. The reactivity of the metals listed decreases from top to bottom.
2. A free metal can displace the ion of a second metal from solution provided that the free metal is above the second metal in the activity series.
3. Free metals above hydrogen react with nonoxidizing acids in solution to liberate hydrogen gas.
4. Free metals below hydrogen do not liberate hydrogen from acids.
5. Conditions such as temperature and concentration may affect the relative position of some of these elements.

Two examples of the application of the activity series are given in the following problems.

Table 17.3 Activity series of metals

$$\begin{array}{ll}
\text{K} & \longrightarrow \text{K}^+ \; + \; e^- \\
\text{Ba} & \longrightarrow \text{Ba}^{2+} + 2e^- \\
\text{Ca} & \longrightarrow \text{Ca}^{2+} + 2e^- \\
\text{Na} & \longrightarrow \text{Na}^+ \; + \; e^- \\
\text{Mg} & \longrightarrow \text{Mg}^{2+} + 2e^- \\
\text{Al} & \longrightarrow \text{Al}^{3+} + 3e^- \\
\text{Zn} & \longrightarrow \text{Zn}^{2+} + 2e^- \\
\text{Cr} & \longrightarrow \text{Cr}^{3+} + 3e^- \\
\text{Fe} & \longrightarrow \text{Fe}^{2+} + 2e^- \\
\text{Ni} & \longrightarrow \text{Ni}^{2+} + 2e^- \\
\text{Sn} & \longrightarrow \text{Sn}^{2+} + 2e^- \\
\text{Pb} & \longrightarrow \text{Pb}^{2+} + 2e^- \\
\text{H}_2 & \longrightarrow 2\,\text{H}^+ + 2e^- \\
\text{Cu} & \longrightarrow \text{Cu}^{2+} + 2e^- \\
\text{As} & \longrightarrow \text{As}^{3+} + 3e^- \\
\text{Ag} & \longrightarrow \text{Ag}^+ \; + \; e^- \\
\text{Hg} & \longrightarrow \text{Hg}^{2+} + 2e^- \\
\text{Au} & \longrightarrow \text{Au}^{3+} + 3e^-
\end{array}$$

Ease of oxidation ↑

PROBLEM

17.8

Will zinc metal react with dilute sulfuric acid?

From Table 17.3 we see that zinc is above hydrogen; therefore zinc atoms will lose electrons more readily than hydrogen atoms. Hence, zinc atoms will reduce hydrogen ions from the acid to form hydrogen gas and zinc ions. In fact, these reagents are commonly used for the laboratory preparation of hydrogen. The equation is

$$\text{Zn(s)} + \text{H}_2\text{SO}_4\text{(aq)} \longrightarrow \text{ZnSO}_4\text{(aq)} + \text{H}_2\text{(g)}$$

$$\text{Zn(s)} + 2\,\text{H}^+\text{(aq)} \longrightarrow \text{Zn}^{2+}\text{(aq)} + \text{H}_2\text{(g)} \qquad \text{Net ionic equation}$$

PROBLEM

17.9

Will a reaction occur when copper metal is placed in an iron(II) sulfate solution?

No, copper lies below iron in the series, loses electrons less easily than iron, and therefore will not displace iron(II) ions from solution. In fact, the reverse is true. When an iron nail is dipped into a copper(II) sulfate solution, it becomes coated with free copper. The equations are

$$\text{Cu(s)} + \text{FeSO}_4\text{(aq)} \longrightarrow \text{no reaction}$$

$$\text{Fe(s)} + \text{CuSO}_4\text{(aq)} \longrightarrow \text{FeSO}_4\text{(aq)} + \text{Cu} \downarrow$$

From Table 17.3 we may abstract the following pair in their relative position to each other:

$$\text{Fe} \longrightarrow \text{Fe}^{2+} + 2\,e^-$$

$$\text{Cu} \longrightarrow \text{Cu}^{2+} + 2\,e^-$$

According to the second principle listed above on the use of the activity series, we can predict that free iron will react with copper(II) ions in solution to form free copper metal and iron(II) ions in solution.

$$Fe(s) + Cu^{2+}(aq) \longrightarrow Fe^{2+}(aq) + Cu(s) \qquad \text{Net ionic equation}$$

17.6 Electrolytic and Voltaic Cells

electrolysis

electrolytic cell

cathode

anode

The process in which electrical energy is used to bring about chemical change is known as **electrolysis.** An **electrolytic cell** uses electrical energy to produce a nonspontaneous chemical reaction. The use of electrical energy has many applications in the chemical industry—for example, in the production of sodium, sodium hydroxide, chlorine, fluorine, magnesium, aluminum, and pure hydrogen and oxygen, and in the purification and electroplating of metals.

What happens when an electric current is passed through a solution? Let us consider a hydrochloric acid solution in a simple electrolytic cell, as shown in Figure 17.2. The cell consists of a source of direct current (a battery) connected to two electrodes that are immersed in a solution of hydrochloric acid. The negative electrode is called the **cathode** because cations are attracted to it. The positive electrode is called the **anode** because anions are attracted to it. The cathode is attached to the negative pole and the anode to the positive pole of the battery. The battery supplies electrons to the cathode.

When the switch is closed, the electric circuit is completed; positive hydronium ions (H_3O^+) migrate to the cathode, where they pick up electrons and evolve hydrogen gas. At the same time the negative chloride ions (Cl^-) migrate to the anode, where they lose electrons and evolve chlorine gas.

Figure 17.2   Electrolysis: During the electrolysis of a hydrochloric acid solution, positive hydronium ions are attracted to the cathode, where they gain electrons and form hydrogen gas. Chloride ions migrate to the anode, where they lose electrons and form chlorine gas. The equation for this process is $2\ HCl(aq) \longrightarrow H_2(g) + Cl_2(g)$.

Reaction at the cathode (reduction)	$H_3O^+ + 1\ e^- \longrightarrow H^0 + H_2O$
	$H^0 + H^0 \longrightarrow H_2(g)$
Reaction at the anode (oxidation)	$Cl^- \longrightarrow Cl^0 + 1\ e^-$
	$Cl^0 + Cl^0 \longrightarrow Cl_2(g)$
Net reaction	$2\ HCl(aq) \xrightarrow{\text{Electrolysis}} H_2(g) + Cl_2(g)$

Note that oxidation–reduction has taken place. Chloride ions lose electrons (are oxidized) at the anode, and hydronium ions gain electrons (are reduced) at the cathode.

Oxidation always occurs at the anode and reduction at the cathode.

When concentrated sodium chloride solutions (brines) are electrolyzed, the products are sodium hydroxide, hydrogen, and chlorine. The overall reaction is

$$2\ Na^+ + 2\ Cl^- + 2\ H_2O \xrightarrow{\text{Electrolysis}} 2\ Na^+ + 2\ OH^- + H_2(g) + Cl_2(g)$$

The net ionic equation is

$$2\ Cl^-(aq) + 2\ H_2O(l) \longrightarrow 2\ OH^-(aq) + H_2(g) + Cl_2(g)$$

During the electrolysis, Na^+ ions move toward the cathode and Cl^- ions move toward the anode. The anode reaction is similar to that of hydrochloric acid; chlorine is liberated.

$$2\ Cl^-(aq) \longrightarrow Cl_2(g) + 2\ e^-$$

Even though Na^+ ions are attracted by the cathode, the facts show that hydrogen is liberated there. No evidence of metallic sodium is found, but the area around the cathode tests alkaline from accumulated OH^- ions. The reaction at the cathode is

$$2\ H_2O(l) + 2\ e^- \longrightarrow H_2(g) + 2\ OH^-(aq)$$

If the electrolysis is allowed to continue until all the chloride is reacted, the solution remaining will contain only sodium hydroxide, which on evaporation yields solid NaOH. Large tonnages of sodium hydroxide and chlorine are made by this process.

When molten sodium chloride (without water) is subjected to electrolysis, metallic sodium and chlorine gas are formed:

$$2\ Na^+(l) + 2\ Cl^-(l) \xrightarrow{\text{Electrolysis}} 2\ Na(l) + Cl_2(g)$$

An important electrochemical application is the electroplating of metals. Electroplating is the art of covering a surface or an object with a thin adherent electrodeposited metal coating. Electroplating is done for protection of the surface of the base metal or for a purely decorative effect. The layer deposited is surprisingly thin, varying from as little as 5×10^{-5} cm to 2×10^{-3} cm, depending on the metal and the intended use. The object to be plated is set up as the cathode and is immersed in a solution containing ions of the metal to be plated. When an electric current passes through the solution, metal ions that migrate to the cathode are reduced, depositing on the object as the free metal. In most cases the metal deposited on the object is replaced in the solution by using an anode of the same metal. The following equations show the chemical changes in the electroplating of nickel:

Reaction at the cathode $Ni^{2+}(aq) + 2\,e^- \longrightarrow Ni(s)$ Ni plated out on an object

Reaction at the anode $Ni(s) \longrightarrow Ni^{2+}(aq) + 2\,e^-$ Ni replenished in solution

Metals commonly used in commercial electroplating are copper, nickel, zinc, lead, cadmium, chromium, tin, gold, and silver.

In the electrolytic cell shown in Figure 17.2, electrical energy from the battery is used to bring about nonspontaneous redox reactions. The hydrogen and chlorine produced have more potential energy than was present in the hydrochloric acid before electrolysis.

Conversely, some spontaneous redox reactions can be made to supply useful amounts of electrical energy. When a piece of zinc is put in a copper(II) sulfate solution, the zinc quickly becomes coated with metallic copper. We expect this coating to happen because zinc is above copper in the activity series; copper(II) ions are therefore reduced by zinc atoms:

$$Zn^0(s) + Cu^{2+}(aq) \longrightarrow Zn^{2+}(aq) + Cu^0(s)$$

This reaction is clearly a spontaneous redox reaction, but simply dipping a zinc rod into a copper(II) sulfate solution will not produce useful electric current. However, when we carry out this reaction in the cell shown in Figure 17.3, an electric current is produced. The cell consists of a piece of zinc immersed in a zinc sulfate solution and connected by a wire through a voltmeter to a piece of copper immersed in copper(II) sulfate solution. The two solutions are connected by a salt bridge. Such a cell produces an electric current and a potential of about 1.1 volts when both solutions are 1.0 M in concentration. A cell that produces electric current from a spontaneous chemical reaction is called a **voltaic cell**. A voltaic cell is also known as a *galvanic cell*.

voltaic cell

The driving force responsible for the electric current in the zinc–copper cell originates in the great tendency of zinc atoms to lose electrons relative to the tendency of copper(II) ions to gain electrons. In the cell shown in Figure 17.3, zinc atoms lose electrons and are converted to zinc ions at the zinc electrode surface; the electrons flow through the wire (external circuit) to the copper electrode. Here copper(II) ions pick up electrons and are reduced to copper atoms, which plate out on the copper electrode. Sulfate ions flow from the $CuSO_4$ solution via the salt bridge into the $ZnSO_4$ solution (internal circuit) to complete

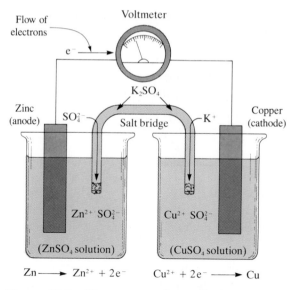

Figure 17.3 Zinc–copper voltaic cell: The cell has a potential of 1.1 volts when $ZnSO_4$ and $CuSO_4$ solutions are 1.0 M. The salt bridge provides electrical contact between the two half-cells.

the circuit. The equations for the reactions of this cell are

Anode	$Zn^0(s) \longrightarrow Zn^{2+}(aq) + 2\ e^-$	Oxidation
Cathode	$Cu^{2+}(aq) + 2\ e^- \longrightarrow Cu^0(s)$	Reduction
Net ionic	$Zn^0(s) + Cu^{2+}(aq) \longrightarrow Zn^{2+}(aq) + Cu^0(s)$	
Overall	$Zn(s) + CuSO_4(aq) \longrightarrow Cu(s) + ZnSO_4(aq)$	

The redox reaction, the movement of electrons in the metallic or external part of the circuit, and the movement of ions in the solution or internal part of the circuit of the copper–zinc cell are very similar to the actions that occur in the electrolytic cell of Figure 17.2. The only important difference is that the reactions of the zinc–copper cell are spontaneous. This spontaneity is the crucial difference between all voltaic and electrolytic cells.

Voltaic cells use chemical reactions to produce electrical energy, and electrolytic cells use electrical energy to produce chemical reactions.

Although the zinc–copper voltaic cell is no longer used commercially, it was used to energize the first transcontinental telegraph lines. Such cells were the direct ancestors of the many different kinds of "dry" cells that operate portable radio and television sets, automatic cameras, tape recorders, and so on.

Figure 17.4 Diagram of an alkaline zinc–mercury cell

One such "dry" cell, the alkaline zinc–mercury cell, is shown diagrammatically in Figure 17.4. The reactions occurring in this cell are

Anode	$Zn^0 + 2\,OH^- \longrightarrow ZnO + H_2O + 2e^-$	Oxidation
Cathode	$HgO + H_2O + 2e^- \longrightarrow Hg^0 + 2\,OH^-$	Reduction
Net ionic	$Zn^0 + Hg^{2+} \longrightarrow Zn^{2+} + Hg^0$	
Overall	$Zn^0 + HgO \longrightarrow ZnO + Hg^0$	

To offset the relatively high initial cost, this cell (a) provides current at a very steady potential of about 1.5 volts, (b) has an exceptionally long service life—that is, high energy output to weight ratio, (c) is completely self-contained, and (d) can be stored for relatively long periods of time when not in use.

An automobile storage battery is an energy reservoir. The charged battery acts as a voltaic cell and through chemical reactions furnishes electrical energy to operate the starter, lights, radio, and so on. When the engine is running, a generator, or alternator, produces and forces an electric current through the battery and, by electrolytic chemical action, restores the battery to the charged condition.

The cell unit consists of a lead plate filled with spongy lead and a lead dioxide plate, both immersed in dilute sulfuric acid solution, which serves as the electrolyte (see Figure 17.5). When the cell is discharging, or acting as a voltaic cell, these reactions occur:

Pb plate (anode)	$Pb^0 \longrightarrow Pb^{2+} + 2\,e^-$	Oxidation
PbO$_2$ plate (cathode)	$PbO_2 + 4\,H^+ + 2\,e^- \longrightarrow Pb^{2+} + 2\,H_2O$	Reduction
Net ionic redox reaction	$Pb^0 + PbO_2 + 4\,H^+ \longrightarrow 2\,Pb^{2+} + 2\,H_2O$	

Figure 17.5 Cross-sectional diagram of a lead storage battery cell

Precipitation
reaction on
plates

$$Pb^{2+} + SO_4^{2-} \longrightarrow PbSO_4(s)$$

Because lead(II) sulfate is insoluble, the Pb^{2+} ions combine with SO_4^{2-} ions to form a coating of $PbSO_4$ on each plate. The overall chemical reaction of the cell is

$$Pb(s) + PbO_2(s) + 2\ H_2SO_4(aq) \xrightarrow[\text{cycle}]{\text{Discharge}} 2\ PbSO_4(s) + 2\ H_2O(l)$$

The cell can be recharged by reversing the chemical reaction. This reversal is accomplished by forcing an electric current through the cell in the opposite direction. Lead sulfate and water are reconverted to lead, lead dioxide, and sulfuric acid:

$$2\ PbSO_4(s) + 2\ H_2O(l) \xrightarrow[\text{cycle}]{\text{Charge}} Pb(s) + PbO_2(s) + 2\ H_2SO_4(aq)$$

The electrolyte in a lead storage battery is a 38% by weight sulfuric acid solution having a density of 1.29 g/mL. As the battery is discharged, sulfuric acid is removed, thereby decreasing the density of the electrolyte solution. The state of charge or discharge of the battery can be estimated by measuring the density (or specific gravity) of the electrolyte solution with a hydrometer. When the density has dropped to about 1.05 g/mL, the battery needs recharging.

In a commercial battery, each cell consists of a series of cell units of alternating lead–lead dioxide plates separated and supported by wood, glass wool, or fiberglass. The energy storage capacity of a single cell is limited, and its electrical potential is only about 2 volts. Therefore, a bank of six cells is connected in series to provide the 12 volt output of the usual automobile battery.

QUESTIONS

A. *Review the meanings of the new terms introduced in this chapter.*

1. Oxidation–reduction
2. Redox
3. Oxidation
4. Reduction
5. Oxidizing agent
6. Reducing agent
7. Activity series of metals
8. Electrolysis
9. Electrolytic cell
10. Cathode
11. Anode
12. Voltaic cell

B. *Information useful in answering the following questions will be found in the tables and figures.*

1. In the equation

$$I_2 + 5\ Cl_2 + 6\ H_2O \longrightarrow 2\ HIO_3 + 10\ HCl$$

   (a) Has iodine been oxidized or has it been reduced?
   (b) Has chlorine been oxidized or has it been reduced? (See Figure 17.1.)

2. Based on Table 17.3, which element of each pair is more active?
   (a) Ag or Al   (b) Na or Ba   (c) Ni or Cu

3. Based on Table 17.3, will the following combinations react in aqueous solution?
   (a) $Zn + Cu^{2+}$ (e) $Ba + FeCl_2$
   (b) $Ag + H^+$ (f) $Pb + NaCl$
   (c) $Sn + Ag^+$ (g) $Ni + Hg(NO_3)_2$
   (d) $As + Mg^{2+}$ (h) $Al + CuSO_4$

4. The reaction between powdered aluminum and iron(III) oxide (in the Thermite process), producing molten iron, is very exothermic.
   (a) Write the equation for the chemical reaction that occurs.
   (b) Explain in terms of Table 17.3 why a reaction occurs.
   (c) Would you expect a reaction between powdered iron and aluminum oxide?
   (d) Would you expect a reaction between powdered aluminum and chromium(III) oxide?

5. Write equations for the chemical reaction of each of the following metals with dilute solutions of (a) hydrochloric acid and (b) sulfuric acid: alumi-

num, chromium, gold, iron, copper, magnesium, mercury, and zinc. If a reaction will not occur, write "no reaction" as the product. (See Table 17.3)

6. A $NiCl_2$ solution is placed in the apparatus shown in Figure 17.2, instead of the HCl solution shown. Write equations for:
   (a) the anode reaction
   (b) the cathode reaction
   (c) the net electrochemical reaction

7. What is the major distinction between the reactions occurring in Figure 17.2 and those in Figure 17.3?

8. In the cell shown in Figure 17.3,
   (a) What would be the effect of removing the voltmeter and connecting the wires shown coming to the voltmeter?
   (b) What would be the effect of removing the salt bridge?

C. *Review questions*

1. What is the oxidation number of the underlined element in each compound?
   (a) $Na\underline{Cl}$ (e) $H_2\underline{S}O_3$ (i) $\underline{N}H_3$
   (b) $Fe\underline{Cl}_3$ (f) $\underline{N}H_4Cl$ (j) $K\underline{Cl}O_3$
   (c) $\underline{Pb}O_2$ (g) $K\underline{Mn}O_4$ (k) $K_2\underline{Cr}O_4$
   (d) $Na\underline{N}O_3$ (h) $\underline{I}_2$ (l) $K_2\underline{Cr}_2O_7$

2. What is the oxidation number of the underlined elements?
   (a) $\underline{S}^{2-}$ (d) $\underline{Mn}O_4^-$ (g) $\underline{As}O_4^{3-}$
   (b) $\underline{N}O_2^-$ (e) $\underline{Bi}^{3+}$ (h) $\underline{Fe}(OH)_3$
   (c) $Na_2\underline{O}_2$ (f) $\underline{O}_2$ (i) $\underline{I}O_3^-$

3. In the following half-reactions, which element is changing oxidation state? Is the half-reaction an oxidation or a reduction? Supply the proper number of electrons to the proper side to balance each equation.
   (a) $Zn^{2+} \longrightarrow Zn$
   (b) $2\ Br^- \longrightarrow Br_2$
   (c) $MnO_4^- + 8\ H^+ \longrightarrow Mn^{2+} + 4\ H_2O$
   (d) $Ni \longrightarrow Ni^{2+}$
   (e) $SO_3^{2-} + H_2O \longrightarrow SO_4^{2-} + 2\ H^+$
   (f) $NO_3^- + 4\ H^+ \longrightarrow NO + 2\ H_2O$
   (g) $S_2O_3^{2-} + 2\ H_2O \longrightarrow 2\ SO_3^{2-} + 4\ H^+$
   (h) $Fe^{2+} \longrightarrow Fe^{3+}$

4. In the following unbalanced equations,
   (a) Identify the element that is oxidized and the element that is reduced.

(b) Identify the oxidizing agent and the reducing agent.
(1) $Cr + HCl \longrightarrow CrCl_3 + H_2$
(2) $SO_4^{2-} + I^- + H^+ \longrightarrow H_2S + I_2 + H_2O$
(3) $AsH_3 + Ag^+ + H_2O \longrightarrow$
$$H_3AsO_4 + Ag + H^+$$
(4) $Cl_2 + NaBr \longrightarrow NaCl + Br_2$

5. Balance these equations by the oxidation-number method:
(a) $Zn + S \longrightarrow ZnS$
(b) $AgNO_3 + Pb \longrightarrow Pb(NO_3)_2 + Ag$
(c) $Fe_2O_3 + CO \longrightarrow Fe + CO_2$
(d) $H_2S + HNO_3 \longrightarrow S + NO + H_2O$
(e) $MnO_2 + HBr \longrightarrow MnBr_2 + Br_2 + H_2O$
(f) $Cl_2 + KOH \longrightarrow KCl + KClO_3 + H_2O$
(g) $Ag + HNO_3 \longrightarrow AgNO_3 + NO + H_2O$
(h) $CuO + NH_3 \longrightarrow N_2 + Cu + H_2O$
(i) $PbO_2 + Sb + NaOH \longrightarrow$
$$PbO + NaSbO_2 + H_2O$$
(j) $H_2O_2 + KMnO_4 + H_2SO_4 \longrightarrow$
$$O_2 + MnSO_4 + K_2SO_4 + H_2O$$

6. Balance the following ionic redox equations using the ion–electron method. All reactions occur in acidic solution.
(a) $Zn + NO_3^- \longrightarrow Zn^{2+} + NH_4^+$
(b) $NO_3^- + S \longrightarrow NO_2 + SO_4^{2-}$
(c) $PH_3 + I_2 \longrightarrow H_3PO_2 + I^-$
(d) $Cu + NO_3^- \longrightarrow Cu^{2+} + NO$
(e) $ClO_3^- + I^- \longrightarrow I_2 + Cl^-$
(f) $Cr_2O_7^{2-} + Fe^{2+} \longrightarrow Cr^{3+} + Fe^{3+}$
(g) $MnO_4^- + SO_2 \longrightarrow Mn^{2+} + SO_4^{2-}$
(h) $H_3AsO_3 + MnO_4^- \longrightarrow H_3AsO_4 + Mn^{2+}$
*(i) $ClO_3^- + Cl^- \longrightarrow Cl_2$
*(j) $Cr_2O_7^{2-} + H_3AsO_3 \longrightarrow Cr^{3+} + H_3AsO_4$

7. Balance the following ionic redox equations using the ion–electron method. All reactions occur in basic solutions.
(a) $Cl_2 + IO_3^- \longrightarrow Cl^- + IO_4^-$
(b) $MnO_4^- + ClO_2^- \longrightarrow MnO_2 + ClO_4^-$
(c) $Se \longrightarrow Se^{2-} + SeO_3^{2-}$
(d) $MnO_4^- + SO_3^{2-} \longrightarrow MnO_2 + SO_4^{2-}$
(e) $ClO_2(g) + SbO_2^- \longrightarrow ClO_2^- + Sb(OH)_6^-$
*(f) $Fe_3O_4 + MnO_4^- \longrightarrow Fe_2O_3 + MnO_2$
*(g) $BrO^- + Cr(OH)_4^- \longrightarrow Br^- + CrO_4^{2-}$
*(h) $P_4 \longrightarrow HPO_3^{2-} + PH_3$
*(i) $Al + OH^- \longrightarrow Al(OH)_4^- + H_2$
*(j) $Al + NO_3^- \longrightarrow NH_3 + Al(OH)_4^-$

8. Why are oxidation and reduction said to be complementary processes?

9. When molten $CaBr_2$ is electrolyzed, calcium metal and bromine are produced. Write equations for the two half-reactions that occur at the electrodes. Label the anode half-reaction and the cathode half-reaction.

10. Why is direct current used instead of alternating current in the electroplating of metals?

11. The chemical reactions taking place during discharge in a lead storage battery are

$$Pb + SO_4^{2-} \longrightarrow PbSO_4$$

$$PbO_2 + SO_4^{2-} + 4H^+ \longrightarrow PbSO_4 + 2H_2O$$

(a) Complete each half-reaction by supplying electrons.
(b) Which reaction is oxidation and which is reduction?
(c) Which reaction occurs at the anode of the battery?

12. What property of lead dioxide and lead(II) sulfate makes it unnecessary to have salt bridges in the cells of a lead storage battery?

13. Explain why the density of the electrolyte in a lead storage battery decreases during the discharge cycle.

14. In one type of alkaline cell used to power devices such as portable radios, Hg^{2+} ions are reduced to metallic mercury when the cell is being discharged. Does this reduction occur at the anode or the cathode? Explain.

15. Differentiate between an electrolytic cell and a voltaic cell.

16. Why is a porous barrier or a salt bridge necessary in some voltaic cells?

17. Which of the following statements are correct?
(a) An atom of an element in the uncombined state has an oxidation number of zero.
(b) The oxidation number of molybdenum in Na_2MoO_4 is +4.
(c) The oxidation number of an ion is the same as the electrical charge on the ion.
(d) The process in which an atom or an ion loses electrons is called reduction.
(e) The reaction $Fe^{3+} + e^- \longrightarrow Fe^{2+}$ is a reduction reaction.
(f) In the reaction

$$2Al + 3CuCl_2 \longrightarrow 2AlCl_3 + 3Cu$$

aluminum is the oxidizing agent.
(g) In a redox reaction the oxidizing agent

is reduced, and the reducing agent is oxidized.

(h) $Cu^0 \longrightarrow Cu^{2+}$ is a balanced oxidation half-reaction.

(i) In the electrolysis of sodium chloride brine (solution), Cl_2 gas is formed at the cathode, and hydroxide ions are formed at the anode.

(j) In any cell, electrolytic or voltaic, reduction takes place at the cathode, and oxidation occurs at the anode.

(k) In the Zn–Cu voltaic cell, the reaction at the anode is $Zn \longrightarrow Zn^{2+} + 2\,e^-$.

The statements in (l)–(o) pertain to this activity series:

Ba Mg Zn Fe H Cu Ag

(l) The reaction $Zn + MgCl_2 \longrightarrow Mg + ZnCl_2$ is a spontaneous reaction.

(m) Barium is more active than copper.

(n) Silver metal will react with acids to liberate hydrogen gas.

(o) Iron is a better reducing agent than zinc.

(p) Oxidation and reduction occur simultaneously in a chemical reaction; one cannot take place without the other.

(q) A free metal can displace from solution the ions of a metal that lies below the free metal in the activity series.

(r) In electroplating, the piece to be electroplated with a metal is attached to the cathode.

(s) In an automobile lead storage battery, the density of the sulfuric acid solution decreases as the battery discharges.

(t) In an electrolytic cell, chemical energy is used to produce electrical energy.

D. *Review problems*

1. How many moles of NO gas will be formed by the reaction of 25.0 g of silver with nitric acid? [See the equation given in Question C.5(g).]

2. How many liters of chlorine gas, measured at STP, are required to react with excess KOH to form 0.300 mol of $KClO_3$? [See the equation given in Question C.5(f).]

3. How many grams of $KMnO_4$ would be needed to react with 100 mL of H_2O_2 solution (d = 1.031 g/mL, 9.0% H_2O_2 by weight)? [See the equation given in Question C.5(j).]

*4. How many milliliters of 0.200 M $K_2Cr_2O_7$ will be required to oxidize 5.00 g of H_3AsO_3? [See the equation given in Question C.6(j).]

*5. How many milliliters of 0.200 M $K_2Cr_2O_7$ will be required to oxidize the Fe^{2+} ion in 60.0 mL of 0.200 M $FeSO_4$ solution? [See the equation given in Question C.6(f).]

6. A sample of crude potassium iodide was analyzed using the following reaction (not balanced):

$$I^- + SO_4^{2-} \longrightarrow I_2 + H_2S \quad \text{(Acidic solution)}$$

If a 4.00 g sample of crude KI produced 2.79 g of iodine, what is the percent purity of the KI?

7. How many grams of copper are formed when 35.0 L of ammonia gas, measured at STP, react with copper(II) oxide? [See the equation given in Question C.5(h).]

*8. How many liters of NO gas, measured at 28°C and 744 torr, will be formed by the reaction of 0.500 mol of Ag reacting with excess nitric acid? [See the equation given in Question C.5(g).]

9. How many moles of H_2 can be produced from 100 g of Al according to the following reaction?

$$Al + OH^- \longrightarrow Al(OH)_4^- + H_2 \quad \text{(Basic solution)}$$

18

Radioactivity and Nuclear Chemistry

After studying Chapter 18, you should be able to

1. Understand the new terms listed in Question A at the end of the chapter.
2. Outline the historical development of nuclear chemistry, giving the major contributions of Henri Becquerel, Marie Curie, Ernest Rutherford, Paul Villard, E. O. Lawrence, Irene Joliot-Curie, Otto Hahn, F. Strassmann, and Edwin McMillan.
3. Write balanced nuclear chemical equations using isotopic notation.
4. Determine the amount of a radioactive nuclide remaining after a given period of time when the starting amount and half-life are given.
5. List the characteristics that distinguish alpha, beta, and gamma rays from the standpoint of mass, charge, relative velocities, and penetrating power.
6. Describe the effect of a magnetic field on alpha particles, beta particles, and gamma rays.
7. Describe a radioactive disintegration series and predict what nuclide (isotope) would be formed by the loss of specified numbers of alpha and beta particles from a given radioactive nuclide.
8. Discuss the transmutation of elements.
9. Describe the use of the Geiger counter in measuring radioactivity and the units for measuring radioactivity.
10. Distinguish between radioactive disintegration and nuclear fission reactions.
11. Tell how the fission of $^{235}_{92}U$ can lead to a chain reaction and why a critical mass is needed for the chain reaction.

12. Explain how the energy from nuclear fission is converted to electrical energy.

13. Tell what the essential difference is between the fission reactions of a nuclear reactor and those of an atomic bomb.

14. Explain what is meant by nuclear fusion and why large-scale efforts to develop controlled nuclear fusion are under way.

15. Discuss the significance of mass defect and nuclear binding energy.

16. Calculate the mass defect and binding energy of a given nuclide from appropriate data.

17. Explain how nuclear radiation can cause acute, long-term, and genetic damage to living organisms.

18. Describe the formation of carbon-14 in the atmosphere and tell how this isotope is used to determine the age of carbon-containing material.

19. Explain the use of radioactive tracers.

Up to this point, we have considered only atomic changes that involve the electron structures of atoms and molecules. We now introduce an entirely different aspect of the atom—reactions of the nucleus. Since the dramatic ending of World War II, nuclear chemistry has become a tremendously important branch of science. The immense amounts of energy available from nuclear reactions can be used for constructive or destructive purposes. The controlled release of nuclear energy has become an important source of power. Nuclear power plants are in operation or are built in virtually every industrialized nation in the world. The use of radioactive tracers is a routine technique in industry and in biological and medical research and applications.

18.1   Discovery of Radioactivity

One of the most important steps leading to the discovery of radioactivity was made in 1895 by Wilhelm Konrad Roentgen (1845–1923). Roentgen discovered X rays when he observed that a vacuum discharge tube, enclosed in a thin, black cardboard box, caused a nearby piece of paper coated with barium platinocyanide to glow with a brilliant phosphorescence. From this and other experiments he concluded that certain rays, which he called X rays, were emitted from the discharge tube, penetrated the box, and caused the salt to glow. Roentgen also showed that X rays could penetrate other bodies and affect photographic plates. This observation led to the development of X-ray photography.

Shortly after this discovery Antoine Henri Becquerel (1852–1908) attempted to show a relationship between X rays and the phosphorescence of uranium salts. In one of his experiments, he wrapped a photographic plate in black paper, placed a sample of uranium salt on it, and exposed it to sunlight. The developed photographic plate showed that rays emitted from the salt had penetrated the paper. Later Becquerel prepared to repeat the experiment, but, because the sunlight was intermittent, he placed the entire setup in a drawer. Several days later he developed the photographic plate, expecting to find it only slightly affected. He was amazed to observe an intense image on the plate. He repeated the experiment in total darkness and obtained the same results, proving that the uranium salt emitted rays that affected the photographic plate without its being exposed to sunlight. In this way Becquerel discovered radioactivity. The name radioactivity was given to this phenomenon two years later (in 1898) by Marie Curie. Becquerel later showed that the rays coming from uranium were able to ionize air and were also capable of penetrating thin sheets of metal.

In 1898 Marie Sklodowska Curie (1867–1934) and her husband Pierre Curie (1859–1906) began to research radioactivity. In a short time the Curies discovered two new elements, polonium and radium, both of which are radioactive. To confirm their work on radium, they processed 1 ton of pitch-blende residue ore to obtain 0.1 g of pure radium chloride, which they used to make further studies on the properties of radium and to determine its atomic weight.

In 1899 Ernest Rutherford began to investigate the nature of the rays emitted from uranium. He found two rays, which he called *alpha* and *beta rays*. Soon he realized that uranium, while emitting these rays, was changing into another element. By 1912, over 30 radioactive isotopes were known, and many more are known today. The *gamma ray*, a third ray emitted from radioactive materials and similar to an X ray, was discovered by Paul Villard in 1900. After the description of the nuclear atom by Rutherford, the phenomenon of radioactivity was attributed to reactions taking place in the nuclei of atoms.

The symbolism and notation described for isotopes in Chapter 5 is very useful in nuclear chemistry and is briefly reviewed here.

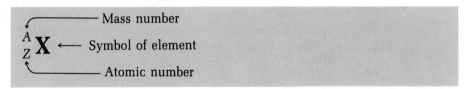

For example, $^{238}_{92}\text{U}$ represents a uranium isotope with an atomic number of 92 and a mass number of 238. This isotope is also designated as U-238 or uranium-238 and contains 92 protons and 146 neutrons. The protons and **nucleons** neutrons collectively are known as **nucleons.** The mass number is the total number of nucleons in the nucleus. Table 18.1 shows the isotopic notations for several particles associated with nuclear chemistry.

Table 18.1 **Symbols in isotopic notation for several particles (and small isotopes) associated with nuclear chemistry**

Particle	Symbol	Atomic number Z	Approximate atomic mass A
Neutron	^1_0n	0	1
Proton	^1_1H	1	1
Beta particle (electron)	$^{\ 0}_{-1}\text{e}$	−1	0
Positron (positive electron)	$^{\ 0}_{+1}\text{e}$	1	0
Alpha particle (helium nucleus)	^4_2He	2	4
Deuteron (heavy hydrogen nucleus)	^2_1H	1	2

nuclide

When we speak of isotopes, we generally mean atoms of the same element with different masses, such as $^{16}_{8}O$, $^{17}_{8}O$, $^{18}_{8}O$. In nuclear chemistry we use the term **nuclide** to mean any isotope of any atom. Thus $^{16}_{8}O$ and $^{235}_{92}U$ are referred to as nuclides.

18.2 Natural Radioactivity

radioactivity

radioactive decay

Radioactivity is the spontaneous emission of radiations from the nucleus of an atom. Elements having this property are said to be radioactive. Radioactive elements continuously undergo **radioactive decay**, or disintegration, to form different elements. The chemical properties of an element are associated with its electronic structure, but radioactivity is a property of the nucleus. Therefore, neither ordinary changes of temperature and pressure nor the chemical or physical state of an element has any effect on its radioactivity.

The principal emissions from the nuclei of radionuclides are known as alpha rays (or particles), beta rays (or particles), and gamma rays. Upon losing an alpha or beta particle, the radioactive element changes into a different element. This process will be explained in detail later.

half-life

Each radioactive nuclide disintegrates at a specific and constant rate, which is expressed in units of half-life. The **half-life** ($t_{1/2}$) is the time required for one-half of a specific amount of a radioactive nuclide to disintegrate. The half-lives of the elements range from a fraction of a second to billions of years. For example, $^{238}_{92}U$ has a half-life of 4.5×10^9 years, $^{226}_{88}Ra$ has a half-life of 1620 years, and $^{15}_{6}C$ has a half-life of 2.4 seconds. To illustrate, if we start today with 1.0 g of $^{226}_{88}Ra$, we will have 0.50 g of $^{226}_{88}Ra$ remaining at the end of 1620 years; at the end of another 1620 years, 0.25 g will remain; and so on.

$$1.0 \text{ g } ^{226}_{88}Ra \xrightarrow[\text{1620 years}]{t_{1/2}} 0.50 \text{ g } ^{226}_{88}Ra \xrightarrow[\text{1620 years}]{t_{1/2}} 0.25 \text{ g } ^{226}_{88}Ra$$

The half-lives of the various radioisotopes of the same element are different from one another. Those for some of the radium isotopes are as follows:

Radium isotope	Half-life
Ra-223	11.7 days
Ra-224	3.64 days
Ra-225	14.8 days
Ra-226	1620 years
Ra-228	6.7 years

A radioactive decay curve is illustrated in Figure 18.1. Note that half of the remaining quantity decays in the half-life of the radioactive nuclide.

PROBLEM

18.1

In how many half-lives will 10.0 g of a radioactive nuclide decay to less than 10% of its original amount.

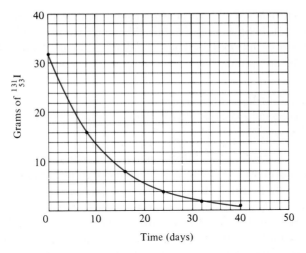

Figure 18.1   Radioactive decay curve for $^{131}_{53}I$, which has a half-life of 8 days:

$$^{131}_{53}I \longrightarrow {}^{131}_{54}Xe + {}^{0}_{-1}e$$

Half of the remaining $^{131}_{53}I$ decays in 8 days. Starting with 32 g, 1 g of $^{131}_{53}I$ will be left after 5 half-lives (40 days).

Ten percent of the original amount is 1.0 g. After the first half-life, half of the original material remains and half has decayed. After the second half-life, one fourth of the original material remains, which is one-half of the starting amount at the end of the first half-life. This progression continues, reducing the quantity remaining by half for each half-life that passes.

Half-lives	0	1	2	3	4
Percent remaining	100%	50%	25%	12.5%	6.25%
Amount remaining	10.0 g	5.00 g	2.50 g	1.25 g	0.625 g

Therefore, the amount remaining will be less than 10% sometime between the third and the fourth half-lives.

Nuclides are said to be either *stable* (nonradioactive) or *unstable* (radioactive). All nuclides of elements that have atomic numbers greater than 83 (bismuth) are naturally radioactive, although some of these nuclides have extremely long half-lives. Some of the naturally occurring nuclides of elements 81, 82, and 83 are radioactive, and some are stable. Only a few naturally occurring nuclides of elements that have atomic numbers less than 81 are radioactive. However, no stable nuclides of element 43 (technetium) or of element 61 (promethium) are known.

Radioactivity is believed to be a result of an unstable ratio of neutrons to protons in the nucleus. Stable nuclides of elements up to about atomic number

20 generally have about a 1:1 neutron to proton ratio. In elements above number 20, the neutron to proton ratio in the stable nuclides gradually increases to about 1.5:1 in element number 83 (bismuth). When the neutron to proton ratio is too high or too low, alpha, beta, or other particles are emitted to achieve a more stable nucleus.

| **18.3** | **Properties of Alpha Particles, Beta Particles, and Gamma Rays** |

alpha particle

(a) Alpha particle. An **alpha particle** consists of two protons and two neutrons, has a mass of about 4 amu, a charge of + 2, and is considered to be a doubly charged helium atom. It is usually given one of the following symbols: α, He^{2+}, or $^{4}_{2}He$. When an alpha particle is emitted from the nucleus, a different element is formed. The atomic number of the new element is 2 less and the mass is 4 amu less than that of the starting element.

Loss of an alpha particle from the nucleus results in
  loss of 4 in the mass number (A)
  loss of 2 in the atomic number (Z)

For example, when $^{238}_{92}U$ loses an alpha particle, $^{234}_{90}Th$ is formed, because two neutrons and two protons are lost from the uranium nucleus. This disintegration may be written as an equation:

$$^{238}_{92}U \longrightarrow ^{234}_{90}Th + \alpha \qquad \text{or} \qquad ^{238}_{92}U \longrightarrow ^{234}_{90}Th + ^{4}_{2}He$$

For the loss of an alpha particle from $^{226}_{88}Ra$, the equation is

$$^{226}_{88}Ra \longrightarrow ^{222}_{86}Rn + ^{4}_{2}He \qquad \text{or} \qquad ^{222}_{88}Rn \longrightarrow ^{222}_{86}Rn + \alpha$$

A nuclear equation, like a chemical equation, consists of reactants and products and must be balanced. To have a balanced nuclear equation, the sum of the mass numbers (superscripts) on both sides of the equation must be equal, and the sum of the atomic numbers (subscripts) on both sides of the equation must be equal.

Sum of mass numbers equals 226.

$$^{226}_{88}Ra \longrightarrow ^{222}_{86}Rn + ^{4}_{2}He$$

Sum of atomic numbers equals 88.

What new nuclide will be formed when $^{230}_{90}Th$ loses an alpha particle? This loss is equivalent to two protons and two neutrons. The new nuclide will have a mass of $(230 - 4)$ or 226 amu and will contain $(90 - 2)$ or 88 protons, so its atomic number is 88. Locate the corresponding element on the periodic chart. It is $^{226}_{88}Ra$ or radium-226.

beta particle

(b) Beta particle. The **beta particle** is identical in mass and charge to an electron; its charge is -1. Both a beta particle and a proton are produced by the decomposition of a neutron:

$$^1_0n \longrightarrow {}^1_1p + {}^0_{-1}e$$

The beta particle leaves, and the proton remains in the nucleus. When an atom loses a beta particle from its nucleus, a different element is formed that has essentially the same mass but an atomic number that is 1 greater than that of the starting element. The beta particle is written as β or ${}^0_{-1}e$.

Loss of a beta particle from the nucleus results in
    no change in the mass number
    increase of 1 in the atomic number

Examples of equations in which a beta particle is lost are

$$^{234}_{90}Th \longrightarrow {}^{234}_{91}Pa + \beta$$

$$^{234}_{91}Pa \longrightarrow {}^{234}_{92}U + {}^0_{-1}e$$

$$^{210}_{82}Pb \longrightarrow {}^{210}_{83}Bi + \beta$$

gamma ray

(c) Gamma ray. **Gamma rays** are photons of energy that have properties similar to those of X rays. They have no electrical charge and no measurable mass. Gamma rays emanate from the nucleus in many radioactive changes along with either alpha or beta particles. The designation for a gamma ray is γ. Gamma radiation does not result in a change of atomic number or the mass of an element.

Loss of a gamma ray from the nucleus results in
    no change in mass number or atomic number

PROBLEM

18.2

(a) Write an equation for the loss of an alpha particle from the nuclide $^{194}_{78}Pt$.

(b) What nuclide is formed when $^{228}_{88}Ra$ loses a beta particle from the nucleus?

(a) Loss of an alpha particle, ^4_2He, means the loss of two neutrons and two protons. This change results in a decrease of 4 in the mass number and a decrease of 2 in the atomic number.

Mass of new nuclide: $A - 4$ or $194 - 4 = 190$

Atomic number of new nuclide: $Z - 2$ or $78 - 2 = 76$

Looking up element number 76 on the periodic table, we find it to be osmium, Os. The equation, then, is

$$^{194}_{78}Pt \longrightarrow {}^{190}_{76}Os + {}^4_2He$$

(b) The loss of a beta particle from a $^{228}_{88}Ra$ nucleus means a gain of 1 in the atomic number with no essential change in mass.

The new nuclide will have an atomic number of $(Z + 1)$ or 89, which is actinium, Ac. The nuclide formed is $^{228}_{89}Ac$.

$$^{228}_{88}Ra \longrightarrow {}^{228}_{89}Ac + {}^0_{-1}e$$

PROBLEM

18.3

What nuclide will be formed when $^{214}_{82}Pb$ successively emits β, β, and α particles from its nucleus? Write successive equations showing these changes.

The changes brought about in the three steps outlined are as follows:

β loss: Increase of 1 in the atomic number; no change in mass
β loss: Increase of 1 in the atomic number; no change in mass
α loss: Decrease of 2 in the atomic number; decrease of 4 in the mass

The equations are

$$^{214}_{82}Pb \xrightarrow{-\beta} {}^{214}_{83}X \xrightarrow{-\beta} {}^{214}_{84}X \xrightarrow{-\alpha} {}^{210}_{82}X$$

where X stands for the new nuclide formed. Looking up each of these elements by their atomic numbers, we rewrite the equations:

$$^{214}_{82}Pb \xrightarrow{-\beta} {}^{214}_{83}Bi \xrightarrow{-\beta} {}^{214}_{84}Po \xrightarrow{-\alpha} {}^{210}_{82}Pb$$

The ability of radioactive rays to pass through various objects is in proportion to the speed at which they leave the nucleus. Gamma rays travel at the velocity of light (186,000 miles per second) and are capable of penetrating several inches of lead. The velocities of beta particles are variable, the fastest being about nine-tenths the velocity of light. Alpha particles have velocities less than one-tenth the velocity of light. Figure 18.2 illustrates the relative penetrating power of these rays. A few sheets of paper will stop alpha particles; a thin sheet of aluminum will stop both alpha and beta particles; and a 5 cm block of lead will reduce, but not completely stop, gamma radiation. In fact it is difficult to stop all gamma radiation. Table 18.2 summarizes the properties of alpha, beta, and gamma radiation.

The classical experiment proving that alpha and beta particles are oppositely charged was performed by Marie Curie (see Figure 18.3). She placed a radioactive source in a hole in a lead block and positioned two poles of a strong

Figure 18.2 Relative penetrating ability of alpha (α), beta (β), and gamma (γ) radiation: (a) Thin sheet of paper; (b) thin sheet of aluminum; (c) 5 cm lead block.

Table 18.2 Characteristics of nuclear radiation

Radiation	Symbol	Mass (amu)	Electrical charge	Velocity	Composition
Alpha	α ^4_2He	4	+2	Variable, less than 10% of the speed of light	Identical to He^{2+}
Beta	β $^0_{-1}\text{e}$	$\dfrac{1}{1837}$	−1	Variable, up to 90% of the speed of light	Identical to an electron
Gamma	γ	0	0	Speed of light	Photons or electromagnetic waves of energy

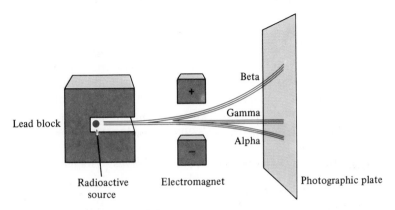

Figure 18.3   The effect of an electromagnetic field on alpha, beta, and gamma rays. Lighter beta particles are deflected considerably more than alpha particles. Alpha and beta particles are deflected in opposite directions. Gamma radiation is not affected by the electromagnetic field.

electromagnet so that the radiations that were given off passed between them. The paths of three different kinds of radiation were detected by means of a photographic plate placed some distance beyond the electromagnet. The lighter beta particles were strongly deflected toward the positive pole of the electromagnet; the heavier alpha particles were less strongly deflected and in the opposite direction. The uncharged gamma rays were not affected by the electromagnet and struck the photographic plates after traveling along a path straight out of the lead block.

18.4 Radioactive Disintegration Series

The naturally occurring radioactive elements with a higher atomic number than lead (Pb) fall into three orderly disintegration series. Each series proceeds from

$$^{238}_{92}\text{U} \xrightarrow[4.51 \times 10^9 \text{ yr}]{\alpha} {}^{234}_{90}\text{Th} \xrightarrow[24.1 \text{ days}]{\beta} {}^{234}_{91}\text{Pa} \xrightarrow[1.18 \text{ min}]{\beta} {}^{234}_{92}\text{U} \xrightarrow[2.48 \times 10^5 \text{ yr}]{\alpha}$$

$$\xrightarrow[3.82 \text{ days}]{\alpha} {}^{222}_{86}\text{Rn} \xleftarrow[1.62 \times 10^3 \text{ yr}]{\alpha} {}^{226}_{88}\text{Ra} \xleftarrow[8.0 \times 10^4 \text{ yr}]{\alpha} {}^{230}_{90}\text{Th} \xleftarrow{}$$

$$\xrightarrow{} {}^{218}_{84}\text{Po} \xrightarrow[3.05 \text{ min}]{\alpha} {}^{214}_{82}\text{Pb} \xrightarrow[26.8 \text{ min}]{\beta} {}^{214}_{83}\text{Bi} \xrightarrow[19.7 \text{ min}]{\alpha} {}^{214}_{84}\text{Po} \xrightarrow[1.6 \times 10^{-4} \text{ s}]{\alpha}$$

$$\begin{array}{c}{}^{206}_{82}\text{Pb} \\ \text{(Stable)}\end{array} \xleftarrow[138 \text{ days}]{\alpha} {}^{210}_{84}\text{Po} \xleftarrow[5.0 \text{ days}]{\beta} {}^{210}_{83}\text{Bi} \xleftarrow[22 \text{ yr}]{\beta} {}^{210}_{82}\text{Pb} \xleftarrow{}$$

Figure 18.4   The uranium disintegration series. Uranium-238 decays by a series of alpha(α) and beta (β) emissions to the stable nuclide lead-206. The type of decay and the corresponding half-life are shown with the arrow.

one element to the next by the loss of either an alpha or a beta particle, finally ending in a nonradioactive stable nuclide. The uranium series starts with $^{238}_{92}\text{U}$ and ends with $^{206}_{82}\text{Pb}$. The thorium series starts with $^{232}_{90}\text{Th}$ and ends with $^{208}_{82}\text{Pb}$. The actinium series starts with $^{235}_{92}\text{U}$ and ends with $^{207}_{82}\text{Pb}$. A fourth series, the neptunium series, starts with the synthetic element $^{241}_{94}\text{Pu}$ and ends with the stable bismuth nuclide $^{209}_{83}\text{Bi}$. The uranium series is shown in Figure 18.4; gamma radiation, which accompanies alpha and beta radiation, is not shown in the figure.

By using such a series and the half-lives of its members, scientists have been able to approximate the age of certain geologic deposits. This approximation was done by comparing the amount of $^{238}_{92}\text{U}$ with the amount of $^{206}_{82}\text{Pb}$ and other nuclides in the series that are present in a particular geologic formation. Rocks found in Canada and Finland have been calculated to be about 3.0×10^9 (3 billion) years old. Some meteorites have been determined to be 4.5×10^9 years old.

18.5   Transmutation of Elements

transmutation

Transmutation is the conversion of one element into another by either natural or artificial means. Transmutation occurs spontaneously in natural radioactive disintegrations. Alchemists tried for centuries to convert lead and mercury into gold by artificial means. But transmutation by artificial means was not achieved until 1919, when Ernest Rutherford succeeded in bombarding the nuclei of nitrogen atoms with alpha particles and produced oxygen nuclides and protons. The nuclear equation for this transmutation can be written as

$$^{14}_{7}\text{N} + \alpha \longrightarrow {}^{17}_{8}\text{O} + {}^{1}_{1}\text{H} \qquad \text{or} \qquad {}^{14}_{7}\text{N} + {}^{4}_{2}\text{He} \longrightarrow {}^{17}_{8}\text{O} + {}^{1}_{1}\text{H}$$

It is believed that the alpha particle enters the nitrogen nucleus, forming $^{18}_{9}\text{F}$ as an intermediate, which then decomposes into the products.

Rutherford's experiments opened the door to nuclear transmutations of all kinds. Atoms were bombarded by alpha particles, neutrons, protons, deuterons

($^2_1$H), electrons, and so forth. Massive instruments were developed for accelerating these particles to very high speeds and energies to aid their penetration of the nucleus. Some of these instruments are the famous cyclotron, developed by E. O. Lawrence at the University of California; the Van de Graaf electrostatic generator; the betatron; and the electron and proton synchrotrons. With these instruments many nuclear transmutations became possible. Equations for a few of these follow.

$$^7_3\text{Li} + ^1_1\text{H} \longrightarrow 2\,^4_2\text{He}$$

$$^{40}_{18}\text{Ar} + ^1_1\text{H} \longrightarrow ^{40}_{19}\text{K} + ^1_0\text{n}$$

$$^{23}_{11}\text{Na} + ^1_1\text{H} \longrightarrow ^{23}_{12}\text{Mg} + ^1_0\text{n}$$

$$^{114}_{48}\text{Cd} + ^2_1\text{H} \longrightarrow ^{115}_{48}\text{Cd} + ^1_1\text{H}$$

$$^2_1\text{H} + ^2_1\text{H} \longrightarrow ^3_1\text{H} + ^1_1\text{H}$$

$$^{209}_{83}\text{Bi} + ^2_1\text{H} \longrightarrow ^{210}_{84}\text{Po} + ^1_0\text{n}$$

$$^{16}_8\text{O} + ^1_0\text{n} \longrightarrow ^{13}_6\text{C} + ^4_2\text{He}$$

$$^{238}_{92}\text{U} + ^{12}_6\text{C} \longrightarrow ^{244}_{98}\text{Cf} + 6\,^1_0\text{n}$$

A shorthand notation for nuclear bombardment reactions includes, in order, the nuclide being bombarded, followed by the bombarding particle, a comma, and the particle released all in parentheses, and finally the nuclide product. The shorthand notation for the last two equations above are

$$^{16}_8\text{O}(\text{n}, \alpha)^{13}_6\text{C} \qquad ^{238}_{92}\text{U}(^{12}_6\text{C}, 6\text{ n})^{244}_{98}\text{Cf}$$

Note that the reactants are to the left and products to the right of the comma.

18.6   Artificial Radioactivity

Irene Joliot-Curie, a daughter of Pierre and Marie Curie, and her husband, Frederic Joliot-Curie, observed that when aluminum-27 was bombarded with alpha particles, neutrons and positrons (positive electrons) were emitted as part of the products. When the source of alpha particles was removed, neutrons ceased to be produced, but positrons continued to be emitted. This observation suggested that the neutrons and positrons were coming from two separate reactions. It also indicated that one of the products of the first reaction was radioactive. After further investigation they discovered that when aluminum-27 is bombarded with alpha particles, phosphorus-30 and neutrons are produced. Phosphorus-30 is radioactive, has a half-life of 2.5 minutes, and decays to silicon-30 with the emission of a positron. The equations for these reactions follow.

$$^{27}_{13}\text{Al} + ^4_2\text{He} \longrightarrow ^{30}_{15}\text{P} + ^1_0\text{n}$$

$$^{30}_{15}\text{P} \longrightarrow ^{30}_{14}\text{Si} + ^0_{+1}\text{e}$$

artificial
radioactivity

The radioactivity of nuclides produced in this manner is known as **artificial radioactivity** or **induced radioactivity**. Artificial radionuclides behave like

Table 18.3   Some commonly used radionuclides

Radionuclide	Radiation emitted	Half-life
$^{14}_{6}C$	β	5668 years
$^{32}_{15}P$	β	14.3 days
$^{35}_{16}S$	β	87 days
$^{60}_{27}Co$	β	5.3 years
$^{90}_{38}Sr$	β	28 years
$^{131}_{53}I$	β	8.1 days
$^{137}_{55}Cs$	β	30 years

induced radioactivity

natural radioactive elements in that they disintegrate in a definite fashion and have a specific half-life for each nuclide. The Joliot-Curies received the Noble prize in chemistry in 1935 for the discovery of artificial, or induced, radioactivity.

A list of some commonly used radionuclides and their mode of decay is given in Table 18.3.

18.7   Measurement of Radioactivity

Radiation from radioactive sources is so energetic that it is called *ionizing radiation*. When it strikes an atom or a molecule, one or more electrons are knocked off, and an ion is created. One of the common instruments used to detect and measure radioactivity, the Geiger counter, depends on this fact. The instrument consists of a Geiger–Müller detecting tube and a counting device. The detector tube is a pair of oppositely charged electrodes in an argon gas–filled chamber fitted with a thin window. When radiation, such as a beta particle, passes through the window into the tube, some argon is ionized, and a momentary pulse of current (discharge) flows between the electrodes. These current pulses are electronically amplified in the counter and appear as signals in the form of audible clicks, flashing lights, meter deflections, or numerical readouts. Figure 18.5 illustrates a simple Geiger counter.

one curie

The *curie* is the unit used to express the amount of radioactivity produced by an element. **One curie** is defined as the quantity of radioactive material giving 3.7×10^{10} disintegrations per second. The basis for this figure is pure radium, which has an activity of 1 curie per gram. Because the curie is such a large quantity, the millicurie and microcurie, representing one-thousandth and one-millionth of a curie, respectively, are more practical and more commonly used. Other units in which radioactivity is expressed are given in Table 18.4.

18.8   Nuclear Fission

nuclear fission

In **nuclear fission** a heavy nuclide splits into two or more intermediate-sized fragments when struck in a particular way by a neutron. The fragments are

Figure 18.5 A Geiger counter, or battery-operated portable Geiger–Müller survey meter: Radioactivity is indicated in a headphone by clicks and by a graduated meter indicating the number of counts per minute or hour. The Geiger tube located on top is the detector; the rest of the instrument is the counting device. (*Courtesy Atomic Accessories, Inc.*)

Table 18.4   Radiation units

Curie (Ci)	A unit of radioactivity indicating the rate of decay of a radioactive substance. One curie is the amount of radioactive material undergoing 3.7×10^{10} disintegrations per second.
Roentgen (R)	A unit of exposure of gamma or X radiation based on the quantity of ionization produced in air
Rad	A unit of absorbed dose of radiation indicating the energy absorbed from any ionizing radiation. 1 rad = 0.01 J of energy absorbed per 1 kg of matter
Rem	A unit of radiation dose equivalent. The rem takes into account that the same dose in rads from different sources of radiation does not produce the same degree of biological effect. 1 rem is equal to the dose in rads multiplied by a factor dependent on the particular type of radiation.
Gray (Gy) (SI unit)	Energy absorbed by tissue; 1 Gy = 1 J/kg tissue (1 Gy = 100 rad)

called *fission products*. As the atom splits, it releases energy and two or three neutrons, each of which can cause another nuclear fission. The first instance of nuclear fission was reported in January 1939 by the German scientists Otto Hahn and F. Strassmann. Detecting isotopes of barium, krypton, cerium, and lanthanum after bombarding uranium with neutrons, the scientists were led to believe that the uranium nucleus had been split.

Figure 18.6 The fission process: When a neutron is captured by a heavy nucleus, the nucleus becomes more unstable. The more energetic nucleus begins to deform, resulting in fission. Two nuclear fragments and three neutrons are produced by this fission process.

Characteristics of nuclear fission are

1. Upon absorption of a neutron, a heavy nuclide splits into two or more smaller nuclides (fission products).
2. The mass of the nuclides formed ranges from about 70 to 160 amu.
3. Two or more neutrons are produced from the fission of each atom.
4. Large quantities of energy are produced as a result of the conversion of a small amount of mass into energy.
5. Most nuclides formed are radioactive and continue to decay until they reach a stable nuclide.

One suggested process by which this fission takes place is illustrated in Figure 18.6. When a heavy nucleus captures a neutron, the energy increase may be sufficient to cause deformation of the nucleus until the mass finally splits into two fragments, releasing radiant energy and usually two or more neutrons.

In a typical fission reaction, a $^{235}_{92}U$ nucleus captures a neutron and forms unstable $^{236}_{92}U$. This $^{236}_{92}U$ nucleus undergoes fission, quickly disintegrating into two fragments, such as $^{139}_{56}Ba$ and $^{94}_{36}Kr$, and three neutrons. The three neutrons in turn may be captured by three other $^{235}_{92}U$ atoms, each of which undergoes fission, producing nine neutrons, and so on. A reaction of this kind, in which the

chain reaction

products cause the reaction to continue or magnify, is known as a **chain reaction.** For a chain reaction to continue, enough fissionable material must be present so that each atomic fission causes, on the average, at least one additional fission. The minimum quantity of an element needed to support a self-sustaining chain

critical mass

reaction is called the **critical mass.** Since energy is released in each atomic fission, chain reactions constitute a possible source of a steady supply of energy. A chain reaction is illustrated in Figure 18.7. Two of the many possible ways in which U-235 may fission are shown by the following equations.

$$^{235}_{92}U + ^{1}_{0}n \longrightarrow ^{139}_{56}Ba + ^{94}_{36}Kr + 3\,^{1}_{0}n$$

$$^{235}_{92}U + ^{1}_{0}n \longrightarrow ^{144}_{54}Xe + ^{90}_{38}Sr + 2\,^{1}_{0}n$$

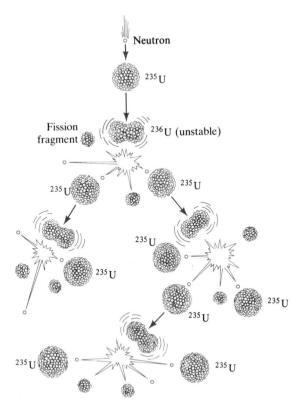

Figure 18.7   Fission and chain reaction of $^{235}_{92}$U: Each fission produces two major fission fragments and three neutrons, which may be captured by other $^{235}_{92}$U nuclei, continuing the chain reaction.

18.9   Nuclear Power

Nearly all electricity for commercial use is produced by machines consisting of a turbine linked by a drive shaft to an electrical generator. The energy required to run the turbine can be supplied by falling water, as in hydroelectric power plants, or by steam generated by heat from fuel, as in thermal power plants. Thermal power plants burn fossil fuel—coal, oil, or natural gas.

The world's demand for energy, largely from fossil fuels, has continued to grow at an ever-increasing rate for about 250 years. Even at present rates of consumption, the estimated world supply of fossil fuels is sufficient for only a few centuries. Although the United States has large coal and oil shale deposits, it is currently importing about 40% of its oil supply. We clearly need to develop alternate energy sources. At present uranium is the most productive alternate energy source, and about 12% of the electrical energy used in the United States is generated in power plants using uranium fuel.

The major disadvantage of nuclear-fueled power plants is that they produce highly radioactive waste in the form of isotopes, some of which have half-lives of thousands of years. As yet, no agreement has been reached on how to dispose of these dangerous wastes safely.

A nuclear power plant is a thermal power plant in which heat is produced by a nuclear reactor instead of by combustion of fossil fuel. The major components of a nuclear reactor are (1) an arrangement of nuclear fuel, called the reactor core; (2) a control system, which regulates the rate of fission and thereby the rate of heat generation; and (3) a cooling system, which removes the heat from the reactor and also keeps the core at the proper temperature. One type of reactor uses metal slugs containing uranium enriched from the normal 0.7% U-235 to about 3% U-235. These slugs are placed in a graphite block to form a nuclear pile. The self-sustaining fission reaction is moderated, or controlled, by the graphite and by adjustable control rods containing substances that slow down and capture some of the neutrons produced. Ordinary water, heavy water, and molten sodium are typical coolants used. Energy obtained from nuclear reactions in the form of heat is used in the production of steam to drive turbines for generating electricity.

In the United States reactors designed for commercial power production use uranium oxide, U_3O_8, that is enriched with the relatively scarce fissionable U-235 isotope. Because the supply of U-235 is limited, a new type of reactor known as the *breeder reactor* has been developed. Breeder reactors are designed to produce additional fissionable material at the same time that the fission reaction is occurring. In a breeder reactor, excess neutrons convert nonfissionable isotopes, such as U-238 or Th-232, to the fissionable isotopes, Pu-239 or U-233.

$$^{238}_{92}\text{U} + ^{1}_{0}\text{n} \longrightarrow {}^{239}_{92}\text{U} \xrightarrow{-\beta} {}^{239}_{93}\text{Np} \xrightarrow{-\beta} {}^{239}_{94}\text{Pu}$$

$$^{232}_{90}\text{Th} + ^{1}_{0}\text{n} \longrightarrow {}^{233}_{90}\text{Th} \xrightarrow{-\beta} {}^{233}_{91}\text{Pa} \xrightarrow{-\beta} {}^{233}_{92}\text{U}$$

These transmutations make it possible to greatly extend the supply of fuel for nuclear reactors. No breeder reactors are presently in commercial operation in the United States, but several are being operated in Europe and Great Britain.

18.10   *The Atomic Bomb*

The atomic bomb is a fission bomb; it operates on the principle of a very fast chain reaction that releases a tremendous amount of energy. An atomic bomb and a nuclear reactor both depend on self-sustaining nuclear fission chain reactions. The essential difference is that in a bomb the fission is "wild," or uncontrolled, whereas in a nuclear reactor the fission is moderated and carefully controlled. A minimum critical mass of fissionable material is needed for a bomb, or a major explosion will not occur. When a quantity smaller than the critical mass is used, too many neutrons formed in the fission step escape without combining with another nucleus, and a chain reaction does not occur. Therefore, the fissionable material of an atomic bomb must be stored as two or more subcritical masses and brought together to form the critical mass at the desired time of explosion. The temperature developed in an atomic bomb is believed to be about 10 million °C. Figure 18.8 shows an atomic bomb of the "Little Boy" type, the World War II nuclear weapon detonated over Hiroshima, Japan.

The nuclides used in atomic bombs are U-235 and Pu-239. Uranium deposits contain about 0.7% of the U-235 isotope, the remainder being U-238. Uranium-238 does not undergo fission except with very-high-energy neutrons. It was discovered, however, that U-238 captures a low-energy neutron without undergoing fission and that the product, U-239, changes to $^{239}_{94}\text{Pu}$ (plutonium) by a beta decay process. Plutonium-239 readily undergoes fission upon capture of a neutron and is therefore useful for nuclear weapons. The equations for the nuclear transformations are

$$^{238}_{92}\text{U} + {}^{1}_{0}\text{n} \longrightarrow {}^{239}_{92}\text{U} \xrightarrow{-\beta} {}^{239}_{93}\text{Np} \xrightarrow{-\beta} {}^{239}_{94}\text{Pu}$$

The hazards of an atomic bomb explosion include not only shock waves from the explosive pressure and tremendous heat, but also intense radiation in the

Figure 18.8 Atomic bomb of the "Little Boy" type detonated over Hiroshima, Japan, in World War II: The bomb is 28 in. in diameter and 120 in. long. The first nuclear weapon ever detonated, it weighed about 9000 lb and had a yield equivalent to approximately 20,000 tons of high explosives. (*Courtesy U.S. Department of Energy, Los Alamos Scientific Laboratory.*)

form of alpha, beta, gamma, and ultraviolet rays. Gamma rays and X rays can penetrate deeply into the body, causing burns, sterilization, and mutation of the genes, which may have an adverse effect on future generations. Both radioactive fission products and unfissioned material are present after the explosion. If the bomb explodes near the ground, many tons of dust are lifted into the air. Radioactive material adhering to this dust, known as *fallout*, is spread by air currents over wide areas of the land and constitutes a lingering source of radiation hazard.

Today nuclear war is probably the most awesome threat facing civilization. Only two rather primitive fission-type atom bombs were used to destroy the Japanese cities of Hiroshima and Nagasaki and bring World War II to an early end. Now tens of thousands of nuclear weapons are in existence, and hundreds more are being manufactured each year. Many of these weapons are at least several hundred times more powerful than the Hiroshima and Nagasaki bombs. The United States and the Soviet Union, the so-called superpowers, have been unable to reach an effective agreement on the control and reduction of nuclear armaments. Finally, the threat of nuclear war is further increased by the fact that the number of nations possessing nuclear weapons is steadily increasing.

18.11   Nuclear Fusion

nuclear fusion

The process of uniting the nuclei of two light elements to form one heavier nucleus is known as **nuclear fusion.** Such reactions can be used for producing energy, because the mass of the two individual nuclei that are fused into a single nucleus is greater than the mass of the nucleus formed by their fusion. The mass differential is liberated in the form of energy. Fusion reactions are responsible for the tremendous energy output of the sun. Thus, aside from relatively small amounts from nuclear fission and radioactivity, fusion reactions are the ultimate source of our energy, even the energy from fossil fuels. They are also responsible for the devastating power of the thermonuclear, or hydrogen, bombs.

Fusion reactions require temperatures on the order of tens of millions of degrees for initiation. Such temperatures are present in the sun but have been produced only momentarily on earth. For example, the hydrogen, or fusion, bomb is triggered by the temperature of an exploding fission bomb.

Two typical fusion reactions are

$$^3_1\text{H} + {}^2_1\text{D} \longrightarrow {}^4_2\text{He} + {}^1_0\text{n} + \text{Energy}$$

Tritium   Deuterium

$$^3_1\text{H} + {}^1_1\text{H} \longrightarrow {}^4_2\text{He} + \text{Energy}$$

3.01495   1.00782   4.00260
amu   amu   amu

The total mass of the reactants in the second equation is 4.02277 amu, which is 0.02017 amu greater than the mass of the product. This difference in mass is manifested in the great amount of energy liberated.

During the past 35 to 40 years, a large amount of research on controlled nuclear fusion reactions has been done in the United States and in other countries, especially the Soviet Union. So far, the goal of controlled nuclear fusion has not been attained, although the required ignition temperature has been reached in several devices. Evidence to date leads us to believe that it is possible to develop a practical fusion power reactor. Fusion power, if it can be developed, will be far superior to fission power because: (1) Virtually infinite amounts of energy are to be had from fusion. Uranium supplies for fission power are limited, but heavy hydrogen, or deuterium (the most likely fusion fuel), is relatively abundant. It is estimated that the deuterium in a cubic mile of seawater is an energy resource (as fusion fuel) greater than the petroleum reserves of the entire world. (2) From an environmental viewpoint, fusion power is much "cleaner" than fission power because fusion reactions, in contrast to uranium and plutonium fission reactions, do not produce large amounts of long-lived and dangerously radioactive isotopes.

18.12 Mass-Energy Relationship in Nuclear Reactions

Because large amounts of energy are released in nuclear reactions, significant amounts of mass are converted to energy. We stated earlier that the amount of mass converted to energy in chemical changes is considered insignificant. In fission reactions about 0.1% of the mass is converted into energy. In fusion reactions as much as 0.5% of the mass may be changed into energy. The Einstein equation, $E = mc^2$, can be used to calculate the energy liberated, or available, when the mass loss is known. For example, in the reaction

$$\underset{\text{7.0160 g}}{^{7}_{3}\text{Li}} \ + \ \underset{\text{1.0078 g}}{^{1}_{1}\text{H}} \ \longrightarrow \ \underset{\text{4.0026 g}}{^{4}_{2}\text{He}} \ + \ \underset{\text{4.0026 g}}{^{4}_{2}\text{He}} \ + \text{Energy}$$

the mass difference between the reactants and the products (8.0238 g − 8.0052 g) is 0.0186 g. The energy equivalent to this amount of mass is 1.67×10^{12} J $(4.0 \times 10^{11}$ cal). By comparison this amount is more than 4 million times greater than the 3.9×10^5 J $(9.4 \times 10^4$ cal) of energy obtained from the complete combustion of 12.0 g (1 mol) of carbon.

The mass of a nucleus is actually less than the sum of the masses of the protons and neutrons that make up that nucleus. The difference between the mass of the protons and the neutrons in a nucleus and the mass of the nucleus is known as the **mass defect.** The energy equivalent to this difference in mass is known as the **nuclear binding energy.** This energy is the amount that would be required to break up a nucleus into its individual protons and neutrons. The higher the binding energy, the more stable is the nucleus. Elements of intermediate atomic masses have high binding energies. For example, iron (element number 26) has a very high binding energy and therefore has a very stable nucleus. Just as electrons attain less energetic and more stable arrangements through ordinary chemical reactions, neutrons and protons attain less energetic and more stable

mass defect

nuclear binding energy

arrangements through nuclear fission or fusion reactions. Thus, when uranium undergoes fission, the products have less mass (and greater binding energy) than the original uranium. In like manner, when hydrogen and lithium fuse to form helium, the helium has less mass (and greater binding energy) than the hydrogen and lithium. It is this conversion of mass to energy that accounts for the very large amounts of energy associated with both nuclear fission and fusion reactions.

18.13   Transuranium Elements

transuranium elements

The elements following uranium on the periodic chart and having atomic numbers greater than 92 are known as the **transuranium elements.** All of them are synthetic radioactive elements; none of them occur naturally.

The first transuranium element, number 93, was discovered in 1939 by Edwin M. McMillan (b. 1907) at the University of California while he was investigating the fission of uranium. He named it neptunium for the planet Neptune. In 1941 element 94, plutonium, was identified as a beta decay product of neptunium:

$$^{238}_{93}\text{Np} \longrightarrow {}^{238}_{94}\text{Pu} + {}^{0}_{-1}\text{e}$$

$$^{239}_{93}\text{Np} \longrightarrow {}^{239}_{94}\text{Pu} + {}^{0}_{-1}\text{e}$$

Plutonium is one of the most important fissionable elements known today.

Since 1964 the discoveries of five new transuranium elements—numbers 104, 105, 106, 107, and 109—have been announced. All of these elements were produced in minute quantities by high-energy particle accelerators. In the case of element 109, the discovery was based on the detection of a single atom of the nuclide $^{266}_{109}\text{X}$, which existed for about five milliseconds! The reported synthesis was achieved by bombarding a bismuth-209 target with highly accelerated iron-58 nuclei.

$$^{209}_{83}\text{Bi} + {}^{58}_{26}\text{Fe} \longrightarrow {}^{266}_{109}\text{X} + {}^{1}_{0}\text{n}$$

Groups of scientists in the United States and the Soviet Union involved in high-energy particle research to produce new elements disagree on the names for elements 104, 105, and 106. Consequently the International Union of Pure and Applied Chemistry (IUPAC) has suggested a systematic method for naming all elements beyond 103. The method combines letters from the Greek and Latin words for the numbers plus the ending *ium*. For example, *un* for 1, *nil* for 0, and *quad* for 4 plus the ending *ium* forms unnilquadium, element 104. Thus unnilpentium is 105 and unnilhexium is 106. Accordingly, 107 is unnilseptium and 109 is unnilennium. Table 18.5 lists all the presently known transuranium elements.

18.14   Biological Effects of Radiation

Radiation that has enough energy to dislocate bonding electrons and create ions when passing through matter is classified as *ionizing radiation*. Alpha, beta, and gamma rays, along with X rays, fall into this classification. Ionizing radiation can

Table 18.5 Transuranium elements

Element	Symbol	Atomic number	Discovery date
Neptunium	Np	93	1939
Plutonium	Pu	94	1941
Americium	Am	95	1944
Curium	Cm	96	1944
Berkelium	Bk	97	1949
Californium	Cf	98	1950
Einsteinium	Es	99	1953
Fermium	Fm	100	1953
Mendelevium	Md	101	1955
Nobelium	No	102	1957
Lawrencium	Lr	103	1961
Unnilquadium	Unq	104	1964
Unnilpentium	Unp	105	1970
Unnilhexium	Unh	106	1974
Unnilseptium	Uns	107	1981
Unnilennium	Une	109	1982

damage or kill living cells. This damage is particularly devastating when it occurs in the cell nuclei and affects molecules involved in cell reproduction. The overall effects of radiation on living organisms fall into these general categories: (1) acute, or short-term, effects; (2) long-term effects, and (3) genetic effects.

Acute radiation damage. High levels of radiation, especially of gamma or X rays, produce nausea, vomiting, and diarrhea. The effect has been likened to a sunburn throughout the body. If the dosage is high enough, death will occur in a few days. The damaging effects of radiation appear to be centered in the nuclei of the cells, and cells that are undergoing rapid cell division are most susceptible to damage. It is for this reason that cancers are often treated with gamma radiation from a cobalt-60 source. Cancerous cells are multiplying rapidly and are destroyed by a level of radiation that does not seriously damage normal cells.

Long-term radiation damage. Protracted exposure to low levels of any form of ionizing radiation can weaken the organism and lead to the onset of malignant tumors, even after fairly long time delays. The largest exposure to man-made sources of radiation is from X rays. Evidence suggests that a number of early workers in radioactivity and X-ray technology may have had their lives shortened by long-term radiation damage.

A number of women who had been employed in the early 1920s to paint luminous numbers on watch dials died some years later from the effects of radiation. These women had ingested radium by using their lips to point the brushes used on the job. Radium was retained in their bodies and, as an alpha emitter with a half-life of about 1620 years, continued to inflict radiation damage.

Strontium-90 isotopes are present in the fallout from atmospheric testing of nuclear weapons. Strontium is in the same periodic-table group as calcium, and its chemical behavior is similar to that of calcium. Hence, when foods contaminated with Sr-90 are eaten, Sr-90 ions are laid down in the bone tissue along with ordinary calcium ions. Strontium-90 is a beta emitter with a half-life of 28 years. Blood cells that are manufactured in bone marrow are affected by the radiation from Sr-90. Hence, there is concern that Sr-90 accumulation in the environment may cause an increase in the incidence of leukemia and bone cancers. Fortunately, the United States and the Soviet Union agreed to stop atmospheric testing of nuclear weapons several years ago; however, some countries are still doing testing in the atmosphere.

Genetic effects.   All the information needed to create an individual of a particular species, be it a bacterial cell or a human being, is contained within the nucleus of a cell. This genetic information is encoded in the structure of DNA (deoxyribonucleic acid) molecules, which make up genes. The DNA molecules form precise duplicates of themselves when cells divide, thus passing genetic information from one generation to the next. Radiation can damage DNA molecules. If the damage is not severe enough to prevent the individual from reproducing, a mutation (a heritable variation in the offspring) may result. Most mutation-induced traits are undesirable. Unfortunately, if the bearer of the altered genes survives to reproduce, these traits are passed along to succeeding generations. In other words, the genetic effects of increased radiation exposure are found in future generations, not in the present generation.

Because radioactive rays are hazardous to health and living tissue, special precautions must be taken in designing laboratories and nuclear reactors, in disposing of waste materials, and in monitoring the radiation exposure of people working in this field. For example, personnel working in areas of hazardous radiation wear film badges or pocket dosimeters to provide them with an accurate indication of cumulative radiation exposure.

18.15   Applications of Radionuclides

To date, the largest uses of radioactive materials have been for making weapons and for the generation of electricity in nuclear power plants. Aside from these major uses, radionuclides have innumerable applications. They are used extensively in chemical, physical, biological, and medical research. Radionuclides now serve in a wide variety of almost routine technological applications in medicine and various branches of industry including chemical, petroleum, and metallurgical processing. A major advantage of using radionuclides in research is that they continuously emit radiations that can be detected and measured. A few of these applications are briefly described here.

Cancer treatment.   For many years, radium has been used in the treatment of cancer; cobalt-60 and cesium-137 are now extensively used for therapy in this field. The effectiveness of radiation therapy for cancer is dependent on the fact that rapidly growing or dividing malignant cells are more susceptible to radiation damage than are normal cells. Therefore, radiation therapy is effective when it can be applied at levels that will destroy cancer cells but not normal cells.

Isotopic tracers. Compounds containing a radioactive nuclide are described as being *labeled*, or *tagged*. These compounds undergo their normal chemical reactions. In addition their location can be detected because of their radioactivity. When such compounds are given to a plant or to an animal, the movement of the radionuclide can be traced through the organism by the use of a Geiger counter or other detecting device. The following are examples of biological research in which such tracer techniques have been employed: the rate of phosphate intake by plants, using radiophosphorus; the utilization of carbon dioxide in photosynthesis, using radioactive carbon; the accumulation of iodine in the thyroid gland, using radioactive iodine; and the absorption of iron by the hemoglobin of the blood, using radioactive iron. In chemistry the uses are unlimited: The study of reaction mechanisms, the measurement of the rates of chemical reactions, and the determination of physical constants are just a few of the areas of application.

Doctors can examine the heart's pumping performance and check for evidence of obstruction in the coronary arteries by *nuclear scanning*. The radionuclide thallium-201, when injected into the bloodstream, lodges in healthy heart muscle. Thallium-201 emits gamma radiation, which is detected by a special imaging device called a *scintillation camera*. The data obtained are simultaneously translated into pictures by a computer. With this technique doctors can observe whether heart tissue has died after a heart attack and whether blood is flowing freely through the coronary passages.

Agriculture. Agricultural research scientists use gamma radiation from cobalt-60 or other sources to develop disease-resistant and highly productive grains and other crops. The seeds are exposed to gamma radiation to induce mutations. The most healthy and vigorous plants grown from the irradiated seed are then selected and propagated to obtain new and improved varieties for commercial use. Preservation of foodstuffs by radiation is another beneficial application of radioactivity.

Insect control. Radioactivity has been used to control and, in some areas, to eliminate the screw-worm fly. The larvae of this obnoxious insect pest burrow into wounds in livestock. The female fly, like a queen bee, mates only once. When large numbers of gamma ray–sterilized male flies are released at the proper time in an area infested with screw-worm flies, the majority of the females mate with sterile males. As a consequence, the flies fail to reproduce sufficiently to maintain their numbers. This technique has also been used to eradicate the Mediterranean fruit fly in some areas.

Age dating. An interesting outgrowth of the use of radionuclide techniques is *radiocarbon dating*. The method is based on the decay rate of carbon-14 and was devised by the American chemist W. F. Libby, who received the Nobel prize in chemistry in 1960 for this work. The principle of radiocarbon dating is as follows: Carbon dioxide in the atmosphere contains a fixed ratio of radioactive carbon-14 to ordinary carbon-12, because carbon-14 is produced at a steady rate in the atmosphere by bombardment of nitrogen-14 by neutrons from cosmic ray sources.

$$^{14}_{7}N + ^{1}_{0}n \longrightarrow ^{14}_{6}C + ^{1}_{1}H$$

Plants that consume carbon dioxide during photosynthesis and animals that eat the plants contain the same proportion of C-14 to C-12 as long as they are alive. When an organism dies, the amount of C-12 remains fixed, but the C-14 content diminishes according to its half-life (5668 years). By comparing the ratio of C-14 to C-12 in an object to the same ratio in living plants, one can estimate the age of the object being evaluated. In 5668 years, one-half the radiocarbon initially present will have undergone decomposition. In 11,336 years, one-fourth of the original C-14 will be left. The age of fossil material, archaeological specimens, and old wood can be determined by this method. The age of specimens from ancient Egyptian tombs calculated by radiocarbon dating correlates closely with the chronological age established by Egyptologists. Charcoal samples obtained at Darrington Walls, a wood-henge in Great Britain, were determined to be about 4000 years old. Radiocarbon dating instruments currently in use enable researchers to date specimens back as far as 70,000 years.

Radioactive decay has been used to date samples other than those containing carbon. For example, the age of rock formations containing uranium has been approximated by determining the ratio of U-238 to Pb-206. Lead-206 is the last isotope formed in the U-238 disintegration series. Thus, a geologic deposit containing a 1:1 ratio of U-238 to Pb-206 would correspond to a time lapse of one half-life of U-238, which is 4.5×10^9 years, assuming that all the Pb-206 came from the decay of U-238.

QUESTIONS

A. *Review the meanings of the new terms introduced in this chapter.*

1. Nucleons
2. Nuclide
3. Radioactivity
4. Radioactive decay
5. Half-life
6. Alpha particle
7. Beta particle
8. Gamma ray
9. Transmutation
10. Artificial radioactivity
11. Induced radioactivity
12. One curie
13. Nuclear fission
14. Chain reaction
15. Critical mass
16. Nuclear fusion
17. Mass defect
18. Nuclear binding energy
19. Transuranium elements

B. *Information useful in answering the following questions will be found in the tables and figures.*

1. To afford protection from radiation injury,

which kind of radiation requires: (a) the most shielding? (b) the least shielding?

2. Why is an alpha particle deflected less than a beta particle in passing through an electromagnetic field?

3. List the first five nuclides in Table 18.3 in order of increasing half-life.

4. What is the half-life of strontium-90?

5. Name three pairs of nuclides that might be obtained by fissioning three U-235 atoms.

6. List the transuranium elements that are named for
   (a) People (b) Geographical places
   (c) Planets

C. *Review questions*

1. Identify the following people and their associations with the early history of radioactivity:
   (a) Antoine Henri Becquerel
   (b) Marie and Pierre Curie
   (c) Wilhelm Roentgen
   (d) Ernest Rutherford
   (e) Paul Villard

2. Why is the radioactivity of an element unaffected by the usual factors that affect the rate of chemical reactions, such as ordinary changes of temperature and concentration?

3. Distinguish between the terms *isotope* and *nuclide*.

4. Indicate the number of protons, neutrons, and nucleons in each of the following nuclei.
   (a) $^{35}_{17}Cl$ (b) $^{226}_{88}Ra$ (c) $^{235}_{92}U$ (d) $^{82}_{35}Br$

5. Explain the phenomenon of half-life for a radionuclide.

6. The half-life of plutonium-244 is 76 million years. If the age of the earth is about 5 billion years, discuss the feasibility of this nuclide's being found as a naturally occurring element.

7. Tell how alpha, beta, and gamma radiation are distinguished from the standpoint of:
   (a) Charge
   (b) Relative mass
   (c) Nature of particle or ray
   (d) Relative penetrating power

8. How are the mass and the atomic number of a nucleus affected by the loss of the following?
   (a) An alpha particle (b) A beta particle

9. Distinguish between natural and artificial radioactivity.

10. What is a radioactive disintegration series?

11. Briefly discuss the transmutation of elements.

12. Write nuclear equations for the alpha decay of:
    (a) $^{218}_{85}At$ (b) $^{221}_{87}Fr$ (c) $^{192}_{78}Pt$ (d) $^{210}_{84}Po$

13. Write nuclear equations for the beta decay of:
    (a) $^{14}_{6}C$ (b) $^{137}_{55}Cs$ (c) $^{239}_{93}Np$ (d) $^{90}_{38}Sr$

14. Stable $^{208}_{82}Pb$ is formed from $^{232}_{90}Th$ in the thorium disintegration series by successive, α, β, β, α, α, α, α, β, β, α particle emissions. Write the symbol (including mass and atomic number) for each nuclide formed in this series.

15. The nuclide $^{237}_{93}Np$ loses a total of seven alpha particles and four beta particles. What nuclide remains after these losses?

16. Bismuth-211 decays by alpha emission to give a nuclide that in turn decays by beta emission to yield a stable nuclide. Show these two steps with nuclear equations.

17. Write nuclear equations for the following:
    (a) Conversion of $^{13}_{6}C$ to $^{14}_{6}C$
    (b) Conversion of $^{30}_{15}P$ to $^{30}_{14}Si$

18. Complete and balance the following nuclear equations by supplying the missing particles:
    (a) $^{27}_{13}Al + ^{4}_{2}He \longrightarrow ^{30}_{15}P + ?$
    (b) $^{27}_{14}Si \longrightarrow _{+1}^{0}e + ?$
    (c) $? + ^{2}_{1}H \longrightarrow ^{13}_{7}N + ^{1}_{0}n$
    (d) $? \longrightarrow ^{82}_{36}Kr + _{-1}^{0}e$
    (e) $^{66}_{29}Cu \longrightarrow ^{66}_{30}Zn + ?$
    (f) $_{-1}^{0}e + ? \longrightarrow ^{7}_{3}Li$
    (g) $^{27}_{13}Al + ^{4}_{2}He \longrightarrow ^{30}_{14}Si + ?$
    (h) $^{85}_{37}Rb + ? \longrightarrow ^{82}_{35}Br + ^{4}_{2}He$
    (i) $^{214}_{83}Bi \longrightarrow ^{4}_{2}He + ?$

19. Write shorthand notations for the following nuclear equations:
    (a) $^{27}_{13}Al + ^{4}_{2}He \longrightarrow ^{30}_{15}P + ^{1}_{0}n$
    (b) $^{14}_{7}N + ^{4}_{2}He \longrightarrow ^{17}_{8}O + ^{1}_{1}H$
    (c) $^{59}_{27}Co + ^{1}_{0}n \longrightarrow ^{60}_{27}Co + \gamma$
    (d) $^{249}_{98}Cf + ^{12}_{6}C \longrightarrow ^{257}_{104}Unq + 4 {}^{1}_{0}n$

20. Write nuclear equations from these shorthand notations:
    (a) $^{23}_{11}Na(p, n)^{23}_{12}Mg$
    (b) $^{209}_{83}Bi(d, n)^{210}_{84}Po$ (d = deuteron, $^{2}_{1}H$)
    (c) $^{238}_{92}U(^{16}_{8}O, 5\ n)^{249}_{100}Fm$
    (d) $^{9}_{4}Be(\alpha, n)^{12}_{6}C$

21. Describe the use of a Geiger counter in measuring radioactivity.

22. What does each of these units represent?
    (a) Curie   (c) Rad or Gray
    (b) Roentgen (d) Rem

23. What was the contribution to nuclear physics of Otto Hahn and Fritz Strassmann?

24. What is a breeder reactor? Explain how it accomplishes the "breeding."

25. What is the essential difference between the nuclear reactions in a nuclear reactor and those in an atomic bomb?

26. Why must a certain minimum amount of fissionable material be present before a self-supporting chain reaction can occur?

27. Are the terms *atomic bomb* and *hydrogen bomb* synonymous? If not, what is the major distinction between them?

28. What is mass defect and nuclear binding energy?

29. Explain why radioactive rays are classified as ionizing radiation.

30. Give a brief description of the biological hazards associated with radioactivity.

31. Strontium-90 has been found to occur in radioactive fallout. Why is there so much concern about this radionuclide being found in cow's milk? (See Table 18.3.)

32. What is a radioactive tracer? How is it used?

33. Describe the radiocarbon method for dating archaeological artifacts.

34. How might radioactivity be used to locate a leak in an underground pipe?

35. Anthropologists have found bones whose age suggests that the human line may have emerged in Africa as much as 4 million years ago. If wood or charcoal were found with such bones, would carbon-14 dating be useful in dating the bones? Explain.

36. Which of the following statements are correct?

    (a) Radioactivity was discovered by Marie Curie.

    (b) An atom of $^{59}_{28}$Ni has 59 neutrons.

    (c) The loss of a beta particle by an atom of $^{75}_{33}$As forms an atom of increased atomic number.

    (d) The emission of an alpha particle from the nucleus of an atom lowers its atomic number by 4 and lowers its atomic mass by 2.

    (e) Emission of gamma radiation from the nucleus of an atom leaves both the atomic number and atomic mass unchanged.

    (f) Relatively few naturally occurring radioactive nuclides have atomic numbers below 81.

    (g) The longer the half-life of a radionuclide, the more slowly it decays.

    (h) The beta ray has the greatest penetrating power of all the rays emitted from the nucleus of an atom.

    (i) Radioactivity is due to an unstable ratio of neutrons to nucleons in an atom.

    (j) The half-life of different nuclides can vary from a fraction of a second to millions of years.

    (k) The symbol $^{0}_{+1}e$ is used to indicate a positron, which is a positively charged particle with the mass of an electron.

    (l) The disintegration of $^{226}_{88}$Ra into $^{214}_{83}$Po involves the loss of three alpha particles and two beta particles.

    (m) If 1.0 g of a radionuclide has a half-life of 7.2 days, the half-life of 0.50 g of that nuclide is 3.6 days.

    (n) If the mass of a radionuclide is reduced by radioactive decay from 12 g to 0.75 g in 22 hours, the half-life of the isotope is 5.5 hours.

    (o) A very high temperature is required to initiate nuclear fusion reactions.

    (p) Radiocarbon dating of archaeological artifacts is based on an increase in the ratio of carbon-14 to carbon-12 in the object.

    (q) Cancers are often treated by radiation from cobalt-60, which destroys the rapidly growing cancer cells.

    (r) High levels of radiation produce nausea, vomiting, and diarrhea.

    (s) Carbon-14, used in radiocarbon dating, is produced in living matter by the beta decay of nitrogen-14.

    (t) Radioactive tracers are small amounts of radioactive nuclides of selected elements whose progress in chemical or biological processes can be followed using a radiation detection instrument.

D. *Review problems*

1. Strontium-90 has a half-life of 28 years. If a 1.00 mg sample of this nuclide were stored for 112 years, what weight of this nuclide would remain?

2. If radium costs $50,000 a gram, how much will 0.0100 g of ^{226}RaCl$_2$ cost if the price is based only on the radium content?

3. Strontium-90 has a half-life of 28 years. If a sample was tested in 1980 and found to be

emitting 240 counts/minute, in what year would the same sample be found to be emitting 30 counts/minute? How much of the original Sr-90 would be left?

4. An archaeological specimen was analyzed and found to be emitting only 25% as much carbon-14 radiation per gram of carbon as newly cut wood. How old is this specimen?

5. Barium-141 is a beta emitter. What is the half-life if a 16.0 g sample of the nuclide decays to 0.500 g in 90 minutes?

*6. Calculate (a) the mass defect and (b) the binding energy of $^{7}_{3}Li$. Mass data: $^{7}_{3}Li = 7.0160$ g; n = 1.0087 g;   p = 1.0073 g;   e = 0.00055 g; 1.0 g = 9.2×10^{13} J (from $E = mc^2$).

*7. For the fission reaction

$$^{235}_{92}U + ^{1}_{0}n \longrightarrow ^{94}_{38}Sr + ^{139}_{54}Xe + 3\,^{1}_{0}n + Energy$$

Mass data: U-235 = 235.0439; Sr-94 = 93.9154; Xe-139 = 138.9179; n = 1.0087; 1.0 g = 9.2×10^{13} J. Calculate:

(a) The energy released in joules for a single event (one uranium atom splitting)

(b) The energy released in joules per mole of uranium splitting

(c) The percentage of the mass that is lost in the reaction

*8. For the fusion reaction

$$^{1}_{1}H + ^{2}_{1}H \longrightarrow ^{3}_{2}He + Energy$$

Mass data: $^{1}_{1}H = 1.00782$; $^{2}_{1}H = 2.01410$; $^{3}_{2}He = 3.01603$; 1.0 g = 9.2×10^{13} J. Calculate:

(a) The energy released in joules per mole of $^{3}_{2}He$ formed

(b) The percentage of the mass that is lost in the reaction

9. In the disintegration series $^{235}_{92}U \longrightarrow ^{207}_{82}Pb$, how many alpha and beta particles are emitted?

19

Chemistry of Some Selected Elements

After studying Chapter 19, you should be able to

1. Understand the new terms listed in Question A at the end of the chapter.
2. List the alkali metals (Group IA) and compare their atomic radii, densities, melting points, and first ionization energies.
3. Write balanced chemical equations for the reaction of any alkali metal with (a) water, (b) any halogen, and (c) hydrogen.
4. Describe the preparation of magnesium metal from seawater and write equations for the reactions involved.
5. Explain, using chemical equations, why it is difficult to extinguish a magnesium fire with water or carbon dioxide.
6. Explain why colors appear when certain elements are heated strongly in a nonluminous flame and list the specific colors obtained from Li, Na, K, Rb, Ca, Sr, and Ba.
7. State the essential chemical difference between pig iron and steel.
8. Explain cathodic protection, and write equations for the anode reactions of two metals used in protecting steel.
9. Explain why aluminum is more expensive than iron or steel even though it is more abundant than iron in the earth's crust.
10. Explain why aluminum and magnesium can be used as structural materials even though they are very reactive elements.
11. Identify the halogen that has the highest electronegativity (and first ionization energy) and explain why it has an especially high electronegativity.

12. Explain why the boiling point of hydrogen fluoride is abnormally high when compared to that of other hydrogen halides.
13. Write balanced equations for the preparation of halogens by (a) electrolysis of the appropriate salt and (b) reaction of the appropriate salt (fluorides excepted) with sulfuric acid and manganese dioxide.
14. Explain why pure HBr or HI cannot be prepared by heating NaBr or NaI with concentrated sulfuric acid.
15. Arrange the halogens in order of increasing strength as oxidizing agents and the halide ions in order of increasing strength as reducing agents.
16. Describe and explain a safe procedure for diluting concentrated sulfuric acid.
17. Write equations illustrating the reactions of sulfuric acid as (a) an acid, (b) a dehydrating agent, (c) an oxidizing agent, and (d) a reagent in the preparation of other acids.
18. Tell which element of Group VA is the most metallic and which is the least metallic.
19. Diagram and discuss the nitrogen cycle.
20. Balance redox equations involving the chemistry of Groups VA, VIA, and VIIA elements.

19.1   Metals: Importance and Properties

More than three-fourths of the chemical elements are metals. Their historical importance to humanity is suggested by the names of the most recent ages of civilization: the Bronze Age and the Iron Age.

Physically, the outstanding properties of metals are: (a) "metallic" luster, (b) good thermal conductivity, (c) generally good electrical conductivity, (d) malleability (capable of being shaped by hammering), and (e) ductility (capable of being drawn out into wire).

Chemically, two outstanding properties of metals are:

(a) Formation of positive ions in compounds:

$$Zn^0 + Br_2^0 \longrightarrow Zn^{2+}Br_2^{1-}$$

(b) Formation of basic oxides, which react with acids to produce salts and, if soluble, with water to produce hydroxide ions in solution:

$$CuO \quad + 2\,HNO_3 \longrightarrow Cu(NO_3)_2 + H_2O$$
Basic oxide   Acid   Salt
(insoluble)

$$BaO \quad + 2\,H_2O \longrightarrow Ba^{2+}(aq) + 2\,OH^-(aq)$$
Basic oxide   Barium hydroxide solution
(soluble)

19.2   Metallurgy

metallurgy

Metallurgy is the science of obtaining and refining metals from their ores, and the study of the properties and applications of metals. With the exception of a few relatively unreactive ones such as gold, silver, and platinum, metals do not occur in the free or uncombined state in nature. They occur instead as compounds or minerals, an ore being the commercial source of the element. To secure a free metal, the appropriate ore must be obtained and processed. Ore processing may involve a variety of physical and chemical treatments, but the essential operation is that of *reduction*, whereby positive metal ions are reduced to metal atoms.

Reduction may be accomplished by (a) reaction with hot carbon or carbon monoxide, (b) reaction with a more active (more electropositive) metal, (c) reaction with hydrogen, (d) electrolysis, and (e) heating. Hot carbon (or carbon monoxide) and electrolysis are the most widely used reduction methods. Heating is effective for only a few thermally unstable oxides, notably Ag_2O and HgO. Equations for some typical reductions follow.

(a) $2\,PbO + C \xrightarrow{\Delta} 2\,Pb + CO_2$

(b) $TiCl_4 + 2\,Mg \xrightarrow{\Delta} Ti + 2\,MgCl_2$

(c) $WO_3 + 3\,H_2 \xrightarrow{\Delta} W + 3\,H_2O$

(d) $MgCl_2 \xrightarrow[\text{current}]{\text{Electric}} Mg + Cl_2$

(e) $2\,Ag_2O \xrightarrow{\Delta} 4\,Ag + O_2$

alloy

Most metals used in the home and in industry are not pure but are alloys. An **alloy** is a homogenous mixture (normally a solid) that usually contains two or more metals and may contain small amounts of nonmetals. Alloys are made to improve the tensile strength, wearing qualities, corrosion resistance, and so on, of pure metals. Steel, for example, is an iron alloy that contains very small amounts of carbon, yet steel is very much harder and stronger than pure iron. Alloys are usually made by combining the materials in the molten state to obtain a uniform mixture. The metals used in electrical wiring, chiefly aluminum and copper, are very pure and are not alloyed because impurities in a metal decrease

amalgam

its electrical conductivity. Alloys of mercury are called **amalgams;** they may be either solid or liquid depending on the amount of mercury present.

It is possible to make an almost limitless number of alloys. Table 19.1 gives a few examples of the thousands of alloys that are available.

19.3   The Alkali Metals

Physical Properties

alkali metal

The elements of Group IA in the periodic table—lithium, sodium, potassium, rubidium, cesium, and francium—are known as the **alkali metals** or the *sodium family.* They are named *alkali metals* because all of them form strong alkalies. An alkali is a substance that has the properties of a base. All Group IA metals are silvery-white in color when freshly cut, are soft and ductile, and are good conductors of electricity. Lithium is the hardest, being only a little softer

Table 19.1   Composition of selected alloys

Alloy	Percent composition
Stainless steel	74 Fe, 18 Cr, 8 Ni, 0.18 C
	(Many others are known.)
Storage battery plates	94 Pb, 6 Sb
Coinage silver (U.S.)	90 Ag, 10 Cu
Plumber's solder	67 Pb, 33 Sn
Babbitt metal	90 Sn, 7 Sb, 3 Cu
Yellow brass	67 Cu, 33 Zn
10 carat gold	42 Au, 38–46 Cu, 12–20 Ag
18 carat gold	75 Au, 10–20 Ag, 5–15 Cu
Nichrome	60 Ni, 40 Cr
Stellite	55 Co, 15 W, 25 Cr, 5 Mo
Spring steel	98.6 Fe, 1 Cr, 0.4 C

than lead. Francium is radioactive; it is so rare that comparatively little is known about its properties.

The alkali metals are among the most reactive elements and are never found in the free state of nature. Their chemical activity increases with size and atomic number. Because these metals react readily with oxygen and moisture, they are stored in a vacuum or under an inert liquid such as kerosene, benzene, or toluene. The similarity in chemical properties of this family is due to a similar electronic structure. An atom of an alkali metal has only one valence electron. Therefore, these elements form ions having only a +1 oxidation number. Variations in their properties and reactivities are due to differences in mass, size, and ease with which they lose their outer-shell electron. Some of the physical properties of the alkali metals are shown in Table 19.2.

Metallic sodium has excellent thermal and electrical conductivity. It does not conduct electricity quite as well as silver, copper, aluminum, or gold; however, for some applications in the electrical power industry, sodium is more economical to use than the usual electrical conductors. For example, sodium metal encased in steel has replaced large copper bus bars in some power stations.

Table 19.2   Physical properties of the alkali metals

Element	Atomic number	Atomic weight	Electron configuration	Metallic atomic radius (nm)	Radius of M^+ ion (nm)	Density (20°C, g/mL)	Melting point (°C)	Boiling point (°C)
Li	3	6.941	[He]$2s^1$	0.158	0.060	0.53	186.0	1,336
Na	11	22.990	[Ne]$3s^1$	0.186	0.095	0.97	97.7	880
K	19	39.098	[Ar]$4s^1$	0.238	0.133	0.86	63.6	760
Rb	37	85.468	[Kr]$5s^1$	0.253	0.148	1.53	39.0	700
Cs	55	132.905	[Xe]$6s^1$	0.272	0.169	1.90	28.4	670

Alkali Metal Mineral Deposits

Salts or minerals of the alkalies, especially sodium, are widespread throughout the earth. Lithium deposits, usually in the form of complex minerals, are widely scattered over the earth. An important commercial source is the mineral spodumene, $LiAl(SiO_3)_2$.

The most important compound of sodium is sodium chloride. It occurs in seawater to the extent of about 3% and as rock salt deposits all over the globe. Most sodium chloride is obtained from subterranean mineral deposits, although the sea remains the largest potential source. The mineral name for sodium chloride is *halite*. Trona ($Na_2CO_3 \cdot NaHCO_3 \cdot 2H_2O$) is found in large deposits at Searles Lake, California. Large deposits of sodium nitrate (Chile saltpeter, $NaNO_3$) are located in Chile and Peru.

Major deposits of potassium salts are located at Stassfurt, Germany; Searles Lake, California; and in the Carlsbad, New Mexico, area. The principal minerals are sylvite (KCl), carnalite ($KCl \cdot MgCl_2 \cdot 6H_2O$), polyhalite ($K_2SO_4 \cdot MgSO_4 \cdot 2CaSO_4 \cdot 2H_2O$), and longbeinite ($K_2SO_4 \cdot 2MgSO_4$).

Small amounts of rubidium and cesium are found in potassium salt deposits. Sodium and potassium are the sixth and seventh most abundant elements in the earth's crust.

Preparation

The alkali metals are usually prepared by electrolysis of the molten chlorides or hydroxides. Graphite and iron electrodes are used; the alkali metal deposits at the cathode and floats to the surface of the more dense salt. The cathode and anode reactions of molten Na^+Cl^- are shown below.

Cathode reaction	$2\,Na^+ + 2e^- \longrightarrow 2\,Na$
Anode reaction	$2\,Cl^- \longrightarrow Cl_2 \uparrow\ + 2e^-$
Total reaction	$2\,Na^+ + 2\,Cl^- \longrightarrow 2\,Na + Cl_2 \uparrow$

The electrolysis of aqueous sodium chloride gives sodium hydroxide, hydrogen, and chlorine as products.

Potassium metal may be prepared by electrolysis of potassium hydroxide. Potassium and hydrogen are liberated at the cathode and oxygen at the anode. Potassium is also prepared by the reaction of sodium with potassium chloride.

$$2\,KOH \xrightarrow{\text{Electrolysis}} 2\,K + H_2(g) + O_2(g)$$

$$Na + KCl \longrightarrow K + NaCl$$

Chemical Properties

The chemical properties of an alkali metal depend on the ease with which it loses its outer-shell electron. The ion formed when an electron is lost from an alkali metal has a noble gas structure and, therefore, has great stability. We have seen (Chapter 7) that the amount of energy required to remove an electron from an atom is known as the ionization energy. A study of ionization energies shows

Table 19.3 Ionization energies of the alkali metals. These values represent the energies required to remove the first and the second electron from one atomic weight of the element, causing the formation of positive ions. Values for hydrogen, helium, and magnesium are included for comparison.

	Ionization energy (kJ/mol)	
Element	First electron	Second electron
Li	520	7,297
Na	496	4,565
K	419	3,055
Rb	403	2,640
Cs	376	2,260
H	1,314	—
He	2,372	5,247
Mg	738	1,444

that the values for the alkali metals are lower than those for all the other metals (see Figure 7.1), indicating their relatively greater reactivity. Table 19.3 shows the ionization energies for the alkali metals and some other elements for comparison. A value of 376 kJ/mol for cesium compared with 496 kJ/mol for sodium means that cesium loses an electron more easily than does sodium, which verifies the fact that cesium is more reactive than sodium. The alkali metals are excellent reducing agents.

Reaction with water. The reaction of the alkali metals with water is vigorous and strongly exothermic, with lithium being the least reactive of the group. Potassium, rubidium, and cesium are so highly reactive that they will even react with ice at −100°C. In the equation below, M represents an alkali metal:

$$2\ M(s) + 2\ H_2O \longrightarrow 2\ MOH(aq) + H_2 \uparrow$$

Alkali metals react violently with dilute acids. The hydrogen gas that is produced with either water or acids may ignite and explode.

All the alkali metal hydroxides, MOH, are readily soluble in water. Lithium hydroxide is the least soluble and cesium hydroxide is the most soluble. All are strong bases. Cesium hydroxide is the strongest base known. Cesium is the most electropositive element and stands first in the activity series of metals.

Reaction with hydrogen. Rubidium and cesium react violently with hydrogen at room temperature. The other three metals require elevated temperatures in order to form the hydride. The general equation is

$$2\ M(s) + H_2(g) \longrightarrow 2\ MH(s)$$

The compounds that are formed (MH) are called *hydrides*. Lithium hydride and sodium hydride are useful sources of hydrogen in organic chemistry reactions. Hydrides react with water to form free hydrogen and metal hydroxides.

$$LiH(s) + H_2O \longrightarrow LiOH(aq) + H_2 \uparrow$$

Reaction with halogens.   All alkali metals react with all of the halogens to form metal halides. Lithium and sodium, for example, react slowly with chlorine at room temperature; but molten sodium burns with a brilliant yellow flame in a chlorine atmosphere to form sodium chloride:

$$2\,Na + Cl_2 \longrightarrow 2\,NaCl$$

Potassium, rubidium, and cesium react vigorously with all the halogens, forming metal halides.

Reaction with oxygen.   When heated, all five alkali metals react vigorously with oxygen. Lithium forms only the monoxide, Li_2O; sodium and potassium form peroxides, Na_2O_2 and K_2O_2. Cesium explodes spontaneously when it is in contact with air or oxygen. By way of comparison, the combustion of the alkali metals is a more violent reaction than the combustion of magnesium in air.

Lithium compounds.   Table 19.4 lists some of the more important lithium compounds and describes their uses.

Sodium compounds.   The principal commercial sodium compounds are sodium chloride, sodium carbonate, and sodium hydroxide. Sodium chloride, because of its abundance and low cost, is the starting material for the manufacture of metallic sodium and a variety of other sodium compounds. See Table 19.5.

Potassium compounds.   Potassium compounds were known in early times; the name *potash* was given to potassium carbonate, which was obtained by leaching the ashes of burned wood or other plant material in iron pots. Mineral salts of potassium are selectively absorbed from the soil by plants. Animals

Table 19.4   Important compounds of lithium

Compound	Uses
Lithium chloride, LiCl	Starting material for the manufacture of Li metal; a 35–40% aqueous solution is used in air-conditioning units for humidity control
Lithium carbonate, Li_2CO_3	Ceramic glazes
Lithium hydride, LiH	Source of H_2; a reducing agent
Lithium hydroxide, LiOH	Excellent absorbent for CO_2: $2LiOH + CO_2 \rightarrow Li_2CO_3 + H_2O$
Lithium stearate, $LiC_{18}H_{35}O_2$	Added to lubricating oils and greases to maintain their viscosity at low temperatures

Table 19.5 Important compounds of sodium

Compound	Uses
Sodium chloride, NaCl	Starting material for preparation of metallic sodium and other sodium compounds; table salt; source of chlorine gas; dietary need for the human body
Sodium carbonate, Na_2CO_3	Also known as *soda ash*; used in manufacture of soap, cleansers, glass; water softening; pulp and paper industry
Sodium hydroxide, NaOH	Also known as *caustic soda* and *lye*; used in manufacture of soap, rayon, and cellulose film; most common base used in the chemical laboratory
Sodium bicarbonate, $NaHCO_3$	Also known as *baking soda*; used in baking as a leavening agent; source of CO_2 in some fire extinguishers
Sodium nitrate, $NaNO_3$	Known as *Chile saltpeter*; formerly used to make HNO_3; now used mainly as a fertilizer
Sodium bromide, NaBr	Photographic emulsions
Sodium iodide, NaI	Photographic emulsions; medicinals
Sodium tetraborate, $Na_2B_4O_7 \cdot 10\, H_2O$	Known as *borax*; used as a water softener and cleansing agent
Sodium thiosulfate, $Na_2S_2O_3$	Known as *hypo*; used as a fixing agent in photography
Sodium sulfate, Na_2SO_4	Diluent for synthetic detergents, many of which contain more than 50% Na_2SO_4
Sodium peroxide, Na_2O_2	Oxidizing agent; preparation of hydrogen peroxide

Table 19.6 Important compounds of potassium

Compound	Uses
Potassium chloride, KCl	Starting material for preparation of most potassium compounds; fertilizer
Potassium hydroxide, KOH	Preparation of soft soaps; textile industry
Potassium carbonate, K_2CO_3	Manufacture of glass and soap
Potassium iodide, KI	Photographic emulsions; medicinals
Potassium nitrate, KNO_3	Known as *saltpeter*; used as the oxidant in black gunpowder; now used for glass, ceramic glazes, fertilizers, and in the curing and pickling of meat
Potassium hydrogen tartrate, $KHC_4H_4O_6$	Known as *cream of tartar*; present in grape juice; an ingredient of baking powder
Potassium sulfate, K_2SO_4	Fertilizer

require both sodium and potassium in their diets; plants require only potassium for proper growth. Table 19.6 lists some potassium compounds.

19.4 The Alkaline Earth Metals

alkaline earth metal

The elements of Group IIA of the periodic table—beryllium, magnesium, calcium, strontium, barium, and radium—are called the **alkaline earth metals.** They were so named because of the alkaline properties of their oxides and

Table 19.7   **Physical properties of the alkaline earth metals**

Element	Atomic number	Atomic weight	Electron configuration	Metallic atomic radius (nm)	Radius of M^{2+} ion (nm)	Density (20°C, g/mL)	Melting point (°C)	Boiling point (°C)
Be	4	9.012	[He]$2s^2$	0.112	0.031	1.85	1278	2970
Mg	12	24.305	[Ne]$3s^2$	0.116	0.065	1.74	651	1107
Ca	20	40.08	[Ar]$4s^2$	0.197	0.099	1.55	843	1487
Sr	38	87.62	[Kr]$5s^2$	0.215	0.113	2.6	769	1384
Ba	56	137.34	[Xe]$6s^2$	0.222	0.135	3.6	725	1140
Ra	88	226.03	[Rn]$7s^2$	0.246	—	5.5	700	<1737

because early chemists called all insoluble nonmetallic substances that were unaffected by fire "earths."

Group IIA metals are too reactive to be found free in nature but are generally harder and less reactive than the Group IA metals. At ordinary temperatures beryllium and magnesium are stable in air, but barium and strontium are so reactive that they are usually stored under an inert solvent such as kerosene. Radium is highly radioactive. Some of the physical properties of the alkaline earth metals are shown in Table 19.7.

Occurrence

Calcium and magnesium rank fifth and eighth, respectively, in order of abundance in the earth's crust. The other Group IIA elements are much less common; all occur as compounds in both igneous and sedimentary rocks. Seawater contains about 0.13% magnesium. A list of the more common naturally occurring minerals of the alkaline earth metals is given in Table 19.8.

Preparation

All alkaline earth metals can be prepared by electrolysis of their fused chlorides; calcium and magnesium are prepared on a commercial scale by this method. Beryllium is prepared commercially by electrolyzing beryllium chloride with sodium chloride added to lower the melting point of the electrolyte mixture. Because sodium ions are harder to reduce than beryllium ions, no free sodium is produced.

$$BeCl_2 \xrightarrow[NaCl]{Electrolysis} Be + Cl_2$$

The small quantities of strontium and barium needed for industrial use are prepared by reducing SrO or BaO with aluminum in an electric vacuum furnace. Either strontium or barium will distill away from the solid aluminum oxide that is produced.

$$3\,SrO + 2\,Al \xrightarrow[Vacuum]{>1000°C} Al_2O_3 + 3\,Sr$$

Table 19.8   Principal naturally occurring minerals of the alkaline earth metals

Mineral	*Chemical composition*
Beryllium	
Beryl	$Be_3Al_2(SiO_3)_6$
Chrysoberyl	$BeO \cdot Al_2O_3$
Magnesium	
Magnesite	$MgCO_3$
Dolomite	$CaCO_3 \cdot MgCO_3$
Epsom salt	$MgSO_4 \cdot 7\,H_2O$
Asbestos	$H_4Mg_3Si_2O_9$
Talc	$Mg_3Si_4O_{10}(OH)_2$
Calcium	
Calcite (limestone)	$CaCO_3$
Gypsum	$CaSO_4 \cdot 2\,H_2O$
Fluorspar	CaF_2
Apatite	$Ca_5F(PO_4)_3$
Strontium	
Celestite	$SrSO_4$
Strontianite	$SrCO_3$
Barium	
Barite	$BaSO_4$
Witherite	$BaCO_3$

Magnesium is the only metal that is obtained commercially from seawater. The process involves the following steps: precipitation of magnesium ions from seawater (which contains approximately 0.13% Mg^{2+}) as magnesium hydroxide by adding calcium oxide; filtering out the $Mg(OH)_2$ and converting it to magnesium chloride by reaction with hydrochloric acid; drying and electrolyzing the $MgCl_2$ to obtain magnesium and chlorine. The chemistry involved is represented by these equations:

$$CaCO_3(s) \xrightarrow{\Delta} CaO(s) + CO_2(g)$$

$$CaO(s) + H_2O(l) \longrightarrow Ca^{2+}(aq) + 2\,OH^-(aq)$$

$$Mg^{2+}(aq) + 2\,OH^-(aq) \longrightarrow Mg(OH)_2(s)$$

$$Mg(OH)_2(s) + 2\,HCl(aq) \longrightarrow MgCl_2(aq) + 2\,H_2O(l)$$

$$MgCl_2(l) \xrightarrow{\text{Electrolysis}} Mg(s) + Cl_2(g)$$

Chemical and Physical Properties

All the Group IIA elements react by losing the outermost pair of s electrons to form + 2 ions. Hence, the formulas of their compounds are similar ($BeSO_4$, $MgSO_4$, $CaSO_4$, and so on). However, these elements differ widely in reactivity.

Beryllium is the least reactive of the alkaline earth metals. It is resistant to oxidation and stable in air at ordinary temperatures, but oxidizes rapidly at about 800°C.

$$2\,Be + O_2 \xrightarrow{\;800°C\;} 2\,BeO$$

Because of its many special properties, beryllium is useful in technology. For example, it is highly permeable to X rays and is therefore used in X-ray tube windows. In nuclear technology beryllium serves as a moderator to slow neutrons; and when bombarded with alpha particles, it is a good source of neutrons.

$$^{9}_{4}Be + ^{4}_{2}He \longrightarrow ^{12}_{6}C + ^{1}_{0}n$$

Magnesium is used because of its high strength-to-weight ratio and resistance to atmospheric corrosion. The corrosion resistance is actually due to its reactivity. When exposed to air, magnesium quickly becomes coated with a thin transparent layer of MgO. This layer protects the surface from further corrosion at ordinary temperatures.

Because magnesium is very reactive, care must be exercised in its use. It will react slowly with boiling water and more rapidly with steam.

$$Mg(s) + 2\,H_2O(l) \xrightarrow{\;100°C\;} Mg(OH)_2(s) + H_2(g)$$

$$Mg(s) + H_2O(g) \longrightarrow MgO(s) + H_2(g)$$
(Steam)

Magnesium burns brilliantly in air or oxygen. Fortunately, any piece large enough to use as a structural material is difficult to ignite. When a large piece is heated at one point, the heat is conducted away so rapidly that it is difficult to reach the ignition point of the metal. A magnesium fire, once started, is very hard to extinguish. Hot magnesium reacts exothermically with common fire extinguishing agents. In effect, the hot magnesium takes the oxygen needed for combustion away from the "fire extinguishing" material—water, carbon dioxide, or sand—and thus continues to burn.

$$Mg + H_2O(g) \longrightarrow MgO + H_2 + 360\,kJ\ (86.0\,kcal)$$

$$2\,Mg + CO_2 \longrightarrow 2\,MgO + C + 810\,kJ\ (194\,kcal)$$

$$2\,Mg + SiO_2 \longrightarrow 2\,MgO + Si + 344\,kJ\ (82.2\,kcal)$$

The alkaline earth metals that are heavier than magnesium are too reactive to be used as structural materials. They react with cold water to form free hydrogen and the corresponding metal hydroxide. Reactivity increases from calcium to radium. Calcium is the only one of the heavier Group IIA elements that is produced in commercially significant amounts. It is used as a minor constituent of some alloys and as a reducing agent.

Compounds

Calcium carbonate is of special importance and occurs in various natural forms such as marble, calcite, travertine, and ordinary limestone. Large areas of the earth's surface are covered with layers of limestone up to several thousand feet thick.

Calcium carbonate is probably the most extensively used raw material in industry. For centuries *lime burning* has been practiced to obtain calcium oxide, or *quicklime*. Lime burning involves the decomposition of calcium carbonate (limestone) in a large tubular furnace or *lime kiln* at about 1000°C.

$$CaCO_3 \xrightarrow{\Delta} CaO + CO_2$$

Huge quantities of calcium oxide (quicklime) are used in making mortar and plaster, softening water, making paper, sugar refining, and chemical manufacturing. Calcium oxide from limestone also enters into the making of glass and portland cement through reactions of this kind.

$$CaCO_3 \xrightarrow{\Delta} CaO + CO_2$$

$$CaO + SiO_2 \longrightarrow \underset{\text{Calcium silicate}}{CaSiO_3}$$

Calcium hydroxide, or slaked lime, is made from calcium oxide and water:

$$CaO + H_2O \longrightarrow Ca(OH)_2$$

The mineral gypsum is another common calcium compound. Although gypsum is much less common than calcium carbonate, the several hundred square miles of "sand" in the Great White Sands Desert in New Mexico is composed of finely divided gypsum. Plaster of paris is made by heating gypsum:

$$2\ CaSO_4 \cdot 2\ H_2O \xrightarrow{\Delta} (CaSO_4)_2 \cdot H_2O + 3\ H_2O$$

Gypsum
(Calcium sulfate
dihydrate)

Plaster of paris
(Calcium sulfate
hemihydrate)

To make surgical casts or plaster molds and impressions, the foregoing reaction is reversed by wetting powdered plaster of paris to form a solid cast of calcium sulfate dihydrate.

Table 19.9 lists the uses of some of the more important and interesting compounds of the Group IIA elements.

Biological Properties

Calcium and magnesium are required for many essential biological processes in both animal and plant life. Magnesium is present in the chlorophyll of green plants, and it is required for the activity of some enzymes involved in the metabolism of animals. Calcium is needed for nitrogen utilization by plants. Calcium serves the human body in a variety of ways; for example, it is present in

Table 19.9   Important compounds of Group IIA elements

Compound	Uses
Beryllium oxide, BeO	Refractory material used in crucibles; neutron reflector in nuclear reactors
Beryllium aluminum silicate, $3\,BeO \cdot Al_2O_3 \cdot 6\,SiO_2$	The precious and semiprecious gems emerald, aquamarine, and beryl have this approximate composition
Magnesium chloride, $MgCl_2$	Principal source of magnesium metal; occurs in underground deposits and dissolved in seawater
Magnesium oxide, MgO	Also known as *magnesia*; refractory material used in furnace linings and other high-temperature applications; milk of magnesia, which is used as an antacid, is a mixture of MgO and $Mg(OH)_2$
Magnesium carbonate, $MgCO_3$	Also known as *magnesite*; used as an insulating material; source of magnesium for other magnesium compounds
Magnesium sulfate, $MgSO_4$	Occurs as the heptahydrate ($MgSO_4 \cdot 7\,H_2O$) and is known as *epsom salts*; this salt is used as a purgative; also used in the tanning and dyeing industries and as a fertilizer for magnesium-deficient soils
Calcium carbonate, $CaCO_3$	Largest volume raw material in chemical industry; flux in steel making; manufacture of cement, mortar, and glass: building material
Calcium oxide, CaO	Also known as *quicklime*; used for mortar and plaster, paper making, sugar refining, water treating, and others
Calcium hydroxide, $Ca(OH)_2$	Known as *slaked lime*; cheapest source of OH^- ions
Calcium phosphate, $Ca_3(PO_4)_2$	Used as fertilizer; source of phosphoric acid and phosphorus compounds
Calcium sulfate, $CaSO_4$	Occurs as gypsum ($CaSO_4 \cdot 2\,H_2O$); used to make plaster of paris and building materials, especially plasterboard
Calcium fluoride, CaF_2	Known as *fluorspar* or *fluorite*; used as a flux in metallurgy; principal source of fluorine for other fluorine compounds
Calcium chloride, $CaCl_2$	Very hygroscopic; used to reduce dust on unpaved roads and to reduce danger of dust explosions in mines; also used to melt ice on streets
Calcium carbide, CaC_2	Source of acetylene
Strontium nitrate, $Sr(NO_3)_2$	Produces an intense red color in flares and fireworks
Barium sulfate, $BaSO_4$	Also known as *barite*; high-density material used in oil-well drilling muds; paint pigment; filler for paper making; also used in X-ray photography of the gastrointestinal tract
Barium nitrate, $Ba(NO_3)_2$	Used to produce a brilliant green color in flares and fireworks

bones and teeth as calcium phosphate, and it has an essential role in the clotting of blood.

Strontium is believed to be a biologically nonessential element and is not toxic to humans. However, the isotope Sr-90, which is present in nuclear fallout, is extremely hazardous due to its radioactivity (Section 18.14).

Soluble beryllium and barium salts are poisonous to humans. Barium salts are so toxic that a quantity of less than 1 g of barium chloride may be fatal to an adult. An exception to this general toxicity is barium sulfate, which is given orally prior to X-ray or fluoroscopic examination of the gastrointestinal tract.

Barium sulfate is used for this purpose because (1) barium is a heavy metal and therefore is opaque to X rays, and (2) it is so highly insoluble that no barium ions are absorbed into the body from the gastrointestinal tract.

19.5 Flame Tests and Spectroscopy

All Group IA elements and calcium, strontium, and barium from Group IIA can be detected by simple flame tests. A Bunsen burner and a piece of clean platinum wire are the only essential pieces of apparatus needed to make flame tests. When salts of the elements are volatilized in the burner flame, the characteristic colors are visible.

Element	Color
Li	Red
Na	Bright yellow (persistent)
K	Violet (short duration)
Rb	Violet
Ca	Brick red (short duration)
Sr	Crimson
Ba	Light green

Flame color has been exploited by spectroscopy both to identify elements and to provide detailed information on the structure of atoms. Electrons can exist only at certain definite quantized energy levels within atoms (Section 5.6). At ordinary temperatures the electrons in atoms are at their lowest, or ground-state, energy levels. When heated in a Bunsen flame (or electric arc for some elements), some ground-state electrons are promoted to higher excited-state energy levels. In falling back to the ground state, each electron releases the same amount of energy (as radiation) that was absorbed when it was promoted to the excited state. If the wavelength of this radiation falls in the visible spectrum (400–700 nm), it is seen as colored light corresponding to a particular wavelength. When such light is passed through a prism (or ruled grating) in a spectroscope, it is found to consist of narrow colored bands called *spectral lines*. Each band (or line) corresponds to the energy emitted when an electron falls from a specific excited state to a specific lower, or ground-state, energy level. Since the number of electrons in each element is different, each element has a characteristic set of spectral lines that is different from that of every other element. This set of spectral lines identifies the element and provides a means of determining the energy levels that are occupied by electrons within the atoms of that element.

19.6 Iron

Physical Properties, Occurrence, and Preparation

Iron is the fourth most abundant element, following oxygen, silicon, and aluminum. It has been the key element to the development of modern civilization. Iron was known in prehistoric times, and its known use dates back almost

Table 19.10   Iron-bearing minerals

Name	Composition
Magnetite	Fe_3O_4
Hematite	Fe_2O_3
Limonite	$Fe_2O_3 \cdot xH_2O$
Siderite	$FeCO_3$
Ilmenite	$FeTiO_3$
Pyrite	FeS_2

8000 years. The first iron to be used was probably obtained from meteorites, but iron was produced from ores as early as 1300 B.C.

Pure iron is a silvery-white, relatively soft, very ductile metal. It has a melting point of 1532°C and it boils at 3000°C. One of its most distinguishing characteristics is its magnetism, which it loses when it is heated to 770°C. In the presence of a magnetic field or electric current, iron shows greater magnetic properties than any other element. (Cobalt and nickel are also strongly magnetic.)

Very little iron is used in its pure form; most of it is used in the form of steel, an iron–carbon alloy. Steel may contain small amounts of other elements such as Mn, Si, Cr, Ni, V, W, Mo, Co, and Ti. These alloying elements enhance certain qualities of the steel such as toughness, hardness, corrosion resistance, and so on. The chief iron-bearing minerals are listed in Table 19.10. Large iron ore deposits are found on all continents. The most important iron ore–producing area in the United States is the Mesabi range in northern Minnesota.

Steel

steel

Steel is an iron–carbon alloy (0.05–1.7% C) that usually contains small amounts of other elements. Steel making is a basic industry; the quantity of steel produced each year in the world far exceeds the combined quantities of all other metals.

The first step in steel making is the reduction of iron ore to impure iron, commonly called *pig iron*. Reduction occurs in a huge reactor called a *blast furnace*. Furnace operation is continuous; ore, coke, and limestone are charged at the top while steady streams of preheated air are blown in through bottom nozzles (*tuyeres*). Furnace temperatures range from about 200°C near the top to about 1900°C near the bottom (the combustion zone). Coke is both the fuel and the source of the principal reducing agent (CO). The limestone reacts with impurities in the ore and coke to form a slag that coats and protects the reduced iron from reoxidation in the combustion zone. Molten pig iron and slag are removed at intervals from the bottom of the furnace. The following are equations for typical blast furnace reactions.

$$2\ C(s) + O_2(g) \longrightarrow 2\ CO(g)$$
Coke

$$Fe_3O_4(s) + CO(g) \longrightarrow 3\ FeO(s) + CO_2(g)$$
Ore

$$FeO(s) + CO(g) \longrightarrow Fe(l) + CO_2(g)$$

$$CaCO_3(s) \longrightarrow CaO(s) + CO_2(g)$$
Limestone

$$CaO(s) + SiO_2(s) \longrightarrow CaSiO_3(l)$$
Slag

Pig iron contains on the average about 1% Si, 0.03% S, 0.27% P, 2.4% Mn, and 4.6% C, the balance being Fe. These impurities must be removed or lowered to carefully controlled levels to convert pig iron into steel.

Several steel-making processes are known. One of the most widely used is the L-D or basic oxygen process (BOP). This process, first operated commercially at Linz, Austria, in 1952, uses a pear-shaped furnace. The furnace is charged with molten pig and scrap iron and a flux consisting of limestone and fluorspar (CaF_2) to form a slag. A long, water-cooled lance is lowered into the furnace until its tip is 4 to 8 feet from the surface of the white-hot metal. Nearly pure oxygen under a pressure of 150 pounds per square inch (approximately 10 atm) is blown into the melt, converting the impurities to oxides. Carbon oxidizes to carbon monoxide, which in turn burns to CO_2. The oxides of sulfur, phosphorus, and silicon are absorbed in the slag. The process is highly exothermic and no outside source of energy is needed. This part of the refining process takes 20 minutes, and a batch of high-quality steel can be made in 50 minutes.

Elements such as manganese, aluminum, vanadium, and silicon are added to molten steel to remove traces of disolved oxygen. However, certain elements may be added in larger portions to produce alloy steels with specific properties. Some important alloying elements and their effects on steel are given in Table 19.11.

Table 19.11 The effects of selected alloying elements on the properties of steel

Alloying element	Effect on steel
Carbon	Makes tempering possible; increases tensile strength (up to 0.83% C); increases hardness
Cobalt	Imparts high-temperature strength
Chromium	Improves hardness, abrasion resistance, corrosion resistance, and high-temperature properties
Manganese	Imparts hardness, toughness, and resistance to wear and abrasion
Molybdenum	Imparts hardness, shock resistance, and high-temperature strength
Nickel	Imparts corrosion resistance; increases toughness and high-temperature strength; reduces brittleness at very low temperatures
Silicon	Increases strength without affecting ductility; modifies magnetic and electrical properties; high Si concentrations impart resistance to acid corrosion
Tungsten	Imparts hardness, which is retained at high temperatures
Vanadium	Increases strength and toughness; improves heat-treating characteristics

Chemical Properties

Iron is a fairly reactive metal and forms two principal series of compounds: iron(II), or ferrous, compounds and iron(III), or ferric, compounds. The two oxidation states of +2 and +3 are the most common, but compounds are known in which iron has a +4 and a +6 oxidation number.

Iron dissolves in both dilute hydrochloric and dilute sulfuric acids to give Fe^{2+} compounds and hydrogen gas. When cold dilute nitric acid (an oxidizing acid) is reacted with iron, iron(II) nitrate and ammonium nitrate are formed; with concentrated nitric acid, iron(III) nitrate and nitrogen oxides are formed.

$$Fe + 2\,HCl \longrightarrow FeCl_2 + H_2 \uparrow$$

$$Fe + H_2SO_4 \longrightarrow FeSO_4 + H_2 \uparrow$$

$$4\,Fe + 10\,HNO_3 \longrightarrow 4\,Fe(NO_3)_2 + NH_4NO_3 + 3\,H_2O$$

$$Fe + 6\,HNO_3 \longrightarrow Fe(NO_3)_3 + 3\,NO_2 + 3\,H_2O$$

Iron reacts with many nonmetals, such as sulfur and the halogens, to form binary compounds:

$$Fe + S \longrightarrow FeS$$

$$2\,Fe + 3\,Cl_2 \longrightarrow 2\,FeCl_3$$

It reacts with steam to form magnetic iron oxide and hydrogen:

$$3\,Fe + 4\,H_2O(Steam) \xrightarrow{\Delta} Fe_3O_4(s) + 4\,H_2(g)$$

Magnetic iron oxide is considered to contain both +2 and +3 iron, $Fe_2O_3 \cdot FeO$. Solutions of ferrous salts are difficult to maintain in the +2 state due to the ease of oxidation of Fe^{2+} to Fe^{3+} by oxygen of the air. The equation for the net ionic reaction may be represented as follows:

$$4\,Fe^{2+} + O_2 \longrightarrow 4\,Fe^{3+} + 2\,O^{2-}$$

Corrosion of iron, commonly called *rusting*, is a serious economic problem that causes losses of billions of dollars annually in the United States. Rusting occurs on the surface of the iron, where it is exposed to oxygen and moisture in the atmosphere. The iron is transformed into reddish-brown rust, a hydrated iron(III) oxide ($Fe_2O_3 \cdot xH_2O$). As the rust is formed, it flakes off the surface, allowing the corrosion to penetrate deeper into the iron. Both oxygen and water are needed for rusting. Iron at first is oxidized to iron(II) hydroxide. This, in turn, is rapidly oxidized to iron(III) hydroxide. The latter loses water to form iron(III) oxide, containing variable amounts of water of hydration.

$$2\,Fe + O_2 + 2\,H_2O \longrightarrow 2\,Fe(OH)_2$$

$$4\,Fe(OH)_2 + O_2 + 2\,H_2O \longrightarrow 4\,Fe(OH)_3$$

$$2\,Fe(OH)_3 \longrightarrow Fe_2O_3 \cdot xH_2O$$

The most common general methods for protecting iron from corrosion are

(1) protective coatings, (2) alloying, and (3) cathodic protection. Protective coatings of paint, enamel, tar, grease, or metal are commonly used to prevent contact with the atmosphere. The term *galvanized* is applied to iron or steel that is protected by a coating of zinc metal.

Highly corrosion-resistant iron alloys are produced industrially. Eighteen-eight (18% Cr and 8% Ni) stainless steel provides almost complete protection from atmospheric corrosion. The high cost of this alloy prevents its general use, although it is used in many special applications. An iron–silicon alloy containing about 12% Si (known as *duriron*) is very resistant to the action of acids.

The ordinary rusting or corrosion of iron can be considered an electrochemical process in which iron acting as an anode is oxidized in this fashion:

$$\text{Anode reaction} \qquad Fe^0 \longrightarrow Fe^{2+} + 2\ e^-$$

To afford *cathodic protection* to a steel pipeline or tank, magnesium (or zinc) stakes or rods are driven into the earth and are connected by wires to the pipeline or tank. This in effect sets up an electrochemical cell, with the more easily oxidized magnesium metal acting as the anode. Electrons flow from the magnesium to the iron, causing the iron to become negatively charged or cathodic with respect to the magnesium. Under these conditions, the magnesium, instead of iron, acts as the anode and is oxidized:

$$Mg^0 \longrightarrow Mg^{2+} + 2\ e^-$$

Oxidation does not occur at the iron cathode, and thus no corrosion occurs on the iron pipe or tank. The following reduction reaction is believed to occur at the iron cathode:

$$2\ H_2O + O_2 + 4\ e^- \longrightarrow 4\ OH^-$$

The magnesium or zinc rods or stakes must be replaced periodically, since they are consumed in affording protection to the iron or steel. The iron hulls of ships can be protected by fastening blocks of magnesium metal to them. The zinc coating on galvanized iron actually provides cathodic protection for the iron.

19.7   Aluminum

Occurrence and Physical Properties

Aluminum (generally spelled *aluminium* in countries other than the United States) is the most abundant metal and the third most abundant element in the earth's crust, being exceeded only by oxygen and silicon. Aluminum is not found as the free metal but occurs mainly in clays, feldspars, and granite as complex aluminum silicates and in bauxite ores as hydrated aluminum oxide. Pure aluminum oxide (Al_2O_3) is known as *alumina*.

Alumina occurs naturally as the mineral corundum. Corundum is a very hard material, standing next to diamond on the hardness scale, and it is used as an abrasive. Emery, also widely used as an abrasive, is an impure corundum consisting of Al_2O_3 and Fe_3O_4. Rubies and sapphires are much sought-after precious gemstones. They consist of corundum colored by small amounts of other metallic oxides. Artificial rubies and sapphires are produced that are practically indistinguishable from the natural stones. In addition to their use as gemstones and bearings for watches and other instruments, artificial rubies and sapphires are used in lasers for the production of intense beams of coherent light.

Although aluminum is the most abundant metal in the earth's crust, free aluminum metal was not known until 1825. In that year the Danish scientist Hans Christian Oersted succeeded in making some impure samples of aluminum metal by heating aluminum chloride with potassium–mercury amalgam. However, the reduction of aluminum by an alkali metal was an inherently costly process, and aluminum remained nearly as expensive as gold and platinum during most of the 19th century. Finally in 1886 a relatively cheap method for the electrolytic production of aluminum was devised. Since then, aluminum has been used in ever-increasing amounts. Aluminum has a density of only 2.7 g/mL, a value about one-third that of other common metals such as iron, copper, and zinc. Because it is a lightweight metal and has the ability to form a variety of useful alloys, aluminum has many important commercial applications.

Aluminum is an excellent conductor of heat. As an electrical conductor, it is surpassed only by silver and copper. However, when a comparison is made with wires having the same mass per unit of length, aluminum wire, being larger, surpasses both copper and silver as an electrical conductor. For this reason—and because of the increasing scarcity of copper—high-voltage transmission cables are now usually made of aluminum wires reinforced with a steel core for additional strength.

Production

The principal aluminum ore is bauxite, which contains 40–60% alumina together with impurities of silica, iron oxide, quartz, and so on. Aluminum is obtained by the electrolysis of alumina dissolved in an electrolyte consisting mainly of fused cryolite (Na_3AlF_6). The process was developed simultaneously by Charles M. Hall (1863–1914) in the United States and by Paul L. Heroult (1863–1914) in France in 1886. Both men were only 22 years old at that time. Their basic electrolytic process is still in use today.

The purified alumina is dissolved in molten cryolite (about 950°C) and electrolyzed between carbon electrodes. Molten aluminum is formed at the cathode, sinks to the bottom of the cell, and is periodically drawn off and poured into molds. Oxygen is formed at the anode and combines with the carbon to form CO and CO_2 (see Figure 19.1). The aluminum obtained by the Hall–Heroult process is 99.5% pure.

Chemical Properties

Since aluminum is a Group IIIA metal, its common oxidation state is +3. It is a very reactive element, but when in contact with air, aluminum forms a protective oxide film that prevents further reaction. This film is so thin (0.001 to 0.1 micrometer) and transparent that the aluminum retains its bright metallic luster.

Figure 19.1 Electrolytic production of aluminum

At temperatures of about 800°C, aluminum reacts vigorously in oxygen to form Al_2O_3 and in air to form both Al_2O_3 and AlN:

$$4\,Al + 3\,O_2 \longrightarrow 2\,Al_2O_3 + 3.34 \times 10^3 \text{ kJ (798 kcal)}$$

Aluminum does not react with water at room temperature, but at 180°C it oxidizes rapidly:

$$2\,Al + 3\,H_2O \longrightarrow Al_2O_3 + 3\,H_2$$

The reaction of aluminum with dry chlorine or hydrogen chloride produces aluminum chloride ($AlCl_3$):

$$2\,Al + 3\,Cl_2 \longrightarrow 2\,AlCl_3$$

$$2\,Al + 6\,HCl \longrightarrow 2\,AlCl_3 + 3\,H_2$$

Anhydrous $AlCl_3$ is used as a catalytic reagent in many organic reactions.

At high temperatures aluminum is a good reducing agent and is capable of reducing the oxides of many other metals (Goldschmidt reaction). For example, Cr_2O_3, WO_3, and MoO_3 are readily reduced by aluminum:

$$2\,Al + Cr_2O_3 \longrightarrow Al_2O_3 + 2\,Cr$$

Aluminum reacts readily with hydrochloric acid and slowly with dilute sulfuric acid but is rendered passive by, and does not react with even concentrated nitric acid. In fact, nitric acid is shipped in aluminum-lined containers.

When aluminum salts react with bases, aluminum hydroxide forms a gelatinous white precipitate. The net ionic equation is

$$Al^{3+} + 3\,OH^- \longrightarrow Al(OH)_3(s)$$

This hydroxide is amphoteric and will dissolve in either a strong base or a strong acid:

$$Al(OH)_3(s) + NaOH(aq) \longrightarrow NaAlO_2(aq) + 2\,H_2O(l)$$

$$2\,Al(OH)_3(s) + 6\,HCl(aq) \longrightarrow 2\,AlCl_3(aq) + 3\,H_2O(l)$$

Applications of Aluminum and Its Compounds

The properties of lightness, strength when alloyed, corrosion resistance, and good heat and electrical conductivity make aluminum and its alloys useful in almost every facet of modern society. Aluminum is used in the building trades as a structural and decorative material; in the construction of aircraft, automobiles, ships, and other kinds of vehicles; and in cooking utensils, kitchen equipment, and household appliances. Aluminum foil is a common article in most households. More than half a million tons of aluminum are used each year in making containers for foods and beverages. Photographic flashbulbs are filled with thin strips of foil or fine wire made of aluminum. Aluminum is used in paints and in coating reflective surfaces.

Concern is sometimes expressed over the possibility of ingesting dangerous quantities of aluminum from acid foods that have been cooked or stored in aluminum utensils. There appears to be no danger from this source, since aluminum is essentially inert in the body. People have taken aluminum hydroxide preparations as antacids for many years without apparent ill effects; these preparations have also been used in the treatment of peptic ulcers.

Certain aluminum salts exert an astringent or constricting action on the skin and mucous membranes. This property is exploited in many commercial antiperspirant preparations. Substances called *aluminum chlorohydrates* are the principal active agents in many of these formulations. Aluminum chlorohydrates are actually aluminum hydroxy chlorides having formulas of the type $Al_2(OH)_5Cl \cdot 2H_2O$ or $Al(OH)_2Cl$. These substances prevent or retard perspiration by constricting the openings of the sweat glands.

19.8 Nonmetals: General Properties

In contrast to the metals, nonmetals have no unique physical characteristic such as "metallic" luster to identify them. Nonmetals generally are (a) poor conductors of heat, (b) extremely poor conductors or nonconductors of electricity, and (c) nonmalleable. In physical state and appearance, they range through colorless and colored gases, one reddish-brown liquid, and several variously colored solids.

As with metals, nonmetals vary greatly in reactivity. In nature the noble gases always occur in the free state, and as recently as 1962 they were believed not to form compounds. The halogens (Group VIIA) always occur as compounds, never in the free state, in nature. Other nonmetals—notably nitrogen, oxygen, carbon, and sulfur—occur both in the free state and as compounds.

Chemically, when undergoing reactions nonmetals tend to

(1) form negative ions in binary compounds with metals—for example, NaCl, Al_2O_3, $CuBr_2$

(2) form covalent bonds with other nonmetals (and with like atoms)—for example, CH_4, CO_2, NH_3, Cl_2, S_8

(3) form acidic oxides that react
   (a) with water to form acids

$$SO_3 + H_2O \longrightarrow H_2SO_4$$

(b) with bases and basic oxides to form salts

$$CO_2 + CaO \longrightarrow CaCO_3$$

19.9 The Halogen Family

halogen family

The **halogen family**, Group VIIA of the periodic table, consists of five elements: fluorine (F), chlorine (Cl), bromine (Br), iodine (I), and astatine (At). None of these are found as free elements in nature. The term *halogen* is derived from the Greek words *halos* and *gen*, which mean "salt producer." Chlorine, bromine, and iodine are easily prepared in the laboratory; fluorine is much more difficult to prepare. Astatine is found only in very small amounts as a radioactive decay product of other elements.

All the halogen atoms have seven electrons in their outermost shell and are followed, in each case, in the periodic table by a noble gas. Consequently, their most stable oxidation state is -1. All the halogens except fluorine are known to exist in several oxidation states. A halogen atom has a great tendency to fill its outer-orbital electron vacancy either by gaining an electron, as in the formation of a sodium halide, Na^+X^- (where X = F, Cl, Br, I), or by sharing electrons and forming a covalent bond. In the free state, the halogens exist as diatomic molecules, F_2, Cl_2, Br_2, and I_2:

$$:\!\overset{..}{\underset{..}{F}}\!:\!\overset{..}{\underset{..}{F}}\!: \qquad :\!\overset{..}{\underset{..}{Cl}}\!:\!\overset{..}{\underset{..}{Cl}}\!: \qquad :\!\overset{..}{\underset{..}{Br}}\!:\!\overset{..}{\underset{..}{Br}}\!: \qquad :\!\overset{..}{\underset{..}{I}}\!:\!\overset{..}{\underset{..}{I}}\!:$$

The differences in reactivity of the halogens are due to differences in their electronegativities. Fluorine, as the most electronegative, has the greatest attraction for electrons and is the most reactive, followed by chlorine, bromine, and iodine, respectively (see Table 19.12).

Since fluorine has the highest electronegativity, it is the most characteristically nonmetallic of all the elements. The general trend of the elements to become less electronegative (from top to bottom within a periodic group), and hence

Table 19.12 Physical characteristics of the halogens

Property	Fluorine	Chlorine	Bromine	Iodine
Molecular formula	F_2	Cl_2	Br_2	I_2
Atomic number	9	17	35	53
Atomic weight	18.998	35.453	79.904	126.904
Electron configuration	$[He]2s^2 2p^5$	$[Ne]3s^2 3p^5$	$[Ar]4s^2 3d^{10} 4p^5$	$[Kr]5s^2 4d^{10} 5p^5$
Atomic radius (nm)	0.072	0.099	0.114	0.133
Radius of X^- ion (nm)	0.136	0.181	0.195	0.216
Appearance	Pale yellow gas	Yellow-green gas	Reddish-brown liquid	Bluish-black solid
Density (g/mL)	1.11 (liquid at bp)	1.57 (liquid at bp)	3.14	4.94
Melting point (°C)	-219.6	-102.4	-7.2	113.6
Boiling point (°C)	-187.9	-34.0	58.8	184.5
Relative electronegativity	4.0	3.0	2.8	2.5

more metallic in characteristics, is clearly evident among the halogens. Fluorine and chlorine are gases, bromine is a liquid, and iodine is a solid with a characteristic metallic luster.

Some of the properties of the halogens are tabulated in Table 19.12.

Fluorine

The principal minerals in which fluorine is found are fluorspar (fluorite), CaF_2, and cryolite, Na_3AlF_6. Elemental fluorine was first obtained by the French chemist Henri Moissan in 1886. Moissan electrolyzed a mixture of hydrogen fluoride and potassium fluoride, the latter acting as the electrolyte. This successful electrolytic preparation came only after many attempts over a time span of about 75 years. Thereafter, because fluorine is the most reactive nonmetal and has greater electronegativity than oxygen, most chemists came to believe it could be obtained only by electrolysis. However, a century later in 1986 Karl Christie, an American, succeeded in preparing fluorine by a purely chemical method without the use of electrolysis. Christie reacted dipotassium hexafluoro-manganate(IV) and antimony pentafluoride. The overall reaction is represented by the equation.

$$2 K_2MnF_6 + 4 SbF_5 \longrightarrow 4 KSbF_6 + 2 MnF_3 + F_2$$

Nearly all elements, including some of the noble gases, form compounds with fluorine. There are two known oxides: oxygen difluoride (OF_2) and dioxygen difluoride (O_2F_2).

Hydrogen fluoride is the most important commercial product of fluorine. It is a colorless gas with a boiling point of 19.4°C and a melting point of −83°C. Hydrogen fluoride is dangerous to inhale, since it causes edema of the lungs; the eyes are also quite sensitive to this compound. The gas is very soluble in water, forming a solution of hydrofluoric acid, a weak acid. The industrial source of hydrogen fluoride is fluorspar and concentrated sulfuric acid:

$$CaF_2(s) + H_2SO_4(l) \longrightarrow 2 HF(g) + CaSO_4(s)$$

Fluorine is the only halogen sufficiently electronegative to form hydrogen bonds (see Section 13.4). In the gaseous state, hydrogen fluoride molecules are bonded together by hydrogen bonds and exist in polymeric forms, $(HF)_x$, where x has values ranging up to 6.

$$6 HF \rightleftharpoons H_6F_6$$

A unique property of hydrogen fluoride is its ability to etch glass. The art of etching glass with hydrogen fluoride was practiced as early as the 16th century. The chemical reaction that takes place is the dissolving of silicon dioxide in glass, forming silicon tetrafluoride:

$$SiO_2(s) + 4 HF(g) \longrightarrow SiF_4(g) + 2 H_2O(l)$$

Fluorine is present in the bones and teeth of mammals. Some fluoride ions are necessary for the development of sound teeth in children; however, too much fluoride can cause mottled teeth. Controlled amounts of sodium fluoride are sometimes added to water supplies that are deficient in fluoride.

Other important uses of fluorine compounds are as refrigerants and plastics. Dichlorodifluoromethane (CCl_2F_2), known as Freon-12, is the commonly used refrigerant in household refrigerators and air conditioners. Polytetrafluoroethylene, $(C_2F_4)_n$, known as Teflon, is a plastic material with high resistance to chemical attack, good temperature stability, and self-lubricating qualities.

Chlorine

Chlorine is prepared commercially by electrolysis of either aqueous sodium chloride solution or molten sodium chloride. In the laboratory, hydrochloric acid or a sodium chloride–sulfuric acid mixture is reacted with manganese dioxide:

$$4 HCl(aq) + MnO_2(s) \longrightarrow MnCl_2(aq) + 2 H_2O + Cl_2(g)$$

$$2 NaCl(s) + 2 H_2SO_4(aq) + MnO_2(s) \longrightarrow$$

$$MnSO_4(aq) + Na_2SO_4(aq) + 2 H_2O + Cl_2(g)$$

A dilute potassium chlorate solution and hydrochloric acid also liberate chlorine, when heated gently:

$$KClO_3(aq) + 6 HCl(aq) \xrightarrow{\Delta} KCl(aq) + 3 H_2O + 3 Cl_2(g)$$

Figure 19.2 shows a laboratory setup for preparing and collecting dry chlorine. Chlorine is about 2.5 times as heavy as air and is collected by the upward displacement of air.

Chlorine is quite reactive, combining directly or indirectly with many metals to form metal chlorides. All the common metal chlorides, except silver, lead, and mercury(I), are soluble in water. This property is used to separate $AgCl$, $PbCl_2$, and $HgCl_2$ from other metals for purposes of identification. With nonmetals, chlorine forms compounds that have covalent bonds. The following are a few examples:

S_2Cl_2	Disulfur dichloride	BCl_3	Boron trichloride
Cl_2O	Dichlorine monoxide	CCl_4	Carbon tetrachloride
NCl_3	Nitrogen trichloride	$SiCl_4$	Silicon tetrachloride
PCl_3	Phosphorus trichloride	ICl	Iodine monochloride
PCl_5	Phosphorus pentachloride	C_2Cl_4	Tetrachloroethylene

Table 19.13 lists the oxides of chlorine.

Hydrogen burns smoothly in an atmosphere of pure chlorine, but mixtures of hydrogen and chlorine ranging from 14–92% chlorine are considered to be explosive.

$$H_2(g) + Cl_2(g) \longrightarrow 2 HCl(g) + 185 \text{ kJ } (44.2 \text{ kcal})$$

One of the most important compounds of chlorine is hydrogen chloride (HCl), which is prepared by combining hydrogen and chlorine or by reacting sodium chloride, or other metal chlorides, with sulfuric acid. At low temperatures

Figure 19.2 Laboratory preparation of chlorine: Reactants in the generator are sodium chloride, sulfuric acid, manganese dioxide, and water. Bottle A contains water, which is used to remove any hydrogen chloride carried over with the product. Bottle B contains concentrated sulfuric acid, which functions as a drying agent to remove moisture from the product. Dry chlorine gas is collected in bottle C.

Table 19.13 Oxides of chlorine

Oxide	Formula	Oxidation number of Cl	Melting point (°C)	Boiling point (°C)
Dichlorine monoxide	Cl_2O	+1	−116	2
Dichlorine trioxide	Cl_2O_3	+3	—	—
Chlorine dioxide	ClO_2	+4	−59	11
Dichlorine hexoxide	Cl_2O_6	+6	3.5	203
Dichlorine heptoxide	Cl_2O_7	+7	−91.5	80

sodium chloride and sulfuric acid react to form sodium hydrogen sulfate and hydrogen chloride. When the mixture is heated to high temperature, the second hydrogen of sulfuric acid reacts and sodium sulfate is formed.

$$NaCl + H_2SO_4 \xrightarrow{\text{Low temp.}} NaHSO_4 + HCl(g)$$

$$NaCl + NaHSO_4 \xrightarrow{\text{High temp.}} Na_2SO_4 + HCl(g)$$

$$\overline{2\ NaCl + H_2SO_4 \longrightarrow Na_2SO_4 + 2\ HCl(g)} \qquad \text{(Overall reaction)}$$

Hydrogen chloride is very soluble in water, forming hydrochloric acid. The concentrated acid contains 36–38% HCl and has a density of about 1.19 g/mL. A demonstration of the solubility of hydrogen chloride in water is illustrated in Figure 19.3, the hydrogen chloride fountain. The top flask contains dry hydrogen chloride; the bottom flask, water. When a small amount of water is squirted into the top flask by the attached medicine dropper, hydrogen chloride dissolves in this water, creating a partial vacuum. The water from the bottom flask is then continuously drawn up into the top flask in a fountainlike effect as the hydrogen chloride dissolves.

Hydrochloric acid—the technical grade is called *muriatic acid*—is used as an acid, in preparing other chlorides, and for "pickling" (cleaning) metals. The acidity of gastric juice is due to hydrochloric acid, which is necessary for digestion.

Because of its germicidal action, chlorine is widely used to disinfect water. It is also an excellent bleaching agent. An aqueous solution of chlorine is

Figure 19.3 Hydrogen chloride fountain: Water from the lower flask rises into the upper flask because of the vacuum created when hydrogen chloride gas dissolves in water. The reaction is initiated by priming with a small amount of water from the attached medicine dropper.

commonly called *chlorine water*. Part of the dissolved chlorine reacts with water, producing hypochlorous and hydrochloric acids:

$$Cl_2(g) + H_2O(l) \longrightarrow \underset{\text{Hypochlorous acid}}{HOCl(aq)} + \underset{\text{Hydrochloric acid}}{HCl(aq)}$$

The behavior of chlorine water as a bleaching agent is due to the decomposition of unstable hypochlorous acid, which liberates *nascent* (atomic) oxygen (O), a powerful oxidant. The oxygen atom either attacks the substance being bleached or combines with another atom to form an oxygen molecule. In the reaction, the chlorine atom is reduced from an oxidation number of $+1$ to -1.

$$HOCl(aq) \longrightarrow HCl(aq) + (O)$$

Sodium hypochlorite (NaOCl) is an important household bleach and disinfectant. An acidified sodium hypochlorite solution reacts similarly to chlorine water and is used as a source of chlorine for purifying swimming pools. The equation for the reaction is

$$NaOCl(aq) + HCl(aq) \longrightarrow NaCl(aq) + HOCl(aq)$$

Organic chlorine compounds are used for refrigeration, gasoline additives, insecticides, pesticides, solvents, paints, and plastics.

Bromine

Bromine is the only nonmetallic element that is liquid at ordinary temperatures. It is readily prepared in the laboratory by oxidizing a bromide–sulfuric acid mixture with manganese dioxide.

$$2\,KBr + 2\,H_2SO_4 + MnO_2 \longrightarrow Br_2 + K_2SO_4 + MnSO_4 + 2\,H_2O$$

Bromine is obtained commercially by passing chlorine into large volumes of seawater. The bromine formed is removed by bubbling a stream of air through the chlorinated seawater. The air–bromine mixture is then passed into a sodium carbonate solution, where the bromine reacts to form sodium bromide and sodium bromate. Bromine is again formed when this mixture is acidified and heated with sulfuric acid. The equations are

$$Cl_2 + 2\,Br^- \longrightarrow Br_2 + 2\,Cl^-$$

$$3\,Br_2 + 6\,Na_2CO_3 + 3\,H_2O \longrightarrow 5\,NaBr + NaBrO_3 + 6\,NaHCO_3$$

$$5\,NaBr + NaBrO_3 + 3\,H_2SO_4 \longrightarrow 3\,Br_2 + 3\,Na_2SO_4 + 3\,H_2O$$

The chemical reactions of bromine are similar to those of chlorine, except that bromine is not as strong an oxidizing agent. With water, it forms hypobromous and hydrobromic acids:

$$Br_2(l) + H_2O(l) \rightleftharpoons \underset{\text{Hypobromous acid}}{HOBr(aq)} + \underset{\text{Hydrobromic acid}}{HBr(aq)}$$

Bromine is more reactive than iodine and oxidizes iodides in solution to free iodine:

$$Br_2(aq) + 2I^-(aq) \longrightarrow I_2(aq) + 2\,Br^-(aq)$$

Pure hydrogen bromide cannot be made from bromide salts and sulfuric acid because hydrogen bromide is a fairly good reducing agent and reacts further with the acid to form sulfur dioxide and bromine:

$$2\,HBr + H_2SO_4 \longrightarrow Br_2 + SO_2 + 2\,H_2O$$

Hydrogen bromide can be prepared from (1) hydrogen and bromine, (2) sodium bromide and phosphoric acid, or (3) phosphorus tribromide and water. The last two are convenient laboratory methods.

$$H_2(g) + Br_2(g) \longrightarrow 2\,HBr(g) + 72.8\text{ kJ (17.4 kcal)} \tag{1}$$

$$3\,NaBr(aq) + H_3PO_4(aq) \longrightarrow Na_3PO_4(aq) + 3\,HBr(aq) \tag{2}$$

$$PBr_3(l) + 3\,H_2O(l) \longrightarrow H_3PO_3(aq) + 3\,HBr(aq) \tag{3}$$
$$\text{Phosphorous}$$
$$\text{acid}$$

The hydrogen bromide dissolves in water to form hydrobromic acid, which is a strong acid.

Bromine compounds are used as pharmaceuticals (for example, mercurochrome), fumigants, tear gas, refrigerants, dyes, and photographic emulsions.

Precautions must be taken when working with bromine, because its fumes are poisonous and it produces painful sores when spilled on the skin.

Iodine

Iodine is a bluish-black solid that forms violet vapors when heated. Compounds of iodine are found in seawater, where they are selectively absorbed and concentrated by certain types of seaweed (kelp). The first commercial source was from ashes of seaweed. Today iodine is obtained commercially from (1) certain oil well brines and (2) Chilean sodium nitrate deposits, where it occurs as sodium iodate ($NaIO_3$). The brines are treated with chlorine to liberate iodine:

$$Cl_2(g) + 2\,I^-(aq) \longrightarrow I_2(s) + 2\,Cl^-(aq)$$

Sodium iodate is separated from other salts found in the nitrate deposits, and then reacted with sodium hydrogen sulfite to liberate free iodine:

$$2\,NaIO_3 + 5\,NaHSO_3 \longrightarrow I_2 + 3\,NaHSO_4 + 2\,Na_2SO_4 + H_2O$$

In the laboratory, iodine is easily prepared and collected by heating a mixture containing sodium iodide, sulfuric acid, and manganese dioxide in a beaker. The iodine vapors are condensed to crystals and collected on a chilled procelain dish covering the beaker.

$$2\,NaI + 2\,H_2SO_4 + MnO_2 \longrightarrow I_2 + Na_2SO_4 + MnSO_4 + 2\,H_2O$$

Chemically, iodine is less reactive than the other three halogens, but it still combines with most of the elements, both metals and nonmetals, to form iodides:

$$2 \, Na(s) + I_2(s) \longrightarrow 2 \, NaI(s)$$

$$2 \, Sb(s) + 3 \, I_2(g) \longrightarrow 2 \, SbI_3(s)$$

$$2 \, P(s) + 3 \, I_2(s) \longrightarrow 2 \, PI_3(s)$$

Pure hydrogen iodide cannot be prepared from sodium iodide and sulfuric acid because of a secondary reaction between hydrogen iodide and the acid, forming iodine and hydrogen sulfide:

$$8 \, HI + H_2SO_4 \longrightarrow 4 \, I_2 + H_2S + 4 \, H_2O$$

Hydrogen iodide is usually made from phosphorus triiodide and water:

$$PI_3 + 3 \, H_2O \longrightarrow H_3PO_3 + 3 \, HI(g)$$

Hydrogen iodide is very soluble in water and forms a strong acid solution known as hydriodic acid.

Iodine is only slightly soluble in water, but it is very soluble in organic solvents such as alcohol, carbon tetrachloride, and carbon disulfide. The brown alcohol solution is known as *tincture* of iodine and is used as an antiseptic and disinfectant for cuts and scratches. The carbon tetrachloride and carbon disulfide solutions are violet. Iodine is soluble in aqueous potassium iodide because of the formation of the soluble complex triiodide ion, I_3^-. The solution is labeled "I_2 in KI" and is brown in color.

$$I_2(s) + KI(aq) \longrightarrow KI_3(aq)$$

$$I_2(s) + I^-(aq) \longrightarrow I_3^-(aq)$$

An intense blue complex is formed when iodine is added to a starch suspension. This iodine–starch color is used as a very sensitive test for iodine; it is a useful indicator that allows iodine to be used in the analysis of other substances.

The thyroid gland is richer in iodine than any other part of the human body. A deficiency of iodine causes this gland to enlarge, creating the condition known as goiter. Iodine and iodides have been used for many years as an effective treatment for goiter. Iodine in the regular diet may be supplemented by iodized salt, which contains a small amount of a soluble iodide.

Silver iodide (AgI) is very sensitive to light; it is used in high-speed photographic films.

Interhalogen Compounds

The ability of halogens to share electrons leads to molecules containing two kinds of halogen atoms. All possible two-element interhalogen compounds, except iodine monofluoride (IF), are known: ClF, BrF, BrCl, ICl, and IBr. Because halogens have different electronegativities, the bonding electrons are not equally shared. This information is utilized in assigning oxidation numbers, writing formulas, and naming compounds. Bromine, for example, is less electronegative than chlorine. Hence, in the compound composed of these two elements, bromine is assigned an oxidation number of +1 and is written first in the formula, BrCl; the compound is called bromine monochloride. Similar considerations apply in writing the formulas and names for other interhalogen compounds.

Additional chlorine can be added to iodine monochloride to form iodine trichloride

$$ICl(l) + Cl_2(g) \longrightarrow ICl_3(s)$$

Other known interhalogen compounds are chlorine trifluoride (ClF_3), bromine trifluoride (BrF_3), bromine pentafluoride (BrF_5), iodine pentafluoride (IF_5), and iodine heptafluoride (IF_7). The chemistry of the interhalogens containing only two atoms is very similar to that of the free halogens. For example, BrCl reacts with water in a manner similar to that of Br_2 and Cl_2.

$$BrCl(l) + H_2O \rightleftharpoons HOBr(aq) + HCl(aq)$$

Comparison of Halogen Reactivities

This section summarizes some of the properties of the halogens and their compounds by comparing their relative reactivities.

Oxidizing strength.   Fluorine is capable of oxidizing all other halide ions to free halogens. The order of oxidizing strength is

$$F_2 > Cl_2 > Br_2 > I_2$$

This order is in agreement with the respective electronegativities of the halogens.

Reducing strength.   The relative ability of an ion or molecule to lose electrons and become oxidized is a measure of its reducing strength. Since oxidation and reduction are opposite phenomena with respect to electrons, the order of reducing strength for halide ions is the reverse of the order of oxidizing strength for halogens. The order is

$$I^- > Br^- > Cl^- > F^-$$

Acidity of hydrohalic acids.   Hydrochloric, hydrobromic, and hydriodic acids are all strong acids. Hydrofluoric acid is a weak acid, a 1 M solution being between 2 and 3% ionized.

Reaction of halogens with water.   Fluorine reacts violently with water, forming as products H_2O_2, OF_2, HF, and O_2. Chlorine and bromine react with water to form HOCl + HCl and HOBr + HBr, respectively. Iodine is only slightly soluble in water but readily dissolves in potassium iodide solution because of the formation of the soluble triiodide ion, I_3^-.

Table 19.14 Oxyacids of the halogens

Fluorine	Bromine	Iodine	Chlorine	Name of chlorine acid	Name and formula of sodium salt	
—	HBrO	HIO	HClO	Hypochlorous acid	NaClO	Sodium hypochlorite
—	—	—	$HClO_2$	Chlorous acid	$NaClO_2$	Sodium chlorite
—	$HBrO_3$	HIO_3	$HClO_3$	Chloric acid	$NaClO_3$	Sodium chlorate
—	—	H_5IO_6	$HClO_4$	Perchloric acid	$NaClO_4$	Sodium perchlorate

Oxyacids of the halogens. The oxyacids of the halogens are listed in Table 19.14. No oxyacids of fluorine have been isolated. In general, the salts are much more stable than the acids.

Biological effects. As free elements, all the halogens are toxic; fluorine is the most dangerous and iodine is the least dangerous of the group.

Many halogen compounds are known to have specific physiological or biological effects in nutrition and medicine. Our diets must contain certain amounts of chloride and iodide ions for normal health. Fluoride ions are needed for sound tooth structure but are definitely harmful when excessive amounts are consumed. Bromide is known to be present in animal tissue, but its function is not definitely established.

19.10 The Sulfur Family

sulfur family

The elements in Group VIA of the periodic table are known as the **sulfur family.** This family includes oxygen, sulfur, selenium, tellurium, and polonium.

Oxygen

Occurrence and physical properties. Oxygen is the most abundant element on earth; it occurs both as free oxygen gas and combined with other elements. It forms compounds with all elements except some noble gases. Water is 88.9% oxygen; the human body is 65% oxygen by weight. The atmosphere contains about 21% oxygen by volume and about 23% oxygen by weight.

The three naturally occurring isotopes of oxygen are $^{16}_{8}O$, $^{17}_{8}O$, and $^{18}_{8}O$; $^{16}_{8}O$ is by far the most abundant. The oxygen molecule is diatomic.

Oxygen is a colorless, odorless, tasteless gas. It is a pale blue solid or liquid, melting at $-218.4°C$ and boiling at $-183°C$. The liquid is *paramagnetic;* that is, it is attracted by a magnet. The solubility of the gas is about 0.03 mL per gram of water at 20°C, a fact that is very important for most marine life.

Preparation of oxygen. We have seen that oxygen can be prepared by heating mercury(II) oxide (Section 3.6), by electrolysis of water (Section 3.10), and by decomposition of hydrogen peroxide (Section 13.12). Many additional methods for the laboratory preparation of oxygen are known.

Oxygen is obtained commercially from air. Air is first freed of carbon dioxide and moisture and then liquefied to give a mixture that is essentially liquid oxygen and nitrogen. Oxygen is separated from nitrogen by fractional distillation.

One of the outstanding properties of oxygen is its ability to support combustion. By *combustion* we generally mean the act of burning or, commonly, the union of oxygen with other substances accompanied by the evolution of light and heat. Oxygen is consumed during combustion but does not burn. We are highly dependent on heat, electrical, and mechanical energy obtained from combustion of fossil fuels.

Animal life as we know it is dependent on oxygen. Absorbed in the blood, oxygen is carried by way of the arteries to all tissues of the body, where it is used in metabolism. Metabolism includes the oxidation of carbohydrates, fats, and proteins and provides the energy needed to carry on the normal life processes. The free oxygen in the atmosphere and that dissolved in fresh water and seawater is constantly replenished by photosynthesis carried on by green plants (Section 32.10).

Certain additional aspects of oxygen, including peroxides and allotropic forms, are discussed in Chapter 13.

Sulfur

Occurrence and physical properties.   Sulfur has been known for thousands of years; evidence of its use dates back 16 to 20 centuries B.C. It is mentioned in the Bible, where it is called *brimstone*, a name also sometimes used today.

Sulfur occurs both in the free state and in compounds. It is found in various metal sulfides and sulfates, hydrogen sulfide, sulfur dioxide, and in a variety of compounds associated with petroleum and natural gas. Sulfur is an essential element in life processes and is present in all living organisms.

On a commercial basis elemental sulfur is obtained from deposits in Sicily, Texas, Louisiana, and in volcanic regions of Japan and Mexico. Large quantities of sulfur and sulfur compounds are recovered as by-products from petroleum, natural gas, and metallurgical processing. Sulfur is widely used in many phases of agriculture and industry. More than four-fifths of all sulfur produced is made into sulfuric acid.

Sulfur is a bright yellow, odorless solid. It occurs as four stable isotopes, $_{16}^{32}S$, $_{16}^{33}S$, $_{16}^{34}S$, and $_{16}^{36}S$. The S-32 isotope accounts for about 95% of natural sulfur. In the solid form, sulfur exists in a crown-shaped ring structure containing eight atoms connected by covalent bonds. The molecular aggregate is actually S_8, but in many of its reactions sulfur is represented by a single S. Figure 19.4 shows several ways of representing the S_8 molecule.

Sulfur is insoluble in water but is soluble in organic solvents such as carbon disulfide and benzene. Several allotropic forms of sulfur are known. The most common are rhombic, monoclinic, and amorphous sulfur. Rhombic sulfur melts at 112.8°C; the monoclinic form melts at 119°C. Sulfur boils at 444.6°C. Figure 19.5 illustrates crystals of rhombic and monoclinic sulfur.

(a)   (b)   (c)

Figure 19.4   Diagrams of the S_8 molecule: (a) crown-shaped ring formation with bond angles of 105°; (b) Lewis dot structure; (c) compact molecular orbital structure. The latter most nearly represents the S_8 molecule.

Figure 19.5   Crystal structures of rhombic and monoclinic sulfur

(a) Rhombic   (b) Monoclinic

Sulfur undergoes unique and interesting changes when it is heated. When sulfur is carefully heated in a test tube it melts at 115°C and forms a straw-colored, mobile liquid that can be poured easily. As the temperature of the liquid is increased, the color of the sulfur darkens, and at about 160°C the viscosity (resistance to flow) begins to increase rapidly. At 187°C the viscosity reaches a maximum, and the dark reddish-brown sulfur is so viscous that it will not pour when the test tube is inverted. As sulfur is heated above 187°C, the color remains dark, the viscosity decreases rapidly, and near its boiling point, sulfur again becomes a mobile liquid. When sulfur near its boiling point is rapidly cooled by pouring into cold water, an amber-colored, rubbery solid called *plastic* or *amorphous sulfur* is formed.

The changes in viscosity are explained on the basis of molecular composition. Rhombic sulfur and monoclinic sulfur consist of S_8 rings. Liquid sulfur, near its melting point, also is composed principally of S_8 rings and has low viscosity. At higher temperatures, the rings begin to break up and form long chains of sulfur atoms (polymers) represented by S_x. Since viscosity increases with increasing molecular size, the chains apparently reach a maximum length at 187°C. Above 187°C the chains begin to break into shorter lengths, resulting in a lower viscosity. Gaseous sulfur is known to contain S_2 molecules.

Chemical properties of sulfur. Since sulfur is less electronegative than oxygen, its compounds are less ionic and more covalent than those of oxygen. Ionic sulfur compounds are formed with only the most electropositive metals—the alkali metals and the alkaline earth metals (Group IIA). The oxidation states of sulfur range from -2 to $+6$. Sulfur combines directly with many elements, both metals and nonmetals. For example,

$$Zn(s) + S(s) \xrightarrow{\Delta} ZnS(s)$$

$$H_2(g) + S(l) \xrightarrow{200°C} H_2S(g)$$

$$C(s) + 2 S(g) \xrightarrow{3000°C} CS_2(g)$$

There are at least ten known oxides of sulfur, two of which are well known—sulfur dioxide (SO_2) and sulfur trioxide (SO_3).

The prefix *thio* is used to indicate the presence of sulfur in a compound. More specifically, it means that sulfur is used in place of oxygen in an analogous compound. Two examples of thio compounds are sodium thiosulfate and thiourea. Their formulas and the formulas of their oxygen analogs are shown below.

Sodium sulfate, Na_2SO_4

Sodium thiosulfate, $Na_2S_2O_3$

Urea

Thiourea

The central sulfur atom in sodium thiosulfate has a $+6$ oxidation number, whereas the thio sulfur has a -2 oxidation number, the same as the oxygen it replaced. Many other compounds with multiple sulfur linkages are known.

Sulfur burns in air or oxygen with a bluish flame to form sulfur dioxide:

$$S(l) + O_2(g) \longrightarrow SO_2(g)$$

Sulfur dioxide is also formed by reacting iron pyrites (FeS_2) or other metal sulfides with oxygen (air) at elevated temperatures:

$$4 FeS_2 + 11 O_2 \xrightarrow{\Delta} 2 Fe_2O_3 + 8 SO_2$$

Sulfur dioxide is a colorless gas that is irritating to the throat, causing choking and coughing. It also causes eye irritation and is an air pollutant known to be damaging to plant life.

Sulfur dioxide is an acid anhydride and forms sulfurous acid (H_2SO_3) when dissolved in water. It is a weak acid, decomposing easily into sulfur dioxide and water.

$$SO_2(g) + H_2O \rightleftharpoons H_2SO_3(aq)$$

Salts of sulfurous acid, called *sulfites* or *bisulfites*, liberate sulfur dioxide when treated with strong acids:

$$Na_2SO_3(s) + 2\, HCl(aq) \longrightarrow 2\, NaCl(aq) + H_2O + SO_2(g)$$
Sodium sulfite

$$NaHSO_3(s) + HCl(aq) \longrightarrow NaCl(aq) + H_2O + SO_2(g)$$
Sodium bisulfite

Much industrial sulfur dioxide goes into the production of sulfuric acid. It is also used as a bleaching agent in the pulp and paper industry, in refining sugar, and in processing dried fruit.

Hydrogen sulfide (H_2S) is the sulfur analog of water, but that is as far as the resemblance goes. It is normally a gas; the liquid boils at $-60°C$. It has a disagreeable odor, like rotten eggs, and is very toxic. The gas is slightly soluble in water, forming an extremely weak acid solution called hydrosulfuric acid.

Hydrogen sulfide is usually detected by its rotten-egg odor, but it may be identified chemically by passing the gas over a strip of filter paper that has been dipped into a lead acetate solution. The formation of black lead(II) sulfide is a positive indication of hydrogen sulfide.

$$H_2S(g) + Pb(C_2H_3O_2)_2(aq) \longrightarrow PbS(s) + 2\, HC_2H_3O_2(aq)$$

Sulfuric acid.   The uses of sulfuric acid (H_2SO_4) are numerous and varied. The current U.S. production is greater than 79 billion lb (3.6×10^{10} kg) annually. Large amounts are used to convert insoluble phosphates into soluble phosphates for fertilizers, and for pickling of metal surfaces. Sulfuric acid is used in the production of hydrochloric acid, ammonium sulfate, and aluminum sulfate. It is also used in petroleum refining; the manufacture of rayon; the making of explosives (nitroglycerin and TNT), alcohols, detergents, and metal sulfates; textile printing; dyeing; and in scores of other applications. Dilute sulfuric acid is the electrolyte used in millions of ordinary automobile storage batteries.

Sulfuric acid is a colorless, oily liquid with a density of 1.84 g/mL. Its freezing point is 10.4°C; its boiling point is 338°C. The acid decomposes as it boils, liberating its anhydride, sulfur trioxide (SO_3):

$$H_2SO_4(l) \xrightarrow{\Delta} H_2O(g) + SO_3(g)$$

Ordinary concentrated sulfuric acid contains about 96–98% H_2SO_4; the remainder is water.

Sulfuric acid is generally manufactured by the *contact process*. The essential steps are:

1. Oxidation of sulfur dioxide to sulfur trioxide in the contact chamber in the presence of a vanadium oxide catalyst. The SO_2 is usually obtained by burning elemental sulfur or metallic sulfides.

$$2\, SO_2 + O_2 \xrightarrow{V_2O_5} 2\, SO_3$$

2. Dissolution of SO_3 in concentrated sulfuric acid to form pyrosulfuric acid ($H_2S_2O_7$). Sulfur trioxide dissolves rapidly in concentrated sulfuric acid but rather slowly in water. Solutions of SO_3 in H_2SO_4 are known as *fuming sulfuric acid* or *oleum*.

$$H_2SO_4 + SO_3 \longrightarrow H_2S_2O_7$$

3. Dilution of the pyrosulfuric acid to obtain the desired concentration of sulfuric acid.

$$H_2S_2O_7 + H_2O \longrightarrow 2\,H_2SO_4$$

Note: Concentrated sulfuric acid reacts exothermically and vigorously with water to form the hydrates $H_2SO_4 \cdot H_2O$ and $H_2SO_4 \cdot 2\,H_2O$. When making dilutions of sulfuric acid in the laboratory, *always add the acid to the water slowly with stirring.* Never add water to concentrated acid because dangerous spattering will be caused by localized overheating and boiling.

The existence of the bisulfate ion (HSO_4^-) and bisulfate salts such as $NaHSO_4$ is explained by the two-stage ionization of sulfuric acid:

Step 1. $H_2SO_4 + H_2O \longrightarrow H_3O^+ + HSO_4^-$

Step 2. $HSO_4^- + H_2O \rightleftharpoons H_3O^+ + SO_4^{2-}$

The first-stage ionization is complete, but the second stage is only about 10% complete in a 0.10 M solution.

There are four general categories of reactivity for sulfuric acid: (1) acid, (2) oxidizing agent, (3) dehydrating agent, and (4) reagent for preparing other acids.

1. **Acid.** An aqueous solution of H_2SO_4 is a strong mineral acid and shows the usual acid reactions with metals, bases, carbonates, and so on (see Section 15.2).
2. **Oxidizing agent.** Concentrated sulfuric acid, especially when hot, is a good oxidizing agent; sulfur is reduced. The acid will react with metals below hydrogen in the activity series; for example,

$$Cu + 2\,H_2SO_4(conc.) \xrightarrow{\Delta} CuSO_4 + 2\,H_2O + SO_2(g)$$

With a stronger reducing agent such as zinc, the sulfur is reduced to -2; hydrogen is not liberated:

$$4\,Zn + 5\,H_2SO_4(conc.) \xrightarrow{\Delta} 4\,ZnSO_4 + H_2S(g) + 4\,H_2O$$

Even carbon is oxidized by hot sulfuric acid:

$$C + 2\,H_2SO_4(conc.) \xrightarrow{\Delta} CO_2(g) + 2\,SO_2(g) + 2\,H_2O$$

3. **Dehydrating agent.** Sulfuric acid has a great affinity for water. This property makes concentrated sulfuric acid an excellent drying agent. Gases, which do not react with sulfuric acid and which contain water vapor, may be dried by bubbling them through concentrated sulfuric acid.

Sulfuric acid is such a good dehydrating agent that it will remove water from sugar (or other carbohydrates), leaving carbon as a residue:

$$C_{12}H_{22}O_{11} + 11\,H_2SO_4 \longrightarrow 12\,C + 11\,H_2SO_4 \cdot H_2O$$

This interesting reaction is easily demonstrated by adding 25 mL of concentrated sulfuric acid to a 50 mL beaker half-filled with sugar. After several seconds have

Figure 19.6   When concentrated sulfuric acid is poured onto sugar, the sugar is dehydrated, leaving a column of black carbon.

elapsed, a black cylinder of carbon rises to a height greater than that of the beaker (see Figure 19.6). This dehydration reaction also occurs when cellulose products such as wood, cotton, and paper turn black when they come into contact with sulfuric acid.

4. **Preparation of other acids.**   The high boiling point of sulfuric acid makes it ideal for preparing acids with lower boiling points. Salts of chlorides or nitrates are mixed with sulfuric acid and heated. The more volatile products, hydrogen chloride (HCl, bp $-84.9°C$) and hydrogen nitrate (HNO_3, bp $86°C$), distill off long before the boiling temperature of sulfuric acid is reached:

$$NaCl + H_2SO_4 \xrightarrow{\Delta} NaHSO_4 + HCl(g)$$

$$KNO_3 + H_2SO_4 \xrightarrow{\Delta} KHSO_4 + HNO_3(g)$$

Other Elements of the Sulfur Family

Selenium and tellurium resemble sulfur much more than they resemble oxygen. Both elements are less electronegative and tend to be more metallic than sulfur. Their hydrogen compounds, hydrogen selenide (H_2Se) and hydrogen telluride (H_2Te), have vile odors and are more acidic than hydrosulfuric acid.

Several allotropic forms of selenium are known. One form, gray selenium, shows the interesting property of having low electric conductivity in darkness and a much higher conductivity when exposed to light. This is the basis for the operation of the selenium photoelectric cell, which is used in controlling automatic equipment of all kinds. Selenium is also used to impart a red color to glass, glazes, and enamels.

Tellurium has a definite metallic luster and is a better conductor of electricity than selenium or sulfur. Its major uses are in metal alloys, glass, and dyestuffs.

The heaviest element of the family, polonium, is very rare and claims fame only as the first radioactive element discovered by Pierre and Marie Curie.

19.11 The Nitrogen Family

nitrogen family   The **nitrogen family,** Group VA of the periodic table, includes the elements nitrogen, phosphorus, arsenic, antimony, and bismuth. These elements, especially nitrogen and phosphorus, are fairly well known. Nitrogen is the most abundant element in the atmosphere, and phosphorus is the 11th most abundant element in the earth's crust. Compounds of nitrogen and phosphorus are essential for all forms of life.

The electron structures of these elements show that they each have five electrons in their outer shell, two s and three p electrons. This structure suggests that their oxidation numbers will range from -3 to $+5$. In fact, nitrogen and phosphorus are known to exist in every possible oxidation state from -3 to $+5$.

The elements of Group VA become increasingly metallic from top to bottom in the group. Nitrogen is a colorless gas with virtually no suggestion of metallic properties, but bismuth is distinctly metallic in character. Some of the physical properties of Group VA elements are listed in Table 19.15.

Nitrogen

Nitrogen occurs as two stable isotopes, $^{14}_{7}N$ and $^{15}_{7}N$; the lighter isotope accounts for more than 99% of the nitrogen atoms. Nitrogen is found in the atmosphere, living organic matter, decayed matter, ammonia, ammonium salts, and nitrate deposits.

Nitrogen can be prepared in the laboratory by decomposing ammonium nitrite; the gas is collected by the displacement of water:

$$NH_4NO_2(s) \xrightarrow{\Delta} N_2(g) + 2\,H_2O$$

The atmosphere is composed of about four-fifths nitrogen and is the commercial source of the element. Nitrogen is obtained as a coproduct in the preparation of oxygen from liquid air. The nitrogen obtained in this manner contains very small amounts of noble gases.

Liquid nitrogen, because of its low boiling temperature, is stored and shipped in Dewar flasks. The liquid is used primarily as a coolant. Purified nitrogen gas is stored and shipped in high-pressure steel cylinders.

Table 19.15 Physical properties of the nitrogen family

Element	Melting point (°C)	Boiling point (°C)	Density (g/mL)
Nitrogen	-210.1	-195.8	0.81^a
Phosphorus	44.2	280	1.82^b
Arsenic	817	615^c	5.7
Antimony	630.5	1380	6.6
Bismuth	271.3	1450	9.8

^{a} Liquid at boiling point
^{b} White phosphorus
^{c} Sublimes

Elemental nitrogen is a diatomic molecule in the gaseous state. Its electron structure contains three shared pairs of electrons, forming a triple bond between the nitrogen atoms:

$$\cdot \ddot{N} \cdot \qquad :N:::N: \qquad :N\equiv N:$$

Nitrogen atom   Nitrogen molecule

The high energy of dissociation (941 kJ/mol; 225 kcal/mol) is evidence of the stability of the nitrogen molecule. As a result, free nitrogen is chemically unreactive except at high temperatures or in the presence of certain catalysts.

Nitrogen oxide is formed when air is passed through an electric arc or when nitrogen and oxygen are reacted at about 3000°C:

$$N_2(g) + O_2(g) \rightleftharpoons 2\,NO(g)$$

This reaction accounts for the formation of oxides of nitrogen during electrical storms.

The known oxides of nitrogen are as follows:

N_2O	Dinitrogen oxide	Colorless gas
NO	Nitrogen oxide	Colorless gas
N_2O_3	Dinitrogen trioxide	Red-brown gas
NO_2	Nitrogen dioxide	Red-brown gas
N_2O_4	Dinitrogen tetroxide	Yellow liquid, colorless solid
N_2O_5	Dinitrogen pentoxide	White solid

Compounds of Nitrogen

Hundreds of useful nitrogen compounds are known. Some of the more important ones, produced and used in large tonnages, are

ammonia	NH_3
nitric acid	HNO_3
ammonium nitrate	NH_4NO_3
ammonium sulfate	$(NH_4)_2SO_4$
ammonium phosphate	$(NH_4)_3PO_4$
urea	$CO(NH_2)_2$
sodium nitrate	$NaNO_3$
calcium cyanamide	$CaCN_2$

Nitrogen combines directly with many metals to form metal nitrides when the gas is passed over the heated metal:

$$6\,Li(s) + N_2(g) \xrightarrow{\Delta} 2\,Li_3N(s)$$

$$3\,Mg(s) + N_2(g) \xrightarrow{\Delta} Mg_3N_2(s)$$

In the Haber process, ammonia is manufactured by passing nitrogen and hydrogen gases over a catalyst at elevated temperatures and pressures:

$$N_2(g) + 3\,H_2(g) \rightleftharpoons 2\,NH_3(g) + 92\ kJ\ (22\ kcal)$$

The current production of ammonia in the United States is over 32 billion lb (1.5×10^{10} kg) annually. By far the greatest consumption of ammonia is in the manufacture of fertilizers or in its direct use as a fertilizer. Other industrial uses of ammonia or its derivatives include the manufacture of nitric acid, plastics, refrigerants, explosives, pulp and paper, and textiles.

Nitric acid is produced in the United States in excess of 15 billion lb (6.8×10^9 kg) annually. The pure material is a colorless liquid; it has a melting point of $-41.6°C$, a boiling point of $86°C$, and a density (at $20°C$) of 1.503 g/mL. Nitric acid has a high vapor pressure at room temperature, fumes strongly in moist air, and is miscible with water in all proportions. The concentrated acid contains 68–70% HNO_3 and has a specific gravity of 1.42. The concentrated acid often appears yellow because it contains dissolved nitrogen dioxide. This NO_2 is formed by slow decomposition of the acid when it is exposed to light:

$$4\,HNO_3 \xrightarrow{\text{Light}} 4\,NO_2 + 2\,H_2O + O_2$$

Most nitric acid is made by the Ostwald process. In this process, an ammonia–air mixture is passed over a platinum catalyst at about $800°C$. Ammonia is first oxidized to nitrogen oxide, which in turn is further oxidized to nitrogen dioxide. The latter is then absorbed in water to form the acid. The equations are

$$4\,NH_3(g) + 5\,O_2(g) \longrightarrow 4\,NO(g) + 6\,H_2O(g)$$

$$2\,NO(g) + O_2(g) \longrightarrow 2\,NO_2(g)$$

$$3\,NO_2(g) + H_2O \longrightarrow 2\,HNO_3(aq) + NO(g)$$

The acid produced is about 60% HNO_3. The nitrogen oxide formed in the last step is recycled back through the process.

Nitric acid is both a strong acid and a powerful oxidizing agent. It will attack all metals except gold, platinum, iridium, rhodium, and tantalum. As an acid, it reacts with bases to form nitrate salts:

$$NaOH(aq) + HNO_3(aq) \longrightarrow NaNO_3(aq) + H_2O$$

$$NH_3(aq) + HNO_3(aq) \longrightarrow NH_4NO_3(aq)$$

$$Na_2CO_3(aq) + 2\,HNO_3(aq) \longrightarrow 2\,NaNO_3(aq) + H_2O + CO_2(g)$$

Nitric acid reacts with metals to form a variety of nitrate reduction products, depending on the concentration of the acid and the reducing ability of the metal. Hydrogen is not formed by the reaction of nitric acid with metals. With concentrated acid and metals, nitrogen dioxide gas is always formed. With dilute acid and metals such as copper and mercury, nitrogen oxide gas is formed. With very dilute acid and stronger reducing metals such as zinc or aluminum, nitric acid is reduced to the ammonium ion. In this last case, the oxidation number of nitrogen is reduced from $+5$ to -3. The following equations illustrate these three different reduction reactions:

$$Hg + 4\,H^+ + 4\,NO_3^- \longrightarrow Hg^{2+} + 2\,NO_3^- + 2\,NO_2(g) + 2\,H_2O$$
Conc. HNO_3

$$3\,Cu + 8\,H^+ + 8\,NO_3^- \longrightarrow 3\,Cu^{2+} + 6\,NO_3^- + 2\,NO(g) + 4\,H_2O$$

Dilute HNO_3

$$4\,Zn + 10\,H^+ + 10\,NO_3^- \longrightarrow 4\,Zn^{2+} + NH_4^+ + 9\,NO_3^- + 3\,H_2O$$

Dilute HNO_3

A mixture of 3 parts of concentrated hydrochloric acid to 1 part of concentrated nitric acid is known as *aqua regia* (royal water); it will attack and dissolve such metals as gold and platinum.

When nitric acid comes into contact with the skin, it reacts with the proteins to cause destruction of the tissues, producing a yellow discoloration of the skin.

The major uses for nitric acid are for manufacturing ammonium nitrate fertilizers, explosives, plastics, pharmaceuticals, dye intermediates, and organic nitro compounds, and for pickling stainless steel in steel refining.

The Nitrogen Cycle

nitrogen cycle

The process by which nitrogen is circulated and recirculated from the atmosphere through living organisms and back to the atmosphere is known as the **nitrogen cycle.**

Nitrogen compounds are required by all living organisms. Despite the fact that the atmosphere is about four-fifths nitrogen, man and all other animals as well as the higher plants are unable to utilize free nitrogen. Higher plants require inorganic nitrogen compounds, and animals must have nitrogen in the form of organic compounds.

Atmospheric nitrogen is *fixed*—that is, converted into chemical compounds that are useful to higher forms of life—by three general routes:

1. **Bacterial action.** Certain soil bacteria are capable of converting N_2 into nitrates. Most of these bacteria live in the soil in association with legumes (for example, peas, beans, clover). Some free-living soil bacteria and the blue-green algae, which live in water, are also capable of fixing nitrogen.
2. **Lightning.** The high temperature of lightning flashes causes the formation of substantial amounts of nitrogen oxide in the atmosphere. This NO is dissolved in rainwater and is eventually converted to nitrate ions in the soil. The combustion of fuels also provides temperatures high enough to form NO in the atmosphere. The total amount of nitrogen fixed by combustion is relatively insignificant on a worldwide basis. However, NO produced by combustion, especially in automobile engines, is a serious air pollution problem in some areas.
3. **Chemical fixation.** Chemical processes have been devised for making nitrogen compounds directly from atmospheric nitrogen. By far the most important of these is the Haber process for making ammonia from nitrogen and hydrogen. This process is the major means of production for the millions of tons of nitrogen fertilizers that are produced synthetically each year.

A schematic diagram of the nitrogen cycle is shown in Figure 19.7. Starting with the atmosphere, the cycle begins with the fixation of nitrogen by any one of the three routes. In the soil, nitrogen or nitrogen compounds are converted to nitrates, taken up by higher plants, and converted to organic compounds. The plants eventually die or are eaten by animals. During the life of the animal, part

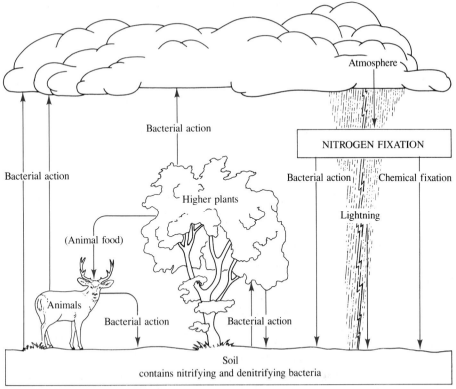

Figure 19.7   The nitrogen cycle

of the nitrogen from plants in its diet is returned to the soil in the form of fecal and urinary excreta. Eventually, after death, both plants and animals are decomposed by bacterial action. Part of the nitrogen from plant and animal tissues is returned to the atmosphere as free nitrogen and part is retained in the soil. The cycle thus continues.

Other Elements of the Nitrogen Family

The physical properties of the other four elements of Group VA—phosphorus, arsenic, antimony, and bismuth—differ markedly from those of nitrogen (see Table 19.15).

Phosphorus.   Phosphorus is the 11th most abundant element in the earth's crust. Free phosphorus is never found in nature. The element occurs mainly in phosphate minerals. Calcium phosphate is present in the bones and teeth of animals, and small amounts of phosphorus compounds are present in the cells of all plants and animals. The free element exists in several allotropic modifications—white, red, and black being the most common. The white form is tetratomic, P_4; the red and black forms exist as polymeric chains of phosphorus atoms.

White phosphorus is a soft, waxy solid, insoluble in water but soluble in carbon disulfide. It is generally stored under water to keep it out of contact with air, in which it fumes and ignites spontaneously, burning to the pentoxide. White phosphorus often appears yellow because of its gradual changing to the more stable red form. Red phosphorus is formed by heating white phosphorus to 250°C. The red modification is much less reactive and more stable than the white and need not be stored under water. Although white phosphorus is extremely poisonous, the red form is not.

Another crystalline form, which is less reactive than the red, is black phosphorus, produced by subjecting white phosphorus to very high pressures.

Two principal oxides of phosphorus are P_4O_6 and P_4O_{10}. These oxides are commonly called phosphorus trioxide and phosphorus pentoxide, respectively. They are named from their empirical formulas, which are P_2O_3 and P_2O_5. Many different oxyacids of phosphorus are known; several are listed here.

H_3PO_2	Hypophosphorous acid	$H_4P_2O_6$	Hypophosphoric acid
HPO_2	Metaphosphorous acid	HPO_3	Metaphosphoric acid
H_3PO_3	Orthophosphorous acid	H_3PO_4	Orthophosphoric acid
$H_4P_2O_5$	Pyrophosphorous acid	$H_4P_2O_7$	Pyrophosphoric acid

Orthophosphoric and orthophosphorous acids are commonly called phosphoric and phosphorous acids, respectively.

Phosphorus compounds are indispensable for both plants and animals. Although phosphorus is fairly abundant in the earth's crust, many soils do not contain enough soluble phosphates for optimum plant growth. Consequently, about two-thirds of the phosphates produced are used in fertilizers.

Arsenic, antimony, and bismuth.   Although nitrogen and phosphorus are nonmetals, arsenic, antimony, and bismuth become progressively more metallic, with bismuth having properties approaching those of a true metal. All three were known in ancient times, and all are found in nature, both in the free and the combined states. Their principal ores are the sulfides. Their most common oxidation states are +3 and +5, and their oxides resemble nitrogen and phosphorus in composition: As_4O_6, As_2O_5, Sb_4O_6, Sb_2O_5, Bi_2O_5.

Arsenic, antimony, and bismuth are mainly used in alloys to increase the hardness of metals. Lead shot is hardened by adding up to 0.5% arsenic; type metal contains 15–18% antimony; pewter contains 6% bismuth and 1.7% antimony; babbitt metal contains 7% antimony. Low-melting alloys containing over 50% bismuth are used in safety sprinkler heads for fire protection. Arsenic and antimony compounds, although very toxic, have been successfully used as medicinals in controlled dosages.

QUESTIONS

A.   *Review the meanings of the new terms introduced in this chapter.*

1. Metallurgy
2. Alloy
3. Amalgam
4. Alkali metal
5. Alkaline earth metal
6. Steel

7. Halogen family
8. Sulfur family
9. Nitrogen family
10. Nitrogen cycle

B. *Review questions*

1. Explain in terms of electronic structure why potassium reacts more violently with water than does lithium.
2. How would the ionization energy of francium be expected to compare with that of cesium?
3. What is oxidized and what is reduced during the electrolysis of potassium hydroxide?
4. What is the starting raw material used in the preparation of most sodium chemicals? Why?
5. Write the formulas of an alkali metal oxide, hydroxide, acetate, bicarbonate, and carbonate using a different metal for each compound.
6. Which would a farmer be more likely to buy in tonnage quantities—sodium sulfate or potassium sulfate? Justify your answer.
7. On the basis of electronic structure, explain why a Group IIA metal is less reactive than the Group IA metal that precedes it in the periodic table.
8. Why can a magnesium fire not be fought successfully with conventional fire extinguishing agents such as water or carbon dioxide? Supplement your answer with appropriate equations.
9. Explain why it is possible to use barium sulfate, but not barium chloride, as an aid to X-ray photography of the gastrointestinal tract.
10. Write equations for the following reactions related to the preparation of magnesium:
    (a) The cathode reaction
    (b) The anode reaction
    (c) The overall chemical reaction
11. Briefly discuss the nature and origin of the colored flames that are used for the quantitative detection of certain Group IA and Group IIA elements.
12. What is the essential chemical difference between pig iron and steel?
13. Bare aluminum and magnesium metal structures are not damaged by prolonged exposure to the atmosphere. Yet bare iron, generally less reactive than either aluminum or magnesium, is severely corroded by long exposure to the atmosphere. Explain.

14. Write the equation for the anode reaction that occurs when steel is afforded cathodic protection by magnesium.
15. In the Hall–Heroult process of aluminum production, oxide ions are oxidized to free oxygen at the anode, but free oxygen is not given off. Explain.
16. At high temperatures, aluminum reacts with nitrogen.
    (a) Write the equation for the reaction.
    (b) Draw the Lewis structure for the compound that is formed.
17. Explain in terms of electronic structure why the reactivity of Group VIIA elements decreases from top to bottom in the periodic table.
18. Use Lewis-dot structures to illustrate how the halogen elements, designated X, can form both covalent bonds (X_2, HX) and ionic bonds (Na^+X^-).
19. Why is the boiling point of HF abnormally high when compared to that of the other hydrogen halides?
20. Arrange the halogens in order of increasing strength as oxidizing agents. Justify the order in terms of electronic structure.
21. What ill effects, if any, would occur from a lack of the following ions in the diet?
    (a) Fluoride ions   (c) Bromide ions
    (b) Chloride ions   (d) Iodide ions
22. Explain why the viscosity of liquid sulfur increases markedly as it is heated in the range of 160–187°C.
23. Explain why free sulfur can act either as an oxidizing agent or as a reducing agent.
24. Explain why the lowest oxidation state of sulfur is −2 and the highest oxidation state is +6.
25. Write equations to illustrate the reaction of sulfuric acid acting as:
    (a) An acid
    (b) An oxidizing agent
    (c) A dehydrating agent
26. Can wet NH_3 gas be dried by bubbling it through concentrated sulfuric acid? Explain.
27. Describe a safe procedure for diluting concentrated sulfuric acid in the laboratory.
28. Why do the oxidation numbers of Group VA elements range from −3 to +5?
29. Does the tendency to become more metallic increase or decrease from top to bottom in Group VA elements? Explain.

30. Draw Lewis-dot structures for:
    (a) A nitrogen molecule
    (b) An ammonia molecule
    (c) A nitride ion
    (d) An ammonium ion
    (e) A nitrate ion
31. Outline and discuss the nitrogen cycle in nature.
32. Which Group VA elements are absolutely essential to our health and well-being?
33. Which of the following statements are correct?
    (a) Most of the common metals are found in the free or uncombined state in nature.
    (b) Metals are alloyed to increase tensile strength, hardness, and electrical conductivity.
    (c) The reactivity of the alkali metals (Group IA) increases from top to bottom in the periodic table.
    (d) In binary compounds between metals and nonmetals, the metals generally form positive ions.
    (e) Chile saltpeter is another name for sodium nitrate.
    (f) Both calcium and magnesium are essential elements for animals, but only calcium is essential for plants.
    (g) Very pure iron is used in some industrial applications because of its great hardness and strength, especially at high temperatures.
    (h) Copper and aluminum alloys are used for electrical wiring because of their excellent electrical conductivity.
    (i) Galvanized steel is protected from rusting or corrosion by a zinc coating.
    (j) Aluminum is the most abundant metal in the earth's crust.
    (k) The electronegativity of the halogens (Group VIIA) increases from top to bottom in the periodic table.
    (l) Fluorine, the most electronegative element, can be prepared only by electrolytic methods.
    (m) The oxidation number of oxygen in oxygen difluoride (OF_2) is +2.
    (n) Pure hydrogen bromide cannot be prepared by reacting sodium bromide and sulfuric acid.
    (o) Pure sulfur is a bright yellow, odorless solid.
    (p) The oxidation states of sulfur range from −1 to +7.
    (q) The Ostwald process is used to prepare ammonia on an industrial scale.
    (r) Phosphorus is indispensable to plants and animals.
    (s) Depending on temperature and concentration, sulfuric acid may act as a dehydrating agent, strong acid, or oxidizing agent.
    (t) The oxidation states of nitrogen range from −3 to +5.

C. *Review problems*

1. (a) How many kilograms of sodium chloride must be electrolyzed to produce 5.00 kg of sodium metal?
   (b) How many moles of chlorine are produced along with the 5.00 kg of sodium from part (a)?
2. Analysis of a pure mineral indicated that it contained 72.4% Fe. Was the mineral hematite, magnetite, or siderite?
3. How many liters of SO_2 (at STP) can be obtained by combustion of 150 g of sulfur?
4. The water coming from a large reservoir is being treated with 0.20 ppm (parts per million) of chlorine. Calculate the number of grams of chlorine required each hour when water is being pumped from the reservoir at a rate of 300,000 L per hour.
5. How many moles of bromine are liberated when 15.0 L of chlorine gas (at STP) are dissolved in seawater? Assume that 80.0% of the chlorine gas reacts with bromide ions present in the seawater.
6. Calculate the molarity of each of the following concentrated acids:
   (a) Sulfuric acid: $d = 1.84$ g/mL, containing 96% H_2SO_4 by weight
   (b) Nitric acid: $d = 1.42$ g/mL, containing 70% HNO_3 by weight
   (c) Hydrochloric acid: $d = 1.19$ g/mL, containing 37% HCl by weight

Organic Chemistry: Saturated Hydrocarbons

1. Understand the new terms listed in Question A at the end of the chapter.
2. Describe the tetrahedral nature of the carbon atom.
3. Explain why the concept of hybridization is used to describe the bonding of carbon in simple compounds such as methane.
4. Explain the bonding in alkanes.
5. Write the Lewis structures for alkanes and halogenated alkanes.
6. Write the names and formulas of the first ten normal alkanes.
7. Understand the concept of isomerization and isomers.
8. Write structural formulas and IUPAC names for the isomers of an alkane or a halogenated alkane.
9. Give the IUPAC name of a hydrocarbon or a halogenated hydrocarbon when given the structural formula, or vice versa.
10. Write equations for the halogenation of an alkane, giving all the possible monohalosubstitution products.
11. Write structural formulas and names for simple cycloalkanes.
12. Name a class of biochemicals that have alkane-like properties.
13. Discuss the octane number rating of gasoline.

20.1 Organic Chemistry: History and Scope

During the late 18th and the early 19th centuries, chemists were baffled by the fact that compounds obtained from animal and vegetable sources defied the established rules for inorganic compounds—namely, that compound formation is due to a simple attraction between positively and negatively charged elements. In their experience with inorganic chemistry, only one, or at most a few, compounds were composed of any group of only two or three elements. However, they observed that a group of only four elements—carbon, hydrogen, oxygen, and nitrogen—gave rise to a large number of different compounds that often were remarkably stable.

vital force theory

Because no organic compounds had been synthesized from inorganic substances and because there was no other explanation for the complexities of organic compounds, chemists believed that organic compounds were formed by some "vital force." The **vital force theory** held that organic substances could originate only from living material. In 1828 Friedrich Wöhler (1800–1882), a German chemist, did a simple experiment that eventually proved to be the death blow to this theory. In attempting to prepare ammonium cyanate (NH_4CNO) by heating cyanic acid (HCNO) and ammonia. Wöhler obtained a white crystalline substance that he identified as urea ($H_2N—CO—NH_2$). Wöhler knew that urea is an authentic organic substance because it is a product of metabolism that had been isolated from urine. Although Wöhler's discovery was not immediately and generally recognized, the vital force theory was overthrown by this simple experiment since one organic compound had been made from nonliving materials.

organic chemistry

After the work of Wöhler, it was apparent that no vital force other than skill and knowledge was needed to make organic chemicals in the laboratory and that inorganic as well as organic substances could be used as raw materials. Today, **organic chemistry** designates the branch of chemistry that deals with carbon compounds but does not imply that these compounds must originate from some form of life. A few special kinds of carbon compounds (for example, carbon oxides, metal carbides, and metal carbonates) are excluded from the organic classification because their chemistry is more conveniently related to that of inorganic substances.

The field of organic chemistry is vast, for it includes not only the composition of all living organisms but also of a great many other materials that we use daily. Examples of organic materials are foodstuffs (fats, proteins, carbohydrates); fuels; fabrics (cotton, wool, rayon, nylon); wood and paper products; paints and varnishes; plastics; dyes; soaps and detergents; cosmetics; medicinals; rubber products; and explosives.

The sources of organic compounds are carbon-containing raw materials—petroleum and natural gas, coal, carbohydrates, fats, and oils. In the United States we produce over 250 billion pounds of organic chemicals per year from these sources. This amounts to more than 1100 pounds per year for every man, woman, and child in the United States. About 90% of this 250 billion pounds comes from petroleum and natural gas. Because there is a finite amount of petroleum and natural gas in the world, sometime in the future we will have to rely on the other sources to make the voluminous amount of organic chemicals that we use. Fortunately we know how to do this, but at much greater expense than from petroleum and natural gas.

An immense and ever-growing number of organic chemical compounds have been prepared and are described in the chemical literature. The number is estimated to be more than 6 million. The elements that make up most of the organic compounds are carbon, hydrogen, oxygen, nitrogen, the halogens, phosphorus, and sulfur. There is no theoretical limit on the number of organic compounds that can exist. Several thousand different organic chemicals are available commercially.

20.2   The Need for Classification of Organic Compounds

functional group

It is impossible for anyone to study the properties of each of the millions of known organic compounds. Hence, organic compounds with similar structural features are grouped into classes. The members of each class of compounds contain a characteristic atom or group of atoms called a **functional group.** This functional group identifies a compound as belonging to a particular class. For example, the hydroxyl group (—OH) is the functional group of the class of compounds called alcohols.

Even within a single class there is such a large number of possible compounds that it is virtually impossible to study each individual compound. The properties of a few members of a class of compounds are studied, and the information obtained is used to predict the behavior of other members of the class. For example, ethyl alcohol, a two-carbon alcohol, can be oxidized to a two-carbon acid. On the basis of this information, it can be predicted and found to be true that hexyl alcohol, a six-carbon alcohol, can be oxidized to a six-carbon acid because the oxidizable structures of the two alcohols are identical. Some of the classes of organic compounds we will study are hydrocarbons, alcohols, phenols, aldehydes, ketones, ethers, carboxylic acids, esters, carbohydrates, and proteins. Table 22.1 lists some of the more common classes of organic compounds and their functional groups.)

20.3   The Carbon Atom: Tetrahedral Structure

The carbon atom is central to all organic compounds. The atomic number of carbon is 6, and its electron structure is $1s^2 2s^2 2p^2$. Two stable isotopes of carbon exist, C-12 and C-13. In addition there are several radioactive isotopes; C-14 is the most widely known of these because of its use in radiocarbon dating. Having four electrons in its outer shell, carbon has oxidation numbers ranging from $+4$ to -4 and forms predominantly covalent bonds. Carbon occurs as the free element in diamond, graphite, coal, coke, carbon black, charcoal, and lampblack.

A carbon atom usually forms four covalent bonds. The most common geometric arrangement of these bonds is tetrahedral (see Figure 20.1). In this structure the four covalent bonds are not planar about the carbon atom but are directed toward the corners of a regular tetrahedron. (A tetrahedron is a solid figure with four sides.) The angle between these tetrahedral bonds is 109.5°.

Figure 20.1 Tetrahedral structure of carbon: (a) A regular tetrahedron; (b) a carbon atom with tetrahedral bonds; (c) a carbon atom within a regular tetrahedron; (d) a methane molecule, CH_4.

20.4 Carbon–Carbon Bonds

With four outer-shell electrons, the carbon atom ($\cdot\overset{\displaystyle\cdot}{\underset{\displaystyle\cdot}{C}}\cdot$), following the octet rule, forms four single covalent bonds by sharing electrons with other atoms. The structures of methane and carbon tetrachloride illustrate this point:

$$H:\overset{\displaystyle H}{\underset{\displaystyle H}{\overset{..}{C}}}:H \qquad H-\overset{\displaystyle H}{\underset{\displaystyle H}{C}}-H \qquad\qquad Cl:\overset{\displaystyle Cl}{\underset{\displaystyle Cl}{\overset{..}{C}}}:Cl \qquad Cl-\overset{\displaystyle Cl}{\underset{\displaystyle Cl}{C}}-Cl$$

Methane   Carbon tetrachloride

Actually, the bond angles (109.5°) in these compounds are tetrahedral (see Figure 20.1), but for convenience of writing, the bonds are drawn at right angles.

The formation of carbon–carbon bonds is due to the ability of a carbon atom to share electrons with other carbon atoms. One, two, or three pairs of electrons can be shared between two carbon atoms, forming a single, double, or triple bond, respectively. Two vertical dots (:) represent a covalent bond.

$$\cdot\overset{\displaystyle\cdot}{\underset{\displaystyle\cdot}{C}}:\overset{\displaystyle\cdot}{\underset{\displaystyle\cdot}{C}}\cdot \qquad\qquad \cdot\overset{\displaystyle\cdot}{C}::\overset{\displaystyle\cdot}{C}\cdot \qquad\qquad \cdot C:::C\cdot$$

$$\cdot\overset{\displaystyle\cdot}{\underset{\displaystyle\cdot}{C}}-\overset{\displaystyle\cdot}{\underset{\displaystyle\cdot}{C}}\cdot \qquad\qquad \cdot\overset{\displaystyle\cdot}{C}=\overset{\displaystyle\cdot}{C}\cdot \qquad\qquad \cdot C\equiv C\cdot$$

Single bond   Double bond   Triple bond

Each dash above represents a covalent bond. Carbon, more than any other element, has the ability to form chains of covalently bonded atoms. This bonding ability is the main reason for the large number of organic compounds. Three examples are shown below. It is easy to see how, because of this bonding ability, a chain of carbon atoms can be formed by the linking of one carbon to another through covalent bonds.

·C:C:C·   ·C—C—C·

Three carbon atoms bonded by single bonds

Seven-carbon chain

Ten carbon atoms bonded together

20.5

20.5 Hydrocarbons

hydrocarbons

Hydrocarbons are compounds that are composed entirely of carbon and hydrogen atoms bonded to each other by covalent bonds. Several classes of hydrocarbons are known. These include the alkanes, alkenes, alkynes, and aromatic hydrocarbons (see Figure 20.2).

Fossil fuels—natural gas, petroleum, and coal—are the principal sources of hydrocarbons. Natural gas is primarily methane with small amounts of ethane, propane, and butane. Petroleum is a mixture of hydrocarbons from which gasoline, kerosene, fuel oil, lubricating oil, paraffin wax, and petrolatum (themselves mixtures of hydrocarbons) are separated. Coal tar, a volatile by-product of

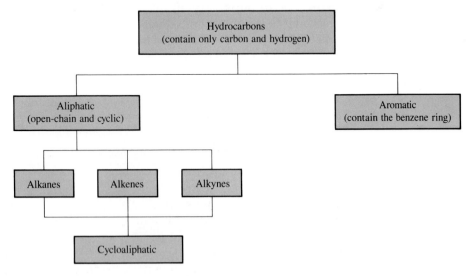

Figure 20.2 Classes of hydrocarbons

the process of making coke from coal for use in the steel industry, is the source of many valuable chemicals including the aromatic hydrocarbons benzene, toluene, and naphthalene.

20.6   *Saturated Hydrocarbons: Alkanes*

alkanes

The **alkanes,** also known as *paraffins* or *saturated hydrocarbons,* are straight- or branched-chain hydrocarbons with only single covalent bonds between the carbon atoms. We shall study the alkanes in some detail because many other classes of organic compounds can be considered as derivatives of these substances. For example, it is necessary to learn the names of the first ten members of the alkane series, because these names are used as a basis for naming other classes of compounds.

Methane (CH_4) is the first member of the alkane series. Members having two, three, and four carbon atoms are ethane, propane, and butane, respectively. The names of the first four alkanes are of common or trivial origin and must be memorized; but the names beginning with the fifth member, pentane, are derived from Greek numbers and are relatively easy to recall. The names and formulas of the first ten members of the series are given in Table 20.1.

homologous series

Adjacent compounds in the alkane series differ from each other in composition by one carbon and two hydrogen atoms. When each member of a series differs from the next member by a CH_2 group, the series is called a **homologous series.** The members of a homologous series are similar in structure but have a regular difference in formula. All common classes of organic compounds exist in homologous series. Each homologous series can be represented by a general formula. For all open-chain alkanes, the general formula is C_nH_{2n+2}, where n corresponds to the number of carbon atoms in the molecule. The formula of any specific alkane is easily determined from this general formula. Thus, for pentane,

Table 20.1   Names, formulas, and physical properties of straight-chain alkanes

Name	Molecular formula C_nH_{2n+2}	Condensed structural formula	Boiling point (°C)	Melting point (°C)
Methane	CH_4	CH_4	−161	−183
Ethane	C_2H_6	CH_3CH_3	−88	−172
Propane	C_3H_8	$CH_3CH_2CH_3$	−45	−187
Butane	C_4H_{10}	$CH_3CH_2CH_2CH_3$	−0.5	−138
Pentane	C_5H_{12}	$CH_3CH_2CH_2CH_2CH_3$	36	−130
Hexane	C_6H_{14}	$CH_3CH_2CH_2CH_2CH_2CH_3$	69	−95
Heptane	C_7H_{16}	$CH_3CH_2CH_2CH_2CH_2CH_2CH_3$	98	−90
Octane	C_8H_{18}	$CH_3CH_2CH_2CH_2CH_2CH_2CH_2CH_3$	125	−57
Nonane	C_9H_{20}	$CH_3CH_2CH_2CH_2CH_2CH_2CH_2CH_2CH_3$	151	−54
Decane	$C_{10}H_{22}$	$CH_3CH_2CH_2CH_2CH_2CH_2CH_2CH_2CH_2CH_3$	174	−30

$n = 5$ and $2n + 2 = 12$, so the formula is C_5H_{12}. For hexadecane, the 16-carbon alkane, the formula is $C_{16}H_{34}$.

20.7   Carbon Bonding in Alkanes

As was pointed out in Section 20.4, a carbon atom is capable of forming single covalent bonds with one, two, three, or four other carbon atoms. To understand this remarkable bonding ability, we must look at the electron structure of carbon. The valence electrons of carbon in their ground state are $2s^2 2p_x^1 2p_y^1$. These are the electrons that enter into bonding. When a carbon atom is bonded to other atoms by single bonds (for example, to four hydrogen atoms in CH_4), it would appear at first that there should be two different types of bonds—bonds involving the $2s$ electrons and bonds involving the $2p$ electrons of the carbon atom. However, this is not the case. All four carbon–hydrogen bonds are found to be identical.

If the carbon atom is to form four equivalent bonds, its electrons in the $2s$ and $2p$ orbitals must rearrange to four equivalent orbitals. To form the four equivalent orbitals, imagine that a $2s$ electron is promoted to a $2p$ orbital, giving carbon an outer-shell electron structure of $2s^1 2p_x^1 2p_y^1 2p_z^1$. The $2s$ orbital and the three $2p$ orbitals then hybridize to form four equivalent hybrid orbitals, which are designated sp^3 orbitals. The orbitals formed (sp^3) are neither s orbitals nor p orbitals but are a hybrid of those orbitals, having one-fourth s orbital character and three-fourths p orbital character. This process is illustrated in Figure 20.3. It is these sp^3 orbitals that are directed toward the corners of a regular tetrahedron (see Figure 20.4).

A single bond is formed when one of the sp^3 orbitals overlaps an orbital of another atom. Thus each C—H bond in methane is the result of the overlapping of a carbon sp^3 orbital and a hydrogen s orbital [Figure 20.4, part (c)]. Once the bond is formed, the pair of bonding electrons constituting it are said to be in a molecular orbital. In a similar way a C—C single bond results from the overlap of sp^3 orbitals between two carbon atoms. This type of bond is called a sigma (σ) bond. A **sigma bond** exists if the electron cloud formed by the pair of bonding electrons is symmetrical about a straight line drawn between the nuclei of the bonded atoms.

sigma bond

Figure 20.3   Schematic hybridization of $2s^2 2p_x^1 2p_y^1$ orbitals of carbon to form four sp^3 electron orbitals

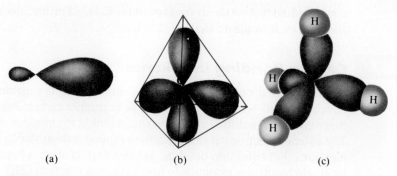

(a)   (b)   (c)

Figure 20.4   Tetrahedral nature of sp^3 orbitals: (a) A single sp^3 hybridized orbital; (b) four sp^3 hybridized orbitals in tetrahedral arrangement; (c) sp^3–s orbitals overlapping to form C—H bonds in methane.

20.8   Structural Formulas and Isomerism

The properties of an organic substance are dependent on its molecular structure. By *structure* we mean the way in which the atoms are bonded together within the molecule. The majority of organic compounds are made from relatively few elements—carbon, hydrogen, oxygen, nitrogen, and the halogens. In these compounds carbon is tetravalent, hydrogen is monovalent, oxygen is divalent, nitrogen is trivalent, and the halogens are monovalent. The valence bonds or points of attachment may be represented in structural formulas by a corresponding number of dashes attached to each atom:

$$ -\overset{\displaystyle |}{\underset{\displaystyle |}{C}}- \qquad H- \qquad -O- \qquad -\overset{\displaystyle |}{N}- \qquad Cl- \qquad Br- \qquad I- \qquad F- $$

Thus carbon will have four bonds to each atom, nitrogen three bonds, oxygen two bonds, and hydrogen and the halogens one bond to each atom.

In an alkane each carbon atom is joined to four other atoms by four single covalent bonds. These bonds are separated by angles of 109.5° (the angles correspond to those formed by lines drawn from the center of a regular tetrahedron to its corners). Alkane molecules contain only carbon–carbon and carbon–hydrogen bonds and are essentially nonpolar. Alkane molecules are nonpolar because (1) carbon–carbon bonds are nonpolar since they are between like atoms; (2) carbon–hydrogen bonds are only slightly polar since there is only a small difference in electronegativity between carbon and hydrogen atoms; and (3) the bonds in an alkane are symmetrically directed toward the corners of a tetrahedron. Because of their low polarity, alkane molecules have very little intermolecular attraction and therefore relatively low boiling points compared with other organic compounds of similar molecular weight.

Without the use of models or perspective drawings, the three-dimensional character of atoms and molecules is difficult to portray accurately. However, concepts of structure can be conveyed to some extent by Lewis (or electron-dot) diagrams of structural formulas. Methane and ethane are represented by Lewis structures as

$$
\begin{array}{cc}
\text{H} & \text{H H} \\
\text{H:C:H} & \text{H:C:C:H} \\
\text{H} & \text{H H} \\
\text{Methane} & \text{Ethane}
\end{array}
$$

But it is more convenient to use conventional structural formulas representing electron pairs by single short lines:

$$
\begin{array}{cc}
\text{H} & \text{H H} \\
| & | \ \ | \\
\text{H—C—H} & \text{H—C—C—H} \\
| & | \ \ | \\
\text{H} & \text{H H}
\end{array}
$$

To write the correct structural formula for propane (C_3H_8), the next member of the alkane series, we must determine how to place each atom in the molecule. An alkane contains only single bonds, and carbon is tetravalent. Therefore, each carbon atom must be bonded to four other atoms by either C—C or C—H bonds. Hydrogen is univalent and therefore must be bonded to only one carbon atom by a C—H bond, since C—H—C bonds do not occur, and an H—H bond would simply represent a hydrogen molecule. Applying this information, we find that the only possible structure for propane is

$$
\begin{array}{c}
\text{H H H} \\
| \ \ | \ \ | \\
\text{H—C—C—C—H} \\
| \ \ | \ \ | \\
\text{H H H} \\
\text{Propane}
\end{array}
$$

However, it is possible to write two structural formulas corresponding to the molecular formula C_4H_{10}:

$$
\begin{array}{ccc}
\text{H H H H} & & \text{H} \\
| \ \ | \ \ | \ \ | & & \text{H} \ | \ \text{H} \\
\text{H—C—C—C—C—H} & \text{and} & \text{C} \\
| \ \ | \ \ | \ \ | & & \text{H} \ | \ \text{H} \\
\text{H H H H} & & \text{H—C—C—C—H} \\
& & | \ \ | \ \ | \\
\text{Butane} & & \text{H H H} \\
& & \text{Isobutane}
\end{array}
$$

Two C_4H_{10} compounds with the structural formulas shown above actually exist. The butane with the unbranched carbon chain is called *butane* or *normal butane* (abbreviated n-butane); it boils at 0.5°C and melts at −138.3°C. The branched-chain butane is called *isobutane*; it boils at −11.7°C and melts at −159.5°C. These differences in physical properties are sufficient to establish that the two compounds, though they have the same molecular formula, are different substances. Models illustrating the structural arrangement of the atoms in methane, ethane, propane, butane, and isobutane are shown in Figure 20.5.

isomerism

This phenomenon of two or more compounds having the same molecular formula but different structural arrangements of their atoms is called **isomerism.** The various individual compounds are called **isomers.** For example, there are 2 isomers of butane, C_4H_{10}. Isomerism is very common among organic compounds and is another reason for the large number of known compounds. There are 3 isomers of pentane, 5 isomers of hexane, 9 isomers of heptane, 18 isomers of octane, 35 isomers of nonane, and 75 isomers of decane. The phenomenon of isomerism is a very compelling reason for the use of structural formulas.

isomers

> **Isomers are compounds that have the same molecular formula but different structural formulas.**

Figure 20.5   Ball-and-stick models illustrating structural formulas of methane, ethane, propane, butane, and isobutane

To save time and space in writing, condensed structural formulas are often used. In the condensed structural formulas, atoms and groups that are attached to a carbon atom are generally written to the right of that carbon atom. Examine these examples.

Molecular formula	Structural formula	Condensed structural formula
CH_4 Methane		CH_4
C_2H_6 Ethane		$CH_3—CH_3$ or CH_3CH_3
C_3H_8 Propane		$CH_3—CH_2—CH_3$ or $CH_3CH_2CH_3$
C_4H_{10} Butane		$CH_3—CH_2—CH_2—CH_3$, $CH_3CH_2CH_2CH_3$, or $CH_3(CH_2)_2CH_3$
C_4H_{10} 2-Methylpropane (Isobutane)		CH_3 CH_3 $CH_3—CH—CH_3$, CH_3CHCH_3, $CH_3CH(CH_3)CH_3$, $CH_3CH(CH_3)_2$, or $CH(CH_3)_3$

Let us interpret the condensed structural formula for propane:

$$\overset{1}{C}H_3—\overset{2}{C}H_2—\overset{3}{C}H_3$$

Carbon number 1 has three hydrogen atoms attached to it and is bonded to carbon number 2, which has two hydrogen atoms on it and is bonded to carbon number 3, which has three hydrogen atoms bonded to it.

When structures are written as in butane, $CH_3CH_2CH_2CH_3$, the bonds (dashes) are often not shown. But when a group is shown above or below the main carbon chain, as in 2-methylpropane, a vertical dash must be used to indicate the point of attachment of the group to the main carbon chain.

PROBLEM

20.1

There are three isomers of pentane, C_5H_{12}. Write structural formulas and condensed structural formulas for these isomers.

In a problem of this kind it is best to start by writing the carbon skeleton of the compound containing the longest continuous carbon chain. In this case it is five carbon atoms:

C—C—C—C—C

Now complete the structure by attaching hydrogen atoms around each carbon atom so that each carbon atom has four bonds attached to it. The carbon atoms at each end of the chain need three hydrogen atoms. The three inner carbon atoms each need two hydrogen atoms to give them four bonds.

$$
\begin{array}{ccccc}
H & H & H & H & H \\
| & | & | & | & | \\
H-C- & C- & C- & C- & C-H \\
| & | & | & | & | \\
H & H & H & H & H
\end{array}
\qquad CH_3CH_2CH_2CH_2CH_3
$$

For the next isomer, start by writing a four-carbon chain and attach the fifth carbon atom to either of the middle carbon atoms—do not use the end ones.

$$
\begin{array}{c}
C \\
| \\
C-C-C-C
\end{array}
\qquad
\begin{array}{c}
C \\
| \\
C-C-C-C
\end{array}
$$

Both of these structures represent the same compound.

Now add the 12 hydrogen atoms to complete the structure:

$$
\begin{array}{c}
H \\
H \ | \ H \\
C \\
H \quad H \quad | \quad H \\
| \quad | \quad | \quad | \\
H-C-C-C-C-H \\
| \quad | \quad | \quad | \\
H \quad H \quad H \quad H
\end{array}
$$

$$CH_3CH_2CHCH_3 \quad (CH_3) \qquad \text{or} \qquad CH_3CH_2CH(CH_3)_2$$

For the third isomer, write a three-carbon chain, attach the other two carbon atoms to the central carbon atom, and complete the structure by adding the 12 hydrogen atoms:

$$
\begin{array}{c}
C \\
| \\
C-C-C \\
| \\
C
\end{array}
$$

$$CH_3CCH_3 \quad (CH_3 \ above,\ CH_3\ below) \qquad \text{or} \qquad C(CH_3)_4$$

Biochemicals such as fats and oils often contain long alkane chains and share the nonpolar properties of the alkanes. The fats and oils tend to have the lowest melting points of all the many large molecules found in living cells. Also, fats and oils do not attract polar water molecules because these biochemicals have only very few polar bonds. These properties are very important in biochemistry. In fact, the physical nature of living cell membranes is determined by the nonpolar character of the fats and oils. The cellular membrane is fluid and also excludes water because of the alkane-like properties of its constituent fats and oils.

It is important to understand that, although isomers have the same molecular formula, they may react in very different ways because of their different structural formulas. This is especially true in biochemistry. For example, linear fatty acid molecules such as arachidic acid,

$$CH_3CH_2CH_2CH_2CH_2CH_2CH_2CH_2CH_2CH_2CH_2CH_2CH_2CH_2CH_2CH_2CH_2CH_2COOH \qquad \text{or} \qquad C_{20}H_{40}O_2$$
Arachidic acid

are easily digested by animals. In contrast, branched fatty acid molecules (even with the same molecular formula) are more difficult to digest. For some individuals, phytanic acid, a fatty acid derived from milk fat,

$$\underset{\text{Phytanic acid}}{CH_3\underset{\displaystyle\vert}{CH}CH_2CH_2CH_2\underset{\displaystyle\vert}{CH}CH_2CH_2CH_2\underset{\displaystyle\vert}{CH}CH_2CH_2CH_2\underset{\displaystyle\vert}{CH}CH_2COOH} \qquad \text{or} \qquad C_{20}H_{40}O_2$$

with CH_3 groups above each marked CH

is undigestible because of its branched structure. The phytanic acid accumulates in body tissues causing serious neurological problems. Note that phytanic acid has the same molecular formula as the straight-chain molecule, $C_{20}H_{40}O_2$. The difference in reactivity arises from the difference in structure between these two isomers.

20.9 Naming Organic Compounds

In the early development of organic chemistry, each new compound was given a name, usually by the person who had isolated or synthesized it. Names were not systematic but often did carry some information—usually about the origin of the substance. Wood alcohol (methanol), for example, was so named because it was obtained by destructive distillation or pyrolysis of wood. Methane, formed during underwater decomposition of vegetable matter in marshes, was originally called *marsh gas*. A single compound was often known by several names. For example, the active ingredient in alcoholic beverages has been called *alcohol, ethyl alcohol, methyl carbinol, grain alcohol, spirit,* and *ethanol*.

Beginning with a meeting in Geneva in 1892, an international system for naming compounds was developed. In its present form the method recommended by the International Union of Pure and Applied Chemistry is systematic, generally unambiguous, and internationally accepted. It is called the IUPAC System. Despite the existence of the official IUPAC System, a great many well-established common, or trivial, names and abbreviations (such as TNT and DDT) are used because of their brevity and/or convenience. So it is necessary to have a knowledge of both the IUPAC System and many common names.

alkyl groups
In order to name organic compounds systematically, you must be able to recognize certain common alkyl groups. **Alkyl groups** have the general formula C_nH_{2n+1} (one less hydrogen atom than the corresponding alkane). The missing H

Table 20.2 Names and formulas of selected alkyl groups

Formula	Name	Formula	Name
CH_3-	Methyl	$\begin{matrix} CH_3 \\ | \\ CH_3CH- \end{matrix}$	Isopropyl
CH_3CH_2-	Ethyl		
$CH_3CH_2CH_2-$	Propyl	$\begin{matrix} CH_3 \\ | \\ CH_3CHCH_2- \end{matrix}$	Isobutyl
$CH_3CH_2CH_2CH_2-$	Butyl		
$CH_3(CH_2)_3CH_2-$	Pentyl		
$CH_3(CH_2)_4CH_2-$	Hexyl	$\begin{matrix} CH_3 \\ | \\ CH_3CH_2CH- \end{matrix}$	sec-Butyl (secondary butyl)
$CH_3(CH_2)_5CH_2-$	Heptyl		
$CH_3(CH_2)_6CH_2-$	Octyl	$\begin{matrix} CH_3 \\ | \\ CH_3C- \\ | \\ CH_3 \end{matrix}$	tert-Butyl or t-Butyl (tertiary butyl)
$CH_3(CH_2)_7CH_2-$	Nonyl		
$CH_3(CH_2)_8CH_2-$	Decyl		

atom can be from any carbon in the alkane. The name of the group is formed from the name of the corresponding alkane by simply dropping -*ane* and substituting a -*yl* ending. The names and formulas of selected alkyl groups up to and including four carbon atoms are given in Table 20.2. The letter R is often used in formulas to mean any of the many possible alkyl groups.

$$R = C_nH_{2n+1} \qquad \text{Any alkyl group}$$

The following relatively simple rules are all that are needed to name a great many alkanes according to the IUPAC System. In later sections these rules will be extended to cover other classes of compounds, but advanced texts or references must be consulted for the complete system. The IUPAC rules for naming alkanes are

1. Select the longest continuous chain of carbon atoms as the parent compound, and consider all alkyl groups attached to it as side chains that have replaced hydrogen atoms of the parent hydrocarbon. The name of the alkane consists of the name of the parent compound prefixed by the names of the side-chain alkyl groups attached to it.
2. Number the carbon atoms in the parent carbon chain starting from the end closest to the first carbon atom that has an alkyl or other group substituted for a hydrogen atom.
3. Name each side-chain alkyl group and designate its position on the parent carbon chain by a number (for example, 2-methyl means a methyl group attached to carbon number 2).
4. When the same alkyl-group side chain occurs more than once, indicate this by a prefix (*di-, tri-, tetra-,* and so forth) written in front of the alkyl-group name (for example, *dimethyl* indicates two methyl groups). The numbers indicating the positions of these alkyl groups are separated by a comma and followed by a hyphen and are placed in front of the name (for example, 2,3-dimethyl).
5. When several different alkyl groups are attached to the parent compound, list them in alphabetical order; for example, *ethyl* before *methyl* in 3-ethyl-4-methyloctane.

The compound shown below is commonly called isopentane. Consider naming it by the IUPAC System:

$$\overset{4}{C}H_3—\overset{3}{C}H_2—\overset{2}{C}H—\overset{1}{C}H_3$$
$$|$$
$$CH_3$$

2-Methylbutane
(Isopentane)

The longest continuous chain contains four carbon atoms. Therefore, the parent compound is butane and the compound is named as a butane. The methyl group ($CH_3—$) attached to carbon number 2 is named as a prefix to butane, the "2-" indicating the point of attachment of the methyl group on the butane chain.

How would we write the structural formula for 2-methylpentane? An analysis of its name gives us this information.

1. The parent compound, pentane, contains five carbons. Write and number the five-carbon skeleton of pentane:

$$\overset{5}{C}—\overset{4}{C}—\overset{3}{C}—\overset{2}{C}—\overset{1}{C}$$

2. Put a methyl group on carbon number 2 ("2-methyl" in the name gives this information):

$$\overset{5}{C}—\overset{4}{C}—\overset{3}{C}—\overset{2}{C}—\overset{1}{C}$$
$$|$$
$$CH_3$$

3. Add hydrogens to give each carbon four bonds. The structural formula is

$$CH_3—CH_2—CH_2—CH—CH_3$$
$$|$$
$$CH_3$$

2-Methylpentane

Should this compound be called 4-methylpentane? No, the IUPAC System specifically states that the parent carbon chain shall be numbered starting from the end nearest to the side or branch chain.

It is very important to understand that it is the sequence of atoms and groups that determines the name of a compound, and not the way the sequence is written. Each of the following formulas represents 2-methylpentane:

$$\overset{1}{C}H_3—\overset{2}{C}H—\overset{3}{C}H_2—\overset{4}{C}H_2—\overset{5}{C}H_3$$
$$|$$
$$CH_3$$

$$\overset{5}{C}H_3—\overset{4}{C}H_2—\overset{3}{C}H_2—\overset{2}{\overset{\displaystyle CH_3}{\overset{\displaystyle |}{C}}}H—\overset{1}{C}H_3$$

$$\overset{1}{C}H_3—\overset{2}{\overset{\displaystyle CH_3}{\overset{\displaystyle |}{C}}}H—\overset{3}{C}H_2$$
$$\overset{4}{|}$$
$$\overset{}{C}H_2—\overset{5}{C}H_3$$

$$\overset{2}{\overset{\displaystyle CH_3}{\overset{\displaystyle |}{C}}}H \qquad \overset{4}{C}H_2$$
$$\diagup \overset{3}{\diagdown} \qquad \diagup \overset{5}{\diagdown}$$
$$\overset{1}{C}H_3 \quad \overset{3}{C}H_2 \quad \overset{5}{C}H_3$$

The following formulas and names demonstrate other aspects of the official nomenclature system:

$$\overset{4}{C}H_3 - \overset{3}{C}H - \overset{2}{C}H - \overset{1}{C}H_3$$
$$\qquad\ \ |\ \quad |$$
$$\qquad\ \ CH_3\ \ CH_3$$

2,3-Dimethylbutane

The name of this compound is 2,3-dimethylbutane. The longest carbon atom chain is four, indicating butane; "dimethyl" indicates two methyl groups; "2,3-" means that one CH_3 is on carbon 2 and one is on carbon 3.

$$\qquad\qquad\quad CH_3$$
$$\qquad\qquad\quad |2$$
$$\overset{4}{C}H_3 - \overset{3}{C}H_2 - \overset{}{C} - \overset{1}{C}H_3$$
$$\qquad\qquad\quad |$$
$$\qquad\qquad\quad CH_3$$

2,2-Dimethylbutane

(Both methyl groups are on the same carbon atom; both numbers are required.)

$$\qquad\qquad\qquad\qquad CH_3$$
$$\qquad\qquad\qquad\qquad |4$$
$$\overset{1}{C}H_3 - \overset{2}{C}H - \overset{3}{C}H_2 - \overset{4}{C}H - \overset{5}{C}H_2 - \overset{6}{C}H_3$$
$$\qquad\quad |$$
$$\qquad\quad CH_3$$

2,4-Dimethylhexane

(The molecule is numbered from left to right.)

$$\qquad\quad \overset{3}{C}H - \overset{4}{C}H_2 - \overset{5}{C}H_2 - \overset{6}{C}H_3$$
$$CH_3 -$$
$$\qquad\quad |2$$
$$\qquad\quad CH_2$$
$$\qquad\quad |1$$
$$\qquad\quad CH_3$$

3-Methylhexane

(There are six carbons in the longest continuous chain.)

$$\qquad\qquad\qquad\qquad\qquad CH_2 - CH_3$$
$$\qquad\qquad\qquad\qquad\qquad |4$$
$$\overset{8}{C}H_3 - \overset{7}{C}H_2 - \overset{6}{C}H_2 - \overset{5}{C}H_2 - \overset{}{C} - \overset{3}{C}H - \overset{2}{C}H - \overset{1}{C}H_3$$
$$\qquad\qquad\qquad\qquad\quad |\qquad |\qquad |$$
$$\qquad\qquad\qquad\qquad\quad CH_3\ \ Cl\ \ \ CH_3$$

3-Chloro-4-ethyl-2,4-dimethyloctane

The longest carbon chain is eight. The groups that are attached or substituted for H on the octane chain are named in alphabetical order.

PROBLEM

20.2

Write the formulas for
(a) 3-Ethylpentane   **(b)** 2,2,4-Trimethylpentane

(a) The name *pentane* indicates a five-carbon chain. Write five connected carbon atoms and number them:

$$\overset{1}{C}-\overset{2}{C}-\overset{3}{C}-\overset{4}{C}-\overset{5}{C}$$

An ethyl group is written as CH_3CH_2-. Attach this group at the open bond to carbon number 3:

$$\overset{1}{C}-\overset{2}{C}-\overset{3}{\underset{|}{C}}-\overset{4}{C}-\overset{5}{C}$$
$$CH_2CH_3$$

Now add hydrogen atoms to give each carbon atom four bonds. Carbons 1 and 5 each need three H atoms; carbons 2 and 4 each need two H atoms; and carbon 3 needs one H atom. The formula is complete:

$$CH_3CH_2\underset{|}{C}HCH_2CH_3$$
$$CH_2CH_3$$

(b) Pentane indicates a five-carbon chain. Write five connected carbon atoms and number them:

$$\overset{1}{C}-\overset{2}{C}-\overset{3}{C}-\overset{4}{C}-\overset{5}{C}$$

There are three methyl groups (CH_3-) in the compound *(trimethyl)*, two attached to carbon 2 and one attached to carbon 4. Attach these three methyl groups to their respective carbon atoms:

$$\qquad CH_3 \quad CH_3$$
$$\overset{1}{C}-\overset{2}{\underset{|}{C}}-\overset{3}{C}-\overset{4}{\underset{|}{C}}-\overset{5}{C}$$
$$\qquad CH_3$$

Now add H atoms to give each carbon atom four bonds. Carbons 1 and 5 each need three H atoms; carbon 2 does not need any H atoms; carbon 3 needs two H atoms; and carbon 4 needs one H atom. The formula is complete:

$$\qquad CH_3 \ CH_3$$
$$CH_3\underset{|}{C}CH_2\underset{|}{C}HCH_3$$
$$\qquad CH_3$$

PROBLEM

20.3

Name the following compounds:

(a)
$$\qquad\qquad CH_3$$
$$CH_3CH_2CH_2CH_2\underset{|}{C}HCH_3$$

(b)
$$\qquad\qquad CH_2CH_3$$
$$CH_3CH_2CH_2\underset{|}{C}HCH_2\underset{|}{C}HCH_3$$
$$\qquad\qquad\qquad\qquad CH_2CH_3$$

(a) The longest continuous carbon chain contains six carbon atoms (Rule 1). Thus the parent name of the compound is hexane. Number the carbon chain from right to left so that the methyl group attached to carbon 2 is given the lowest possible number (Rule 2). With a methyl group on carbon 2, the name of the compound is 2-methyl-hexane (Rule 3).

(b) The longest continuous carbon chain contains eight carbon atoms:

$$
\begin{array}{c}
\mathrm{C{-}C} \\
\underset{8\ \ \ \ 7\ \ \ \ 6}{\mathrm{C{-}C{-}C{-}}}\overset{5\ \ \ 4\ \ \ 3}{\underset{|}{\mathrm{C{-}C{-}C{-}C}}} \\
\underset{2\ \ \ 1}{\mathrm{C{-}C}}
\end{array}
$$

Thus the parent name is octane. As the chain is numbered, there is a methyl group on carbon 3 and an ethyl group on carbon 5. Thus the name of the compound is 5-ethyl-3-methyloctane. Note that ethyl is named before methyl (alphabetical order) (Rule 5).

20.10 Reactions of Alkanes

One single type of reaction of alkanes has inspired people to explore equatorial jungles, endure the heat and sandstorms of the deserts of Africa and the Middle East, mush across the frozen Arctic, and drill holes in the earth more than 30,000 feet deep! These strenuous and expensive activities have been undertaken because alkanes, as well as other hydrocarbons, undergo combustion with oxygen with the evolution of large amounts of heat energy. Methane, for example, reacts with oxygen:

$$CH_4(g) + 2\,O_2(g) \longrightarrow CO_2(g) + 2\,H_2O(g) + 802.5 \text{ kJ (191.8 kcal)}$$

The thermal energy can be converted to mechanical and electrical energy. Combustion reactions overshadow all other reactions of alkanes in economic importance. But combustion reactions are not usually of great interest to organic chemists, since carbon dioxide and water are the only chemical products of complete combustion.

Aside from their combustibility, alkanes are relatively sluggish and limited in reactivity. But with proper activation, such as high temperature and/or catalysts, alkanes can be made to react in a variety of ways. Some important noncombustion reactions of alkanes are the following:

1. *Halogenation* (substitution of halogens for hydrogen). *Halogenation* is a general term. When a specific halogen such as chlorine is used, the reaction is called chlorination. RH is an alkane (alkyl group +H atom).

$$RH + X_2 \longrightarrow RX + HX \qquad (X = Cl \text{ or } Br)$$

$$\underset{\text{Chloroethane}}{CH_3CH_3 + Cl_2 \longrightarrow CH_3CH_2Cl + HCl}$$

This reaction yields alkyl halides (RX), which are useful as intermediates for the manufacture of other substances.

2. *Dehydrogenation* (removal of hydrogen)

$$C_nH_{2n+2} \xrightarrow{700-900°C} C_nH_{2n} + H_2$$

$$CH_3CH_2CH_3 \xrightarrow{\Delta} CH_3CH{=}CH_2 + H_2$$
$$\text{Propene}$$

This reaction yields alkenes, which, like alkyl halides, are useful chemical intermediates. Hydrogen is a valuable by-product.

3. *Cracking* (breaking up large molecules to form smaller ones)

$$\textit{Example:} \quad C_{16}H_{34} \xrightarrow{\Delta} C_8H_{18} + C_8H_{16} \quad \text{(one of several possibilities)}$$
$$\text{Alkane} \qquad \text{Alkane} \quad \text{Alkene}$$

4. *Isomerization* (rearrangment of molecular structures)

$$\textit{Example:} \quad CH_3{-}CH_2{-}CH_2{-}CH_2{-}CH_3 \longrightarrow CH_3{-}CH_2{-}CH(CH_3){-}CH_3$$

Halogenation is used extensively in the manufacture of petrochemicals (chemicals derived from petroleum and used for purposes other than fuels). The other three reactions—dehydrogenation, cracking, and isomerization—singly or in combination, are of great importance in the production of motor fuels and petrochemicals.

A well-known reaction of methane and chlorine is shown by the equation

$$CH_4 + Cl_2 \longrightarrow CH_3Cl + HCl$$
$$\text{Chloromethane}$$
$$\text{(Methyl chloride)}$$

The reaction of methane and chlorine will give a mixture of mono-, di-, tri-, and tetra-substituted chloromethanes.

$$CH_4 \xrightarrow{Cl_2} CH_3Cl \xrightarrow{Cl_2} CH_2Cl_2 \xrightarrow{Cl_2} CHCl_3 \xrightarrow{Cl_2} CCl_4 + 4\,HCl$$

However, if an excess of chlorine is used, the reaction can be controlled to give all tetrachloromethane (carbon tetrachloride). On the other hand, if a large ratio of methane to chlorine is used, the product will be predominantly chloromethane (methyl chloride). Table 20.3 shows the formulas and names for all the chloromethanes. The names for the other halogen-substituted methanes follow the same pattern as for the chloromethanes; for example, CH_3Br is bromomethane, or methyl bromide, and CHI_3 is triiodomethane, or iodoform.

Table 20.3 Chlorination products of methane

Formula	*IUPAC name*	*Common name*
CH_3Cl	Chloromethane	Methyl chloride
CH_2Cl_2	Dichloromethane	Methylene chloride
$CHCl_3$	Trichloromethane	Chloroform
CCl_4	Tetrachloromethane	Carbon tetrachloride

**mono-
substitution**

Chloromethane is a monosubstitution product of methane. The term **monosub-stitution** refers to the fact that one hydrogen atom in an organic molecule is substituted by another atom or by a group of atoms. In hydrocarbons, for example, when we substitute one chlorine atom for a hydrogen atom, the new compound is a monosubstitution (monochlorosubstitution) product. In a like manner we can have di-, tri-, tetra-, and so on, substitution products.

This kind of chlorination (or bromination) is general with alkanes. There are nine different chlorination products of ethane. See if you can write the structural formulas for all of them.

When propane is chlorinated, two isomeric monosubstitution products are obtained, because a hydrogen atom may be replaced on either the first or second carbon:

$$CH_3CH_2CH_3 + Cl_2 \xrightarrow[25^\circ C]{\text{Light}} CH_3CH_2CH_2Cl \ + \ CH_3CHClCH_3 \ + \ HCl$$

1-Chloropropane   2-Chloropropane
(*n*-Propyl chloride)   (Isopropyl chloride)

alkyl halide

The letter X is commonly used to indicate a halogen atom. The formula RX indicates a halogen atom attached to an alkyl group and represents the class of compounds known as the **alkyl halides.** When R = CH_3, then CH_3X can be CH_3F, CH_3Cl, CH_3Br, or CH_3I.

Alkyl halides are named systematically in the same general way as alkanes. Halogen atoms are identified as *fluoro-, chloro-, bromo-,* or *iodo-* and are named as substituents like side-chain alkyl groups. Study these examples:

CH_3—$CHCl$—CH_2—CH_3 CH_2Cl—$CHBr$—CH_3

2-Chlorobutane   2-Bromo-1-chloropropane

$$CH_3-CH_2-\underset{\underset{\displaystyle CH_3}{|}}{CH}-CHCl-CH_3$$

2-Chloro-3-methylpentane

PROBLEM

20.4

How many monochlorosubstitution products can be obtained from pentane? First write the formula for pentane:

$$\overset{5}{C}H_3\overset{4}{C}H_2\overset{3}{C}H_2\overset{2}{C}H_2\overset{1}{C}H_3$$

Now rewrite the formula five times substituting a Cl atom for an H atom on each C atom:

I	$CH_3CH_2CH_2CH_2\overset{1}{C}H_2Cl$	Cl on carbon 1
II	$CH_3CH_2CH_2\overset{2}{C}HClCH_3$	Cl on carbon 2
III	$CH_3CH_2\overset{3}{C}HClCH_2CH_3$	Cl on carbon 3
IV	$CH_3\overset{4}{C}HClCH_2CH_2CH_3$	Cl on carbon 4
V	$\overset{5}{C}H_2ClCH_2CH_2CH_2CH_3$	Cl on carbon 5

Compounds I and V are identical. By numbering compound V from left to right, we find that both compounds (I and V) are 1-chloropentane. Compounds II and IV are identical. By numbering compound IV from left to right, we find that both compounds (II and IV) are 2-chloropentane. Thus there are three monochlorosubstitution products of pentane: 1-chloropentane, 2-chloropentane, and 3-chloropentane.

20.11 Sources of Alkane Hydrocarbons

The two main sources of alkane hydrocarbons are natural gas and petroleum. Natural gas was formed by the anaerobic decay of plants and animals. The composition of natural gas varies in different locations. Its main component is methane (80–95%), the balance being varying amounts of other hydrocarbons, hydrogen, nitrogen, carbon monoxide, carbon dioxide, and in some locations, hydrogen sulfide. Economically significant amounts of methane are now obtained by the decomposition of sewage, garbage, and other organic waste products.

Petroleum, also called *crude oil*, is a viscous black liquid consisting of a mixture of hydrocarbons with smaller amounts of nitrogen and sulfur-containing organic compounds. Petroleum was formed by the decomposition of plants and animals over millions of years. The composition of petroleum varies widely from one locality to another. Crude oil is refined into many useful products such as gasoline, kerosene, diesel fuel, jet fuel, lubricating oil, heating oil, paraffin wax, petroleum jelly (petrolatum), tars, and asphalt. Petroleum jelly is a jellylike semisolid that is used in preparing medicinal ointments and for lubrication.

At the rate that natural gas and petroleum are being used, these sources of hydrocarbons are destined to be in short supply and virtually exhausted in the not-too-distant future. Long before this happens, alternate sources of fuels must be developed.

Fortunately, our country has very large coal deposits, and coal is a good alternative source of gaseous and liquid hydrocarbons. The chemistry for converting coal into mixtures of gaseous and liquid hydrocarbons, called *synthetic fuels* or *syn fuels*, has been known for many years. However, because of relatively inexpensive natural gas and petroleum, it has not been economically feasible to produce synthetic fuels on a large scale in the United States.

Another important source of hydrocarbons is shale oil. Shale oil is found in sedimentary rocks, and vast deposits are widely distributed in the western United States. When it becomes economically feasible, shale oil will provide another major source of hydrocarbons.

20.12 Octane Rating of Gasoline

Gasoline, aside from the additives put into it, consists primarily of hydrocarbons. Gasoline, as it is distilled from crude oil, causes "knocking" when burned in high-compression automobile engines. Knocking, which is due to a too-rapid combustion or detonation of the air–gasoline mixture, is a severe problem in high-compression engines. The knock-resistance of gasolines, a quality that varies widely, is usually expressed in terms of *octane number*, or *octane rating*.

Isooctane (2,2,4-trimethylpentane), because of its highly branched chain structure, is a motor fuel that is resistant to knocking. Mixtures of isooctane and n-heptane, a straight-chain alkane that knocks badly, have been used as standards to establish octane ratings of gasolines. Isooctane is arbitrarily assigned an octane number of 100 and n-heptane an octane number of 0. To determine the octane rating, a gasoline is compared with mixtures of isooctane and n-heptane in a test engine. The octane number of the gasoline corresponds to the percentage of isooctane present in the isooctane and n-heptane mixture that matches the knocking characteristics of the gasoline being tested. Thus a 90 octane gasoline has knocking characteristics matching those of a mixture of 90% isooctane and 10% n-heptane.

When first used to establish octane numbers, isooctane was the most knock-resistant substance available. Substances even more resistant to knocking than isooctane have since been manufactured, and it is now possible to buy gasolines with octane numbers greater than 100.

Two general methods are available for increasing the octane number of gasoline. One method is to process the crude oil so as to increase the percentages of branched-chain alkanes and/or aromatic hydrocarbons in the product. Both branched-chain alkanes and aromatic hydrocarbons have excellent antiknock properties, but these materials are present only in small quantities in most crude oils. So this method involves breaking up molecules and rearranging the fragments to form new molecules. Numerous processes, usually involving high pressure, high temperature, and special catalysts, have been developed for the production of high-octane gasoline by this method.

The second general method is the use of additives such as tetraethyl lead, $(C_2H_5)_4Pb$, in "ethyl fluid." This approach is relatively inexpensive and very effective and can increase the rating of some motor fuels by as much as 15 octane numbers. The highest-octane gasolines now commercially available are produced by combining the two methods; for example, "ethyl fluid" is added to gasoline stocks containing high percentages of branched-chain alkanes and aromatics.

Although lead compounds, specifically tetraethyl lead, are without question effective antiknock agents, their use in gasoline is currently open to the following serious objections and is being phased out.

1. In the modern automobiles catalytic devices are used in exhaust systems to reduce the level of exhaust air pollutants (carbon monoxide, hydrocarbons, and nitrogen oxides). The use of leaded gasoline makes pollutant control more difficult because the lead in the exhaust deactivates most metal catalysts.

2. Lead is a poisonous substance. The continued use of lead in gasoline means that the environmental level of finely divided lead compounds is being increased. This environmental accumulation is mostly in the soil since the lead compounds in exhausts are not volatile enough to remain as atmospheric pollutants for long periods of

time. Legal restrictions have been established to govern the maximum amounts of lead in gasoline.

3. Tetraethyl lead is a volatile poison. Its presence in gasoline constitutes an additional hazard to persons who handle this volatile and highly combustible material. Leaded gasoline should never be used in gasoline stoves, lanterns, catalytic heaters, or similar devices.

20.13 Cycloalkanes

cycloalkanes

Cyclic, or closed-chain, alkanes also exist. These substances, called **cycloalkanes,** *cycloparaffins,* or *naphthenes,* have the general formula C_nH_{2n}. Note that this series of compounds has two fewer hydrogen atoms than the open-chain alkanes. The bonds for the two missing hydrogen atoms are accounted for by an additional carbon–carbon bond in forming the cyclic ring of carbon atoms. Structures for the four smallest cycloalkanes are shown in Figure 20.6.

With the exception noted below for cyclopropane and cyclobutane, cycloalkanes are generally similar to open-chain alkanes in both physical properties and chemical reactivity. Cycloalkanes are saturated hydrocarbons; they contain only single bonds between carbon atoms.

The reactivity of cyclopropane, and to a lesser degree that of cyclobutane, is greater than that of other alkanes. This greater reactivity exists because the carbon–carbon bond angles in these substances deviate substantially from the normal tetrahedral angle. The carbon atoms form a triangle in cyclopropane, and in cyclobutane they approximate a square. Cyclopropane molecules therefore have carbon–carbon bond angles of 60°, and in cyclobutane the bond angles are about 90°. In the open-chain alkanes and in larger cycloalkanes, the carbon atoms are in a three-dimensional zigzag pattern in space and have normal (tetrahedral) bond angles of about 109.5°.

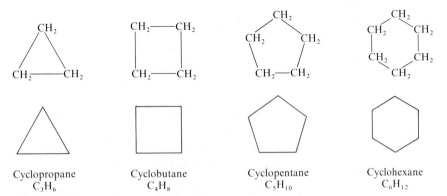

Figure 20.6 Cycloalkanes: In the line representations, each corner of the diagram represents a CH_2 group.

n-Hexane $CH_3CH_2CH_2CH_2CH_2CH_3$

Cyclopropane

Cyclohexane

Figure 20.7   Ball-and-stick models illustrating cyclopropane, hexane, and cyclohexane: In cyclopropane all the carbon atoms are in one plane. The angle between carbon atoms is 60°, not the usual 109.5°; therefore the cyclopropane ring is strained. In cyclohexane the carbon–carbon bonds are not strained. This is because the molecule is puckered, with carbon–carbon bond angles of 109.5°, as found in normal hexane.

Bromine will add to cyclopropane readily and to cyclobutane to some extent. In this reaction the ring breaks and an open-chain dibromopropane is formed:

$$CH_2 \atop CH_2\!-\!CH_2 + Br_2 \longrightarrow BrCH_2CH_2CH_2Br$$

Cyclopropane   1,3-Dibromopropane

Cyclopropane and cyclobutane react in this way because their carbon–carbon bonds are strained and therefore weakened. Cycloalkanes with rings having more than four carbon atoms do not react in this way because their molecules take the shape of nonplanar puckered rings. These rings can be considered to be formed by simply joining the end carbon atoms of the corresponding normal alkanes. The resulting cyclic molecules are nearly strain-free, with carbon atoms arranged in space so that the bond angles are close to 109.5° (Figure 20.7).

Cyclopropane is a useful general anesthetic and, along with certain other cycloalkanes, is used as an intermediate in some chemical syntheses. The high reactivity of cyclopropane requires great care in its use as an anesthetic because it is an extreme fire and explosion hazard. The cyclopentane and cyclohexane ring structures are present in many naturally occurring molecules such as prostaglandins, steroids (for example, cholesterol and sex hormones), and some vitamins.

QUESTIONS

A. *Review the meanings of the new terms introduced in this chapter.*

1. Vital force theory
2. Organic chemistry
3. Functional group
4. Hydrocarbons
5. Alkanes
6. Homologous series
7. Sigma bond
8. Isomerism
9. Isomers
10. Alkyl groups
11. Monosubstitution
12. Alkyl halide
13. Cycloalkanes

B. *Review questions*

1. What is the major reason for the large number of organic compounds?
2. Why is it believed that a carbon atom must form hybrid electron orbitals when it bonds to hydrogen atoms to form methane?
3. Write Lewis structures for:
   (a) CCl_4 (b) C_2Cl_6 (c) $CH_3CH_2CH_3$
4. Write the names and formulas for the first ten normal alkanes.
5. The name of the compound of formula $C_{11}H_{24}$ is undecane. What is the formula for dodecane, the next higher homologue in the alkane series?
6. How many sigma bonds are in a molecule of
   (a) Ethane (b) Butane (c) Isobutane
7. Which of these formulas represent isomers?
   (a) $CH_3CH_2CH_2CH_3$
   (b) $CH_3CH_2CH_2CH_2CH_3$

(c) CH_3CHCH_3
     |
     CH_3CH_2

(d) $CH_3CH_2CH_2CH_2CH_2CH_3$

(e) $CH_3 \qquad CH_3$
    \quad \diagdown \qquad \diagup
    \qquad CH—CH
    \quad \diagup \qquad \diagdown
    $CH_3 \qquad CH_3$

(f) CH_2—CH_2
    |\qquad |
    $CH_2 \quad CH_2$
    \quad \diagdown \diagup
    \qquad CH_2

(g) $CH_3CHCH_2CH_2CH_3$
     |
     CH_3

(h) CH_2
    \diagdown
    \quad $CHCH_2CH_3$
    \diagup
    CH_2

(i) CH_3CH_2
    |
    CH_2CH_3

8. (a) How many methyl groups are in each formula in Question 7?
   (b) How many ethyl groups?
9. Which of these formulas represent the same compound?

   (a) $CH_3CHCH_2CHCH_3$
        |\qquad\qquad |
        $CH_3 \quad CH_3$

   (b) \qquad CH_3
       \qquad |
       $CH_2CHCH_2CHCH_3$
       |\qquad\qquad |
       $CH_3 \qquad CH_3$

(c)
$$CH_3CHCH_2CH_2CHCH_3$$
with CH_3 above first CH and CH_3 below

(c)
             CH_3
$CH_3CHCH_2CH_2CHCH_3$
         CH_3

(d)
          CH_3
$CH_3CHCHCH_2CH_2$
        CH_3 CH_3

(e)
       CH_3
CH_3CHCH_2
$CH_3CH_2CHCH_3$

(f)
      CH_3
CH_3CH
    CH_2CHCH_3
       CH_2CH_3

10. Draw structural formulas for all the isomers of
   (a) CH_3Br (d) C_3H_7Br (g) C_3H_6BrCl
   (b) CH_2Cl_2 (e) C_4H_9I (h) $C_4H_8Cl_2$
   (c) C_2H_5Cl (f) $C_3H_6Cl_2$

11. What is the molecular weight of an alkane that contains 30 carbon atoms?

12. Write condensed structural formulas for:
   (a) The five isomers of hexane
   (b) The nine isomers of heptane

13. Give common and IUPAC names for the following:
   (a) CH_3CH_2Cl (d) $CH_3CH_2CH_2Cl$
   (b) $CH_3CHClCH_3$ (e) $(CH_3)_3CCl$
   (c) $(CH_3)_2CHCH_2Cl$ (f) $CH_3CHClCH_2CH_3$

14. The following names are incorrect. Tell why the name is wrong and give the correct name.
   (a) 3-Methylbutane
   (b) 2-Ethylbutane
   (c) 2-Dimethylpentane
   (d) 3-Methyl-5-ethyloctane
   (e) 3,5,5-Triethylhexane

15. Draw structural formulas of the following compounds
   (a) 2,4-Dimethylpentane
   (b) 2,2-Dimethylpentane
   (c) 3-Isopropyloctane
   (d) 4-Ethyl-2-methylhexane
   (e) 4-t-Butylheptane
   (f) 4-Ethyl-7-isopropyl-2,4,8-trimethyldecane

16. Give the IUPAC name for each of the following compounds:
   (a) $CH_3CH_2CHCH_3$
           CH_3
   (b) $(CH_3)_2CHCH_2CH(CH_3)_2$
   (c) CH_2
      ▷$CHCH_3$
    CH_2

             CH_3CHCH_3
   (d) $CH_3CH_2CH_2CHCH_3$

17. Complete the equations for (a) the monochlorination and (b) complete combustion of butane.
   (a) $CH_3CH_2CH_2CH_3 + Cl_2 \xrightarrow{hv}$
   (b) $CH_3CH_2CH_2CH_3 + O_2 \xrightarrow{\Delta}$

18. The structure for hexane is

   $CH_3CH_2CH_2CH_2CH_2CH_3$

   Draw structural formulas for all the monochlorohexanes, $C_6H_{13}Cl$, that have the same carbon structures as hexane.

19. Draw structures for the ten dichlorosubstituted isomers ($C_5H_{10}Cl_2$) of 2-methylbutane.

20. A hydrocarbon sample of formula C_4H_{10} was brominated, and four different monobromo compounds of formula C_4H_9Br were isolated. Was the sample a pure compound or a mixture of compounds? Explain your answer.

21. There are two cycloalkanes that have the formula C_4H_8. Draw their structures and name them.

22. Which of these statements are correct?
   (a) Alkane hydrocarbons are essentially nonpolar.
   (b) The C—H sigma bond in methane is made from an overlap of an s electron orbital and an sp^3 electron orbital.
   (c) The valence electrons of every carbon atom in an alkane are in sp^3-hybridized orbitals.
   (d) The four carbon–hydrogen bonds in methane are equivalent.
   (e) Hydrocarbons are composed of carbon and water.
   (f) In the alkane homologous series, the formula of each member differs from its preceding member by CH_3.

(g) Carbon atoms can form single, double, and triple bonds with other carbon atoms.

(h) The name for the alkane C_5H_{12} is propane.

(i) There are eight carbon atoms in a molecule of 2,3,3-trimethylpentane.

(j) The general formula for an alkyl halide is RX.

(k) The IUPAC name for $CH_3CH_2CH_2CHClCH_3$ is 4-chloropentane.

(l) Isopropyl chloride is also called 2-chloropropane.

(m) The formula for chlorocyclohexane is $C_6H_{11}Cl$.

(n) Chlorocyclohexane and 1-chlorohexane are isomers.

(o) The products of complete combustion of a hydrocarbon are carbon monoxide and water.

(p) When pentane is chlorinated, three monochlorosubstitution products can be obtained.

(q) Isobutane, 2-methylpropane, and 1,1-dimethylethane are all correct names for the same compound.

(r) Only one monochloro-substituted product will result from the chlorination of butane.

(s) Cycloalkanes have the general formula C_nH_{2n}.

Hydrocarbons ( )
1. Alkanes {saturated H/c}
2. Alkenes
3. Alkynes
4. Aromatics

21

Unsaturated Hydrocarbons: Alkenes, Alkynes, and Aromatic Hydrocarbons

Basic reactions
1. combustion
2. substitution
3. Cracking
4.

After studying Chapter 21, you should be able to

1. Understand the new terms listed in Question A at the end of the chapter.
2. Explain the sp^2 and sp hybridization of carbon atoms.
3. Explain the formation of a pi bond.
4. Explain the formation of double and triple bonds.
5. Distinguish, by formulas, the difference between saturated and unsaturated hydrocarbons.
6. Name and write structural formulas of alkenes, alkynes, and cycloalkenes.
7. Determine from structural formulas whether a compound can exist as geometric isomers.
8. Name geometric isomers by the cis–trans method.
9. Write equations for addition reactions of alkenes and alkynes.
10. Explain the formation of carbocations and the role they play in chemical reactions.
11. Apply Markovnikov's rule to the addition of HCl, HBr, HI, and H_2O/H^+ to alkenes and alkynes.
12. Explain the Baeyer test for unsaturation.
13. Distinguish, using simple chemical tests, among alkanes, alkenes, and alkynes.
14. Describe the nature of benzene and how its properties differ from open-chain unsaturated compounds.

15. Name monosubstituted, disubstituted, and polysubstituted benzene compounds.
16. Draw structural formulas of substituted benzene compounds.
17. Recognize the more common fused aromatic ring compounds.
18. Write equations for the following reactions of benzene and substituted benzenes: halogenation (chlorination or bromination), nitration, alkylation (Friedel–Crafts reaction), and side-chain oxidation.
19. Describe and write equations for the mechanism by which benzene compounds are brominated in the presence of $FeBr_3$ or chlorinated in the presence of $FeCl_3$.

The bulk of the organic compounds manufactured in the United States are derived from seven starting materials: ethylene, propylene, benzene, butylene, toluene, xylene, and methane. Of the seven substances listed, all are unsaturated hydrocarbons except methane. Ethylene is the base for almost half the petrochemicals made in the country. Over 28 billion pounds of ethylene are produced each year, making it the sixth-ranking chemical in production volume in the United States.

21.1 Alkenes and Alkynes

alkene

alkyne

Both **alkenes** and **alkynes** are classified as unsaturated hydrocarbons. They are said to be unsaturated because, unlike alkanes, their molecules do not contain the maximum possible number of hydrogen atoms. Alkenes (also known as *olefins*) contain at least one double bond between adjacent carbon atoms. Alkynes (also known as *acetylenes*) contain at least one triple bond between adjacent carbon atoms. The simplest alkene is ethylene (or ethene, $CH_2{=}CH_2$), and the simplest alkyne is acetylene (or ethyne, $CH{\equiv}CH$). Ethylene and

Ethylene (common name)
Ethene (IUPAC)

Acetylene (common name)
Ethyne (IUPAC)

Table 21.1 Names and formulas for several alkenes and alkynes

IUPAC name	Common name	Formula
Ethene	Ethylene	$CH_2{=}CH_2$
Propene	Propylene	$CH_3CH{=}CH_2$
1-Butene	Butylene	$CH_3CH_2CH{=}CH_2$
2-Butene		$CH_3CH{=}CHCH_3$
2-Methylpropene	Isobutylene	$CH_3C{=}CH_2$ $\quad\ \ \vert$ $\quad\ \ CH_3$
Ethyne	Acetylene	$HC{\equiv}CH$
Propyne	Methyl acetylene	$CH_3C{\equiv}CH$
1-Butyne	Ethyl acetylene	$CH_3CH_2C{\equiv}CH$
2-Butyne	Dimethyl acetylene	$CH_3C{\equiv}CCH_3$

acetylene are the first members of homologous series in which the formulas of successive members differ by increments of CH_2 (for example, $CH_2{=}CH_2$, $CH_3CH{=}CH_2$, $CH_3CH_2CH{=}CH_2$, and so on). Huge quantities of alkenes are made by cracking and dehydrogenating alkanes during the processing of crude oils. These alkenes are used to manufacture motor fuels, polymers, and petrochemicals. Alkene molecules, like those of alkanes, have very little polarity. Hence, the physical properties of alkenes are very similar to those of the corresponding saturated hydrocarbons.

General formula for alkenes: C_nH_{2n}

General formula for alkynes: C_nH_{2n-2}

Note that the general formula for alkenes is the same as that for cycloalkanes. Alkenes and cycloalkanes have two hydrogen atoms less than alkanes. Table 21.1 gives the names and formulas for several alkenes and alkynes.

21.2 Bond Formation in Alkenes and Alkynes

In alkanes each carbon atom is bonded to four other atoms utilizing electrons in sp^3 hybrid orbitals. In ethylene each carbon atom is bonded to three other atoms, two hydrogen atoms and one carbon atom. The fourth electron of each carbon atom in ethylene is shared between the two carbon atoms, thus forming the second bond of the carbon–carbon double bond.

The formation of double bonds in alkenes is explained by a different type of hybridization of electrons. The hybridization may be visualized in the following way. One of the $2s$ electrons of carbon is promoted to a $2p$ orbital forming the

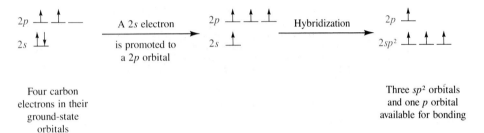

Four carbon
electrons in their
ground-state
orbitals

Three sp^2 orbitals
and one p orbital
available for bonding

Figure 21.1 Schematic hybridization of $2s^2 2p_x^1 2p_y^1$ orbitals of carbon to form three sp^2 electron orbitals and one p electron orbital

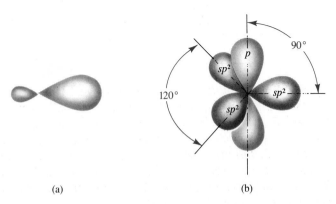

(a)

(b)

Figure 21.2 (a) A single sp^2 electron orbital and (b) a side view of three sp^2 orbitals all lying in the same plane with a p orbital perpendicular to the three sp^2 orbitals

four half-filled orbitals, $2s^1 2p_x^1 2p_y^1 2p_z^1$. Three of these orbitals $(2s^1 2p_x^1 2p_y^1)$ hybridize forming three equivalent orbitals designated as sp^2. Thus the four orbitals available for bonding are three sp^2 orbitals and one p orbital. This process is illustrated in Figure 21.1.

The three sp^2 hybrid orbitals form angles of 120° with each other and lie in a single plane. The remaining 2p orbital is oriented perpendicular to this plane, with one lobe above and one lobe below the plane (see Figure 21.2). In the formation of a double bond, an sp^2 orbital of one carbon atom overlaps an identical sp^2 orbital of another carbon to form a sigma bond. At the same time the two perpendicular p orbitals (one on each carbon atom) overlap to form a **pi (π) bond** between the two carbon atoms. This pi bond consists of two electron clouds, one above and one below the sigma bond (see Figure 21.3). The $H_2C{=}CH_2$ molecule is completed as the remaining sp^2 orbitals (two on each carbon atom) overlap hydrogen s orbitals to form sigma bonds between the carbon and hydrogen atoms. Thus there are five sigma bonds and one pi bond in an ethylene molecule.

pi bond

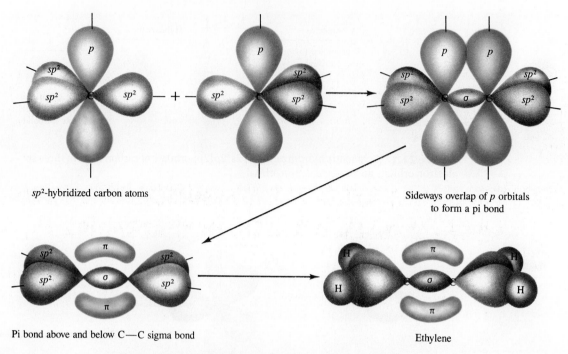

sp²-hybridized carbon atoms

Sideways overlap of *p* orbitals
to form a pi bond

Pi bond above and below C—C sigma bond

Ethylene

Figure 21.3   Pi (π) and sigma (σ) bonding in ethylene

In the formula commonly used to represent ethylene ($CH_2{=}CH_2$), no distinction is made between the sigma bond and the pi bond in the carbon–carbon double bond. Each bond is represented by a dash. However, these bonds are actually very different from each other. The sigma bond is formed by the overlap of sp^2 orbitals; the pi bond is formed by the overlap of p orbitals. The sigma bond electron cloud is distributed about a line joining the carbon nuclei, but the pi bond electron cloud is distributed above and below the sigma bond region (see Figure 21.3). The carbon–carbon pi bond is much weaker and, as a consequence, much more reactive than the carbon–carbon sigma bond.

The formation of a triple bond between carbon atoms, as in acetylene, $HC{\equiv}CH$, may be visualized as follows:

1. A carbon atom 2s electron is promoted to a 2p orbital ($2_s^1 2p_x^1 2p_y^1 2p_z^1$).
2. The 2s orbital hybridizes with one of the 2p orbitals to form two equivalent orbitals known as sp orbitals. These two hybrid orbitals lie on a straight line that passes through the center of the carbon atom. The remaining two unhybridized 2p orbitals are oriented at right angles to these sp orbitals and to each other.
3. In forming carbon–carbon bonds, one carbon sp orbital overlaps an identical sp orbital on another carbon atom to establish a sigma bond between the two carbon atoms.
4. The remaining sp orbitals (one on each carbon atom) overlap s orbitals on hydrogens to form sigma bonds and establish the H—C—C—H bond sequence. Because all the atoms forming this sequence lie in a straight line, the acetylene molecule is linear.

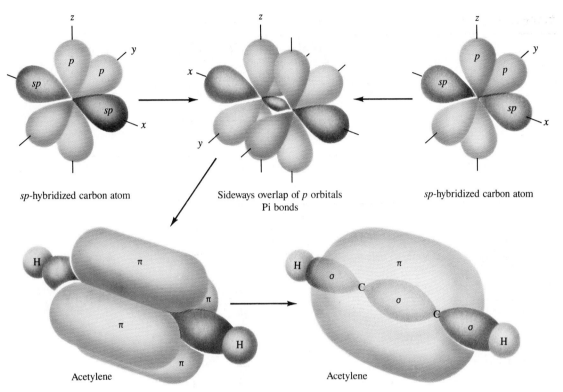

sp-hybridized carbon atom   Sideways overlap of *p* orbitals   *sp*-hybridized carbon atom
                                              Pi bonds

Acetylene   Acetylene

Figure 21.4 Pi (π) and sigma (σ) bonding in acetylene

5. Simultaneously the two 2p orbitals on each carbon overlap to form two pi bonds. These two pi bond orbitals occupy sufficient space that they overlap each other to form a continuous tubelike electron cloud surrounding the sigma bond between the carbon atoms (Figure 21.4). These pi bond electrons (as in ethylene) are not as tightly held by the carbon nuclei as are the sigma bond electrons. Acetylene, consequently, is a very reactive substance.

21.3 Naming Alkenes and Alkynes

The names of alkenes and alkynes are derived from the names of corresponding alkanes. To name an alkene (or alkyne) by the IUPAC System:

1. Select the longest carbon–carbon chain that contains the double or triple bond.
2. Name this parent compound as you would an alkane but change the *-ane* ending to *-ene* for an alkene or to *-yne* for an alkyne; for example, propane is changed to propene or propyne.

$$CH_3CH_2CH_3 \qquad CH_3CH\!=\!CH_2 \qquad CH_3C\!\equiv\!CH$$
Propane   Propene   Propyne

3. Number the carbon chain of the parent compound starting with the end nearer to the double or triple bond. Use the smaller of the two numbers on the double- or triple-bonded carbon atoms to indicate the position of the double or triple bond. Place this number in front of the alkene or alkyne name; for example, 2-butene means that the carbon–carbon double bond is between carbon numbers 2 and 3.

4. Side chains and other groups are treated as in naming alkanes, by numbering and assigning them to the carbon atom to which they are bonded.

Study the following examples of named alkenes and alkynes:

$$\overset{4}{C}H_3\overset{3}{C}H_2\overset{2}{C}H{=}\overset{1}{C}H_2 \qquad \overset{1}{C}H_3\overset{2}{C}H{=}\overset{3}{C}H\overset{4}{C}H_3$$

1-Butene   2-Butene

$$\begin{array}{c} CH_3 \\ | \\ \overset{4}{C}H_3\overset{3}{C}H\overset{2}{C}H{=}\overset{1}{C}H_2 \end{array} \qquad \begin{array}{c} \overset{6}{C}H_3\overset{5}{C}H_2\overset{4}{C}H_2 \\ _{3}_{2}_{1} \\ CHCH{=}CH_2 \\ CH_3CH_2CH_2 \end{array}$$

3-Methyl-1-butene   3-Propyl-1-hexene

$$\overset{4}{C}H_3\overset{3}{C}H_2\overset{2}{C}{\equiv}\overset{1}{C}H \qquad \begin{array}{c} CH_3 \\ | \\ \overset{1}{C}H_3{-}\overset{2}{C}{\equiv}\overset{3}{C}{-}\overset{4}{C}H{-}\overset{5}{C}H{-}\overset{6}{C}H_3 \\ | \\ CH_3 \end{array}$$

1-Butyne   4,5-Dimethyl-2-hexyne

To write a structural formula from a systematic name, the naming process is reversed. For example, how would we write the structural formula for 4-methyl-2-pentene? The name indicates:

1. Five carbons in the longest chain
2. A double bond between carbons 2 and 3
3. A methyl group on carbon 4

Write five carbon atoms in a row. Place a double bond between carbons 2 and 3, and place a methyl group on carbon 4:

$$\overset{1}{C}{-}\overset{2}{C}{=}\overset{3}{C}{-}\overset{4}{C}{-}\overset{5}{C}$$
$$| $$
$$CH_3$$

Carbon skeleton

Now add hydrogen atoms to give each carbon atom four bonds. Carbons 1 and 5 each need three H atoms; carbons 2, 3, and 4 each need one H atom. The complete formula is

$$\begin{array}{c} CH_3CH{=}CHCHCH_3 \\ | \\ CH_3 \end{array}$$

4-Methyl-2-pentene

PROBLEM

21.1

Write structural formulas for **(a)** 2-pentene, **(b)** 7-methyl-2-octene, and **(c)** 3-hexyne.

(a) The stem *pent-* indicates a five-carbon chain; the suffix *-ene* indicates a carbon–carbon double bond; the number 2 locates the double bond between carbons 2 and 3. Write five carbon atoms in a row and place a double bond between carbons 2 and 3:

$$\overset{1}{C}-\overset{2}{C}=\overset{3}{C}-\overset{4}{C}-\overset{5}{C}$$

Add hydrogen atoms to give each carbon atom four bonds. Carbons 1 and 5 each need three H atoms; carbons 2 and 3 each need one H atom; carbon 4 needs two H atoms. The complete formula is

$$CH_3CH=CHCH_2CH_3$$
2-Pentene

(b) Octene, like octane, indicates an eight-carbon chain. The chain contains a double bond between carbons 2 and 3 and a methyl group on carbon 7. Write eight carbon atoms in a row, place a double bond between carbons 2 and 3, and place a methyl group on carbon 7:

$$\overset{1}{C}-\overset{2}{C}=\overset{3}{C}-\overset{4}{C}-\overset{5}{C}-\overset{6}{C}-\overset{7}{C}-\overset{8}{C}$$
$$\underset{CH_3}{|}$$

Now add hydrogen atoms to give each carbon atom four bonds. The complete formula is

$$CH_3CH=CHCH_2CH_2CH_2CHCH_3$$
$$\underset{CH_3}{|}$$
7-Methyl-2-octene

(c) The stem *hex-* indicates a six-carbon chain; the suffix *-yne* indicates a carbon–carbon triple bond; the number 3 locates the triple bond between carbons 3 and 4. Write six carbon atoms in a row and place a triple bond between carbons 3 and 4:

$$\overset{1}{C}-\overset{2}{C}-\overset{3}{C}\equiv\overset{4}{C}-\overset{5}{C}-\overset{6}{C}$$

Now add hydrogen atoms to give each carbon atom four bonds. Carbons 3 and 4 do not need any H atoms. The complete formula is

$$CH_3CH_2C\equiv CCH_2CH_3$$
3-Hexyne

PROBLEM

21.2

Name this compound:

$$CH_3CH_2CCH_2CH_2CH_3$$
$$\underset{CH_2}{||}$$

The longest carbon chain contains six carbons. However, since the compound is an alkene, we must include the double bond in the chain. The longest carbon chain containing the double bond has five carbons. Therefore, the compound is named as a pentene.

$$\underset{\overset{1\|}{\underset{\text{CH}_2}{}}}{\overset{2\quad3\quad\;4\quad\;5}{\text{CH}_3\text{CH}_2\text{CCH}_2\text{CH}_2\text{CH}_3}}$$

Attached to carbon 2 is an ethyl group. The name is 2-ethyl-1-pentene.

21.4 Geometric Isomerism

There are only two dichloroethanes: 1,1-dichloroethane ($CHCl_2CH_3$) and 1,2-dichloroethane (CH_2ClCH_2Cl). But surprisingly there are three dichloro-ethenes—namely, 1,1-dichloroethene ($CCl_2=CH_2$) and *two* isomers of 1,2-dichloroethene ($CHCl=CHCl$). There is only one 1,2-dichloroethane be-cause carbon atoms can rotate freely about a single bond. Thus, the structural formulas I and II given below represent the same compound. The chlorine atoms are simply shown in different relative positions in the two formulas due to rotation of the CH_2Cl group about the carbon–carbon single bond.

1,2-Dichloroethane

Compounds containing a carbon–carbon double bond have restricted rotation about that double bond. Restricted rotation in a molecule gives rise to a type of isomerism known as *geometric isomerism*. Isomers that differ from each other only in the geometry of the molecules and not in the order of their atoms are known as **geometric isomers.** They are also called cis–trans isomers. Two isomers of 1,2-dichloroethene exist because of geometric isomerism.

geometric isomers

For a further explanation, let us look at the geometry of an ethylene molecule. This molecule is planar, or flat, with all six atoms lying in a single plane as in a rectangle:

Because the hydrogen atoms are identical, only one structural arrangement is possible for ethylene. But if one hydrogen atom on each carbon atom is replaced by chlorine, for example, two different geometric isomers are possible:

cis-1,2-Dichloroethene   and   trans-1,2-Dichloroethene
(bp = 60.1°C)   (bp = 48.4°C)

Both of these isomers are known and have been isolated. The fact that they have different boiling points as well as other different physical properties is proof that they are not the same compound. Note that, in naming these geometric isomers, the prefix *cis-* is used to designate the isomer having the substituent groups (chlorine atoms) on the same side of the double bond, and the prefix *trans-* is used to designate the isomer having the substituent groups on opposite sides of the double bond.

Molecules of *cis-* and *trans-*1,2-dichloroethene are not superimposable. That is, we cannot pick up one molecule and place it over the other in such a way that all the atoms in each molecule occupy the same relative positions in space. Nonsuperimposability is a general test for isomerism that all kinds of isomers must meet.

An alkene will show cis–trans isomerism when each of the carbon atoms of the double bond has two different kinds of groups attached to it.

cis isomer   trans isomer

An alkene will not show cis–trans isomerism if one of the carbon atoms of the double bond has two identical groups attached to it. Thus there are no geometric isomers of ethene or propene.

Four structural isomers of butene (C_4H_8) are known. Two of these, 1-butene and 2-methylpropene, do not show geometric isomerism.

1-Butene   2-Methylpropene

The other two butenes are the cis–trans isomers shown below.

cis-2-Butene   trans-2-Butene

PROBLEM

21.3

Draw structures for **(a)** *trans*-3-heptene and **(b)** *cis*-5-chloro-2-hexene.

(a) The compound contains seven carbon atoms with a double bond between C 3 and C 4. First draw a C=C double bond in a planar arrangement:

$$>C=C<$$

In the trans positions attach a two-carbon chain to one carbon atom and a three-carbon chain to the other carbon atom:

Now attach hydrogen atoms to give each carbon atom four bonds. C 3 and C 4 need only one hydrogen atom apiece; these two hydrogen atoms are also trans to each other. The structure is

(b) The compound contains six carbons, a double bond between C 2 and C 3, and a Cl atom on C 5. Draw a C=C double bond in a planar arrangement:

$$>C=C<$$

In the cis positions attach a —CH$_3$ to one carbon and a three-carbon chain to the other carbon. Place a Cl on C 5.

Now add H atoms to give each carbon four bonds. C 2, C 3, and C 5 each need only one H atom. The structure is

PROBLEM

21.4

Draw structural formulas and names for all the isomers of pentene, C$_5$H$_{10}$. Identify all geometric isomers.

Start by drawing the isomers of the five-carbon chain, placing the C=C in all possible positions (there are two possible isomers). Then proceed to the four-carbon chains with a methyl-group side chain. Locate the C=C and the CH$_3$ group in all possible positions. Check for duplications from the names of the compounds.

$$CH_2=CHCH_2CH_2CH_3$$
1-Pentene

$$CH_3CH=CHCH_2CH_3$$
2-Pentene

$$
\begin{array}{c}
CH_3 \\
| \\
CH_2=CCH_2CH_3
\end{array}
$$
2-Methyl-1-butene

$$
\begin{array}{c}
CH_3 \\
| \\
CH_3C=CHCH_3
\end{array}
$$
2-Methyl-2-butene

$$
\begin{array}{c}
CH_3 \\
| \\
CH_2=CHCHCH_3
\end{array}
$$
3-Methyl-1-butene

Of these five compounds, only 2-pentene will have cis–trans isomers. All of the others have two identical groups on one of the carbon atoms of the double bond. Draw the cis–trans isomers:

cis-2-Pentene   trans-2-Pentene

PROBLEM

21.5

Is the compound below the cis or the trans isomer?

$$
\begin{array}{c}
\overset{1}{CH_3} \quad _2 \quad _3 \quad CH_3 \\
 C=C \quad _4 \quad _5 \\
H CH_2CH_3
\end{array}
$$

In branched-chain alkenes, the cis–trans designation ordinarily is given to the structure containing the longest carbon chain that includes the carbon–carbon double bond. In this case the longest chain is the 2-pentene, in which the methyl group on carbon 2 and the ethyl group on carbon 3 are trans to each other. Thus the name of the compound shown is trans-3-methyl-2-pentene. The cis isomer is

Enzymes (biological catalysts) test molecules for superimposability. In order to react with an enzyme, a molecule must twist and turn in solution until it achieves a specific shape. If this specific shape cannot be attained, the molecule won't react. For example, our bodies commonly use the cis isomer of unsaturated fatty acids but not the trans isomer in building more complex fats. That is why the great majority of unsaturated fatty acids in most cells are cis isomers.

$$
\begin{array}{c}
H CH_2CH_2CH_2CH_2CH_2CH_2CH_2COOH \\
 C \\
 || \\
 C \\
H CH_2CH_2CH_2CH_2CH_2CH_2CH_2CH_3
\end{array}
$$
cis isomer

$$CH_3CH_2CH_2CH_2CH_2CH_2CH_2CH_2$$
$$\underset{H}{\overset{}{C}}\!=\!\underset{}{\overset{H}{C}}$$
$$H \qquad CH_2CH_2CH_2CH_2CH_2CH_2CH_2COOH$$

trans isomer

Enzymes differentiate between the "hairpin" shape of the cis isomer and the more linear trans form. Although these molecules are constantly tumbling and vibrating in solution, they cannot normally attain the same shape due to restricted rotation about the carbon–carbon double bond. Because the two shapes cannot be superimposed, the two isomers are treated differently by the body's enzymes.

21.5   Cycloalkenes

cycloalkenes

As the name implies, **cycloalkenes** are cyclic compounds that contain a carbon–carbon double bond in the ring. The two most common cycloalkenes are cyclopentene and cyclohexene. The double bond may be placed between any two carbon atoms in cyclopentene and cyclohexene.

Cyclopentene (C_5H_8)

Cyclohexene (C_6H_{10})

In cycloalkenes the carbons of the double bond are assigned numbers 1 and 2. Thus the position of the double bond need not be indicated in the name of the compound. Other substituents on the ring are named in the usual manner, and their position on the ring is indicated with the smallest possible numbers.

In the examples below note that a Cl or a CH_3 has replaced one H atom in the molecule. The ring is numbered either clockwise or counterclockwise starting with the carbon–carbon double bond so that the substituted group(s) will have the smallest possible numbers.

3-Chlorocyclohexene
(C_6H_9Cl)

1-Methylcyclopentene
($C_5H_7CH_3$)

1,3-Dimethylcyclohexene
[$C_6H_8(CH_3)_2$]

No cis–trans designation is necessary for cycloalkenes containing up to seven carbon atoms in the ring. Cyclooctene has been shown to exist in both cis and trans forms.

<table>
<tr><td>**21.6**</td><td></td></tr>
</table>

21.6 Reactions of Alkenes

The alkenes are much more reactive than the corresponding alkanes. This greater reactivity is due to the carbon–carbon double bonds.

Addition

addition
reaction

A reaction in which two substances join together to produce one compound is called an **addition reaction.** Addition at the carbon–carbon double bond is the most common reaction of alkenes. Hydrogen, halogens (Cl_2 or Br_2), hydrogen halides, sulfuric acid, and water are some of the reagents that can be added to unsaturated hydrocarbons. Ethylene (ethene), for example, reacts in the presence of a platinum catalyst in this fashion:

$$CH_2{=}CH_2 + H_2 \xrightarrow[\text{1 atm}]{\text{Pt, 25°C}} CH_3{-}CH_3$$
Ethylene $\qquad\qquad$ Ethane

$$CH_2{=}CH_2 + Br{-}Br \longrightarrow CH_2Br{-}CH_2Br$$
$\qquad\qquad\qquad\qquad\qquad$ 1,2-Dibromoethane

The product in the foregoing reaction is colorless. Therefore the disappearance of the reddish-brown bromine color provides visible evidence of reaction. Other reactions of ethylene follow.

$$CH_2{=}CH_2 + HCl \longrightarrow CH_3CH_2Cl$$
$\qquad\qquad\qquad\qquad$ Chloroethane
$\qquad\qquad\qquad\qquad$ (Ethyl chloride)

$$CH_2{=}CH_2 + HOSO_3H(conc.) \longrightarrow CH_3CH_2OSO_3H$$
$\qquad\qquad$ Sulfuric acid $\qquad\qquad\qquad$ Ethyl hydrogen sulfate

$$CH_2{=}CH_2 + HOH \xrightarrow{H^+} CH_3CH_2OH$$
$\qquad\qquad\qquad\qquad\qquad$ Ethanol
$\qquad\qquad\qquad\qquad\qquad$ (Ethyl alcohol)

The H^+ indicates that the reaction is carried out under acidic conditions.

Note that the double bond is broken and the unsaturated alkene molecules become saturated by an addition reaction.

The preceding examples dealt with ethylene, but reactions of this kind can be made to occur on almost any molecule that contains a carbon–carbon double bond. If a symmetrical molecule such as Cl_2 is added to propene, only one product, 1,2-dichloropropane, is formed:

$$CH_2{=}CH{-}CH_3 + Cl_2 \longrightarrow CH_2Cl{-}CHCl{-}CH_3$$
$\qquad\qquad\qquad\qquad\qquad$ 1,2-Dichloropropane

But if an unsymmetrical molecule such as HCl is added to propene, two products are theoretically possible, depending upon which carbon atom adds the hydrogen. The two possible products are 1-chloropropane and 2-chloropropane.

Experimentally we find that 2-chloropropane is formed almost exclusively:

$$CH_3CHClCH_3 \quad \text{(About 100\%)}$$

$$CH_3—CH=CH_2 + HCl$$

$$CH_3CH_2CH_2Cl \quad \text{(Trace)}$$

A single product is obtained because the reaction proceeds stepwise according to the following mechanism:

1. A proton (H^+) from HCl bonds to the number 1 carbon of propene utilizing the pi bond electrons. The intermediate formed is a positively charged alkyl group, or carbocation. The positive charge is localized on the number 2 carbon atom of this carbocation.

$$CH_2=CH—CH_3 + HCl \longrightarrow CH_3—\overset{\oplus}{C}H—CH_3 + Cl^-$$

Isopropyl carbocation

2. The chloride ion then adds to the positively charged carbon atom to form a molecule of 2-chloropropane:

$$CH_3—\overset{\oplus}{C}H—CH_3 + Cl^- \longrightarrow CH_3—CHCl—CH_3$$

2-Chloropropane

carbocation

An ion in which a carbon atom has a positive charge is known as a **carbocation.** There are four types of carbocations: methyl, primary (1°), secondary (2°), and tertiary (3°). Examples of these four types follow:

$$H—\overset{\overset{\displaystyle H}{|}}{\underset{\underset{\displaystyle H}{|}}{C^\oplus}} \qquad CH_3—\overset{\overset{\displaystyle H}{|}}{\underset{\underset{\displaystyle H}{|}}{C^\oplus}} \qquad CH_3CH_2—\overset{\overset{\displaystyle H}{|}}{\underset{\underset{\displaystyle H}{|}}{C^\oplus}} \qquad CH_3—\overset{\overset{\displaystyle \oplus}{}}{\underset{\underset{\displaystyle H}{|}}{C}}—CH_3 \qquad CH_3—\overset{\overset{\displaystyle CH_3}{|}}{\underset{\underset{\displaystyle CH_3}{|}}{C^\oplus}}$$

| Methyl carbocation | Ethyl carbocation (primary) | n-Propyl carbocation (primary) | Isopropyl carbocation (secondary) | t-Butyl carbocation (tertiary) |

A carbon atom is designated as primary if it is bonded to one carbon atom, secondary if it is bonded to two carbon atoms, and tertiary if it is bonded to three carbon atoms. In a primary carbocation the positive carbon atom is bonded to only one carbon atom. In a secondary carbocation the positive carbon atom is bonded to two carbon atoms. In a tertiary carbocation the positive carbon atom is bonded to three carbon atoms.

The order of stability of carbocations and hence the ease with which they are formed is tertiary > secondary > primary. Thus, in the reaction of propene and HCl, isopropyl carbocation (secondary) is formed as an intermediate in preference to n-propyl carbocation (primary).

Stability of carbocations: $3° > 2° > 1° > CH_3^+$

In the middle of the 19th century, a Russian chemist, V. Markovnikov, observed reactions of this kind, and in 1869 he formulated a useful generaliza-

Markovnikov's   tion now known as **Markovnikov's rule.** This rule in essence states:
rule

> When an unsymmetrical molecule such as HX(HCl) adds to a carbon–carbon double bond, the hydrogen from HX goes to the carbon atom that has the greater number of hydrogen atoms.

As you can see, the addition of HCl to propene discussed above follows Markovnikov's rule. The addition of HI to 2-methylpropene (isobutylene) is another example illustrating this rule:

$$
\begin{array}{ccc}
& CH_3 & & CH_3 \\
& | & & | \\
CH_3-C=CH_2 + HI & \longrightarrow & CH_3-C-CH_3 \\
& & & | \\
& & & I
\end{array}
$$

2-Iodo-2-methylpropane
(tert-Butyl iodide)

General rules of this kind are useful in predicting the products of reactions. However, exceptions are known for most such rules.

PROBLEM

21.6

Write formulas for the organic products formed when 2-methyl-1-butene reacts with **(a)** H_2, Pt/25°C; **(b)** Cl_2; **(c)** HCl; **(d)** H_2O, H^+.

First write the formula for 2-methyl-1-butene:

$$
\begin{array}{c}
CH_3 \\
| \\
\overset{1}{CH_2}=\overset{2}{C}-\overset{3}{CH_2}-\overset{4}{CH_3}
\end{array}
$$

(a) The double bond is broken when a hydrogen molecule adds. One H atom adds to each carbon atom of the double bond. Platinum, Pt, is a necessary catalyst in this reaction. The product is

$$
\begin{array}{c}
CH_3 \\
| \\
CH_3CHCH_2CH_3
\end{array}
$$
2-Methylbutane

(b) The Cl_2 molecule adds to the carbons of the double bond. One Cl atom adds to each carbon atom of the double bond. The product is

$$
\begin{array}{c}
CH_3 \\
| \\
CH_2CCH_2CH_3 \\
| \quad | \\
Cl \quad Cl
\end{array}
$$
1,2-Dichloro-2-methylbutane

(c) HCl adds to the double bond according to Markovnikov's rule. The H^+ goes to C 1 (the more stable 3° carbocation is formed as an intermediate product), and the Cl⁻ goes to C 2. The product is

$$
\begin{array}{c}
\mathrm{CH_3} \\
| \\
\mathrm{CH_3CCH_2CH_3} \\
| \\
\mathrm{Cl}
\end{array}
$$

2-Chloro-2-methylbutane

(d) The net result of this reaction is a molecule of water added across the double bond. The H adds to C 1 (the carbon with the greater number of hydrogen atoms), and the OH adds to C 2 (the carbon of the double bond with the lesser number of hydrogen atoms). The product is

$$
\begin{array}{c}
\mathrm{CH_3} \\
| \\
\mathrm{CH_3CCH_2CH_3} \\
| \\
\mathrm{OH}
\end{array}
$$

2-Methyl-2-butanol
(an alcohol)

PROBLEM

21.7

Write equations for the addition of HCl to **(a)** 1-pentene and **(b)** 2-pentene.

(a) In the case of 1-pentene, $CH_3CH_2CH_2CH{=}CH_2$, the proton from HCl adds to carbon 1 to give the more stable secondary carbocation, followed by the addition of Cl⁻ to give the product 2-chloropentane. The addition is directly in accordance with Markovnikov's rule.

$$CH_3CH_2CH_2CH{=}CH_2 + HCl \longrightarrow CH_3CH_2CH_2CHClCH_3$$
$$\text{2-Chloropentane}$$

(b) In 2-pentene, $CH_3CH_2CH{=}CHCH_3$, each carbon of the double bond has one hydrogen atom, and the addition of a proton to either one forms a secondary carbocation. After the addition of Cl⁻, the result is two isomeric products that are formed in almost equal quantities:

$$CH_3CH_2CH{=}CHCH_3 + HCl \longrightarrow CH_3CH_2CH_2CHClCH_3 + CH_3CH_2CHClCH_2CH_3$$
$$\text{2-Chloropentane} \qquad \text{3-Chloropentane}$$

Oxidation

Another typical reaction of alkenes is oxidation at the double bond. For example, when shaken with a cold, dilute solution of potassium permanganate ($KMnO_4$), an alkene is converted to a glycol (glycols are dihydroxy alcohols). Ethylene reacts in this manner:

$$
\mathrm{CH_2{=}CH_2} + \mathrm{KMnO_4}(aq) + \mathrm{H_2O} \longrightarrow \underset{\underset{\mathrm{OH}\quad\mathrm{OH}}{|\qquad|}}{\mathrm{CH_2{-}CH_2}} + \mathrm{MnO_2} + \mathrm{KOH}
$$

Ethylene   (Purple)   (Brown)

Ethylene glycol

The *Baeyer test* makes use of this reaction to detect or confirm the presence of double (or triple) bonds in hydrocarbons. Evidence of reaction (positive Baeyer test) is the disappearance of the purple color of permanganate ions. The Baeyer test is not specific for detecting unsaturation in hydrocarbons, since other classes of compounds may also give a positive Baeyer test.

Carbon–carbon double bonds (ethylenic linkages) are found in many different kinds of molecules. Most of these substances will react with potassium permanganate and will undergo somewhat similar reactions with other oxidizing agents including oxygen in the air and, especially, with ozone. Such reactions are frequently troublesome. For example, premature aging and cracking of tires in smoggy atmospheres occur because ozone attacks the ethylenic linkages in rubber molecules. Cooking oils and fats sometimes develop disagreeable odors and flavors because the oxygen of the air reacts with the double bonds present in these materials. Potato chips, because of their large surface area, are especially subject to flavor damage caused by oxidation of the unsaturated cooking oils that they contain.

21.7 *Acetylenes: Preparation and Properties*

Acetylene (ethyne), $HC{\equiv}CH$, is the simplest alkyne and is an industrial chemical of prime importance. It can be prepared from relatively inexpensive raw materials—lime and coke, or from methane. Lime and coke are heated to form calcium carbide, which is then reacted with water to form acetylene:

$$CaO \ + \ 3\,C \ \xrightarrow[\text{Electric furnace}]{2500^\circ C} \ CaC_2 \ + \ CO$$

Calcium oxide   Carbon   Calcium carbide
(Lime)   (Coke)

$$CaC_2 + 2\,H_2O \ \longrightarrow \ HC{\equiv}CH + Ca(OH)_2$$

Acetylene

Until about 1940 nearly all acetylene was made from calcium carbide. Then cheaper methods of production, using methane as the raw material, were devised. When methane is subjected to high temperatures for a very short time (0.01–0.1 second) and the products are cooled rapidly, a reasonably high yield of acetylene is obtained. The equation for the reaction, which is endothermic, is

$$2\,CH_4 \ + \ 400 \text{ kJ (95.5 kcal)} \ \xrightarrow{1500^\circ C} \ HC{\equiv}CH + 3\,H_2$$

Methane   Acetylene

Special precautions must be taken when handling acetylene. Like all hydrocarbon gases it forms explosive mixtures with air or oxygen. In addition to this hazard, acetylene is unstable at room temperature. When highly compressed or liquefied, acetylene may decompose violently (explode) either spontaneously or from a slight shock:

$$HC{\equiv}CH \ \longrightarrow \ H_2 + 2\,C + 227 \text{ kJ (54.3 kcal)}$$

To eliminate the danger of explosions, acetylene is dissolved under pressure in acetone and is packed in cylinders that contain a porous inert material.

Acetylene is used mainly (1) as fuel for oxyacetylene cutting and welding torches and (2) as an intermediate in the manufacture of other substances. Both uses are dependent upon the great reactivity of acetylene. Acetylene and oxygen mixtures produce flame temperatures of about 2800°C. Acetylene readily undergoes addition reactions rather similar to those of ethylene. It will react with chlorine and bromine and will decolorize a permanganate solution (Baeyer's test). Either one or two molecules of bromine or chlorine can be added:

$$HC\equiv CH + Br_2 \longrightarrow CHBr\!=\!CHBr$$
1,2-Dibromoethene

or

$$HC\equiv CH + 2\ Br_2 \longrightarrow CHBr_2\!-\!CHBr_2$$
1,1,2,2-Tetrabromoethane

It is apparent that either unsaturated or saturated compounds can be obtained as addition products of acetylene. Often, unsaturated compounds capable of undergoing further reactions are made from acetylene. For example, vinyl chloride, which is used to make the plastic polyvinyl chloride (PVC), can be made by simple addition of HCl to acetylene:

$$CH\equiv CH + HCl \longrightarrow CH_2\!=\!CHCl$$
Chloroethene
(Vinyl chloride)

Note: The common name for the $CH_2\!=\!CH-$ group is *vinyl*.
If the reaction is not properly controlled, another HCl will add to the chloroethene:

$$CH_2\!=\!CHCl + HCl \longrightarrow CH_3CHCl_2$$
1,1-Dichloroethane

Hydrogen chloride reacts with other alkynes in a similar fashion to form substituted alkenes. The addition follows Markovnikov's rule. Alkynes can react with 1 or 2 moles of HCl. Consider the reaction of propyne with HCl:

$$CH_3C\equiv CH + HCl \longrightarrow CH_3CCl\!=\!CH_2$$
2-Chloropropene

$$CH_3CCl\!=\!CH_2 + HCl \longrightarrow CH_3CCl_2CH_3$$
2,2-Dichloropropane

Acetylenic hydrogen atoms—that is, hydrogen atoms attached to a carbon bearing a triple bond—are somewhat acidic and can be replaced by metals, thus forming metal salts. Sodium, silver, and copper(I) are some of the metal salts that can be easily prepared. Acetylene reacts with molten sodium and with ammoniacal silver nitrate or copper(I) chloride to form insoluble precipitates according to the following equations:

$$2\ HC\equiv CH + 2\ Na(molten) \longrightarrow 2\ HC\equiv C^-\ Na^+(s) + H_2(g)$$
Sodium acetylide

$$HC\!\equiv\!CH + 2\ Ag(NH_3)_2NO_3 \longrightarrow AgC\!\equiv\!CAg(s) + 2\ NH_4NO_3 + 2\ NH_3$$

Silver acetylide

$$HC\!\equiv\!CH + 2\ Cu(NH_3)_2Cl \longrightarrow CuC\!\equiv\!CCu(s) + 2\ NH_4Cl + 2\ NH_3$$

Copper(I) acetylide

Silver and copper(I) acetylides (*alkynides* in general) are unstable when dry and can be detonated by heat or shock. Compounds of the type R—C≡CH (the —C≡CH is at the end of the carbon chain) yield solid metal alkynides, whereas compounds of the type R—C≡C—R (the C≡C is in the middle of the carbon chain) do not form metal alkynides.

The reactions of other alkynes are similar to those of acetylene. Although many other alkynes are known, from an industrial viewpoint, acetylene is by far the most important.

21.8   Aromatic Hydrocarbons: Structure

aromatic compounds

Benzene and all substances that have structures and chemical properties resembling benzene are classified as **aromatic compounds.** The word *aromatic* originally referred to the rather pleasant odor possessed by many of these substances, but this meaning has been dropped. Benzene, the parent substance of the aromatic hydrocarbons, was first isolated by Michael Faraday in 1825; its correct molecular formula, C_6H_6, was established a few years later. The establishment of a reasonable structural formula that would account for the properties of benzene was a very difficult problem for chemists in the mid-19th century.

Finally, in 1865, August Kekulé proposed that the carbon atoms in a benzene molecule are arranged in a six-membered ring with one hydrogen atom bonded to each carbon atom and with three carbon–carbon double bonds, as shown in the following formula:

Kekulé soon realized that there should be two dibromobenzenes, based on double- and single-bond positions relative to the two bromine atoms:

Since only one dibromobenzene (with bromine atoms on adjacent carbons) could be produced, Kekulé suggested that the double bonds are in rapid oscillation within the molecule. He therefore proposed that the structure of benzene could be represented in this fashion:

Kekulé's concepts are a landmark in the history of chemistry. They are the basis of the best representation of the benzene molecule devised in the 19th century, and they mark the beginning of our understanding of structure in aromatic compounds.

Kekulé's formulas have one serious shortcoming: They represent benzene and related substances as highly unsaturated compounds. Yet benzene does not react like a typical alkene (olefin); it does not decolorize bromine solutions rapidly, nor does it destroy the purple color of permanganate ions (Baeyer's test). Instead, the chemical behavior of benezene resembles that of an alkane. Its typical reactions are the substitution type, wherein a hydrogen atom is replaced by some other group; for example,

$$C_6H_6 + Cl_2 \xrightarrow{Fe} C_6H_5Cl + HCl$$

This problem was not fully resolved until the technique of X-ray diffraction, developed in the years following 1912, permitted us to determine the actual distances between the nuclei of carbon atoms in molecules. The center-to-center distances between carbon atoms in different kinds of hydrocarbon molecules are

Ethane (single bond)	0.154 nm
Ethylene (double bond)	0.134 nm
Benzene	0.139 nm

Because only one carbon–carbon distance (bond length) is found in benzene, it is apparent that alternating single and double bonds do not exist in the benzene molecule.

Modern theory accounts for the structure of the benzene molecule in this way: The orbital hybridization of the carbon atoms is sp^2 (see structure of ethylene in Section 21.2). A planar hexagonal ring is formed by the overlapping of two sp^2 orbitals on each of six carbon atoms. The other sp^2 orbital on each carbon atom overlaps an s orbital of a hydrogen atom, bonding the carbon to the hydrogen by a sigma bond. The remaining six p orbitals, one on each carbon atom, overlap each other and form doughnut-shaped pi electron clouds above and below the plane of the ring (see Figure 21.5). The electrons comprising these clouds are not attached to particular carbon atoms but are delocalized and associated with the entire molecule. This electronic structure imparts unusual

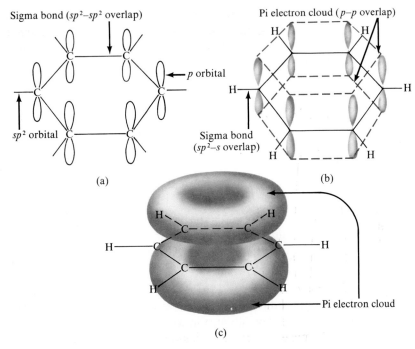

Figure 21.5 Bonding in a benzene molecule: (a) sp^2–sp^2 orbital overlap to form the carbon ring structure; (b) carbon–hydrogen bonds formed by sp^2–s orbital overlap and overlapping of p orbitals; (c) pi electron clouds above and below the plane of the carbon ring

stability to benzene and is responsible for many of the characteristic properties of aromatic compounds.

For convenience present-day chemists usually write the structure of benzene as one or the other of these abbreviated forms:

In all of these representations, it is understood that there is a carbon atom and a hydrogen atom at each corner of the hexagon. The classical Kekulé structures are represented by formulas A and B. However, neither of these Kekulé structures actually exists. The real benzene molecule is a hybrid of these structures and is commonly represented by either formula C or D. The circle or the dotted circle represents the pi cloud of electrons, as shown in Figure 21.5. We will use the hexagon with the solid circle to represent a benzene ring.

Hexagons are used in representing the structural formulas of benzene derivatives—that is, substances in which one or more hydrogen atoms in the ring have been replaced by other atoms or groups. Chlorobenzene (C_6H_5Cl), for example, is written in this fashion:

Cl

Chlorobenzene, C_6H_5Cl

This notation indicates that the chlorine atom has replaced a hydrogen atom and is bonded directly to a carbon atom in the ring. Thus, the correct formula for chlorobenzene is C_6H_5Cl, not C_6H_6Cl.

21.9 Naming Aromatic Compounds

A substituted benzene is derived by replacing one or more hydrogen atoms of benzene by another atom or group of atoms. Thus, a monosubstituted benzene has the formula C_6H_5G, where G is the group replacing a hydrogen atom.

Monosubstituted Benzenes

Some monosubstituted benzenes are named by adding the name of the substituent group as a prefix to the word *benzene*. The name is written as one word. Several examples follow:

Nitrobenzene   Ethylbenzene   Chlorobenzene   Bromobenzene

Certain monosubstituted benzenes have special names. These are used as parent names for further substituted compounds, so they should be learned.

| Toluene | Phenol | Styrene |
| (Methylbenzene) | (Hydroxybenzene) | (Vinylbenzene) |

Benzoic acid   Benzaldehyde   Aniline
(Benzene carboxylic acid)   (Benzene carboxaldehyde)

All the hydrogen atoms in benzene are equivalent; therefore, it does not matter at which corner of the ring the substituted group is located. Each of the following formulas shown below represents chlorobenzene:

The C_6H_5— group is known as the phenyl group, and the name *phenyl* is used to name compounds that cannot easily be named as benzene derivatives. For example, the following compounds are named as derivatives of alkanes:

3-Chloro-2-phenylpentane   Diphenylmethane

Disubstituted Benzenes

When two substituent groups replace two hydrogen atoms in a benzene molecule, three different isomeric compounds are possible. The prefixes *ortho-*, *meta-*, and *para-* (abbreviated *o-*, *m-*, and *p-*) are used to name these disubstituted benzenes. In the ortho compound the substituents are located on adjacent carbon atoms. In the meta compound they are one carbon apart. And in the para compound the substituents are located on opposite sides of the ring:

ortho   meta   para

Let us examine the dichlorobenzenes, $C_6H_4Cl_2$. Note that the three isomers have different physical properties, indicating that they are truly different substances:

ortho-Dichlorobenzene   *meta*-Dichlorobenzene   *para*-Dichlorobenzene
(1,2-Dichlorobenzene)   (1,3-Dichlorobenzene)   (1,4-Dichlorobenzene)
(mp −17.2°C, bp 180.4°C)   (mp −24.8°C, bp 172°C)   (mp 53.1°C, bp 174.4°C)

When the two substituents are different and neither is part of a compound with a special name, the names of the two substituents are given in alphabetical order, followed by the word *benzene*. For example,

o-Bromochlorobenzene   m-Ethylnitrobenzene

The dimethylbenzenes have the special name *xylene*.

ortho-Xylene   meta-Xylene   para-Xylene

When one of the substituents corresponds to a monosubstituted benzene that has a special name, the disubstituted compound is named as a derivative of that parent compound. In the following examples the parent compounds are phenol, aniline, and toluene:

o-Nitrophenol   p-Bromoaniline   m-Nitrotoluene

The numbering system as described under polysubstituted benzenes is also used to name disubstituted benzenes.

Polysubstituted Benzenes

When there are more than two substituents on a benzene ring, the carbon atoms in the ring are numbered starting at one of the substituted groups. Numbering may be either clockwise or counterclockwise but must be done in the direction that gives the lowest possible numbers to the substituent groups. When the compound is named as a derivative of one of the special parent compounds, the substituent of the parent compound is considered to be on carbon 1 of the ring (the CH_3 group is on C 1 in 2,4,6-trinitrotoluene). The following examples illustrate this system:

NO₂ structure — 1,3,5-Trinitrobenzene

Br structure — 1,2,4-Tribromobenzene

CH₃ structure — 2,4,6-Trinitrotoluene

Br/OH structure — 5-Bromo-2-chlorophenol

1,3,5-Trinitrobenzene

1,2,4-Tribromobenzene
(not 1,4,6-)

2,4,6-Trinitrotoluene
(TNT)

5-Bromo-2-chlorophenol

PROBLEM

21.8

Write formulas and names for all the possible isomers of **(a)** chloronitrobenzene, $C_6H_4Cl(NO_2)$, and **(b)** tribromobenzene, $C_6H_3Br_3$.

(a) The name and formula indicate a chloro group (Cl) and a nitro group (NO_2) attached to a benzene ring. There are six positions in which to place these two groups. They can be ortho, meta, or para to each other.

o-Chloronitrobenzene   *m*-Chloronitrobenzene   *p*-Chloronitrobenzene

(b) For tribromobenzene start by placing the three bromo groups in the 1-, 2-, and 3-positions; then the 1-, 2-, and 4-positions; and so on until all the possible isomers are formed. The name of each isomer will allow you to check that no duplication of formulas has been written.

Br structure — 1,2,3-Tribromobenzene

Br structure — 1,2,4-Tribromobenzene

Br structure — 1,3,5-Tribromobenzene

1,2,3-Tribromobenzene   1,2,4-Tribromobenzene   1,3,5-Tribromobenzene

There are only three isomers of tribromobenzene. If one erroneously writes the 1,2,5- compound, a further check will show that, by numbering the ring as indicated, it is in reality the 1,2,4- isomer:

Br structure — 1,2,4-Tribromobenzene

1,2,5-Tribromobenzene
(erroneous name)

1,2,4-Tribromobenzene
(correct name)

21.10 Polycyclic Aromatic Compounds

polycyclic or fused aromatic ring systems

There are many other aromatic ring systems besides benzene. Their structures consist of two or more rings in which two carbon atoms are common to two rings. These compounds are known as **polycyclic** or **fused aromatic ring systems.** Three of the most common hydrocarbons in this category are naphthalene, anthracene, and phenanthrene. As you can see in the structures below, one hydrogen is attached to each carbon atom except at the carbons that are common to two rings.

Naphthalene, $C_{10}H_8$

Anthracene, $C_{14}H_{10}$ Phenanthrene, $C_{14}H_{10}$

All three of these substances may be obtained from coal tar. Naphthalene is known as moth balls and has been used as a moth repellant for many years. A number of the polycyclic aromatic hydrocarbons (and benzene) have been shown to be carcinogenic (cancer-producing). Formulas for some of the more notable ones, found in coal tar, tar from cigarette smoke, and soot in urban environments follow.

1,2-Benzanthracene   1,2,5,6-Dibenzanthracene

3,4-Benzpyrene   Methylcholanthrene

21.11 ## Sources and Properties of Aromatic Hydrocarbons

When coal is heated to high temperatures (450–1200°C) in the absence of air to produce coke (C), coal gas and a complex mixture of condensable substances called *coal tar* are driven off:

$$\text{Coal} \xrightarrow{\Delta} \text{Coke} + \text{Coal gas} + \text{Coal tar}$$

The aromatic hydrocarbons, such as benzene, toluene, xylene, naphthalene, and anthracene, were first obtained in quantity from coal tar. Since coal tar itself is a by-product of the manufacture of coke, the total amount of aromatics that can be obtained from this source is limited. The demand for aromatic hydrocarbons, which are used in the production of a vast number of materials such as drugs, dyes, detergents, explosives, insecticides, plastics, and synthetic rubber, became too great to be obtained from coal tar alone. Processes were devised to make aromatic hydrocarbons from the relatively inexpensive alkanes found in petroleum. Currently, about one-third of our benzene supply, and the greater portion of our toluene and xylene supplies, are obtained from petroleum. For example, toluene is made by cyclizing and dehydrogenating n-heptane:

$$\text{CH}_3\text{CH}_2\text{CH}_2\text{CH}_2\text{CH}_2\text{CH}_2\text{CH}_3 \xrightarrow[500°C]{\text{Cr}_2\text{O}_3-\text{SiO}_2-\text{Al}_2\text{O}_3} \underset{\text{Toluene}}{\bigcirc\!\!-\!\text{CH}_3} + 4\,\text{H}_2$$

n-Heptane

Aromatic hydrocarbons are essentially nonpolar substances, insoluble in water but soluble in many organic solvents. They are liquids or solids and usually have densities less than that of water. Aromatic hydrocarbons burn readily, usually with smoky yellow flames as a result of incomplete carbon combustion. Some are good motor fuels with excellent antiknock properties.

21.12 ## Reactions of Aromatic Hydrocarbons

The most characteristic reactions of aromatic hydrocarbons involve the substitution of some group for a hydrogen on one of the ring carbons. The following are examples of typical aromatic substitution reactions. In each of these reactions, a functional group is substituted for a hydrogen atom.

1. *Halogenation* (chlorination or bromination)   When benzene reacts with chlorine or bromine in the presence of a catalyst such as iron(III) chloride or iron(III) bromide, a Cl or a Br atom replaces an H atom to form the products.

$$\underset{\text{Benzene}}{\bigcirc} + \underset{\substack{\text{Chlorine}\\\text{or bromine}}}{\text{X}_2} \xrightarrow{\text{FeX}_3} \underset{\substack{\text{Chlorobenzene}\\\text{or bromobenzene}}}{\bigcirc\!\!-\!\text{X}} + \text{HX}$$

2. *Nitration*   When benzene reacts with a mixture of concentrated nitric acid and concentrated sulfuric acid at about 50°C, nitrobenzene is formed. In this reaction a nitro group, —NO_2, is substituted for an H atom of benzene.

$$\text{Benzene} + HO-NO_2 \xrightarrow{H_2SO_4} \text{Nitrobenzene}-NO_2 + H_2O$$

Benzene   Nitric acid   Nitrobenzene

3. *Alkylation* (Friedel–Crafts reaction)   There are many variations of the Friedel–Crafts reaction. In this type the alkyl group from an alkyl halide (RX), in the presence of $AlCl_3$ catalyst, substitutes for an H atom on the benzene ring.

$$\text{Benzene} + CH_3CH_2Cl \xrightarrow{AlCl_3} \text{Ethylbenzene}-CH_2CH_3 + HCl$$

Benzene   Chloroethane   Ethylbenzene

From about 1860 onward, especially in Germany, a great variety of useful substances such as dyes, explosives, and drugs were synthesized from aromatic hydrocarbons by reactions of the types just described. These early syntheses were developed by trial-and-error methods. A good picture of the reaction mechanism, or step-by-step sequence of intermediate stages in the overall reaction, was not obtained until about 1940.

It is now recognized that aromatic substitution reactions usually proceed by a mechanism called *electrophilic substitution*. Three steps are involved: (1) the formation of an electrophile (electron-seeking group), (2) the attachment of the electrophile to the benzene ring forming a positively charged carbocation intermediate, and finally (3) the loss of a hydrogen ion from the carbocation to form the product. This reaction mechanism is illustrated in the chlorination of benzene catalyzed by iron(III) chloride.

Step 1. $FeCl_3 + Cl_2 \longrightarrow FeCl_4^- + Cl^+$

Iron(III) chloride   Chloronium ion

Step 2. $\text{Benzene} + Cl^+ \longrightarrow \left[\begin{array}{c} H \quad Cl \\ \text{(+)} \end{array}\right]$

A carbocation

Step 3. $\left[\begin{array}{c} H \quad Cl \\ \text{(+)} \end{array}\right] + FeCl_4^- \longrightarrow \text{Chlorobenzene}-Cl + FeCl_3 + HCl$

Chlorobenzene

In Step (1) the electrophile (chloronium ion) is formed. In Step (2) the chloronium ion adds to benzene to form an intermediate carbocation, which loses a proton (H^+) in Step (3) to form the products, C_6H_5Cl and HCl. The catalyst, $FeCl_3$, is regenerated in Step (3).

This same mechanism is used by living organisms when aromatic rings gain or lose substituents. For example, the thyroxines (thyroid gland hormones) contain aromatic rings that are iodinated by following an electrophilic substitution mechanism. Iodination is a key step in producing these potent hormones. In general, scientists find that most of life's reactions follow mechanisms that have been elucidated in the organic chemist's laboratory.

4. *Oxidation of side chains* Carbon chains attached to an aromatic ring are fairly easy to oxidize. Reagents most commonly used to accomplish this in the laboratory are $KMnO_4$ or $K_2Cr_2O_7 + H_2SO_4$. No matter how long the side chain is, the carbon atom attached to the aromatic ring is oxidized to a carboxylic acid group, —COOH. For example, toluene, ethylbenzene, and propylbenzene are all oxidized to benzoic acid:

Toluene   Benzoic acid

Ethylbenzene

Propylbenzene

Aromatic substitution products of hydrocarbons are valuable in themselves and also serve as intermediates in the manufacture of other products. Thus, benzene can be nitrated to introduce a nitro group into the molecule. The product, nitrobenzene, is capable of a variety of reactions. Numerous drugs and dyes can be made by syntheses starting with nitrobenzene. These syntheses usually involve several steps. As an illustration, acetanilide, which is used in some pain- and fever-reducing drugs, can be made by the following sequence of reactions:

Nitrobenzene   Aniline   Acetanilide

Organic compounds containing nitro groups are toxic and may also have explosive properties. Therefore, special safety precautions must be taken when handling nitro compounds. A number of nitro compounds are synthesized specifically for use as explosives. For example, the highly explosive trinitrotoluene, or TNT, is made by nitrating toluene:

Toluene → 2,4,6-Trinitrotoluene (TNT)

QUESTIONS

A. *Review the meanings of the new terms introduced in this chapter.*

1. Alkene
2. Alkyne
3. Pi bond
4. Geometric isomers
5. Cycloalkenes
6. Addition reaction
7. Carbocation
8. Markovnikov's rule
9. Aromatic compounds
10. Polycyclic or fused aromatic ring systems

B. *Review questions*

1. The double bond in ethylene (C_2H_4) is made up of a sigma bond and a pi bond. Explain how the pi bond differs from the sigma bond.
2. Draw Lewis structures to represent the following molecules:
   (a) Ethane (b) Ethene (c) Ethyne
3. (a) Draw structural formulas for the four isomeric chloropropenes, C_3H_5Cl.
   (b) There is another compound with this same molecular formula. What is its structure?
4. There are 17 possible isomeric hexenes including geometric isomers.
   (a) Write the structural formula for each isomer.
   (b) Name each isomer and include the prefix *cis*- or *trans*- where appropriate.
5. Draw structural formulas for the following:
   (a) 2,5-Dimethyl-3-hexene
   (b) 2-Ethyl-3-methyl-1-pentene
   (c) *cis*-4-Methyl-2-pentene
   (d) *cis*-1,2-Diphenylethene

(e) 3-Pentene-1-yne
(f) 3-Phenyl-1-butyne
(g) Vinyl bromide
(h) Cyclopentene
(i) *trans*-3-hexene
(j) 1-Methylcyclohexene
(k) 3-Methyl-1-pentyne
(l) 3-Isopropylcyclopentene
(m) 3-Methyl-2-phenylhexane

6. Name the following compounds:

(a)

(b)

(c)

(d)

(e)

(f) $CH_3CHBrCHBrC{\equiv}CCH_3$

7. Write the structural formulas and IUPAC names for all the (a) pentynes and (b) hexynes.
8. Why is it possible to obtain cis and trans isomers of 1,2-dichloroethene but not of 1,2-dichloroethane?
9. Which of the following molecules have struc-

tural formulas that permit cis–trans isomers to exist?

(a) $(CH_3)_2C=CHCH_3$

(b) $CH_2=CHCl$

(c) $CH_3CH_2C≡CCH_3$

(d) $CH_3CH=CHCl$

(e) $CCl_2=CBr_2$

(f) $CH_2ClCH=CHCH_2Cl$

10. The following names are incorrect. Tell why each name is wrong and give the correct name.

(a) 3-Methyl-3-butene

(b) 3-Pentene

(c) *cis*-2-Methyl-2-pentene

(d) 3-Ethyl-1-butene

(e) 2-Chlorocyclohexene

11. Complete the following equations:

(a) $CH_3CH_2CH_2CH=CH_2 + Br_2 \longrightarrow$

(b) $CH_3CH_2CH_2CH=CH_2 + HCl \longrightarrow$

(c) $CH_3CH_2C=CHCH_3 + HI \longrightarrow$
     |
     CH_3

(d) $CH_3CH_2CH=CHCH_3 + HBr \longrightarrow$

(e) $CH_3CH_2CH=CH_2 + H_2O \xrightarrow{H^+}$

(f)

![benzene ring with CH=CH2] $-CH=CH_2 + HCl \longrightarrow$

(g)

![benzene ring with CH=CH2] $-CH=CH_2 + H_2 \xrightarrow[atm]{Pt.\ 25°C}$

(h) $CH_2=CHCl + HBr \longrightarrow$

(i) $CH_3CH=CHCH_3 + KMnO_4 \xrightarrow[Cold]{H_2O}$

12. Complete the following equations:

(a) $CH_3C≡CH + 2 H_2 \xrightarrow[1\ atm]{Pt,\ 25°C}$

(b) $CH_3C≡CCH_3 + Br_2\ (1\ mol) \longrightarrow$

(c) $CH_3C≡CCH_3 + Br_2\ (2\ mol) \longrightarrow$

(d) The two-step reaction

$CH≡CH + HCl \longrightarrow \xrightarrow{HCl}$

(e) The two-step reaction

$CH_3C≡CH + HCl \longrightarrow \xrightarrow{HCl}$

(f) $CH_3CH_2C≡CH + Ag(NH_3)_2NO_3 \longrightarrow$

13. Write the formula and name for the product when cyclohexene reacts with

(a) Br_2 (c) $H_2O,\ H^+$

(b) HI (d) $KMnO_4(aq)(cold)$

14. Write equations to show how 2-butyne can be converted to

(a) 2,3-Dibromobutane

(b) 2,2-Dibromobutane

(c) 2,2,3,3-Tetrabromobutane

15. Two alkyl bromides are possible when 2-methyl-1-pentene is reacted with HBr. Which one will predominate? Why?

16. You are given three unlabeled samples with the information that they are pentane, 1-pentene, and 1-pentyne. Describe a series of simple visible chemical tests that will identify these hydrocarbons.

17. Cyclohexane and 2-hexene both have the formula C_6H_{12}. How could you readily distinguish one from the other by chemical tests?

18. Why do many rubber products deteriorate rapidly in smog-ridden areas?

19. Explain the two different kinds of explosion hazards present when acetylene is being handled.

20. Write structural formulas for

(a) Benzene   (f) Phenol

(b) Toluene   (g) *o*-Bromochlorobenzene

(c) *p*-Xylene   (h) 1,3-Dichloro-5-nitrobenzene

(d) Styrene   (i) *m*-Dinitrobenzene

(e) Aniline

21. Write structural formulas for

(a) Ethylbenzene

(b) Benzoic acid

(c) 1,3,5-Tribromobenzene

(d) Naphthalene

(e) Anthracene

(f) *tert*-Butylbenzene

(g) 1,1-Diphenylethane

22. Write structural formulas and names for all the isomers of:

(a) Trichlorobenzene $(C_6H_3Cl_3)$

(b) Dichlorobromobenzene $(C_6H_3Cl_2Br)$

(c) The benzene derivatives of formula C_8H_{10}

23. (a) Write the structures for all the isomers that can be written by substituting a third chlorine atom in *o*-dichlorobenzene.

(b) Write the structure for all the isomers that can be written by substituting an additional chlorine atom in *o*-chlorobromobenzene.

24. Name the following compounds:

(c) —CH$_2$CH$_2$CH$_3$ (d)

(e)   (f)

(g)   (h)

(i)

25. Explain how the reactions of benzene provide evidence that its structure does not include double bonds like those found in alkenes.

26. Complete the following equations and name the organic products:

(a) + Br$_2$ $\xrightarrow{\text{FeBr}_3}$

(b) + CH$_3$CHCH$_3$ $\xrightarrow{\text{AlCl}_3}$
      |
      Cl

(c) + HNO$_3$ $\xrightarrow{\text{H}_2\text{SO}_4}$

(d) + KMnO$_4$ $\xrightarrow{\text{H}_2\text{O}}$

27. Describe the reaction mechanism by which ben-

zene is brominated in the presence of FeBr$_3$ [Question 26, part (a)]. Show equations.

28. In terms of historical events, why did the major source of aromatic hydrocarbons shift from coal tar to petroleum during the 10 year period 1935–1945?

29. Which of the following statements are correct?

(a) The compound with the formula C$_5$H$_{10}$ can be either an alkene or a cycloalkane.

(b) If C$_8$H$_{10}$ is an open-chain compound with multiple double bonds, it needs an additional ten hydrogen atoms to become a saturated hydrocarbon.

(c) Propene and propane are isomers.

(d) The pi bond is formed from two sp^2 electron orbitals.

(e) A double bond consists of two equivalent bonds called pi bonds.

(f) A triple bond consists of one sigma bond and two pi bonds.

(g) The hybridized electron structure of a carbon atom in alkynes is sp, sp, p, p.

(h) The acetylene molecule is linear.

(i) A molecule of 2,3-dimethyl-1-pentene contains seven carbon atoms.

(j) When an alkene is reacted with cold KMnO$_4$, a glycol is formed.

(k) The compound C$_6$H$_{10}$ can have in its structure: two carbon–carbon double bonds, or one carbon–carbon triple bond, or one cyclic ring and one carbon–carbon double bond.

(l) The disappearance of the purple color when KMnO$_4$ reacts with an alkene is known as the Markovnikov test for unsaturation.

(m) CH$_3$CH$_2$CH$_2^+$ is a primary carbocation.

(n) A secondary carbocation is more stable than a primary carbocation and less stable than a tertiary carbocation.

(o) After bromine has added to an alkene, the product is no longer unsaturated.

(p) Alkynes have the general formula C$_n$H$_{2n-4}$.

(q) 1-butyne will yield hydrogen gas when reacted with sodium.

(r) Cis–trans isomerism occurs in alkenes and alkynes.

(s) Geometric isomers are superimposable on each other.

(t) All six hydrogen atoms in benzene are equivalent.

(u) The chemical behavior of benzene is similar to that of alkenes.

(v) Toluene and benzene are isomers.

(w) Two substituents on a benzene ring that are in the 1,2-position are ortho to each other.

(x) 1,4-Dichlorobenzene and p-dichlorobenzene are different names for the same compound.

(y) The oxidation of toluene with hot $KMnO_4$ yields benzoic acid.

Alcohols, Phenols, and Ethers

After studying Chapter 22, you should be able to

1. Understand the new terms listed in Question A at the end of the chapter.
2. Name alcohols by common and IUPAC methods.
3. Write the structural formula when given the name of an alcohol.
4. Write the structural formulas for all the isomeric alcohols of a given molecular formula.
5. Recognize and identify primary, secondary, and tertiary alcohols.
6. Compare and explain the relative solubilities of alcohols and ethers in water.
7. Name a class of biochemicals that has many of the same properties as the polyhydroxy alcohols.
8. Write equations for the oxidation of alcohols.
9. Write equations for the dehydration of alcohols to ethers and to alkenes.
10. Write equations for the synthesis of alcohols from alkyl halides and from alkenes.
11. Write equations for the reactions of alcohols with sodium metal.
12. Explain the relative reactivities of primary, secondary, and tertiary alcohols.
13. Understand the common methods of preparing methyl alcohol, ethyl alcohol, isopropyl alcohol, ethylene glycol, and glycerol, and know the properties of these alcohols.
14. Name phenols and write their formulas.
15. Understand the differences in properties of the hydroxyl group (—OH) when bonded to an aromatic ring (a phenol) and to an aliphatic group (an alcohol).

16. Be familiar with the general properties of phenols.
17. Write equations for the cumene–hydroperoxide synthesis of phenol.
18. Name ethers and write their formulas.
19. Write equations for preparing ethers by the Williamson synthesis.
20. Discuss relative boiling points and water solubilities of comparable hydrocarbons, alcohols, dihydroxy alcohols, and ethers.
21. Discuss the hazards of using ethers in the laboratory.

22.1 Functional Groups

Organic compounds were obtained originally from plants and animals, which, even today, are still the direct sources of many important chemicals. As a case in point, millions of tons of sucrose (table sugar) are obtained from sugar cane and sugar beet juices each year. As chemical knowledge developed, many naturally occurring compounds were synthesized, often at far less cost than the natural products. Of even greater significance than the cheaper manufacture of natural substances was the synthesis of new substances totally unlike any natural product. The synthesis of new substances was aided greatly by the realization that organic chemicals can be divided into a relatively small number of classes and studied on the basis of similar chemical properties. The various classes of compounds are identified by the presence of certain characteristic groups called functional groups. For example, if a hydroxyl group (—OH) is substituted for a

alcohol

hydrogen atom in an alkane molecule, the resulting compound is an **alcohol.** Thus alcohols are a class of compounds in which the functional group is the hydroxyl group.

Each class of compounds exists as a homologous series that exhibits similar chemical properties as a result of having a common functional group. Examples of the more common classes of compounds and their functional groups are shown in Table 22.1.

Through the chemical reactions of functional groups, it is possible to create or synthesize new substances. The synthesis of new and possibly useful compounds or the more economical synthesis of known compounds is a main concern of modern organic chemistry. Most chemicals used today do not occur in nature but are synthesized from naturally occurring materials. The chemical and physical properties of an organic compound depend on (1) the kinds and number of functional groups present and (2) the shape and size of the molecule.

The structures of alcohols, ethers, and phenols may be derived from water by replacing the hydrogen atoms of water with alkyl groups (R) or aromatic rings:

Water	Alcohol	Ether	Phenol

The R— groups in ethers can be the same or different and can be alkyl groups or aromatic rings.

Table 22.1 Classes of organic compounds

Class	General formula	Structure of functional group	Sample structural formula	Name IUPAC	Common
Alkane	RH	R—H	CH_4 CH_3CH_3	Methane Ethane	Methane Ethane
Alkene	R—CH=CH₂	C=C	$CH_2=CH_2$ $CH_3CH=CH_2$	Ethene Propene	Ethylene Propylene
Alkyne	R—C≡C—H	—C≡C—	$CH\equiv CH$ $CH_3C\equiv CH$	Ethyne Propyne	Acetylene Methyl acetylene
Alkyl halide	RX	—X (X = F, Cl, Br, I)	CH_3Cl CH_3CH_2Cl	Chloromethane Chloroethane	Methyl chloride Ethyl chloride
Alcohol	ROH	—OH	CH_3OH CH_3CH_2OH	Methanol Ethanol	Methyl alcohol Ethyl alcohol
Ether	R—O—R	R—O—R	CH_3—O—CH_3 CH_3CH_2—O—CH_2CH_3	Methoxymethane Ethoxyethane	Dimethyl ether Diethyl ether
Aldehyde	$\begin{matrix} H \\ \| \\ R-C=O \end{matrix}$	$\begin{matrix} H \\ \| \\ -C=O \end{matrix}$	$\begin{matrix} H \\ \| \\ H-C=O \end{matrix}$ $\begin{matrix} CH_3-C=O \\ \| \\ H \end{matrix}$	Methanal Ethanal	Formaldehyde Acetaldehyde
Ketone	$\begin{matrix} R-C-R \\ \| \| \\ O \end{matrix}$	$\begin{matrix} R-C-R \\ \| \| \\ O \end{matrix}$	$\begin{matrix} CH_3-C-CH_3 \\ \| \| \\ O \end{matrix}$ $\begin{matrix} CH_3-C-CH_2CH_3 \\ \| \| \\ O \end{matrix}$	Propanone 2-Butanone	Acetone Methyl ethyl ketone
Carboxylic acid	$\begin{matrix} O \\ \| \| \\ R-C-OH \end{matrix}$	$\begin{matrix} O \\ \| \| \\ -C-OH \end{matrix}$	HCOOH CH_3COOH	Methanoic acid Ethanoic acid	Formic acid Acetic acid
Ester	$\begin{matrix} O \\ \| \| \\ R-C-OR \end{matrix}$	$\begin{matrix} O \\ \| \| \\ -C-OR \end{matrix}$	$HCOOCH_3$ CH_3COOCH_3	Methyl methanoate Methyl ethanoate	Methyl formate Methyl acetate
Amide	$\begin{matrix} O \\ \| \| \\ R-C-NH_2 \end{matrix}$	$\begin{matrix} O \\ \| \| \\ -C-NH_2 \end{matrix}$	$\begin{matrix} O \\ \| \| \\ HC-NH_2 \end{matrix}$ $\begin{matrix} O \\ \| \| \\ CH_3C-NH_2 \end{matrix}$	Methanamide Ethanamide	Formamide Acetamide

Table 22.1 (continued)

Class	General formula	Structure of functional group	Sample structural formula	Name	
				IUPAC	Common
Amine	R—NH$_2$	—NH$_2$	CH$_3$NH$_2$ CH$_3$CH$_2$NH$_2$	Aminomethane Aminoethane	Methylamine Ethylamine
Nitrile	R—C≡N	—C≡N	CH$_3$C≡N CH$_3$CH$_2$C≡N	Ethanonitrile Propanonitrile	Acetonitrile Propiononitrile
Amino acid	R—CH—COOH | NH$_2$	R | H$_2$N—CH—COOH	H$_2$NCH$_2$COOH	2-Aminoethanoic acid	Glycine
			CH$_3$CH—COOH | NH$_2$	2-Aminopropanoic acid	Alanine

22.2 Classification of Alcohols

Structurally, an alcohol is derived from a nonaromatic hydrocarbon by the replacement of at least one hydrogen atom with a hydroxyl group (—OH). Alcohols are represented by the general formula ROH, with methanol (CH$_3$OH) being the first member of the homologous series. R represents an alkyl or substituted alkyl group. Models illustrating the structural arrangements of the atoms in methanol and ethanol are shown in Figure 22.1.

primary alcohol

secondary alcohol

tertiary alcohol

Alcohols are classified as **primary** (1°), **secondary** (2°), or **tertiary** (3°), depending on whether the carbon atom to which the —OH group is attached is directly bonded to one, two, or three other carbon atoms, respectively. Generalized formulas for 1°, 2°, and 3° alcohols follow.

$$
\begin{array}{ccc}
\text{H} & \text{R} & \text{R} \\
| & | & | \\
\text{R—C—OH} & \text{R—C—OH} & \text{R—C—OH} \\
| & | & | \\
\text{H} & \text{H} & \text{R}
\end{array}
$$

Primary alcohol   Secondary alcohol   Tertiary alcohol

Formulas of specific examples of these classes of alcohols are shown in Table 22.2. Methanol (CH$_3$OH) is grouped with the primary alcohols.

Molecular structures with more than one —OH group attached to a single carbon atom are generally not stable. But an alcohol molecule can contain two or more —OH groups if each —OH is attached to a different carbon atom. Accordingly, alcohols are also classified as monohydroxy, dihydroxy, trihydroxy, and so on, on the basis of the number of hydroxyl groups per molecule.

polyhydroxy alcohol

Polyhydroxy alcohols and *polyols* are general terms for alcohols that have more than one —OH group per molecule. Polyhydroxy compounds are very important molecules in living cells as they include the carbohydrate class of biochemicals.

H|O—H H—C—H | H	CH₃OH Methanol

H O—H | | H—C—C—H | | H H	CH₃CH₂OH Ethanol

Figure 22.1 Ball-and-stick models illustrating structural formulas of methanol and ethanol

Table 22.2 **Names and classification of alcohols**

Class	Formula	IUPAC name	Common name[a]	Boiling point (°C)
Primary	CH₃OH	Methanol	Methyl alcohol	65.0
Primary	CH₃CH₂OH	Ethanol	Ethyl alcohol	78.5
Primary	CH₃CH₂CH₂OH	1-Propanol	n-Propyl alcohol	97.4
Primary	CH₃CH₂CH₂CH₂OH	1-Butanol	n-Butyl alcohol	118
Primary	CH₃(CH₂)₃CH₂OH	1-Pentanol	n-Amyl or n-pentyl alcohol	138
Primary	CH₃(CH₂)₆CH₂OH	1-Octanol	n-Octyl alcohol	195
Primary	CH₃CHCH₂OH | CH₃	2-Methyl-1-propanol	Isobutyl alcohol	108
Secondary	CH₃CHCH₃ | OH	2-Propanol	Isopropyl alcohol	82.5
Secondary	CH₃CH₂CHCH₃ | OH	2-Butanol	sec-Butyl alcohol	91.5
Tertiary	CH₃ | CH₃—C—OH | CH₃	2-Methyl-2-propanol	t-Butyl alcohol	82.9
Dihydroxy	HOCH₂CH₂OH	1,2-Ethanediol	Ethylene glycol	197
Trihydroxy	HOCH₂CHCH₂OH | OH	1,2,3-Propanetriol	Glycerol or glycerine	290

[a] The abbreviations n, sec, and t stand for normal, secondary, and tertiary, respectively.

An alcohol such as 2-butanol can be written in a single-line formula by putting the —OH group in parentheses and placing it after the carbon to which it is bonded. For example, the following two formulas represent the same compound:

$$CH_3CH_2\underset{\underset{OH}{|}}{C}HCH_3 \qquad CH_3CH_2CH(OH)CH_3$$

22.3   Naming Alcohols

If you know how to name alkanes, it is easy to name alcohols by the IUPAC System. Unfortunately, several of the alcohols are generally known by common or nonsystematic names, so it is often necessary to know more than one name for a given alcohol. The common name is usually formed from the name of the alkyl group that is attached to the —OH group, followed by the word *alcohol*. See examples given below and in Table 22.2. To name an alcohol by the IUPAC System:

1. Select the longest continuous chain of carbon atoms containing the hydroxyl group.
2. Number the carbon atoms in this chain so that the one bearing the —OH group has the lowest possible number.
3. Form the parent alcohol name by replacing the final *e* of the corresponding alkane name by *ol*. When isomers are possible, locate the position of the —OH by placing the number (hyphenated) of the carbon atom to which the —OH is bonded immediately before the parent alcohol name.
4. Name each alkyl side chain (or other group) and designate its position by number.

For example, let us go through the steps above to name $CH_3CH_2CH_2CH_2OH$.

Step 1. The longest carbon chain containing the —OH group has four carbons.
Step 2. Number the carbon atoms, giving the carbon bonded to the —OH the number 1.

$$\overset{4}{C}-\overset{3}{C}-\overset{2}{C}-\overset{1}{C}-OH$$

Step 3. The name of the four-carbon alkane is butane. Replace the final *e* in butane with *ol*, forming the name *butanol*. Since the —OH is on carbon 1, place a 1 before butanol to give the complete alcohol name 1-butanol.
Step 4. No groups of atoms other than hydrogen are attached to the butanol chain so the name of this alcohol is 1-butanol.

Study the application of this naming system to these examples and to those shown in Table 22.2.

$$\overset{3}{C}H_3-\overset{2}{C}H_2-\overset{1}{C}H_2OH \qquad \overset{1}{C}H_3-\underset{\underset{OH}{|}}{\overset{2}{C}}H-\overset{3}{C}H_3$$

1-Propanol
(n-Propyl alcohol)

2-Propanol
(Isopropyl alcohol)

Cyclohexanol

$$\overset{4}{C}H_3-\overset{3}{C}H-\overset{2}{C}H_2-\overset{1}{C}H_2OH \qquad HO\overset{2}{C}H_2-\overset{1}{C}H_2OH$$
$$\qquad\quad |$$
$$\qquad\ CH_3$$

3-Methyl-1-butanol
(Isoamyl alcohol or
isopentyl alcohol)

1,2-Ethanediol
(Ethylene glycol)

PROBLEM

22.1

Name this alcohol by the IUPAC method.

$$CH_3CH_2CHCH_2CHCH_3$$
$$\qquad\quad |\qquad\ \ |$$
$$\qquad\ CH_3\quad OH$$

Step 1. The longest continuous carbon chain containing the —OH group has six carbon atoms.

Step 2. This carbon chain is numbered from right to left so that the —OH group has the smallest possible number:

$$\overset{6}{C}-\overset{5}{C}-\overset{4}{C}-\overset{3}{C}-\overset{2}{C}-\overset{1}{C}$$
$$\qquad\qquad |\qquad\ |$$
$$\qquad\ CH_3\quad OH$$

In this case, the —OH is on carbon 2.

Step 3. The name of the six-carbon alkane is hexane. Replace the final e in hexane by *ol*, forming the name *hexanol*. Since the —OH is on carbon 2, place a *2* before hexanol to give the parent alcohol name 2-hexanol.

Step 4. A methyl group (—CH₃) is located on carbon 4. Therefore the full name of the compound is 4-methyl-2-hexanol.

PROBLEM

22.2

Write the structural formula of 3,3-dimethyl-2-hexanol.

Step 1. The "2-hexanol" refers to a six-carbon chain with an —OH group on carbon 2. Write the skeleton structure as follows:

$$\overset{1}{C}-\overset{2}{C}-\overset{3}{C}-\overset{4}{C}-\overset{5}{C}-\overset{6}{C}$$
$$\qquad\ |$$
$$\qquad OH$$

Step 2. Place the two methyl groups ("3,3-dimethyl") on carbon 3:

$$\qquad\qquad\ CH_3$$
$$\qquad\qquad\ |$$
$$\overset{1}{C}-\overset{2}{C}-\overset{3}{C}-\overset{4}{C}-\overset{5}{C}-\overset{6}{C}$$
$$\quad |\quad\ |$$
$$\ HO\quad CH_3$$

Step 3. Finally, add H atoms to give each carbon atom four bonds:

$$
\begin{array}{c}
\overset{\displaystyle CH_3}{\underset{\displaystyle |}{|}} \\
CH_3CH-\overset{|}{\underset{|}{C}}-CH_2CH_2CH_3 \\
\overset{\displaystyle |}{OH}\ \ \overset{\displaystyle |}{CH_3}
\end{array}
$$

3,3-Dimethyl-2-hexanol

22.4   Physical Properties of Alcohols

The physical properties of alcohols are related to those of both water and alkane hydrocarbons. This is easily understandable if we recall certain facts about water and the alkanes. Water molecules are quite polar. The properties of water, such as its high boiling point and its ability to dissolve many polar substances, are largely due to the polarity of its molecules. Alkane molecules possess almost no polarity. The properties of the alkanes reflect this lack of polarity—for example, their relatively low boiling points and inability to dissolve water and other polar substances. An alcohol molecule is made up of a water-like hydroxyl group joined to a hydrocarbon-like alkyl group.

    Water   Alcohol

One striking property of alcohols is their relatively high boiling points. The simplest alcohol, methanol, boils at 65°C. But methane, the simplest hydrocarbon, boils at −162°C. The boiling points of the normal alcohols increase in a regular fashion with increasing number of carbon atoms. Branched-chain alcohols have lower boiling points than the corresponding straight-chain alcohols (see Table 22.2).

Alcohols containing up to three carbon atoms are infinitely soluble in water. With one exception (*t*-butyl alcohol), alcohols with four or more carbon atoms have limited solubility in water. In contrast, all hydrocarbons are essentially insoluble in water.

The hydroxyl group on the alcohol molecule is responsible for both the water solubility and the relatively high boiling points of the low-molecular-weight alcohols. Hydrogen bonding (see Section 13.4) between water and alcohol molecules accounts for the solubility, and hydrogen bonding between alcohol molecules accounts for their high boiling points.

    Water–Alcohol   Alcohol–Alcohol

Table 22.3 Boiling points of alkanes and monohydroxy alcohols

Name	Boiling point (°C)	Name	Boiling point (°C)
Hexane	69	1-Hexanol	156
Octane	126	1-Octanol	195
Decane	174	1-Decanol	228

Table 22.4 Comparison of the boiling points of ethanol, ethylene glycol, and 1-propanol

Name	Formula	Molecular weight	Boiling point (°C)
Ethanol	CH_3CH_2OH	46	78
Ethylene glycol	$CH_2(OH)CH_2OH$	62	197
1-Propanol	$CH_3CH_2CH_2OH$	60	97

As the length of the hydrocarbon chain increases, the effect of the hydroxyl group becomes relatively less important. Alcohols with 5 to 11 carbons are oily liquids of slight water solubility, and in physical behavior they resemble the corresponding alkane hydrocarbons. However, the effect of the —OH group is still noticeable in that their boiling points are higher than those of alkanes with similar molecular weights (see Table 22.3). Alcohols containing 12 or more carbons are waxlike solids that resemble solid alkanes in physical appearance.

In alcohols with two or more hydroxyl groups, the effect of the hydroxyl groups on intermolecular attractive forces is, as we might suspect, even more striking than in monohydroxy alcohols. Ethanol, CH_3CH_2OH, boils at 78°C, but the boiling point of ethylene glycol or 1,2-ethanediol, $CH_2(OH)CH_2OH$, is 197°C. Comparison of the boiling points of ethanol, 1-propanol, and ethylene glycol shows that increased molecular weight does not account for the high boiling point of ethylene glycol (see Table 22.4). The higher boiling point is primarily a result of additional hydrogen bonding due to the two —OH groups in the ethylene glycol molecule.

PROBLEM

22.3

Glucose is one of the most important carbohydrates in biochemistry. It has six carbons and five alcohol groups (molecular weight = 180 g/mol). How would you predict the water solubility of glucose will differ from that of hexanol?

Each polar alcohol group attracts water molecules and increases the solubility of organic compounds in water. Because glucose contains five —OH groups whereas hexanol contains only one, glucose should dissolve to a much greater extent than hexanol. In fact, only about 0.6 g of hexanol will dissolve in 100 g of water (at 20°C). In contrast, about 95 g of glucose will dissolve in 100 g of water. The high water solubility of glucose is important because this molecule is transported in a water solution to the body's cells.

22.5 Reactions of Alcohols

Oxidation

We will consider only a few of the many reactions that alcohols are known to undergo. One important reaction is oxidation. We saw in Chapter 17 that the oxidation number of an element increases as a result of oxidation. Carbon can exist in several oxidation states, ranging from −4 to +4. In the −4 oxidation state, such as in methane, the carbon atom is considered to be completely reduced. In carbon dioxide the carbon atom is completely oxidized; that is, it is in its highest oxidation state (+4). The greater the number of bonds from carbon to oxygen, the higher is the oxidation state of the carbon atom. Table 22.5 illustrates the progression of oxidation states for various compounds containing one carbon atom.

Carbon atoms exist in progressively higher stages of oxidation in different functional-group compounds:

$$\text{Alkanes} \longrightarrow \text{Alcohols} \longrightarrow \left\{ \begin{array}{l} \text{Aldehydes} \\ \text{Ketones} \end{array} \right\} \longrightarrow \begin{array}{c} \text{Carboxylic} \\ \text{acids} \end{array} \longrightarrow \begin{array}{c} \text{Carbon} \\ \text{dioxide} \end{array}$$

Increasing oxidation state $\longrightarrow$

The different stages shown do not necessarily indicate direct methods of synthesis. For example, some, but not all alcohols can be converted to aldehydes by oxidation; but it is not practical to convert alkanes directly to alcohols. The following equations represent generalized oxidation reactions in which the oxidizing agent is represented by [O].

Table 22.5 Oxidation states of carbon in one-carbon compounds

	Compound	Number of C—O bonds	Oxidation state
CH_4	Methane	0	−4
CH_3OH	Methanol	1	−2
$H_2C{=}O$	Methanal (Formaldehyde)	2	0
$HC\overset{\displaystyle O}{\underset{\displaystyle OH}{\big\langle}}$	Methanoic acid (Formic acid)	3	+2
$O{=}C{=}O$	Carbon dioxide	4	+4

Primary alcohols are converted to aldehydes by oxidation:

$$RCH_2OH + [O] \longrightarrow RC\overset{\displaystyle O}{\overset{\|}{{}}}\!\!-H + H_2O$$

Primary alcohol   Aldehyde

This reaction goes easily, but is not always a practical method for making aldehydes, because aldehydes are easily oxidized further to carboxylic acids:

$$RC\overset{\displaystyle O}{\overset{\|}{{}}}\!\!-H + [O] \longrightarrow RC\overset{\displaystyle O}{\overset{\|}{{}}}\!\!-OH$$

Aldehyde   Carboxylic acid

Secondary alcohols yield ketones upon oxidation:

$$\underset{\underset{\displaystyle OH}{|}}{R\!-\!CH\!-\!R} + [O] \longrightarrow R\!-\!\underset{\underset{\displaystyle O}{\|}}{C}\!-\!R + H_2O$$

Secondary alcohol   Ketone

Unlike aldehydes, ketones cannot be oxidized further except by drastic procedures that break carbon–carbon bonds or by combustion. Almost any desired ketone can be made from the corresponding secondary alcohol by the action of an appropriate oxidizing agent.

Some common oxidizing agents used for specific reactions are potassium permanganate ($KMnO_4$) in an alkaline solution, potassium dichromate ($K_2Cr_2O_7$) in an acid solution, or oxygen of the air. A complete equation for an alcohol oxidation may be fairly complex. For example, the equation for the oxidation of ethanol to ethanal by potassium dichromate in sulfuric acid solution is

$$3\ CH_3CH_2OH + K_2Cr_2O_7 + 4\ H_2SO_4 \longrightarrow 3\ CH_3C\overset{\displaystyle O}{\overset{\|}{{}}}\!\!-H + K_2SO_4 + Cr_2(SO_4)_3 + 7\ H_2O$$

Ethanol   Ethanal

Since our main interest is in the changes that occur in the functional groups, we can convey this information in abbreviated form:

$$CH_3CH_2OH \xrightarrow[\Delta]{K_2Cr_2O_7/H_2SO_4} CH_3C\overset{\displaystyle O}{\overset{\|}{{}}}\!\!-H + H_2O$$

Although the abbreviated equation lacks some of the details, it does show the overall reaction involving the organic compounds. Additional information is provided by notations above and below the arrow, which indicate that this reaction is carried out in heated potassium dichromate–sulfuric acid solution. Abbreviated equations of this kind will be used frequently in the remainder of this book.

Oxidation of a primary alcohol to an aldehyde or of a secondary alcohol to a ketone involves the removal of two hydrogen atoms from the alcohol molecule.

One of these hydrogens is from the —OH group; the other is from the carbon atom to which the —OH group is attached.

$$\underset{\substack{\text{Ethanol}}}{\overset{\displaystyle \underset{\displaystyle H}{\overset{\displaystyle H}{|}}}{CH_3C-OH}} + [O] \longrightarrow \underset{\substack{\text{Ethanal}\\\text{(Acetaldehyde)}}}{\overset{\displaystyle \overset{O}{\parallel}}{CH_3C-H}} + H_2O$$

$$\underset{\substack{\text{2-Propanol}}}{\overset{\displaystyle \overset{H}{|}}{\underset{\displaystyle \underset{OH}{|}}{CH_3CCH_3}}} + [O] \longrightarrow \underset{\substack{\text{Propanone}\\\text{(Acetone)}}}{CH_3-\overset{\displaystyle \underset{\parallel}{C}}{\underset{O}{}}-CH_3} + H_2O$$

But in a tertiary alcohol no hydrogen atom is directly bonded to the carbon atom that is attached to the —OH group. Consequently, a tertiary alcohol cannot be oxidized except by such drastic procedures as combustion.

$$CH_3-\underset{\displaystyle \underset{CH_3}{|}}{\overset{\displaystyle \overset{CH_3}{|}}{C}}-OH + [O] \longrightarrow \text{No reaction}$$

PROBLEM

22.4

What are the products when **(a)** 1-propanol, **(b)** 2-propanol, and **(c)** cyclohexanol are oxidized with $K_2Cr_2O_7$—H_2SO_4?

(a) The formula for 1-propanol is $CH_3CH_2CH_2OH$. Since it is a primary alcohol, it can be oxidized to an aldehyde or a carboxylic acid. The oxidation occurs at the carbon bonded to the —OH group, and this carbon atom becomes an aldehyde or a carboxylic acid. The rest of the molecule remains the same.

$$CH_3CH_2CH_2OH \begin{cases} \underset{\text{Propanal}}{\overset{\displaystyle \overset{H}{|}}{CH_3CH_2C=O}} \\ \underset{\text{Propanoic acid}}{CH_3CH_2COOH} \end{cases}$$

(b) 2-Propanol is a secondary alcohol and will be oxidized to a ketone. Ketones resist further oxidation. The oxidation occurs at the carbon bonded to the —OH group.

$$\underset{\displaystyle \underset{OH}{|}}{CH_3CHCH_3} \longrightarrow \underset{\substack{\text{Propanone (Acetone)}}}{CH_3\overset{\displaystyle \underset{\parallel}{C}}{\underset{O}{}}CH_3}$$

(c) Cyclohexanol is also a secondary alcohol and will be oxidized to cyclohexanone, a ketone.

Cyclohexanone

Dehydration

The term *dehydration* implies the elimination of water. Alcohols can be dehydrated to form alkenes or ethers. One of the more effective dehydrating reagents is sulfuric acid. Whether an ether or an alkene is formed depends on the ratio of alcohol to sulfuric acid, the reaction temperature, and the type of alcohol. With primary alcohols, intermolecular (between molecules) dehydration to an ether occurs with excess alcohol and a temperature lower than that required to dehydrate the alcohol to an alkene.

When ethanol and concentrated sulfuric acid are heated to 140°C, one molecule of water is eliminated per two molecules of alcohol to form diethyl ether. At 180°C, intramolecular (within a molecule) dehydration occurs within individual molecules, and ethylene is formed. The equations are

The dehydration to ethers is useful only for primary alcohols. Dehydration of secondary and tertiary alcohols yields predominantly the most highly substituted alkene. Thus, the dehydration of 2-butanol gives chiefly 2-butene, and the dehydration of 2-methyl-2-butanol gives 2-methyl-2-butene as the chief product.

The $C{=}C$ double bond in 2-butene is the more highly substituted, having two alkyl groups bonded to the $C{=}C$. Only one alkyl group is bonded to the $C{=}C$ double bond in 1-butene.

$$\underset{\substack{\text{OH}\\ \text{2-Methyl-2-butanol}}}{\overset{\overset{\displaystyle CH_3}{|}}{CH_3CH_2\overset{|}{C}CH_3}} \xrightarrow[\text{90°C}]{\text{45\% } H_2SO_4} \underset{\substack{\text{2-Methyl-2-butene}\\ \text{(chief product)}}}{CH_3CH{=}\overset{\overset{\displaystyle CH_3}{|}}{C}CH_3} + \underset{\substack{\text{2-Methyl-1-butene}}}{CH_3CH_2\overset{\overset{\displaystyle CH_3}{|}}{C}{=}CH_2} + H_2O$$

The C=C double bond in 2-methyl-2-butene is the more highly substituted, having three alkyl groups bonded to the C=C. Only two alkyl groups are bonded to the C=C double bond in 2-methyl-1-butene.

Dehydration reactions are often used in industry to make relatively high-priced ethers from cheaper alcohols. But since alkenes are generally lower-priced than the corresponding alcohols, the industrial preparation of alkenes from alcohols does not make economic sense.

Reaction with Active Metals

Although alcohols are less acidic than water, they react with active metals such as sodium and potassium to replace the hydrogen atom of the alcohol —OH group. The products formed are a salt and hydrogen gas. The salt is an ionic compound and is called an alkoxide (CH_3CH_2ONa is sodium ethoxide). The equation is

$$2\text{ ROH} + 2\text{ Na} \longrightarrow \underset{\text{Alkoxide}}{2\text{ RONa}} + H_2(g)$$

$$2\underset{\text{Ethanol}}{CH_3CH_2OH} + 2\text{ Na} \longrightarrow 2\underset{\text{Sodium ethoxide}}{CH_3CH_2ONa} + H_2(g)$$

The order of reactivity of alcohols with sodium is primary > secondary > tertiary. Methanol and ethanol react vigorously with sodium, but not as vigorously as do sodium and water. The reactivity of an alcohol also decreases as its molecular weight increases. This is because the —OH group becomes a relatively smaller and less significant part of the molecule.

Esterification (Conversion of Alcohols to Esters)

An alcohol can react with a carboxylic acid to form an ester and water. The reaction is represented as follows:

$$\underset{\substack{\text{Carboxylic acid}}}{R\overset{\overset{\displaystyle O}{\|}}{C}\!-\!(OH)} + (H)\!-\!\underset{\substack{\text{Alcohol}}}{\boxed{OR'}} \xrightleftharpoons{H^+} \underset{\text{Ester}}{R\overset{\overset{\displaystyle O}{\|}}{C}\!-\!OR'} + HOH$$

$$\underset{\text{Acetic acid}}{CH_3\overset{\overset{\displaystyle O}{\|}}{C}\!-\!OH} + \underset{\text{Ethanol}}{HOCH_2CH_3} \xrightleftharpoons{H^+} \underset{\text{Ethyl acetate}}{CH_3\overset{\overset{\displaystyle O}{\|}}{C}\!-\!OCH_2CH_3} + HOH$$

Esterification is an important reaction of alcohols and is discussed in greater detail in Chapter 24.

22.6 Preparation and Properties of Common Alcohols

Three general methods for making alcohols are

1. *Hydrolysis of an ester*

$$
\underset{\text{Ester}}{\overset{\displaystyle O}{\overset{\|}{RC}}-OR'} + HOH \xrightarrow[\Delta]{H^+} \underset{\text{Carboxylic acid}}{\overset{\displaystyle O}{\overset{\|}{RC}}-OH} + \underset{\text{Alcohol}}{R'OH}
$$

2. *Alkaline hydrolysis of an alkyl halide (1° and 2° alcohols only)*

$$
\underset{\text{Alkyl halide}}{RX} + NaOH(aq) \longrightarrow \underset{\text{Alcohol}}{ROH} + NaX
$$

$$
CH_3CH_2Cl + NaOH(aq) \longrightarrow CH_3CH_2OH + NaCl
$$

hydrolysis   **Hydrolysis** is a reaction of water with another species in which the water molecule is split (see Section 16.13). The hydrolysis of an ester is the reverse reaction of esterification. A carboxylic acid and an alcohol are formed as products. The reaction can be conducted in an acid or an alkaline medium.

3. *Catalytic reduction of aldehydes and ketones* to produce primary and secondary alcohols. These reactions are discussed in Chapter 23.

In theory, these general methods provide a way to make almost any desired alcohol, but they may not be practical for a specific alcohol because the necessary starting material—ester, alkyl halide, aldehyde, or ketone—cannot be obtained at a reasonable cost. Hence, for economic reasons most of the widely used alcohols are made on an industrial scale by special methods that have been developed for specific alcohols. The preparation and properties of several of these alcohols are described in the following paragraphs.

Methanol

When wood is heated to a high temperature in an atmosphere lacking oxygen, methanol (wood alcohol) and other products are formed and driven off. The process is called *destructive distillation* and, until about 1925, nearly all methanol was obtained in this way. In the early 1920s the synthesis of methanol by high-pressure catalytic hydrogenation of carbon monoxide was developed in Germany. The reaction is

$$
CO + 2\,H_2 \xrightarrow[\text{300–400°C, 200 atm}]{ZnO-Cr_2O_3} CH_3OH
$$

Nearly all methanol is now manufactured by this method.

Methanol is a volatile (bp 65°C), highly flammable liquid. It is poisonous and capable of causing blindness or death if taken internally. Exposure to methanol vapors for even short periods of time is dangerous. Despite this danger, over 3.6×10^9 kg (7.9×10^9 lb) annually are manufactured and used for

1. Conversion to formaldehyde (methanal) primarily for use in the manufacture of polymers
2. Manufacture of other chemicals, especially various kinds of esters
3. Denaturing ethyl alcohol (rendering it unfit as a beverage)
4. An industrial solvent
5. An inexpensive and temporary antifreeze for radiators (it is not a satisfactory permanent antifreeze, because its boiling point is lower than that of water)

The experimental use of 5–30% methanol or ethanol in gasoline *(gasohol)* has shown promising results in reducing the amount of air pollutants emitted in automobile exhausts. Another benefit of using methanol in gasoline is that methanol can be made from nonpetroleum sources. The most economical non-petroleum source of carbon monoxide for making methanol is coal. In addition to coal, burnable materials such as wood, agricultural wastes, and sewage sludge also are potential sources of methanol.

Ethanol

Ethanol is without doubt the earliest and most widely known alcohol. It is or has been known by a variety of names such as ethyl alcohol, "alcohol," grain alcohol, methyl carbinol, spirit, and *aqua vitae*. The preparation of ethanol by fermentation is recorded in the Old Testament. Huge quantities of this substance are still prepared by fermentation. Starch and sugar are the raw materials. Starch is first converted to sugar by enzyme- or acid-catalyzed hydrolysis. (An enzyme is a biological catalyst, as discussed in Chapter 29.) Conversion of simple sugars to ethanol is accomplished by yeast:

$$C_6H_{12}O_6 \xrightarrow{\text{Yeast}} 2 \text{ CH}_3\text{CH}_2\text{OH} + 2 \text{ CO}_2$$

Glucose   Ethanol

For legal use in beverages, ethanol is made by fermentation; but a large part of the alcohol for industrial uses (5.9×10^8 kg [about 1.3×10^9 lb] annually) is made from petroleum-derived ethylene. Ethylene is passed into an aqueous acid solution to form ethanol:

$$\text{CH}_2\!\!=\!\!\text{CH}_2 + \text{H}_2\text{O} \xrightarrow{\text{H}^+} \text{CH}_3\text{CH}_2\text{OH}$$

Some of the economically significant uses of ethanol are the following:

1. Intermediate in the manufacture of other chemicals such as acetaldehyde, acetic acid, ethyl acetate, and diethyl ether
2. Solvent for many organic substances
3. Compounding ingredient for pharmaceuticals, perfumes, flavorings, and so on
4. Essential ingredient of alcoholic beverages

Ethanol acts physiologically as a food, as a drug, and as a poison. It is a food in the limited sense that the body is able to metabolize it to carbon dioxide and water with the production of energy. As a drug, ethanol is often mistakenly considered to be a stimulant, but it is in fact a depressant. In moderate quantities ethanol causes drowsiness and depresses brain functions so that activities requiring skill and judgment (such as automobile driving) are impaired. In larger quantities ethanol causes nausea, vomiting, impaired perception, and incoordination. If a very large amount is consumed, unconsciousness and ultimately death may occur.

Authorities maintain that the effects of ethanol on automobile drivers are a factor in about half of all fatal traffic accidents in the United States. The gravity of this problem can be grasped when you realize that traffic accidents are responsible for about 50,000 deaths each year in the United States.

Heavy taxes are imposed on alcohol in beverages. A gallon of pure alcohol costs only a dollar or two to produce, but in a distilled beverage it bears a tax of about 20 dollars or more.

Ethanol for industrial use is often denatured (rendered unfit for drinking) and, thus, is not taxed. Denaturing is done by adding small amounts of methanol and other denaturants that are extremely difficult to remove. Denaturing is required by the federal government to protect the beverage-alcohol tax source. Special tax-free use permits are issued to scientific and industrial users who require pure ethanol for nonbeverage uses.

Isopropyl Alcohol (2-Propanol)

Isopropyl alcohol (2-propanol) is made from propene derived from petroleum. This synthesis is analogous to that used for making ethanol from ethylene:

$$CH_3CH{=}CH_2 + H_2O \xrightarrow{\ H^+\ } CH_3\underset{\underset{\displaystyle OH}{|}}{CH}CH_3$$

Propene

Isopropyl alcohol (2-propanol)

Note that 2-propanol, not 1-propanol, is produced. This is because, in the first step of the reaction, an H^+ adds to carbon 1 of propene according to Markovnikov's rule (Section 21.6). The —OH group then ends up on carbon 2 to give the final product.

Isopropyl alcohol is a relatively low-cost alcohol that is manufactured in large quantities, about 7.3×10^8 kg (1.6×10^9 lb) annually. It is not a potable alcohol, and even breathing large quantities of the vapor may cause dizziness, headache, nausea, vomiting, mental depression, and coma. Isopropyl alcohol is used (1) to manufacture other chemicals (especially acetone), (2) as an industrial solvent, and (3) as the principal ingredient in rubbing alcohol formulations.

Ethylene Glycol (1,2-Ethanediol)

Ethylene glycol is the simplest alcohol containing two —OH groups. Like most other relatively cheap, low-molecular-weight alcohols, it is commercially derived from petroleum. One industrial synthesis is from ethylene via ethylene oxide (oxirane).

$$2 \ CH_2{=}CH_2 + O_2 \xrightarrow[200-300°C]{Ag \ catalyst} 2 \ \overset{O}{\overset{\diagup \diagdown}{CH_2{-}CH_2}}$$

Ethylene   Oxirane
                                  (Ethylene oxide)

$$\overset{O}{\overset{\diagup \diagdown}{CH_2{-}CH_2}} + H_2O \xrightarrow{H^+} HOCH_2CH_2OH$$

1,2-Ethanediol
(Ethylene glycol)

Major uses of ethylene glycol are (1) in the preparation of the synthetic polyester fibers Dacron and Terylene, (2) as a major ingredient in "permanent type" antifreeze for cooling systems, (3) as a solvent in the paint and plastics industries, and (4) in the formulations of printing ink and ink for ballpoint pens.

The low molecular weight, complete water solubility, low freezing point, and high boiling point make ethylene glycol a nearly ideal antifreeze. A 58% by weight aqueous solution of ethylene glycol freezes at −48°C. Its high boiling point and high heat of vaporization prevent it from being boiled away and permit higher, and therefore more efficient, engine operating temperatures than are possible with water alone. The U.S. production of ethylene glycol amounts to about 1.8×10^8 kg (4.0×10^8 lb) annually. Ethylene glycol is extremely toxic when ingested.

Glycerol

Glycerol, also known as *glycerine* or 1,2,3-propanetriol, is an important trihydroxy alcohol. Glycerol is a syrupy liquid with a sweet, warm taste. It is about 0.6 times as sweet as cane sugar. It is obtained as a by-product of processing animal and vegetable fats to make soap and other products, and it is also synthesized commercially from propene. The major uses of glycerol are (1) as a raw material in the manufacture of polymers and explosives, (2) as an emollient in cosmetics, (3) as a humectant in tobacco products, and (4) as a sweetener. Each use is directly related to the three —OH groups on glycerol.

The —OH groups provide sites through which the glycerol unit may be bonded to other molecules to form a polymer (Chapter 25). The explosive nitroglycerine or glyceryltrinitrate, is made by reacting the —OH groups with nitric acid:

$$
\begin{array}{l}
CH_2OH \\
| \\
CHOH \\
| \\
CH_2OH
\end{array}
+ 3 \ HONO_2
\longrightarrow
\begin{array}{l}
CH_2ONO_2 \\
| \\
CHONO_2 \\
| \\
CH_2ONO_2
\end{array}
+ 3 \ H_2O
$$

Glycerol   Nitric acid   Glyceryltrinitrate
                                 (Nitroglycerine)

The three polar —OH groups on the glycerol molecule are able to hold water molecules by hydrogen bonding. Consequently, glycerol is a hygroscopic substance; that is, it has the ability to take up water vapor from the air. It is therefore used as a skin moisturizer in cosmetic preparations. Glycerol is also used as an additive in tobacco products; by taking up moisture from the air, it prevents the tobacco from becoming excessively dry and crumbly.

22.7 Phenols

phenol

The term **phenol** is used for the class of compounds that have a hydroxy group attached to an aromatic ring. The parent compound is called *phenol* (C_6H_5OH) and is also known as carbolic acid.

Naming Phenols

Many phenols are named as derivatives of the parent compound using the general methods for naming aromatic compounds. For example,

| Phenol (Carbolic acid) | *m*-Bromophenol | *p*-Aminophenol | 2,4,6-Trinitrophenol (Picric acid) |

The *ortho-*, *meta-*, and *para*-dihydroxybenzenes have the special names catechol, resorcinol, and hydroquinone, respectively. The catechol structure occurs in many natural substances; and hydroquinone, a manufactured product, is commonly used as a photographic reducer and developer.

Catechol   Resorcinol   Hydroquinone

The *ortho-*, *meta-*, and *para*-methylphenols are present in coal tar and are known as cresols. They are all useful disinfectants.

| *o*-Cresol (*o*-Methylphenol) | *m*-Cresol (*m*-Methylphenol) | *p*-Cresol (*p*-Methylphenol) |

22.8 Selected Phenolic Compounds

Many well-known natural substances have phenolic groups in their structures. The formulas and brief descriptions of several examples follow.

Vanillin

Eugenol

Urushiols

Thymol

Menthol
(not a phenol)

2,6-di-t-Butyl-4-methylphenol
(Butylated hydroxytoluene, BHT)

Vanillin is the principal odorous component of the vanilla bean. It is one of the most widely used flavorings and is also used for masking undesirable odors in many products such as paints.

Eugenol is the essence of oil of cloves. Two of its uses are as a dental analgesic and for the manufacture of synthetic vanillin. Thymol occurs in the oil of thyme. It has a pleasant odor and flavor and is used as an antiseptic in preparations such as mouthwashes. Thymol is the starting material for the synthesis of menthol, the main constituent of oil of peppermint. Thymol is a widely used flavoring and pharmaceutical.

Butylated hydroxytoluene (BHT) is used in small amounts as an antioxidant preservative for food, synthetic rubber, vegetable oils, soap, and some plastics.

The active irritants in poison ivy and poison oak are called urushiols. They are catechol derivatives with an unbranched 15-carbon side chain in position 3 on the phenol ring.

Tetrahydrocannibinol
(from Marijuana)

Phenolphthalein

OH
OH

HO—CHCH$_2$NHCH$_3$
Adrenalin.
(Epinephrine)

COOH
OCCH$_3$
‖
O
Aspirin
(Acetylsalicylic acid)

The widely discussed active principle of marijuana is tetrahydrocannibinol. It is obtained from the dried leaves and flowering tops of the hemp plant and has been used since antiquity for its physiological effects. The common acid–base indicator phenolphthalein is a phenol derivative. Phenolphthalein is also used as a medical cathartic. Epinephrine (adrenalin) is secreted by the adrenal gland in response to stress, fear, anger, or other heightened emotional states. It stimulates the conversion of glycogen to glucose in the body. Phenol is the starting material for the manufacture of aspirin, one of the most widely used drugs for self-medication.

22.9 Properties of Phenols

In the pure state, phenol is a colorless crystalline solid with a melting point at about 41°C and a characteristic odor. Phenol is highly poisonous. Ingestion of even small amounts of it may cause nausea, vomiting, circulatory collapse, and death from respiratory failure.

Phenol is a weak acid; it is more acidic than alcohols and water but less acidic than acetic and carbonic acids. The pH values are as follows: acetic acid (0.1 M), 2.87; water, 7.0; phenol (0.1 M), 5.5. Thus, phenol will react with sodium hydroxide solution to form a salt but will not react with sodium bicarbonate. The salt formed is called sodium phenoxide or sodium phenolate. Sodium hydroxide will not remove a hydrogen atom from an alcohol because alcohols are weaker acids than water.

OH
+ NaOH ⟶
ONa
+ H$_2$O

Sodium phenoxide
(Sodium phenolate)

In general the phenols are toxic to microorganisms. They are widely used as antiseptics and disinfectants. Phenol was the first compound to be used extensively as an operating room disinfectant. Joseph Lister (1827–1912) first used phenol for this purpose in 1867. The antiseptic power of phenols is increased by substituting alkyl groups (up to six carbons) in the benzene ring. For example, 4-hexylresorcinol is used as an antiseptic in numerous pharmaceuticals.

OH

$$\text{4-Hexylresorcinol}$$

OH

$CH_2(CH_2)_4CH_3$

4-Hexylresorcinol

22.10   Production of Phenol

Phenol is obtained from coal tar. In addition, there are several commercial methods used to produce phenol synthetically. The most economical of these methods starts with benzene and propylene, which react to form cumene (isopropylbenzene). Cumene is then oxidized by air to cumene hydroperoxide, which is treated with dilute sulfuric acid to obtain phenol and acetone. The economic feasibility of the process is due to the fact that two important commercial products are produced. The equations for the reactions are

Benzene   Propylene   Cumene
                                          (Isopropylbenzene)

Cumene hydroperoxide   Phenol   Acetone

Over 1.1×10^9 kg (2.4×10^9 lb) of synthetic phenol are produced annually in the United States. The chief use of phenol is for the manufacture of phenol–formaldehyde resins and plastics (see Section 25.7).

22.11   Ethers

ether

Ethers have the general formula ROR′. The groups, R and R′, can be derived from saturated, unsaturated, or aromatic hydrocarbons; and, for a given ether, R and R′ may be alike or different. Cyclic ethers are formed by joining the ends of a single hydrocarbon chain through an oxygen atom to form a ring structure. Table 22.6 shows structural formulas and names for some of the different kinds of ethers.

Naming Ethers

Individual ethers, like alcohols, may be known by several names. The ether having the formula $CH_3CH_2—O—CH_2CH_3$ and formerly widely used as an

Table 22.6 Names and structural formulas of ethers

Name[a]	Formula	Boiling point (°C)
Dimethyl ether (Methoxymethane)	CH_3-O-CH_3	−25
Methyl ethyl ether (Methoxyethane)	$CH_3CH_2-O-CH_3$	8
Diethyl ether (Ethoxyethane)	$CH_3CH_2-O-CH_2CH_3$	35
Ethyl isopropyl ether (2-Ethoxypropane)	$CH_3CH_2-O-\overset{\textstyle \vert}{C}HCH_3$ CH_3	54
Divinyl ether	$CH_2{=}CH-O-CH{=}CH_2$	39
Anisole (Methoxybenzene) (Methyl phenyl ether)	⬡—OCH_3	154
Diphenyl ether	⬡—O—⬡	259
Tetrahydrofuran	CH_2-CH_2 CH_2 CH_2 O	66

[a] The IUPAC name is in parentheses when given.

anesthetic is called diethyl ether, ethyl ether, ethoxyethane, or simply ether. Common names of ethers are formed from the names of the groups attached to the oxygen atom, followed by the word *ether*.

$$CH_3 \boxed{O} CH_3 \qquad CH_3 \boxed{O} CH_2CH_3$$

Methyl   Ether   Methyl   Methyl   Ether   Ethyl

Dimethyl ether   Methyl ethyl ether

In the IUPAC System, ethers are named as alkoxy (RO—) derivatives of the alkane corresponding to the longest carbon–carbon chain in the molecule. To name an ether by this system:

1. Select the longest carbon–carbon chain and label it with the name of the corresponding alkane.
2. Change the *yl* ending of the other hydrocarbon group to *oxy* to obtain the alkoxy group name. For example, CH_3O- is called *methoxy*.
3. Combine the two names from Steps 1 and 2, giving the alkoxy name first, to form the ether name.

$$CH_3—O—CH_2CH_3$$

This is the longest C—C chain, so call it *ethane*.

$CH_3O—$ is the other group; modify its name from *methyl* to *methoxy* and combine with *ethane* to obtain the name of the ether, methoxyethane. Thus

$CH_3CH_2—O—CH_2CH_3$ is ethoxyethane

$CH_3CH_2CH_2—O—CH_2CH_2CH_2CH_3$ is propoxybutane

Additional examples named by both methods are found in Table 22.6.

22.12 Structures and Properties of Ethers

An oxygen atom linking together two carbon atoms is the key structural feature of an ether molecule. This oxygen atom causes ether molecules to have a bent shape somewhat like that of water and alcohol molecules:

Water   Alcohol   Ether

Ethers are somewhat more polar than alkanes, because alkanes lack the oxygen atom with its exposed, nonbonded electrons. But ethers are much less polar than alcohols, since no hydrogen is attached to the oxygen atom in an ether. The solubility and boiling point (vapor pressure) characteristics of ethers are related to the C—O—C structure. Alkanes have virtually no solubility in water or acid. But about 7.5 g of diethyl ether will dissolve in 100 g of water at 20°C. Diethyl ether will also dissolve in sulfuric acid. Hydrogen bonding between ether and water molecules and between ether and acid molecules is responsible for this solubility.

Ether ···· Water   Ether ···· Acid

Because no —OH group is present, hydrogen bonding does not occur between ether molecules. This lack of hydrogen bonding can be seen by comparing the boiling points of a hydrocarbon, an ether, and an alcohol of similar molecular weight, as in Table 22.7. The boiling point of the ether is somewhat above that of the hydrocarbon but much lower than that of the more polar alcohol.

Ethers, especially diethyl ether, are exceptionally good solvents for organic compounds. Many polar compounds, including water, acids, alcohols, and other

Table 22.7 Boiling points of ethers, alkanes, and alcohols

Name	Formula	Molecular weight	Boiling point (°C)
Dimethyl ether	CH_3OCH_3	46	−24
Propane	$CH_3CH_2CH_3$	44	−42
Ethanol	CH_3CH_2OH	46	78
Methoxyethane	$CH_3OCH_2CH_3$	60	8
Butane	$CH_3CH_2CH_2CH_3$	58	−0.6
1-Propanol	$CH_3CH_2CH_2OH$	60	97
2-Propanol	$CH_3CH(OH)CH_3$	60	83

oxygenated organic compounds, will dissolve, at least to some extent, in ethers. This solubility is a result of intermolecular attractions between the slightly polar ether molecules and the molecules of the other polar substance. Nonpolar compounds such as hydrocarbons and alkyl halides will also dissolve in ethers. These substances dissolve because the ether molecules are not very polar and therefore are not strongly attracted either to one another or to the other kinds of molecules. Thus, ether molecules are able to intermingle freely with the molecules of a nonpolar substance and form a solution by simple mixing.

In summary, ethers are polar enough to dissolve some polar substances; but their polarity is so slight that they act as nonpolar solvents for a great many nonpolar substances.

Ethers have little chemical reactivity, but because a great many organic substances dissolve readily in ethers, they are often used as solvents in laboratory and manufacturing operations. Their use may be dangerous, since low-molecular-weight ethers are volatile, and their highly flammable vapors form explosive mixtures with air. Another hazard of ethers is that, despite their generally low chemical reactivity, oxygen of the air slowly reacts with them to form unstable peroxides that are subject to explosive decomposition:

$$CH_3CH_2\text{—}O\text{—}CH_2CH_3 + O_2 \longrightarrow CH_3CH\text{—}O\text{—}CH_2CH_3$$
$$|$$
$$O\text{—}O\text{—}H$$

Diethyl ether hydroperoxide

22.13   Preparation of Ethers

We have seen that ethers can be made by intermolecular dehydration of alcohols by heating in the presence of an acid (see Section 22.5). Ethers are also made from sodium alkoxides or sodium phenoxides and alkyl halides, a reaction called the *Williamson synthesis*.

$$\underset{\text{Sodium alkoxide}}{\text{RONa}} \quad + \quad \underset{\text{Alkyl halide}}{\text{R}'\text{X}} \quad \longrightarrow \quad \underset{\text{Ether}}{\text{ROR}'} \quad + \quad \underset{\text{Sodium halide}}{\text{NaX}}$$

The Williamson synthesis is especially useful in the preparation of mixed ethers (where $R \neq R'$) and aromatic ethers:

$$\underset{\substack{\text{Sodium}\\\text{ethoxide}}}{\text{CH}_3\text{CH}_2\text{ONa}} \quad + \quad \underset{\text{Bromomethane}}{\text{CH}_3\text{Br}} \quad \longrightarrow \quad \underset{\substack{\text{Methoxyethane}\\\text{(Methyl ethyl ether)}}}{\text{CH}_3\text{CH}_2—\text{O}—\text{CH}_3} + \text{NaBr}$$

It is interesting to note that organic chemistry is replete with "name reactions," such as the Williamson synthesis, named after the scientists who invented the reactions.

22.14 Ether as an Anesthetic

The most widely known use of ethyl ether has been as a general anesthetic for surgery. The introduction of ether for this purpose is one of the great landmarks of medicine. Two Americans, Crawford W. Long and William T. Morton, played important roles in this development. Long, a physician, used ether in a surgical operation as early as 1842 but did not publish his discovery until 1849. Morton, a dentist, used ether as an anesthetic for dental work in 1846. He publicly demonstrated its effectiveness by administering ether to a patient undergoing surgery at the Massachusetts General Hospital on October 16, 1846.

The word *anesthesia* is from the Greek, meaning insensibility, and was suggested to Morton by the poet and physician Oliver Wendell Holmes. A **general anesthetic** is a substance or combination of substances that produces both unconsciousness and insensitivity to pain. Many other substances, including other ethers such as divinyl ether (Vinethene) and methoxyflurane (Penthrane), are general inhalation anesthetics. These substances are superior in some respects, and in recent years have replaced ethyl ether as a general anesthetic.

general anesthetic

$$\underset{\text{Divinyl ether}}{\text{CH}_2\text{=CH}—\text{O}—\text{CH=CH}_2} \qquad \underset{\text{Methoxyflurane}}{\text{CHCl}_2\text{CF}_2—\text{O}—\text{CH}_3}$$

The nonpolar nature of ethers is critical to their use as inhalation anesthetics. Because they are nonpolar, ether molecules interact readily with the oily, alkane-like cell membranes, and this interaction leads to unconsciousness and insensitivity to pain.

QUESTIONS

A. *Review the meanings of the new terms introduced in this chapter.*

1. Alcohol
2. Primary alcohol
3. Secondary alcohol
4. Tertiary alcohol
5. Polyhydroxy alcohol
6. Hydrolysis
7. Phenol
8. Ether
9. General anesthetic

B. *Review questions*

1. Write structural formulas for and give an example of
   (a) An alkyl halide   (e) A ketone
   (b) A phenol   (f) A carboxylic acid
   (c) An ether   (g) An ester
   (d) An aldehyde
2. Although it is possible to make alkenes from alcohols, alkenes are seldom, if ever, made in this way on an industrial scale. Why not?
3. Isopropyl alcohol is usually used in rubbing alcohol formulations. Why is this alcohol used in preference to normal propyl alcohol?
4. What classes of compounds can be formed by the oxidation of primary alcohols? Cite examples.
5. What is the molecular weight of myricyl alcohol, an open-chain saturated alcohol containing 30 carbon atoms? Myricyl alcohol is present in beeswax as an ester.
6. Why is ethylene glycol (1,2-ethanediol) superior to methyl alcohol (methanol) as an antifreeze for automobile radiators?
7. Briefly outline the physiological effects of
   (a) Methanol   (b) Ethanol
8. Explain, in terms of molecular structure, why ethanol (CH_3CH_2OH, molecular weight = 46) is a liquid at room temperature and dimethyl ether (CH_3OCH_3, molecular weight = 46) is a gas.
9. Write structural formulas for
   (a) Methanol
   (b) 2-Butanol
   (c) 3-Methyl-1-hexanol
   (d) 2-Methyl-2-butanol
   (e) Propylene glycol
   (f) Isopropyl alcohol
   (g) 1-Phenylethanol
   (h) Cyclopentanol
   (i) 2,3-Butanediol
   (j) *sec*-Butyl alcohol
   (k) Sodium propoxide
   (l) Sodium isopropoxide

10. Write structures for all the isomers (alcohols and ethers) with the formula
    (a) C_3H_8O (b) $C_4H_{10}O$
11. There are eight open-chain isomeric alcohols that have the formula $C_5H_{11}OH$. Write the structural formula and the IUPAC name for each of these alcohols.
12. Which of the isomers in Question 11 are
    (a) Primary alcohols?
    (b) Secondary alcohols?
    (c) Tertiary alcohols?
13. Write the structural formula of a glycol that is both a primary and a secondary alcohol.
14. Name the following compounds:
    (a) CH_3CH_2OH
    (b) $CH_3CH(OH)CH_3$
    (c)

    (d) $CH_3CH_2CH(OH)CH_2CH_3$

    (e) $CH_3\overset{\overset{\displaystyle CH_2CH_3}{|}}{\underset{\underset{\displaystyle OH}{|}}{C}}CH_2CH_3$

    (f)

    (g)

    (h) $CH_2\!\!-\!\!CH_2$ with O bridge

    (i) $CH_3\overset{}{\underset{\underset{\displaystyle OH}{|}}{C}}H\!\!-\!\!\overset{}{\underset{\underset{\displaystyle OH}{|}}{C}}H_2$

    (j) $HOCH_2\overset{\overset{\displaystyle CH_3}{|}}{C}H\!\!-\!\!\overset{\overset{\displaystyle CH_3}{|}}{C}HCH_2OH$

15. Cyclic glycols show cis–trans isomerism because of restricted rotation about the carbon–carbon bonds in the ring. Draw and label the structures for *cis*- and *trans*-cyclopentane-1,2-diol.

16. Write the formula and the name of the chief product when the following alcohols are dehydrated to alkenes:

(a) $CH_3CHCHCH_3$
$\quad\quad\;\; |\quad\;\;|$
$\quad\quad\; CH_3\;\; OH$

(b) $CH_3CHCH_2CH_2CH_3$
$\quad\quad\;\; |$
$\quad\quad\; OH$

(c) (cyclohexyl)—OH

17. When 1-butanol is dehydrated to an alkene, it yields mainly 2-butene rather than 1-butene. This indicates that the dehydration process is at least a two-step reaction. Suggest a mechanism to explain the reaction. (*Hint:* n-Butyl carbocation is formed initially.)

18. Alcohols can be made by reacting alkyl halides with aqueous sodium hydroxide, as follows:

$$RX + NaOH(aq) \longrightarrow ROH + NaX(aq)$$

Give the names and formulas of the alkyl bromides (RBr) needed to prepare the following alcohols by this method:
(a) Isopropyl alcohol (c) Cyclohexanol
(b) 3-Methyl-1-butanol
Write the equation for the preparation of each alcohol.

19. Write the equation for the preparation of an alcohol by reacting each of the following alkenes with sulfuric acid and water:
(a) Propene   (d) 1-Pentene
(b) 1-Butene   (e) 2-Methyl-2-butene
(c) 2-Butene

20. Write equations to show how each of the following transformations can be accomplished. Some conversions may require more than one step, and some reactions studied in previous chapters may be needed.

(a) $CH_3CHCH_3 \longrightarrow CH_3CCH_3$
$\quad\quad\;\; |\quad\quad\quad\quad\quad\quad\; \|$
$\quad\quad\; OH\quad\quad\quad\quad\quad\quad\; O$

(b) $CH_3CH_2CH_2CH{=}CH_2 \longrightarrow$
$\quad\quad\quad\quad\quad CH_3CH_2CH_2CHCH_3$
$\quad\quad\quad\quad\quad\quad\quad\quad\quad\;\; |$
$\quad\quad\quad\quad\quad\quad\quad\quad\quad\; OH$

(c) $CH_3CH_2OH \longrightarrow CH_3CH_2O^- \; Na^+$

(d) $CH_3CH_2CH{=}CH_2 \longrightarrow CH_3CH_2CCH_3$
$\quad\quad\quad\quad\quad\quad\quad\quad\quad\quad\quad\;\; \|$
$\quad\quad\quad\quad\quad\quad\quad\quad\quad\quad\quad\; O$

(e) $CH_3CH_2CH_2CH_2OH \longrightarrow CH_3CH_2CHCH_3$
$\quad\quad\quad\quad\quad\quad\quad\quad\quad\quad\quad\quad\quad\quad\;\; |$
$\quad\quad\quad\quad\quad\quad\quad\quad\quad\quad\quad\quad\quad\quad\; Cl$

(f) $CH_3CH_2CH_2Cl \longrightarrow CH_3CH_2C{=}O$
$\quad\quad\quad\quad\quad\quad\quad\quad\quad\quad\quad\quad\quad\;\; |$
$\quad\quad\quad\quad\quad\quad\quad\quad\quad\quad\quad\quad\quad\; H$

21. Complete the following equations and name the principal organic product formed in each case:

(a) $CH_3CH_2OH \xrightarrow[\Delta]{Cu}$

(b) $2\; CH_3CH_2OH \xrightarrow[140°C]{96\% \; H_2SO_4}$

(c) $CH_3CH_2CH_2OH \xrightarrow[180°C]{96\% \; H_2SO_4}$

(d) $CH_3CH(OH)CH_2CH_3 \xrightarrow[\Delta]{K_2Cr_2O_7/H_2SO_4}$

(e) $CH_3CH_2\overset{\displaystyle O}{\overset{\displaystyle \|}{C}}{-}OCH_2CH_3 + H_2O \xrightarrow{H^+}$

22. Benzyl alcohol ($C_6H_5CH_2OH$) is a primary alcohol. Write the formulas of two different organic compounds that can be obtained by oxidizing benzyl alcohol.

23. Name the following compounds:

(a) phenol with OH

(b) benzene with OH and OH (ortho)

(c) benzene with OH and CH₃ (meta)

(d) benzene with OH, Br, and NO₂

(e) benzene with OH, OH, and CH₂(CH₂)₄CH₃

(f) benzene with OH, NO₂, and NO₂

24. Write structural formulas for each of the following:
(a) o-Cresol
(b) p-Nitrophenol
(c) Resorcinol
(d) 2,6-Dimethylphenol
(e) 4-Hydroxy-3-methoxybenzaldehyde (vanillin)
(f) 2-Isopropyl-5-methylphenol (thymol)

25. Summarize the general properties of phenols.
26. Write equations for the cumene–hydroperoxide synthesis of phenol and acetone.
27. Which of the following compounds would you expect to react with (a) sodium metal and (b) sodium hydroxide solution? Write equations for those that react.

(a) [benzene ring]—OH   (c) [benzene ring]—O—[benzene ring]

(b) [benzene ring]—CH$_2$OH

28. Starting with p-cresol and ethane, show equations for the synthesis of ethyl-p-methylphenyl ether (p-CH$_3$C$_6$H$_4$OCH$_2$CH$_3$).
29. What two hazards may be present when working with low-molecular-weight ethers?
30. Arrange the following substances in order of increasing solubility in water:
    (a) CH$_3$CH$_2$—O—CH$_2$CH$_2$CH$_3$
    (b) CH$_3$CH(OH)CH$_2$CH$_2$CH$_3$
    (c) CH$_3$CH$_2$CH$_2$CH$_2$CH$_3$
    (d) CH$_3$CH(OH)CH(OH)CH$_2$CH$_3$
31. Arrange these three compounds in order of increasing acidity:

[benzene ring]—CH$_2$OH   [benzene ring with OH and CH$_3$]   H$_2$O

32. There are six isomeric saturated ethers that have the formula C$_5$H$_{12}$O. Write the structural formula and name for each of these ethers.
33. Write the balanced chemical equation for the complete combustion of diethyl ether,

    CH$_3$CH$_2$—O—CH$_2$CH$_3$

34. Write the formulas of all the possible combinations of RONa and RCl for making each of these ethers by the Williamson synthesis:
    (a) CH$_3$CH$_2$—O—CH$_3$
    (b) CH$_3$CH$_2$CH$_2$—O—CH$_2$CH$_2$CH$_3$
    (c) [benzene ring]—CH$_2$—O—CH$_2$CH$_3$

(d) HC—O—CH$_2$CH$_2$CH$_3$ with CH$_3$ groups above and below

35. Write equations for the following transformations. Name each of the products.

(a) [benzene ring]—CH$_2$OH $\longrightarrow$

[benzene ring]—CH$_2$—O—CH$_2$CH$_3$

(b) [cyclopentane ring]—Br $\longrightarrow$ [cyclopentane ring]—O—[cyclopentane ring]

36. Give a simple chemical test that will distinguish between the compounds in each of the following pairs:
    (a) Ethanol and dimethyl ether
    (b) 1-Pentanol and 1-pentene
    (c) p-Cresol and methyl phenyl ether
37. Which of the following statements are correct?
    (a) Another name for isopropyl alcohol is 2-propanol.
    (b) Ethanol and dimethyl ether are isomers.
    (c) Alcohols and phenols are more acidic than water.
    (d) Sodium ethoxide can be prepared by reacting ethyl alcohol and sodium hydroxide solution.
    (e) Methyl alcohol is a very poisonous substance that can lead to blindness if ingested.
    (f) Tertiary alcohols are easier to oxidize than primary alcohols.
    (g) A correct name for CH$_3$CH$_2$CH(OH)CH$_3$ is sec-butyl alcohol.
    (h) (CH$_3$)$_3$CCH$_2$OH is a primary alcohol.
    (i) When a secondary alcohol is oxidized, a ketone is formed.
    (j) Alcohols have higher boiling points than ethers with comparable molecular weights due to hydrogen bonding between the alcohol molecules.
    (k) The product formed when a molecule of water is split out between an alcohol and a carboxylic acid is called an ether.

(l) When 1-butene is reacted with dilute H_2SO_4, the alcohol formed is 1-butanol.

(m) Ethanol used for industrial purposes and rendered unfit for use in beverages is said to be denatured.

(n) The common name for 1,2,3-propanetriol is ethylene glycol.

(o) Although ethyl alcohol is used in beverages, it is still classified physiologically as a depressant and a poison.

(p) Cyclohexanol is a primary alcohol.

(q) Dihydroxy alcohols are more soluble in water than monohydroxy alcohols.

(r) Aldehydes and ketones may be prepared by the oxidation of primary alcohols.

23

Aldehydes and Ketones

After studying Chapter 23, you should be able to

1. Understand the new terms listed in Question A at the end of the chapter.
2. Recognize aldehydes and ketones from their formulas.
3. Give IUPAC and common names of aldehydes and ketones.
4. Write formulas of aldehydes and ketones when given their names.
5. Understand why aldehydes and ketones have lower boiling points than alcohols.
6. Write equations showing the oxidation of alcohols to aldehydes and ketones.
7. Write the structure of the alcohol formed when an aldehyde or a ketone is reduced.
8. Discuss the Tollens test and the Fehling test, including the reagents used, evidence of a positive test, and the equations for the reactions that occur in positive tests.
9. Use the Tollens and Fehling tests to differentiate between aldehydes and ketones.
10. Recognize whether an aldehyde or a ketone will undergo the aldol condensation.
11. Write equations showing the aldol condensation of aldehydes and ketones.
12. Write equations for the formation and hydrolysis of cyanohydrins.
13. Write equations for the formation and/or decomposition of hemiacetals, hemiketals, acetals, and ketals.
14. Understand what a positive iodoform test is.

15. Identify, from their structural formulas, compounds that will show a positive iodoform test.
16. Write an equation for the preparation of a Grignard reagent.
17. Write equations for the reaction of a Grignard reagent with a given aldehyde or ketone.
18. Choose the reagents for a Grignard reaction that will produce a given alcohol.

23.1 Structure of Aldehydes and Ketones

carbonyl group

aldehydes

ketones

The aldehydes and ketones are closely related classes of compounds. Their structures contain the **carbonyl group,** $\diagup$C$=$O, a carbon–oxygen double bond. **Aldehydes** have at least one hydrogen atom bonded to the carbonyl group, whereas **ketones** have only alkyl or aryl (aromatic, denoted Ar) groups bonded to the carbonyl group.

$$\underset{\text{Aldehydes}}{R-\overset{\overset{\displaystyle O}{\|}}{C}-H \qquad Ar-\overset{\overset{\displaystyle O}{\|}}{C}-H} \qquad \underset{\text{Ketones}}{R-\overset{\overset{\displaystyle O}{\|}}{C}-R \qquad R-\overset{\overset{\displaystyle O}{\|}}{C}-Ar \qquad Ar-\overset{\overset{\displaystyle O}{\|}}{C}-Ar}$$

In a linear expression, the aldehyde group is often written as CHO or CH$=$O. For example,

$$CH_3CHO \quad \text{is equivalent to} \quad CH_3\overset{\overset{\displaystyle O}{\|}}{C}-H$$

In the linear expression of a ketone, the carbonyl group is written as CO; for example,

$$CH_3COCH_3 \quad \text{is equivalent to} \quad CH_3\overset{\overset{\displaystyle O}{\|}}{C}CH_3$$

The general formula for the saturated homologous series of aldehydes and ketones is $C_nH_{2n}O$.

23.2 Naming Aldehydes and Ketones

Aldehydes

The IUPAC names of aliphatic aldehydes are obtained by dropping the final *e* and adding *al* to the name of the parent hydrocarbon (that is, the longest carbon–carbon chain carrying the —CHO group). The aldehyde carbon is always at the end of the carbon chain, is understood to be carbon number 1, and does not need to be numbered. The first member of the homologous series, H$_2$C$=$O, is methanal. The name *methanal* is derived from the hydrocarbon methane, which contains one carbon atom. The second member of the series is ethanal; the third member of the series is propanal; and so on.

$$CH_4 \qquad H-\overset{\overset{\displaystyle O}{\|}}{C}-H \qquad CH_3CH_3 \qquad CH_3\overset{\overset{\displaystyle O}{\|}}{C}-H$$

Methane   Methanal   Ethane   Ethanal

          (from methane + *al*)   (from ethane + *al*)

The longest carbon chain containing the aldehyde group is the parent compound. Other groups attached to this chain are numbered and named as we have done previously. For example,

$$CH_3CH_2\overset{\overset{\displaystyle CH_3}{|}}{C}HCH_2CH_2\overset{\overset{\displaystyle O}{\|}}{C}-H$$

4-Methylhexanal

Common names for some aldehydes are widely used. The common names for the aliphatic aldehydes are derived from the common names of the carboxylic acids (see Table 24.1). The *-ic acid* or *-oic acid* ending of the acid name is dropped and is replaced with the suffix *-aldehyde*. Thus, the name of the one-carbon acid, formic acid, becomes formaldehyde for the one-carbon aldehyde.

$$H-\overset{\overset{\displaystyle O}{\|}}{C}-OH \qquad\qquad H-\overset{\overset{\displaystyle O}{\|}}{C}-H$$

Formic acid   Formaldehyde

Naming aldehydes by both methods is illustrated in Table 23.1.

Table 23.1 IUPAC and common names of selected aldehydes

Formula	IUPAC name	Common name
$H-\overset{\overset{O}{\|}}{C}-H$	Methanal	Formaldehyde
$CH_3\overset{\overset{O}{\|}}{C}-H$	Ethanal	Acetaldehyde
$CH_3CH_2\overset{\overset{O}{\|}}{C}-H$	Propanal	Propionaldehyde
$CH_3CH_2CH_2\overset{\overset{O}{\|}}{C}-H$	Butanal	Butyraldehyde
$CH_3\overset{\overset{O}{\|}}{C}H\overset{}{C}-H$ with CH_3	2-Methylpropanal	Isobutyraldehyde

Aromatic aldehydes contain an aldehyde group bonded to an aromatic ring. They are also named after the corresponding carboxylic acids. Thus the name benzaldehyde is derived from benzoic acid, and the name p-tolualdehyde is from p-toluic acid.

| Benzaldehyde | Benzoic acid | p-Tolualdehyde | p-Toluic acid |

In dialdehydes the suffix -*dial* is added to the corresponding hydrocarbon name; for example,

$$H-\overset{\overset{\displaystyle O}{\|}}{C}CH_2CH_2\overset{\overset{\displaystyle O}{\|}}{C}-H$$

is named butanedial.

Ketones

The IUPAC name of a ketone is derived from the name of the alkane corresponding to the longest carbon chain that contains the ketone carbonyl group. The parent name is formed by changing the e ending of the alkane to *one*. If the chain is longer than four carbons, it is numbered so that the carbonyl carbon has the smallest number possible; and this number is prefixed to the name of the ketone. Other groups bonded to the parent chain are named and numbered as previously indicated for hydrocarbons and alcohols. See the following examples:

| Propanone | 2-Pentanone | 4-Methyl-3-hexanone |

Note that in 4-methyl-3-hexanone the carbon chain is numbered from left to right to give the ketone group the lowest possible number.

An alternate non-IUPAC method commonly used to name simple ketones is to list the names of the alkyl or aromatic groups attached to the carbonyl carbon together with the word *ketone*. Thus, butanone ($CH_3COCH_2CH_3$) is methyl ethyl ketone:

$$CH_3-\overset{\overset{\displaystyle O}{\|}}{C}-CH_2CH_3$$

Methyl Ketone Ethyl

Two of the most widely used ketones have special common names: Propanone is called acetone, and butanone is known as methyl ethyl ketone, or MEK.

Aromatic ketones are named in a fashion similar to that for aliphatic ketones and often have special names as well.

Methyl phenyl ketone
Acetophenone
1-Phenylethanone

Ethyl phenyl ketone
Propiophenone
1-Phenylpropanone

PROBLEM

23.1

Write the formulas and the names for the straight-chain five- and six-carbon aldehydes.

The IUPAC names are based on the five- and six-carbon alkanes. Drop the e of the alkane name and add the suffix al. Pentane (C_5) becomes pentanal and hexane (C_6) becomes hexanal. (The aldehyde group does not need to be renumbered; it is understood to be on carbon 1.) The common names are derived from valeric acid and caproic acid, respectively.

Pentanal (Valeraldehyde)   Hexanal (Caproaldehyde)

PROBLEM

23.2

Give two names for each of the following ketones:

(a) The parent carbon chain that contains the carbonyl group has six carbons. Number this chain from the end nearer to the carbonyl group. The ketone group is on carbon 3, and a methyl group is on carbon 5. The six-carbon alkane is hexane. Drop the e from hexane and add one to give the parent name, hexanone. Prefix the name hexanone with a 3- to locate the ketone group and with 5-methyl- to locate the methyl group. The name is 5-methyl-3-hexanone. The common name is ethyl isobutyl ketone since the C=O has an ethyl group and an isobutyl group bonded to it.

(b) The longest aliphatic chain has four carbons. The parent ketone name is butanone, derived by dropping the e of butane and adding one. The butanone has a phenyl group attached to carbon 1. The IUPAC name is therefore 1-phenyl-1-butanone. The common name for this compound is phenyl n-propyl ketone, since the C=O group has a phenyl and an n-propyl group bonded to it.

23.3 Bonding and Physical Properties

The carbon atom of the carbonyl group is sp^2 hybridized and is joined to three other atoms by sigma bonds. The fourth bond is made by overlapping p electrons of carbon and oxygen to form a pi bond between the carbon and oxygen atoms.

Because the oxygen atom is considerably more electronegative than carbon, the carbonyl group is polar, with the electrons shifted toward the oxygen atom. This makes the oxygen atom partially negative (δ^-) and leaves the carbon atom partially positive (δ^+). Many of the chemical reactions of aldehydes and ketones are due to this polarity.

Polarity

Unlike alcohols, aldehydes and ketones cannot interact with themselves through hydrogen bonding, because there is no hydrogen atom attached to the oxygen atom of the carbonyl group. Aldehydes and ketones, therefore, have lower boiling points than alcohols of comparable molecular weight (Table 23.2).

Low-molecular-weight aldehydes and ketones are soluble in water, but for five or more carbons, the solubility decreases markedly. Ketones are very efficient organic solvents.

The lower-molecular-weight aldehydes have a penetrating, disagreeable odor and are partially responsible for the taste of some rancid and stale foods. As the molecular weight increases, the odor of both aldehydes and ketones, especially the aromatic ones, becomes more fragrant. Some are even used in flavorings and perfumes. A few of these and other selected aldehydes and ketones are shown in Figure 23.1.

Table 23.2 Comparison of the boiling points of selected aldehydes and ketones with those of corresponding alcohols

Name	Molecular weight	Boiling point (°C)
1-Propanol	60	97
Propanal	58	49
Propanone	58	56
1-Butanol	74	118
Butanal	72	76
Butanone	72	80
1-Pentanol	86	138
Pentanal	84	103
2-Pentanone	84	102

Benzaldehyde
(oil of bitter almonds)

Cinnamaldehyde
(oil of cinnamon)

Carvone
(chief component of spearmint oil)

Muscone
(gland of male musk deer, used in perfume)

Civetone
(secretion of the civet cat, used in perfume)

Camphor
(from the camphor tree)

Cortisone
(hormone; regulation of carbohydrate
and protein metabolism; used to
reduce inflammation)

Glucose
(sugar)

Ribose
(sugar)

Fructose
(sugar)

Citral
(oil of lemon)

Vitamin K_1
(antihemorrhagic vitamin)

Figure 23.1   Selected naturally occurring aldehydes and ketones

23.4   Reactions of Aldehydes and Ketones

The carbonyl group undergoes a great variety of reactions. Although there are differences, aldehydes and ketones undergo many similar reactions. However, ketones are generally less reactive than aldehydes. Some typical reactions follow.

Oxidation

Aldehydes are easily oxidized to carboxylic acids by a variety of oxidizing agents, including (under some conditions) oxygen of the air. Oxidation is the reaction in which aldehydes differ most from ketones. In fact, aldehydes and ketones may be separated into classes by their relative susceptibilities to oxidation. Aldehydes are easily oxidized to carboxylic acids by $K_2Cr_2O_7 + H_2SO_4$ and by mild oxidizing agents such as Ag^+ and Cu^{2+} ions; ketones are unaffected by such reagents. Ketones can be oxidized under drastic conditions—for example, by treatment with hot potassium permanganate solution. However, under these conditions carbon–carbon bonds are broken, and a variety of products is formed. Equations for the oxidation of aldehydes by dichromate are

$$3 \ \underset{\text{Carboxylic acid}}{RC-H} + Cr_2O_7^{2-} + 8 \ H^+ \longrightarrow 3 \ RC-OH + 2 \ Cr^{3+} + 4 \ H_2O$$

$$3 \ \underset{\text{acetic acid}}{CH_3C-H} + Cr_2O_7^{2-} + 8 \ H^+ \longrightarrow 3 \ CH_3C-OH + 2 \ Cr^{3+} + 4 \ H_2O$$

The Tollens test (silver-mirror test) for aldehydes is based on the ability of silver ions to oxidize aldehydes. The Ag^+ ions are thereby reduced to metallic silver. In practice a little of the suspected aldehyde is added to a solution of silver nitrate and ammonia in a clean test tube. The appearance of a silver mirror on the inner wall of the tube is a positive test for the aldehyde group. The abbreviated equation is

$$RC-H + 2 \ Ag^+ \xrightarrow[H_2O]{NH_3} RC-O^- \ NH_4^+ + 2 \ Ag(s) \qquad \text{(general reaction)}$$

$$CH_3C-H + 2 \ Ag^+ \xrightarrow[H_2O]{NH_3} CH_3COO^- \ NH_4^+ + 2 \ Ag(s)$$

Fehling's and Benedict's solutions contain Cu^{2+} ions in an alkaline medium. In the Fehling and the Benedict tests, the aldehyde group is oxidized to an acid by Cu^{2+} ions. The blue Cu^{2+} ions are reduced and form brick-red copper(I) oxide (Cu_2O), which precipitates during the reaction. These tests can be used for detecting carbohydrates that have an available aldehyde group. The abbreviated equation is

$$\underset{\text{(Blue)}}{RC-H + Cu^{2+}} \xrightarrow[H_2O]{NaOH} \underset{\text{(Brick-red)}}{RCOO^- \ Na^+ + Cu_2O(s)}$$

Most ketones do not give a positive test with Tollens', Fehling's, or Benedict's solutions. These tests are used to distinguish between aldehydes and ketones.

$$\overset{\text{O}}{\underset{}{\text{R}-\overset{\|}{\text{C}}-\text{R}}} + \text{Ag}^+ \xrightarrow[\text{H}_2\text{O}]{\text{NH}_3} \text{No reaction}$$

$$\overset{\text{O}}{\underset{}{\text{R}-\overset{\|}{\text{C}}-\text{R}}} + \text{Cu}^{2+} \xrightarrow[\text{H}_2\text{O}]{\text{OH}^-} \text{No reaction}$$

Aldehydes and ketones are highly combustible, yielding carbon dioxide and water when completely burned. Their vapors, like those of nearly all volatile organic substances, form explosive mixtures with air. Adequate safety precautions must be taken to guard against fire and explosions when working with aldehydes and ketones or other volatile organic compounds, especially hydrocarbons, alcohols, and ethers.

The oxidation of aldehydes is a very important reaction in biochemistry. When our cells "burn" carbohydrates, they take advantage of the aldehyde reactivity. The aldehyde group is oxidized to a carboxylic acid and is eventually converted to carbon dioxide, which is then exhaled. This stepwise oxidation provides some of the energy necessary to sustain life.

Reduction

Aldehydes and ketones are easily reduced to alcohols, either by elemental hydrogen in the presence of a catalyst or by chemical reducing agents such as lithium aluminum hydride ($LiAlH_4$) or sodium borohydride ($NaBH_4$). Aldehydes yield primary alcohols; ketones yield secondary alcohols:

$$\overset{\text{O}}{\underset{}{\text{R}-\overset{\|}{\text{C}}-\text{H}}} \xrightarrow[\Delta]{\text{H}_2/\text{Ni}} \underset{1° \text{ alcohol}}{\text{RCH}_2\text{OH}} \qquad \text{(general reaction)}$$

$$\overset{\text{O}}{\underset{}{\text{R}-\overset{\|}{\text{C}}-\text{R}}} \xrightarrow[\Delta]{\text{H}_2/\text{Ni}} \underset{2° \text{ alcohol}}{\overset{\text{OH}}{\underset{}{\text{R}-\overset{|}{\text{C}}\text{H}-\text{R}}}} \qquad \text{(general reaction)}$$

$$\overset{\text{O}}{\underset{}{\text{CH}_3\overset{\|}{\text{C}}-\text{H}}} \xrightarrow[\Delta]{\text{H}_2/\text{Ni}} \text{CH}_3\text{CH}_2\text{OH}$$

$$\overset{\text{O}}{\underset{}{\text{CH}_3\overset{\|}{\text{C}}\text{CH}_3}} \xrightarrow[\Delta]{\text{H}_2/\text{Ni}} \overset{\text{OH}}{\underset{}{\text{CH}_3\overset{|}{\text{C}}\text{HCH}_3}}$$

Aldol Condensation

Many of the reactions of aldehydes and ketones involve the *addition* of a new substituent to the carbonyl carbon:

$$\overset{\text{O}}{\underset{}{-\overset{\|}{\text{C}}-}} + \text{HX} \longrightarrow \overset{\text{OH}}{\underset{|}{-\overset{|}{\text{C}}-\text{X}}}$$

This general reaction links two groups together and is very useful in synthetic organic chemistry.

In the reaction known as the aldol condensation, two aldehyde or two ketone molecules react in the presence of dilute sodium hydroxide to form a hydroxy aldehyde or ketone. For example, acetaldehyde reacts in this fashion:

$$
2\ CH_3\overset{\overset{\displaystyle O}{\|}}{C}\!-\!H \xrightarrow{\text{Dilute NaOH}} CH_3\underset{\underset{\displaystyle OH}{|}}{CH}CH_2\overset{\overset{\displaystyle O}{\|}}{C}\!-\!H
$$

Aldol
(3-Hydroxybutanal)

Note that the product is both an aldehyde and an alcohol, from which the name *aldol* is derived.

To explain the aldol condensation, we need to define some additional terms. The carbon atoms in a carbonyl compound are labeled alpha (α), beta (β), gamma (γ), delta (δ), and so on, according to their positions with respect to the carbonyl group. The alpha carbon is adjacent to the carbonyl carbon, the beta carbon is next, the gamma carbon is third, and so forth. In addition, the hydrogen atoms attached to the alpha-carbon atom are called alpha hydrogens, and so on, as shown below:

$$
-\overset{\delta}{C}\!-\!\overset{\gamma}{C}\!-\!\overset{\beta}{\underset{\underset{\displaystyle H}{|}}{C}}\!-\!\overset{\alpha}{\underset{\underset{\displaystyle H}{|}}{C}}\!-\!C\!=\!O
$$

beta H atom   H H   alpha H atom

The aldol condensation is a fairly general-type reaction. Aldehydes that have at least one alpha hydrogen will react in a manner similar to acetaldehyde. The net result is that the alpha hydrogen of one molecule transfers to the oxygen of the carbonyl group of a second molecule. The carbon atom that lost the alpha hydrogen bonds to the carbonyl carbon atom that accepted the hydrogen atom:

Aldol

Acetone will also undergo the aldol condensation:

Acetone   Acetone   Diacetone alcohol
(4-Hydroxy-4-methyl-2-pentanone)

In the foregoing reaction an alpha hydrogen first transfers from one molecule to the oxygen of the other molecule. This breaks the $C=O$ pi bond, leaving a carbon atom of each molecule with three bonds. The two carbon atoms then bond to each other, forming the product, diacetone alcohol.

PROBLEM

23.3

Write the equation for the aldol condensation of propanal.
First write the structure for propanal and locate the alpha-hydrogen atoms:

$$
\begin{array}{c}
\text{H} \\
| \\
\text{CH}_3\text{CHC}=\text{O} \\
| \\
\text{(H)} \longleftarrow \; \alpha\,\text{H}
\end{array}
$$

Now write two propanal molecules and transfer an alpha hydrogen from one molecule to the oxygen of the second molecule. After the pi bond breaks, the two carbon atoms that are bonded to only three other atoms are attached to each other to form the product.

$$
\begin{array}{ccccc}
\overset{O}{\overset{\|}{\text{CH}_3\text{CH}_2\text{C}-\text{H}}} & \xrightarrow[\text{NaOH}]{\text{Dilute}} & \overset{\text{OH}}{\overset{|}{\text{CH}_3\text{CH}_2\overset{+}{\text{C}}}} & \longrightarrow & \overset{\text{OH}\quad O}{\overset{|\qquad\|}{\text{CH}_3\text{CH}_2\text{CHCHC}-\text{H}}} \\
& & | & & | \\
\text{H}\;\;\text{O} & & \text{H} & & \text{CH}_3 \\
| \quad \| & & | & & \\
\text{CH}_3\text{CHC}-\text{H} & & \text{CH}_3\text{C}^-\text{HC}-\text{H} & & \text{3-Hydroxy-2-methylpentanal}
\end{array}
$$

The aldol condensation reaction is used often by living cells. By means of this reaction, smaller biochemicals can be combined to make larger molecules. For example, most cells can join two three-carbon carbohydrates to make one six-carbon sugar using the aldol condensation. Ultimately, this reaction sequence leads to the formation of glucose (see Chapter 33).

Addition of Alcohols

hemiacetal

hemiketal

acetal

ketal

Compounds derived from aldehydes and ketones that contain an alkoxy and a hydroxy group on the same carbon atom are known as **hemiacetals** and **hemiketals.** In a like manner, compounds that have two alkoxy groups on the same carbon atom are known as **acetals** and **ketals.**

$$
\begin{array}{cccc}
\underset{\text{Hemiacetal}}{\overset{R}{\underset{H}{\diagdown}}\text{C}\overset{\text{OH}}{\underset{\text{OR}'}{\diagup}}} &
\underset{\text{Hemiketal}}{\overset{R}{\underset{R}{\diagdown}}\text{C}\overset{\text{OH}}{\underset{\text{OR}'}{\diagup}}} &
\underset{\text{Acetal}}{\overset{R}{\underset{H}{\diagdown}}\text{C}\overset{\text{OR}'}{\underset{\text{OR}'}{\diagup}}} &
\underset{\text{Ketal}}{\overset{R}{\underset{R}{\diagdown}}\text{C}\overset{\text{OR}'}{\underset{\text{OR}'}{\diagup}}}
\end{array}
$$

Most open-chain hemiacetals and hemiketals are so unstable that they cannot be isolated. On the other hand, acetals and ketals are stable in alkaline solutions but are unstable in acid solutions, in which they are hydrolyzed back to the original aldehyde or ketone. The hemiacetal and acetal structures are important in the study of carbohydrate chemistry (Chapter 27).

In the reactions below we show only aldehydes in the equations, but keep in mind that ketones behave in a similar fashion, although they are not as reactive.

Aldehydes react with alcohols in the presence of a trace of acid to form hemiacetals:

$$CH_3CH_2\overset{\displaystyle O}{\overset{\|}{C}}-H + CH_3OH \underset{}{\overset{H^+}{\rightleftharpoons}} CH_3CH_2CH\overset{\diagup OH}{\underset{\diagdown OCH_3}{}}$$

Propanal   Methanol

1-Methoxy-1-propanol
(Propionaldehyde methyl hemiacetal)

In the presence of excess alcohol and a strong acid such as dry HCl, aldehydes or hemiacetals react with a second molecule of the alcohol to give an acetal:

$$CH_3CH_2CH\overset{\diagup OH}{\underset{\diagdown OCH_3}{}} + CH_3OH \underset{}{\overset{Dry\ HCl}{\rightleftharpoons}} CH_3CH_2CH\overset{\diagup OCH_3}{\underset{\diagdown OCH_3}{}} + H_2O$$

1,1-Dimethoxypropane
(Propionaldehyde dimethyl acetal)

A hemiacetal has both an alcohol and an ether group attached to the aldehyde carbon. An acetal has two ether groups attached to the aldehyde carbon.

Cyclic acetals or ketals can be formed by using an alcohol having two —OH groups and two or three carbon atoms. A five- or a six-membered ring is formed. For example, one molecule of ethylene glycol can furnish both of the hydroxyl groups for acetal formation in the following reaction:

Benzaldehyde   Ethylene glycol   Ethylene glycol acetal of benzaldehyde

All hemiacetal and acetal reactions are reversible.

Addition of Hydrogen Cyanide

cyanohydrin

The addition of hydrogen cyanide, HCN, to aldehydes and ketones forms a class of compounds known as cyanohydrins. **Cyanohydrins** have a cyano (—CN) group and a hydroxyl group on the same carbon atom. The reaction is catalyzed by a small amount of base:

$$CH_3\overset{\displaystyle O}{\overset{\|}{C}}-H + HCN \overset{OH^-}{\longrightarrow} CH_3\overset{\displaystyle OH}{\overset{|}{C}}HCN$$

Acetaldehyde   Acetaldehyde cyanohydrin

$$CH_3\overset{\displaystyle ||}{\underset{\displaystyle O}{C}}CH_3 + HCN \xrightarrow{OH^-} CH_3\overset{\displaystyle CH_3}{\underset{\displaystyle OH}{C}}{-}CN$$

Acetone   Acetone cyanohydrin

In the cyanohydrin reaction, the more positive H atom of HCN adds to the oxygen of the carbonyl group, and the —CN group adds to the carbon atom of the carbonyl group. In the aldehyde addition, the length of the carbon chain is increased by one carbon. The ketone addition product also contains an additional carbon atom.

Cyanohydrins are useful intermediates for the synthesis of several important compounds. For example, the hydrolyses of cyanohydrins produce α-hydroxy acids:

$$CH_3\underset{\displaystyle OH}{CH}{-}CN + H_2O \xrightarrow{H^+} CH_3\underset{\displaystyle OH}{CH}COOH + NH_4^+$$

Lactic acid

23.5   Preparation and Properties of Common Aldehydes and Ketones

Numerous methods have been devised for making aldehydes and ketones. The oxidation of alcohols is a very general method. Special methods are often used for the commercial production of individual aldehydes and ketones.

Formaldehyde (methanal).   This aldehyde is made from methanol by reaction with oxygen (air) in the presence of a silver or copper catalyst:

$$2\ CH_3OH + O_2 \xrightarrow[400°C]{Ag\ or\ Cu} 2\ H_2C{=}O + 2\ H_2O$$

Formaldehyde
(methanal)

Formaldehyde is a poisonous, irritating gas that is very soluble in water. It is marketed as a 40% aqueous solution called *formalin*. Because formaldehyde is a powerful germicide, it is used in embalming and to preserve biological specimens. Formaldehyde is also used for disinfecting dwellings, ships, and storage houses; for destroying flies; for tanning hides; and as a fungicide for plants and vegetables. But by far the largest use of this chemical is in the manufacture of polymers (Chapter 25). About 2.59×10^9 kg (5.7 billion lb) of formaldehyde are manufactured annually in the United States.

Formaldehyde vapors are intensely irritating to the mucous membranes. Ingestion may cause severe abdominal pains, leading to coma and death.

It is of interest that formaldehyde may have had a significant role in chemical evolution. Formaldehyde is believed to have been a component of the primitive atmosphere of the earth. It is theorized that the reactivity of this single-carbon aldehyde enabled it to form more complex organic molecules—molecules that were precursors of the still more complicated substances that today are essential components of every living organism.

Acetaldehyde (ethanal). This aldehyde is made by vapor-phase oxidation of ethanol by a process similar to the one used for formaldehyde:

$$2\ CH_3CH_2OH + O_2 \xrightarrow[450°C]{Ag\ or\ Cu} 2\ CH_3\overset{\displaystyle O}{\overset{\|}{C}}-H + 2\ H_2O$$

Acetaldehyde
(ethanal)

One of the newest commercial processes for making acetaldehyde is known as the Wacker reaction. It is a direct oxidation of ethylene to acetaldehyde using palladium chloride as a catalyst:

$$CH_2{=}CH_2 + O_2 \xrightarrow[HCl/H_2O]{PdCl_2/CuCl_2} CH_3\overset{\displaystyle O}{\overset{\|}{C}}-H$$

Acetaldehyde is a volatile liquid (bp 21°C) with a pungent, irritating odor. It has a general narcotic action and in large doses may cause respiratory paralysis. Its principal use is as an intermediate in the manufacture of other chemicals such as acetic acid, 1-butanol, and paraldehyde. Acetic acid, for example, is made by air oxidation of acetaldehyde:

$$2\ CH_3\overset{\displaystyle O}{\overset{\|}{C}}-H + O_2 \xrightarrow[\Delta]{Mn^{2+}} 2\ CH_3\overset{\displaystyle O}{\overset{\|}{C}}-OH$$

Acetaldehyde undergoes reactions in which three or four molecules condense or polymerize to form the cyclic compounds paraldehyde and metaldehyde:

Paraldehyde
(bp 125°C)

Paraldehyde is used in medical practice as a hypnotic or sleep-inducing drug.

$$4 \ CH_3\overset{\displaystyle O}{\overset{\displaystyle \|}{C}}-H \ \xrightarrow[-20°C]{Ca(NO_3)_2 + HBr}$$

Metaldehyde
(mp 246°C)

Metaldehyde is very attractive to slugs and snails, and it is also very poisonous to them. For this reason it is an active ingredient in some pesticides that are sold for lawn and garden use. Metaldehyde is also used as a solid fuel.

Benzaldehyde.   Benzaldehyde (C_6H_5CHO) is known as *oil of bitter almonds*. It is found in almonds and in the seeds of stone fruits—for example, apricots and peaches. Benzaldehyde is made synthetically and used in the manufacture of artificial flavors. The synthesis begins with the free-radical chlorination of toluene, as shown in the following sequence of reactions:

Toluene   Benzyl chloride

Benzal chloride   Benzaldehyde   + 2 HCl

(*Note:* $C_6H_5CH_2$— is called the benzyl group.)

Cinnamaldehyde, $C_6H_5CH=CHCHO$, is the principal substance contributing to the flavor of oil of cinnamon. Like benzaldehyde, it is made synthetically and used in the preparation of artificial flavoring agents.

Cinnamaldehyde

Acetone and methyl ethyl ketone.   Ketones are widely used organic solvents. Acetone, in particular, is used in very large quantities for this purpose. U.S. production of acetone is about 8.2×10^8 kg (1.8×10^9 lb) annually. It is used as a solvent in the manufacture of drugs, chemicals, and explosives; for removal of paints, varnishes, and fingernail polish; and as a solvent in the plastics industry. Methyl ethyl ketone (MEK) is also widely used as a solvent, especially for lacquers. Both acetone and MEK are made by oxidation (dehydrogenation) of secondary alcohols. Acetone is also a coproduct in the manufacture of phenol (see Section 22.10).

$$CH_3CHCH_3 \xrightarrow[250-300°C]{Cu} CH_3CCH_3 + H_2$$

$$\underset{OH}{|} \qquad\qquad \underset{O}{||}$$

2-Propanol   Acetone
                             (Propanone)

$$CH_3CH_2CHCH_3 \xrightarrow[250-300°C]{Cu} CH_3CH_2CCH_3 + H_2$$

$$\underset{OH}{|} \qquad\qquad\qquad \underset{O}{||}$$

2-Butanol   Methyl ethyl ketone
                           (2-Butanone)

23.6 Iodoform Test

Iodoform (CHI_3) is a canary-yellow solid with a distinctive, somewhat unpleasant odor. Iodoform is formed when a methyl ketone, acetaldehyde, ethyl alcohol, or a secondary alcohol that contains at least one methyl group bonded to the alcohol group is treated with sodium hypoiodite (NaOI) solution (NaOH + I_2). All these substances either contain the methyl carbonyl (acetyl) group ($CH_3C=O$) or are easily oxidized to form this structure. The **iodoform test** is useful in the qualitative examination of organic compounds. A positive test is the appearance of a yellow precipitate of iodoform. The reactions involved are represented by the following equations:

$$\underset{R-C-CH_3}{\overset{O}{||}} + 3\ NaOI \longrightarrow \underset{RC-CI_3}{\overset{O}{||}} + 3\ NaOH$$

$$\underset{RC-CI_3}{\overset{O}{||}} + NaOH \longrightarrow \underset{RC-ONa}{\overset{O}{||}} + CHI_3(s)$$
$$\qquad\qquad\qquad\qquad\qquad\qquad\text{Iodoform}$$

Ethyl alcohol gives a positive test because it is first oxidized to acetaldehyde, which contains the $CH_3C=O$ group:

$$CH_3CH_2OH \xrightarrow{NaOI} \underset{CH_3C-H}{\overset{O}{||}} \xrightarrow[NaOH]{NaOI} CHI_3(s) + HCOONa$$

The reaction that occurs in the iodoform test is sometimes called the haloform reaction, since similar reactions occur when chlorine or bromine is used. However, iodine is usually used because chloroform ($CHCl_3$) and bromoform ($CHBr_3$) are more difficult to detect than iodoform.

23.7   Grignard Reactions

Grignard reagent

A **Grignard reagent** is an organic magnesium halide. It can be either an alkyl or an aryl compound (RMgX or ArMgX). Grignard (pronounced *green yard*) reagents were first prepared in France around 1900 by Victor Grignard (1871–1935). Grignard was awarded the Nobel prize in organic chemistry in 1912.

Grignard reagents are usually prepared by reacting an organic halide and magnesium metal in an ether solvent:

$$RX + Mg \xrightarrow{\text{Ether}} RMgX$$

Grignard reagent
(X = Cl, Br, or I)

$$ArX + Mg \xrightarrow{\text{Ether}} ArMgX$$

Grignard reagent
(X = Br)

In the Grignard reagent, the bonding electrons between carbon and magnesium are shifted away from the electropositive Mg to form a strongly polar covalent bond. As a result the charge distribution in the Grignard reagent is such that the organic group (R) is partially negative (δ^-) and the —MgX group is partially positive ($\delta+$). This charge distribution directs the manner in which the Grignard reacts with other compounds.

$$\overset{\delta^- \quad \delta^+}{\textbf{RMgX}}$$

The Grignard reagent is one of the most versatile and widely used reagents in organic chemistry. We will consider only its reactions with aldehydes and ketones at this time. Grignards react with aldehydes and ketones to give intermediate products that form alcohols when hydrolyzed. With formaldehyde, primary alcohols are formed; with other aldehydes, secondary alcohols are formed; with ketones, tertiary alcohols are formed:

Grignard reagent + Formaldehyde $\longrightarrow$ 1° ROH
Grignard reagent + Other aldehydes $\longrightarrow$ 2° ROH
Grignard reagent + Ketones $\longrightarrow$ 3° ROH

Specific examples of each type of reaction follow.

$$H_2C{=}O + CH_3MgBr \xrightarrow{\text{Ether}} \overset{\overset{\textstyle CH_3}{\textstyle |}}{H_2C}{-}OMgBr \xrightarrow{H_2O} CH_3CH_2OH + Mg(OH)Br$$

$$CH_3CCH_3 + CH_3CH_2MgBr \xrightarrow{\text{Ether}} CH_3\overset{CH_2CH_3}{\underset{OMgBr}{C}}CH_3 \xrightarrow{H_2O} CH_3\overset{CH_2CH_3}{\underset{OH}{C}}CH_3 + Mg(OH)Br$$

Acetone Ethyl magnesium bromide 2-Methyl-2-butanol

The Grignard reaction with acetone may be explained as follows. In the first step of the addition of ethyl magnesium bromide, the partially positive —MgBr of the Grignard bonds to the oxygen atom, and the partially negative CH_3CH_2— bonds to the carbon atom of the carbonyl group of acetone:

In the hydrolysis step, a proton (H^+) from water bonds to the oxygen atom, leaving an hydroxide ion (^-OH) to combine with the ^+MgBr. Thus the alcohol is formed.

PROBLEM

23.4

What combination(s) of aldehyde or ketone and Grignard reagent will react to give 2-butanol, $CH_3CHCH_2CH_3$?

$\underset{OH}{|}$

Since the alcohol is secondary, the reactants must be an aldehyde (other than formaldehyde) and a Grignard reagent. If the two organic groups attached to the $>CH(OH)$ of the alcohol are the same, only one combination is possible; if they are different, two combinations are possible. Isolate the groups as follows:

This part from   This part from   This part from   This part from
the aldehyde   the Grignard   the Grignard   the aldehyde

In the first case the aldehyde and Grignard each have two carbon atoms. Therefore, one possible combination to make 2-butanol is ethanal and ethyl magnesium bromide:

$$CH_3\overset{\displaystyle O}{\overset{\|}{C}}-H \qquad \text{and} \qquad CH_3CH_2MgBr$$

In the second case the aldehyde has three carbon atoms and the Grignard has one carbon atom. Thus another combination to make 2-butanol is propanal and methyl magnesium bromide:

$$CH_3CH_2\overset{\displaystyle O}{\overset{\|}{C}}-H \qquad \text{and} \qquad CH_3MgBr$$

QUESTIONS

A. *Review the meanings of the new terms introduced in this chapter.*

1. Carbonyl group
2. Aldehydes
3. Ketones
4. Hemiacetal
5. Hemiketal
6. Acetal
7. Ketal
8. Cyanohydrin
9. Iodoform test
10. Grignard reagent

B. *Review questions*

1. Write generalized structures for
   (a) An aldehyde   (f) An acetal
   (b) A ketone   (g) A ketal
   (c) A dialdehyde   (h) A cyanohydrin
   (d) A hemiacetal   (i) A Grignard reagent
   (e) A hemiketal

2. Name each of these aldehydes:

   (a) $CH_2{=}O$ (two names)

   (b) $CH_3CH_2CH_2\overset{\displaystyle O}{\overset{\|}{C}}-H$ (two names)

   (c) $CH_3\underset{\underset{\displaystyle CH_3}{|}}{C}HCH_2\overset{\displaystyle O}{\overset{\|}{C}}-H$ (one name)

   (d) ⬡$-\overset{\displaystyle O}{\overset{\|}{C}}-H$ (one name)

   (e) $O{=}\underset{\underset{\displaystyle H}{|}}{C}CH_2CH_2\overset{\displaystyle O}{\overset{\|}{C}}-H$ (one name)

   (f) Cl-⬡$-\overset{\displaystyle O}{\overset{\|}{C}}-H$ with $\underset{\displaystyle CH_3 \quad CH_3}{CH}$ (one name)

   (g) ⬡$-CH{=}CH-\overset{\displaystyle O}{\overset{\|}{C}}-H$ (one name)

   (h) $CH_3\underset{\underset{\displaystyle OH}{|}}{C}HCH_2\overset{\displaystyle O}{\overset{\|}{C}}-H$ (two names)

(i)

$$\underset{H}{\overset{CH_3}{\diagup}}C=C\underset{H}{\overset{\overset{\displaystyle O}{\overset{\|}{C}}-H}{}}$$

3. Name each of these ketones:
 (a) CH_3COCH_3 (three names)
 (b) $CH_3CH_2COCH_3$ (two names)

(c)

$$\text{⬡}-\overset{\overset{\displaystyle O}{\|}}{C}-CH_2CH_3 \quad \text{(two names)}$$

(d) $CH_3\overset{\overset{\displaystyle O}{\|}}{C}-\underset{\underset{\displaystyle CH_3}{|}}{\overset{\overset{\displaystyle CH_3}{|}}{C}}-CH_3$ (two names)

(e) ⬠$=O$ (one name)

(f) $CH_3\overset{\overset{\displaystyle O}{\|}}{C}CH_2CH_2\overset{\overset{\displaystyle O}{\|}}{C}CH_3$ (one name)

(g) $CH_3\underset{\underset{\displaystyle OH}{|}}{\overset{\overset{\displaystyle CH_3}{|}}{C}}-CH_2\overset{\overset{\displaystyle O}{\|}}{C}CH_3$ (two names)

(h) $\text{⬡}-CH_2\overset{\overset{\displaystyle O}{\|}}{C}CH_3$ (two names)

4. Write structural formulas for
 (a) 1,3-Dichloropropanone
 (b) Phenylacetaldehyde
 (c) 3-Butenal
 (d) 3-Hydroxypropanal
 (e) Diisopropyl ketone
 (f) 4-Methyl-3-hexanone
 (g) Hexanal
 (h) Cyclohexanone
5. Write structural formulas for propanal and pro-panone. Judging from these formulas, do you think that aldehydes and ketones are isomeric with each other? Show evidence and substanti-ate your answer by testing with a four-carbon aldehyde and a four-carbon ketone.
6. Explain, in terms of structure, why aldehydes and ketones have lower boiling points than alcohols of similar molecular weights.

7. Which compound in each of the following pairs has the higher boiling point? (Try to answer without consulting tables.)
 (a) 1-Pentanol or pentanal
 (b) Pentane or pentanal
 (c) Benzaldehyde or benzyl alcohol
 (d) 2-Pentanone or 2-pentanol
 (e) Propanone or butanone
8. Write equations to show how each of the follow-ing is oxidized by (1) $K_2Cr_2O_7 + H_2SO_4$ and (2) air + Cu or Ag + heat:
 (a) 1-Propanol
 (b) 3-Pentanol
 (c) 2,3-Dimethyl-2-butanol
9. Ketones are prepared by oxidation of secondary alcohols. Which alcohol should be used to prepare
 (a) Diethyl ketone
 (b) Diisopropyl ketone
 (c) 4-Phenyl-2-butanone
10. (a) What functional group is present in a com-pound that gives a positive Tollens test?
 (b) What is the visible evidence for a positive Tollens test?
 (c) Write an equation showing the reaction in-volved in a positive Tollens test.
11. (a) What functional group is present in a com-pound that gives a positive Fehling test?
 (b) What is the visible evidence for a positive Fehling test?
 (c) Write an equation showing the reaction in-volved in a positive Fehling test.
12. Give the products of the reaction of the follow-ing with Tollens' reagent:
 (a) Butanal
 (b) Benzaldehyde
 (c) Methyl ethyl ketone
13. Write equations showing the aldol condensation for the following compounds:
 (a) Acetaldehyde (c) Butanal
 (b) Propanal (d) 3-Pentanone
14. How many aldol condensation products are pos-sible if a mixture of acetaldehyde and propanal is reacted with dilute NaOH?
15. Complete the following equations:

(a) $CH_3CH_2\overset{\overset{\displaystyle O}{\|}}{C}-H + CH_3CH_2CH_2OH \xrightarrow[]{\text{Dry HCl}} \rightleftharpoons$

(b) $CH_3\overset{\overset{}{\underset{\underset{\displaystyle O}{\|}}{C}}}{}CH_3 + \underset{\underset{\displaystyle OH\ OH}{|\ \ |}}{CH_2CH_2} \xrightarrow[]{\text{Dry HCl}} \rightleftharpoons$

(c) $CH_3CH_2\overset{\displaystyle O}{\overset{\|}{C}}-H + CH_3CH_2OH \underset{}{\overset{H^+}{\rightleftharpoons}}$

(d) ⬡$=O + CH_3OH \underset{}{\overset{H^+}{\rightleftharpoons}}$

(e) $CH_3CH_2CH_2CH(OCH_3)_2 \underset{H^+}{\overset{H_2O}{\longrightarrow}}$

16. 3-Hydroxypropanal can form an intramolecular cyclic hemiacetal. What is the structure of the hemiacetal?

17. Write equations for the following sequence of reactions:
  (a) Benzaldehyde + HCN $\longrightarrow$
  (b) Product from part (a) + $H_2O \longrightarrow$
  (c) Product from part (b)
  $\qquad + K_2Cr_2O_7 + H_2SO_4 \longrightarrow$

18. Write equations to show how you could prepare lactic acid, $CH_3CH(OH)COOH$, from acetaldehyde through a cyanohydrin intermediate.

19. What structural grouping must a molecule have, or be easily converted to, in order to give a positive iodoform test?

20. Which of these compounds will give a positive iodoform test?
  (a) CH_3OH
  (b) CH_3CH_2OH
  (c) $CH_3CH_2CH_2OH$
  (d) $CH_3\underset{\displaystyle OH}{\underset{|}{CH}}CH_3$

  (e) $CH_3\overset{\displaystyle O}{\overset{\|}{C}}-H$

  (f) $CH_3CH_2\overset{\displaystyle O}{\overset{\|}{C}}CH_3$

  (g) $CH_3-\underset{\displaystyle CH_3}{\underset{|}{\overset{|}{\overset{\displaystyle CH_3}{C}}}}-OH$

  (h) $CH_3\underset{}{CH}-\underset{\displaystyle O}{\overset{\displaystyle CH_3}{\overset{|}{\underset{|}{C}}}}-CH_3$

  (i) ⬡$-CH_2OH$

  (j) ⬡$-\overset{\displaystyle O}{\overset{\|}{C}}-CH_3$

21. There are four isomeric butyl alcohols. Which of them will give a positive iodoform test?

22. (a) Write an equation for the preparation of the Grignard reagent ethyl magnesium bromide, starting with ethyl bromide.
  (b) Using the Grignard reagent from part (a) and whatever other reagents are needed, write equations for the preparation of the following alcohols:

(1) 1-Propanol
(2) 3-Hexanol
(3) 3-Methyl-3-pentanol
(4) 2-Methyl-3-pentanol
(5) 1-Phenyl-2-butanol

23. What combination(s) of Grignard reagent and aldehyde or ketone are needed to prepare the following?
  (a) t-Butyl alcohol (d) Benzyl alcohol
  (b) 2-Pentanol (e) 1-Phenylethanol
  (c) 1-Hexanol

24. Give a simple visible chemical test that will distinguish between the compounds in each of the following pairs:

  (a) $CH_3CH_2\overset{\displaystyle O}{\overset{\|}{C}}-H$ and $CH_3\overset{\displaystyle O}{\overset{\|}{C}}CH_3$

  (b) $CH_3\overset{\displaystyle O}{\overset{\|}{C}}-H$ and $CH_3CH_2\overset{\displaystyle O}{\overset{\|}{C}}-H$

  (c) $CH_3CH_2\overset{\displaystyle O}{\overset{\|}{C}}-H$ and $CH_2{=}CH\overset{\displaystyle O}{\overset{\|}{C}}-H$

  (d) ⬡$-CH_2\overset{\displaystyle O}{\overset{\|}{C}}-H$ and ⬡$-\overset{\displaystyle O}{\overset{\|}{C}}-CH_3$

  (e) ⬡$-CH_2CH_2OH$ and ⬡$-\underset{\displaystyle OH}{\underset{|}{CH}}CH_3$

25. Three alcohols, A, B, and C, each have the formula $C_4H_{10}O$. Each compound was reacted with $K_2Cr_2O_7 + H_2SO_4$. Compounds A and B reacted; compound C did not react. The oxidation product of compound A gave a positive Tollens test; the oxidation product of compound B gave a positive iodoform test. Write structural formulas for compounds A, B, and C.

* **26.** Compound A, $C_5H_{12}O$, when reacted with $K_2Cr_2O_7 + H_2SO_4$ formed compound B, $C_5H_{10}O$. Compound B did not show a silver mirror when reacted with Tollens' reagent and gave a negative iodoform test. Identify compounds A and B.

* **27.** Compound D, $C_5H_{12}O$, when passed through a heated copper tube together with O_2, formed compound E, $C_5H_{10}O$. Compound E gave a positive Tollens test and a negative iodoform test. Upon dehydration followed by hydrogenation, compound D gave compound F, C_5H_{12} (2-methylbutane). Write all possible structures for compounds D and E.

28. Which of the following statements are correct?

(a) The functional group that characterizes aldehydes and ketones is called a carboxyl group.

(b) The carbonyl group contains a sigma and a pi bond.

(c) The carbonyl group is polar, with the oxygen atom being more electronegative than the carbon atom.

(d) The higher-molecular-weight aldehydes and ketones are very soluble in water.

(e) Ketones, like aldehydes, are easily oxidized to carboxylic acids.

(f) A compound of formula $C_6H_{12}O$ can be either an aliphatic aldehyde or ketone.

(g) Diethyl ketone has the same molecular formula as butyraldehyde.

(h) In aldehydes and ketones, the hydrogen atoms that are bonded to carbon atoms adjacent to the carbonyl group (alpha position) are more reactive than other hydrogen atoms in the molecule.

(i) In order for an aldehyde or a ketone to undergo the aldol condensation, it must have at least one alpha-hydrogen atom.

(j) Primary, secondary, and tertiary alcohols can be prepared by reacting aldehydes with a Grignard reagent.

(k) A hemiacetal has an alcohol and an ether group bonded to the same carbon atom.

(l) Acetals are stable in acid solution but not in alkaline solution.

(m) The reagent used for the iodoform test is NaOI (NaOH + I_2).

(n) The formula for iodoform is $CH_3\overset{\displaystyle O}{\overset{\|}{C}}-CI_3$.

(o) Formaldehyde is a gas, but it is usually handled in a solution.

(p) The major use for formaldehyde is for making plastics.

(q) Ethanal may be distinguished from propanal by use of Tollens reagent.

(r) The general formula for the saturated homologous series of aldehydes and ketones is $C_nH_{2n}O$.

(s) The compound C_2H_4O can be an aldehyde or a ketone.

(t) The name for $O\!\!=\!\!\overset{\displaystyle |}{\underset{\displaystyle H}{C}}-\overset{\displaystyle |}{\underset{\displaystyle H}{C}}\!\!=\!\!O$ is ethanedial.

(u) The oxidation product of 3-pentanol is diethylketone.

(v) $C_6H_5CH_2CH(OC_2H_5)_2$ is a ketal.

(w) When hydrolyzed, cyanohydrins form α-hydroxy acids.

(x) Of the three compounds ethanal, propanal, and butanal, ethanal has the lowest vapor pressure.

(y) Of the three compounds ethanal, propanal, and butanal, butanal has the highest boiling point.

(z) Reduction of aldehydes yields secondary alcohols.

24

Carboxylic Acids, Their Derivatives, and Amines

**After studying
Chapter 24,
you should be
able to**

1. Understand the new terms listed in Question A at the end of the chapter.
2. Give the common and IUPAC names of carboxylic acids.
3. Write structural formulas for saturated carboxylic acids, unsaturated acids, hydroxy acids, aromatic carboxylic acids, and dicarboxylic acids.
4. Tell how the water solubility of carboxylic acids varies with increasing molecular weight.
5. Relate the boiling points of carboxylic acids to their structures.
6. Write equations showing the effect of heat on malonic, succinic, and glutaric acids.
7. Write equations for the preparation of carboxylic acids by (a) oxidation of alcohols and aldehydes, (b) hydrolysis or saponification of esters and fats, (c) oxidation of aromatic hydrocarbons, and (d) hydrolysis of nitriles.
8. Write equations for reactions of carboxylic acids to form (a) salts, (b) esters, (c) amides, (d) N-substituted amides, and (e) acid chlorides.
9. Write equations for reactions of acid chlorides to form esters and amides.
10. Name and write structural formulas for amides.
11. Write common names, IUPAC names, and formulas of esters.
12. Identify the carboxylic acid and alcohol needed to prepare an ester.
13. Write the structure of a triacylglycerol (triglyceride) when given the fatty acid composition.
14. Tell how a fat differs from an oil.

15. Write equations illustrating the (a) hydrogenation, (b) hydrogenolysis, (c) hydrolysis, and (d) saponification of a fat or an oil.
16. Write the structural formulas for the three principal unsaturated carboxylic acids found in fats and oils.
17. Explain how a soap or synthetic detergent acts as a cleansing agent.
18. Explain why syndets are effective and soaps are not effective as cleansing agents in hard water.
19. Write structural formulas for a soap, a biodegradable synthetic detergent, and a nonbiodegradable detergent.
20. Explain how cationic, anionic, and nonionic detergents differ in how they act as cleansing agents.
21. Name and write structural formulas for amines.
22. Distinguish among primary, secondary, and tertiary amines.
23. Show that amines are bases in their reactions with water and with acids.
24. Write equations for reactions of amines to form substituted amides.
25. Write equations for the formation of amines from (a) alkyl halides plus ammonia, (b) reduction of amides with $LiAlH_4$, (c) reduction of nitriles with H_2 and Ni, and (d) reduction of aromatic nitro compounds.
26. Identify and write equations for the formation of quaternary ammonium salts.

Carboxylic acids and their derivatives are among the most widely distributed substances in nature. Acetic acid, the familiar substance that gives vinegar its sour taste, has been known since antiquity. Salicylic acid is the acid from which aspirin is made. Butyric acid is one of the foulest smelling substances imaginable, yet derivatives of butyric acid are found in butter and are used as flavorings and perfumes. Some acid derivatives are important to the sustenance of life. Two of the principal classes of foods are acid derivatives: Proteins consist primarily of amino acids, and fats are esters of carboxylic acids. A number of organic acids play essential roles in metabolic and energy-producing processes in plant and animal life.

24.1 Carboxylic Acids

carboxyl group   The functional group of the carboxylic acids is called a **carboxyl group** and is represented in the following ways:

$$-\overset{\overset{\displaystyle O}{\|}}{C}-OH \qquad or \qquad -COOH \qquad or \qquad -CO_2H$$

Carboxylic acids can be either aliphatic or aromatic:

$$R\overset{\overset{\displaystyle O}{\|}}{C}-OH \qquad CH_3\overset{\overset{\displaystyle O}{\|}}{C}-OH \qquad Ar\overset{\overset{\displaystyle O}{\|}}{C}-OH \qquad \text{⬡}\overset{\overset{\displaystyle O}{\|}}{C}-OH$$

Aliphatic   Aromatic

24.2   Nomenclature and Sources of Aliphatic Carboxylic Acids

Aliphatic carboxylic acids form a homologous series. The carboxyl group is always at the beginning of a carbon chain, and the C atom in this group is understood to be carbon number 1 in naming the compound.

To name a carboxylic acid by the IUPAC System, first identify the longest carbon chain including the carboxyl group. Then form the acid name by dropping the final e from the corresponding parent hydrocarbon name and add *oic acid*. Thus, the names corresponding to the one-, two-, and three-carbon acids are methanoic acid, ethanoic acid, and propanoic acid. These names are derived from methane, ethane, and propane.

CH_4	Methane	HCOOH	Methanoic acid
CH_3CH_3	Ethane	CH_3COOH	Ethanoic acid
$CH_3CH_2CH_3$	Propane	CH_3CH_2COOH	Propanoic acid

Other groups bonded to the parent chain are numbered and named as we have done previously. For example,

$$\overset{5}{C}H_3\overset{4}{C}H_2\overset{3}{C}H\overset{2}{C}H_2\overset{1}{C}OOH$$
$$|$$
$$CH_3$$

3-Methylpentanoic acid

Unfortunately the IUPAC method is not the only, nor the most used, method of naming acids. Organic acids are usually known by common names. Methanoic, ethanoic, and propanoic acids are called formic, acetic, and propionic acids, respectively. These names usually refer to a natural source of the acid and are not systematic. Formic acid was named from the Latin word *formica*, meaning ant. This acid contributes to the stinging sensation of ant bites. Acetic acid is found in vinegar and is so named from the Latin word for vinegar. The name of butyric acid is derived from the Latin term for butter, since it is a constituent of butterfat. The 6-, 8-, and 10-carbon acids are found in goat fat and have names derived from the Latin word for goat. These three acids—caproic, caprylic, and capric—along with butyric acid have characteristic and disagreeable odors. In a similar way the names of the 12-, 14-, and 16-carbon acids—lauric, myristic, and palmitic—are from plants from which the corresponding acid has been isolated. The name stearic acid is derived from a Greek word meaning beef fat or tallow, which is a good source of this acid. Many of the carboxylic acids, principally those having even numbers of carbon atoms ranging from 4 to about 20, exist in combined form in plant and animal fats. These are called *fatty acids* (see Chapter 28). Table 24.1 lists the common and IUPAC names, together with some of the physical properties, of the more important saturated aliphatic acids.

Another common nomenclature method using letters of the Greek alphabet ($\alpha, \beta, \gamma, \delta, \ldots$) has traditionally been used in naming certain acid derivatives,

Table 24.1 Names, formulas, and physical properties of saturated carboxylic acids

Common name (IUPAC name)	Formula	Melting point (°C)	Boiling point (°C)	Solubility in water[a]
Formic acid (Methanoic acid)	HCOOH	8.4	100.8	∞
Acetic acid (Ethanoic acid)	CH_3COOH	16.6	118	∞
Propionic acid (Propanoic acid)	CH_3CH_2COOH	−21.5	141.4	∞
Butyric acid (Butanoic acid)	$CH_3(CH_2)_2COOH$	−6	164	∞
Valeric acid (Pentanoic acid)	$CH_3(CH_2)_3COOH$	−34.5	186.4	3.3
Caproic acid (Hexanoic acid)	$CH_3(CH_2)_4COOH$	−3.4	205	1.1
Caprylic acid (Octanoic acid)	$CH_3(CH_2)_6COOH$	16.3	239	0.1
Capric acid (Decanoic acid)	$CH_3(CH_2)_8COOH$	31.4	269	Insoluble
Lauric acid (Dodecanoic acid)	$CH_3(CH_2)_{10}COOH$	44.1	225[b]	Insoluble
Myristic acid (Tetradecanoic acid)	$CH_3(CH_2)_{12}COOH$	54.2	251[b]	Insoluble
Palmitic acid (Hexadecanoic acid)	$CH_3(CH_2)_{14}COOH$	63	272[b]	Insoluble
Stearic acid (Octadecanoic acid)	$CH_3(CH_2)_{16}COOH$	69.6	287[b]	Insoluble
Arachidic acid (Eicosanoic acid)	$CH_3(CH_2)_{18}COOH$	77	298[b]	Insoluble

[a] Grams of acid per 100 g of water
[b] Boiling points of acids beginning with lauric acid are given at 100 mm Hg pressure instead of atmospheric pressure because thermal decomposition occurs before these acids reach their boiling points at atmospheric pressure.

especially hydroxy, amino, and halogen acids. When Greek letters are used, the carbon atoms, beginning with the one adjacent to the carboxyl group are labeled $\alpha, \beta, \gamma, \delta, \ldots$. When numbers are used, the numbers begin with the carbon in the —COOH group. Common and IUPAC nomenclature systems should not be intermixed.

$$\overset{\delta}{\underset{5}{C}} - \overset{\gamma}{\underset{4}{C}} - \overset{\beta}{\underset{3}{C}} - \overset{\alpha}{\underset{2}{C}} - \overset{\overset{\displaystyle O}{\parallel}}{\underset{1}{C}} - OH$$

$CH_3CH_2\underset{\underset{OH}{\mid}}{CH}COOH$	$CH_3\underset{\underset{NH_2}{\mid}}{CH}COOH$	CH_2ClCH_2COOH
Common name: α-Hydroxybutyric acid	α-Aminopropionic acid	β-Chloropropionic acid
IUPAC name 2-Hydroxybutanoic acid	2-Aminopropanoic acid	3-Chloropropanoic acid

PROBLEM

24.1

Write formulas for the following:
(a) 3-Chloropentanoic acid   **(b)** γ-Hydroxybutyric acid   **(c)** Phenylacetic acid

(a) *Pentanoic* (from pentane) indicates a five-carbon acid. Substituted on carbon 3 is a chlorine atom. Write five carbon atoms in a row. Make carbon 1 a carboxyl group, place a Cl on carbon 3, and add hydrogens to give each carbon four bonds. The formula is

$$CH_3CH_2CHClCH_2COOH$$

(b) *Butyric* (from butane) indicates a four-carbon acid. The gamma (γ) position is three carbons removed from the carboxyl group. Therefore, the formula is

$$HO—CH_2CH_2CH_2COOH$$

(c) *Acetic acid* is the familiar two-carbon acid. There is only one place to substitute the phenyl group and still call the compound an acid—that is, at the CH_3 group. Substitute a phenyl group for one of the three H atoms to give the formula:

$$⬡—CH_2COOH$$

24.3   **Physical Properties of Carboxylic Acids**

Each aliphatic carboxylic acid molecule is polar and consists of a carboxyl group and a hydrocarbon radical. These two unlike parts have great bearing on the physical, as well as chemical, behavior of the molecule as a whole. The first four acids, formic through butyric, are completely soluble (miscible) in water (Table 24.1). Beginning with pentanoic acid (valeric acid), the water solubility falls sharply and is only about 0.1 g of acid per 100 g of water for octanoic acid (caprylic acid). Acids of this series with more than eight carbons are virtually insoluble in water. The water-solubility characteristics of the first four acids are evidently determined by the highly soluble polar carboxyl group. Thereafter the water insolubility of the nonpolar hydrocarbon chain is dominant.

The polarity due to the carboxyl group is evident in the boiling-point data. Formic acid (HCOOH) boils at about 101°C. Carbon dioxide, a nonpolar substance of similar molecular weight, remains in the gaseous state until it is cooled to −78°C. In like manner, the boiling point of acetic acid (molecular weight 60) is 118°C, whereas nonpolar butane (molecular weight 58) boils at −0.6°C. The comparatively high boiling points for carboxylic acids are due to intermolecular attractions resulting from hydrogen bonding. In fact, molecular weight determinations on gaseous acetic acid (near its boiling point) show a value of about 120, indicating that two molecules are joined together to form a *dimer*, $(CH_3COOH)_2$.

Hydrogen bonding in
carboxylic acids

Acetic acid dimer

Saturated monocarboxylic acids that have fewer than ten carbon atoms are liquids at room temperature, whereas those with more than ten carbon atoms are waxlike solids.

Carboxylic acids and phenols, like mineral acids such as HCl, ionize in water to produce hydronium ions and anions. Carboxylic acids are generally weak; that is, they are only slightly ionized in water. Phenols are, in general, even weaker acids than carboxylic acids. For example, the ionization constant for acetic acid is 1.8×10^{-5} and that for phenol is 1.1×10^{-10}. Equations illustrating these ionizations are given below.

$$\text{HCl} + \text{H}_2\text{O} \longrightarrow \text{H}_3\text{O}^+ + \text{Cl}^-$$

Hydrogen chloride   Hydronium ion   Chloride ion

$$\text{CH}_3\overset{\text{O}}{\overset{\|}{\text{C}}}-\text{OH} + \text{H}_2\text{O} \rightleftharpoons \text{H}_3\text{O}^+ + \text{CH}_3\overset{\text{O}}{\overset{\|}{\text{C}}}-\text{O}^-$$

Acetic acid   Hydronium ion   Acetate ion

Phenol   Hydronium ion   Phenoxide ion

Carboxylic acids are very common in biological systems. Their tendency to ionize and form anions means that many biological molecules carry negative charges.

24.4 Classification of Carboxylic Acids

Thus far our discussion has dealt mainly with a single type of acid—that is, saturated monocarboxylic acids. But various other kinds of carboxylic acids are known. Some of the more important ones are discussed here.

Unsaturated Acids

An unsaturated acid contains one or more carbon–carbon double bonds. The first member of the homologous series of unsaturated carboxylic acids containing one carbon–carbon double bond is acrylic acid, $\text{CH}_2{=}\text{CHCOOH}$. The IUPAC name for $\text{CH}_2{=}\text{CHCOOH}$ is propenoic acid. Derivatives of acrylic acid are used to manufacture a class of synthetic polymers known as the acrylates (see Chapter 25). These polymers are widely used as textiles and in paints and lacquers.

Unsaturated carboxylic acids undergo the reactions of both an unsaturated hydrocarbon and a carboxylic acid.

Even one carbon–carbon double bond in the molecule exerts a major influence on the physical and chemical properties of an acid. The effect of a double bond can be seen when comparing the two 18-carbon acids, stearic and oleic. Stearic acid, $CH_3(CH_2)_{16}COOH$, a solid that melts at 70°C, shows only the reactions of a carboxylic acid. On the other hand, oleic acid, $CH_3(CH_2)_7CH{=}CH(CH_2)_7COOH$ (mp 16°C), with one double bond, is a liquid at room temperature and shows the reactions of an unsaturated hydrocarbon as well as those of a carboxylic acid.

Aromatic Carboxylic Acids

In an aromatic carboxylic acid, the carbon of the carboxyl group (—COOH) is bonded directly to a carbon in an aromatic nucleus. The parent compound of this series is benzoic acid. Other common examples are the three isomeric toluic acids:

Benzoic acid   *o*-Toluic acid   *m*-Toluic acid   *p*-Toluic acid

Dicarboxylic Acids

Acids of both the aliphatic and aromatic series that contain two or more carboxyl groups are known. These are called dicarboxylic acids. The simplest member of the aliphatic series is oxalic acid. The next member in the homologous series is malonic acid. Several dicarboxylic acids and their names are listed in Table 24.2.

The IUPAC names for dicarboxylic acids are formed by modifying the corresponding hydrocarbon names to end in *dioic acid*. Thus the two-carbon

Table 24.2   Names and formulas of selected dicarboxylic acids

Common name	IUPAC name	Formula
Oxalic acid	Ethanedioic acid	$HOOCCOOH$
Malonic acid	Propanedioic acid	$HOOCCH_2COOH$
Succinic acid	Butanedioic acid	$HOOC(CH_2)_2COOH$
Glutaric acid	Pentanedioic acid	$HOOC(CH_2)_3COOH$
Adipic acid	Hexanedioic acid	$HOOC(CH_2)_4COOH$
Fumaric acid	*trans*-2-Butenedioic acid	$HOOCCH{=}CHCOOH$
Maleic acid	*cis*-2-Butenedioic acid	$HOOCCH{=}CHCOOH$

acid is ethanedioic acid (derived from ethane). However, the common names for dicarboxylic acids are frequently used.

Oxalic acid is found in various plants including spinach, cabbage, and rhubarb. Among its many uses are bleaching straw and leather and removing rust and ink stains. Although oxalic acid is poisonous, the amounts present in the above-mentioned vegetables are usually not harmful.

Malonic acid is made synthetically but was originally prepared from malic acid, which is commonly found in apples and many fruit juices. Malonic acid is one of the major compounds used in the manufacture of the class of drugs known as barbiturates. When heated above their melting points, malonic acid and substituted malonic acids lose carbon dioxide to give monocarboxylic acids. Thus, malonic acid yields acetic acid when strongly heated:

$$\overset{\displaystyle \text{COOH}}{\underset{\displaystyle \text{COOH}}{\overset{\displaystyle |}{\underset{\displaystyle |}{\text{CH}_2}}}} \quad \xrightarrow{150°C} \quad \text{CH}_3\text{COOH} + \text{CO}_2\uparrow$$

Malonic acid   Acetic acid

Malonic acid is used as the biological precursor for the synthesis of fatty acids. In living cells, when malonic acid loses carbon dioxide, the acetic acid units are linked together to begin formation of fatty acids.

Succinic acid has been known since the 16th century, when it was obtained as a distillation product of amber. Succinic, fumaric, and citric acids are among the important acids in the energy-producing metabolic pathway known as the citric acid cycle (see Chapter 33). Citric acid is a *tricarboxylic acid* that is widely distributed in plant and animal tissue, especially in citrus fruits (lemon juice contains 5–8%). The formula for citric acid is

$$\underset{\displaystyle \text{CH}_2\text{COOH}}{\overset{\displaystyle \text{CH}_2\text{COOH}}{\text{HO}\!-\!\overset{\displaystyle |}{\underset{\displaystyle |}{\text{C}}}\!-\!\text{COOH}}}$$

Citric acid

When succinic acid is heated, it loses water, forming succinic anhydride, an acid anhydride. Glutaric acid behaves similarly.

$$\begin{array}{c}\text{CH}_2-\text{C} \diagup^{\displaystyle O} \diagdown_{\displaystyle O\,H} \\ | \qquad\qquad\qquad \diagdown_{\displaystyle O\,H} \\ \text{CH}_2-\text{C} \diagdown_{\displaystyle O} \end{array} \xrightarrow{\Delta} \begin{array}{c}\text{CH}_2-\text{C} \diagup^{\displaystyle O} \\ | \qquad\qquad \diagdown_{\displaystyle O} \\ \text{CH}_2-\text{C} \diagdown_{\displaystyle O} \end{array} + \text{H}_2\text{O}$$

Succinic acid   Succinic anhydride

Adipic acid is the most important commercial dicarboxylic acid. It is made from benzene by converting it first to cyclohexene and then by oxidation to adipic acid. About 5.9×10^8 kg (1.3×10^9 lb) of adipic acid are produced annually in the United States. Most of the adipic acid is used to produce nylon (Chapter 25). It is also used in polyurethane foams, plasticizers, and lubricating-oil additives.

Aromatic dicarboxylic acids contain two carboxyl groups attached directly to an aromatic nucleus. Examples are the three isomeric phthalic acids, $C_6H_4(COOH)_2$:

o-Phthalic acid
(Phthalic acid)

m-Phthalic acid
(Isophthalic acid)

p-Phthalic acid
(Terephthalic acid)

Dicarboxylic acids are *bifunctional*; that is, they have two sites where reactions can occur. Therefore they are often used as monomers in the preparation of synthetic polymers such as Dacron polyester (Section 25.7).

Hydroxy Acids

Lactic acid, found in sour milk, sauerkraut, and dill pickles, has the functional groups of both a carboxylic acid and an alcohol. Lactic acid is the end product when our muscles use glucose for energy in the absence of oxygen, a process called *glycolysis* (see Chapter 33). Salicylic acid is both a carboxylic acid and a phenol. It is of special interest because a family of useful drugs—the salicylates—are derivatives of this acid. The salicylates include aspirin and function as *analgesics* (pain relievers) and as *antipyretics* (fever reducers). The structural formulas of several hydroxy acids are shown below:

$CH_3CHCOOH$
  |
 OH

Lactic acid
(α-Hydroxypropionic acid)

Malic acid
(α-Hydroxysuccinic acid)

Salicylic acid
(o-Hydroxybenzoic acid)

Tartaric acid
(2,3-Dihydroxybutanedioic acid)

Amino Acids

Naturally occurring amino acids have this general formula; the amino group is in the alpha position:

$$
\begin{array}{c}
\quad\quad\ \ \overset{\displaystyle O}{\overset{\|}{}} \\
R\!-\!CH\!-\!C\!-\!OH \\
\quad\ |\\
\quad NH_2
\end{array}
$$

Each amino acid molecule has a carboxyl group that acts as an acid and an amino group that acts as a base. About 20 biologically important amino acids, each with a different group represented by R, have been found in nature. (In amino acids, R does not always represent an alkyl group.) The immensely complicated protein molecules, found in every form of life, are built from amino acids. Some protein molecules contain more than 10,000 amino acid units. Amino acids and proteins are discussed in more detail in Chapter 29.

24.5 Preparation of Carboxylic Acids

Many different methods of preparing carboxylic acids are known. We will consider only a few examples.

Oxidation of an aldehyde or a primary alcohol.   This is a general method that can be used to convert an aldehyde or primary alcohol to the corresponding carboxylic acid:

$$RCH_2OH + [O] \longrightarrow RCOOH$$

$$
\begin{array}{c}
\ \ \overset{\displaystyle O}{\overset{\|}{}} \\
RC\!-\!H + [O] \longrightarrow RCOOH
\end{array}
$$

Butyric acid (butanoic acid) can be obtained by oxidizing either 1-butanol or butanal with potassium dichromate in the presence of sulfuric acid. Aromatic acids may be prepared by the same general method. For example, benzoic acid is obtained by oxidizing benzyl alcohol.

$$CH_3CH_2CH_2CH_2OH \xrightarrow[\substack{H_2SO_4 \\ \Delta}]{Cr_2O_7^{2-}} CH_3CH_2CH_2COOH$$
$$\text{1-Butanol}\qquad\qquad\qquad\qquad\text{Butanoic acid}$$

$$
\underset{\text{Butanal}}{\overset{\displaystyle O}{\overset{\|}{CH_3CH_2CH_2C\!-\!H}}} \xrightarrow[\substack{H_2SO_4 \\ \Delta}]{Cr_2O_7^{2-}} \underset{\text{Butanoic acid}}{CH_3CH_2CH_2COOH}
$$

Benzyl alcohol   Benzoic acid

Carboxylic acids can also be obtained by the hydrolysis or saponification of esters (see Sections 24.7 and 24.8).

Oxidation of alkyl groups attached to aromatic rings.   When reacted with a strong oxidizing agent (alkaline permanganate solution or potassium dichromate and sulfuric acid), alkyl groups bonded to aromatic rings are oxidized to carboxyl groups. Regardless of the size or length of the alkyl group, the carbon atom adjacent to the ring remains bonded to the ring and is oxidized to a carboxyl group. The remainder of the alkyl group goes either to carbon dioxide or to a salt of a carboxylic acid. Thus sodium benzoate is obtained when toluene, ethylbenzene, or propylbenzene is heated with alkaline permanganate solution:

Toluene   Sodium benzoate

Ethylbenzene   Sodium benzoate

Propylbenzene   Sodium benzoate   Sodium acetate

Since the reaction is conducted in an alkaline medium, a salt of the carboxylic acid (sodium benzoate) is formed instead of the free acid. To obtain the free carboxylic acid, the reaction mixture is acidified with a strong mineral acid (HCl or H_2SO_4) in a second step.

Sodium benzoate   Benzoic acid

Hydrolysis of nitriles.   Nitriles, RCN, which can be prepared by adding HCN to aldehydes and ketones (Section 23.4) or by reacting alkyl halides with KCN, can be hydrolyzed to carboxylic acids:

$$RX \quad + \quad KCN \longrightarrow \quad RCN \; + \; KX$$

Alkyl halide   A nitrile

$$RCN + 2\,H_2O \xrightarrow{\;H^+\;} RCOOH + NH_4^+$$

$$CH_3CN + 2\,H_2O \xrightarrow{\;H^+\;} CH_3COOH + NH_4^+$$

24.6 Reactions of Carboxylic Acids

Acid–base reactions. Because of their ability to form hydrogen ions in solution, acids in general have the following properties:

1. Sour taste
2. Change blue litmus to red and affect other suitable indicators
3. Form water solutions with pH values of less than 7
4. Undergo neutralization reactions with bases to form water and a salt

All of the foregoing general properties of an acid are readily seen in low-molecular-weight carboxylic acids such as acetic acid. However, these general acid properties can be greatly influenced by the size of the hydrocarbon chain attached to the carboxyl group. In stearic acid, for example, taste, effect on indicators, and pH are not detectable because the large size of the hydrocarbon chain makes the acid insoluble in water. But it is an acid, and it will react with a base to form water and a salt. With sodium hydroxide, the equation for the reaction is

$$C_{17}H_{35}COOH + NaOH \longrightarrow C_{17}H_{35}COONa + H_2O$$

Stearic acid   Sodium stearate

Ester formation. Carboxylic acids react with alcohols to form esters:

$$\underset{\text{Carboxylic acid}}{RC\!-\!\boxed{OH}} \;+\; \underset{\text{Alcohol}}{R'O\,\boxed{H}} \;\underset{\text{H}^+}{\rightleftharpoons}\; \underset{\substack{\text{Ester} \\ \text{(R can be H,} \\ \text{but R' cannot be H)}}}{RC\!-\!OR'} \;+\; H_2O$$

(with the carbonyl $\overset{O}{\overset{\|}{}}$ groups shown above each RC)

$$\underset{\text{Formic acid}}{H\!-\!\overset{O}{\overset{\|}{C}}\!-\!OH} + CH_3CH_2OH \underset{\text{H}^+}{\rightleftharpoons} \underset{\text{Ethyl formate}}{H\!-\!\overset{O}{\overset{\|}{C}}\!-\!OCH_2CH_3} + H_2O$$

Many biologically important substances are esters (see Section 24.7).

Amide formation. Carboxylic acids react with ammonia to form ammonium salts:

$$\underset{\text{Carboxylic acid}}{RC\!-\!OH} + \underset{\text{Ammonia}}{NH_3} \longrightarrow \underset{\text{Ammonium salt}}{RC\!-\!O^-\,NH_4^+}$$

$$\underset{\text{Acetic acid}}{CH_3C\!-\!OH} + NH_3 \longrightarrow \underset{\text{Ammonium acetate}}{CH_3C\!-\!O^-\,NH_4^+}$$

Ammonium salts of carboxylic acids are ionic substances. Ammonium acetate, for example, is ionized and exists as ammonium ions and acetate ions both in the crystalline form and when dissolved in water.

When heated, ammonium salts of carboxylic acids are converted to *amides*:

$$
\underset{\text{Ammonium salt}}{\overset{\overset{\displaystyle O}{\|}}{RC-ONH_4}} \quad \overset{\Delta}{\longrightarrow} \quad \underset{\text{Amide}}{\overset{\overset{\displaystyle O}{\|}}{RC-NH_2}} + H_2O
$$

$$
\underset{\text{Ammonium acetate}}{\overset{\overset{\displaystyle O}{\|}}{CH_3C-ONH_4}} \quad \overset{\Delta}{\longrightarrow} \quad \underset{\substack{\text{Acetamide}\\ \text{(Ethanamide)}}}{\overset{\overset{\displaystyle O}{\|}}{CH_3C-NH_2}} + H_2O
$$

Amides are molecular substances and exist as molecules (not ions) both in the crystalline form and when dissolved in water. An amide contains the following characteristic structure:

$$
R-\boxed{\overset{\overset{\displaystyle O}{\|}}{C-N}}H_2
$$

Amide structure

In amides the carbon atom of a carbonyl group is bonded directly to a nitrogen atom of an —NH_2, —NHR, or —NR_2 group. The amide structure occurs in numerous substances, including proteins and some synthetic polymers such as nylon.

Two systems are in use for naming amides. The IUPAC name is based on the longest carbon chain that includes the amide group. The amide name is formed by dropping the *oic acid* ending from the corresponding IUPAC acid name and adding the suffix *amide*. Thus,

Methanoic acid   becomes   Methanamide

HCOOH

$$
HC\overset{\displaystyle O}{\underset{\displaystyle NH_2}{<}}
$$

Ethanoic acid   becomes   Ethanamide

CH_3COOH

$$
CH_3C\overset{\displaystyle O}{\underset{\displaystyle NH_2}{<}}
$$

In a like manner, the common names for amides are formed from the common names of the corresponding carboxylic acids by dropping the *ic* or *oic acid* ending and adding the suffix *amide*. Thus,

Formic acid   becomes   Formamide

HCOOH

$$HC\overset{\displaystyle O}{\underset{\displaystyle NH_2}{\diagup}}$$

Butyric acid   becomes   Butyramide

$CH_3CH_2CH_2COOH$

$$CH_3CH_2CH_2C\overset{\displaystyle O}{\underset{\displaystyle NH_2}{\diagup}}$$

Benzoic acid   becomes   Benzamide

—COOH

$$\overset{\displaystyle O}{\overset{\|}{C}}-NH_2$$

Formulas and names of selected amides are shown in Table 24.3.

Acid chloride formation. Thionyl chloride ($SOCl_2$) reacts with carboxylic acids to form acid chlorides, which are very reactive and can be used to synthesize other substances such as amides and esters:

$$\underset{\text{Acid}}{R\overset{\displaystyle O}{\overset{\|}{C}}-OH} + \underset{\substack{\text{Thionyl}\\\text{chloride}}}{SOCl_2} \longrightarrow \underset{\text{Acid chloride}}{R\overset{\displaystyle O}{\overset{\|}{C}}-Cl} + SO_2 + HCl$$

Table 24.3 Formulas and names of selected amides

Formula	IUPAC name	Common name
$HC\overset{O}{\overset{\|}{}}-NH_2$	Methanamide	Formamide
$CH_3C\overset{O}{\overset{\|}{}}-NH_2$	Ethanamide	Acetamide
$CH_3CH_2C\overset{O}{\overset{\|}{}}-NH_2$	Propanamide	Propionamide
$CH_3\overset{CH_3}{\overset{\|}{C}H}-\overset{O}{\overset{\|}{C}}-NH_2$	2-Methylpropanamide	Isobutyramide

$$\underset{\text{Acetyl chloride}}{CH_3\overset{\displaystyle O}{\overset{\|}{C}}-OH + SOCl_2 \longrightarrow CH_3\overset{\displaystyle O}{\overset{\|}{C}}-Cl + SO_2 + HCl}$$

Acid chlorides are extremely reactive substances. They must be kept away from moisture, or they will hydrolyze back to the acid:

$$R\overset{\displaystyle O}{\overset{\|}{C}}-Cl + H_2O \longrightarrow R\overset{\displaystyle O}{\overset{\|}{C}}-OH + HCl$$

Acid chlorides are more reactive than acids and can be used in place of acids to prepare esters and amides:

$$\underset{\text{Methyl acetate}}{CH_3\overset{\displaystyle O}{\overset{\|}{C}}-Cl + CH_3OH \longrightarrow CH_3\overset{\displaystyle O}{\overset{\|}{C}}-OCH_3 + HCl}$$

$$\underset{\text{Acetamide}}{CH_3\overset{\displaystyle O}{\overset{\|}{C}}-Cl + 2\,NH_3 \longrightarrow CH_3\overset{\displaystyle O}{\overset{\|}{C}}-NH_2 + NH_4Cl}$$

Acid anhydride formation.   Acid anhydrides (Section 13.9), like acid chlorides, are very reactive and can be used to synthesize carboxylic acid derivatives such as amides or esters. Acetic anhydride (ethanoic anhydride) is the most commonly used anhydride in laboratory synthesis and is produced by first dehydrating acetic acid to ketene, which then reacts with another acetic acid molecule to form the anhydride:

$$CH_3\overset{\displaystyle O}{\overset{\|}{C}}-OH \xrightarrow[\text{AlPO}_4]{700^\circ C} \underset{\text{Ketene}}{CH_2{=}C{=}O} + H_2O$$

$$CH_3\overset{\displaystyle O}{\overset{\|}{C}}-OH + CH_2{=}C{=}O \longrightarrow \underset{\text{Acetic anhydride}}{\begin{array}{c}CH_3-C\diagdown^{O} \\ \diagdown O \\ CH_3-C\diagup_{\diagup O}\end{array}}$$

The acid anhydrides are not used in organic synthesis as often as are the acid chlorides. However, in living cells, acid anhydrides are commonly used to activate carboxylic acids for further reaction.

24.7 Esters

Esters of carboxylic acids have the general formula RCOOR':

$$\begin{array}{c} O \\ \parallel \\ R\!-\!C\!-\!O\!-\!R' \end{array}$$

Ester structure

Carboxylic acids react with alcohols to form esters in an equilibrium reaction represented by this equation:

$$\begin{array}{c} O \\ \parallel \\ R\!-\!C\!-\!\boxed{OH} \\ \\ R'\!-\!O\!-\!\boxed{H} \end{array} \quad \overset{H^+}{\rightleftharpoons} \quad \begin{array}{c} O \\ \parallel \\ R\!-\!C\!-\!O\!-\!R' \end{array} + HOH$$

Ester

At first glance this looks like the familiar acid–base neutralization reaction. But this is not the case, because the alcohol does not yield OH^- ions, and the ester, unlike a salt, is a molecular not an ionic substance. The forward reaction of an acid and an alcohol is called *esterification*; the reverse reaction of an ester with water is called *hydrolysis*. The work of a chemist may call for manipulating reaction conditions to favor the formation of either esters or their component parts, alcohols and acids.

Naming Esters

Esters are alcohol derivatives of carboxylic acids. They are named in much the same way as salts. The alcohol part is named first, followed by the name of the acid modified to end in ate. The *ic* ending of the organic acid name is replaced by the ending *ate*. Thus in the IUPAC System, *ethanoic acid* becomes *ethanoate*. In the common names, *acetic acid* becomes *acetate*. To name an ester it is necessary to recognize the portion of the ester molecule that comes from the acid and the portion that comes from the alcohol. In the general formula for an ester, the RC=O comes from the acid, and the R'O comes from the alcohol:

Acid   Alcohol

The R' in R'O is named first, followed by the name of the acid modified by replacing *ic acid* with *ate*. The ester derived from ethyl alcohol and acetic acid is called ethyl acetate or ethyl ethanoate. Consider the ester formed from

CH_3CH_2COOH and CH_3OH:

Propanoic acid	Methanol	Methyl propanoate
(Propionic acid)	(Methyl alcohol)	(Methyl propionate)

Esters of aromatic acids are named in the same general way as those of aliphatic acids. For example, the ester of benzoic acid and isopropyl alcohol is

Isopropyl benzoate

Formulas and names for additional esters are given in Table 24.4.

Occurrence and Properties of Esters

Since many acids and many alcohols are known, the number of esters theoretically possible is very large. In fact, both natural and man-made esters exist in almost endless variety. Simple esters derived from monocarboxylic acids and monohydroxy alcohols are colorless, generally nonpolar liquids or solids. The low polarity of ester molecules is substantiated by the fact that both their water solubility and boiling points are lower than those of either acids or alcohols of similar molecular weights.

Table 24.4   Formulas and names of selected esters

Formula	IUPAC name	Common name	Odor or flavor
$CH_3C\!-\!OCH_2CH_2CHCH_3$ (with O, CH_3)	Isopentyl ethanoate	Isoamyl acetate	Banana, pear
$CH_3CH_2CH_2C\!-\!OCH_2CH_3$ (with O)	Ethyl butanoate	Ethyl butyrate	Pineapple
$HC\!-\!OCH_2CHCH_3$ (with O, CH_3)	Isobutyl methanoate	Isobutyl formate	Raspberry
$CH_3C\!-\!OCH_2(CH_2)_6CH_3$ (with O)	Octyl ethanoate	n-Octyl acetate	Orange
(benzene ring) $C\!-\!OCH_3$, OH (with O)	Methyl-2-hydroxy-benzoate	Methyl salicylate	Wintergreen

Low- and intermediate-molecular-weight esters (from both acids and alcohols up to about ten carbons) are liquids with characteristic, usually fragrant or fruity odors. The distinctive odor and flavor of many fruits is caused by one or more of these esters. The difference in properties between an acid and its esters is remarkable. For example, in contrast to the extremely unpleasant odor of butyric acid, ethyl butyrate has the pleasant odor of pineapple and methyl butyrate the odor of artificial rum. Esters are used in flavoring and scenting agents (see Table 24.4). They are generally good solvents for organic substances, and those having relatively low molecular weights are volatile. Therefore esters such as ethyl acetate, butyl acetate, and isoamyl acetate are extensively used in paints, varnishes, and lacquers.

High-molecular-weight esters (formed from acids and alcohols of 16 or more carbons) are waxes and are obtained from various plants. They are used in furniture wax and automobile wax preparations; for example, carnauba wax contains esters of 24- and 28-carbon fatty acids and 32- and 34-carbon alcohols. Polyesters with very high molecular weights, such as Dacron, are widely used in the textile industries (see Chapter 25).

PROBLEM

24.2

Name the following esters:

(a) $H-\overset{\overset{\displaystyle O}{\|}}{C}-OCH_2CH_2CH_3$ (b) $\underset{\bigcirc}{}-\overset{\overset{\displaystyle O}{\|}}{C}-OCH_2CH_3$ (c) $\begin{array}{c} O=C-OCH_2CH_3 \\ | \\ CH_2 \\ | \\ O=C-OCH_2CH_3 \end{array}$

(a) First identify the acid and alcohol components. The acid contains one carbon and is formic acid. The alcohol is propyl alcohol.

$H-\overset{\overset{\displaystyle O}{\|}}{C}-O-CH_2CH_2CH_3$

Formic acid   Propyl alcohol

Change the *ic* ending of the acid to *ate*, making the name formate or methanoate. The name of the ester then is propyl formate or propyl methanoate.

(b) The acid is benzoic acid; the alcohol is ethyl alcohol. Using the same procedure as in part (a), the name of the ester is ethyl benzoate.

(c) The acid is the three-carbon dicarboxylic acid, malonic acid. The alcohol is ethyl alcohol. Both acid groups are in the ester form. The name, therefore, is diethyl malonate.

Hydrolysis or saponification of esters. Both a carboxylic acid, RCOOH, and an alcohol, R'OH, can be obtained from the hydrolysis of an ester. This preparation of an acid from an ester is practical only when an ester of the desired acid is available. As a rule, a chemist is more likely to want to make an ester from an acid than to make an acid from an ester. However, large quantities of fatty acids and their salts (soaps) are obtained commercially by hydrolysis or saponification of animal and vegetable fats and oils. These fats and oils are esters of fatty acids and glycerol (Section 24.8).

Hydrolysis of an ester involves reaction with water to form an acid and an alcohol. The hydrolysis is catalyzed by strong acids (H_2SO_4 and HCl) or by certain enzymes.

$$\underset{\text{Ester}}{\overset{\displaystyle O}{\overset{\|}{RC}}-OR'} + H_2O \xrightarrow[\text{or enzyme}]{H^+} \underset{\text{Acid}}{\overset{\displaystyle O}{\overset{\|}{RC}}-OH} + \underset{\text{Alcohol}}{R'OH}$$

$$\underset{\text{Methyl propanoate}}{CH_3CH_2\overset{\displaystyle O}{\overset{\|}{C}}-OCH_3} + H_2O \xrightarrow{H^+} \underset{\text{Propanoic acid}}{CH_3CH_2COOH} + \underset{\text{Methanol}}{CH_3OH}$$

$$\underset{\text{Methyl salicylate}}{\overset{\displaystyle O}{\underset{\|}{}}} + H_2O \xrightarrow{H^+} \underset{\text{Salicylic acid}}{} + \underset{\text{Methanol}}{CH_3OH}$$

saponification   **Saponification** is the hydrolysis of an ester by a strong base (NaOH or KOH) to produce an alcohol and a salt (or soap):

$$\underset{\text{Ester}}{\overset{\displaystyle O}{\overset{\|}{RC}}-OR'} + NaOH \xrightarrow[\Delta]{H_2O} \underset{\substack{\text{Salt} \\ \text{(or soap)}}}{\overset{\displaystyle O}{\overset{\|}{RC}}-O^- \, Na^+} + \underset{\text{Alcohol}}{R'OH}$$

$$\underset{\text{Ethyl stearate}}{CH_3(CH_2)_{16}\overset{\displaystyle O}{\overset{\|}{C}}-OCH_2CH_3} + NaOH \xrightarrow[\Delta]{H_2O} \underset{\text{Sodium stearate}}{CH_3(CH_2)_{16}\overset{\displaystyle O}{\overset{\|}{C}}ONa} + CH_3CH_2OH$$

The carboxylic acid may be obtained by reacting the salt with a strong acid such as HCl:

$$CH_3(CH_2)_{16}COONa + HCl \longrightarrow \underset{\text{Stearic acid}}{CH_3(CH_2)_{16}COOH} + NaCl$$

24.8   Glycerol Esters

fats, oils

triacylglycerols

Fats and oils are esters of glycerol and predominantly long-chain fatty acids. Fats and oils are also called **triacylglycerols** or triglycerides, since each molecule is derived from one molecule of glycerol and three molecules of fatty acid.

Glycerol portion →

$$CH_2-O-C(=O)-R$$

$$R'-C(=O)-O-CH$$

$$CH_2-O-C(=O)-R''$$

General formula
for a triacylglycerol

$$CH_2-O-C(=O)-C_{17}H_{35}$$ (Stearic)

$$C_{15}H_{31}C(=O)-O-CH$$ (Palmitic)

$$CH_2-O-C(=O)-C_{11}H_{23}$$ (Lauric)

Typical triacylglycerol
containing three different
fatty acids

The structural formulas of triacylglycerol molecules vary because

1. The length of the fatty acid chain may vary from 4 to 20 carbons, but the number of carbon atoms in the chain is nearly always even.
2. Each fatty acid may be saturated or may be unsaturated and contain one, two, or three carbon–carbon double bonds.
3. A triacylglycerol may, and frequently does, contain three different fatty acids.

The most abundant saturated fatty acids in fats and oils are lauric, myristic, palmitic, and stearic acids (Table 24.1). The most abundant unsaturated acids in fats and oils contain 18 carbon atoms and have one, two, or three carbon–carbon double bonds. In all of these naturally occurring unsaturated acids, the configuration about the double bond is cis. Their formulas are:

$$CH_3(CH_2)_7CH=CH(CH_2)_7COOH$$
Oleic acid

$$CH_3(CH_2)_4CH=CHCH_2CH=CH(CH_2)_7COOH$$
Linoleic acid

$$CH_3CH_2CH=CHCH_2CH=CHCH_2CH=CH(CH_2)_7COOH$$
Linolenic acid

The major physical difference between fats and oils is that fats are solid and oils are liquid at room temperature (see Section 28.2). Since the glycerol part of the structure is the same for a fat and an oil, the difference must be due to the fatty acid end of the molecule. Fats contain a higher proportion of saturated fatty acids, whereas oils contain greater amounts of unsaturated fatty acids. The term *polyunsaturated* has been popularized in recent years; it means that each molecule of fat in a particular product contains several double bonds.

Fats and oils are obtained from natural sources. In general, fats come from animal sources and oils from vegetable sources. Thus, lard is obtained from hogs and tallow from cattle and sheep. Olive, cottonseed, corn, peanut, soybean, linseed, and other oils are obtained from the fruit or seed of their respective vegetable sources. Table 24.5 shows the major constituents of several fats and oils.

Table 24.5   Fatty acid composition of selected fats and oils

	Fatty acid (%)				
Fat or oil	Myristic acid	Palmitic acid	Stearic acid	Oleic acid	Linoleic acid
Animal fat					
Butter[a]	7–10	23–26	10–13	30–40	4–5
Lard	1–2	28–30	12–18	41–48	6–7
Tallow	3–6	24–32	14–32	35–48	2–4
Vegetable oil					
Olive	0–1	5–15	1–4	49–84	4–12
Peanut	—	6–9	2–6	50–70	13–26
Corn	0–2	7–11	3–4	43–49	34–42
Cottonseed	0–2	19–24	1–2	23–33	40–48
Soybean	0–2	6–10	2–4	21–29	50–59
Linseed[b]	—	4–7	2–5	9–38	3–43

[a] Butyric acid, 3–4%
[b] Linolenic acid, 25–58%

Triacylglycerols are the principal form in which energy is stored in the body. The caloric value per unit of mass is over twice as great as that for carbohydrates and proteins. As a source of energy, triacylglycerols can be completely replaced by either carbohydrates or proteins. However, some minimum amount of fat is needed in the diet, because fat supplies the nutritionally essential unsaturated fatty acids (linoleic, linolenic, and arachidonic) required by the body (see Section 28.2).

Hydrogenation of glycerides.   Addition of hydrogen is a characteristic reaction of the carbon–carbon pi bonds in ethylenic linkages. Industrially, low-cost vegetable oils are partially hydrogenated to obtain solid fats that are useful as shortening in baking or in making oleomargarine. In this process, hydrogen gas is bubbled through hot oil containing a finely dispersed nickel catalyst. The hydrogen adds to the carbon–carbon double bonds of the oil to saturate the double bonds and form fats:

$$H_2 + -CH=CH- \xrightarrow{\text{Ni}} -CH_2-CH_2-$$
$$\text{In oil or fat}$$

In actual practice, only some of the double bonds are allowed to become saturated. The degree of hydrogenation can be controlled to obtain a product of any desired degree of saturation. The products resulting from the partial hydrogenation of oils are marketed as solid shortening (Crisco, Spry, and so on) and are used for cooking and baking. Oils and fats are also partially hydrogenated to improve their keeping qualities. Rancidity in fats and oils results from air oxidation at points of unsaturation, producing low-molecular-weight aldehydes and acids of disagreeable odor and flavor.

Hydrogenolysis.   Triacylglycerols can be split and reduced in a reaction called hydrogenolysis (splitting by hydrogen). Hydrogenolysis requires higher temperatures and pressures and a different catalyst (copper chromite) than does hydrogenation of double bonds. Each triacylglycerol molecule yields a molecule of glycerol and three primary alcohol molecules. The hydrogenolysis of glyceryl trilaurate is represented as follows:

$$
\begin{array}{c}
\underset{\text{Glyceryl trilaurate}}{
\begin{array}{l}
\text{CH}_2\text{—O—}\overset{\displaystyle O}{\overset{\|}{\text{C}}}\text{—C}_{11}\text{H}_{23}\\[2mm]
\overset{\displaystyle O}{\overset{\|}{\text{C}_{11}\text{H}_{23}\text{—C}}}\text{—O—CH}\\[2mm]
\text{CH}_2\text{—O—}\overset{\displaystyle O}{\overset{\|}{\text{C}}}\text{—C}_{11}\text{H}_{23}
\end{array}}
\end{array}
\;+\;6\,\text{H}_2\;\xrightarrow[\Delta,\ \text{pressure}]{\substack{\text{Copper}\\ \text{chromite}}}\; 3\,\underset{\substack{\text{Lauryl alcohol}\\ \text{(1-Dodecanol)}}}{\text{CH}_3(\text{CH}_2)_{10}\text{CH}_2\text{OH}} \;+\; \underset{\text{Glycerol}}{\begin{array}{l}\text{CH}_2\text{OH}\\ \text{CHOH}\\ \text{CH}_2\text{OH}\end{array}}
$$

Long-chain primary alcohols obtained by this reaction are important, since they are used to manufacture other products, especially synthetic detergents (see Section 24.9).

Hydrolysis.   Triacylglycerols can be hydrolyzed, yielding fatty acids and glycerol. The hydrolysis is catalyzed by digestive enzymes at room temperatures and by mineral acids at high temperatures:

$$
\begin{array}{c}
\underset{\text{Triacylglycerol}}{
\begin{array}{l}
\text{CH}_2\text{—O—}\overset{\displaystyle O}{\overset{\|}{\text{C}}}\text{—R}\\[2mm]
\overset{\displaystyle O}{\overset{\|}{\text{R}'\text{—C}}}\text{—O—CH}\\[2mm]
\text{CH}_2\text{—O—}\overset{\displaystyle O}{\overset{\|}{\text{C}}}\text{—R}''
\end{array}}
\end{array}
\;+\;3\,\text{H}_2\text{O}\;\xrightarrow[\text{enzymes}]{\text{H}^+\ \text{or}}\; \underset{\substack{\text{Fatty acids}\\ \text{(3 molecules)}}}{\begin{array}{l}\text{RCOOH}\\ \text{R}'\text{COOH}\\ \text{R}''\text{COOH}\end{array}} \;+\; \underset{\text{Glycerol}}{\begin{array}{l}\text{CH}_2\text{OH}\\ \text{CHOH}\\ \text{CH}_2\text{OH}\end{array}}
$$

The enzyme-catalyzed reaction occurs in digestive reactions and in biological degradation (or metabolic) processes. The acid-catalyzed reaction is employed in the commercial preparation of fatty acids and glycerol.

Saponification.   Saponification of a fat or oil involves the alkaline hydrolysis of a triester. The products formed are glycerol and the alkali metal salts of fatty acids, which are called soaps. As a specific example, glyceryl tripalmitate reacts with sodium hydroxide to produce sodium palmitate and glycerol:

$$
\begin{array}{c}
\underset{\displaystyle\substack{| \\ \text{CH}_2\text{—O—C—C}_{15}\text{H}_{31}}}{\overset{\displaystyle\overset{O}{\|}}{}} \\
\end{array}
$$

$$
\text{C}_{15}\text{H}_{31}\overset{\overset{\displaystyle O}{\|}}{\text{C}}\text{—O—CH} \qquad + \ 3\ \text{NaOH} \ \xrightarrow{\ \Delta\ } \ 3\ \text{C}_{15}\text{H}_{31}\text{COONa} \ + \ \begin{array}{c} \text{CH}_2\text{OH} \\ | \\ \text{CHOH} \\ | \\ \text{CH}_2\text{OH} \end{array}
$$

$$
\underset{\text{Glyceryl tripalmitate}}{\overset{\displaystyle\overset{O}{\|}}{\text{CH}_2\text{—O—C—C}_{15}\text{H}_{31}}}
$$

Sodium palmitate (a soap)   Glycerol

Glycerol, fatty acids, and soaps are valuable articles of commerce, and the processing of fats and oils to obtain these products is a major industry.

24.9   Soaps and Synthetic Detergents

In the broadest sense possible, a detergent is simply a cleansing agent. Soap has been used as a cleansing agent for at least 2000 years and thereby is classified as a detergent under this definition. Beginning about 1930 a number of new cleansing agents that were superior in many respects to ordinary soap began to appear on the market. Because they were both synthetic organic products and detergents, they were called **synthetic detergents,** or syndets. A soap is distinguished from a synthetic detergent on the basis of chemical composition and not on the basis of function or usage.

synthetic detergents

Soaps

In former times soap-making was a crude operation. Surplus fats were boiled with wood ashes or with some other alkaline material. Today, soap is made in large manufacturing plants under controlled conditions. Salts of long-chain fatty acids are called **soaps.** However, only the sodium and potassium salts of carboxylic acids containing 12 to 18 carbon atoms are of great value as soaps, because of their abundance in fats.

soaps

Fat or oil + NaOH $\longrightarrow$ Soap + Glycerol

In order to understand how a soap works as a cleansing agent, let us consider sodium palmitate, $\text{CH}_3(\text{CH}_2)_{14}\text{COONa}$, as an example of a typical soap. In water this substance exists as sodium ions, Na^+, and palmitate ions, $\text{CH}_3(\text{CH}_2)_{14}\text{COO}^-$. The sodium ion is an ordinary hydrated metal ion. The cleansing property, then, must be centered in the palmitate ion. The palmitate ion contains both a **hydrophilic** (water-loving) and a **hydrophobic** (water-fearing) group. The hydrophilic end is the polar, negatively charged carboxylate group. The hydrophobic end is the long hydrocarbon group. The hydrocarbon group is soluble in oils and greases, but is not soluble in water. The hydrophilic carboxylate group is soluble in water.

hydrophilic

hydrophobic

The cleansing action of a soap is explained in this fashion: When the soap comes in contact with grease on a soiled surface, the hydrocarbon end of the soap dissolves in the grease, leaving the negatively charged carboxylate end exposed on the grease surface. Because the negatively charged carboxylate groups are strongly attracted by water, small droplets are formed, and the grease is literally lifted or floated away from the soiled object (see Figure 24.1).

The cleansing property of a soap is due to its ability to act as an emulsifying agent between water and water-insoluble greases and oils. The grease–soap emulsion is stable because the oil droplets repel each other due to the negatively charged carboxyl groups on their surfaces. Some insoluble particulate matter is carried away with the grease; the remainder is wetted and mechanically washed away in the water. Synthetic detergents function in a similar way.

Ordinary soap is a good cleansing agent in soft water, but it is not satisfactory in hard water because insoluble calcium, magnesium, and iron(III) salts are formed. Palmitate ions for example, are precipitated by calcium ions:

$$Ca^{2+}(aq) + 2\ CH_3(CH_2)_{14}COO^-(aq) \longrightarrow [CH_3(CH_2)_{14}COO]_2Ca(s)$$

Palmitate ion   Calcium palmitate

These precipitates are sticky substances and are responsible for "bathtub ring" and the sticky feel of hair after being shampooed with soap in hard water.

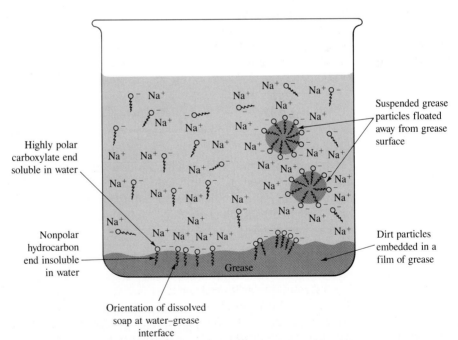

Figure 24.1 Cleansing action of soap: Dirt particles are embedded in a surface film of grease. The hydrocarbon ends of negative soap ions dissolve in the grease film, leaving exposed carboxylate groups. These carboxylate groups are attracted to water, and small droplets of grease-bearing dirt are formed and floated away from the surface.

Soaps are ineffective in acidic solutions because water-insoluble molecular fatty acids are formed:

$$CH_3(CH_2)_{14}COO^- + H^+ \longrightarrow CH_3(CH_2)_{14}COOH$$

Palmitic acid molecule

Synthetic Detergents

Once it was recognized that the insoluble hydrocarbon radical joined to a highly polar group was the key to the detergent action of soaps, chemists set out to make new substances that would have similar properties. About 1930, synthetic detergents (syndets) began to replace soaps, and at present about four pounds of syndets are sold for each pound of soap.

Although hundreds of substances having detergent properties are known, an idea of their general nature can be obtained from consideration of sodium lauryl sulfate and sodium dodecylbenzene sulfonate. Sodium lauryl sulfate is made by the following sequence of reactions, starting with lauryl alcohol (1-dodecanol) obtained from triacylglycerols or from petroleum:

$$CH_3(CH_2)_{10}CH_2OH \xrightarrow{H_2SO_4} CH_3(CH_2)_{10}CH_2OSO_3H \xrightarrow{NaOH} CH_3(CH_2)_{10}CH_2OSO_3^- \, Na^+$$

Lauryl alcohol   Lauryl hydrogen sulfate   Sodium lauryl sulfate

Sodium dodecylbenzene sulfonate is prepared from dodecylbenzene, which is synthesized from petroleum:

Dodecylbenzene   p-Dodecylbenzene sulfonic acid   Sodium p-dodecylbenzene sulfonate

Sodium lauryl sulfate and sodium p-dodecylbenzene sulfonate act in water in much the same way as sodium palmitate. The negative ion of each substance is the detergent. For example, like the palmitate ion, the negative lauryl sulfate ion has a long hydrocarbon chain that is soluble in grease and a sulfate group that is attracted to water:

$$CH_3CH_2CH_2CH_2CH_2CH_2CH_2CH_2CH_2CH_2CH_2CH_2{-}OSO_3^-$$

Nonpolar hydrophobic end,   Polar hydrophilic end,
grease soluble   water soluble

The one great advantage these synthetic detergents have over soap is that their calcium, magnesium, and iron(III) salts, as well as their sodium salts, are soluble in water. Therefore, they are nearly as effective in hard water as in soft water.

The foregoing are anionic detergents, because the detergent activity is located in negative ions. Other detergents, both cationic and nonionic, have been developed for special purposes. The detergent activity of a cationic detergent is located in a cation that has a long hydrocarbon chain and a positive charge.

$$CH_3(CH_2)_{14}CH_2 \overset{+}{\underset{\text{Water soluble,}}{\text{—N(CH}_3)_3}}$$

Grease soluble,   Water soluble,
hydrophobic   hydrophilic

Nonionic detergents are molecular substances. The molecule of a nonionic detergent contains a grease-soluble component and a water-soluble component. Some of these substances are especially useful in automatic washing machines because they have good detergent but low sudsing properties. The structure of a representative nonionic detergent is

$$CH_3(CH_2)_{10}CH_2 \text{—O—} (CH_2CH_2O)_7 \text{—CH}_2CH_2OH$$

Grease soluble   Water soluble

Biodegradability

biodegradable

Organic substances that are readily decomposed by microorganisms in the environment are said to be **biodegradable.** All naturally occurring organic substances are eventually converted to simple inorganic molecules and ions such as CO_2, H_2O, N_2, Cl^-, and SO_4^{2-}. Most of these conversions are catalyzed by enzymes produced by microorganisms. These enzymes are capable of attacking only certain specific molecular configurations that are found in substances occurring in nature.

Several years ago a serious environmental pollution problem arose in connection with synthetic detergents. Some of the early syndets containing highly branched-chain hydrocarbons had no counterparts in nature. Therefore, enzymes capable of degrading them do not exist, and the detergents were essentially nonbiodegradable and broke down very, very slowly. As a result these syndets accumulated in water supplies, where they caused severe pollution problems due to excessive foaming and other undesirable effects.

Happily, this particular pollution problem has been eliminated or at least greatly diminished. Detergent manufacturers, acting on the recommendations of chemists and biologists, changed from a branched-chain alkyl benzene to a straight-chain alkyl benzene raw material. Detergents containing the straight-chain alkyl groups are biodegradable.

$$CH_3CHCH_2CHCH_2CHCH_2CH \text{—} \bigcirc \text{—} SO_3^- Na^+$$
$$| | | |$$
$$CH_3 CH_3 CH_3 CH_3$$

A nonbiodegradable detergent

$$CH_3CH_2CH_2CH_2CH_2CH_2CH_2CH_2CH_2CH_2CH_2CH_2 \text{—} \bigcirc \text{—} SO_3^- Na^+$$

A biodegradable detergent

24.10   Amines

amine

An **amine** is a substituted ammonia molecule and has the general formula RNH_2, R_2NH, or R_3N, where R is an alkyl or an aryl group. Amines are classified as primary (1°), secondary (2°) or tertiary (3°), depending on the number of hydrocarbon groups attached to the nitrogen atom. Examples are given below.

Ammonia

Methylamine
(1° amine)

Methylethylamine
(2° amine)

Triethylamine
(3° amine)

Aniline
(1° amine)

Naming Amines

Common names for aliphatic amines are formed by naming the alkyl group or groups attached to the nitrogen atom followed by the ending *amine*. Thus, CH_3NH_2 is methylamine, $(CH_3)_2NH$ is dimethylamine, and $(CH_3)_3N$ is trimethylamine. A few more examples follow:

$CH_3CH_2NH_2$ $CH_3CH_2CH_2NH_2$

Ethylamine   Propylamine   Cyclohexylamine ($C_6H_{11}NH_2$)

In the IUPAC System—NH_2 is called an amino group, and amines are named as amino-substituted hydrocarbons using the longest carbon chain as the parent compound (for example, $CH_3CH_2CH_2NH_2$ is called 1-aminopropane).

The most important aromatic amine is aniline ($C_6H_5NH_2$). Derivatives are named as substituted anilines. To identify a substituted aniline in which the substituent group is attached to the nitrogen atom, an N- is placed before the group name to indicate that the substituent is bonded to the nitrogen atom and not to a carbon atom in the ring. For example, the following compounds are called N-methylaniline and N,N-dimethylaniline:

N-Methylaniline   N,N-Dimethylaniline

When a group is substituted for a hydrogen atom in the ring, the resulting ring-substituted aniline is named as we have previously done for naming aromatic compounds. The monomethyl ring-substituted anilines are known as toluidines. Study the names for the following substituted anilines:

Aniline

p-Toluidine
(p-Methylaniline)

N-Ethylaniline

m-Ethylaniline

o-Toluidine
(o-Methylaniline)

2,3-Dimethylaniline

p-Chloroaniline

Physiologically, aniline is a toxic substance. It is easily absorbed through the skin and affects both the blood and the nervous system. Aniline reduces the oxygen-carrying capacity of the blood by converting hemoglobin to methemoglobin. Methemoglobin is the oxidized form of hemoglobin in which the iron has gone from a +2 to a +3 oxidation state.

PROBLEM

24.3

Name the two compounds given:

(a) $CH_3CHCH_2-NH_2$ (with CH_3 branch)

(b) benzene ring with COOH and NH₂

(a) The alkyl group attached to NH_2 is an isobutyl group. Thus the common name is isobutylamine. The longest chain containing the NH_2 has three carbons. Therefore the parent carbon chain is propane, and the compound is called 1-amino-2-methylpropane.

(b) The parent compound on which the name is based is benzoic acid. With an amino group in the para position, the name is p-aminobenzoic acid. The acronym for p-aminobenzoic acid is PABA. In the human body PABA is a growth factor for certain bacteria. The main source of PABA for the human body is folic acid, an essential vitamin in the diet. Esters of PABA are some of the most effective ultraviolet screening agents and are used in sun-tanning lotions.

heterocyclic compounds Ring compounds in which all the atoms in the ring are not alike are known as **heterocyclic compounds.** The most common heteroatoms are oxygen, nitrogen, and sulfur. A number of the nitrogen-containing heterocyclic compounds are present in naturally occurring biological substances such as DNA, which controls heredity. The structural formulas of several nitrogen-containing heterocyclics follow:

Pyrrole	Pyridine	Piperidine	Pyrimidine	Purine
(C_4H_5N)	(C_5H_5N)	($C_5H_{11}N$)	($C_4H_4N_2$)	($C_5H_4N_4$)

Physical Properties

Amines are capable of hydrogen bonding with water. As a result the aliphatic amines with up to six carbons are quite soluble in water. The methylamines and ethylamine are flammable gases with a strong ammoniacal odor. Trimethylamine has a "fishy" odor. Higher-molecular-weight amines have obnoxious odors. The foul odors arising from dead fish and decaying flesh are due to amines released by bacterial decomposition. Two of these compounds are diamines, 1,4-butanediamine and 1,5-pentanediamine. Each compound contains two amino groups.

$$H_2NCH_2CH_2CH_2CH_2NH_2 \qquad\qquad H_2NCH_2CH_2CH_2CH_2CH_2NH_2$$

1,4-butanediamine	1,5-pentanediamine
(Putrescine)	(Cadaverine)

Simple aromatic amines are all liquids or solids. They are colorless or almost colorless when freshly prepared but become dark brown or red when exposed to air and light.

Alkaline Properties of Amines

In many respects amines resemble ammonia in their reactions. Thus, amines are bases and, like ammonia, ionize in water to produce OH^- ions:

$$\ddot{N}H_3 + \textcircled{H}OH \rightleftharpoons NH_4^+ + OH^-$$

Ammonia molecule	Ammonium ion	Hydroxide ion

Methylamine and aniline react in the same manner:

$$CH_3\ddot{N}H_2 + \textcircled{H}OH \rightleftharpoons CH_3NH_3^+ + OH^-$$

Methylamine molecule	Methylammonium ion	Hydroxide ion

Aniline molecule	Anilinium ion	Hydroxide ion

The ions formed are substituted ammonium ions. They are named by replacing the amine ending by ammonium and, for the aromatic amines, by replacing the aniline name by anilinium.

Dimethylammonium ion   o-Methylanilinium ion   N-Methylanilinium ion

Like ammonia, amines are weak bases. Methylamine is a slightly stronger base than ammonia, and aniline is considerably weaker than ammonia. The pH values for $0.1\,M$ solutions are: methylamine, 11.8; ammonia, 11.1; and aniline, 8.8.

Because amine groups form substituted ammonium ions under physiological conditions, they provide the positive charge that is found on some biological molecules. For example, neurotransmitters are often positively charged. The structures of two such transmitter compounds, dopamine and serotonin, are shown here:

Dopamine   Serotonin

The hormone epinephrine (adrenaline) carries a positive charge due to its amine functional group:

Epinephrine
(Adrenaline)

These amines, which are important in biological systems, are termed *biogenic amines*.

Preparation of Amines

Alkylation of ammonia and amines. The substitution of alkyl groups for hydrogen atoms of ammonia can be done by reacting ammonia with alkyl halides. Thus, in successive reactions, a primary, a secondary, and a tertiary amine can be formed.

$$NH_3 \xrightarrow{CH_3Br} CH_3NH_2 \xrightarrow{CH_3Br} (CH_3)_2NH \xrightarrow{CH_3Br} (CH_3)_3N$$

Methylamine   Dimethylamine   Trimethylamine

Tertiary amines can be further alkylated so that there are four organic groups bonded to the nitrogen atom. These types of compounds are called **quaternary ammonium salts.** For example,

$$CH_3-\ddot{N}-CH_3 + CH_3Br \longrightarrow CH_3-N^+-CH_3 \ Br^-$$

with CH_3 groups on each nitrogen.

Tetramethylammonium bromide

Quaternary ammonium salts are well known in biologically active compounds and in many popular medicinals. For example, acetylcholine, an active neurotransmitter in the brain is a quaternary salt. Choline is an important component of many biological membranes. Vitamin B_1 is marketed as the quaternary ammonium salt thiamine hydrochloride. Many well-known fabric softening agents used in laundering clothes are quaternary ammonium salts.

$$CH_3-N^+-CH_2CH_2OH \qquad CH_3-N^+-CH_2CH_2OCCH_3$$

Choline   Acetylcholine

Reduction of amides and nitriles.

Amides can be reduced with lithium aluminum hydride to give amines. For example, acetamide can be reduced to ethylamine; and when *N,N*-diethylacetamide is reduced, triethylamine is formed:

$$CH_3C-NH_2 \xrightarrow{LiAlH_4} CH_3CH_2NH_2$$

Ethylamine

$$CH_3C-N\begin{matrix}CH_2CH_3\\CH_2CH_3\end{matrix} \xrightarrow{LiAlH_4} (CH_3CH_2)_3N$$

Triethylamine

Nitriles, RCN, are also reducible to amines using hydrogen and a metal catalyst:

$$CH_3CH_2C\equiv N \xrightarrow{H_2/Ni} CH_3CH_2CH_2NH_2$$

Propionitrile   *n*-Propylamine

Reduction of aromatic nitro compounds.

Aniline, the most widely used aromatic amine, is made by reducing nitrobenzene. The nitro group can be reduced by several reagents; Fe and HCl, or Sn and HCl, are commonly used.

$$\text{C}_6\text{H}_5-\text{NO}_2 \xrightarrow[\text{HCl}]{\text{Sn}} \text{C}_6\text{H}_5-\text{NH}_3^+ \; \text{Cl}^- \xrightarrow{\text{NaOH}} \text{C}_6\text{H}_5-\text{NH}_2$$

Reactions of Amines

1. An amine will react with a strong acid to form a salt; for example, methylamine and hydrogen chloride react in this fashion:

$$\underset{\substack{\text{Methylamine} \\ \text{molecule}}}{\text{CH}_3\text{NH}_2(g)} \;+\; \underset{\substack{\text{Hydrogen chloride} \\ \text{molecule}}}{\text{HCl}(g)} \longrightarrow \underset{\substack{\text{Methylammonium} \\ \text{chloride (salt)}}}{(\text{CH}_3\text{NH}_3)^+ \; \text{Cl}^-}$$

Methylammonium chloride is made up of methylammonium ions, CH_3NH_3^+, and chloride ions, Cl^-. It is a white crystalline salt that in physical appearance resembles ammonium chloride very closely.

Aniline reacts in a similar manner, forming anilinium chloride:

$$\text{C}_6\text{H}_5-\text{NH}_2 + \text{HCl} \longrightarrow \text{C}_6\text{H}_5-\text{NH}_3^+\text{Cl}^-$$

Anilinium chloride

Many amines or amino compounds are more stable in the form of the hydrochloride salt. When the free amine is wanted, the HCl is neutralized to liberate the free amine. Thus,

$$\underset{\text{An amine hydrochloride salt}}{\text{RNH}_3^+ \; \text{Cl}^- \; (\text{or RNH}_2 \cdot \text{HCl})} + \text{NaOH} \longrightarrow \underset{\text{Free amine}}{\text{RNH}_2} + \text{NaCl} + \text{H}_2\text{O}$$

2. Amines react with organic acids as well as with mineral acids. For example, methylamine reacts with acetic acid according to the following equation:

$$\text{CH}_3\overset{\text{O}}{\overset{\|}{\text{C}}}-\text{O}(\text{H})(aq) + \text{CH}_3\ddot{\text{N}}\text{H}_2(aq) \longrightarrow \text{CH}_3\overset{\text{O}}{\overset{\|}{\text{C}}}-\text{O}^- \; \text{NH}_3^+\text{CH}_3(aq)$$

N-Methylammonium acetate

3. Primary and secondary amines react with acid chlorides to form substituted amides. For example,

$$\text{CH}_3\overset{\text{O}}{\overset{\|}{\text{C}}}-\text{Cl} + 2\,(\text{CH}_3\text{CH}_2)_2\text{NH} \longrightarrow \text{CH}_3\overset{\text{O}}{\overset{\|}{\text{C}}}-\text{N}\overset{\text{CH}_2\text{CH}_3}{\underset{\text{CH}_2\text{CH}_3}{\Big\langle}} + (\text{CH}_3\text{CH}_2)_2\text{NH}_2^+\text{Cl}^-$$

N,N-Diethylacetamide

Sources and Uses of Amines

Nitrogen compounds are found throughout the entire plant and animal kingdoms. Amines, substituted amines, and amides occur in every living cell.

Colorful dyes, vitamins, and many medicinals including the alkaloids quinine and morphine, sulfa drugs, and amphetamines are but a few of the classes of substances in which organic nitrogen compounds are found. The formulas for several well-known nitrogen compounds are shown below:

Sulfanilamide
(antibacterial agent)

Benzocaine (Ethyl-p-aminobenzoate)
(topical anesthetic)

Caffeine
(stimulant and diuretic)

Procaine hydrochloride (novocaine)
(local anesthetic)

Amphetamine (Benzedrene)
(stimulant)

Nicotinamide (niacin)
(antipellagra vitamin)

Nicotine
(from tobacco leaves, used as
an agricultural insecticide)

Methadone
(narcotic analgesic, substitute
for heroin)

Lysergic acid diethylamide (LSD)
(hallucinogen)

Benadryl
(antihistamine)

Ampicillin
(antibacterial agent)

QUESTIONS

A. *Review the meanings of the new terms intro-duced in this chapter.*

1. Carboxyl group
2. Saponification
3. Fats, oils
4. Triacylglycerols (triglycerides)
5. Synthetic detergents
6. Soaps
7. Hydrophilic
8. Hydrophobic
9. Biodegradable
10. Amine
11. Heterocyclic compounds
12. Quaternary ammonium salts

B. *Review questions*

1. Using a specific compound in each case, write structural formulas for the following:
   (a) An aliphatic carboxylic acid
   (b) An aromatic carboxylic acid
   (c) An α-hydroxy acid
   (d) An α-amino acid
   (e) A β-chloro acid
   (f) A dicarboxylic acid
   (g) An unsaturated acid
   (h) An ester
   (i) A nitrile
   (j) A sodium salt of a carboxylic acid
   (k) An amide
   (l) An acid halide
   (m) A triacylglycerol
   (n) A primary, a secondary, and a tertiary amine
   (o) An aromatic amine
   (p) A heterocyclic compound
   (q) A quaternary ammonium salt

2. Name the following compounds:
   (a) $CH_3(CH_2)_5COOH$

   (b)

   (c) $CH_3CH{=}CHCOOH$
   (d) $CH_3(CH_2)_7CH{=}CH(CH_2)_7COOH$

   (e)

   (f)

   (g) $CH_3(CH_2)_{16}COOH$
   (h) $CH_3CH_2CHCOOH$
        $\quad\quad\quad\ \ |$
        $\quad\quad\quad\ OH$
   (i) $CH_3CH_2COO^- \ Na^+$
   (j) $CH_3CH_2COO^- \ NH_4^+$

3. Write structures for the following compounds:
   (a) Caproic acid
   (b) Adipic acid
   (c) *o*-Toluic acid
   (d) Oxalic acid
   (e) β-Hydroxybutyric acid
   (f) *p*-Phthalic acid
   (g) Sodium benzoate
   (h) Linoleic acid
   (i) 2-Chloropropanoic acid
   (j) Ammonium benzoate
   (k) *p*-Aminobenzoic acid
   (l) *o*-Phthalic acid

4. Which of the following would have the more objectionable odor?
   (a) A 1% solution of butyric acid (C_3H_7COOH)
   (b) A 1% solution of sodium butyrate (C_3H_7COONa)
   Cite a satisfactory reason for your answer.

5. Suggest a logical scheme for obtaining reasonably pure stearic acid from a solution containing 2.0% sodium stearate, $CH_3(CH_2)_{16}COONa$, dissolved in water.

6. Assume that you have a 0.01 M solution of each of the following substances:
   (a) CH_3NH_2 (c) NaCl   (e) CH_3COOH

   (b) HCl   (d) NaOH   (f) ![benzene ring with OH]

   Arrange them in order of increasing pH (list the most acidic solution first).

7. Give at least one name, more if you can, for each of the following:
   (a) $\quad O$
        $\quad\quad \|$
        $HC{-}OCH_3$

(b)

(c)

(d)

$$CH_3CH_2C-OCH_2CH_3$$
with O double bonded to C

(e)

$$CH_3CH_2O-C-C-OCH_2CH_3$$
with two O double bonded

(f)

$$CH_2=CHC-OCH_3$$
with O double bonded to C

8. Write structural formulas for each:
(a) Methyl formate   (c) n-Propyl propanoate
(b) n-Octyl acetate   (d) Ethyl benzoate

9. Write the structural formula and name of the principal organic product for each of the following reactions:

(a) $CH_3(CH_2)_7CHCH(CH_2)_7COH + H_2 \xrightarrow{Ni}$ (with O double bonded)

(b) $CH_3CH_2C-OH + NH_3 \xrightarrow{\Delta}$ (with O double bonded)

(c)

$\xrightarrow[H_2SO_4]{Na_2Cr_2O_7}$

(d)

$\xrightarrow[\Delta]{NaMnO_4/NaOH}$

(e)

$\xrightarrow[\Delta]{NaMnO_4/NaOH}$

(f) $CH_3CH_2COOH + NaOH \longrightarrow$

(g) $CH_3(CH_2)_3CH_2COCH_2CH_2CH_3 + NaOH \xrightarrow{\Delta}$ (with O double bonded)

10. For each of the first eight acids listed in Table 24.1, give the common and IUPAC names of the corresponding amides.

11. Write structural formulas for the organic products of the following reactions:

(a)

$+ CH_3NH_2 \longrightarrow$

(b)

$+ H_2O \xrightarrow{H^+}$

(c) $CH_3CH_2CH_2Br + KCN \rightarrow A \xrightarrow{LiAlH_4} B$
Write structures for Products A and B.

(d) $CH_3CH_2C-NHCH_3 \xrightarrow{LiAlH_4}$ (with O double bonded)

(e) $CH_3CH_2CH_2CN \xrightarrow{H_2/Ni}$

12. Write structural formulas for the organic products of the following reactions:

(a)
$$\begin{array}{c} COOH \\ | \\ CH_3-CH \xrightarrow{150°C} \\ | \\ COOH \end{array}$$

(b)
$$\begin{array}{c} COOH \\ / \\ CH_2 \\ | \\ CH_2 \xrightarrow{\Delta} \\ \backslash \\ CH_2COOH \end{array}$$
Glutaric acid

(c)

$+ H_2O \xrightarrow[\Delta]{H^+}$

(d)

$+ CH_3CHCH_3 \xrightarrow[\Delta]{H^+}$ (with OH on middle carbon)

(e)
$$CH_3CH_2C-OH +$$ (with O double bonded)

$\xrightarrow{H^+}$

(f)
$$\begin{array}{c} COOH \\ | \\ CH_2 \quad + 2\ C_2H_5OH \xrightarrow{H^+} \\ | \\ COOH \quad (2\ mol) \end{array}$$

13. Write the structural formulas for the organic products formed in the following reactions:

(a)

$$\text{C}_6\text{H}_5\text{—}\overset{\overset{\displaystyle O}{\|}}{\text{C}}\text{—Cl} + \text{H}_2\text{O} \longrightarrow$$

(b) $\text{CH}_2\!\!=\!\!\text{CHCOOH} + \text{Br}_2 \longrightarrow$

(c) $\text{CH}_3\text{COOH} + \text{SOCl}_2 \longrightarrow$

(d) $\text{CH}_3\overset{\overset{\displaystyle O}{\|}}{\text{C}}\text{—Cl} + \text{NH}_3 \longrightarrow$

(e) $\text{CH}_3\overset{\overset{\displaystyle O}{\|}}{\text{C}}\text{—Cl} + \text{CH}_3\text{CH}_2\text{OH} \longrightarrow$

(f) $\text{CH}_3\overset{\overset{\displaystyle O}{\|}}{\text{C}}\text{—Cl} + \text{C}_6\text{H}_5\text{—NH}_2 \longrightarrow$

14. Write the structural formula of the ester that when hydrolyzed would yield
    (a) Methanol and acetic acid
    (b) Ethanol and formic acid
    (c) 1-Octanol and acetic acid
    (d) 2-Propanol and benzoic acid
    (e) Methanol and salicylic acid

15. Explain how the amide formed from ammonia and acetic acid differs in properties from the ammonium salt formed from ammonia and acetic acid.

16. Write structural formulas for the following compounds:
    (a) Isopropyl formate
    (b) Methyl palmitate
    (c) Diethyl adipate
    (d) Benzyl benzoate
    (e) Phenyl propionate
    (f) Methyl-2-aminopentanoate

17. What simple tests can be used to distinguish between the following pairs of compounds?
    (a) Benzoic acid and sodium benzoate
    (b) Maleic acid and malonic acid

18. The geometric configuration of naturally occurring unsaturated 18-carbon acids is all cis. Draw structural formulas for
    (a) *cis*-Oleic acid (b) *cis,cis*-Linoleic acid

19. Write the structural formula of a triacylglycerol that contains one unit each of lauric acid, pal-

mitic acid, and stearic acid. How many other triacylglycerols each containing all three of these acids, are possible?

20. Triolein (glyceryl trioleate) has this structure:

$$\begin{array}{l} \text{CH}_2\text{—O—}\overset{\overset{\displaystyle O}{\|}}{\text{C}}(\text{CH}_2)_7\text{CH}\!\!=\!\!\text{CH}(\text{CH}_2)_7\text{CH}_3 \\[2pt] \,| \\[2pt] \text{CH—O—}\overset{\overset{\displaystyle O}{\|}}{\text{C}}(\text{CH}_2)_7\text{CH}\!\!=\!\!\text{CH}(\text{CH}_2)_7\text{CH}_3 \\[2pt] \,| \\[2pt] \text{CH}_2\text{—O—}\overset{\overset{\displaystyle O}{\|}}{\text{C}}(\text{CH}_2)_7\text{CH}\!\!=\!\!\text{CH}(\text{CH}_2)_7\text{CH}_3 \end{array}$$

Write the names and formulas of all products expected when triolein is
    (a) Reacted with hydrogen in the presence of Ni
    (b) Reacted with water at high temperature and pressure in the presence of mineral acid
    (c) Boiled with potassium hydroxide
    (d) Reacted with hydrogen at relatively high pressure and temperature in the presence of a copper chromite catalyst

21. Which has the greater solubility in water?
    (a) Methyl propanoate or propanoic acid
    (b) Sodium palmitate or palmitic acid
    (c) Decylamine or decylammonium chloride
    (d) Sodium stearate or barium stearate
    (e) Phenol or sodium phenoxide

22. Write the structural formulas for each pair of compounds mentioned in Question 21.

23. Explain the difference between
    (a) A fat and an oil
    (b) A soap and a syndet
    (c) Hydrolysis and saponification

24. Cite the principal advantages synthetic detergents (syndets) have over soaps.

25. Would $\text{CH}_3(\text{CH}_2)_{12}\text{COOH}$ or $\text{CH}_3(\text{CH}_2)_{12}\text{COONa}$ be the more useful cleansing agent in soft water? Explain.

26. Would $\text{CH}_3(\text{CH}_2)_{11}\text{OSO}_3\text{Na}$ (sodium lauryl sulfate) or $\text{CH}_3\text{CH}_2\text{CH}_2\text{OSO}_3\text{Na}$ (sodium propyl sulfate) be the more effective detergent in hard water? Explain.

27. Explain the cleansing action of detergents.

28. Which one of the following substances is a good detergent in water? Is this substance a nonionic, anionic, or cationic detergent?

(a) $C_{16}H_{33}N(CH_3)_3^+\ Cl^-$
Hexadecyltrimethyl
ammonium chloride

(b) $C_{16}H_{34}$
Hexadecane

(c) $C_{15}H_{31}COOH$
Palmitic acid
(Hexadecanoic acid)

(d)
$$C_{15}H_{31}\overset{\overset{O}{\|}}{C}-O-C_{16}H_{33}$$
Cetyl palmitate
(Hexadecyl hexadecanoate)

29. Oleomargarine consists principally of a relatively small amount of water emulsified in vegetable or animal fats and oils. Monoacylglycerols (monoglycerides) such as glycerol monooleate,

$$C_{17}H_{33}\overset{\overset{O}{\|}}{C}-O-CH_2-\underset{\underset{OH}{|}}{CH}-\underset{\underset{OH}{|}}{CH_2}$$

are often used in small quantities in making oleomargarine.
(a) What is the function of the monoacylglycerols?
(b) Explain how this function is achieved.

30. If 1.00 kg of triolein (glyceryl trioleate) is converted to tristearin (glyceryl tristearate) by hydrogenation.
(a) How many liters of hydrogen (at STP) are required?
(b) What is the weight of the tristearin that is produced?

31. Low-molecular-weight aliphatic amines generally have odors suggestive of ammonia and/or stale fish. Which would have the more objectionable odor? Give a satisfactory reason for your answer.
(a) A 1% trimethylamine solution in 1.0 M H_2SO_4 or
(b) A 1% trimethylamine solution in 1.0 M NaOH

32. Draw structural formulas for
(a) All the amines of formula C_3H_9N
(b) All the amines of formula $C_4H_{11}N$
(c) All the quaternary ammonium salts of formula $C_4H_{12}N^+Cl^-$

33. Name the following compounds:

(a)

(b) $CH_3CH_2NH_3^+Br^+$

(c)

(d)

(e)

(f) $CH_3\overset{\overset{}{}}{C}-NHC_2H_5$ with O below

(g)

(h)

(i)

(j) $(C_2H_5)_4N^+\ I^-$

(k)

34. Draw structural formulas for the following compounds:
(a) Methylethylamine
(b) Tributylamine
(c) Aniline
(d) Ethylammonium chloride
(e) N-Methylanilinium chloride
(f) 1,4-Butanediamine
(g) N,N-dimethylaniline
(h) Ethylisopropylmethylamine
(i) Pyridine
(j) 2-Amino-1-pentanol

35. Write equations to show how each conversion may be accomplished. (Some conversions may require more than one step.)
(a) $CH_3CH_2CH_2Br \longrightarrow CH_3CH_2CH_2NH_2$
(b) $CH_3CH_2CH_2Br \longrightarrow CH_3CH_2CH_2CH_2NH_2$

(c)

36. (a) What is a heterocyclic compound?

(b) How many heterocyclic rings are present in (1) LSD, (2) ampicillin, (3) methadone, and (4) nicotine?

37. Which acid will require more base for neutralization?
    (a) 1 g of acetic acid or
    (b) 1 g of propanoic acid
    Explain your answer.

38. Starting with ethyl alcohol as the only source of organic material and using any other reagents you desire, write equations to show the synthesis of
    (a) Acetic acid   (c) N-Ethylacetamide
    (b) Ethyl acetate (d) β-Hydroxybutyric acid

39. Upon hydrolysis, an ester of formula $C_6H_{12}O_2$ yields an acid A and an alcohol B. When B is oxidized, it yields a product identical to A. What is the structure of the ester? Explain your answer.

40. Which of these statements are correct?
    (a) Carboxylic acids can be either aliphatic or aromatic.
    (b) The functional group —COOH is known as a carboxyl group.
    (c) The name for $CH_3CH_2CHBrCH_2COOH$ is γ-bromovaleric acid.
    (d) Acetic acid is a stronger acid than hydrochloric acid.
    (e) Benzoic acid is more soluble in water than sodium benzoate.
    (f) Carboxylic acids have relatively high boiling points because of hydrogen bonding between molecules.
    (g) The formula $C_{17}H_{33}COOH$ represents oleic acid.
    (h) Fumaric and maleic acids are cis–trans isomers.
    (i) If $CH_3CH_2CH_2COCl$ is allowed to come into contact with water, it will be hydrolyzed to butyric acid.
    (j) Volatile esters generally have a pleasant smell.
    (k) The common name for CH_3CONH_2 is methanamide.
    (l) The general formula for a primary amine is

    $$RC\!-\!NH_2$$
    $$\|$$
    $$O$$

    (m) Glycerol is a trihydroxy alcohol.
    (n) Fatty acids in fats usually have an even number of carbon atoms.
    (o) Fats and oils are esters of glycerol.
    (p) Oils are largely of vegetable origin.
    (q) The presence of unsaturation in the acid component of a fat tends to raise its melting point compared with the corresponding saturated compound.
    (r) Alkali metal salts of long-chain fatty acids are called soaps.
    (s) The name for $[(CH_3)_2CH]_2NH$ is isopropyl amine.
    (t) Aniline is soluble in dilute HCl because it forms a soluble salt.
    (u) Most amines have pleasant odors.
    (v) Lactic acid is an α-amino acid.
    (w) Sulfanilamide is an aniline derivative.
    (x) Isopropyl amine is a secondary amine.
    (y) Butylamine and diethylamine are isomers.
    (z) Aniline is made by the reduction of nitrobenzene.

25

Polymers: Macromolecules

After studying Chapter 25, you should be able to

1. Understand the new terms listed in Question A at the end of the chapter.
2. Write formulas for addition polymers when given the monomer(s).
3. Write formulas for condensation polymers when given the monomers.
4. Describe the properties of a thermoplastic polymer and a thermosetting polymer.
5. Explain the free radical mechanism for polymer formation.
6. Identify polymers from their trade names (for example, Dacron, nylon, and Teflon).
7. Explain the effect of cross-linking in polymers.
8. Draw a segment of the structural formula of natural rubber to illustrate the all-cis configuration.
9. Explain how butadiene-type polymers are formed.
10. Explain vulcanization and its effect on rubber.
11. Identify polymers by type (such as vinyl, polyester, polyamide, or polyurethane).

25.1 Introduction

Up to now we have dealt mainly with rather small organic molecules that contain up to 50 atoms and some (fats) that contain up to about 150 atoms. But there exist in nature some very large molecules (macromolecules) containing tens of thousands of atoms. Some of these, such as starch, glycogen, cellulose, proteins, and DNA, have molecular weights in the millions and are central to many of our life processes. Man-made macromolecules touch every phase of modern living. It is hard today to imagine a world without polymers. Textiles for clothing, carpeting, and draperies, shoes, toys, automobile parts, construction materials, synthetic rubber, chemical equipment, medical supplies, cooking utensils, synthetic leather, recreational equipment—the list could go on and on. All these and a host of others that we consider to be essential in our daily life are wholly or partly man-made polymers. Most of these polymers were unknown 60 years ago. The vast majority of these polymeric materials are based on petroleum. Because petroleum is a nonreplaceable resource, our dependence on polymers is another good reason for not squandering the limited world supply of petroleum.

Polyethylene is an example of a synthetic polymer. Ethylene, derived from petroleum, is made to react with itself to form polyethylene (or polythene). Polyethylene is a long-chain hydrocarbon made from many ethylene units:

$$n\ CH_2{=}CH_2 \longrightarrow -CH_2CH_2CH_2[CH_2CH_2]_nCH_2CH_2CH_2-$$

Ethylene   Polyethylene

A typical polyethylene molecule is made up of about 2,500–25,000 ethylene molecules joined in a continuous structure.

polymerization

polymer

monomer

The process of forming very large, high-molecular-weight molecules from smaller units is called **polymerization.** The large molecule, or unit, is called the **polymer** and the small unit, the **monomer.** The term *polymer* is derived from the Greek word *polumerēs*, meaning "having many parts." Ethylene is a monomer, and polyethylene is a polymer. Because of their large size, polymers are often called *macromolecules*. Another commonly used term is *plastics*. The word *plastic* means "to be capable of being molded, or pliable." Although not all polymers are pliable and capable of being remolded, the word *plastics* has gained general use and has come to mean any of a variety of polymeric substances.

25.2 Synthetic Polymers

Some of the early commercial polymers were merely modifications of naturally occurring substances. One chemically modified natural polymer, nitrated cellulose, was made and sold as Celluloid late in the 19th century. But the first commercially successful fully synthetic polymer, Bakelite, was made from phenol and formaldehyde by Leo Baekeland in 1909. This was the beginning of the modern plastics industry. Chemists began to create many synthetic polymers in the late 1920s. Since then, ever-increasing numbers of synthetic macromolecular materials have become articles of commerce. Even greater numbers of polymers have been made and discarded for technical or economic reasons. Polymers are presently used extensively in nearly every industry. For example, the electronics industry uses "plastics" in applications ranging from microchip production to fabrication of heat- and impact-resistant cases for the assembled products. In the auto industry, huge amounts of polymers are used as body, engine, transmission, and electrical-system components, as well as for tires. Vast quantities of polymers, with varied and sometimes highly specialized characteristics are used for packaging; for example, packaging for frozen foods must withstand subfreezing temperatures as well as those met in either conventional or microwave ovens.

Although there is a great variety of synthetic polymers on the market, they can be classified into the following general groups based on properties and uses:

1. Rubberlike materials or elastomers
2. Flexible films
3. Synthetic textiles and fibers
4. Resins (or plastics) for casting, molding, and extruding
5. Coating resins for dip, spray, or solvent-dispersed applications
6. Miscellaneous, including hydraulic fluids, foamed insulation, ion-exchange resins

25.3 Polymer Types

addition polymer

condensation polymer

thermoplastic polymers

thermosetting polymers

Two general types of polymers—addition and condensation—are known. An **addition polymer** is one that is produced by the successive addition of repeating monomer molecules. Polyethylene is an example of an addition polymer. A **condensation polymer** is one that is formed from monomers that react to split out water or some other simple substance.

Polymers are also classified as being either thermoplastic or thermosetting. Those that soften on reheating are **thermoplastic polymers;** those that set to an infusible solid and do not soften on reheating are **thermosetting polymers.** Thermoplastic polymers are formed when monomer molecules join end to end in a linear chain with little or no cross-linking between the chains. Thermosetting polymers are macromolecules in which the polymeric chains are cross-linked to form a network structure. The structures of thermoplastic and thermosetting polymers are illustrated in the schematic diagram in Figure 25.1.

25.4 Addition Polymerization

Ethylene polymerizes by addition to form polyethylene according to the reaction shown in Section 25.1. Polyethylene is the most important and widely used polymer on the market today. It is a tough, inert, but flexible thermoplastic material. Over 6.9×10^9 kg (1.5×10^{10} lb) of polyethylene are produced annually in the United States. Polyethylene is made into hundreds of different articles such as bread wrappers, toys, squeeze bottles, containers of all kinds, and electrical insulation.

The double bond is the key structural feature involved in the polymerization of ethylene. Ethylene derivatives, in which one or more hydrogen atoms have been replaced by other atoms or groups, can also be polymerized. This is often called *vinyl polymerization.* Many of our commercial synthetic polymers are

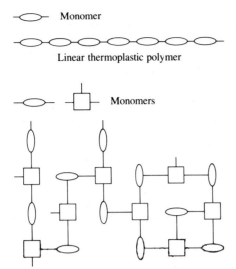

Figure 25.1   Schematic diagrams of thermoplastic and thermosetting polymer structures

made from such modified ethylene monomers. The names, structures, and uses of some of these polymers are given in Table 25.1.

Free radicals catalyze or initiate many addition polymerizations. Organic peroxides, ROOR, are frequently used for this purpose. The steps in the reaction are as follows.

Step 1. *Free radical formation.*   The peroxide splits into free radicals:

$$RO:OR \longrightarrow 2\ RO\cdot$$

Step 2. *Propagation of polymeric chain.*

$$RO\cdot + CH_2{=}CH_2 \longrightarrow ROCH_2CH_2\cdot$$

$$ROCH_2CH_2\cdot + CH_2{=}CH_2 \longrightarrow ROCH_2CH_2CH_2CH_2\cdot \quad \text{(and so on)}$$

Step 3. *Termination.*   Polymerization stops when the free radicals are used up:

$$RO(CH_2CH_2)_n\cdot + \cdot OR \longrightarrow RO(CH_2CH_2)_nOR$$

$$RO(CH_2CH_2)_n\cdot + \cdot(CH_2CH_2)_nOR \longrightarrow RO(CH_2CH_2)_n(CH_2CH_2)_nOR$$

Addition (or vinyl) polymerization of ethylene and its substituted derivatives yields saturated polymers—that is, polymer chains without carbon–carbon double bonds. The pi bond is eliminated when a free radical adds to an ethylene molecule. One of the electrons of the pi bond pairs with the unpaired electron of the free radical, thus bonding the radical to the ethylene unit. The other pi bond electron remains unpaired, generating a new and larger free radical. This new free radical then adds another ethylene molecule, continuing the building of the

Table 25.1 Polymers derived from modified ethylene monomers

Monomer	Polymer	Uses
$CH_2\!=\!CH_2$ Ethylene	$+CH_2\!-\!CH_2+_n$ Polyethylene	Packing material, molded articles, containers, toys
$CH_2\!=\!CH$ $\quad\;\; \mid$ $\quad\;\; CH_3$ Propylene	$\left(CH_2\!-\!CH\!-\!\right)$ $\qquad\;\; \mid$ $\qquad\;\; CH_3 \Big)_n$ Polypropylene	Textile fibers, molded articles, lightweight ropes, autoclavable biological equipment
$CH_2\!=\!C\!\!<^{CH_3}_{CH_3}$ Isobutylene	$+CH_2\!-\!C\!\!<^{CH_3}_{CH_3}\Big)_n$ Polyisobutylene	Pressure-sensitive adhesives, butyl rubber (contains some isoprene as copolymer)
$CH_2\!=\!CH$ $\quad\;\; \mid$ $\quad\;\; Cl$ Vinyl chloride	$+CH_2\!-\!CH+$ $\qquad\;\; \mid$ $\qquad\;\; Cl\;\Big)_n$ Polyvinyl chloride (PVC)	Phonograph records, garden hoses, pipes, molded articles, floor tile, electrical insulation, vinyl leather
$CH_2\!=\!CCl_2$ Vinylidene chloride	$+CH_2\!-\!CCl_2+_n$ Saran	Food packaging, textile fibers, pipes, tubing (contains some vinyl chloride as copolymer)
$CH_2\!=\!CH$ $\quad\;\; \mid$ $\quad\;\; CN$ Acrylonitrile	$+CH_2\!-\!CH+$ $\qquad\;\; \mid$ $\qquad\;\; CN\;\Big)_n$ Orlon, Acrilan	Textile fibers
$CF_2\!=\!CF_2$ Tetrafluoroethylene	$+CF_2\!-\!CF_2+_n$ Teflon	Gaskets, valves, insulation, heat-resistant and chemical-resistant coatings, linings for pots and pans
$CH_2\!=\!CH$ ⬡ Styrene	$+CH_2\!-\!CH+$ ⬡ $\;_n$ Polystyrene	Molded articles, styrofoam, insulation, toys, disposable food containers
$CH_2\!=\!CH$ $\quad\;\; \mid$ $\quad\;\; OC\!-\!CH_3$ $\qquad \| \!\!\!$ $\qquad O$ Vinyl acetate	$+CH_2\!-\!CH\longrightarrow$ $\qquad\;\; \mid$ $\qquad\;\; OC\!-\!CH_3$ $\qquad\quad \|$ $\qquad\quad O\;\Big)_n$ Polyvinyl acetate	Adhesives, paint, and varnish
$CH_2\!=\!C\!-\!CH_3$ $\qquad \mid$ $\qquad C\!-\!O\!-\!CH_3$ $\qquad \|$ $\qquad O$ Methylmethacrylate	$+CH_2\!-\!C(CH_3)\longrightarrow$ $\qquad\quad \mid$ $\qquad\quad C\!-\!OCH_3$ $\qquad\quad \|$ $\qquad\quad O\;\Big)_n$ Lucite, Plexiglas (acrylic resins)	Contact lenses, clear sheets for windows and optical uses, molded articles, automobile finishes

polymeric chain. This process is illustrated by the following electron-dot diagram:

$$H-\underset{RO\cdot}{\underset{|}{\overset{H}{\underset{|}{C}}}}::\underset{|}{\overset{H}{\underset{|}{C}}}-H \longrightarrow H-\underset{\underset{RO}{..}}{\underset{|}{\overset{H}{\underset{|}{C}}}}:\overset{H}{\underset{|}{C}}-H \quad (ROCH_2CH_2\cdot)$$

25.5 Butadiene Polymers

A diene is a compound that contains two carbon–carbon double bonds. Another type of addition polymer is based on the compound 1,3-butadiene or its derivatives.

$$\overset{1}{CH_2}=\overset{2}{CH}-\overset{3}{CH}=\overset{4}{CH_2}$$

1,3-Butadiene

Natural rubber is a polymer of isoprene (2-methyl-1,3-butadiene). Many synthetic elastomers or rubberlike materials are polymers of isoprene or of butadiene. Unlike the saturated ethylene polymers, these polymers are unsaturated; that is, they have double bonds in their polymeric structures.

$$n\ CH_2=\overset{\overset{\displaystyle CH_3}{|}}{C}-CH=CH_2 \longrightarrow -(CH_2-\overset{\overset{\displaystyle CH_3}{|}}{C}=CH-CH_2)_n-$$

Isoprene   Rubber polymer chain (Polyisoprene)

$$n\ CH_2=CH-CH=CH_2 \longrightarrow -(CH_2-CH=CH-CH_2)_n-$$

1,3-Butadiene   Butadiene polymer chain

$$n\ CH_2=\overset{\overset{\displaystyle Cl}{|}}{C}-CH=CH_2 \longrightarrow -(CH_2-\overset{\overset{\displaystyle Cl}{|}}{C}=CH-CH_2)_n-$$

2-Chloro-1,3-butadiene (Chloroprene)   Neoprene polymer chain (Polychloroprene)

In this kind of polymerization, the free radical adds to the butadiene monomer at carbon 1 of the carbon–carbon double bond. At the same time, a double bond is formed between carbon 2 and carbon 3, and a new free radical is formed at carbon 4. This process is illustrated in the following diagram:

$$H-\underset{RO\cdot}{\overset{\overset{\displaystyle H}{|}}{\underset{1}{C}}}:\overset{\overset{\displaystyle H}{|}}{\underset{2}{C}}:\overset{\overset{\displaystyle H}{|}}{\underset{3}{C}}:\overset{\overset{\displaystyle H}{|}}{\underset{4}{C}}-H \longrightarrow RO:\overset{\overset{\displaystyle H}{|}}{C}:\overset{\overset{\displaystyle H}{|}}{\underset{H}{C}}::\overset{\overset{\displaystyle H}{|}}{C}:\overset{\overset{\displaystyle H}{|}}{\underset{H}{C}}\cdot$$

Free radical   1,3-Butadiene   Radical chain lengthened by four carbon atoms

copolymer

One of the outstanding synthetic rubbers (styrene–butadiene rubber, SBR) is made from two monomers, styrene and 1,3-butadiene. These substances form a **copolymer**—that is, a polymer containing two different kinds of monomer units. Styrene and butadiene do not necessarily have to combine in a 1:1 ratio. In the actual manufacture of SBR polymers, about three moles of butadiene are used per mole of styrene. Thus, the butadiene and styrene units are intermixed, but in a ratio of about 3:1.

$$-CH_2CH=CHCH_2 + CH_2CH + CH_2CH=CHCH_2 + CH_2CH=CHCH_2-$$

Styrene	Butadiene
unit	unit

Segment of styrene–butadiene rubber (SBR)

The presence of double bonds at intervals along the chains of rubber and rubberlike synthetic polymers designed for use in tires is almost a necessity and, at the same time, a disadvantage. On the positive side, double bonds make vulcanization possible. On the negative side, double bonds afford sites where ozone, present especially in smoggy atmospheres, can attack the rubber, causing "age hardening" and cracking. Vulcanization extends the useful temperature range of rubber products and imparts greater abrasion resistance to them. The vulcanization process is usually accomplished by heating raw rubber with sulfur and other auxiliary agents. It consists of introducing sulfur atoms that connect or cross-link the long strands of polymeric chains. Vulcanization was devised through trial-and-error experimentation by the American inventor Charles Goodyear in 1839, long before any real understanding of the chemistry of the process was known. Goodyear's patent on "Improvement in India Rubber" was issued on June 15, 1844. In the segment of vulcanized rubber shown below, the chains of polymerized isoprene are cross-linked by sulfur–sulfur bonds giving the polymer more strength and elasticity.

$$
\begin{array}{ccc}
CH_3 & CH_3 & CH_3 \\
| & | & | \\
-CH_2C=CHCHCH_2C=CHCH_2CHC=CHCH_2- \\
| & | \\
S & S \\
| & | \\
S & S \\
| & | \\
-CH_2C=CHCHCH_2C=CHCH_2CHC=CHCH_2- \\
| & | & | \\
CH_3 & CH_3 & CH_3
\end{array}
$$

25.6 Geometric Isomerism in Polymers

The recurring double bonds in isoprene and butadiene polymers make it possible to have polymers with specific spatial orientation as a result of cis–trans isomerism. Recall from Section 21.4 that two carbon atoms joined by a double bond are not free to rotate and thus give rise to cis–trans isomerism. An isoprene polymer can have all-cis, all-trans, or a random distribution of cis and trans configurations about the double bonds.

Natural rubber is *cis*-polyisoprene with an all-cis configuration about the carbon–carbon double bonds. Gutta-percha, also obtained from plants, is a *trans*-polyisoprene with an all-trans configuration. Although these two polymers have the same composition, their properties are radically different. The cis natural rubber is a soft, elastic material, whereas the trans gutta-percha is a tough, nonelastic, hornlike substance. Natural rubber has many varied uses. Some uses of gutta-percha are for electrical insulation, dentistry, and golf balls.

All-cis configuration of natural rubber

All-trans configuration of gutta-percha

Chicle is another natural substance containing polyisoprenes. It is obtained by concentrating the latex from the sapodilla tree and contains about 5% cis-polyisoprene and 12% *trans*-polyisoprene. The chief use of chicle is in chewing gum.

Only random or nonstereospecific polymers are obtained by free radical polymerization. Synthetic polyisoprenes made by free radical polymerization are much inferior to natural rubber, since they contain both the cis and the trans isomers. But in the 1950s Karl Ziegler (1898–1973) of Germany and Guilio Natta (1903–1973) of Italy developed catalysts [for example, $(C_2H_5)_3Al/TiCl_4$] that allowed polymerization to proceed by an ionic mechanism, producing stereochemically controlled polymers. Ziegler–Natta catalysts made possible the synthesis of polyisoprene with an all-cis configuration and with properties fully comparable to those of natural rubber. This material is known by the odd but logical name *synthetic natural rubber*. In 1963 Natta and Ziegler were jointly awarded the Nobel prize for their work on stereochemically controlled polymerization reactions.

25.7 Condensation Polymers

Condensation polymers are formed by reactions between functional groups on adjacent monomer molecules. As a rule a smaller molecule, usually water, is eliminated in the reaction. The monomers must be at least bifunctional, and if cross-linking is to occur, there must be more than two functional groups on some monomer molecules.

Most biochemical polymers are of the condensation type. Proteins are polyamides, whereas nucleic acids are polyesters. Just as with synthetic polymers, biological polymers can have varied physical properties and varied functions. The collagen protein is used to make durable structures such as feathers, hair, and hooves. The elastin protein can be used for structures that need to stretch, such as tendons. Other proteins provide the mucous coating that protects our nasal passages. These differences in physical properties are determined by (1) the functional groups that are incorporated in the polymer and (2) the structure into which the atoms have been bonded. This generalization applies to synthetic polymers as well.

Many different condensation polymers have been synthesized. Important classes include the polyesters, polyamides, phenol–formaldehyde polymers, and polyurethanes.

Polyesters

Polyesters are joined by ester linkages between carboxylic acid and alcohol groups; the macromolecule formed may be linear or cross-linked. From the bifunctional monomers terephthalic acid and ethylene glycol, a linear polyester is obtained. Esterification occurs between the alcohol and acid groups on both ends of both monomers, forming long-chain macromolecules:

$$HOOC\text{—}\langle\bigcirc\rangle\text{—}COOH \qquad HOCH_2CH_2OH$$

Terephthalic acid   Ethylene glycol

$$-OCH_2CH_2O\left[\underset{\underset{}{\overset{O}{\overset{\|}{C}}}}{}\text{—}\langle\bigcirc\rangle\text{—}\underset{\underset{}{\overset{O}{\overset{\|}{C}}}}{}\text{—}OCH_2CH_2O\right]_n \underset{\underset{}{\overset{O}{\overset{\|}{C}}}}{}\text{—}\langle\bigcirc\rangle\text{—}\underset{\underset{}{\overset{O}{\overset{\|}{C}}}}{}-$$

This polymer may be drawn into fibers or formed into transparent films of great strength. Dacron and Terylene synthetic textiles and Mylar films are made from this polyester. In actual practice the dimethyl ester of terephthalic acid is used, and the molecule split out is methyl alcohol instead of water.

When trifunctional acids or alcohols are used as monomers, cross-linked thermosetting polyesters are obtained (see Figure 25.1). One common example is the reaction of glycerol and o-phthalic acid. The polymer formed is one of a group of polymers known as alkyd resins. Glycerol has three functional —OH groups, and phthalic acid has two functional —COOH groups:

$$\overset{\displaystyle OH}{\underset{\displaystyle |}{HOCH_2CHCH_2OH}} \qquad \langle\bigcirc\rangle\!\!\begin{array}{l}\text{—COOH}\\\text{—COOH}\end{array}$$

Glycerol   o-Phthalic acid

A cross-linked macromolecular structure is formed that, with modifications, has proved to be one of the most outstanding materials used in the coatings industry. Alkyd resins have been used as "baked-on" finishes for automobiles and household appliances. Each year more than 3.6×10^8 kg (800 million lb) of these resins are used in paints, varnishes, lacquers, electrical insulation, and so on.

Polyamides

Although there are several nylons, one of the best known and the first commercially successful polyamide is Nylon-66. This polymer was so named because it was made from two six-carbon monomers, adipic acid [$HOOC(CH_2)_4COOH$] and 1,6-diaminohexane [$H_2N(CH_2)_6NH_2$]. The polymer chains of polyamides contain recurring amide linkages. The amide linkage can be made by reacting a carboxylic acid group with an amine group:

$$R-\overset{\overset{\text{O}}{\|}}{C}-\underset{\substack{\text{Carboxylic} \\ \text{acid group}}}{\boxed{OH}} + \underset{\substack{\text{Amine} \\ \text{group}}}{H\boxed{N}-CH_2-R'} \xrightarrow{\Delta} R-\overset{\overset{\text{O}}{\|}}{C}-\underset{\substack{\text{Amide} \\ \text{linkage}}}{NH}-CH_2-R' + H_2O$$

The repeating structural unit of the Nylon-66 chain consists of one adipic acid unit and one 1,6-diaminohexane unit:

$$\underset{\text{Adipic acid}}{HOOC-(CH_2)_4-COOH} \qquad \underset{\substack{\text{1,6-Diaminohexane} \\ \text{(Hexamethylenediamine)}}}{H_2N-(CH_2)_6-NH_2}$$

$$-NH(CH_2)_6-NH\left[\overset{\overset{\text{O}}{\|}}{C}(CH_2)_4-\overset{\overset{\text{O}}{\|}}{C}-NH(CH_2)_6-NH\right]_n\overset{\overset{\text{O}}{\|}}{C}-(CH_2)_4-\overset{\overset{\text{O}}{\|}}{C}-$$

Segment of Nylon-66 polyamide

Nylon was developed as a synthetic fiber for the production of stockings and other wearing apparel. It was introduced to the public at the New York World's Fair in 1939. Nylon is used to make fibers for clothing and carpeting, filaments for fishing lines and ropes, bristles for brushes, and molded objects such as gears and bearings. For the latter application no lubrication is required, because nylon surfaces are inherently slippery.

Phenol–Formaldehyde Polymers

As noted earlier, a phenol–formaldehyde condensation polymer (Bakelite) was first marketed over 70 years ago. Polymers of this type are still widely used, especially in electrical equipment, because of their insulating and fire-resistant properties.

Each phenol molecule can react with formaldehyde to lose an H atom from the para position and from each of the ortho positions (indicated by arrows):

Each formaldehyde molecule reacts with two phenol molecules to eliminate water:

Similar reactions occur at the other two reactive sites on each phenol molecule, leading to the formation of the polymer. This polymer is thermosetting because it has an extensively cross-linked network structure. A typical section of this structure is illustrated as follows:

Phenol–formaldehyde polymer

Polyurethanes

The compound urethane has structural features of both an ester and an amide. Its formula is

$$H_2N-\overset{O}{\underset{\|}{C}}-OCH_2CH_3$$

Amide bond   Ester bond

A substituted urethane can be made by reacting an isocyanate with an alcohol. For example,

Phenyl isocyanate   N-Phenyl urethane

Diisocyanates and diols are both difunctional; therefore, they yield polymers called *polyurethanes*. The polyurethanes are classified as condensation polymers, although no water or other small molecule is split out when they are formed. From phenylene diisocyanate and ethylene glycol, we obtain a polyurethane that has a structure as shown:

p-Phenylene diisocyanate   Ethylene glycol

Segment of a polyurethane

Some polyurethanes are soft elastic materials that are widely used as *foam rubber* in upholstery and similar applications. There are many other applications, including automobile safety padding, insulation, life preservers, elastic fibers, and semirigid or rigid foams. Polyurethane can be made into a foam or spongy polymer by adding water during the polymerization or during the molding process. Water reacts with the isocyanate to produce carbon dioxide, which causes the polymer to foam. The effect is similar to that of baking powder releasing carbon dioxide in dough, causing it to rise and become light. The result is a polymer containing innumerable tiny gas-filled cavities that give the product a spongelike quality.

25.8 Silicone Polymers

The silicones are an unusual group of polymers. They include oils and greases, molding resins, rubbers (elastomers), and Silly Putty, the latter being a remarkable material that bounces like a rubber ball when dropped but that can be shaped like putty! Silicones have properties common to both organic and inorganic compounds. The mineral quartz (found in igneous rocks and sand) has the empirical formula SiO_2 and is actually an inorganic high polymer. Each silicon atom is bonded to four oxygen atoms, and each oxygen to two silicon atoms to form a three-dimensional structure:

$$
\begin{array}{ccccccc}
 & & | & & | & & \\
 & & O & & O & & \\
 & & | & & | & & \\
| & & | & & | & & | \\
-\text{Si}-\text{O}-\text{Si}-\text{O}-\text{Si}-\text{O}-\text{Si}- \\
| & & | & & | & & | \\
 & & O & & O & & \\
 & & | & & | & & \\
 & & -\text{Si}- & & -\text{Si}- & & \\
 & & | & & | & &
\end{array}
$$

The silicon–oxygen bonds are very strong, and quartz is stable at very high temperatures. But it is also very hard and brittle and therefore difficult to form into useful shapes.

Linear silicone polymers, also called silicones or polysiloxanes, consist of silicon–oxygen chains with two alkyl groups attached to each silicon atom:

$$
\begin{array}{ccccc}
\text{R} & & \left[\begin{array}{c}\text{R}\end{array}\right. & & \text{R} \\
| & & | & & | \\
-\text{O}-\text{Si}-\text{O}- & & \text{Si}-\text{O}- & & \text{Si}-\text{O}- \\
| & & | & & | \\
\text{R} & & \left.\begin{array}{c}\text{R}\end{array}\right]_n & & \text{R}
\end{array}
$$

The physical properties of silicones can be modified by (1) varying the length of the polymer chain, (2) varying the R groups, and (3) introducing cross-linking between the chains.

Because of their special properties, silicones have found a variety of uses despite their high cost. Some of their useful qualities are (1) good insulating properties (used in high-temperature applications), (2) little viscosity change over a wide temperature range (therefore they are used as lubricating oils and greases at extreme temperatures), (3) excellent water repellency (used to waterproof many types of surfaces), and (4) good biological compatibility (hence their use in medical and plastic-surgery applications). A few of the specific uses of silicone polymers are for coatings on printed electronic circuits, synthetic lubricants, hydraulic systems, brake fluids, electrical insulation, foam shields for nuclear power plants, solar energy, heat-transfer systems, hair sprays, body and hand lotions, automobile and furniture polishes, and urethane foams. Because of their stability and tissue compatibility, silicones are frequently used for permanent surgical implants. For example, heart pacemakers are encased in protective casings made of silicone, and silicones are used to replace destroyed nose cartilage.

QUESTIONS

A. *Review the meanings of the new terms introduced in this chapter.*

1. Polymerization
2. Polymer
3. Monomer
4. Addition polymer
5. Condensation polymer
6. Thermoplastic polymers
7. Thermosetting polymers
8. Copolymer

B. *Review questions*

1. How does condensation polymerization differ from addition polymerization?
2. What property distinguishes a thermoplastic polymer from a thermosetting polymer?
3. Show the free radical mechanism for the polymerization of propylene to polypropylene.
4. How many ethylene units are in a polyethylene molecule that has a molecular weight of approximately 25,000?
5. Write a structural formula showing the polymer that can be formed from
   (a) Ethylene   (c) 1-Butene
   (b) Propylene   (d) 2-Butene
6. Write structural formulas for the following polymers:
   (a) Saran   (d) Polystyrene
   (b) Orlon   (e) Lucite
   (c) Teflon
7. Write structures showing two possible ways in which vinyl chloride can polymerize to form polyvinyl chloride. Show four units in each structure.
8. (a) Write the structure for a polymer that can be formed from 2,3-dimethyl-1,3-butadiene.
   (b) Can 2,3-dimethyl-1,3-butadiene form cis and trans polymers? Explain.
9. Write the chemical structures for the monomers of
   (a) Natural rubber
   (b) Synthetic (SBR) rubber
   (c) Synthetic natural rubber
10. Why is the useful life of natural rubber and that of many synthetic rubbers shortened in smoggy atmospheres?
11. How are rubber molecules modified by vulcanization?
12. Natural rubber is the all-cis polymer of isoprene, and gutta-percha is the all-trans isomer. Write the structure for each polymer, showing at least three isoprene units.
13. Nitrile rubber (Buna N) is a copolymer of two parts of 1,3-butadiene to one part of acrylonitrile (CH_2=CHCN). Write a structure for this synthetic rubber, showing at least two units of the polymer.
14. Ziegler–Natta catalysts can orient the polymerization of propylene to form isotactic polypropylene—that is, polypropylene with all the methyl groups on the same side of the long carbon chain. Write the structure for (a) isotactic polypropylene and (b) another possible geometric form of polypropylene.
15. Write formulas showing the structure of
    (a) Dacron   (c) Bakelite
    (b) Nylon-66   (d) Polyurethane
16. Using p-cresol (p-CH_3—C_6H_4—OH) in place of phenol to form a phenol–formaldehyde polymer results in a thermoplastic rather than a thermosetting polymer. Explain why this occurs.

(continued on page 654)

17. Write structures for the monomers of each of the polymers shown below, and classify each as polyvinyl, polyester, polyamide, or polyurethane.

(a) $-CH_2CHCH_2CHCH_2CHCH_2CH-$

   $\quad\quad\quad C=O \quad C=O \quad C=O \quad C=O$

   $\quad\quad\quad OC_2H_5 \quad OC_2H_5 \quad OC_2H_5 \quad OC_2H_5$

(b) $-C-\bigcirc-C-OCH_2-\bigcirc-CH_2O-C-\bigcirc-C-OCH_2-\bigcirc-CH_2O-$

   with $\parallel\atop O$ groups

(c) $-C-NH$

   $\parallel\atop O$

   $\bigcirc-NHCOCH_2CH_2-O-C-NH-\bigcirc(CH_3)$

   $\quad\quad CH_3 \quad\quad\quad\quad O \quad\quad\quad\quad O$

   $\quad\quad\quad\quad\quad\quad NH-C-OCH_2CH_2O-$

   $\quad\quad\quad\quad\quad\quad\quad\quad\parallel\atop O$

(d) $-C-(CH_2)_8-C-NH-(CH_2)_6-NH-C-(CH_2)_8-C-NH-(CH_2)_6-NH-$

   $\quad\parallel\atop O \quad\quad\quad\quad\parallel\atop O \quad\quad\quad\quad\quad\quad\parallel\atop O \quad\quad\quad\quad\parallel\atop O$

(e) $\quad\quad CH_3 \quad\quad CH_3 \quad\quad CH_3$

   $-CH_2C-CH_2-C-CH_2-C-$

   $\quad\quad Cl \quad\quad\quad Cl \quad\quad\quad Cl$

(f) $\left[OCH_2-\bigcirc-CH_2O-C-\bigcirc-C \right]_n$

   with $\parallel\atop O$ groups

18. Why must at least some monomer molecules be trifunctional to form a thermosetting polyester?

19. Glyptal polyesters are made from glycerol and phthalic acid. Would this kind of polymer more likely be thermoplastic or thermosetting? Explain.

20. How is "foam" introduced into foam or sponge rubber materials?

21. Silicone polymers are more resistant to high temperatures than the usual organic polymers. Suggest an explanation for this property of the silicones.

22. Which of these statements are correct?
    (a) The process of forming macromolecules from small units is called polymerization.
    (b) The monomers in condensation polymerization must be at least bifunctional.
    (c) The monomers of Nylon-66 are a dicarboxylic acid and a diol.
    (d) Dacron and Mylar are both made from the same monomers.
    (e) Hexamethylene diamine is a secondary amine.
    (f) Teflon is an addition polymer.
    (g) Vulcanization was invented by Charles Goodrich.
    (h) The monomer for polystyrene is

    $\bigcirc-CH_2CH=CH_2$

    (i) Polyurethanes have both ester and amide bonds in their structure.
    (j) Bakelite is a copolymer of phenol and ethylene glycol.
    (k) The monomer of natural rubber is 2-methyl-1,3-butadiene.

26

Stereoisomerism

After studying Chapter 26, you should be able to

1. Understand the new terms listed in Question A at the end of the chapter.
2. Identify all asymmetric (chiral) carbon atoms in a given formula.
3. Explain the use of a polarimeter.
4. Explain how polarized light is obtained.
5. Calculate the specific rotation of a compound.
6. Explain the phenomenon of optical isomerism.
7. Determine whether a compound is chiral.
8. Draw projection formulas for all possible stereoisomers of a given compound. Label enantiomers, diastereomers, and meso compounds.
9. Calculate the maximum possible optical isomers given the formula of a compound.
10. Understand the meaning of (+) and (−) relative to the optical activity of a compound.
11. Draw the mirror image of a given structure.
12. Compare projection formulas to ascertain whether they represent identical compounds or enantiomers.
13. Compare the physical properties of enantiomers, diastereomers, and racemic mixtures.
14. Explain why meso compounds are optically inactive.
15. Determine whether optical isomers are formed in simple chemical reactions.

26.1   Review of Isomerism

The phenomenon of two or more compounds having the same number and kinds of atoms is isomerism. Thus isomers are different compounds that have the same composition and the same molecular formula.

There are two types of isomerism. In the first type, known as structural isomerism, the difference between isomers is due to a different structural arrangement of the atoms to form different molecules. For example, butane and isobutane, ethanol and dimethyl ether, and 1-chloropropane and 2-chloropropane are structural isomers:

$CH_3CH_2CH_2CH_3$ CH_3CH_2OH $CH_3CH_2CH_2Cl$
    Butane   Ethanol   1-Chloropropane

CH_3CHCH_3 CH_3OCH_3 $CH_3CHClCH_3$
    | Dimethyl ether   2-Chloropropane
   CH_3
  Isobutane

stereoisomerism

stereoisomers

In the second type of isomerism, the isomers have the same structural formulas but differ in the arrangement of the atoms in space. This type of isomerism is known as **stereoisomerism.** Thus, compounds that have the same structural formulas but differ in their spatial arrangement are called **stereoisomers.** There are two types of stereoisomers: cis–trans or geometric isomers, which we have already considered, and optical isomers, the subject of this chapter. The outstanding feature of optical isomers is that they have the ability to rotate plane-polarized light.

26.2   Plane-Polarized Light

plane-polarized light

Plane-polarized light is light that is vibrating in only one plane. Ordinary (unpolarized) light consists of electromagnetic waves vibrating in all directions (planes) perpendicular to the direction in which it is traveling. When ordinary light passes through a polarizer, it emerges vibrating in only one plane and is called plane-polarized light (Figure 26.1).

Polarizers can be made from calcite or tourmaline crystals or from a Polaroid filter, which is a transparent plastic containing properly oriented embedded crystals. Two Polaroid filters with their axes parallel will allow the passage of plane-polarized light. But when one filter is placed so that its axis is at right angles to that of the other filter, the passage of light is blocked and the filters appear black (Figure 26.2).

Specific Rotation

The rotation of plane-polarized light is quantitatively measured with a polarimeter. The essential features of this instrument are (1) a light source (usually a sodium lamp), (2) a polarizer, (3) a sample tube, (4) an analyzer (which is another matched polarizer), and (5) a calibrated scale (360°) to measure the number of

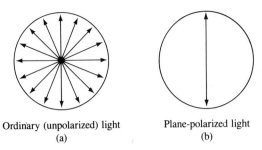

Ordinary (unpolarized) light   Plane-polarized light
(a)   (b)

Figure 26.1 (a) Diagram of ordinary light vibrating in all possible directions (planes) and (b) diagram of plane-polarized light vibrating in a single plane: The beam of light is coming toward the reader.

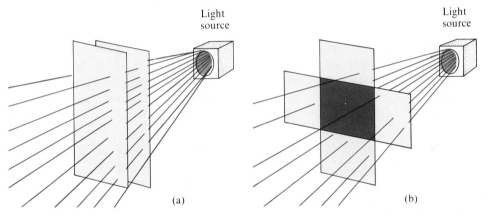

(a)   (b)

Figure 26.2 Two Polaroid filters (a) with axes parallel and (b) with axes at right angles: In (a), light passes through both filters and emerges polarized. In (b) the polarized light that emerges from one filter is blocked and does not pass through the second filter, which is at right angles to the first. With no light emerging, the filters appear black.

degrees the plane of polarized light is rotated. The calibrated scale is attached to the analyzer (see Figure 26.3). When the sample tube contains a solution of an optically inactive material, the axes of the polarizer and the analyzer are parallel and the scale is at zero degrees; the light passing through is at maximum intensity. When a solution of an optically active substance is placed in the sample tube, the plane in which the polarized light is vibrating is rotated through an angle (α). The analyzer is then rotated to the position where the emerging light is at maximum intensity. The number of degrees and the direction of rotation by the solution is then read from the scale as the observed rotation.

specific rotation

The **specific rotation**, [α], of a compound is the number of degrees that polarized light would be rotated by passage through 1 decimeter (dm) of a solution of the substance at a concentration of 1 gram per milliliter. The specific

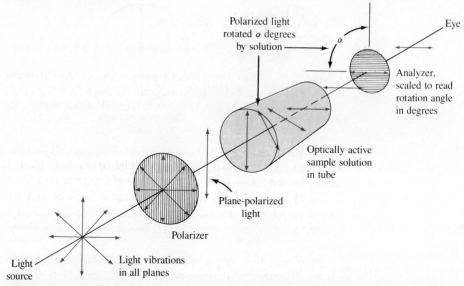

Figure 26.3   Schematic diagram of a polarimeter: This instrument is used to measure the angle α through which an optically active substance rotates the plane of polarized light.

rotation of optically active substances is listed in chemical handbooks along with other physical properties. The following formula is used to calculate specific rotation from polarimeter data:

$$[\alpha] = \frac{\text{Observed rotation in degrees}}{\left(\begin{array}{c}\text{Length of}\\\text{sample tube in decimeters}\end{array}\right)\left(\begin{array}{c}\text{Sample concentration in}\\\text{grams per milliliter}\end{array}\right)}$$

26.3   Optical Activity

optical activity

dextrorotatory

levorotatory

Many naturally occurring substances are able to rotate the plane of polarized light. Because of this ability to rotate polarized light, such substances are said to be **optically active.** When plane-polarized light passes through an optically active substance, the plane of the polarized light is rotated. If the rotation is to the right (clockwise), the substance is said to be **dextrorotatory;** if the rotation is to the left (counterclockwise), the substancce is said to be **levorotatory.**

Some minerals, notably quartz, rotate the plane of polarized light (in fact, optical activity was discovered in minerals). However, when such mineral crystals are melted, the optical activity disappears. This means that the optical activity of these crystals must be due to an ordered arrangement within the crystals.

In 1848 Louis Pasteur (1822–1895) observed that sodium ammonium tartrate,

= Carbon atom

A, B, C, D = Four different atoms or groups of atoms

Figure 26.4 Three-dimensional representation of an asymmetric carbon atom with four different groups bonded to it: The carbon atom is a sphere. Bonds to A and B project from the sphere toward the observer. Bonds to C and D project from the sphere away from the observer.

a salt of tartaric acid, exists as a mixture of two kinds of crystals. Pasteur carefully hand-separated the two kinds of crystals. Investigating their properties, he found that solutions made from either kind of crystal would rotate the plane of polarized light, but in opposite directions. Since this optical activity was present in a solution, it could not be caused by a specific arrangement within a crystal.

The tetrahedral arrangement of single bonds around a carbon atom makes asymmetry (lack of symmetry) possible in organic molecules. When four different atoms or functional groups are bonded to a carbon atom, the molecule formed will be asymmetric, and the carbon atom is called an **asymmetric carbon atom** (see Figure 26.4). In 1874 J. H. van't Hoff (1852–1911) and J. A. Le Bel (1847–1930) concluded that the presence of at least one asymmetric carbon atom in a molecule of an optically active substance is a key factor for optical activity. The first Nobel prize in chemistry was awarded to van't Hoff in 1901.

asymmetric carbon atom

Molecules of optically active substances must have at least one center of dissymmetry. Although optically active compounds are known that do not contain asymmetric carbon atoms (their center of dissymmetry is due to some other structural feature), most optically active organic substances do contain one or more asymmetric carbon atoms.

26.4 Projection Formulas

Molecules of a compound that contain one asymmetric carbon atom occur in two optically active isomeric forms. This is because the four different groups bonded to the asymmetric carbon atom can be oriented in space in two different configurations. It is important to understand how we represent such isomers on paper.

Let us consider the spatial arrangement of a lactic acid molecule, $CH_3CH(OH)COOH$, which contains one asymmetric carbon atom:

$$^1COOH$$
$$|$$
$$H—^2C^*—OH \qquad C^* = \text{Asymmetric carbon atom}$$
$$|$$
$$^3CH_3$$

Lactic acid

Figure 26.5 Methods of representing three-dimensional formulas of a compound that contains one asymmetric carbon atom. All three structures represent the same molecule.

Three-dimensional models are the best means of representing such a molecule, but by adopting certain conventions and using imagination, we can formulate the images on paper. The geometrical arrangement of the four groups about the asymmetric carbon (carbon 2) is the key to the stereoisomerism of lactic acid. The four bonds attached to carbon 2 are separated by angles of about 109.5°. Diagram I in Figure 26.5 is a three-dimensional representation of lactic acid in which the asymmetric carbon atom is represented as a sphere, with its center in the plane of the paper. The—H and—OH groups are projected forward from the paper (toward the observer), and the—COOH and—CH₃ groups are projected back from the paper (away from the observer).

For convenience of expression, simpler diagrams such as II and III are used. These are much easier and faster to draw. In II, it is understood that the groups (—H and —OH) attached to the horizontal bonds are coming out of the plane of the paper toward the observer, and the groups attached to the vertical bonds are projected back from the paper. The molecule represented by formula III is made by drawing a cross and attaching the four groups in their respective positions, as in formula II. The asymmetric carbon atom is understood to be located where the lines cross. Formulas II and III are called **projection formulas.**

projection formula

It is important to be careful when comparing projection formulas. Two rules apply: (1) projection formulas must not be turned 90°; (2) projection formulas must not be lifted or flipped out of the plane of the paper. Projection formulas may, however, be turned 180° in the plane of the paper. Consider the following projection formulas:

Formulas I, III, IV, and V represent identical molecules. Formula IV was obtained by turning formula III 180°. Formula V is formula IV drawn in a three-dimensional representation. If formula III is turned 90°, the other stereoisomer of lactic acid is represented, as shown in formulas VI and VII.

VI   VII

PROBLEM

26.1

(a) Redraw the three-dimensional formula (A) into a projection formula. (b) Draw the three-dimensional formula represented by the projection formula (B).

(A)

$CH_3CHBrCH_2NH_2$

(B) H———CH_2CH_3 with CH_3 on top and OH on bottom

$CH_3CH(OH)CH_2CH_3$

(a) Draw a vertical and a horizontal line crossing each other. Place the CH_3 at the top and the Br at the bottom of the vertical line. Place the H at the left and the CH_2NH_2 at the right of the horizontal line to complete the projection formula:

$$CH_3$$
$$H———CH_2NH_2$$
$$Br$$

(b) Draw a small circle to represent the asymmetric carbon atom (C2) that is located where the two lines cross in the projection formula. Draw a short line extending from the top and from the bottom of the circle. Place the CH_3 on the top and the OH on the bottom at the end of these lines. Now draw two short lines from within the circle coming toward your left and right arms. Place the H at the end of the left line and the CH_2CH_3 at the end of the right line. The finished formula should look like this.

CH_3 ... H ... CH_2CH_3

26.5 Enantiomers

Your right and your left hands are mirror images of each other; that is, the left hand is a mirror reflection of the right hand and vice versa. Furthermore, the two

super-
imposable

chiral

hands are not superimposable on each other (see Figure 26.6). **Superimposable** means that, when we lay one object upon another, all parts of both objects coincide exactly.

A molecule that is not superimposable on its mirror image is said to be **chiral.** The word *chiral* comes from the Greek word *cheir,* meaning hand. Chiral molecules have the property of "handedness"; that is, they are related to each other in the same manner as the right and left hands. An asymmetric carbon atom

| (a) Left hand | Mirror image of right hand | Right hand | (b) Right and left hands are not superimposable |

Figure 26.6 (a) Left hand shown is the same as the mirror image of the right hand. (b) Right and left hands are not superimposable; hence they are chiral. The palm of the left hand is up, and the palm of the right hand is down.

Glove   Shoe   Screw   Golf club   Coat

(a)

Ball   Tetrahedron   Hydrogen molecule   Letter X   Cube

(b)

Figure 26.7 (a) Chiral and (b) achiral objects

achiral

is often referred to as a chiral carbon or a chiral center. Molecules, or objects, that are superimposable are **achiral.** Some chiral and achiral objects are shown in Figure 26.7.

The formulas developed in Section 26.4 dealt primarily with a single kind of lactic acid molecule. But two stereoisomers of lactic acid are known, one that rotates the plane of polarized light to the right and one that rotates it to the left. These two forms of lactic acid are shown in Figure 26.8. If we examine these two structural formulas carefully, we can see that they are mirror images of each other. The reflection of either molecule in a mirror corresponds to the structure of the other molecule. Even though the two molecules have the same molecular formula and the same four groups attached to the central carbon atom, they are not superimposable. Therefore, the two molecules are not identical but are isomers. One molecule will rotate the plane of polarized light to the left and is termed *levorotatory;* the other molecule will rotate it to the right and is dextro-*rotatory.* A plus (+) or a minus (−) sign written in parentheses and placed in front of a name or formula indicates the direction of rotation of polarized light and becomes part of the name of the compound. Plus (+) indicates rotation to the right and minus (−) to the left. Using projection formulas, we write the two lactic acids as follows:

$$
\begin{array}{cc}
\mathrm{COOH} & \mathrm{COOH} \\
| & | \\
\mathrm{H-C-OH} & \mathrm{HO-C-H} \\
| & | \\
\mathrm{CH_3} & \mathrm{CH_3} \\
(-)\text{-Lactic acid} & (+)\text{-Lactic acid}
\end{array}
$$

enantiomer

Originally it was not known which lactic acid structure was the (+) or the (−) compound. However, it is now known that they are as shown. Isomers that are mirror images of each other are called **enantiomers.** The word *enantiomer* comes from the Greek word *enantios,* which means opposite.

Many, but not all, molecules that contain an asymmetric carbon are chiral. Most of the molecules we shall study that have an asymmetric carbon atom are chiral. To decide whether a molecule is chiral and has an enantiomer, make

Figure 26.8 Mirror-image isomers of lactic acid. Each isomer is the mirror reflection of the other. (−)-Lactic acid rotates plane-polarized light to the left, and (+)-lactic acid rotates plane-polarized light to the right.

models of the molecule and of its mirror image and see if they are superimposable. This is the ultimate test, but instead of making models every time, first examine the formula to see if it has an asymmetric carbon atom. If an asymmetric carbon atom is found, draw a cross and attach the four groups on the asymmetric carbon to the four ends of the cross. The asymmetric carbon is understood to be located where the lines cross. Remember that an asymmetric carbon atom has four different groups attached to it. Let us test the compounds 2-butanol and 2-chloropropane:

$$CH_3CH_2CHCH_3 \qquad CH_3CHCH_3$$
$$\quad\quad\quad | \qquad\qquad\qquad |$$
$$\quad\quad\quad OH \qquad\qquad\quad\; Cl$$
2-Butanol   2-Chloropropane

In 2-butanol, carbon 2 is asymmetric. The four groups attached to carbon 2 are H, OH, CH$_3$, and CH$_2$CH$_3$. Draw the structure and its mirror image;

CH$_3$	Mirror	CH$_3$		CH$_3$
H——OH		HO——H		CH$_2$
CH$_2$		CH$_2$		H——OH
CH$_3$		CH$_3$		CH$_3$
VIII		IX		X (IX turned 180°)

Enantiomers

Turning structure IX 180° in the plane of the paper allows H and OH to coincide with their position in VIII, but CH$_3$ and CH$_2$CH$_3$ do not coincide. Therefore, we conclude that the mirror-image structures VIII and IX are enantiomers since they are not superimposable.

In 2-chloropropane, the four groups attached to carbon 2 are H, Cl, CH$_3$, and CH$_3$. Note that two groups are the same. Draw the structure and its mirror image:

CH$_3$	Mirror	CH$_3$		CH$_3$
H——Cl		Cl——H		H——Cl
CH$_3$		CH$_3$		CH$_3$
XI		XII		XIII (XII turned 180°)

When we turn structure XII 180° in the plane of the paper, the two structures XI and XIII are superimposable, proving that 2-chloropropane, which does not have an asymmetric carbon, does not exist in enantiomeric forms.

PROBLEM

26.2

Draw mirror-image isomers for any of the following compounds that can exist as enantiomers:

(a) CH$_3$CH$_2$CH$_2$OH   (b) CH$_3$CH$_2$CHClCH$_2$CH$_3$ (c) CH$_3$CH$_2$CHClCH$_2$CH$_2$CH$_3$

First check each formula for asymmetric carbon atoms:
(a) No asymmetric carbon atoms; each carbon has at least two groups that are the same.
(b) No asymmetric carbon atoms; carbon 3 has H, Cl, and two CH_2CH_3 groups.
(c) Carbon 3 is asymmetric; the four groups on carbon 3 are H, Cl, CH_3CH_2, and $CH_3CH_2CH_2$. Draw mirror images:

$$CH_3CH_2-\underset{\underset{\displaystyle Cl}{|}}{\overset{\overset{\displaystyle H}{|}}{C}}-CH_2CH_2CH_3 \qquad \leftarrow Mirror \qquad CH_3CH_2CH_2-\underset{\underset{\displaystyle Cl}{|}}{\overset{\overset{\displaystyle H}{|}}{C}}-CH_2CH_3$$

The relationship between enantiomers is such that, if we change the positions of any two groups on a compound containing only one asymmetric carbon atom, we obtain the structure of its enantiomer. If we make a second change, the structure of the original isomer is obtained again. In both cases shown below, (+)-lactic acid is formed by interchanging the positions of two groups on (−)-lactic acid:

$$\underset{\text{(+)-Lactic acid}}{H-\overset{\overset{\displaystyle CH_3}{|}}{\underset{\underset{\displaystyle COOH}{|}}{|}}-OH} \xleftarrow[\text{CH}_3\text{ and COOH}]{\text{Change position of}} \underset{\text{(−)-Lactic acid}}{H-\overset{\overset{\displaystyle COOH}{|}}{\underset{\underset{\displaystyle CH_3}{|}}{|}}-OH} \xrightarrow[\text{H and OH}]{\text{Change position of}} \underset{\text{(+)-Lactic acid}}{HO-\overset{\overset{\displaystyle COOH}{|}}{\underset{\underset{\displaystyle CH_3}{|}}{|}}-H}$$

To compare two projection formulas to test whether they are the same structure or are enantiomers, (1) turn one structure 180° in the plane of the paper and compare to see if they are superimposable, or (2) make successive group interchanges until the formulas are identical. If an odd number of interchanges is made, the two original formulas represent enantiomers; if an even number of interchanges is made, the two formulas represent the same compound. The following two examples illustrate this method. Are structures XIV and XV the same compound?

$$\underset{\text{XIV}}{Br-\overset{\overset{\displaystyle CH_3}{|}}{\underset{\underset{\displaystyle Cl}{|}}{|}}-H} \qquad \underset{\text{XV}}{Br-\overset{\overset{\displaystyle H}{|}}{\underset{\underset{\displaystyle CH_3}{|}}{|}}-Cl}$$

$$\underset{\text{XV}}{Br-\overset{\overset{\displaystyle H}{|}}{\underset{\underset{\displaystyle CH_3}{|}}{|}}-Cl} \xrightarrow[\text{CH}_3\text{ and Cl}]{\text{Interchange}} Br-\overset{\overset{\displaystyle H}{|}}{\underset{\underset{\displaystyle Cl}{|}}{|}}-CH_3 \xrightarrow[\text{CH}_3\text{ and H}]{\text{Interchange}} \underset{\text{XIV}}{Br-\overset{\overset{\displaystyle CH_3}{|}}{\underset{\underset{\displaystyle Cl}{|}}{|}}-H}$$

Two interchanges were needed to make structure XV identical to structure XIV. Therefore, structures XIV and XV represent the same compound.

Do structures XVI and XVII represent the same compound?

$$
\begin{array}{c}
CH_3 \\
HO \overline{|} H \\
CH_2CH_3 \\
XVI
\end{array}
\qquad
\begin{array}{c}
OH \\
CH_3CH_2 \overline{|} CH_3 \\
H \\
XVII
\end{array}
$$

$$
\begin{array}{c}
OH \\
CH_3CH_2 \overline{|} CH_3 \\
H \\
XVII
\end{array}
\xrightarrow[CH_3CH_2 \text{ and } OH]{\text{Interchange}}
\begin{array}{c}
CH_2CH_3 \\
HO \overline{|} CH_3 \\
H
\end{array}
\xrightarrow[CH_3 \text{ and } H]{\text{Interchange}}
$$

$$
\begin{array}{c}
CH_2CH_3 \\
HO \overline{|} H \\
CH_3
\end{array}
\xrightarrow[CH_3 \text{ and } CH_3CH_2]{\text{Interchange}}
\begin{array}{c}
CH_3 \\
HO \overline{|} H \\
CH_2CH_3 \\
XVI
\end{array}
$$

Three interchanges were needed to make structure XVII identical to structure XVI. Therefore, structures XVI and XVII do not represent the same compound; they are enantiomers.

Enantiomers ordinarily have the same chemical properties and the same physical properties other than optical rotation (see Table 26.1). They rotate plane-polarized light the same number of degrees but in opposite directions. Enantiomers differ in their physiological properties. Since their reactions are stereoselective, enzymes act on only one of a pair of enantiomers. For example, enzyme-catalyzed reduction of pyruvic acid in muscle tissue yields only (+)-lactic acid, but reduction of pyruvic acid catalyzed with H_2/Pt yields both (+)- and (−)-lactic acids (see Section 26.6).

A summary of the key factors of enantiomers and optical isomerism follows:

1. A carbon atom that has four different groups bonded to it is called an asymmetric or a chiral carbon atom.
2. A compound with one asymmetric carbon atom can exist in two isomeric forms called enantiomers.
3. Enantiomers are nonsuperimposable mirror-image isomers.
4. Enantiomers are optically active; that is, they are able to rotate plane-polarized light.
5. One isomer of an enantiomeric pair rotates polarized light to the left (counterclockwise). The other isomer rotates polarized light to the right (clockwise). The degree of rotation is the same but in opposite directions.
6. Rotation of polarized light to the right is indicated by (+), placed in front of the name of the compound. Rotation to the left is indicated by (−), example, (+)-lactic acid and (−)-lactic acid.

26.6 Racemic Mixtures

racemic
mixture

A mixture containing equal amounts of a pair of enantiomers is known as a **racemic mixture.** Such a mixture is optically inactive and will show no rotation of polarized light when tested in a polarimeter. Each of the enantiomers rotates the plane of polarized light by the same amount but in opposite directions. Thus the rotation by each isomer is canceled. The (±) symbol is often used to designate racemic mixtures. For example, a racemic mixture of lactic acid is written as (±)-lactic acid because this mixture contains equal molar amounts of (+)-lactic acid and (−)-lactic acid.

Racemic mixtures are usually obtained in laboratory syntheses of compounds in which an asymmetric carbon atom is formed. Thus, catalytic reduction of pyruvic acid (an achiral compound) to lactic acid produces a racemic mixture containing equal amounts of (+)- and (−)-lactic acid:

$$CH_3CCOOH + H_2 \xrightarrow{\text{Ni}} CH_3CHCOOH$$

$$\underset{\underset{\text{Pyruvic acid}}{O}}{\|} \qquad\qquad \underset{\underset{(\pm)\text{-Lactic acid}}{OH}}{|}$$

As a general rule, in the biological synthesis of potentially optical active compounds, only one of the isomers is produced. For example, (+)-lactic acid is produced by reactions occurring in muscle tissue, and (−)-lactic acid is produced by lactic acid bacteria in the souring of milk. These stereospecific reactions occur because biochemical syntheses are enzyme catalyzed. The preferential production of one isomer over another is apparently due to the configuration (shape) of the specific enzyme involved. Returning to the hand analogy, if the "right-handed" enantiomer is produced, then the enzyme responsible for the product can be likened to a right-handed glove.

The mirror-image isomers (enantiomers) of a racemic mixture are alike in all ordinary physical properties except in their action on polarized light. It is possible to separate or resolve racemic mixtures into their optically active components. In fact, Pasteur's original work with sodium ammonium tartrate involved such a separation. But a general consideration of the methods involved in such separations is beyond the scope of our present discussion.

Enantiomers usually differ in their biochemical properties. In fact, most living cells are able to use only one isomer of a mirror-image pair. For example, (+)-glucose ("blood sugar") can be used for metabolic energy, whereas (−)-glucose cannot. Enantiomers are truly different molecules and are treated as such by most organisms.

26.7 Diastereomers and Meso Compounds

The enantiomers discussed in the preceding sections are stereoisomers. That is, they differ only in the spatial arrangement of the atoms and groups within the molecule. The number of stereoisomers increases as the number of asymmetric carbon atoms increases. The maximum number of stereoisomers for a given compound is obtained by the formula 2^n, where n is the number of asymmetric carbon atoms in the compound.

> 2^n = Maximum number of stereoisomers for a given chiral compound
>
> n = Number of asymmetric carbon atoms in a molecule

As we have seen, there are two ($2^1 = 2$) stereoisomers of lactic acid. But for a substance with two nonidentical asymmetric carbon atoms, such as 2-bromo-3-chlorobutane ($CH_3CHBrCHClCH_3$), four stereoisomers are possible ($2^2 = 4$). These four possible stereoisomers are written as projection formulas in this way (carbons 2 and 3 are asymmetric):

CH$_3$	CH$_3$	CH$_3$	CH$_3$
H——Br	Br——H	H——Br	Br——H
H——Cl	Cl——H	Cl——H	H——Cl
CH$_3$	CH$_3$	CH$_3$	CH$_3$
XVIII	XIX	XX	XXI
Enantiomers		Enantiomers	

Remember that, for comparison, projection formulas may be turned 180° in the plane of the paper, but they cannot be lifted (flipped) out of the plane. Formulas XVIII and XIX, and formulas XX and XXI, represent two pairs of nonsuperimposable mirror-image isomers and are, therefore, two pairs of enantiomers. All four compounds are optically active. But the properties of XVIII and XIX differ from the properties of XX and XXI because they are not mirror-image isomers of each other. Stereoisomers that are not enantiomers (not mirror images of each **diastereomer** other) are called **diastereomers.** There are four different pairs of diastereomers of 2-bromo-3-chlorobutane: They are XVIII and XX, XVIII and XXI, XIX and XX, and XIX and XXI.

The 2^n formula indicates that four stereoisomers of tartaric acid are possible. The projection formulas of these four possible stereoisomers are written in this way (carbons 2 and 3 are asymmetric):

COOH	COOH	COOH	COOH
HO——H	H——OH	H——OH	HO——H
H——OH	HO——H	H——OH	HO——H
COOH	COOH	COOH	COOH
XXII	XXIII	XXIV	XXV

Formulas XXII and XXIII represent nonsuperimposable mirror-image isomers and are, therefore, enantiomers. Formulas XXIV and XXV are also mirror images. But by turning XXV 180°, we see that it is exactly superimposable on XXIV. Therefore XXIV and XXV represent the same compound, and only *three* stereoisomers of tartaric acid actually exist. Compound XXIV is achiral and does not rotate polarized light. A plane of symmetry can be passed between carbons 2 and 3 so that the top and bottom halves of the molecule are mirror images:

COOH
|
H—C—OH
------+------ ← Plane of symmetry
H—C—OH
|
COOH

Table 26.1   Properties of tartaric acid [HOOCCH(OH)CH(OH)COOH]

Name	Specific gravity	Melting point (°C)	Solubility (g/100 g H$_2$O)	Specific rotation [α]
(+)-Tartaric acid	1.760	170	147$^{20°C}$	+12°
(−)-Tartaric acid	1.760	170	147$^{20°C}$	−12°
(±)-Tartaric acid (racemic mixture)	1.687	206	20.6$^{20°C}$	0°
meso-Tartaric acid	1.666	140	125$^{15°C}$	0°

meso compound

meso structure

Thus the molecule is internally compensated. The rotation of polarized light in one direction by half of the molecule is exactly compensated by an opposite rotation by the other half. Stereoisomers that contain asymmetric carbon atoms and are superimposable on their own mirror images are called **meso compounds,** or **meso structures.** All meso compounds are optically inactive.

The term *meso* comes from the Greek word *mesos*, meaning middle. It was first used by Pasteur to name a kind of tartaric acid that was optically inactive and could not be separated into different forms by any means. Pasteur called it *meso*-tartaric acid, because it seemed intermediate between the (+)- and (−)-tartaric acid. The three stereoisomers of tartaric acid are represented and designated in this fashion:

COOH   COOH   COOH
| | |
HO—C—H   H—C—OH   H—C—OH
| | |
H—C—OH   HO—C—H   H—C—OH
| | |
COOH   COOH   COOH

(−)-Tartaric acid   (+)-Tartaric acid   *meso*-Tartaric acid

The physical properties of tartaric acid stereoisomers are given in Table 26.1. Note that the properties of (+)-tartaric acid and (−)-tartaric acid are identical except for opposite rotation of polarized light. However, *meso*-tartaric acid has properties that are entirely different from those of the other isomers. But most surprising is the fact that the racemic mixture, though composed of equal parts of the (+) and (−) enantiomers, differs from them in specific gravity, melting point and solubility. Why, for example, is the melting point of the racemic mixture higher than that of any of the other forms? The melting point of any substance is largely dependent on the attractive forces holding the ions or molecules together. The melting point of the racemic mixture is higher than that of either enantiomer. Therefore, we can conclude that the attraction between molecules of the (+) and (−) enantiomers in the racemic mixture is greater than the attraction between molecules of the (+) and (+) or the (−) and (−) enantiomers.

PROBLEM

26.3

How many stereoisomers can exist for the following compounds? Write their structures and lable any pairs of enantiomers and meso compounds. Point out any diastereomers.

(a) $CH_3CHBrCHBrCH_2CH_3$ (b) $CH_2BrCHClCHClCH_2Br$

(a) Carbons 2 and 3 are asymmetric, so there can be a maximum of four stereoisomers ($2^2 = 4$). Write structures around the asymmetric carbons:

$$
\begin{array}{cccc}
\text{CH}_3 & \text{CH}_3 & \text{CH}_3 & \text{CH}_3 \\
\text{H}-\!\!\!\!-\text{Br} & \text{Br}-\!\!\!\!-\text{H} & \text{H}-\!\!\!\!-\text{Br} & \text{Br}-\!\!\!\!-\text{H} \\
\text{H}-\!\!\!\!-\text{Br} & \text{Br}-\!\!\!\!-\text{H} & \text{Br}-\!\!\!\!-\text{H} & \text{H}-\!\!\!\!-\text{Br} \\
\text{CH}_2 & \text{CH}_2 & \text{CH}_2 & \text{CH}_2 \\
\text{CH}_3 & \text{CH}_3 & \text{CH}_3 & \text{CH}_3 \\
\text{I} & \text{II} & \text{III} & \text{IV}
\end{array}
$$

Enantiomers   Enantiomers

There are four stereoisomers: two pairs of enantiomers (I and II, and III and IV) and no meso compounds. Structures I and III, I and IV, II and III, and II and IV are diastereomers.

(b) Carbons 2 and 3 are asymmetric, so there can be a maximum of four stereoisomers. Write structures around the asymmetric carbons:

$$
\begin{array}{cccc}
\text{CH}_2\text{Br} & \text{CH}_2\text{Br} & \text{CH}_2\text{Br} & \text{CH}_2\text{Br} \\
\text{H}-\text{C}-\text{Cl} & \text{Cl}-\text{C}-\text{H} & \text{Cl}-\text{C}-\text{H} & \text{H}-\text{C}-\text{Cl} \\
\text{H}-\text{C}-\text{Cl} & \text{Cl}-\text{C}-\text{H} & \text{H}-\text{C}-\text{Cl} & \text{Cl}-\text{C}-\text{H} \\
\text{CH}_2\text{Br} & \text{CH}_2\text{Br} & \text{CH}_2\text{Br} & \text{CH}_2\text{Br} \\
\text{V} & \text{VI} & \text{VII} & \text{VIII}
\end{array}
$$

Meso compound   Enantiomers

There are three stereoisomers: one pair of enantiomers (VII and VIII) and one meso compound V. Structures V and VI represent the meso compound because there is a plane of symmetry between carbons 2 and 3, and turning VI 180° makes it superimposable on V. Structures V, VII, and VIII are diastereomers.

QUESTIONS

A. Review the meanings of the new terms introduced in this chapter.

1. Stereoisomerism
2. Stereoisomers
3. Plane-polarized light
4. Specific rotation
5. Optical activity
6. Dextrorotatory
7. Levorotatory
8. Asymmetric carbon atom
9. Projection formula
10. Superimposable
11. Chiral
12. Achiral
13. Enantiomer
14. Racemic mixture
15. Diastereomer
16. Meso compound, or meso structure

B. Review questions

1. Which of these objects are chiral?
   (a) A wood screw   (d) The letter G
   (b) A pair of pliers   (e) A coiled spring
   (c) The letter O   (f) Your ear
2. What is an asymmetric carbon atom? Draw structural formulas of three different compounds that contain one asymmetric carbon atom, and mark the asymmetric carbon in each with an asterisk.
3. How can you tell when the axes of two Polaroid

filters are parallel? When one filter has been rotated by 90°?

4. How many asymmetric carbon atoms are present in each of the following?

(a) Cl—C—C—Br
 with H Cl on top, H H on bottom

(b) H—C—C—H
 with Br Cl on top, H H on bottom

(c) $CH_3CH_2CH_2CHClCH_3$

(d)
H—C=O
H—C—OH
H—C—OH
H—C—OH
H

(e) $CH_3CH_2CHCH_2CH_3$ with OH below the CH

(f)
H—C—OH (with H on top)
C=O
HO—C—H
H—C—OH
H—C—OH
H—C—OH
H

(g) HO—C—C—C—OH
 with H H O on top, H NH₂ on bottom
$$HO—\underset{H}{\overset{H}{C}}—\underset{NH_2}{\overset{H}{C}}—\overset{O}{C}—OH$$

5. Write the formulas and decide which of the following compounds will show optical activity:
(a) 1-Chloropentane
(b) 2-Chloropentane
(c) 3-Chloropentane
(d) 1-Chloro-2-methylpentane
(e) 2-Chloro-2-methylpentane
(f) 3-Chloro-2-methylpentane
(g) 4-Chloro-2-methylpentane
(h) 3-Chloro-3-methylpentane

6. Suppose a carbon atom is located at the center of a square with four different groups attached to the corners in a planar arrangement. Would the compound rotate polarized light? Explain.

7. What is a necessary and sufficient condition for a compound to show enantiomerism?

8. Glucose ($C_6H_{12}O_6$) has four asymmetric carbon atoms. How many stereoisomers of glucose are theoretically possible?

9. Do structures A and B represent enantiomers or the same compound? Justify your answer.

(A) Br—C—H with Cl on top, F on bottom
(B) H—C—Cl with Br on top, F on bottom

10. Which of these projection formulas represent (−)-lactic acid and which represent (+)-lactic acid?

(a) CH₃ top, HO—H, COOH bottom

(b) OH top, H—COOH, CH₃ bottom

(c) COOH top, H—CH₃, OH bottom

(d) CH₃ top, H—OH, COOH bottom

(e) COOH top, CH₃—H, OH bottom

(f) H top, CH₃—OH, COOH bottom

11. Draw projection fomulas for all the possible stereoisomers of the following compounds. Label pairs of enantiomers and meso compounds.
(a) 1,2-Dibromopropane
(b) 2,3-Dichlorobutane
(c) 2-Butanol
(d) 2,4-Dibromopentane
(e) 3-Chlorohexane

12. Draw projection formulas for all the stereoisomers of 1,2,3-trihydroxybutane. Point out enantiomers, meso compounds, and diastereomers, where present.

*13. Write structures for the four stereoisomers of 3-pentene-2-ol.

*14. Some substituted cycloalkanes are chiral. Draw the structures and enantiomers for any of the following that are chiral:

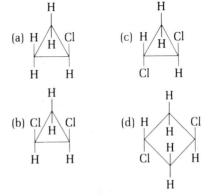

15. The physical properties for (+)-2-methyl-1-butanol are specific rotation. +5.76°; bp, 129°C

density, 0.819 g/mL. What are these same properties for (−)-2-methyl-1-butanol?

*16. Draw projection formulas for all the stereoisomers of 2,3,4-tribromopentane and point out enantiomers and meso compounds, where present.

17. (a) Draw the nine structural isomers of $C_4H_8Cl_2$.
    (b) Identify which structures represent chiral molecules, and draw all possible pairs of enantiomers and meso compounds, if any.

18. (+)-2-Chlorobutane is further chlorinated to give dichlorobutanes ($C_4H_8Cl_2$). Write structures for all the possible isomers formed and indicate which of these isomers will be optically active. [Remember that (+)-2-chlorobutane is optically active.]

19. In the chlorination of butane, 1-chlorobutane and 2-chlorobutane are obtained as products. After separation by distillation, neither product rotates the plane of polarized light. Explain these results.

20. (a) Explain why it is not possible to separate enantiomers by ordinary chemical and physical means.
    (b) Explain why diastereomers can usually be separated by ordinary physical and chemical means.

21. The observed rotation of polarized light was 12.5° for a solution of compound X at a concentration of 10.0 g/100 mL. The measurement was made using a polarimeter sample tube 20.0 cm in length. Calculate the specific rotation, $[\alpha]$, for compound X.

22. Which, if any, of the following are meso compounds?

(a)
```
      COOH
   H──┼──OH
  HO──┼──COOH
       H
```

(b)
```
      CH3
   H──┼──Cl
 CH3──┼──Cl
       H
```

(c)
```
      CH3
   H──┼──Cl
  Br──┼──CH3
       H
      CH3
```

(d)
```
   H──┼──Cl
   H──┼──Br
   H──┼──Cl
      CH3
```

*23. Substances of the type RR′R″R‴N⁺X⁻ are known

to rotate the plane of polarized light. What inference can be drawn regarding the spatial character of the nitrogen bonds?

*24. (a) A chiral substance was identified as a primary alcohol of formula $C_5H_{12}O$. What is its structure?
    (b) The compound $C_6H_{14}O_3$ has three primary alcohol groups and is chiral. What is its structure?

*25. What is the structure of a substance of formula $C_3H_8O_2$ that is (a) chiral and contains two—OH groups; (b) chiral and contains one—OH group; (c) achiral and contains two—OH groups? (Only one—OH group can be bonded to a carbon atom.)

26. Which of these statements are correct?
    (a) The polarizer and the analyzer of a polarimeter are made of the same material.
    (b) The specific rotation of a compound is dependent on the number of molecules in the path of the plane-polarized light.
    (c) Very few natural products are optically active.
    (d) Cis–trans isomers are not considered to be stereoisomers.
    (e) J. A. Le Bel received the first Nobel prize in chemistry in 1901.
    (f) A compound that rotates plane-polarized light +25° would be at the same position on the polarimeter as one that rotates the light −335°.
    (g) Molecules that contain only one asymmetric carbon atom are chiral, but not all chiral, molecules contain an asymmetric carbon atom.
    (h) The compound $CH_3CHBrCHBrCH_2OH$ will have eight optical isomers.
    (i) The compounds shown in these projection formulas are enantiomers:

```
      Cl              H
   Br─┼─H         Br─┼─Cl
      CH3             CH3
```

    (j) Diastereomers have identical melting points.
    (k) A molecule that contains two asymmetric carbon atoms may not be chiral.
    (l) A racemic mixture contains equal amounts of dextrorotatory and levorotatory molecules of a compound.

27

Carbohydrates

1. Understand the new terms listed in Question A at the end of the chapter.
2. List three important characteristics of an energy-providing food.
3. Compare the oxidation state of carbon in carbohydrates with that of carbon in carbon dioxide.
4. Classify carbohydrates as mono-, di-, oligo-, or polysaccharides.
5. Explain the use of D, L, (+), and (−) in naming carbohydrates.
6. Identify and write pyranose and furanose ring structures of carbohydrates.
7. Identify and write Fischer projection, "tree," and Haworth formulas for carbohydrates.
8. Identify the structural feature of a carbohydrate that makes it a reducing sugar.
9. Explain the phenomenon of mutarotation.
10. Distinguish between hemiacetal and acetal structures in a carbohydrate.
11. Understand what a glycoside linkage is.
12. Understand monosaccharide composition and the manner in which monosaccharides are linked together in sucrose, lactose, and maltose.
13. Identify monosaccharides that are epimers.
14. List the major sources of glucose, galactose, fructose, sucrose, lactose, and maltose.
15. Describe some disadvantages to a diet high in sucrose.
16. Describe how starch, cellulose, glycogen, and inulin differ in structure and monomer composition.

17. Identify three disaccharides that are derived from polysaccharides.
18. Describe the Benedict test and tell what evidence must be seen to indicate a positive test.
19. Write chemical equations for the oxidation of monosaccharides by bromine and by nitric acid.
20. Write chemical equations for the reduction of monosaccharides.
21. Write chemical equations for the formation of osazones.
22. Identify monosaccharides that give identical osazones.
23. Identify monosaccharides that give optically inactive (meso) products when reduced to polyhydroxy alcohols or when oxidized to dicarboxylic acids.
24. Discuss the structural differences between amylose and amylopectin.
25. Rate the relative sweetness of the common monosaccharides and disaccharides.

27.1　Introduction

Carbohydrates are among the most widespread and important biochemicals. Most of the matter in plants, except water, consists of these substances. Carbohydrates are one of the three principal classes of energy-yielding nutrients; the other two are fats and proteins. Because of their widespread distribution and their role in many vital metabolic processes such as photosynthesis, carbohydrates have been subjected to a great deal of scientific study over the last 150 years.

The name *carbohydrates* was given to this class of compounds many years ago by French scientists who called them *hydrates de carbone*, because their empirical formulas approximated $(C \cdot H_2O)_n$. It was found later that not all substances classified as carbohydrates conform to this formula (for example, rhamnose, $C_6H_{12}O_5$, and deoxyribose, $C_5H_{10}O_4$). It seems clear that carbohydrates are not simply hydrated carbon; they are complex substances containing from three to many thousands of carbon atoms. The general definition is:

carbohydrates　　**Carbohydrates** are polyhydroxy aldehydes or polyhydroxy ketones or substances that yield these compounds when hydrolyzed.

The simplest carbohydrates are glyceraldehyde and dihydroxyacetone:

$$
\begin{array}{ll}
\text{H—C=O} & \text{H—C—OH} \\
| & | \\
\text{H—C—OH} & \text{C=O} \\
| & | \\
\text{H—C—OH} & \text{H—C—OH} \\
| & | \\
\text{H} & \text{H} \\
\text{Glyceraldehyde} & \text{Dihydroxyacetone}
\end{array}
$$

These substances are "polyhydroxy" because each molecule has more than one hydroxyl group. Glyceraldehyde contains a carbonyl carbon in a terminal position and, therefore is an aldehyde. The internal carbonyl of dihydroxyacetone classifies it as a ketone. Much of the chemistry and biochemistry of carbohydrates can be understood from a basic knowledge of the chemistry of the hydroxyl and carbonyl functional groups (see Chapters 22 and 23 for review)

As we begin to study carbohydrates, it is worthwhile to consider this question: What are the essential characteristics that allow carbohydrates to act as foodstuffs and major sources of biological energy? In answer to this question, three relevant biochemical principles must be set forth.

First, a foodstuff must contain carbon. The preceding formulas show that carbohydrates provide much carbon. The average carbohydrate is about 40% carbon by weight.

Second, the carbon atoms in an energy-providing molecule must be in a more reduced state than those in carbon dioxide. Reduced carbon atoms can react with atmospheric oxygen to produce carbon dioxide and much energy (witness the heat of a wood fire or the energy of a gasoline engine). A useful estimate of a carbon's reduced state is the oxidation number (see Table 27.1). The lower the

Table 27.1 The relative potential energy of carbon in different oxidation states: The more reduced the carbon, the more energy that is potentially available.

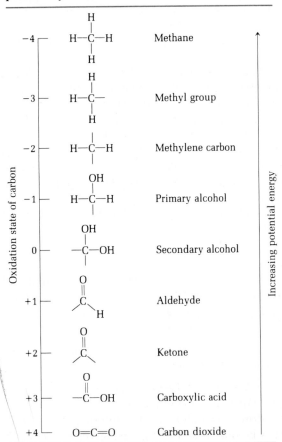

oxidation number, the more reduced the carbon is and the more energy it can supply. Carbohydrates are energy-yielding nutrients partly because they contain carbons in an intermediate state of reduction, with oxidation numbers ranging from -1 to $+1$. As these carbons are oxidized to carbon dioxide during metabolism, much energy is released.

Third, an energy-providing foodstuff not only must contain reduced carbons, but it also must have a chemical reactivity and a physical structure appropriate for use in cells. Carbohydrate metabolism is aided by the presence of reactive hydroxyl and carbonyl functional groups. Thus, a knowledge of carbohydrate structure and chemistry will greatly facilitate an understanding of carbohydrate metabolism.

27.2 Classification

A carbohydrate is classified as a monosaccharide, a disaccharide, an oligosaccharide, or a polysaccharide, depending on the number of monosaccharide units linked together to form a molecule. A **monosaccharide** is a carbohydrate that cannot be hydrolyzed to simpler carbohydrate units. The monosaccharide is the basic carbohydrate unit of cellular metabolism. A **disaccharide** yields two monosaccharides—either alike or different—when hydrolyzed:

**mono-
saccharide**

disaccharide

$$\text{Disaccharide} + \text{Water} \xrightarrow{\text{H}^+ \text{ or enzyme}} \text{2 Monosaccharides}$$

Disaccharides are often used by plants or animals to transport monosaccharides from one cell to another. The monosaccharides and disaccharides generally have names ending in *ose*—for example, glucose, sucrose, and lactose. These water-soluble carbohydrates, which have a characteristically sweet taste, are also called *sugars*.

oligosaccharide

An **oligosaccharide** has two to six monosaccharide units linked together. *Oligo* comes from the Greek word *oligos*, which means small or few. Free oligosaccharides containing more than two monosaccharide units are rarely found in nature.

polysaccharide

A **polysaccharide** is a macromolecular substance that can be hydrolyzed to yield many monosaccharide units:

$$\text{Polysaccharide} + \text{Water} \xrightarrow{\text{H}^+ \text{ or enzyme}} \text{Many monosaccharide units}$$

Polysaccharides are important as structural supports (particularly in plants) and also serve as a storage depot for monosaccharides (which cells use for energy).

Carbohydrates also can be classified in other ways. A monosaccharide might be described with respect to several of these categories:

1. As a *triose, tetrose, pentose, hexose,* or *heptose.* Theoretically, a monosaccharide can have any number of carbons greater than three, but only monosaccharides of three to seven carbons are commonly found in the biosphere.

    Trioses $C_3H_6O_3$
    Tetroses $C_4H_8O_4$

Pentoses $C_5H_{10}O_5$
Hexoses $C_6H_{12}O_6$
Heptoses $C_7H_{14}O_7$

2. As an *aldose* or *ketose*, depending on whether an aldehyde group (—CHO) or keto group ($>$C$=$O) is present.

3. As a D or L isomer, depending on the spatial orientation of the —H and —OH groups attached to the carbon atom that is adjacent to the terminal primary alcohol group. When the —OH is written to the right of this carbon in the *projection formula*, the D isomer is represented. When the —OH is written to the left, the L isomer is represented. The reference compounds for this classification are the trioses D-glyceraldehyde and L-glyceraldehyde, whose formulas follow. Also shown are two aldohexoses (D- and L-glucose) and a ketohexose (D-fructose).

D-configuration →

H—C$=$O
H—C—OH
CH₂OH   ← Terminal 1° ROH

D-Glyceraldehyde

H—C$=$O
HO—C—H   ← L-configuration
CH₂OH   ← Terminal 1° ROH

L-Glyceraldehyde

L configuration

H—C$=$O
HO—C—H
H—C—OH
HO—C—H
HO—C—H
CH₂OH   ← Terminal 1° ROH

L-Glucose

H—C$=$O
H—C—OH
HO—C—H
H—C—OH
H—C—OH   ← D configuration
CH₂OH   ← Terminal 1° ROH

D-Glucose

CH₂OH
C$=$O
HO—C—H
H—C—OH
H—C—OH
CH₂OH

D-Fructose

The letters D and L do not in any way refer to the direction of optical rotation of a carbohydrate. The D and L forms of any specific compound are *enantiomers* (for example, D- and L-glucose).

4. As a (+) or (−) isomer, depending on whether the monosaccharide rotates the plane of polarized light to the right (+) or to the left (−). (See Section 26.5.)

5. As a *furanose* or a *pyranose*, depending on whether the cyclic structure of the carbohydrate is related to that of the five-membered or six-membered heterocyclic ring compound furan or pyran (a heterocyclic ring contains more than one kind of atom in the ring):

Furan, C_4H_4O
(five-membered ring containing oxygen in the ring)

Pyran, C_5H_6O
(six-membered ring containing oxygen in the ring)

6. As having an alpha (α) or beta (β) configuration, based on the orientation of the —H and —OH groups about a specific asymmetric carbon in the cyclic form of the monosaccharide (Section 27.5).

PROBLEM

27.1

Write projection formulas for **(a)** an L-aldotriose, **(b)** a D-ketotetrose, and **(c)** a D-aldopentose. Determine which carbons can provide the most energy for a cell.

(a) *Triose* indicates a three-carbon carbohydrate; *aldo* indicates that the compound is an aldehyde; L- indicates that the —OH on carbon 2 (adjacent to the terminal CH_2OH) is on the left. The aldehyde group is carbon 1.

$$
\begin{array}{c}
H{-}C{=}O \\
| \\
HO{-}C{-}H \\
| \\
CH_2OH
\end{array}
$$

An L-aldotriose

The aldehyde carbon has an oxidation number of $+1$; the secondary alcohol, 0; the primary alcohol, -1. The primary alcohol carbon is most reduced and should provide the most energy.

(b) *Tetrose* indicates a four-carbon carbohydrate; *keto* indicates a ketone group (on carbon 2); D- indicates that the —OH on carbon 3 (adjacent to the terminal CH_2OH) is on the right. Carbons 1 and 4 are primary alcohols.

$$
\begin{array}{c}
CH_2OH \\
| \\
C{=}O \\
| \\
H{-}C{-}OH \\
| \\
CH_2OH
\end{array}
$$

A D-ketotetrose

The ketone carbon has an oxidation number of $+2$; the secondary alcohol carbon, 0; each primary alcohol carbon, -1. The primary alcohol carbons are the most reduced and have the most potential energy.

(c) *Pentose* indicates a five-carbon carbohydrate; *aldo* indicates an aldehyde group (on carbon 1); D- indicates that the —OH on carbon 4 (adjacent to the terminal CH_2OH) is on the right. The orientation of the —OH groups on carbons 2 and 3 is not specified here and therefore can be written in either direction for this problem.

$$
\begin{array}{c}
H{-}C{=}O \\
| \\
H{-}C{-}OH \\
| \\
H{-}C{-}OH \\
| \\
H{-}C{-}OH \\
| \\
CH_2OH
\end{array}
$$

A D-aldopentose

The aldehyde carbon has an oxidation number of $+1$; each secondary alcohol carbon, 0; the primary alcohol carbon, -1. The primary alcohol carbon is the most reduced and has the most potential energy.

27.3   Monosaccharides

Although a great many monosaccharides have been synthesized, only a very few appear to be of much biological significance. One pentose monosaccharide (ribose) and its deoxy derivative are essential components of ribonucleic acid (RNA) and of deoxyribonucleic acid (DNA) (see Chapter 30). However, the hexose monosaccharides are the most important carbohydrate sources of cellular energy. Three hexoses—glucose, galactose, and fructose—are of major significance in nutrition. All three have the same molecular formula, $C_6H_{12}O_6$, and thus contain an equal number of reduced carbons. They differ in structure but are biologically interconvertible. Glucose plays a central role in carbohydrate energy utilization. Other carbohydrates are usually converted to glucose before cellular utilization. The structure of glucose is considered in detail in Section 27.4.

Glucose

Glucose is the most important of the monosaccharides. It is an aldohexose and is found in the free state in plant and animal tissue. Glucose is commonly known as *dextrose*, or *grape sugar*. It is a component of the disaccharides sucrose, maltose, and lactose, and is also the monomer of the polysaccharides starch, cellulose, and glycogen. Among the common sugars, glucose is of intermediate sweetness (see Table 27.2 on page 691).

Glucose is the key sugar of the body and is carried by the bloodstream to all body parts. The concentration of glucose in the blood is normally 80–100 mg per 100 mL of blood. Because glucose is the most abundant carbohydrate in the blood, it is also sometimes known as *blood sugar*. Glucose requires no digestion and therefore may be given intravenously to patients who cannot take food by mouth. Glucose is found in the urine of those who have diabetes mellitus (sugar diabetes). The condition in which glucose is excreted in the urine is called glycosuria.

Galactose

Galactose is also an aldohexose and occurs, along with glucose, in lactose and in many oligo- and polysaccharides such as pectin, gums, and mucilages. Galactose is an isomer of glucose, differing only in the spatial arrangement of the —H and —OH groups around carbon 4 (see Section 27.4). Galactose is synthesized in the mammary glands to make the lactose of milk. It is also a constituent of glycolipids and glycoproteins in nervous tissue. Galactose is less than half as sweet as glucose.

A severe inherited disease, called galactosemia, is the inability of infants to metabolize galactose. The galactose concentration increases markedly in the blood, and also appears in the urine. Galactosemia causes vomiting, diarrhea, enlargement of the liver, and often mental retardation. If not recognized within a few days after birth, it can lead to death. If diagnosis is made early and lactose is excluded from the diet, the symptoms disappear and normal growth may be resumed.

Fructose

Fructose, also known as *levulose*, is a ketohexose that occurs in fruit juices, honey, and (along with glucose) as a constituent of sucrose. Fructose is the major constituent of the polysaccharide inulin, a starchlike substance present in many plants such as dahlia tubers, chicory roots, and Jerusalem artichokes. Fructose is the sweetest of all the sugars, being about twice as sweet as glucose. This accounts for the sweetness of honey. The enzyme invertase, present in bees, splits sucrose into glucose and fructose. Fructose is metabolized directly but is also readily converted to glucose in the liver.

27.4 Structure of Glucose and Other Aldoses

In one of the classic feats of research in organic chemistry, Emil Fischer (1852–1919), working in Germany, established the structural configuration of glucose along with that of many other sugars. He received the Nobel prize in chemistry in 1902. Fischer devised projection formulas that relate the structure of a sugar to one or the other of the two enantiomeric forms of glyceraldehyde. These projection formulas represent three-dimensional stereoisomers (see Chapter 26) in a two-dimensional plane. (Remember that stereoisomers cannot be interconverted without breaking and reforming covalent bonds. Each carbohydrate isomer has a different shape and thus reacts differently in biological systems.)

In Fischer projection formulas, the molecule is represented with the aldehyde (or ketone) group at the top. The —H and —OH groups attached to interior carbons are written to the right or to the left as they would appear when projected toward the observer. The two glyceraldehydes are represented thus:

D-Glyceraldehyde (three-dimensional representation) | D-Glyceraldehyde (projection formula) | L-Glyceraldehyde (three-dimensional representation) | L-Glyceraldehyde (projection formula)

In the three-dimensional molecules represented by these formulas, the number-2 carbon atoms are in the plane of the paper. The —H and —OH groups project forward (toward the observer); the —CHO and —CH$_2$OH groups project backward (away from the observer). Any two monosaccharides that differ only in the configuration around a single carbon atom are called **epimers**. Thus D- and L-glyceraldehyde are epimers.

epimer

Fischer recognized that there were two enantiomeric forms of glucose. To these forms he assigned the following structures and names:

$$
\begin{array}{ll}
H-^1C{=}O & H-^1C{=}O \\
H-^2C{-}OH & HO-^2C{-}H \\
HO-^3C{-}H & H-^3C{-}OH \\
H-^4C{-}OH & HO-^4C{-}H \\
H-^5C{-}OH & HO-^5C{-}H \\
\quad^6CH_2OH & \quad^6CH_2OH
\end{array}
$$

D-Glucose   L-Glucose

The structure called D-glucose is so named because the —H and —OH on carbon 5 are in the same configuration as the —H and —OH on carbon 2 in D-glyceraldehyde. The configuration of the —H and —OH on carbon 5 in L-glucose corresponds to the —H and —OH on carbon 2 in L-glyceraldehyde.

Fischer recognized that 16 different aldohexoses, 8 with the D configuration and 8 with the L configuration, were possible. This follows our formula 2^n for optical isomers (see Section 26.7). Glucose has four asymmetric carbon atoms and should have 16 stereoisomers (2^4). The configurations of the D-aldose family are shown in Figure 27.1. The shorthand "tree" formulas in this figure use the following symbols:

○   denotes   H—C=O

├   denotes   H—C—OH

┤   denotes   HO—C—H

▽   denotes   CH₂OH

For example,

represents
$$
\begin{array}{l}
H-C{=}O \\
H-C{-}OH \\
CH_2OH
\end{array}
$$

In this family (Figure 27.1) new asymmetric carbon atoms are formed as we go from triose to tetrose to pentose to hexose. Each time a new asymmetric carbon is added, a pair of epimers is formed that differ only in the structure around carbon 2. This sequence continues until eight D-aldohexoses are created. A similar series starting with L-glyceraldehyde is known, making a total of 16 aldohexoses.

All 16 aldohexoses have been synthesized, but only D-glucose and D-galactose appear to be of considerable biological importance. Since the metabolism of most living organisms revolves about D-glucose, our discussion will be centered on this substance.

The laboratory conversion of one aldose into another aldose containing one more carbon atom is known as the Kiliani–Fischer synthesis. This synthesis

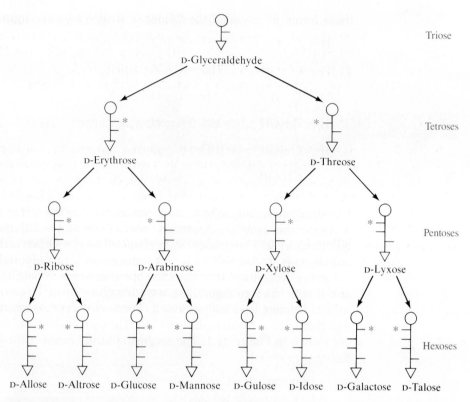

Figure 27.1 Configurations of the D family of aldoses: An asterisk is adjacent to the new asymmetric carbon atom in going from triose to tetrose to pentose to hexose.

Figure 27.2 An example of the Kiliani–Fischer synthesis in which two aldotetrose molecules are formed from an aldotriose molecule makes use of the aldehyde's ability to bond to an additional group (see Section 23.4). The synthesis involves (1) the addition of HCN to form a cyanohydrin, (2) hydrolysis of the —CN group to —COOH, and (3) reduction with sodium amalgam, Na(Hg), to form the aldehyde. As an example, the formation of two aldotetroses from an aldotriose is shown in Figure 27.2.

27.5   Cyclic Structure of Glucose; Mutarotation

Two crystalline forms of D-(+)-glucose are known. These two forms are diastereomers and differ with respect to their rotation of polarized light. One form, labeled α-D-glucopyranose, has a specific rotation, $[\alpha]$, of $+112°$; the other, labeled β-D-glucopyranose, has a specific rotation of $+18.7°$. An interesting phenomenon occurs when these two forms of glucose are put into separate solutions and allowed to stand for several hours. The specific rotation of each

mutarotation   solution changes to $+52.7°$. This phenomenon is known as **mutarotation.** An explanation of mutarotation is that D-glucose exists in solution as an equilibrium mixture of two cyclic forms and the open-chain form (see Figure 27.3). The two cyclic molecules are optical isomers, differing only in the orientation of the —H and —OH groups about carbon 1. When dissolved, some α-D-glucopyranose

Modified Fischer projection formulas

α-D-(+)-Glucopyranose
$[\alpha] = +112°$

D-(+)-Glucose
(open-chain form)

β-D-(+)-Glucopyranose
$[\alpha] = +18.7°$

Haworth perspective formulas

α-D-(+)-Glucopyranose

D-(+)-Glucose
(open-chain form)

β-D-(+)-Glucopyranose

Figure 27.3   Mutarotation of D-glucose, shown in both the modified Fischer projection formulas and the Haworth perspective formulas molecules are transformed into β-D-glucopyranose, and vice versa, until an equilibrium is reached between the α and β forms. (Note that no other chiral centers in D-glucose are altered when this sugar is dissolved.) The equilibrium solution contains about 36% α molecules and 64% β molecules, with a trace of open-chain molecules. When two cyclic isomers differ only in their stereo arrangement about the carbon involved in mutarotation, they are called

anomer **anomers.** For example, α- and β-D-glucopyranose are anomers (see Figure 27.3). Mutarotation is the process by which anomers are interconverted.

The cyclic forms of D-glucose may be represented by either Fischer projection formulas or by Haworth perspective formulas. These structures are shown in Figure 27.3. In the cyclic Fischer projection formulas of the D-aldoses, the α form has the —OH on carbon 1 written to the right; in the β form the —OH on carbon 1 is on the left. The Haworth structure represents the molecule as a flat hexagon with the —H and —OH groups above and below the plane of the hexagon. In the α form the —OH on carbon 1 is written below the plane; in the β form the —OH on carbon 1 is above the plane. In converting the projection formula of a D-aldohexose to the Haworth formula, the —OH groups on carbons 2, 3, and 4 are written below the plane if they project to the right and above the plane if they project to the left. Carbon 6 is written above the plane.

Haworth formulas are sometimes shown in abbreviated schematic form. For example, α-D-(+)-glucopyranose is shown in these diagrams:

α-D-(+)-Glucopyranose

At best, any two-dimensional representation is a compromise in portraying the three-dimensional configuration of such molecules. Structural models are much more effective, especially if constructed by the student.

The two cyclic forms of D-glucose differ only in the relative positions of the —H and —OH groups attached to carbon 1. Yet, this seemingly minor structural difference has important biochemical consequences. Often the physical shape of a molecule determines its biological use. For example, the fundamental structural difference between starch and cellulose is that starch is a polymer of α-D-glucopyranose, whereas cellulose is a polymer of β-D-glucopyranose. As a consequence, starch is a major and easily digested human food, but we are totally unable to digest cellulose.

27.6 Hemiacetals and Acetals

In Chapter 23 we studied the reactions of aldehydes (and ketones) to form hemiacetals and acetals. The hemiacetal structure consists of an ether linkage and an alcohol linkage on the same carbon atom, whereas the acetal structure has two ether linkages to the same carbon atom:

Hemiacetal

Acetal

Cyclic structures of monosaccharides are intramolecular hemiacetals. Five- or six-membered rings are especially stable.

Hemiacetal structure in α-D-glucopyranose

Hemiacetal structure in α-D-ribofuranose

However, in an aqueous solution, the ring often opens and the hemiacetal momentarily reverts to the open-chain aldehyde. When the open chain closes, it forms either the α or the β anomer. Mutarotation results from this opening and closing of the hemiacetal ring (see Figure 27.3).

When an alcohol, ROH, reacts with another alcohol, R'OH, the product formed can be an ether, ROR'. Carbohydrates are alcohols and behave in a similar manner. When a monosaccharide hemiacetal reacts with an alcohol, the product is an acetal. In carbohydrate terminology this acetal structure is called a **glycoside.** In the case of glucose, it would be a glucoside; if galactose, a galactoside; and so on.

glycoside

Acetal structure

Glycosidic linkage

An α-glycoside
(R = a variety of groups)

A glycoside differs significantly from a monosaccharide with respect to chemical reactivity.

When α-D-glucopyranose is heated with methyl alcohol and a small quantity of hydrogen chloride is added, two optically active isomers are formed—methyl α-D-glucopyranoside and methyl β-D-glucopyranoside:

α-D-Glucopyranose

Methyl α-D-glucopyranoside
(mp 165°C, $[\alpha] = +158°$)

Methyl β-D-glucopyranoside
(mp 107°C, $[\alpha] = -33°$)

Unlike D-glucose, the two glycoside products no longer undergo mutarotation. They do not form open-chain compounds in aqueous solution. Acetals tend to be more stable and less reactive than hemiacetals.

The glycosidic linkage occurs in a wide variety of natural substances. All carbohydrates other than monosaccharides are glycosides. Heart stimulants such as digitalis and ouabain are known as heart glycosides. Several antibiotics such as streptomycin and erythromycin are also glycosides.

27.7   Structures of Galactose and Fructose

Galactose, like glucose, is an aldohexose and differs structurally from glucose only in the configuration of the —H and —OH group on the fourth carbon:

D-Galactose

D-Glucose

Galactose, like glucose, also exists primarily in two cyclic pyranose forms that have hemiacetal structures and undergo mutarotation:

α-D-Galactopyranose

β-D-Galactopyranose

Fructose is a ketohexose. The open-chain form may be represented in a Fischer projection formula:

$$^1CH_2OH$$
$$^2C{=}O \quad \longleftarrow \text{ Keto group}$$
$$HO{-}^3C{-}H$$
$$H{-}^4C{-}OH$$
$$H{-}^5C{-}OH$$
$$^6CH_2OH$$

← This portion has the same configuration as D-glucose.

D-Fructose

Like glucose and galactose, fructose exists in both cyclic and open-chain forms. One common cyclic structure is a five-membered furanose ring in the β configuration:

$^6CH_2OH$ O OH ← β configuration

C^5 C^2

H   OH

H C^1H_2OH

$C^4{-}C^3$

OH   H

β-D-Fructofuranose

27.8 **Pentoses**

An open-chain aldopentose has three asymmetric carbon atoms. Therefore eight (2^3) isomeric aldopentoses are possible. The four possible D-pentoses, written in shorthand tree form, are shown in Figure 27.1. Arabinose and xylose occur in some plants as polysaccharides called pentosans. D-ribose and its derivative D-2-deoxyribose are the most interesting pentoses because of their relationship to nucleic acids and the genetic code (Chapter 30). Note the difference between the two names D-ribose and D-2-deoxyribose. In the latter name, the 2-deoxy means that oxygen is missing from the D-ribose molecule at carbon 2. Check the formulas that follow to verify this differences.

$$H{-}^1C{=}O$$
$$H{-}^2C{-}OH$$
$$H{-}^3C{-}OH$$
$$H{-}^4C{-}OH$$
$$^5CH_2OH$$

D-Ribose

$^5CH_2OH$ O OH

^{4}H   H ^{1}

H   H

OH   OH

β-D-Ribofuranose

or

CH_2OH O

H—^{1}C=O

H—^{2}C—H

H—^{3}C—OH

H—^{4}C—OH

^{5}CH$_2$OH

D-2-Deoxyribose

^{5}CH$_2$OH O OH

^{4}H H ^{1}

H $_3$ $_2$ H

OH H

β-D-2-Deoxyribofuranose

or

CH$_2$OH O

The ketose that is closely related to D-ribose is named D-ribulose. (Ketose names are often derived from the corresponding aldose name by modifying the suffix -*ose* to -*ulose*.) This ketose is an intermediate that allows cells to make many other monosaccharides. In photosynthetic organisms, D-ribulose is used to capture carbon dioxide and thus make new carbohydrates.

CH$_2$OH

C=O

H—C—OH

H—C—OH

CH$_2$OH

D-Ribulose

27.9 Disaccharides

Disaccharides are carbohydrates composed of two monosaccharide residues united by a glycosidic linkage. The two important disaccharides that are found in the free state in nature are sucrose and lactose. Sucrose, commonly known as *table sugar*, exists throughout the plant kingdom. Sugar cane contains 15–20% sucrose, and sugar beets 10–17%. Maple syrup and sorghum are also good sources of sucrose. Lactose, also known as *milk sugar*, is found free in nature mainly in the milk of mammals. Human milk contains about 6.7% lactose and cow milk about 4.5% of this sugar.

Unlike sucrose and lactose, several other important disaccharides are derived directly from polysaccharides by hydrolysis (see Section 27.13). For example, maltose, isomaltose and cellobiose are formed when specific polysaccharides are hydrolyzed. Of this group, maltose is the most common and is found as a constituent of sprouting grain.

Upon hydrolysis, disaccharides yield two monosaccharide molecules. The hydrolysis is catalyzed by hydrogen ions (acids), usually at elevated temperatures, or by certain enzymes that act effectively at room or body temperatures. A different enzyme is required for the hydrolysis of each of the three disaccharides:

$$\text{Sucrose} + \text{Water} \xrightarrow{\text{H}^+ \text{ or Sucrase}} \text{Glucose} + \text{Fructose}$$

$$\text{Lactose} + \text{Water} \xrightarrow{\text{H}^+ \text{ or Lactase}} \text{Galactose} + \text{Glucose}$$

$$\text{Maltose} + \text{Water} \xrightarrow{\text{H}^+ \text{ or Maltase}} \text{Glucose} + \text{Glucose}$$

27.10 Structures and Properties of Disaccharides

Disaccharides contain an acetal structure (glycosidic linkage), and some also contain a hemiacetal structure. The acetal structure in maltose may be considered as being derived from two glucose molecules by the elimination of a molecule of water between the —OH group on carbon 1 of one glucose unit and the —OH group of carbon 4 on the other glucose unit. This is an α-1,4-glycosidic linkage, since the glucose units have the α configuration and are joined at carbons 1 and 4. In a more systematic nomenclature, this form of maltose is known as α-D-glucopyranosyl-(1-4)-α-D-glucopyranose. If the structure of glucose is known, this name provides a complete description for drawing the maltose formula.

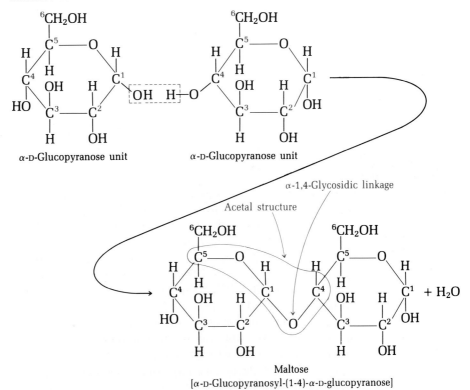

Maltose
[α-D-Glucopyranosyl-(1-4)-α-D-glucopyranose]

Common lactose consists of a β-D-galactopyranose unit linked to an α-D-glucopyranose unit. These are joined by a β-1,4-glycosidic linkage from carbon 1 on galactose to carbon 4 on glucose. The more systematic name for lactose is β-D-galactopyranosyl-(1-4)-α-D-glucopyranose. Note that, although glycosidic bonds are straight carbon–oxygen linkages, the structural formula represents them in a bent fashion. This is designed to provide stereochemical information. Carbon 1 of the galactose is in a β configuration, so its bent bond initially points up. The oxygen on carbon 4 of the glucose is below the carbon in the Haworth formula, and thus the bent bond initially points down.

β-1,4-Glycosidic linkage

β-D-Galactopyranose unit

α-D-Glucopyranose unit

Lactose

[β-D-galactopyranosyl-(1-4)-α-D-glucopyranose]

Sucrose consists of an α-D-glucopyranose unit and a β-D-fructofuranose unit. These monosaccharides are joined by an oxygen bridge from carbon 1 on glucose to carbon 2 on fructose—that is, by an α-1,2-glycosidic linkage.

α-1-2-Glycosidic linkage

α-D-Glucopyranose unit

β-D-Fructofuranose unit

Sucrose

[α-D-glucopyranosyl-(1-2)-β-D-fructofuranose]

In this perspective formula, the fructose unit has been turned through 180° to bring its number 2 carbon close to the number 1 carbon on the glucose unit. The groups on the fructose unit are therefore shown reversed from the perspective representation in Section 27.7.

Lactose and maltose both show mutarotation, which indicates that one of the monosaccharide units has a hemiacetal ring that can open and close to interchange anomers. Sucrose has no hemiacetal structure and hence does not mutarotate.

The three disaccharides sucrose, lactose, and maltose have physical properties associated with large polar molecules. All three are crystalline solids and are quite soluble in water; the solubility of sucrose amounts to 179 g per 100 g of water at 0°C. Hydrogen bonding between the polar —OH groups on the sugar molecules and the water molecules is a major factor in this high solubility. These sugars are not easily melted. In fact, lactose is the only one with a clearly defined melting point (201.6°C). Sucrose and maltose begin to decompose when heated to 186°C and 102.5°C, respectively. When sucrose is heated to melting, it darkens and undergoes partial decomposition. The resulting mixture is known as caramel, or burnt sugar, and is used as coloring and as a flavoring agent in foods.

Sucrose (table sugar) is the most commonly used of the disaccharides. There are no essential chemical differences between cane sugar and beet sugar. Astonishingly large amounts of sugar are produced: World production is on the order of 90 million tons annually. In the United States, approximately 20–30% of the average caloric intake is sucrose (about 150 g/day of sucrose per person). Low price and sweet taste are the major reasons for high sucrose consumption.

A scale of relative sweetness of common sugars, in which fructose is assigned a value of 100, is given in Table 27.2. Note that sucrose is only 58% as sweet as fructose. However, because sucrose is inexpensive to produce and is amenable to a variety of food processing techniques, approximately 60–80% of all sweeteners consumed is sucrose.

Unfortunately, high sucrose consumption has presented problems. This disaccharide has the appropriate structure and chemical reactivity for easy metabolism. Thus, for many people, sucrose is a source of too many calories. Oral bacteria also find sucrose easy to metabolize, increasing the incidence of dental caries. Finally, because the component monosaccharides of sucrose, fructose, and glucose, are quickly absorbed from the small intestine, sucrose consumption leads to a rapid increase in blood sugar. A sharp rise in blood sugar can be dangerous for people with impaired carbohydrate metabolism—for example, diabetes mellitus.

Scientists have searched for sucrose substitutes. The ideal substitute might be sweeter than sucrose but lack the structural features and chemical reactivity that allows sucrose to be absorbed and metabolized. Purely artificial, noncarbohydrate sweeteners have been developed, such as saccharin and sodium cyclamate, but these substances have dangerous or potentially dangerous long- or short-term side effects. Certain polypeptide and protein sweeteners, both natural and artificial, are also alternatives to sucrose. These substances are sweet but are not metabolizable as carbohydrate.

Table 27.2   Relative sweetness of sugars

Fructose	100	Galactose	19
Sucrose	58	Lactose	9.2
Glucose	43	Invert sugar	75
Maltose	19		

HN—SO$_3^-$ Na$^+$

Sodium cyclamate

Saccharin

$$H_2NCHCNHCHC—OCH_3$$

Aspartame

Sucrose has a tendency to crystallize from concentrated solutions or syrups. Therefore, in commercial food preparations (for example, candies, jellies, and canned fruits) the sucrose is often hydrolyzed:

$$Sucrose + H_2O \xrightarrow{H^+} Glucose + Fructose$$

invert sugar

The resulting mixture of glucose and fructose, usually in solution, is called **invert sugar.** Invert sugar has less tendency to crystallize than sucrose, and it has greater sweetening power than the corresponding amount of sucrose. The nutritive value of the sucrose is not affected in any way by conversion to invert sugar, because the same hydrolysis reaction occurs in normal digestion.

27.11 Reducing Sugars

reducing sugar

Some sugars are capable of reducing silver ions to free silver, and copper(II) ions to copper(I) ions, under prescribed conditions. Such sugars are called **reducing sugars.** This reducing ability, which is useful in classifying sugars and in certain clinical tests, is dependent on the presence of (1) aldehydes, (2) α-hydroxyketone groups (—CH$_2$COCH$_2$OH) such as in fructose, or (3) hemiacetal structures in cyclic molecules such as maltose. These groups are easily oxidized to carboxylic acid (or carboxylate ion) groups; the metal ions are thereby reduced (Ag$^+$ ⟶ Ag^0; Cu^{2+} ⟶ Cu$^+$). Several different reagents, including Tollens', Fehling's, Benedict's, and Barfoed's reagents, are used to detect reducing sugars (see Section 23.4). The Benedict, Fehling, and Barfoed tests depend on the formation of copper(I) oxide precipitate to indicate a positive reaction.

$$\underset{\substack{\text{Aldehyde} \\ \text{group}}}{RC\!\!=\!\!O} + 2\ Cu^{2+} + 5\ OH^- \longrightarrow \underset{\substack{\text{Carboxylate} \\ \text{ion group}}}{RC—O^-} + \underset{\substack{\text{Copper(I)} \\ \text{oxide (brick red)}}}{Cu_2O(s)} + 3\ H_2O$$

(blue)

Barfoed's reagent contains Cu^{2+} ions in the presence of acetic acid. It is used to distinguish reducing monosaccharides from reducing disaccharides. Under the same reaction conditions, the reagent is reduced more rapidly by monosaccharides.

Glucose and galactose contain aldehyde groups; fructose contains an α-hydroxyketone group. Therefore, all three of these monosaccharides are reducing sugars.

A carbohydrate molecule need not have a free aldehyde or α-hydroxyketone group to be a reducing sugar. A hemiacetal structure (see below) is a potential aldehyde group. Maltose and the cyclic form of glucose are examples of molecules with the hemiacetal structure.

Glucose

Maltose

Under mildly alkaline conditions, the rings open at the points indicated by the arrows to form aldehyde groups:

Glucose (ring structure)

Glucose (open-chain structure)

Any sugar that has the hemiacetal structure is classified as a reducing sugar. Among the disaccharides, lactose and maltose have hemiacetal structures and are therefore reducing sugars. Sucrose is not a reducing sugar because it does not have the hemiacetal structure.

Many clinical tests monitor glucose as a reducing sugar. For example, Benedict's and Fehling's reagents are used to detect the presence of glucose in urine. Initially the reagents are deep blue in color. A positive test is indicated by a color change to greenish-yellow, yellowish-orange, or brick-red, corresponding to an increasing glucose (reducing sugar) concentration. These tests are used for estimating the amount of glucose in the urine of diabetics in order to adjust the amount of insulin needed for proper glucose utilization.

Alternatively, a clinical test (glucose oxidase test) makes use of an enzyme-catalyzed oxidation of glucose to test for urine sugar. The inclusion of an enzyme ensures a reaction that is specific for the glucose structure, allowing a more selective test for glucose in the urine.

27.12   Reactions of Monosaccharides

Oxidation

The oxidation of monosaccharides by copper ions is described in Section 27.11. The aldehyde groups in monosaccharides are also oxidized to monocarboxylic acids by other mild oxidizing agents such as bromine water. The carboxylic acid group is formed at carbon 1. The name of the resulting acid is formed by changing the *ose* ending to *onic acid*. Glucose yields gluconic acid; galactose, galactonic acid; and so on.

$$
\begin{array}{c}
\text{H}-\text{C}=\text{O} \\
\text{H}-\text{C}-\text{OH} \\
\text{HO}-\text{C}-\text{H} \\
\text{H}-\text{C}-\text{OH} \\
\text{H}-\text{C}-\text{OH} \\
\text{CH}_2\text{OH}
\end{array}
\;+\; \text{Br}_2 + \text{H}_2\text{O} \longrightarrow
\begin{array}{c}
\text{COOH} \\
\text{H}-\text{C}-\text{OH} \\
\text{HO}-\text{C}-\text{H} \\
\text{H}-\text{C}-\text{OH} \\
\text{H}-\text{C}-\text{OH} \\
\text{CH}_2\text{OH}
\end{array}
\;+\; 2\,\text{HBr}
$$

D-Glucose   D-Gluconic acid

Dilute nitric acid, a vigorous oxidizing agent, oxidizes both carbon 1 and carbon 6 of aldohexoses to form dicarboxylic acids. The resulting acid is named by changing the *ose* sugar suffix to *aric acid*. Glucose yields glucaric acid (saccharic acid); galactose, galactaric acid (mucic acid).

$$
\begin{array}{c}
\text{H}-\text{C}=\text{O} \\
\text{H}-\text{C}-\text{OH} \\
\text{HO}-\text{C}-\text{H} \\
\text{H}-\text{C}-\text{OH} \\
\text{H}-\text{C}-\text{OH} \\
\text{CH}_2\text{OH}
\end{array}
\xrightarrow{\text{Warm HNO}_3}
\begin{array}{c}
\text{COOH} \\
\text{H}-\text{C}-\text{OH} \\
\text{HO}-\text{C}-\text{H} \\
\text{H}-\text{C}-\text{OH} \\
\text{H}-\text{C}-\text{OH} \\
\text{COOH}
\end{array}
\qquad
\begin{array}{c}
\text{COOH} \\
\text{H}-\text{C}-\text{OH} \\
\text{HO}-\text{C}-\text{H} \\
\text{HO}-\text{C}-\text{H} \\
\text{H}-\text{C}-\text{OH} \\
\text{COOH}
\end{array}
$$

D-Glucose   Glucaric acid   Galactaric acid

This reaction serves as the basis of the *galactaric (mucic) acid test,* which is sometimes used to distinguish glucose from galactose. Galactaric acid is only slightly soluble in dilute nitric acid, whereas glucaric acid is quite soluble. Hence, when oxidized with nitric acid, galactose (and lactose, which hydrolyzes to form glucose and galactose) yields a precipitate of galactaric acid crystals. When glucose is oxidized under the same conditions, the glucaric acid does not precipitate. Note also that galactaric acid is an optically inactive meso compound, whereas glucaric acid is an optically active compound (see Section 26.3).

PROBLEM

27.2

Two samples labeled A and B are known to be D-threose and D-erythrose. Water solutions of each sample are optically active. However, when each solution was warmed with nitric acid, the solution from sample A was optically inactive and that from sample B was still optically active. Determine which sample (A or B) contains D-threose and which sample contains D-erythrose.

In this problem we need to examine the structures of D-threose and D-erythrose, write equations for the reaction with nitric acid, and examine the products to see why one is optically active and the other optically inactive. Start by writing the formulas for D-threose and D-erythrose:

$$
\begin{array}{cc}
\begin{array}{c}
\text{H—C=O} \\
\text{HO—C—H} \\
\text{H—C—OH} \\
\text{CH}_2\text{OH}
\end{array}
&
\begin{array}{c}
\text{H—C=O} \\
\text{H—C—OH} \\
\text{H—C—OH} \\
\text{CH}_2\text{OH}
\end{array}
\\
\text{D-Threose} & \text{D-Erythrose}
\end{array}
$$

The oxidation of these tetroses would yield dicarboxylic acids:

$$
\begin{array}{c}
\text{H—C=O} \\
\text{HO—C—H} \\
\text{H—C—OH} \\
\text{CH}_2\text{OH}
\end{array}
\xrightarrow{\text{Warm HNO}_3}
\begin{array}{c}
\text{COOH} \\
\text{HO—C—H} \\
\text{H—C—OH} \\
\text{COOH}
\end{array}
\qquad
\begin{array}{c}
\text{H—C=O} \\
\text{H—C—OH} \\
\text{H—C—OH} \\
\text{CH}_2\text{OH}
\end{array}
\xrightarrow{\text{Warm HNO}_3}
\begin{array}{c}
\text{COOH} \\
\text{H—C—OH} \\
\text{H—C—OH} \\
\text{COOH}
\end{array}
$$

I   II

Product I is a chiral molecule and is optically active. Product II is a meso compound and is optically inactive. Therefore, sample A is D-erythrose, since the meso acid results from its oxidation. Sample B then must be D-threose.

Osazone Formation

Phenylhydrazine ($C_6H_5NHNH_2$) reacts with carbons 1 and 2 of reducing sugars to form derivatives called osazones. The formation of these distinctive crystalline derivatives is useful for comparing the structures of sugars. Glucose and fructose react as shown in Figure 27.4.

Identical osazones are obtained from D-glucose and D-fructose. This demonstrates that carbons 3 through 6 of D-glucose and D-fructose molecules are identical. The same osazone is also obtained from D-mannose. This indicates that carbons 3 through 6 of the D-mannose molecule are the same as those of D-glucose and D-fructose molecules. In fact, D-mannose differs from D-glucose only in the configuration of the —H and —OH groups on carbon 2.

```
   H—C=O                    H—C=NNHC₆H₅              H—C=NNHC₆H₅
   H—C—OH                   H—C—OH                      C=O
 HO—C—H    C₆H₅NHNH₂      HO—C—H    C₆H₅NHNH₂      HO—C—H
   H—C—OH    ────────►      H—C—OH    ────────►      H—C—OH
   H—C—OH                   H—C—OH                   H—C—OH
    CH₂OH                    CH₂OH                    CH₂OH
  D-Glucose
```

C₆H₅NHNH₂

```
                              H—C=NNHC₆H₅
                                C=NNHC₆H₅
                             HO—C—H
                               H—C—OH
                               H—C—OH
                                CH₂OH
                               Osazone
                          (from either glucose
                              or fructose)
```

C₆H₅NHNH₂

```
    CH₂OH                    CH₂OH                    H—C=O
     C=O                      C=NNHC₆H₅                 C=NNHC₆H₅
  HO—C—H    C₆H₅NHNH₂      HO—C—H    C₆H₅NHNH₂      HO—C—H
    H—C—OH    ────────►      H—C—OH    ────────►      H—C—OH
    H—C—OH                   H—C—OH                   H—C—OH
     CH₂OH                    CH₂OH                    CH₂OH
  D-Fructose
```

Figure 27.4 Reaction of glucose and fructose to form osazones

Reduction

Monosaccharides may be reduced to their corresponding polyhydroxy alcohols by reducing agents such as H_2/Pt or sodium amalgam, Na(Hg). For example, glucose yields sorbitol (glucitol), galactose yields galactitol (dulcitol), and mannose yields mannitol; all of these are hexahydric alcohols (containing six —OH groups).

```
    H—C=O                         CH₂OH
    H—C—OH                        H—C—OH
  HO—C—H      H₂/Pt            HO—C—H
    H—C—OH    ────────►           H—C—OH
    H—C—OH                        H—C—OH
     CH₂OH                         CH₂OH
  D-Glucose                     D-Glucitol
                                 (Sorbitol)
```

Hexahydric alcohols have properties resembling those of glycerol (Section 22.6). Because of their affinity for water, they are used as moisturizing agents in food and cosmetics. Sorbitol, galactitol, and mannitol occur naturally in a variety of plants.

27.13 Polysaccharides

Although many naturally occurring polysaccharides are known, three—starch, cellulose, and glycogen—are of outstanding importance. All three, when hydrolyzed, yield D-glucose as the only product, according to this approximate general equation:

$$(C_6H_{10}O_5)_n \quad + \quad n\,H_2O \longrightarrow n\,C_6H_{12}O_6$$

Polysaccharide molecule   D-Glucose
(approximate
formula)

This hydrolysis reaction establishes that all three polysaccharides are polymers made up of glucose monosaccharide units. It also means that the differences in properties among the three polysaccharides must be due to differences in the structures and/or sizes of these molecules.

Many years of research were required to determine the detailed structures for polysaccharide molecules. Consideration of all this work is beyond the scope of our discussion, but an abbreviated summary of the results is given in the following paragraphs.

Starch

Starch is found in plants, mainly in the seeds, roots, or tubers. Corn, wheat, potatoes, rice, and cassava are the chief sources of dietary starch. The two main components of starch are amylose and amylopectin. Amylose molecules are unbranched chains composed of about 25 to 1300 α-D-glucose units joined by α-1,4-glycosidic linkages, as shown in Figure 27.5. The disaccharide maltose is obtained by partial hydrolysis of amylose.

Amylopectin is a branched-chain polysaccharide with much larger molecules than those of amylose. Amylopectin molecules consist on the average of several thousand α-D-glucose units with molecular weights ranging up to 1 million or more. The main chain contains glucose units connected by α-1,4-glycosidic linkages. Branch chains are linked to the main chain through α-1,6-glycosidic linkages about every 25 glucose units, as shown in Figure 27.5. Thus, partial hydrolysis of amylopectin yields both maltose and the related disaccharide isomaltose, α-D-glucopyranosyl-(1-6)-α-D-glucopyranose.

Despite the presence of many polar —OH groups, starch molecules are insoluble in cold water, apparently because of their very large size. Starch readily forms colloidal dispersions in hot water. Such starch "solutions" form an intense blue-black color in the presence of free iodine. Hence, a starch solution can be used to detect free iodine, or a dilute iodine solution can be used to detect starch.

Starch is readily converted to glucose by heating with water and a little acid (for example, hydrochloric or sulfuric acid). It is also readily hydrolyzed at room

Figure 27.5   Structure of (a) amylose and (b) amylopectin, the two chief components of starch

temperature by certain digestive enzymes. One of these enzymes, salivary amylase, converts starch to maltose. The hydrolysis of starch to maltose and glucose is shown in the following equations:

$$\text{Starch} \xrightarrow[\text{or amylase}]{\text{Acid} + \Delta,} \text{Dextrins} \xrightarrow[\text{or amylase}]{\text{Acid} + \Delta,} \text{Maltose} \xrightarrow[\text{or maltase}]{\text{Acid} + \Delta,} \text{D-Glucose}$$

Dextrins are intermediate-size polysaccharides.

The hydrolysis of starch can be followed qualitatively by periodically testing samples from a mixture of starch and saliva with very dilute iodine solution. The change of color sequence is blue-black $\longrightarrow$ blue $\longrightarrow$ purple $\longrightarrow$ pink $\longrightarrow$ colorless as the starch molecules are broken down into smaller and smaller fragments.

Starch is the most important energy storage carbohydrate of the plant kingdom. In turn, humans, as well as many other animals, use huge quantities of starch as food. The reduced carbons from starch provide much of our daily energy needs as the carbons are oxidized to carbon dioxide. These reduced carbons can be used because starch has the appropriate structure to serve as a ready source of D-glucose.

Glycogen

Glycogen is the energy storage carbohydrate of the animal kingdom. It is formed in the body by polymerization of glucose and stored in the liver and in muscle tissues. Structurally, it is very similar to the amylopectin fraction of starch except that it is more highly branched. The α-1,6-glycosidic linkages occur on one of every 12 to 18 glucose units.

Cellulose

Cellulose is the most abundant organic substance found in nature. It is the chief structural component of plants and wood. Cotton fibers are almost pure cellulose; wood, after removal of moisture, consists of about 50% cellulose. Cellulose is an important substance in the textile and paper industries.

Cellulose, like starch and glycogen, is a polymer of glucose. But cellulose differs from starch and glycogen because the glucose units are joined by β-1,4-glycosidic linkages instead of α-1,4-glycosidic linkages. A portion of a cellulose molecule is represented in Figure 27.6. A partial hydrolysis of cellulose produces the disaccharide cellobiose, β-D-glucopyranosyl-(1-4)-β-D-glucopyranose. However, cellulose has greater resistance to hydrolysis than either starch or glycogen. It is not appreciably hydrolyzed when boiled in a 1% sulfuric acid solution. It does not show a color reaction with iodine. Humans cannot digest cellulose, because they have no enzymes capable of catalyzing its hydrolysis. Fortunately, some microorganisms found in soil and in the digestive tracts of certain animals produce enzymes that do catalyze the breakdown of cellulose. The presence of these microorganisms explains why cows and other herbivorous animals thrive on grass—and also why termites thrive on wood.

The —OH groups of starch and cellulose can be reacted without destruction of the macromolecular structures. For example, nitric acid converts an —OH group to a nitrate group in this fashion:

Cellulose—$\boxed{\text{OH} + \text{H}}$ ONO$_2$ $\longrightarrow$ Cellulose—ONO$_2$ + H$_2$O

| Hydroxyl group on cellulose molecule | Nitric acid | Nitrate group on cellulose molecule | Water |

Figure 27.6 Portion of a cellulose molecule: Cellulose molecules consist of thousands of glucose anhydride units joined together by β-1,4-glycosidic linkages. Cellulose molecules are mostly unbranched.

If only a portion of the —OH groups on the cellulose molecule are nitrated, a plastic nitrocellulose material known as Celluloid or pyroxylin is obtained. This material has been used to make such diverse articles as billiard balls, Celluloid collars, and photographic film. By nitration of nearly all —OH groups, a powerful high explosive is obtained. This highly nitrated cellulose, or "guncotton," is the basic ingredient in modern "smokeless" gunpowder.

Another modified cellulose, cellulose acetate, is made by esterification of —OH groups with acetic acid (acetic anhydride). About two-thirds of the —OH groups are esterified:

$$\text{Cellulose—O} \boxed{\text{H} + \text{CH}_3\text{—C—O}} \text{—C—CH}_3$$

Hydroxyl group on cellulose molecule   Acetic anhydride

$$\longrightarrow \text{Cellulose—O—C—CH}_3 + \text{CH}_3\text{COOH}$$

Acetate group on cellulose molecule

Cellulose acetate, unlike the dangerously flammable cellulose nitrate, can be made to burn only with difficulty. For this reason, cellulose acetate has displaced cellulose nitrate in almost all kinds of photographic films. The textile known as acetate rayon is made from cellulose acetate. Cellulose acetate is also used as a clear, transparent packaging film. In another process, cellulose reacts with carbon disulfide in the presence of sodium hydroxide to form a soluble cellulose derivative called cellulose xanthate, from which cellulose can be regenerated. Viscose rayon textiles and cellophane packaging materials are made of regenerated cellulose prepared by this process.

Not all polysaccharides are polymers of glucose. For example, inulin is a starchlike substance that is largely a polymer composed of fructose units joined by 1,2-glycosidic linkages. It has a molecular weight of about 5000. Inulin is found in the tubers of artichokes and dahlias and in the roots of dandelions and chicory. It is not digestable by animal enzymes. Clinically, inulin is used as a diagnostic aid in testing kidney function.

QUESTIONS

A. *Review the meanings of the new terms introduced in this chapter.*

1. Carbohydrates
2. Monosaccharide
3. Disaccharide
4. Oligosaccharide
5. Polysaccharide
6. Epimer
7. Mutarotation
8. Anomer
9. Glycoside
10. Invert sugar
11. Reducing sugar

B. *Review questions*

1. Why is the oxidation state of a carbohydrate carbon important in metabolism?
2. What is the significance of the notations D and L in the name of a carbohydrate?
3. What is the significance of the notations (+) and (−) in the name of a carbohydrate?

4. Explain how a carbohydrate with a pyranose structure differs from one with a furanose structure.

5. What is galactosemia and what are its effects on humans?

6. Which of the D-aldohexoses in Figure 27.1 are epimers?

7. Write the cyclic structures for α-D-glucopyranose, β-D-galactopyranose, and α-D-mannopyranose.

8. Explain how α-D-glucopyranose differs from β-D-glucopyranose.

9. Write the structure of L-glyceraldehyde and show, using oxidation numbers, which carbon is most reduced.

10. Would D-mannose provide more metabolic energy than D-galactose? Explain.

11. Starting with the proper D-tetrose, show the steps for the synthesis of D-glucose by the Kiliani–Fischer synthesis.

12. Are the cyclic forms of monosaccharides hemiacetals or glycosides?

13. Explain the phenomenon of mutarotation.

14. Is D-2-deoxyarabinose the same as D-2-deoxyribose? Explain.

15. What is (are) the major source(s) of each?
    (a) Sucrose (b) Lactose (c) Maltose

16. What is the monosaccharide composition of each of the following?
    (a) Sucrose   (c) Lactose   (e) Amylose
    (b) Maltose   (d) Glycogen

17. How does the structure of cellobiose differ from that of isomaltose?

18. Cite two advantages of aspartame, as a sweetener, over sucrose.

19. Explain why invert sugar is sweeter than sucrose.

20. Which of the disaccharides sucrose, maltose, and lactose will show mutarotation? Explain why.

21. Draw structural formulas for maltose and sucrose. Point out the portion of the structure that is responsible for one of these disaccharides being classified as a reducing sugar.

22. Give the systematic names for isomaltose and lactose.

23. What visual difference would you expect between a dilute glucose solution and a concentrated glucose solution in the Benedict test?

24. Which of the D-aldopentoses (Figure 27.1) will be optically inactive when reduced with H_2/Pt? Write structures for the reduced products and explain why they are optically inactive.

25. Glyceraldehyde, $CH_2(OH)CH(OH)CHO$, is the simplest aldose.
    (a) Write projection formulas for and identify the D and L forms of glyceraldehyde.
    (b) Write the structural formula of the product obtained by reacting glyceraldehyde with hydrogen in the presence of a platinum catalyst.

26. Consider the eight aldohexoses given in Figure 27.1 and answer the following:
    (a) Which of these aldohexoses will give the same osazone?
    (b) The eight aldohexoses are oxidized by nitric acid to dicarboxylic acids. Which of these will give meso (optically inactive) dicarboxylic acids?
    (c) Write the structures and names for the enantiomers of D-(+)-mannose and D-(−)-idose.

27. Describe the principal structural differences and similarities between the members of each of the following pairs:
    (a) D-Glucose and D-fructose
    (b) D-Ribose and D-2-deoxyribose
    (c) Maltose and sucrose
    (d) Amylose and amylopectin
    (e) Cellulose and glycogen
    (f) D-(−)-Ribose and D-(+)-glucose

28. When glucose is oxidized with nitric acid, glucaric acid is formed. Write the structural formula and the name of the dicarboxylic acid that is formed when galactose is oxidized with nitric acid.

29. Write the formulas for the four L-aldopentoses. Indicate which pair (or pairs) of the L-aldopentoses will give identical osazones with phenylhydrazine.

30. Write the structure of a disaccharide that hydrolyzes to give only D-glucose and (a) is a reducing sugar, shows mutarotation, and will form an osazone; (b) is a nonreducing sugar, does not mutarotate, and will not form an osazone.

31. What are the structural differences between starch and cellulose?

32. What are the two main components of starch? How are they alike and how do they differ?

33. Write the structure for cellobiose, a disaccharide obtained by the hydrolysis of cellulose.
34. Draw the Haworth formulas for
    (a) β-D-glucopyranosyl-(1-4)-α-D-galactopyranose
    (b) β-D-galactopyranosyl-(1-6)-β-D-mannopyranose
35. A molecular weight value of about 325,000 was calculated for a sample of amylopectin. Approximately how many glucose units are present in an average molecule of this amylopectin? (*Hint:* As each glucose is added to a growing amylopectin chain, a molecule of water is removed).
36. Draw enough of the structural formula of cellulose acetate to show the repeating units and how they are linked.
37. Write three units of the polymeric structure of inulin.
38. Which of these statements are correct?
    (a) α-D-Glucopyranose and β-D-glucopyranose are enantiomers.
    (b) The carbon of a secondary alcohol is more reduced than the carbon of a primary alcohol.
    (c) D-Glyceraldehyde and L-glyceraldehyde are epimers.
    (d) D-Threose and L-threose are epimers.
    (e) There are eight stereoisomers of the aldopentoses.
    (f) D-Glucose and L-glucose will form identical osazones.
    (g) Raffinose, which consists of one unit each of galactose, glucose, and fructose, is an oligosaccharide.
    (h) Two aldohexoses that react with phenylhydrazine to yield identical osazones are epimers.
    (i) Dextrose is another name for glucose.
    (j) D-Mannitol is obtained from D-mannose by oxidation.
    (k) Methyl glucosides are capable of reducing Fehling's and Barfoed's reagents.
    (l) Humans are incapable of using cellulose directly as a food.
    (m) Fructose can be classified as a hexose, a monosaccharide, and an aldose.
    (n) The change in the specific rotation of a carbohydrate solution to an equilibrium value is called mutarotation.
    (o) The disaccharide found in mammalian milk is galactose.
    (p) The reserve carbohydrate of animals is glycogen.
    (q) Starch consists of two polysaccharides known as amylose and amylopectin.
    (r) Carbohydrates that are capable of reducing copper ions in Benedict's reagent are called reducing sugars.
    (s) The polysaccharides cellulose, starch, and glycogen are all composed of glucose units.
    (t) Invert sugar is sweeter than fructose.
    (u) Sucrose, glucose, galactose, and fructose are reducing sugars.
    (v) Methyl glycosides do not undergo mutarotation.
    (w) Oxidation of D-erythrose with dilute HNO_3 yields *meso*-tartaric acid.

28

Lipids

28.1 Classification of Lipids

lipids   **Lipids** are water-insoluble, oily or greasy biochemical compounds that can be extracted from cells by nonpolar solvents such as ether, chloroform, or benzene. Unlike carbohydrates, lipids share no common chemical structure but are a "catch-all" class. Still, the above definition is a starting point for describing some similarities among the structural features of lipids.

What makes a molecule, such as a lipid, insoluble in water? There are many reasons, but two of the most important are (1) large size and (2) lack of polar bonds or charged groups. Water molecules are attracted to polar bonds or charged groups. Without these constituents, a molecule will tend to be water-insoluble. In addition, water molecules have more difficulty dissolving larger molecules. Thus, a molecule that is both large *and* nonpolar will likely be water-insoluble. Such a nonpolar molecule is said to be hydrophobic ("water-fearing"). Conversely, a molecule that dissolves easily in water is said to be hydrophilic ("water-loving").

For example, consider fatty acids, which are common components of lipids. As shown in Table 28.1, as the number of atoms in a fatty acid molecule increases, the water solubility of the fatty acid decreases drastically.

$$\text{Butyric acid (4 carbons)} \longleftrightarrow \text{Stearic acid (18 carbons)}$$
$$\qquad\text{Hydrophilic} \qquad\qquad\qquad\qquad \text{Hydrophobic}$$

The many saturated carbons of fatty acids contribute to their hydrophobic character, since saturated carbons are relatively nonpolar. However, if the fatty acid loses a hydrogen ion from its carboxylic acid end, the resulting negative charge imparts some hydrophilic character, creating a soap:

$$CH_3(CH_2)_{14}COOH \xrightarrow{OH^-} CH_3(CH_2)_{14}COO^- + H_2O$$

Palmitic acid   Palmitate ion
(hydrophobic)   (relatively hydrophilic)

Lipids do not dissolve easily in water because they are large, relatively nonpolar molecules. Their water-insolubility allows them to form barriers to aqueous solutions. This property, as we shall see later, is of great importance when lipids form cellular membranes. Lipids are classified as follows:

1. **Simple lipids**
   (a) *Fats and oils:* esters of fatty acids and glycerol
   (b) *Waxes:* esters of high-molecular-weight fatty acids and high-molecular-weight alcohols
2. **Compound lipids**
   (a) *Phospholipids:* substances that yield glycerol, phosphoric acid, fatty acids, and nitrogen-containing bases upon hydrolysis
   (b) *Sphingolipids:* substances that yield an unsaturated amino alcohol (sphingosine), a long-chain fatty acid, and either a carbohydrate or phosphate and a nitrogen base (choline) upon hydrolysis
   (c) *Glycolipids:* substances that yield an alcohol other than glycerol, fatty acids, a nitrogen-containing base, and a carbohydrate upon hydrolysis.

Table 28.1 Some naturally occurring fatty acids in fats

Fatty acid	Number of C atoms	Formula	Solubility (g/100 g water)	Melting point (°C)
Saturated acids				
Butyric acid	4	$CH_3CH_2CH_2COOH$	∞	−4.7
Caproic acid	6	$CH_3(CH_2)_4COOH$	1.08	−1.5
Caprylic acid	8	$CH_3(CH_2)_6COOH$	0.07	16
Capric acid	10	$CH_3(CH_2)_8COOH$	0.015	32
Lauric acid	12	$CH_3(CH_2)_{10}COOH$	0.006	48
Myristic acid	14	$CH_3(CH_2)_{12}COOH$	0.002	57
Palmitic acid	16	$CH_3(CH_2)_{14}COOH$	0.0007	63
Stearic acid	18	$CH_3(CH_2)_{16}COOH$	0.0003	70
Arachidic acid	20	$CH_3(CH_2)_{18}COOH$	—	77
Unsaturated acids				
Palmitoleic acid	16	$CH_3(CH_2)_5CH{=}CH(CH_2)_7COOH$	—	32
Oleic acid	18	$CH_3(CH_2)_7CH{=}CH(CH_2)_7COOH$	—	4
Linoleic acid	18	$CH_3(CH_2)_4CH{=}CHCH_2CH{=}CH(CH_2)_7COOH$	—	−5
Linolenic acid	18	$CH_3CH_2CH{=}CHCH_2CH{=}CHCH_2CH{=}CH(CH_2)_7COOH$	—	−11
Arachidonic acid	20	$CH_3(CH_2)_4(CH{=}CHCH_2)_4CH_2CH_2COOH$	—	−50

3. **Steroids**
   Substances possessing the steroid nucleus, which is a 17-carbon structure consisting of four fused carboxcyclic rings. Cholesterol and several hormones are in this class.
4. **Miscellaneous lipids**
   Substances that do not fit into the preceding classifications; these include the fat-soluble vitamins A, D, E, and K.

The most abundant lipids are the fats and oils. These substances constitute one of the three important classes of foods. The discussion that follows is centered on fats and oils. A more complete consideration of the properties and composition of various fats and oils is given in Section 24.8.

28.2 Simple Lipids

Fats and Oils

Chemically, fats and oils are esters of glycerol and the higher-molecular-weight fatty acids. They have the general formula where the R's can be either long-chain saturated or unsaturated hydrocarbon groups.

Fats may be considered to be triesters formed from the trihydroxy alcohol glycerol and three molecules of fatty acids. Most of the fatty acids in these esters have 14 to 18 carbons. Because there are three ester groups per glycerol, these molecules are called triacylglycerols, or triglycerides (an older name that is still commonly used). The three R groups are usually different.

$$
\begin{array}{cccc}
\mathrm{CH_2-O-[H + H-O]-C-R} & & \mathrm{CH_2-O-C-R} & \\
\qquad\qquad\qquad\quad\ \underset{\mathrm O}{\|} & & \qquad\qquad\underset{\mathrm O}{\|} & \\
\mathrm{CH-O-[H + H-O]-C-R'} & \longrightarrow & \mathrm{R'-C-O-CH} & +\ 3\,\mathrm{H_2O} \\
\qquad\qquad\qquad\quad\ \underset{\mathrm O}{\|} & & \underset{\mathrm O}{\|} & \\
\mathrm{CH_2-O-[H + H-O]-C-R''} & & \mathrm{CH_2-O-C-R''} & \\
\qquad\qquad\qquad\quad\ \underset{\mathrm O}{\|} & & \qquad\qquad\underset{\mathrm O}{\|} & \\
\end{array}
$$

Glycerol   Fatty acids   A triacylglycerol

Fats and oils fit the general description of a lipid. They are large molecules, averaging more than 50 carbon atoms per molecule, with many nonpolar, uncharged groups. Because they contain large numbers of saturated carbons, the triacylglycerols are hydrophobic and water-insoluble. The formulas for some of the most common fatty acids found in fats are shown in Table 28.1. All these acids are straight-chain carbon compounds. Five of these fatty acids— palmitoleic, oleic, linoleic, linolenic, and arachidonic—are unsaturated, having carbon–carbon double bonds in their structures.

Double bonds impart some special characteristics to unsaturated fatty acids. Remember that the presence of double bonds raises the possibility of geometric isomerism (Section 21.4). To emphasize the effect of these double bonds, the following two fatty acid structures, portray each of the many —(CH₂—) groups as a simple bond in the fatty acid chain. Unsaturated fatty acids found in nature are almost always cis isomers. Each double bond adds a "hairpin" turn to the fatty acid structure. These kinked fatty acids cannot stack closely together. Hence they do not solidify easily and are liquids at ordinary temperatures (see Table 28.1). These characteristics are reflected in triacylglycerols that contain unsaturated fatty acids. Thus, the triacylglycerols purchased from your market as cooking oils are liquids at room temperature because a high percentage of their fatty acids are unsaturated. In like manner, biological membranes are very fluid because of the presence of double bonds in their component fatty acids (see Section 28.5).

Three unsaturated fatty acids—linoleic, linolenic, and arachidonic—are essential for animal nutrition and must be present in the diet. Diets lacking these fatty acids lead to impaired growth and reproduction, and skin disorders such as eczema and dermatitis. A dermatitis disorder can be attributed to an unsaturated fatty acid deficiency if the symptoms clear up when that fatty acid is supplied in the diet.

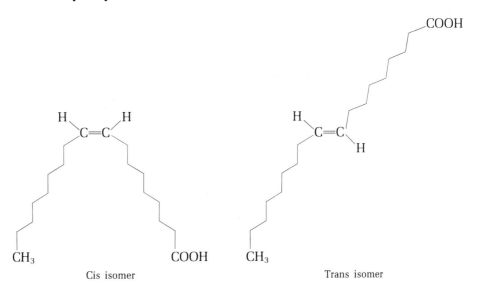

Cis isomer   Trans isomer

Recent research shows that arachidonic acid is used by the body to make two types of hormonelike substances—the prostaglandins and leukotrienes. Under certain circumstances such as infection, allergic reactions, and bee stings, cell membranes release arachidonic acid. Enzymes in the surrounding fluid convert this fatty acid to various prostaglandins or leukotrienes. These reactions involve the addition of oxygen to the arachidonic double bonds. Some examples of prostaglandins and leukotrienes are shown in Figure 28.1.

Prostaglandins cause a variety of tissue changes. They also modify the action of some hormones. Prostaglandins are a primary cause of the swelling, redness, and pain associated with tissue inflammation. Aspirin relieves this condition by blocking the reaction of oxygen with arachidonic acid and thus preventing the formation of prostaglandins. Other anti-inflammatory drugs, like cortisone, stop prostaglandin formation by decreasing the cell membrane release of arachidonic acid.

Fats are an important food source for humans and normally account for about 25–50% of their caloric intake. When oxidized to carbon dioxide and water, fats supply about 38 kJ of energy per gram, which is more than twice the amount obtained from carbohydrates or proteins.

The energy from a fat is released when the reduced carbons are oxidized. In general, the more reduced a carbon, the more energy it contains (see Section 27.1). Triacylglycerol carbons are more reduced than those of most other foods. The typical carbon from a fat has an oxidation number of -2, whereas the typical carbon from a carbohydrate has an oxidation number of 0:

$$C-\underset{\underset{H}{|}}{\overset{\overset{OH}{|}}{C}}-C \qquad \text{0 (Oxidation number)}$$

$$C-\underset{\underset{H}{|}}{\overset{\overset{H}{|}}{C}}-C \qquad \text{-2 (Oxidation number)}$$

In a carbohydrate   In a fat

Figure 28.1 Several examples of prostaglandins and leukotrienes

This difference in oxidation numbers makes it clear that fats contain and will release more energy than carbohydrates. In addition, on a weight basis, the average fat contains about 75% carbon, whereas the average carbohydrate contains only about 40% carbon.

Waxes

waxes

Waxes are esters of high-molecular-weight fatty acids and high-molecular-weight alcohols. They have the general formula

$$R'-\overset{\overset{\displaystyle O}{\|}}{C}-O-R$$

in which the alcohol (ROH) contributes up to about 30 carbons, and the fatty acid (R′COOH) provides an equivalent number of carbons. Waxes are very large molecules with almost no polar groups. They represent one of the most hydrophobic lipid classes.

Their extreme water-insolubility allows waxes to serve a protective function.

Leaves, feathers, fruit, and fur are often naturally coated with a wax. Hardwood floors, cars, and leather goods are just a few of the man-made products that can be protected by a wax. Other biological functions for waxes may also prove important. Recently a component of beeswax, $CH_3(CH_2)_{28}CH_2OH$ (1-triacontanol), has been found to be a potent plant-growth stimulator. When combined with calcium ion, this 30-carbon alcohol has been shown to enhance sweet corn, tomato, and bean yields from 50–70% under certain conditions.

28.3 Compound Lipids

Phospholipids

phospholipids

The **phospholipids** are a group of compounds that yield one or more fatty acid molecules, a phosphate group, and usually a nitrogenous base upon hydrolysis. The phosphate group and the nitrogenous base, which are found at one end of the phospholipid molecule, often have negative and positive charges. Consequently, in contrast to the triacylglycerols, phospholipids have hydrophobic ends that repel water and hydrophilic ends that interact with water.

A triacylglycerol

A phospholipid

As will be seen later in this chapter, a lipid with both hydrophobic and hydrophilic character is needed to make membranes. It is not surprising that phospholipids are one of the most important membrane components.

Phospholipids are also involved in the metabolism of other lipids and nonlipids. Although they are produced to some extent by almost all cells, most of the phospholipids that enter the blood stream are formed in the liver. Representative phospholipids are described below.

Phosphatidic acids. Phosphatidic acids are glyceryl esters of fatty acids and phosphoric acid. The phosphatidic acids are important intermediates in the synthesis of triacylglycerols and other phospholipids.

$$\begin{array}{c} CH_2-O-C-R \\ \qquad\quad \|\ \\ \qquad\quad O \\ R'-C-O-CH \\ \ \|\ \\ O \qquad\qquad O \\ \qquad\quad \|\ \\ CH_2-O-P-O^- \\ \qquad\qquad\ | \\ \qquad\qquad\ O^- \end{array} \quad \begin{array}{l} \text{Hydrophobic} \\[2em] \text{Hydrophilic} \end{array}$$

A phosphatidic acid

Other phospholipids are formed from a given phosphatidic acid when specific nitrogen-containing compounds are linked to the phosphate group by an ester bond. Three commonly used nitrogen compounds are choline, ethanolamine, and L-serine:

$$\begin{array}{c} CH_3 \\ | \\ HOCH_2CH_2N^+-CH_3 \\ | \\ CH_3 \end{array} \qquad HOCH_2CH_2NH_3^+ \qquad HOCH_2CH\!\!\begin{array}{c} \nearrow COO^- \\ \searrow NH_3^+ \end{array}$$

Choline   Ethanolamine   L-Serine

Because other phospholipids are structurally related to phosphatidic acids, their names are also closely related.

Lecithins (phosphatidyl cholines). Phosphatidyl cholines (lecithins) are glyceryl esters of fatty acids, phosphoric acid, and choline. The synonym *lecithin* is an older term that is still used, particularly in commercial products that contain phosphatidyl choline. Phosphatidyl cholines are synthesized in the liver and are present in considerable amounts in nerve tissue and brain substance. Most commercial phosphatidyl choline is obtained from soybean oil and contains palmitic, stearic, palmitoleic, oleic, linoleic, linolenic, and arachidonic acids. Phosphatidyl choline is an edible and digestible emulsifying agent that is used extensively in the food industry. For example, chocolate and margarine are generally emulsified with phosphatidyl choline. Phosphatidyl choline is also used as an emulsifier in many pharmaceutical preparations.

$$\begin{array}{c} CH_2-O-C-R \\ \qquad\quad |\quad \|\ \\ R'-C-O-CH \quad O \\ \ \|\ \\ O \qquad\qquad\qquad\qquad\quad \text{Choline} \\ \qquad\qquad\ O \qquad\qquad\ CH_3 \\ \qquad\qquad \|\ \qquad\qquad\quad | \\ CH_2-O-P-O-CH_2CH_2N^+\!-CH_3 \\ \qquad\qquad\ | \qquad\qquad\qquad\ | \\ \qquad\qquad\ O^- \qquad\qquad\quad CH_3 \end{array} \quad \begin{array}{l} \text{Hydrophobic} \\[3em] \text{Hydrophilic} \end{array}$$

A phosphatidyl choline (lecithin) molecule

Cephalins (phosphatidyl ethanolamines). Phosphatidyl ethanolamines (cephalins) are glyceryl esters of fatty acids, phosphoric acid, and ethanolamine ($HOCH_2CH_2NH_2$). The cephalins are found in all living organisms. They are a significant constituent of the nerve tissue and brain substance. Cephalin is essential to the clotting of blood. It is the predominant substance in thromboplastin, which initiates the clotting process.

$$
\begin{array}{l}
\text{CH}_2\text{—O—C—R} \\
\quad\quad\quad\quad \| \\
\text{R}'\text{—C—O—CH} \quad\quad \text{O} \\
\quad \| \\
\quad \text{O} \\
\quad\quad\quad\quad\quad\quad \text{O} \\
\quad\quad\quad\quad\quad\quad \| \\
\quad\quad\quad \text{CH}_2\text{—O—P—OCH}_2\text{CH}_2\text{NH}_3^+ \\
\quad\quad\quad\quad\quad\quad | \\
\quad\quad\quad\quad\quad\quad \text{O}^-
\end{array}
$$

Hydrophobic
Ethanolamine
Hydrophilic

A cephalin (phosphatidyl ethanolamine) molecule

Sphingolipids

sphingolipids

Sphingolipids are compounds that, when hydrolyzed, yield a long-chain fatty acid (18 to 26 carbons), a hydrophilic group (either phosphate and choline or a carbohydrate), and sphingosine (an unsaturated amino alcohol). Sphingosine substitutes for glycerol in these lipids. When drawn as follows, sphingosine can be seen as similar to glycerol esterified to one fatty acid:

$$
\begin{array}{l}
\text{OH} \\
| \\
\text{CH—CH}=\text{CH(CH}_2)_{12}\text{CH}_3 \\
| \\
\overset{*}{\text{NH}}_2\text{—CH} \\
| \\
\text{CH}_2\text{—}\overset{*}{\text{OH}}
\end{array}
$$

Sphingosine

$$
\begin{array}{l}
\quad\quad\quad\quad \text{O} \\
\quad\quad\quad\quad \| \\
\text{CH}_2\text{—O—C(CH}_2)_n\text{CH}_3 \\
| \\
\overset{*}{\text{HO}}\text{—CH} \\
| \\
\text{CH}_2\text{—}\overset{*}{\text{OH}}
\end{array}
$$

Glycerol esterified with one fatty acid

The starred atoms on sphingosine react further to make sphingolipids, just as the starred atoms on the glycerol compound react further to give triacylglycerols or phospholipids.

Sphingolipids are common membrane components because they have both hydrophobic and hydrophilic character. Sphingomyelins are found in the myelin sheath membranes that surround nerves:

$$
\begin{array}{c}
\text{OH} \\
| \\
\overset{\displaystyle O}{\underset{\displaystyle \parallel}{}} \quad \text{CH--CH=CH(CH}_2)_{12}\text{CH}_3 \\
\text{R--C--NH--CH}
\end{array}
$$

$$
\text{CH}_2\text{--O--}\overset{\displaystyle O}{\underset{\displaystyle O^-}{\overset{\parallel}{\underset{\displaystyle |}{P}}}}\text{--O--CH}_2\text{CH}_2\text{--}\overset{+}{\text{N}}\text{--CH}_3
$$

Hydrophobic

Hydrophilic

A sphingomyelin

Notice the hydrophobic and hydrophilic parts of this molecule. Sphingomyelins can also be classified as phospholipids.

Glycolipids

glycolipids

Sphingolipids that contain carbohydrate groups are also known as **glycolipids.** The two most important classes of glycolipids are the cerebrosides and gangliosides. These substances are found mainly in the cell membranes of nerve and brain tissue. A cerebroside may contain either D-galactose or D-glucose. The following formula of a galactocerebroside shows the typical structure of cerebrosides:

A galactocerebroside

Gangliosides are similar to cerebrosides in structure but contain complex oligosaccharides instead of simple monosaccharides.

28.4 Steroids

steroids

Steroids are compounds that have the steroid nucleus, which consists of four fused carbocyclic rings. This nucleus contains 17 carbon atoms in one five-membered and three six-membered rings. Modifications of this nucleus in the various steroid compounds include added side chains, hydroxyl groups, carbonyl groups, ring double bonds, and so on.

Steroid ring nucleus

Steroids are closely related in structure but are highly diverse in function. Examples of steroids and steroid-containing materials are (1) cholesterol, the most abundant steroid in the body, which is widely distributed in all cells and serves as a major membrane component; (2) bile salts, which aid in the digestion of fats; (3) ergosterol, a yeast steroid, which is converted to vitamin D by ultraviolet radiation; (4) digitalis and related substances called cardiac glycosides, which are potent heart drugs; (5) the adrenal cortex hormones, which are involved in metabolism; and (6) the sex hormones, which control sexual characteristics and reproduction. The formulas for several steroids are given in Figure 28.2.

Most steroid hormones are produced by animals. However, brassinolide, a steroid-like hormone in plants has recently been characterized:

Brassinolide

This compound is isolated from pollen and is an amazingly effective growth promoter. One gram of brassinolide spread over five acres will increase crop yield from 6–30% for such vegetables as radishes, lettuce, beans, peppers, and potatoes.

Cholesterol is a steroid of special interest not only because it is the precursor of many other steroids, but because of its association with atherosclerosis, a disease of the large arteries. The body synthesizes about 1 g of cholesterol per day, whereas about 0.3 g per day is ingested in the average diet. The major sources of cholesterol in the diet are meat, liver, and eggs. A large part of the ingested cholesterol is esterified with long-chain fatty acids. Cholesterol does not need to be digested to be absorbed from the intestines.

The biosynthesis of cholesterol begins with an ester of acetic acid (acetyl CoA; see Chapter 34). Through the use of radioactive carbon-14 tracer atoms, it has been shown that all 27 carbon atoms in cholesterol originate from the acetic acid portion of this ester. The main site of cholesterol synthesis is the liver.

Figure 28.2 Structures of selected steroids

Cholesterol is also produced in many other places such as the adrenal glands and the reproductive organs. Large concentrations of cholesterol are found in the brain, the spinal cord, and the liver.

Cholesterol is used to build cell membranes. It is also used to form cholic acid, which is further modified into the bile salts associated with the digestion of fats. Small amounts of cholesterol are converted to adrenocortical hormones by the adrenal glands, to the estrogens and progesterone by the ovaries, and to testosterone by the testes. A rather large amount of cholesterol is deposited under the skin, making the skin resistant to the absorption of water-soluble substances and helping, along with other lipids, to prevent excessive evaporation of water through the skin.

Cholesterol has been associated with atherosclerosis, the deposition of cholesterol and other lipids on the inner walls of the large arteries. These deposits are called *plaque*. The accumulation of plaque causes the arterial passages to become progressively narrower. The walls of the arteries also lose their elasticity and their ability to expand to accommodate the volume of blood pumped by the heart. Blood pressure increases as the heart works to pump sufficient blood through the narrowed passages; this may eventually lead to a heart attack. The build-up of plaque also causes the inner walls to have a rough rather than the normal smooth surface. This condition is favorable to coronary thrombosis (heart attack due to blood clots).

Because of the variety of both beneficial and dangerous effects of cholesterol, the body has developed a careful distribution system for this steroid. Dietary cholesterol is transferred to the liver, which is the clearinghouse for cholesterol transport to the rest of the body. Cholesterol leaves the liver in association with other lipids and certain proteins in the form of an aggregate known as the *very low density lipoprotein* (VLDL). As the other lipids are removed from this aggregate, it is converted first to an *intermediate density lipoprotein* (IDL) and then to a *low density lipoprotein* (LDL). Cells needing cholesterol are able to absorb the low density lipoprotein. Proper transfer of cholesterol also depends on a fourth lipoprotein, the *high density lipoprotein* (HDL). A normal cholesterol metabolism must involve a proper balance of these lipoprotein factors.

Atherosclerosis can result from an imbalance in the cholesterol distribution system. High-cholesterol diets may contribute to plaque formation. However, any defect in the steroid distribution system can also cause this disease. People with high plasma LDL concentrations are prone to atherosclerosis, even though they may be on low-cholesterol diets. In contrast, large amounts of HDL seem to prevent plaque formation. Many of the hereditary and dietary factors that lead to atherosclerosis cause an imbalance in the cholesterol distribution system.

28.5   Biological Membranes

Biological membranes are thin, semipermeable cellular barriers. The general function of these barriers is to exclude dangerous chemicals from the cell while allowing nutrients to enter. Membranes also confine special molecules to specific sections of the cell. Because almost all the dangerous chemicals, nutrients, and special molecules are water-soluble, the membranes can act as effective barriers only if they impede the movement of hydrophilic (water-soluble) molecules.

To act as such a barrier, a membrane must have some special properties. To exclude water and water solutes, the bulk of a membrane must be hydrophobic. But a membrane necessarily touches water both inside and outside the cell. Therefore, the surface of a membrane must be hydrophilic. Thus a membrane can be visualized as being layered much like a piece of laminated plywood.

Plywood model of a simple membrane

The interior provides the barrier while the exterior interacts with the aqueous environment.

The cell uses lipids to give the membrane its hydrophobic nature. In fact, by selecting the right lipids, both the hydrophobic and hydrophilic portions of a membrane can be assembled. There are several classes of membrane lipids. The most important of these are the phospholipids and sphingolipids. Remember that these lipids have both a hydrophobic and a hydrophilic section.

$$
\begin{array}{l}
\qquad\qquad\qquad\overset{\displaystyle O}{\overset{\displaystyle \|}{CH_2-O-C(CH_2)_nCH_3}} \\[2pt]
\qquad\qquad\qquad\big| \\
\overset{\displaystyle O}{\overset{\displaystyle \|}{CH_3(CH_2)_nC-O-CH}} \\[2pt]
\qquad\qquad\qquad\big| \\
CH_2-O-\overset{\displaystyle O}{\overset{\displaystyle \|}{P}}-O-CH_2CH_2-\overset{\displaystyle CH_3}{\overset{\displaystyle |}{N^+}}-CH_3 \\[2pt]
\qquad\qquad\quad\;\; \underset{\displaystyle O^-}{|}\qquad\qquad\qquad\underset{\displaystyle CH_3}{|}
\end{array}
$$

Hydrophobic

Hydrophilic

A phosphatidyl choline (lecithin) molecule

A membrane lipid can be pictured as having two long, hydrophobic tails (the fatty acids in the example given) and a small, hydrophilic end (the phosphate and choline in the example). Often a membrane lipid is drawn schematically as follows:

Hydrophilic

Hydrophobic

By stacking these lipids together, a basic membrane is formed. This structure is known as a **lipid bilayer.** It has the necessary properties of a membrane—a hydrophobic barrier and a hydrophilic surface.

lipid bilayer

Lipid gives this barrier an oily or fluid appearance. The more unsaturated fatty acids in the membrane, the more fluid it will be. Other lipids, most importantly cholesterol, cause the membrane to be less fluid.

Membrane fluidity can have important consequences on cell function. It is thought that general anesthetics (for example, ether, halothane) are effective partly because they dissolve in membranes, altering the fluidity of the lipid bilayer. During severe cirrhosis of the liver, red cells are forced to take abnormally large amounts of cholesterol into their membranes, causing these membranes to be less fluid. The red cells become more rigid, have greater difficulty passing through narrow capillaries, and are destroyed more easily.

The lipid bilayer acts as a barrier to water and hydrophilic molecules because of its hydrophobic interior. Because a cell is surrounded by a lipid bilayer, most charged or polar molecules have difficulty entering the cell. But the cell must have nutrients, so it is faced with a dilemma. How can it selectively allow some hydrophilic molecules to cross the lipid bilayer while excluding others?

Proteins in the fluid bilayer solve this dilemma. These proteins allow specific molecular transport through the hydrophobic interior. (For a general discussion of proteins, see Chapter 29.) They recognize specific molecules on the exterior of a cell membrane and shuttle these molecules into the cell. This process may be as simple as providing a tunnel through the membrane for selected nutrients. If the protein helps (facilitates) transport without using energy, the process is **facilitated** called **facilitated diffusion.** Some transport requires energy, such as when **diffusion** molecules are moved from areas of low concentration to areas of high concentration (the opposite direction from that of diffusion). This energy-requiring **active** transport is termed **active transport** (see Figure 28.3).

transport   Other proteins are located in the lipid bilayer to allow special reactions to occur. These special reactions, which often could be harmed by water, are enclosed in the hydrophobic interior of the lipid bilayer. Much of the cellular energy production (oxidation–reduction reactions) occurs in this environment.

Thus a complete cellular membrane must have both lipid and protein. A typical membrane includes about 60% protein, 25% phospholipid, 10% cholesterol, and 5% sphingolipid. The fluid lipid bilayer is studded with many solid proteins. The proteins form a random pattern on the outer surface of **fluid-mosaic** the oily lipid. This general membrane is called the **fluid-mosaic model** (see Fig-**model** ure 28.4). Proteins that are primarily inside the lipid bilayer are termed *intrinsic membrane proteins,* and those on the surface are named *extrinsic membrane proteins.*

Human nerve tissue is a good example of the importance of membranes. Nerves coordinate many of the body processes, allowing life to continue. Their ability to function depends primarily on the characteristics of their membranes.

If we could examine a human nerve, it would look like the sketch in Figure 28.5. Notice the thickness of the membranes that wrap the nerve cell. These

Figure 28.3   An illustration of how membrane transport is aided by proteins: Molecules or ions (symbolized by Y and x) can move from high concentration to low concentration without energy (facilitated diffusion), but movement in the reverse direction requires energy (active transport).

membranes are so important that two cells join together to provide them; the outer wrapping from one cell is the myelin sheath, and the thin inner neuronal membrane is from the other cell.

The neuronal membrane transmits electrical nerve impulses. To accomplish this task the neuron, using energy, slowly concentrates potassium ions inside the cell while expelling sodium ions (active transport; see Figure 28.5). Throughout

Figure 28.4   The fluid-mosaic model of a membrane

Cross section of human nerve

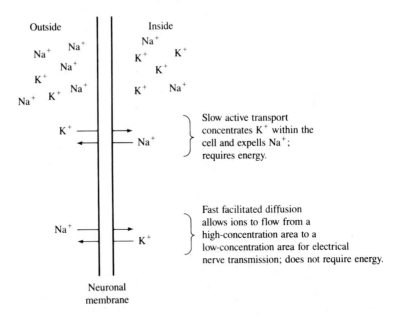

Figure 28.5 Sketch of a human nerve showing the myelin sheath and ion movement across the neuronal membrane

life, proteins within the neuronal membranes constantly pump these ions. When a neuron transmits a signal, membrane proteins allow a small portion of the potassium ions to flow rapidly out of the cell while sodium ions flow in. The sodium and potassium ions now flow from areas of high concentration to areas of low concentration without using energy. This is an example of facilitated diffusion. The rapid ion movement is an electrical nerve impulse.

The myelin sheath serves as insulation for electrical nerve transmission (like the plastic around a copper wire). It is made up of concentric wrappings of a membrane that is high in lipid but low in protein (about 30% protein and 70% lipid). Remember that a lipid bilayer impedes movement of hydrophilic groups such as ions. The major function of the myelin sheath is to act as a barrier.

If the myelin sheath is removed, nerve transmission is faulty. Multiple sclerosis is a disease that causes destruction of the myelin sheath in portions of the central nervous system. The cause of this crippling disease is not completely understood. As the myelin disappears, the affected person experiences vision impairment, muscle weakness, and lack of coordination. These nerve-based symptoms arise because of poor nerve electrical transmission.

QUESTIONS

A. *Review the meanings of the new terms introduced in this chapter.*

1. Lipids
2. Waxes
3. Phospholipids
4. Sphingolipids
5. Glycolipids
6. Steroids
7. Lipid bilayer
8. Facilitated diffusion
9. Active transport
10. Fluid-mosaic model

B. *Review questions*

1. Why are the lipids, which are dissimilar substances, classified as a group?
2. Briefly explain why caproic acid is more water-soluble than stearic acid.
3. Write the structural formula of a triacylglycerol that contains one unit each of palmitic, stearic, and oleic acids. How many other triacylglycerols are possible, each containing one unit of each of these acids?
4. Draw formulas for the products of a hydrolysis reaction involving a triacylglycerol that contains palmitic acid, oleic acid, and linoleic acid.
5. What are the three essential fatty acids? What are the consequences of their being absent from the diet?
6. Briefly explain why arachidonic acid is of special biological importance.

7. List two reasons why fats contain more biochemical energy than carbohydrates.
8. How is aspirin thought to relieve inflammation?
9. Wax serves a protective function on many types of leaves. How does it do this?
10. What two properties must a membrane lipid possess?
11. In what organ in the body are phospholipids mainly produced?
12. Lecithins and cephalins are both derivatives of phosphatidic acid. Indicate how they differ from each other.
13. Draw the structure of phosphatidyl serine.
14. In what ways is sphingosine similar to a glycerol molecule that has been esterified to one fatty acid?
15. Show the structure of a glucocerebroside.
16. What two structural features allow sphingomyelin to serve as a membrane lipid?
17. What common structural feature is possessed by all steroids? Write the structural formulas of two steroids.
18. Where is cholesterol found in the body? Where is it primarily produced?
19. What is atherosclerosis? How is it produced and what are its symptoms?

20. Briefly describe the body's cholesterol distribution system.
21. Why can a lipid bilayer be described as a barrier?
22. Draw the structure of a membrane lipid.
23. Why is the myelin sheath known as an insulator?
24. Would you expect an intrinsic protein to be hydrophobic? Explain.
25. Distinguish active transport from facilitated diffusion.
26. Which of these statements are correct?
    (a) A lipid will dissolve in water.
    (b) Lipids are often small molecules.
    (c) A triacylglycerol is high in biochemical energy because it contains many oxidized carbons.
    (d) Linoleic acid has a lower melting point than stearic acid.
    (e) Phosphatidyl choline is also known as lecithin.
    (f) A sphingolipid always contains carbohydrate.
    (g) Cholesterol is often found in membranes.
    (h) Movement of potassium ion into a nerve cell is an example of facilitated diffusion.
    (i) A lipid bilayer has a hydrophilic interior.
    (j) The "fluid" in the fluid-mosaic model refers to the lipid bilayer.

29

Amino Acids, Polypeptides, and Proteins

After studying Chapter 29, you should be able to

1. Understand the new terms listed in Question A at the end of the chapter.
2. List five foods that are major sources of proteins.
3. List the elements that are contained in proteins.
4. Write formulas for and know the abbreviations for the common amino acids.
5. Write the zwitterion formula of an amino acid and know how it behaves in a dilute acidic and in a dilute basic solution.
6. Understand why a protein in solution at its isoelectric pH will not migrate in an electrolytic cell.
7. Combine amino acids into polypeptide chains.
8. Understand how peptide chains are named and numbered.
9. Understand what is meant by the N-terminal and C-terminal residues of a peptide chain.
10. Briefly explain the primary, secondary, and tertiary structure of a protein.
11. Explain the meaning of the statement "The primary structure helps establish a protein's three-dimensional structure."
12. Define quaternary structure and explain its importance in the function of hemoglobin.
13. Understand the bonding in the α-helical and β-pleated-sheet structure of a protein.
14. Give an example of a structural protein.
15. Explain the role cysteine plays in the structure of polypeptides and proteins.

16. Briefly explain why living cells need catalysts.
17. Define an enzyme active site.
18. Discuss the role of enzymes in the body.
19. List the six main classes of enzymes and their functions.
20. Define the symbols K_m and V_{max}.
21. Briefly describe the action of an enzyme inhibitor.
22. Tell what is meant by the specificity of an enzyme.
23. Discuss the role of specific enzymes in the hydrolysis of proteins.
24. Explain how Edman degradation allows the primary structure to be determined.
25. Describe Sanger's work on determining the primary structure of proteins.
26. Reconstruct a peptide chain from a knowledge of its hydrolysis products.
27. Describe chromatographic methods of separating amino acids.
28. State the physical evidence observed in a positive reaction in the (a) xanthoproteic reaction, (b) biuret test, and (c) ninhydrin test.
29. Know what is meant by denaturation and the various methods by which proteins can be denatured.

29.1 Introduction

Proteins are present in every living cell. Their very name, derived from the Greek work *proteios*, which means holding first place, signifies the importance of these substances. Proteins are one of the three major classes of foods. The other two, carbohydrates and fats, are needed for energy; proteins are needed for growth and maintenance of body tissue. Some common foods with high (over 10%) protein content are fish, beans, nuts, cheese, eggs, poultry, and meat. These foods tend to be scarce and relatively expensive. Proteins are, therefore, the class of foods that is least available to the undernourished people of the world. Hence, the question of how to secure an adequate supply of high-quality protein for an ever-increasing population is one of our more critical problems (see Chapter 31).

Proteins function as structural materials and as enzymes (catalysts) that regulate the countless chemical reactions taking place in every living organism, including the reactions involved in the decomposition and synthesis of proteins.

simple proteins

conjugated proteins

All proteins are polymeric substances that yield amino acids on hydrolysis. Those that yield only amino acids when hydrolyzed are classified as **simple proteins;** those that yield amino acids and one or more additional products are classified as **conjugated proteins.** There are approximately 200 different known amino acids in nature. Some are found in only one particular species of plant or animal, others in only a few life forms. But 20 of these amino acids are found in almost all proteins. Furthermore, these same 20 amino acids are used by all forms of life in the synthesis of proteins.

All proteins contain carbon, hydrogen, oxygen, and nitrogen. Some proteins contain additional elements, usually sulfur, phosphorus, iron, copper, or zinc. The significant presence of nitrogen in all proteins sets them apart from carbohydrates and lipids. The average nitrogen content is about 16%.

Proteins are highly specific in their functions. The amino acid units in a given protein molecule are arranged in a definite sequence. An amazing fact about proteins is that in some cases if just one of the hundreds or thousands of amino acid units is missing or out of place, the biological function of that protein is seriously damaged or destroyed. The sequence of amino acids in a protein establishes the function of that protein.

This relationship between structure and function contrasts sharply with that for other classes of biochemicals. For example, carbohydrates can provide cellular energy because they contain one particular type of atom, reduced carbon, that is readily oxidizable. This important function does not depend directly on the sequence in which the atoms are arranged. On the other hand, an appropriate sequence of amino acids will produce a protein strong enough to form a horse's hoof, a different sequence will produce a protein capable of absorbing oxygen in the lung and releasing it to needy cells; yet another sequence will produce a hormone capable of directing carbohydrate metabolism for an entire organism. As will be seen, full understanding of the function of a protein requires that the structure of that protein be understood.

29.2 The Nature of Amino Acids

Each amino acid has two functional groups, an amino group ($-NH_2$) and a carboxyl group ($-COOH$). The amino acids that are found in proteins are called alpha (α) amino acids because the amino group is attached to the first or alpha carbon atom adjacent to the carboxyl group. The beta (β) position is the next adjacent carbon; the gamma (γ) position the next carbon; and so on. The following formula represents an alpha (α) amino acid:

$$\overset{\gamma}{C}H_3\overset{\beta}{C}H_2\overset{\alpha}{C}HCOOH$$
$$|$$
$$NH_2$$

α-Amino butyric acid

Alpha amino acids are represented by this general formula:

The portion of the molecule designated R is commonly referred to as the *amino acid side chain*. It is not restricted to alkyl groups and may contain (a) open chain, cyclic, or aromatic hydrocarbon groups; (b) additional amino or carboxyl groups; (c) hydroxyl groups; or (d) sulfur-containing groups.

Amino acids are divided into three groups: neutral, acidic, and basic. They are classified as neutral amino acids when their molecules have the same number of amino and carboxyl groups, as acidic when their molecules have more carboxyl groups than amino groups, or as basic when their molecules have more amino groups than carboxyl groups.

The names, formulas, and abbreviations of the common amino acids are given in Table 29.1. Two of these, aspartic acid and glutamic acid, are classified as acidic; three—lysine, arginine, and histidine—as basic; the remainder are classified as neutral amino acids.

Table 29.1 Common amino acids derived from proteins

Name	Abbreviation	Formula
Alanine	Ala	$CH_3CHCOOH$ $\quad\ \ \vert$ $\quad\ \ NH_2$
Arginine	Arg	$NH_2\!-\!\underset{\underset{NH}{\vert\vert}}{C}\!-\!NH\!-\!CH_2CH_2CH_2\underset{\underset{NH_2}{\vert}}{C}HCOOH$
Asparagine	Asn	$NH_2\underset{\underset{O}{\vert\vert}}{C}\!-\!CH_2\underset{\underset{NH_2}{\vert}}{C}HCOOH$
Aspartic acid	Asp	$HOOCCH_2CHCOOH$ $\qquad\qquad\ \vert$ $\qquad\qquad\ NH_2$
Cysteine	Cys	$HSCH_2CHCOOH$ $\qquad\quad\ \vert$ $\qquad\quad\ NH_2$
Glutamic acid	Glu	$HOOCCH_2CH_2CHCOOH$ $\qquad\qquad\qquad\vert$ $\qquad\qquad\qquad NH_2$
Glutamine	Gln	$NH_2\underset{\underset{O}{\vert\vert}}{C}CH_2CH_2\underset{\underset{NH_2}{\vert}}{C}HCOOH$
Glycine	Gly	$HCHCOOH$ $\quad\ \vert$ $\quad\ NH_2$
Histidine	His	$\begin{array}{c} N\!-\!\!-\!CH \\ \vert\vert\qquad\vert\vert \\ HC\underset{\underset{\underset{H}{\vert}}{N}}{}\ \ C\!-\!CH_2\underset{\underset{NH_2}{\vert}}{C}HCOOH \end{array}$
Isoleucine[a]	Ile	$CH_3CH_2CH\!-\!CHCOOH$ $\qquad\qquad\ \vert\qquad\ \vert$ $\qquad\qquad CH_3\ NH_2$
Leucine[a]	Leu	$(CH_3)_2CHCH_2CHCOOH$ $\qquad\qquad\qquad\ \vert$ $\qquad\qquad\qquad\ NH_2$
Lysine[a]	Lys	$NH_2CH_2CH_2CH_2CH_2CHCOOH$ $\qquad\qquad\qquad\qquad\ \vert$ $\qquad\qquad\qquad\qquad\ NH_2$
Methionine[a]	Met	$CH_3SCH_2CH_2CHCOOH$ $\qquad\qquad\qquad\vert$ $\qquad\qquad\qquad NH_2$

[a] Amino acids essential in human nutrition.

(continued)

Table 29.1 (continued)

Name	Abbreviation	Formula
Phenylalanine[a]	Phe	
Proline	Pro	
Serine	Ser	$HOCH_2CHCOOH$ $\quad\quad\;\; NH_2$
Threonine[a]	Thr	$CH_3CH{-}CHCOOH$ $\quad\;\;\, OH\;\;\; NH_2$
Tryptophan[a]	Trp	
Tyrosine	Tyr	
Valine[a]	Val	$(CH_3)_2CHCHCOOH$ $\quad\quad\quad\;\; NH_2$

[a] Amino acids essential in human nutrition.

29.3 Essential Amino Acids

essential amino acids

Dietary protein is broken down during digestion into its constituent amino acids, which supply much of the body's need for amino acids (see Chapter 31). Eight of the amino acids are **essential amino acids.** These amino acids—isoleucine, leucine, lysine, methionine, phenylalanine, threonine, tryptophan, and valine—are essential to the functioning of the human body. Since the body is not capable of synthesizing them, they must be supplied in our diets if we are to enjoy normal health. It is known that some other animals require amino acids in addition to those listed for humans. Rats, for example, require two additional amino acids—arginine and histidine—in their diets.

On a nutritional basis, proteins are classified as complete or incomplete. A complete protein supplies all the essential amino acids; an incomplete protein is deficient in one or more essential amino acids. Many proteins, especially those from vegetable sources, are incomplete. For example, protein from corn (maize) is deficient in lysine. The nutritional quality of such vegetable proteins can be greatly improved by supplementing them with the essential amino acids that are lacking, if these can be synthesized at reasonable costs. Lysine, methionine, and tryptophan are being sold at present for enriching human food and livestock feed. This is another way to extend the world's limited supply of high-quality food protein. In still another approach to the problem of obtaining more high-quality protein, plant breeders have recently developed maize varieties with greatly improved lysine content. Genetic engineering may hold the key to further significant improvements in plant protein quality.

29.4 D-Amino Acids and L-Amino Acids

All amino acids, except glycine, have at least one asymmetric carbon atom. For example, two stereoisomers of alanine are possible:

$$
\begin{array}{cc}
\text{COOH} & \text{COOH} \\
| & | \\
\text{H—C*—NH}_2 & \text{H}_2\text{N—C*—H} \\
| & | \\
\text{CH}_3 & \text{CH}_3 \\
\text{D-(—)-Alanine} & \text{L-(+)-Alanine}
\end{array}
$$

The D and L configurations of amino acids are shown in projection formulas in the same way as in the configuration of D- and L-glyceraldehyde (Section 27.2). The —COOH group is written at the top of the projection formula, and the D configuration is indicated by writing the alpha —NH_2 group to the right of carbon 2. The L configuration is indicated by writing the alpha —NH_2 group to the left of carbon 2 (see the projection formulas of alanine above). Although some D-amino acids occur in nature, only L-amino acids occur in proteins. The (+) and (—) signs in the name indicate the direction of rotation of plane polarized light by the amino acid.

29.5 Amphoterism

Amino acids are *amphoteric* (or *amphiprotic*); that is, they can react either as an acid or as a base. For example, with a strong base such as sodium hydroxide, alanine reacts as an acid, as shown in equation (1); with a strong acid such as HCl, alanine reacts as a base as shown in equation (2).

$$
\begin{array}{ll}
\text{CH}_3\text{CHCOOH} + \text{NaOH} \longrightarrow \text{CH}_3\text{CHCOO}^- \text{ Na}^+ + \text{H}_2\text{O} & \quad (1) \\
\quad | & \quad | \\
\quad \text{NH}_2 & \quad \text{NH}_2 \\
\quad \text{Alanine} & \quad \text{Sodium alanate}
\end{array}
$$

$$
\begin{array}{ll}
\text{CH}_3\text{CHCOOH} + \text{HCl} \longrightarrow \text{CH}_3\text{CHCOOH} & \quad (2) \\
\quad | & \quad | \\
\quad \text{NH}_2 & \quad \text{NH}_3^+ \text{ Cl}^- \\
& \quad \text{Alanyl ammonium chloride}
\end{array}
$$

Even in neutral biological solutions, amino acids do not actually exist in the molecular form shown in equations (1) and (2). Instead, they exist mainly as **zwitterions** dipolar ions called **zwitterions**. Again using alanine as an example, the proton on the carboxyl group transfers to the amino group, forming a zwitterion by an acid–base reaction within the molecule:

$$CH_3CHCOO\ \textcircled{H} \longrightarrow CH_3CHCOO^-$$

$$H_2N: \longleftarrow \qquad\qquad NH_3^+$$

Alanine molecule   Alanine zwitterion

On an ionic basis, the reaction of alanine with NaOH and HCl is

$$CH_3CHCOO^- + OH^- \longrightarrow CH_3CHCOO^- + H_2O \qquad (3)$$

$$NH_3^+ \qquad\qquad\qquad NH_2$$

Alanine zwitterion   Alanate anion

$$CH_3CHCOO^- + H^+ \longrightarrow CH_3CHCOOH \qquad (4)$$

$$NH_3^+ \qquad\qquad\qquad NH_3^+$$

Alanine zwitterion   Alanyl ammonium cation

Other amino acids behave like alanine. Together with protein molecules that contain —COOH and —NH_2 groups, they help to buffer or stabilize the pH of the blood at about 7.4. The pH is maintained close to 7.4 because any excess acid or base in the blood is neutralized by reactions such as shown in equations (3) and (4).

$$RCHCOOH \underset{OH^-}{\overset{H^+}{\rightleftharpoons}} RCHCOO^- \underset{H^+}{\overset{OH^-}{\rightleftharpoons}} RCHCOO^- \qquad (5)$$

$$NH_3^+ \qquad\qquad NH_3^+ \qquad\qquad NH_2$$

Cation form   Zwitterion form   Anion form

II   I   III

When an amino acid in solution has equal positive and negative charges, as in formula I of equation (5), it is electrically neutral and does not migrate toward either the positive or negative electrode when placed in an electrolytic cell. The pH at which there is no migration toward either electrode is called the **isoelectric point** (see Table 29.2). If acid (H^+) is added to an amino acid at its isoelectric point, the equilibrium is shifted toward formula II, and the cation formed will migrate toward the negative electrode. When base (OH^-) is added,

isoelectric point

Table 29.2   Isoelectric points of selected amino acids

Amino acid	pH at isoelectric point
Arginine	10.8
Lysine	9.7
Alanine	6.0
Glycine	6.0
Serine	5.7
Glutamic acid	3.2
Aspartic acid	2.9

the anion formed (formula III) will migrate toward the positive electrode. Differences in isoelectric points are important in isolating and purifying amino acids and proteins, since their rates and directions of migration can be controlled in an electrolytic cell by adjusting the pH. This method of separation is called *electrophoresis*.

Amino acids are classified as basic, neutral, or acidic depending on whether the ratio of —NH_2 to —COOH groups in the molecules is greater than 1:1, equal to 1:1, or less than 1:1, respectively. Furthermore, this ratio differs from 1:1 only if the amino acid side chain (R—) contains an additional amino or carboxyl group. For example, if the side chain contains a carboxyl group, the amino acid is considered acidic. Thus, the R—group determines whether an amino acid is classified as basic, neutral, or acidic.

Isoelectric points are found at pH values ranging from 7.8 to 10.8 for basic amino acids, 4.8 to 6.3 for neutral amino acids and 2.8 to 3.3 for acidic amino acids. It is logical that a molecule such as glutamic acid, with one amino group and two carboxyl groups, would be classified as acidic and that its isoelectric point would be at a pH lower than 7.0. It might also seem that the isoelectric point of an amino acid that is classified as neutral, such as alanine, with one amino and one carboxyl group, would have an isoelectric point of 7.0. However, the isoelectric point of alanine is 6.0, not 7.0. This is because the carboxyl group and the amino group are not equally ionized. The carboxyl group of alanine ionizes to a greater degree as an acid than the amino group ionizes as a base.

29.6 Formation of Polypeptides

peptide linkage

Proteins are polyamides consisting of amino acid units joined through amide structures. If we react two glycine molecules, with the elimination of a molecule of water, we form a compound containing the amide structure, also called the **peptide linkage**, or peptide bond. The elimination of water occurs between the carboxyl group of one amino acid and the α-amino group of a second amino acid (see Section 24.6). The product formed from two glycine molecules is called glycylglycine (abbreviated Gly-Gly). Because it contains two amino acid units, it is a dipeptide.

Glycylglycine
(Gly-Gly)

polypeptide

If three amino acid units are included in a molecule, it is a tripeptide; if four, a tetrapeptide; if five, a pentapeptide; and so on. Peptides containing up to about 40–50 amino acid units in a chain are called **polypeptides**. The units making up the peptide are amino acids less the elements of water and are referred to as *amino acid residues* or, simply, residues. Still larger chains of amino acids are known as proteins.

When amino acids form a polypeptide chain, a carboxyl group and an α-amino group are involved in each peptide bond (amide bond). While these groups are joined in peptide bonds, they cannot ionize as acids or bases. Consequently, the physico-chemical properties of a polypeptide/protein are determined to a large extent by the side chains of the amino acid residues.

In linear peptides one end of the chain has a free amino group and the other end a free carboxyl group. The amino-group end is called the *N-terminal residue* and the other end the *C-terminal residue*:

1   2   3   4   5   6   7

Ala-Pro-Tyr-Met-Gly-Lys-Gly

N-Terminal residue   C-Terminal residue

The sequence of amino acids in a chain is numbered starting with the N-terminal residue, which is written to the left with the C-terminal residue at the right. Any segment of the sequence that is not specifically known is placed in parentheses. Thus in the heptapeptide above, if the order of tyrosine and methionine were not known, the structure would be written as

Ala-Pro-(Met, Tyr)-Gly-Lys-Gly

Peptides are named as acyl derivatives of the C-terminal amino acid with the C-terminal unit keeping its complete name. The *ine* ending of all but the C-terminal amino acid is changed to *yl*, and these are listed in the order in which they appear, starting with the N-terminal amino acid.

CH_3CHC — $NHCHC$ — $NHCH_2COOH$

NH$_2$ CH$_2$

OH

Alanyl   Tyrosyl   Glycine

Ala-Tyr-Gly

Thus Ala-Tyr-Gly is called alanyltyrosylglycine. The name of Arg-Gln-His-Ala is arginylglutamylhistidylalanine.

Alanine and glycine can form two different dipeptides, Gly-Ala and Ala-Gly, using each amino acid only once:

CH_2—C—N—CH—C—OH   and CH_3CH—C—N—CH_2—C—OH

NH$_2$ H   CH$_3$ NH$_2$ H

Glycylalanine (Gly-Ala)   Alanylglycine (Ala-Gly)

If three different amino acids react—for example, glycine, alanine, and threonine—six tripeptides in which each amino acid appears only once are possible.

Gly-Ala-Thr	Ala-Thr-Gly	Thr-Ala-Gly
Gly-Thr-Ala	Ala-Gly-Thr	Thr-Gly-Ala

The number of possible peptides rises very rapidly as the number of amino acid units increases. For example, there are 120 ($1 \times 2 \times 3 \times 4 \times 5 = 120$) different ways to combine five different amino acids to form a pentapeptide, using each amino acid only once in each molecule. If the same constraints are applied to 15 different amino acids, the number of possible combinations is greater than 1 trillion (10^{12})! Since a protein molecule may contain several hundred amino acid units, with individual amino acids occurring several times, the number of possible combinations from 20 amino acids is simply beyond imagination.

There are a number of small, naturally occurring polypeptides with significant biochemical functions. In general these substances serve as hormones or nerve transmitters. Their functions range from controlling pain and pleasure responses in the brain to controlling smooth-muscle contraction or kidney fluid excretion rates (see Table 29.3). The amino acid sequence and chain length give a polypeptide its biological effectiveness and specificity.

For example, recent research has shown that the effects of opiates (opium

Table 29.3 Primary structures and functions of some selected biological polypeptides[a]

Name	Primary structure	General biological function
Substance P	Arg-Pro-Lys-Pro-Gln-Gln-Phe- Phe-Gly-Leu-Met-NH$_2$	Is a pain-producing agent
Bradykinin	Arg-Pro-Pro-Gly-Phe-Ser- Pro-Phe-Arg	Affects tissue inflammation and blood pressure
Angiotensin II	Asp-Arg-Val-Tyr-Val- His-Pro-Phe	Maintains water balance and blood pressure
Leu-enkephalin Met-enkephalin	Tyr-Gly-Gly-Phe-Leu Tyr-Gly-Gly-Phe-Met	Relieves pain, produces sense of well-being
Vasopressin	┌────S—S────┐ Cys-Tyr-Phe-Gly-Asn-Cys- Pro-Arg-Gly-NH$_2$	Increases blood pressure, decreases kidney water excretion
Oxytocin	┌────S—S────┐ Cys-Tyr-Ile-Gln-Asn-Cys- Pro-Leu-Gly-NH$_2$	Initiates childbirth labor, causes mammary gland milk release, affects kidney excretion of water and sodium

[a] Where —NH$_2$ is indicated at the end of the sequence, the C-terminal amino acid has an amide structure rather than a free —COOH.

derivatives) on the brain are also exhibited by two naturally occurring penta-peptides, Leu-enkephalin (Tyr-Gly-Gly-Phe-Leu) and Met-enkephalin (Tyr-Gly-Gly-Phe-Met). These two polypeptides are natural painkillers. Alterations of the amino acid sequence—which alters the side-chain characteristics—cause drastic changes in the analgesic effects of these pentapeptides. The substitution of L-alanine for either of the glycine residues in these compounds (simply changing one side-chain group from —H to —CH$_3$) causes an approximately 1000-fold decrease in effectiveness as a pain killer! The substitution of L-tyrosine for L-phenylalanine causes a comparable loss of activity. Even the substitution of D-tyrosine for the L-tyrosine residue causes a considerable loss in the analgesic effectiveness of the pentapeptides.

It is clearly evident that a particular sequence of amino acid residues is essential for proper polypeptide function. This sequence aligns the side-chain characteristics (large or small; polar or nonpolar; acidic, basic, or neutral) in the proper positions for a specific polypeptide function.

Oxytocin and vasopressin are similar nonapeptides, differing only at three positions in their primary structure (see Table 29.3). Yet their biological functions differ dramatically. Oxytocin controls uterine contractions during labor in childbirth and also causes contraction of the smooth muscles of the mammary gland, resulting in milk excretion. Vasopressin in high concentration raises the blood pressure and has been used in treatment of surgical shock for this purpose. Vasopressin is also an antidiuretic, regulating the excretion of fluid by the kidneys. The absence of vasopressin leads to diabetes insipidus. This condition is characterized by excretion of up to 30 liters of urine per day, but can be controlled by administration of vasopressin or its derivatives.

The isolation and synthesis of oxytocin and vasopressin was accomplished by Vincent du Vigneaud (1901–1978) and co-workers at Cornell University. Du Vigneaud was awarded the Nobel prize in chemistry in 1955 for this work. Synthetic oxytocin is indistinguishable from the natural material. It is available commercially and is used for the induction of labor in the late stages of pregnancy.

29.7 Protein Structure

By 1940 a great deal of information concerning proteins had been assembled. Their elemental composition was known, and they had been carefully classified according to solubility in various solvents. Proteins were known to be polymers of amino acids, and the different amino acids had, for the most part, been isolated and identified. Protein molecules were known to be very large in size, with molecular weights ranging from several thousand to several million.

Knowledge of protein structure could help to answer many chemical and biological questions. But for a while the task of determining the actual structure of molecules of such colossal size appeared to be next to impossible. Then Linus Pauling (b. 1901), at the California Institute of Technology, attacked the problem by a new approach. Using X-ray diffraction techniques, Pauling and his collaborators painstakingly determined the bond angles and dimensions of amino acids and of dipeptides and tripeptides. After building accurate scale models of the dipeptides and tripeptides, they determined how these could be fitted into likely polypeptide configurations. Based on this work, Pauling and R. B. Corey proposed in 1951 that two differential conformations—the *α-helix* and the *β-pleated-sheet*—were the most probable stable polypeptide chain configurations of protein molecules. These two macromolecular structures are illustrated in Figure 29.1. Within a short time it was established that many proteins do have structures corresponding to those predicted by Pauling and Corey. This work was a very great achievement. Pauling received the 1954 Nobel prize in chemistry for this work on protein structure. Pauling's and Corey's work provided the inspiration for another great biochemical breakthrough—the concept of the double-helix structure for deoxyribonucleic acid, DNA (see Section 30.6).

Proteins are very large molecules. But just how many amino acid units must be present for a substance to be a protein? There is no universally agreed upon answer to this question. Some authorities state that a protein must have a molecular weight of at least 6000 or contain about 50 amino acid units. Smaller amino acid polymers, containing from 5–50 amino acid units, are classified as polypeptides and are not proteins. In reality, there is no clearly defined lower limit to the molecular size of proteins. The distinction is made to emphasize (1) that proteins often serve structural or enzymatic functions, whereas polypeptides often serve hormone-related functions and (2) that the three-dimensional conformation of proteins is directly related to function, whereas the relation is not so clear-cut with polypeptides.

In general, if a protein molecule is to perform a specific biological function, it must have a highly detailed overall conformation, or shape. This overall conformation consists of (1) a primary structure, (2) a secondary structure, (3) a tertiary structure, and sometimes (4) a quaternary structure.

primary structure

The **primary structure** of a protein is established by the number, kind, and sequence of amino acid units comprising the polypeptide chain or chains making up the molecule. The primary structure determines the alignment of side-chain characteristics, which, in turn, determines the three-dimensional shape into which the protein folds. In this sense the amino acid sequence is of primary importance in establishing protein shape.

Determining the sequence of the amino acids in even one protein molecule was a formidable task. The amino acid sequence of beef insulin was announced in 1955 by the British biochemist Frederick Sanger (b. 1918). This determination required several years of effort by a team under Sanger's direction. He was awarded the 1958 Nobel prize in chemistry for this work. Insulin is a hormone that regulates the blood-sugar level. A deficiency of insulin leads to the condition of diabetes. Beef insulin consists of 51 amino acid units in two polypeptide chains. The two chains are connected by disulfide linkages (—S—S—) of two cysteine residues at two different sites. The primary structure is shown in Figure 29.2. Insulins from other animals, including humans, differ slightly by one, two, or three amino acid residues in chain A.

α-helix

Collagen

β-pleated sheet

← Chain 1

← Chain 2

Figure 29.1 α-helix, β-pleated-sheet, and the special collagen protein structures: Collagen is composed of three helical protein chains wound together in a three-stranded helix. As the most abundant protein in the animal world, collagen's function in the body is mainly as connective tissue.

$$
\begin{array}{c}
\underset{15}{\hspace{4cm}}\overset{20}{\hspace{1cm}}\overset{21}{\hspace{0.5cm}} \\
\text{Gln—Leu—Glu—Asn—Tyr—Cys—Asn}
\end{array}
$$

Tyr
|
Leu
|
Ser
|
Cys—Val 10
|
S   Ser
|
S   Ala
|
1   5
Gly—Ile—Val—Glu—Gln—Cys—Cys
Chain A
|
S
|
S
|
1   5   10
Phe—Val—Asn—Gln—His—Leu—Cys—Gly—Ser—His—Leu—Val
Chain B

S
|
S
|
Cys—Gly 20
|
Val   Glu
| |
Leu   Arg
| |
Tyr   Gly
| |
15 Leu   Phe
| |
Ala   Phe 25
| |
Glu   Tyr
|
Thr
|
Pro
|
Lys
|
Ala 30

Figure 29.2 Amino acid sequence of beef insulin

secondary structure

The **secondary structure** of proteins can be characterized as a regular, three-dimensional structure held together by hydrogen bonding between the oxygen of the $\text{C}{=}\text{O}$ and the hydrogen of the $\text{H}{-}\text{N}$ groups in the polypeptide chains:

$$\text{C}{=}\text{O} \cdots \text{H}{-}\text{N}$$

Hydrogen bond

The α-helical and β-pleated-sheet structures of Pauling and Corey are two examples of secondary structure. As shown in Figure 29.1, essentially every peptide bond is involved in at least one hydrogen bond in these structures. Proteins having α-helical or β-pleated-sheet secondary structures are strongly held in particular conformations by virtue of the large number of hydrogen bonds.

The fibrous proteins are an important class of proteins that contain highly developed secondary structures. Because these structures provide strength, these proteins tend to function in support roles. For example, collagen in the form of a three-stranded helix (see Figure 29.1) is the principal protein in connective tissues. The α-keratins depend on the α-helix for strength and to provide support for such diverse structures as hair, fingernails, feathers, and hooves. The silk protein, fibroin, is folded into a β-pleated-sheet structure. In each case the repeating secondary structure with its multitude of hydrogen bonds provides the protein with strength and some degree of rigidity.

tertiary structure

The **tertiary structure** of a protein refers to the distinctive and characteristic conformation, or shape, of a protein molecule. This overall three-dimensional conformation is held together by a variety of interactions between amino acid side chains. These interactions include (1) hydrogen bonding, (2) ionic bonding, and (3) disulfide bonding. For example,

1. Glutamic acid–tyrosine hydrogen bonding

2. Glutamic acid–lysine ionic bonding

3. Cysteine–cysteine disulfide bonding

The tertiary structure depends on the number and location of these interactions, variables that are fixed when the primary structure is synthesized. Thus, the tertiary structure depends on the primary structure. For example, there are three locations in the insulin molecule (Fig. 29.2) where the primary sequence permits disulfide bonding. This, in turn, has an obvious bearing on the shape of insulin.

Hair is especially rich in disulfide bonds. These can be broken by certain reducing agents and restored by an oxidizing agent. This fact is the key to "cold" permanent waving of hair. Some of the disulfide bonds are broken by applying a reducing agent to the hair. The hair is then styled with the desired curls or waves. These are then permanently set by using an oxidizing agent to reestablish the disulfide bonds at different points.

$$-CH_2-S-S-CH_2- \xrightarrow{\text{Reducing agent}}$$

Bonds in
normal hair

$$-CH_2-S-H \ H-S-CH_2- \xrightarrow{\text{Oxidizing agent}} -CH_2-S-S-CH_2-$$

Broken bonds
of "reduced" form

Reestablished
bonds of permanently
waved hair

Myoglobin, a small oxygen-carrying protein of the muscle, was the first protein for which a three-dimensional structure was determined (see Figure 29.3). It can be described as having a folded-sausage structure, each section of the sausage representing a segment of the α-helix. Under normal conditions the folds of the myoglobin structure are held firmly in place by interactions between amino acid side chains. The conformation of myoglobin closely accommodates an organically bound iron atom (in the heme group, shown in Figure 29.3 by the rectangular solid), which allows myoglobin to store and transport oxygen in the muscles. The oxygen transport and storage function is determined by myoglobin's specific primary, secondary, and tertiary structures. It is worth noting that myoglobin is a *conjugated* protein—that is, a protein that contains groups other than amino acid residues.

quaternary structure

The fourth type of structure, called **quaternary structure,** is found in some complex proteins. These proteins are made up of two or more smaller protein subunits (polypeptide chains). Nonprotein molecules may also be present. The quaternary structure refers to the shape of the entire complex molecule and is determined by the way in which the subunits are held together by *noncovalent* bonds—that is, by hydrogen bonding, ionic bonding, and so on.

Quaternary structure is commonly important in proteins that are involved in the control of metabolic processes. For example, hemoglobin, the oxygen

Myoglobin

Figure 29.3   Tertiary structure of a protein, represented by myoglobin: The gray portion represents a heme group.

Hemoglobin

Figure 29.4   Quaternary structure of a protein, represented by hemoglobin: A set of axes has been drawn through the molecule to help visualize the position of each protein chain. The heme groups are symbolized by rectangular solids located in the middle of each protein chain.

transport protein of the blood, is composed of four subunits (see Figure 29.4). Each subunit is similar to myoglobin in that a set of helical segments surround the oxygen-binding heme group. Of course, the important structural difference is that hemoglobin has a quaternary structure. This leads to an equally important functional difference. Whereas myoglobin always binds and releases oxygen in the same way, hemoglobin changes its oxygen-binding characteristics depending on the available O_2. When hemoglobin binds oxygen on one subunit, the protein's conformation changes to facilitate the binding of three additional oxygen molecules (see Figure 29.5). The oxygen binding is said to be *cooperative*—that is, the binding of an oxygen at one site promotes oxygen binding on the other three sites. In an oxygen-rich environment, hemoglobin becomes saturated with oxygen.

Conversely, the loss of one oxygen from hemoglobin facilitates the release of oxygen from the other sites. As hemoglobin moves to the oxygen-needy body

Figure 29.5   A schematic representation of the oxygen–hemoglobin binding process: The circles and the squares represent two different conformations of the hemoglobin molecule. Oxygen binding or release causes hemoglobin to change its conformation.

tissues, its oxygen is cooperatively released. The presence of a quaternary structure allows the binding or removal of one oxygen molecule to control the binding or removal of three other oxygen molecules. Hence, the oxygen transport effectiveness of hemoglobin is multiplied by the quaternary structure.

Even minor alterations in primary structure may have drastic effects on the three-dimensional structural function of a protein. A graphic example of this fact is provided by sickle-cell anemia. This crippling genetic disease is due to red blood cells assuming a sickle shape. Sickled cells have impaired vitality and function. Sickle-cell anemia has been traced to a small change in the primary structure, or amino acid residue sequence, of hemoglobin. Normal hemoglobin molecules contain four polypeptide subunits—two identical α-polypeptide chains and two identical β-polypeptide chains (see Figure 29.4). Sickle-cell and normal β-polypeptide chains of hemoglobin each contain 146 amino acid residues and differ only in the residue at the sixth position. In the sickle-cell hemoglobin chain, a glutamic acid residue has been replaced by a valine residue in this position. This change is sufficient, under some circumstances, to cause hemoglobin to aggregate into long filaments—a different quaternary structure. Large amounts of hemoglobin are present in red blood cells, and the changed quaternary structure causes sickling of the cell and greatly diminishes cell vitality. This cell affliction has led to the premature deaths of many affected individuals.

To summarize, there are four classes of protein structure, and each has a different function.

1. Primary structure is defined by the amino acid residue sequence of the polypeptide chain. This sequence determines the shapes, or conformations, into which a protein can be arranged.
2. Secondary structure is a regular, repeating three-dimensional conformation held together by hydrogen bonding between components of the amide bonds of the primary chain. Hydrogen bonding can be between bonds in the same chain (for instance, the α-helix) or between bonds in adjacent chains (for instance, the β-pleated sheet). The secondary structure imparts strength to proteins.
3. Tertiary structure is the overall three-dimensional structural conformation of the protein molecule. Various kinds of bonding interactions between components of the amino acid side chains stabilize the tertiary structure. The biological function of a protein is ultimately determined by the tertiary structure.
4. Quaternary structure, present in some proteins, describes the three-dimensional arrangement of subunits linked together by noncovalent bonds. The subunits have their own primary, secondary, and tertiary structures. Quaternary structure is often a prerequisite for proteins involved in the control of metabolic processes.

29.8   Enzymes

enzymes

Enzymes are the catalysts of biochemical reactions. Enzymes catalyze nearly all of the myriad reactions that occur in living cells. Uncatalyzed reactions that require hours of boiling in the presence of a strong acid or a strong base can occur in a fraction of a second in the presence of the proper enzyme at room temperature and nearly neutral pH. The catalytic functions of enzymes are directly dependent on their three-dimensional structures. It was generally believed until quite recently that all enzymes were proteins. However, research under way since about 1980 has shown that certain ribonucleic acids (RNA's, see Chapter 30) also may function as enzymes.

Louis Pasteur was one of the first scientists to study enzyme-catalyzed reactions. He believed that living yeasts or bacteria were required for these reactions, which he called *fermentations*—for example, the conversion of glucose to alcohol by yeasts. In 1897 Eduard Büchner (1860–1917) made a cell-free filtrate that contained enzymes prepared by grinding yeast cells with very fine sand. The enzymes in this filtrate converted glucose to alcohol, thus proving that the presence of living cells was not required for enzyme activity. For this work Büchner received the Nobel prize in chemistry in 1907.

It is important to realize that enzymes are essential to life. The critical biochemical reactions go too slowly for life to be maintained in the absence of enzymes. The typical biochemical reaction occurs about one million times faster when catalyzed by an enzyme. For example, we know that the reduced carbons of carbohydrates can react with oxygen to produce carbon dioxide and energy.

Yet the sucrose in the sugar bowl at home never reacts significantly with the oxygen in the air. These sucrose molecules must overcome an energy barrier (activation energy) before reaction can occur (see Figure 29.6). In the sugar bowl, the energy barrier is too large. But in the cell, enzymes lower the activation energy and enable sucrose to react rapidly enough to provide the energy needed for life processes.

Each organism contains thousands of enzymes. Some are simple proteins consisting only of amino acid units. Others are conjugated and consist of a protein part, or *apoenzyme*, and a nonprotein part, or *coenzyme*. Both parts are essential, and a functioning enzyme consisting of both the protein and nonprotein parts is called a *holoenzyme*:

Apoenzyme + Coenzyme = Holoenzyme

Often the coenzyme is a vitamin, and one coenzyme may be associated with many different enzymes.

For some enzymes an inorganic component such as a metal ion (for example, Ca^{2+}, Mg^{2+}, or Zn^{2+}) is required. This inorganic component is an *activator*. From the standpoint of function, an activator is analogous to a coenzyme, but inorganic components are not called coenzymes.

Another remarkable property of enzymes is their specificity of reaction; that is, a certain enzyme will catalyze the reaction of a specific type of substance. For example, the enzyme maltase catalyzes the reaction of maltose and water to form glucose. Maltase has no effect on the other two common disaccharides, sucrose and lactose. Each of these sugars requires a specific enzyme—sucrase to

Figure 29.6 A typical reaction energy profile: The lower activation energy in the cell is due to the catalytic effect of enzymes.

hydrolyze sucrose, lactase to hydrolyze lactose. These reactions are indicated by the following equations:

$$C_{12}H_{22}O_{11} + H_2O \xrightarrow{\text{Maltase}} C_6H_{12}O_6 + C_6H_{12}O_6$$

$$\text{Maltose} \qquad\qquad\qquad\qquad\quad \text{Glucose} \qquad \text{Glucose}$$

$$C_{12}H_{22}O_{11} + H_2O \xrightarrow{\text{Sucrase}} C_6H_{12}O_6 + C_6H_{12}O_6$$

$$\text{Sucrose} \qquad\qquad\qquad\qquad\quad \text{Glucose} \qquad \text{Fructose}$$

$$C_{12}H_{22}O_{11} + H_2O \xrightarrow{\text{Lactase}} C_6H_{12}O_6 + C_6H_{12}O_6$$

$$\text{Lactose} \qquad\qquad\qquad\qquad\quad \text{Glucose} \qquad \text{Galactose}$$

The substance acted on by an enzyme is called the *substrate*. Sucrose is the substrate of the enzyme sucrase. Enzymes have been named by adding the suffix *-ase* to the root of the substrate name. Note the derivations of maltase, sucrase, and lactase from maltose, sucrose, and lactose. Many enzymes, especially digestive enzymes, have common names such as pepsin, rennin, trypsin, and so on. These names have no systematic significance.

In the International Union of Biochemistry (IUB) System, enzymes are assigned to one of six classes, the names of which clearly describe the nature of the reaction they catalyze. Each of the classes has several subclasses. In this system the name of the enzyme has two parts; the first gives the name of the substrate, and the second, ending in *-ase*, indicates the type of reactions catalyzed by all enzymes in the group. The six main classes of enzymes are

1. *Oxidoreductases:* Enzymes that catalyze the oxidation–reduction between two substrates.
2. *Transferases:* Enzymes that catalyze the transfer of a functional group between two substrates.
3. *Hydrolases:* Enzymes that catalyze the hydrolysis of esters, carbohydrates, and proteins (polypeptides).
4. *Lyases:* Enzymes that catalyze the removal of groups from substrates by mechanisms other than hydrolysis.
5. *Isomerases.* Enzymes that catalyze the interconversion of stereoisomers and structural isomers.
6. *Ligases:* Enzymes that catalyze the linking together of two compounds with the breaking of a pyrophosphate bond in adenosine triphosphate (ATP, see Chapter 30).

Because the systematic name is usually long and often complex, working or practical names are used for enzymes. For example, adenosine triphosphate creatine phosphotransferase is called creatine kinase, and acetylcholine acylhydrolase is called cholinesterase.

29.9   Enzyme Catalysis

Around the turn of the century, scientists began to study enzyme action. In 1913 two Germans, Leonor Michaelis (1875–1949) and Maud Menten, observed that most enzyme-catalyzed reactions show an increasing rate with increasing

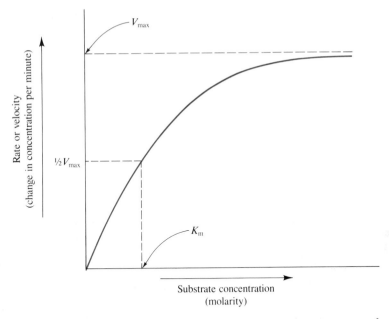

Figure 29.7 A Michaelis–Menten plot showing rate of an enzyme-catalyzed reaction as a function of substrate concentration

substrate (reactant) concentration *but* only to a specific maximum velocity [V_{max}, which commonly has units of mol/L per minute (M/min), see Figure 29.7]. There is a characteristic maximum rate of catalysis for each different enzyme. At rates below V_{max}, each enzyme is sensitive to changes in substrate concentration. A graph like that in Figure 29.7 is often called a Michaelis–Menten plot.

As shown in the Michaelis–Menten plot, enzymes not only have a limited catalytic capacity but also are effective over only a limited substrate-concentration range. Some enzymes work well at low substrate concentrations, whereas others require much higher concentrations before they operate efficiently. A numerical measure of the effective substrate-concentration range is the Michaelis constant, K_m, which gives the substrate concentration needed for the enzyme to operate at one-half of its maximum rate.

PROBLEM

29.1

Two enzymes are studied under identical conditions. Enzyme A is found to have a V_{max} of 0.001 M/min and a K_m of 0.00001 M, whereas enzyme B shows a V_{max} of 0.1 M/min and a K_m of 0.001 M. Compare **(a)** the catalytic efficiency of the two enzymes and **(b)** their respective effective substrate-concentration ranges.

(a) V_{max} is a measure of catalytic ability. Under identical conditions the larger the V_{max}, the more efficient the enzyme is as a catalyst. Enzyme B is a more efficient catalyst than enzyme A.

(b) K_m is a measure of the effective substrate-concentration range for an enzyme. A lower K_m value means that an enzyme works well at lower substrate concentrations. Enzyme A is effective at a lower substrate-concentration range than enzyme B.

By examining values such as V_{max} and K_m, scientists have gained a basic understanding of enzyme action. Each enzyme must retain a specific three-dimensional conformation (structure). This natural conformation includes a small portion of the structure, called the *active site*, where catalysis occurs. (In an analogous fashion, the myoglobin structure forms a small area where oxygen binding occurs). An enzyme's particular function, like that of other proteins, depends on a specific three-dimensional conformation.

To function effectively an enzyme active site must attract and bind the substrate. This is accomplished by noncovalent forces. For some enzymes this attractive force may be quite strong, allowing the enzyme to bind the substrate at concentrations in the micromolar (1×10^{-6} mol/L) range. In general, the smaller the K_m, the stronger the attraction between substrate and enzyme active site.

Once the substrate is bound, a chemical reaction is catalyzed. Thus the following general sequence applies. Enzyme (E) and substrate (S) combine to form an enzyme–substrate intermediate (E–S). This intermediate decomposes to give the product (P) and regenerate the enzyme:

$$E + S \rightleftharpoons E\text{–}S \longrightarrow E + P$$

For the hydrolysis of maltose, the sequence is

$$\text{Maltase} + \text{Maltose} \longrightarrow \text{Maltase–Maltose}$$
$$\quad\;\; E \qquad\qquad S \qquad\qquad\qquad E\text{–}S$$

$$\text{Maltase–Maltose} + H_2O \longrightarrow \text{Maltase} + \text{Glucose}$$
$$\qquad E\text{–}S \qquad\qquad\qquad\qquad E \qquad\quad P$$

For each enzyme a different conformation supports a differently shaped active site. The shape of the active site determines, in part, which substrates can bind. Enzymes are said to be stereospecific, *i.e.*, each different enzyme can only catalyze reactions for a limited number of different reactant structures. Thus, not only can maltase distinguish maltose from lactose (galactose coupled to glucose), in which the disaccharides contain different monosaccharides, but this enzyme can also distinguish maltose from cellobiose (glucose coupled to glucose by a β-1,4 linkage), in which only the glucosidic linkage is different. This enzyme specificity is believed to be partially due to a complementary relationship between the active site and substrate structures. This "lock-and-key" hypothesis envisions the substrate as a key that fits into the appropriate active site, the lock. Because some substrates bind to the active site but do not react, a modification called the "induced-fit" theory was proposed. The induced-fit model proposes that the active site bends to a certain degree when the appropriate substrate binds, in order to prepare the complex for catalysis. Enzyme stereospecificity is thus explained in terms of an active site having a somewhat flexible shape. This shape is rigid enough to exclude very dissimilar substrates (lock-and-key hypothesis) but flexible enough to accommodate (induced-fit model) and allow catalysis of appropriate substrates (see Figure 29.8).

Knowledge of enzyme specificity sometimes proves to be important in treating disease. For example, it is known that cancer cells divide rapidly and depend on enzymes to reproduce their genetic information continuously. A number of different substances, capable of binding strongly to the active sites of these enzymes, have been synthesized. These substances preferentially occupy the active sites and prevent the enzymes from acting on their natural substrates.

enzyme inhibitors

Such molecules are known as **enzyme inhibitors,** substances that are capable of blocking an enzyme reaction. Because cancer cells need new genetic material in far greater amounts than most normal cells, these specific enzyme inhibitors have a greater effect on cancerous than on normal cells and, in effect, selectively poison the cancers. Cancer chemotherapy often involves treatment with one or a combination of enzyme inhibitors. One such inhibitor, methotrexate, has increased the life expectancy of acute leukemia patients from 3–6 months to more than 5 years.

Enzymes also show reaction specificity; that is, an enzyme generally catalyzes only one type of chemical reaction. (In recognition of this generalization, the IUB System of enzyme nomenclature classifies enzymes on the basis of their reaction specificity.) Thus, an enzyme that catalyzes an oxidation–reduction reaction (oxidoreductase) usually cannot also catalyze the hydrolysis of an ester (hydrolase). The ability of an enzyme to catalyze a particular reaction often depends on the presence of particular amino acid side chains at the active site.

Enzyme technology is being used for the commercial production of an increasing number of products. It holds the promise of converting such substances as cellulose to glucose, which can then be used as a source of food or in the manufacture of such products as ethanol and acetone. Enzymes have long been used in fermentation processes for the production of a myriad of compounds. More recently, enzymes have been used to convert cornstarch into

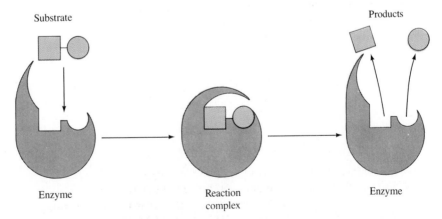

Figure 29.8 Enzyme–substrate interaction illustrating specificity of an enzyme based on both the lock-and-key hypothesis and the induced-fit model

syrups that are equivalent in sweetness and in calories to ordinary table sugar. More than 5 billion pounds of such syrups are produced annually. The process uses three enzymes: The first, α-amylase, catalyzes the liquefaction of starch to dextrins; the second, a glucoamylase, catalyzes the breakdown of oligosaccharides and other carbohydrates to glucose; and the third, glucose isomerase, converts glucose to fructose:

$$\text{Starch} \xrightarrow{\alpha\text{-Amylase}} \text{Dextrins} \xrightarrow{\text{Glucoamylase}} \text{Glucose} \xrightarrow[\text{isomerase}]{\text{Glucose}} \text{Fructose}$$

The product is a high-fructose syrup equivalent in sweetness to sucrose. One of these syrups, sold commercially since 1968, contains by dry weight about 42% fructose, 50% glucose, and 8% other saccharides (on a dry basis).

The ability to isolate purified enzymes has raised the possibility of a number of potential medical applications. For a genetic disease that has caused the loss of a specific enzyme, a treatment known as enzyme-replacement therapy may be useful. For example, a lysosomal storage disease, such as Tay–Sachs disease, leads to the accumulation of excess intracellular polysaccharides because specific digestive enzymes are unavailable. Polysaccharide buildup can lead to mental retardation, paralysis, blindness, and death. Current research is aimed at developing an appropriate microcapsule package that will transport additional digestive enzymes to the affected cells. Such enzyme-replacement therapy has also been proposed for removing toxic substances from the bloodstream.

29.10 Hydrolysis of Proteins

Proteins ultimately yield amino acids when hydrolyzed. Proteins can be hydrolyzed by boiling in a solution containing a strong acid such as HCl or in a solution containing a strong base such as NaOH. Many enzymes that will catalyze the hydrolysis of proteins are known. These enzymes, which are themselves proteins, catalyze the hydrolysis at ordinary temperatures. Such enzymes are called proteolytic enzymes. The essential reaction of hydrolysis is the breaking of a peptide linkage and the addition of the elements of water:

($\sim\sim$ = rest of protein chain)

Any molecule with one or more peptide bonds, from the smallest dipeptide to the largest protein molecule, can be hydrolyzed. During hydrolysis, proteins are broken down into smaller and smaller fragments as follows:

$$\text{Proteins} \longrightarrow \text{Proteoses} \longrightarrow \text{Peptones} \longrightarrow \text{Peptides} \longrightarrow \text{Amino acids}$$

Proteoses and peptones are protein degradation products containing large polypeptides that differ from proteins in that they do not coagulate with heat.

Table 29.4 Enzymes that hydrolyze peptide linkages in proteins (proteolytic enzymes)

Enzyme	Peptide linkage hydrolyzed
Pepsin	Hydrolyzes proteins to proteoses and peptones; attacks the amino end of tyrosine and phenylalanine
Trypsin	Hydrolyzes the polypeptide chain on the carboxyl side of arginine and lysine
Chymotrypsin	Hydrolyzes the polypeptide chain on the carboxyl side of tyrosine, phenylalanine, and tryptophan
Carboxypeptidase	Hydrolyzes C-terminal amino acids
Aminopeptidase	Hydrolyzes N-terminal amino acids
Dipeptidase	Hydrolyzes dipeptides

The enzymes that catalyze the hydrolysis of proteins to amino acids do so at specific peptide linkages. These enzymes show two types of specificity that are characteristic of nearly all enzymes: (1) *reaction specificity*, hydrolysis of the peptide bond and (2) *active-site binding specificity*, each enzyme that catalyzes protein hydrolysis selects a different portion of the protein substrate for reaction. Some enzymes attack only N- or C-terminal amino acids, whereas others break the polypeptide chain at specific internal amino acids. Table 29.4 shows the enzymes involved in protein digestion and the amino acids they hydrolyze.

Sanger partially hydrolyzed beef insulin and then determined the amino acid sequences of a large number of the fragments. He used these data, with the aid of a computer, to determine the amino acid sequence, or primary structure, of the entire insulin molecule.

29.11   Denaturation of Proteins

denaturation

Denaturation refers to a process that causes loss of a protein's natural conformation without peptide-bond hydrolysis. Thus, denaturation involves alteration or disruption of the secondary, tertiary, or quaternary—but not primary—structure of proteins (see Figure 29.9). Because a protein's function depends on its natural conformation, denaturation causes loss of biological activity. An enzyme loses its function when denaturation leads to loss of the active site structure. Denaturation may involve changes ranging from the subtle and reversible alterations caused by a slight change of pH to the extreme alterations involved in tanning a skin to form leather. Noticeable coagulation or precipitation often, but not always, occurs when a protein is denatured. One reason for cooking meats is to denature and thereby tenderize their protein structure. The white of a fried or poached egg is an example of heat-denatured protein.

Protein conformation tends to be fragile because it is held together predominately by noncovalent, relatively weak bonds. As gentle an act as pouring a protein solution can cause denaturation. Purified proteins must often be stored

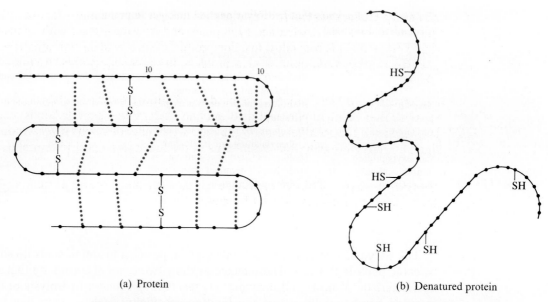

(a) Protein   (b) Denatured protein

Figure 29.9 Structure change when a protein molecule is denatured: The relatively weak hydrogen, electrostatic, and disulfide bonds are broken, resulting in a change of structure and properties. (···· denotes the noncovalent bonds that stabilize a protein's natural conformation.)

under ice-cold conditions because room temperature will denature them. It is not surprising that a wide variety of chemical and physical agents can denature proteins. To name a few: strong acids and strong bases; salts, especially those of heavy metals; certain specific reagents such as tannic acid and picric acid; alcohol and other organic solvents; detergents; mechanical action such as whipping; high temperature; and ultraviolet (UV) radiation.

Egg white contains the protein albumin. If it is stirred vigorously (as with an egg beater) or heated above 70°C, the protein structure is broken, and the albumin coagulates. Denatured proteins are generally less soluble than undenatured proteins. Consequently, the denaturation of a protein will often cause it to coagulate or precipitate from solution.

In clinical laboratories the analysis of blood serum for small molecules such as glucose and uric acid is hampered by the presence of serum protein. This problem is resolved by first treating the serum with an acid to denature and precipitate the protein. The precipitate is removed and the protein-free liquid is then analyzed.

29.12   Tests for Proteins and Amino Acids

Many tests have been devised for detecting and distinguishing among amino acids, peptides, and proteins. Some examples are described here.

Xanthoproteic reaction. Proteins containing a benzene ring—for example, the amino acids phenylalanine, tryptophan, and tryosine—react with concentrated nitric acid to give yellow reaction products. Nitric acid on skin produces a positive xanthoproteic test, as skin proteins are modified by this reaction.

Biuret test. A violet color is produced when dilute copper(II) sulfate is added to an alkaline solution of a peptide or protein. At least two peptide bonds must be present, as the color change occurs only when peptide bonds can surround the Cu^{2+} ion. Thus, amino acids and dipeptides do not give a positive biuret test.

Ninhydrin test. Triketohydrindene hydrate, generally known as *ninhydrin*, is an extremely sensitive reagent for amino acids:

Ninhydrin

All amino acids, except proline and hydroxyproline, give a blue solution with ninhydrin. Proline and hydroxyproline produce a yellow solution. Less than 1 μg (10^{-6} g) of an amino acid can be detected with ninhydrin.

Chromatographic Separation

Complex mixtures of amino acids are readily separated by thin-layer, paper, or column chromatography. In chromatographic methods the components of a mixture are separated by means of differences in their distributions between two phases. Separation depends on the relative tendencies of the components to remain in one phase or the other. In *thin-layer chromatography* (TLC), for example, a liquid and a solid phase are used. The procedure is as follows: A tiny drop of a solution containing a mixture of amino acids (obtained by hydrolyzing a protein) is spotted on a strip (or sheet) coated with a thin layer of dried alumina or some other adsorbant. After the spot has dried, the bottom edge of the strip is put into a suitable solvent. The solvent ascends the strip (by diffusion), carrying the different amino acids upward at different rates. When the solvent front nears the top, the strip is removed from the solvent and dried. The locations of the different amino acids are established by spraying the strip with ninhydrin solution and noting where colored spots appear. The pattern of colored spots is called a chromatogram. The identities of the amino acids in an unknown mixture can be established by comparing the chromatogram of the mixture with a chromatogram produced by known amino acids. A typical chromatogram of amino acids is shown in Figure 29.10.

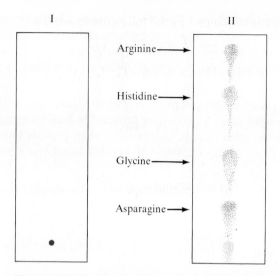

Figure 29.10 Chromatogram showing separation of selected amino acids: On the left, spotted on the chromatographic strip, is an amino acid mixture containing arginine, histidine, glycine, and asparagine. On the right is the developed chromatogram showing the separated amino acids after treatment with ninhydrin. The solvent is a 250:60:250 volume ratio of 1-butanol–acetic acid–water.

Since proteins tend to denature during thin-layer chromatography, they are often separated by column chromatography. In this technique a solution containing a mixture of proteins (liquid phase) is allowed to percolate through a column packed with beads of a suitable polymer (solid phase). Separation of the mixture is accomplished as the proteins partition between the solid and liquid phases. The separated proteins move at different rates and are collected as they leave the column. Unlike amino acid chromatography, mild conditions must be maintained to limit protein denaturation. In the past it was not uncommon for a protein-column chromatography to take from 6–12 hours. Recent developments in the field of high-performance liquid chromatography (HPLC) have shortened this time to minutes.

29.13   Determination of the Primary Structure of Polypeptides

Sanger's reagent.   The pioneering work of Frederick Sanger gave us the first complete primary structure of a protein, insulin, in 1955. He used specific enzymes to hydrolyze insulin into smaller peptides and amino acids, then separated and identified the hydrolytic products by various chemical reactions.

Sanger's reagent, 2-4-dinitrofluorobenzene (DNFB), reacts with the α-amino group of the N-terminal amino acid of a polypeptide chain. The reaction of

Sanger's reagent is illustrated in the following equations:

The carbon–nitrogen bond between the amino acid and the benzene ring is more resistant to hydrolysis than are the remaining peptide linkages. Thus, when the substituted polypeptide is hydrolyzed, the terminal amino acid remains with the dinitrobenzene radical and can be isolated and identified. The remaining peptide chain is hydrolyzed to free amino acids in the process. This method marked an important step in the determination of the amino acid sequence in a protein.

From the DNFB hydrolysis, Sanger learned which amino acids were present in insulin. By less drastic hydrolysis, he split the insulin molecule into peptide fragments consisting of two, three, four, or more amino acid residues. After analyzing vast numbers of fragments utilizing the N-terminal method, he pieced them together in the proper sequence by combining fragments with overlapping structures at their ends, finally elucidating the entire insulin structure. As an example, consider the overlap that occurs between the hexapeptide and heptapeptide shown below:

Gly-Glu-Arg-Gly-Phe-Phe	Hexapeptide
Gly-Phe-Phe-Tyr-Thr-Pro-Lys	Heptapeptide
Gly-Glu-Arg-Gly-Phe-Phe-Tyr-Thr-Pro-Lys	Decapeptide

The three residues Gly-Phe-Phe at the end of the hexapeptide match the three residues at the beginning of the heptapeptide. By using these three residues in common, the structure of the decapeptide shown, which occurs in chain B of insulin (residues 20–29), is determined. (See Figure 29.2, which shows the sequence of insulin.)

Edman degradation.   More recently, the Edman degradation method has been developed to split off amino acids one at a time from the N-terminal end of a polypeptide chain. In this procedure the reagent, phenylisothiocyanate, is first added to the N-terminal amino group. The N-terminal amino acid–phenylisothiocyanate addition product is then cleaved from the polypeptide chain. The resultant substituted phenylthiohydantoin is then isolated and identified. The shortened polypeptide chain is then ready to undergo another Edman degradation. By repeating this set of reactions, one can determine directly the amino acid sequence of a polypeptide. A machine, the protein sequenator, which carries out protein sequencing by Edman degradation automatically, is now available.

Phenylisothiocyanate   Polypeptide chain

Phenylthiohydantoin   Shortened polypeptide chain

29.14   Synthesis of Peptides and Proteins

Since each amino acid has two functional groups, it is not difficult to form dipeptides or even fairly large polypeptide molecules. As mentioned in Section 29.6, glycine and alanine react to form two different dipeptides, glycylalanine and alanylglycine. If threonine, alanine, and glycine react, six tripeptides, each made up of three different amino acids, are obtained. By reacting a mixture of several amino acids, polypeptides are produced that contain a random arrangement of the amino acid units. This fact makes it clear that even a small protein like insulin could not be produced by simply reacting a mixture of the required amino acids. When such a large polypeptide is synthesized, it is formed by joining amino acids one by one in the proper sequence. Within cells, the proper sequence is maintained by careful genetic control (see Section 30.10).

When a polypeptide chain of known primary structure is synthesized in vitro (synthesis in glass without the aid of living tissue), the process must be controlled so that only one particular amino acid is added at each stage. Remarkable progress has been made in developing the necessary techniques. Amino acids are used in which either the amino or carboxylic acid group has been inactivated or blocked with a suitable *blocking agent*. The blocked amino or carboxylic acid group is reactivated by removing the blocking agent in the next stage of the synthesis. For example, if the tripeptide Thr-Ala-Gly is to be made, amino-blocked threonine is reacted with carboxyl-blocked alanine to make the doubly-blocked Thr-Ala dipeptide. The carboxyl-blocked alanine end of the dipeptide can then be reactivated and reacted with carboxyl-blocked glycine to make the blocked Thr-Ala-Gly tripeptide. The free tripeptide can then be obtained by removing the blocking agents from both ends. Using $\boxed{B}$ to designate the blocking agents, this synthesis is represented in schematic form as follows:

$$\boxed{B}\ H_2NCHCOOH + H_2NCHCOOH\ \boxed{B} \longrightarrow \boxed{B}\ H_2NCH\overset{\overset{\displaystyle O}{\|}}{C}-NHCHCOOH\ \boxed{B}$$

$$\underset{\underset{CH_3}{|}}{\overset{|}{H-C-OH}} \qquad \underset{CH_3}{|} \qquad \qquad \underset{\underset{CH_3}{|}}{\overset{|}{H-C-OH}} \quad \underset{CH_3}{|}$$

Amino-blocked   Carboxyl-blocked   Blocked Thr-Ala dipeptide
threonine   alanine

$$\boxed{B}\ H_2NCH\overset{\overset{\displaystyle O}{\|}}{C}-NHCHCOOH + H_2NCH_2COOH\ \boxed{B}$$

$$\underset{\underset{CH_3}{|}}{\overset{|}{H-C-OH}} \quad \underset{CH_3}{|} \qquad \qquad \text{Carboxyl-blocked}$$
glycine

Amino-blocked Thr-Ala
dipeptide

$$\boxed{B}\ H_2NCH\overset{\overset{\displaystyle O}{\|}}{C}-NHCH\overset{\overset{\displaystyle O}{\|}}{C}NHCH_2COOH\ \boxed{B}$$

$$\underset{\underset{CH_3}{|}}{\overset{|}{H-C-OH}} \quad \underset{CH_3}{|}$$

Blocked Thr-Ala-Gly tripeptide

Longer polypeptide chains of specified amino acid sequence can be made by this general technique. The procedure is very tedious. The synthesis of insulin required an effort equivalent to one person working steadily for several years.

It is not necessary to prepare an entire synthetic protein polypeptide chain by starting at one end and adding amino acids one at a time. Previously prepared shorter polypeptide chains of known structure can be joined to form a longer polypeptide chain. This method was used in making synthetic insulin. The insulin molecule, shown in Figure 29.2, consists of two polypeptide chains bonded together by two disulfide bonds. A third disulfide bond, between two amino acids in one chain, makes a small loop in that chain. Once the two chains had been assembled from fragments, a seemingly formidable problem remained—how to form the disulfide bonds in the correct positions. As it turned out, it was necessary only to bring the two chains together, with the cysteine side chains in the reduced condition, and to treat them with an oxidizing agent. Disulfide bonds formed at the right places, and biologically active insulin molecules were obtained. (See Figure 29.2.)

In the mid-1960s a machine capable of automatically synthesizing polypeptide chains of known amino acid sequence was designed by R. B. Merrifield of Rockefeller University. The starting amino acid is bonded to a plastic surface (polystyrene bead) in the reaction chamber of the apparatus. Various reagents needed for building a chain of predetermined structures are automatically delivered to the reaction chamber in a programmed sequence. Twelve reagents and about 100 operations are needed to lengthen the chain by a single amino acid residue. But the machine is capable of adding residues to the chain at the rate of six a day. Such a machine makes it possible to synthesize complex molecules like insulin in a few days. The first large polypeptide (pancreatic ribonuclease), containing 124 amino acid residues, was synthesized by this method in 1969. More recently a human growth hormone (HGH) containing 188 amino acid residues was synthesized using this technique.

QUESTIONS

A. *Review this meanings of the new terms introduced in this chapter.*

1. Simple proteins
2. Conjugated proteins
3. Essential amino acids
4. Zwitterions
5. Isoelectric point
6. Peptide linkage
7. Polypeptide
8. Primary structure
9. Secondary structure
10. Tertiary structure
11. Quaternary structure
12. Enzymes
13. Enzyme inhibitors
14. Denaturation

B. *Review questions*

1. List four foods that are major sources of proteins.
2. Why are the amino acids of proteins called α-amino acids?

3. What elements are present in amino acids and proteins?
4. Why are proteins from some foods of greater nutritional value than others?
5. Write the names of the amino acids that are essential to humans.
6. What two general methods are now available for improving the nutritional value of corn protein?
7. Which amino acids contain a heterocyclic ring?
8. Write the structural formulas for D-serine and L-serine. Which form is found in proteins?
9. Why are the amino acids amphoteric? Why are they optically active?
10. Write the structural formula representing threonine at its isoelectric point.
11. For phenylalanine write
    (a) The molecular formula
    (b) The zwitterion formula
    (c) The formula in 0.1 M H_2SO_4
    (d) The formula in 0.1 M NaOH

12. Write ionic equations to show how alanine acts as a buffer toward
    (a) H^+ ion (b) OH^- ion

13. (a) At what pH will arginine not migrate to either electrode in an electrolytic cell?
    (b) In what pH range will it migrate toward the positive electrode?

14. What can you say about the number of positive and negative charges on a protein molecule at its isoelectric point?

15. At what pH will the following amino acids be at their isoelectric points?
    (a) Histidine
    (b) Phenylalanine
    (c) Glutamic acid

16. Write out the full structural formula of the two dipeptides containing glycine and phenylalanine. Indicate the location of the peptide bonds.

17. Write structures for
    (a) Glycylglycine
    (b) Glycylglycylalanine
    (c) Leucylmethionylglycylserine

18. Using amino acid abbreviations, write all the possible tripeptides containing one unit each of glycine, phenylalanine, and leucine.

19. How many dipeptides containing glycine can be written using the 20 amino acids from Table 29.1?

20. Explain what is meant by (a) the primary structure, (b) the secondary structure, and (c) the tertiary structure of a protein.

21. What special role does the sulfur-containing amino acid cysteine have in protein structure?

22. How do myoglobin and hemoglobin differ in structure and function?

23. What is the general mechanism by which enzymes change the rates of essential biochemical reactions?

24. What are enzymes and what is their role in the body?

25. Distinguish between a coenzyme and an apoenzyme.

26. Give the names of the enzymes that catalyze the hydrolysis of
    (a) Sucrose (b) Lactose (c) Maltose

27. Explain how enzymes function as catalysts. Why is an enzyme usually specific for one particular reaction?

28. What are the six general classes of enzymes?

29. Why are K_m's reported in units of concentration—for example, molarity?

30. Under identical conditions, enzyme A has a V_{max} of 0.003 M/min, and enzyme B has a V_{max} of 0.05 M/min. Which enzyme is the more effective catalyst under these conditions? Briefly explain.

31. How does an enzyme inhibitor differ from an enzyme substrate?

32. Suggest a major reason why proteins tend to be easily denatured.

33. Explain how hydrolysis of a protein differs from denaturation.

34. What chemical change occurs when a protein is hydrolyzed to amino acids?

35. When proteins are partially hydrolyzed, what products are formed?

36. What are the specific functions of the enzymes trypsin and chymotrypsin?

37. What is the visible evidence observed in a positive reaction for the following tests?
    (a) Xanthoproteic reaction
    (b) Biuret test
    (c) Ninhydrin test

38. Would Thr-Ala-Gly react with each of the following?
    (a) Sanger's reagent
    (b) Concentrated HNO_3 to give a positive xanthoproteic test
    (c) Ninhydrin

39. Which amino acids give a positive xanthoproteic test?

40. (a) What is thin-layer chromatography?
    (b) Describe how amino acids are separated using this technique.
    (c) What reagent is used to locate the amino acids in the chromatogram?

41. Briefly describe protein column chromatography.

42. Given the decapeptide Ala-Tyr-Gly-Gln-Lys-Phe-Gly-Arg-Ser-Gly, what peptide fragments would be found in hydrolysis using the following?
    (a) Pepsin   (e) Aminopeptidase
    (b) Trypsin   (f) Sanger's reagent
    (c) Chymotrypsin   (g) Edman's reagent
    (d) Carboxypeptidase

43. Threonine has two asymmetric carbon atoms. Write Fischer projection formulas for its stereoisomers.

44. Show the reactants and products for one complete cycle of the Edman degradation on the tripeptide Ala-Leu-Gly.
45. What is the amino acid sequence of heptapeptides A and B, which upon hydrolysis yield these tripeptides:
    (A) Gly-Phe-Leu, Phe-Ala-Gly, Leu-Ala-Tyr
    (B) Phe-Gly-Tyr, Phe-Ala-Ala, Ala-Leu-Phe
    Both A and B contain one residue each of Gly, Leu, and Tyr and two residues each of Ala and Phe.
46. A nonapeptide is obtained from blood plasma by treatment with the enzyme trypsin. Analysis using Sanger's reagent and carboxypeptidase showed that both terminal amino acids are arginine. Total hydrolysis of this peptide yielded Gly, Ser, 2 Arg, 2 Phe, 3 Pro. Partial hydrolysis gave Phe-Ser, Phe-Arg, Arg-Pro, Pro-Pro, Pro-Gly-Phe, Ser-Pro-Phe. What is the amino acid sequence of the nonapeptide?
47. One hundred grams (100.0 g) of a food product was analyzed and found to contain 6.0 g of nitrogen. If protein contains an average of 16% nitrogen, what percentage of the food is protein?
48. Human hemoglobin contains 0.33% iron. If each hemoglobin molecule contains four iron atoms, what is the molecular weight of hemoglobin?
49. Which of these statements are correct?
    (a) Proteins, like fats and carbohydrates, are primarily for supplying heat and energy to the body.
    (b) Proteins differ from fats and carbohydrates in that they contain a large amount of nitrogen.
    (c) A complete protein is one that contains all the essential amino acids.
    (d) Except for glycine, amino acids that are found in proteins have the L configuration.

(e) All amino acids have an asymmetric carbon atom and are therefore optically active.
(f) The amide linkages by which amino acids are joined together are called peptide linkages.
(g) Two different dipeptides can be formed from the amino acids glycine and phenylalanine.
(h) The compound Ala-Phe-Tyr has two peptide bonds and is therefore known as a dipeptide.
(i) A zwitterion is a dipolar ion form of an amino acid.
(j) The primary structure of a protein is the α-helical or β-pleated-sheet form that it takes.
(k) The tertiary structure of a protein determines that protein's primary structure.
(l) The amino acid residues in a peptide chain are numbered beginning with the C-terminal amino acid.
(m) Insulin contains two polypeptide chains, one with 21 amino acids and the other with 30 amino acids.
(n) Enzymes are proteins.
(o) Enzymes increase the activation energy for a reaction.
(p) An enzyme active site is where catalysis occurs.
(q) The substance acted upon by an enzyme is called the coenzyme.
(r) When a protein is denatured, the polypeptide bonds are broken, liberating the amino acids.
(s) Irreversible coagulation or precipitation of proteins is called denaturation.
(t) Sanger's reagent reacts with peptide chains, isolating the N-terminal amino acid.

30

Nucleic Acids and Heredity

After studying Chapter 30, you should be able to

1. Understand the new terms listed in Question A at the end of the chapter.
2. Write the structural formulas for the two purine and three pyrimidine bases found in nucleotides.
3. Distinguish between ribonucleotides and deoxyribonucleotides.
4. List the compositions, abbreviations, and structures for the ten nucleotides in DNA and RNA.
5. Write the structural formulas for ADP and ATP.
6. Identify where energy is stored in ADP and ATP.
7. Write a structural formula of a segment of a polynucleotide that contains four nucleotides.
8. Describe the double-helix structure of DNA according to Watson and Crick.
9. Explain the concept of complementary bases.
10. Describe and illustrate the replication process of DNA.
11. Understand how heredity factors are stored in DNA molecules.
12. Distinguish between mitosis and meiosis.
13. Understand how the genetic code is used in the synthesis of proteins.
14. Describe a potential cause of cancer involving an oncogene.
15. Explain the genetic code.
16. State the functions of the three different kinds of RNA.
17. Describe the transcription of the genetic code from DNA to RNA.
18. Describe the biosynthesis of proteins.

19. Understand how mutations are caused.
20. Describe the Ames test.
21. Briefly describe genetic engineering.

30.1 Introduction

The question of how hereditary material duplicates itself was for a long time one of the most baffling problems of biology. For many years biologists attempted in vain to solve this problem and also to find an answer to the question "Why are the offspring of a species undeniably of that species?" Many thought the chemical basis for heredity lay in the structure of the proteins. But no one was able to provide evidence showing how protein could reproduce itself. The answer to the heredity problem was finally found in the structure of the nucleic acids.

The unit structure of all living things is the cell. Suspended in the nuclei of cells are chromosomes, which consist largely of proteins and nucleic acids. A **nucleoprotein** simple protein bonded to a nucleic acid is called a **nucleoprotein.** There are two types of **nucleic acids**—those that contain the sugar deoxyribose and those that **nucleic acids** contain the sugar ribose. Accordingly, they are called deoxyribonucleic acid (DNA) and ribonucleic acid (RNA). DNA was discovered in 1869 by the Swiss physiologist Friedrich Miescher (1844–1895), who extracted it from the nuclei of cells.

30.2 Nucleosides

Nucleosides are important cellular molecules that are used by living cells to make nucleic acids. Nucleosides are derived from the two parent bases purine and pyrimidine:

Purine, $C_5H_4N_4$ Pyrimidine, $C_4H_4N_2$

There are five major bases found in living matter—two purine bases (adenine and guanine) and three pyrimidine bases (cytosine, thymine, and uracil) (see **nucleoside** Figure 30.1). A **nucleoside** is composed of either a purine or pyrimidine base linked to a sugar molecule, usually D-ribose or D-2-deoxyribose. The nucleoside is formed when a bond links carbon 1 of the sugar to either the purine nitrogen at position 9 or the pyrimidine nitrogen at position 1. Typical structures of nucleosides are shown in Figure 30.2.

The name of each nucleoside emphasizes the importance of the base to the chemistry of the molecule. Thus, adenine and D-ribose react to yield adenosine, whereas cytosine and D-2-deoxyribose yield deoxycytidine. The root of the nucleoside name derives from the purine or pyrimidine name. The compositions of the *ribonucleosides* and the *deoxyribonucleosides* are given in Table 30.1.

Figure 30.1 Purine and pyrimidine bases found in living matter

Adenine
(6-Aminopurine)

Guanine
(2-Amino-6-oxypurine)

Cytosine
(2-Oxy-4-amino-
pyrimidine)

Thymine
(2,4-Dioxy-5-methyl-
pyrimidine)

Uracil
(2,4-Dioxypyrimidine)

Adenosine

Deoxyadenosine

Cytidine

Deoxycytidine

Figure 30.2 Typical structures of ribonucleosides and deoxyribonucleosides

Table 30.1 Composition of ribonucleosides
and deoxyribonucleosides

Name	*Composition*	*Abbreviation*
Adenosine	Adenine–ribose	A
Deoxyadenosine	Adenine–deoxyribose	dA
Guanosine	Guanine–ribose	G
Deoxyguanosine	Guanine–deoxyribose	dG
Cytidine	Cytosine–ribose	C
Deoxycytidine	Cytosine–deoxyribose	dC
Thymidine	Thymine–ribose	T
Deoxythymidine	Thymine–deoxyribose	dT
Uridine	Uracil–ribose	U
Deoxyuridine	Uracil–deoxyribose	dU

30.3 Nucleotides: Phosphate Esters

nucleotides

Nucleotides are phosphate esters of nucleosides. **Nucleotides** consist of a purine or a pyrimidine base linked to a sugar, which in turn is linked to a phosphate group. The ester may be a monophosphate, a diphosphate, or a triphosphate. When two or more phosphates are linked together, a high-energy phosphate anhydride bond is formed (see Section 30.4). The ester linkage may be to the hydroxyl group of position 2′, 3′, or 5′ of ribose or of position 3′ or 5′ of deoxyribose. A prime is added to the position number in order to differentiate the sugar numbering system from the purine or pyrimidine numbering system.

Nucleoside + Phosphoric acid = Nucleotide

Each nucleotide consists of the following sequence:

A typical nucleotide is adenosine-5′-monophosphate (AMP), also called adenylic acid. The abbreviations for the five nucleosides containing D-ribose are

Adenosine   A
Guanosine   G
Cytidine   C
Thymidine   T
Uridine   U

The letters *MP* (monophosphate) can be added to any of these to designate the corresponding nucleotide. Thus GMP is guanosine monophosphate. A lowercase *d* is placed in front of GMP if the nucleotide contains the deoxyribose sugar (dGMP). When the letters such as *AMP* or *GMP* are given, it is generally understood that the phosphate group is attached to position 5′ of the ribose unit (5′-AMP). If attachment is elsewhere, it will be designated—for example, 3′-AMP. In naming these compounds, the prime designation (as in 5′) indicates the position on the ribose or deoxyribose unit. Thus, adenosine-5′-monophosphate means that the phosphate group is attached to position 5′ of ribose. Examples of nucleotide structures are shown in Figure 30.3.

Two other important adenosine phosphate esters are adenosine diphosphate (ADP) and adenosine triphosphate (ATP). Note that the letters *DP* are used for diphosphate and *TP* for triphosphate. In these molecules the phosphate groups are linked together. The structures are similar to AMP except that they contain two and three phosphate residues, respectively (see Figure 30.4). All the nucleosides form mono-, di-, and triphosphate nucleotides.

Adenosine-5′-monophosphate
(AMP)

Deoxyadenosine-5′-monophosphate
(dAMP)

Figure 30.3 Examples of nucleotides

Adenosine-5′-diphosphate
(ADP)

Adenosine-5′-triphosphate
(ATP)

Figure 30.4 Structures of ADP and ATP

30.4 High-Energy Nucleotides

The nucleotides have a central role in the energy transfers in many metabolic processes. ATP and ADP are especially important in these processes. The role of these two nucleotides is to store and release energy to the cells and tissues. The source of energy is the foods we eat, particularly carbohydrates and fats. Energy is released as the carbons from these foods are oxidized (see Chapter 32). Part of this energy is used to maintain body temperature, and part is stored in the phosphate anhydride bonds of such molecules as ADP and ATP. Because a relatively large amount of energy is stored in these bonds, they are known as high-energy phosphate anhydride bonds.

High-energy phosphate anhydride bonds
(ATP)

High-energy anhydride bond
(ADP)

Chemical energy is needed for many of the complex reactions that are essential to life processes. This energy is obtained from the hydrolysis of high-energy phosphate anhydride bonds in ADP and ATP. In the hydrolysis, ATP forms ADP and inorganic phosphate (P_i) with the release of about 35 kJ of energy per mole of ATP:

$$\text{ATP} + \text{H}_2\text{O} \underset{\substack{\text{Energy} \\ \text{storage}}}{\overset{\substack{\text{Energy} \\ \text{utilization}}}{\rightleftarrows}} \text{ADP} + \text{P}_i + \approx 35 \text{ kJ}$$

The hydrolysis reaction is reversible, with ADP being converted to ATP by still-higher-energy molecules. In this manner, energy is supplied to the cells from ATP, and energy is stored by the synthesis of ATP from ADP and AMP. All these processes are enzyme catalyzed. Processes such as muscle movement, nerve sensations, vision, and even the maintenance of our heartbeats, are all dependent on energy from ATP.

30.5   Polynucleotides; Nucleic Acids

Starting with two nucleotides, a dinucleotide is formed by splitting out a molecule of water between the —OH of the phosphate group of one nucleotide and the —OH on C 3 of the ribose or deoxyribose of the other nucleotide. Then another and another nucleotide can be added in the same manner until a polynucleotide chain is formed. Each nucleotide is linked to its neighbors by phosphate ester bonds (see ester formation in Section 24.6).

Two series of polynucleotide chains are known, one containing D-ribose and the other D-2-deoxyribose. One polymeric chain consists of the monomers AMP, GMP, CMP, and UMP and is known as a polyribonucleotide. The other chain contains the monomers dAMP, dGMP, dCMP, and dTMP is known as a polydeoxyribonucleotide:

Polyribonucleotide (RNA)

Polydeoxyribonucleotide (DNA)

ribonucleic acid (RNA)

deoxyribo-nucleic acid (DNA)

The nucleic acids DNA and RNA are polynucleotides. **Ribonucleic acid (RNA)** is a polynucleotide that upon hydrolysis yields ribose, phosphoric acid, and the four purine and pyrimidine bases adenine, guanine, cytosine, and uracil. **Deoxyribonucleic acid (DNA)** is a polynucleotide that yields D-2-deoxyribose, phosphoric acid, and the four bases adenine, guanine, cytosine, and thymine. Note that RNA and DNA contain one different pyrimidine nucleotide. RNA contains uridine, whereas DNA contains thymidine. A segment of a ribonucleic acid chain is shown in Figure 30.5. As will be described later, RNA and DNA also commonly differ in function: DNA serves as the storehouse for genetic information; RNA aids in expressing genetic characteristics.

Figure 30.5 A segment of ribonucleic acid (RNA) consisting of the four nucleotides adenosine monophosphate, cytidine monophosphate, guanosine monophosphate, and uridine monophosphate: A schematic of the four combined nucleotides is shown at the right.

30.6 Structure of DNA

Deoxyribonucleic acid (DNA) is a polymeric substance made up of thousands of the four nucleotides dAMP, dGMP, dCMP, and dTMP. The order in which these four nucleotides occur varies in different DNA molecules, and it is this order that stores the genetic information within each DNA molecule.

The nucleotide composition of many DNA's has been determined as scientists have tried to understand the structure of DNA. For a long time it was thought that

Table 30.2   Relative amounts of purines and pyrimidines in samples of DNA

Source	Adenine	Thymine	Ratio A/T	Guanine	Cytosine	Ratio G/C
Beef thymus	29.0	28.5	1.02	21.2	21.2	1.00
Beef liver	28.8	29.0	0.99	21.0	21.1	1.00
Beef sperm	28.7	27.2	1.06	22.2	22.0	1.01
Human thymus	30.9	29.4	1.05	19.9	19.8	1.00
Human liver	30.3	30.3	1.00	19.5	19.9	0.98
Human sperm	30.9	31.6	0.98	19.1	18.4	1.04
Hen red blood cells	28.8	29.2	0.99	20.5	21.5	0.96
Herring sperm	27.8	27.5	1.01	22.2	22.6	0.98
Wheat germ	26.5	27.0	0.98	23.5	23.0	1.02
Yeast	31.7	32.6	0.97	18.3	17.4	1.05
Vaccinia virus	29.5	29.9	0.99	20.6	20.0	1.03
Bacteriophage T_2	32.5	32.6	1.00	18.2	18.6	0.98

the four nucleotides occurred in equal amounts in DNA. However, more refined analyses showed that the amounts of purine and pyrimidine bases varied in different DNA molecules. Surprisingly, careful consideration of these data also showed that the ratios of adenine to thymine and guanine to cytosine were always essentially 1:1. This observation served as an important key to unraveling the structure of DNA. The analyses of DNA from several species are shown in Table 30.2.

A second important clue to the special configuration and structure of DNA came from X-ray diffraction studies. Most significant was the work of Maurice H. F. Wilkins (b. 1916) of Kings College in London. Wilkins' X-ray pictures implied that the nucleotide bases were stacked one on top of another like a stack of saucers. From his work as well as that of others, the American biologist James D. Watson (b. 1928) and British physicist Francis H. C. Crick (b. 1916), working at Cambridge University, designed and built a scale model of a DNA molecule. In 1953 Watson and Crick announced their now-famous double-stranded helical structure for DNA. This was a milestone in the history of biology, and in 1962 Watson, Crick, and Wilkins were awarded the Nobel prize in medicine and physiology for their studies of DNA.

The structure of DNA, according to Watson and Crick, consists of two polymeric strands of nucleotides in the form of a double helix, with both nucleotide strands coiled around the same axis (see Figure 30.6). Along each strand are alternate phosphate and deoxyribose units with one of the four bases adenine, guanine, cytosine, or thymine attached to deoxyribose as a side group. The double helix is held together by hydrogen bonds extending from the base on one strand of the double helix to a complementary base on the other strand. The structure of DNA has been likened to a ladder that has been twisted into a double helix, with the rungs of the ladder kept perpendicular to the twisted railings. The phosphate and deoxyribose units alternate along the two railings of the ladder, and two nitrogen bases form each rung of the ladder.

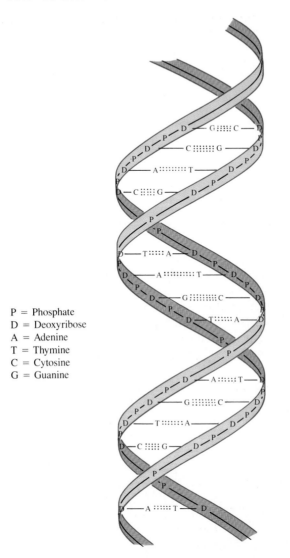

P = Phosphate
D = Deoxyribose
A = Adenine
T = Thymine
C = Cytosine
G = Guanine

Figure 30.6   Double-stranded helical structure of DNA. (···· denotes a hydrogen bond between adjoining bases.)

In the Watson–Crick model of DNA, the distance between the two nucleotide strands is such that it can accommodate one purine and one pyrimidine base. This allows for four possible structures, A–T, A–C, G–C, and G–T. However, it was shown that, because of the hydrogen bonding that occurs between them, the complementary bases are adenine–thymine and guanine–cytosine. The order of bases along each DNA strand may vary but, between strands, adenine always pairs with thymine and guanine always pairs with cytosine. This pairing

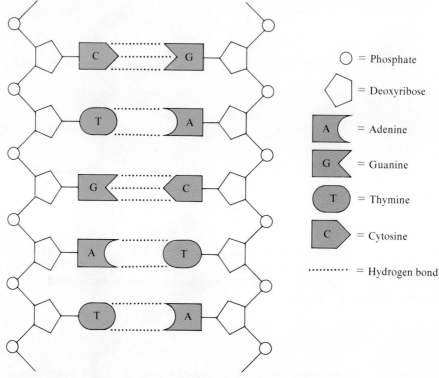

Figure 30.7 Schematic diagram of a DNA segment showing phosphate, deoxyribose, and complementary base pairings held together by hydrogen bonds

results in A : T and G : C ratios of 1 : 1, as substantiated by the data in Table 30.2. A schematic diagram of a double-stranded DNA segment is shown in Figure 30.7. The hydrogen bonding of complementary base pairs is shown in Figure 30. 8. Note that complementary base pairing means that the two DNA strands are complementary to each other. If the sequence of one strand is known, the sequence of the other strand can be determined. During the biological synthesis of DNA (DNA replication), the cell chemically "reads" one strand in order to form its complementary partner.

30.7   DNA: The Genetic Substance

The foundations of our present concepts of heredity and evolution were laid within the span of a decade. Charles Darwin (1809–1882), in *The Origin of Species* (1859), presented evidence supporting the concept of organic evolution and his theory of natural selection. Gregor Johann Mendel (1822–1884) discovered the basic laws of heredity in 1866, and Friedrich Miescher discovered nucleic acid in 1869. Although Darwin's views were widely discussed and

Figure 30.8 Hydrogen bonding between the complementary bases thymine and adenine (T ⦂⦂⦂ A) and cytosine and guanine (C ⦂⦂⦂⦂ G): Note that one pair of bases has two hydrogen bonds and the other pair has three hydrogen bonds.

generally accepted by biologists within a few years, Mendel's and Miescher's work went unnoticed for many years.

Mendel's laws were rediscovered about 1900 and led to our present understanding of heredity and the science of genetics. Interest in nucleic acids lagged until nearly the 1950s, when chemical and X-ray data provided the basis for the suggestion by Watson and Crick that DNA exists in a double helix and that DNA has the possible copying mechanism for genetic material.

Heredity is the process by which the physical and mental characteristics of parents are transferred to their offspring. In order for this to occur, it is necessary for the material responsible for genetic transfer to be able to make exact copies of itself. The polymeric DNA molecule is the chemical basis for heredity. The genetic information needed for transmittal of a species' characteristics is coded along the polymeric chain. Although the chain is made from only four different nucleotides, the information content of DNA resides in the sequence of these nucleotides.

genome

The **genome** is the sum of all hereditary material contained in a cell. Within the eucaryotic (see Section 32.5) genome are chromosomes, which are long, threadlike bodies composed of nucleic acids and proteins that contain the basic units of heredity, called genes. **Genes** are segments of the DNA chain that control the formation of molecules of RNA. The molecules of RNA, in turn, control the sequence of amino acids in specific polypeptides or proteins. In most cases this is a one-to-one relationship, with one gene directing the synthesis of only one polypeptide or protein molecule. Hundreds of genes can exist along a

genes

DNA chain. Furthermore, a gene may be repeated in various places in a DNA molecule.

Genetic information must be reproduced exactly each time a cell divides. The design for replication is built into the DNA structure of Watson and Crick, first by the nature of its double helical structure and second by the complementary nature of its nitrogen bases in which adenine will bond only to thymine and guanine only to cytosine. The DNA double helix unwinds or simply "unzips" at the hydrogen bonds between the bases. As each DNA strand separates, it serves as a template. Nucleotides with complementary bases hydrogen-bond to each template and are incorporated into a new DNA strand. Every double-stranded DNA molecule that is produced contains one template strand and one newly formed, complementary strand. This form of DNA synthesis, known as *semiconservative* replication, is illustrated in Figure 30.9.

The DNA content of cells doubles just before the cell divides, and one-half of the DNA goes to each daughter cell. After cell division is completed, each daughter cell contains DNA and the full genetic code that was present in the **mitosis**   original cell. This process of ordinary cell division is known as **mitosis** and occurs in all the cells of the body except the reproductive cells.

As we have indicated before, DNA is an integral part of the chromosomes. Each species carries a specific number of chromosomes in the nucleus of each of its cells. The number of chromosomes varies with different species. Humans have 23 pairs, or 46 chromosomes. The fruit fly has 4 pairs, or 8 chromosomes. Each chromosome contains DNA molecules. Mitosis produces cells with the same chromosomal content as the parent cell. However, in the sexual reproductive cycle, cell division occurs by a different process known as meiosis.

In sexual reproduction, two cells, the sperm cell from the male and the egg cell (or ovum) from the female, unite to form the cell of the new individual. If reproduction took place with mitotic cells, the normal chromosome content **meiosis**   would double when two cells united. However, in **meiosis** the cell splits in such a way as to reduce the number of chromosomes to one-half of the number normally present (23 in humans). The sperm cell carries only half of the chromosomes from its original cell, and the egg cell also carries half of the chromosomes from its original cell. When the sperm and the egg cells unite during fertilization, the cell once again contains the correct number of chromosomes and the hereditary characteristics of the species. Thus, the offspring derives half its genetic characteristics from the father and half from the mother.

30.8   RNA, Genetic Transcription

One of the main functions of DNA is to direct the synthesis of ribonucleic acids (RNA's). RNA differs chemically from DNA in the following ways: (1) it consists of a single polymeric strand of nucleotides rather than a double helix; (2) it contains the pentose D-ribose instead of D-2-deoxyribose and (3) it contains the pyrimidine base uracil instead of thymine. RNA also differs functionally from DNA. Whereas DNA serves as the storehouse of genetic information, RNA is used to process this information into proteins. Because this processing is

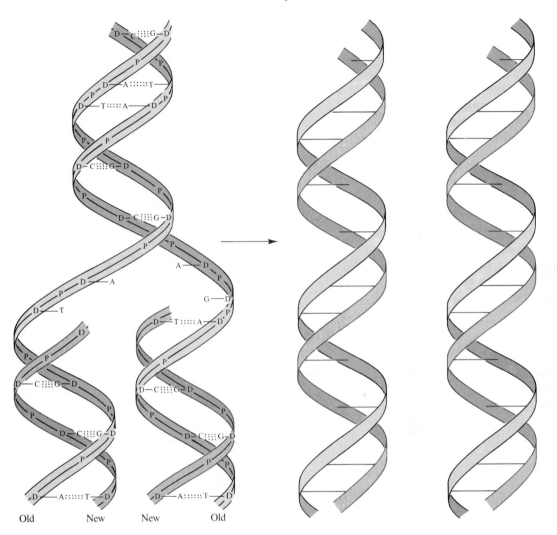

Figure 30.9 Method of replication of DNA: The two helices unwind, separating at the hydrogen bonds. Each strand then serves as a template, recombining with the proper nucleotides to form a new double-stranded helix. The newly synthesized DNA strands are shown in color.

complex, there are three types of RNA: ribosomal RNA (rRNA), messenger RNA (mRNA), and transfer RNA (tRNA).

More than 80% of the cellular RNA is ribosomal RNA. It is found in the ribosomes, where it is associated with protein in proportions of about 60–65% protein to 30–35% rRNA. Ribosomes are the sites where mRNA and tRNA interact to assemble amino acids into proteins.

Messenger RNA carries genetic information from DNA to the ribosomes. It is a template made from DNA and carries the code that directs the synthesis of proteins. The size of mRNA varies according to the length of the polypeptide chain it will encode.

The primary function of tRNA is to bring amino acids to the ribosomes for incorporation into protein molecules. Consequently there exists at least one tRNA for each of the 20 amino acids required for proteins. Transfer RNA molecules have a number of structural features in common. The end of the chain of all tRNA molecules terminates in a CCA nucleotide sequence to which is attached the amino acid to be transferred to a protein chain. The primary structure of tRNA allows extensive folding of the molecule such that complementary bases are hydrogen bonded to each other to form a structure that appears like a cloverleaf. The cloverleaf model of tRNA has an anticodon loop consisting of seven unpaired nucleotides. Three of these nucleotides make up an *anticodon* (see Figure 30.10). The anticodon is complementary to, and hydrogen bonds with, three bases on an mRNA. The other two loops in the cloverleaf

Figure 30.10   Cloverleaf model representation of tRNA: The anticodon triplet (CUU) located at the lower loop is complementary to GAA (which is the code for glutamic acid) on mRNA.

structure enable the tRNA to bind to the ribosome and other specific enzymes during protein synthesis (see Section 30.10.)

transcription   The making of RNA from DNA is called **transcription.** The verb *transcribe* literally means to copy, often into a different format. When the nucleotide sequence of one strand of DNA is transcribed into a single strand of RNA, genetic information is copied from DNA to RNA. This transcription occurs in a complementary fashion. Where there is a guanine base in DNA, a cytosine base will occur in RNA. Cytosine is transcribed to guanine, thymine to adenine, and adenine to uracil (see Figure 30.11).

Transcription is the initial step in the expression of genetic information. Normally, only a fraction of the total information is used at any one time. Thus, the cell needs stringent control to select and use only the appropriate genes. In procaryotic cells (see Section 32.5), related genes are often located together so that they can be controlled and used in concert. The control of eucaryotic transcription is more complex.

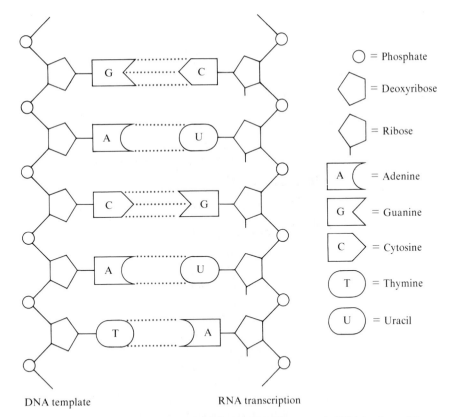

DNA template   RNA transcription

Figure 30.11   Transcription of RNA from DNA: The sugar in RNA is ribose. The complementary base of adenine is uracil. After transcription is complete, the new RNA separates from its DNA template and travels to another location for further use. (···· denotes a hydrogen bond between adjoining bases.)

The importance of transcription control is illustrated by the recently discovered *oncogenes*. These genes, which cause cells to become malignant or cancerous, were originally discovered as part of the genome of cancer-causing viruses. To the surprise of many investigators, it was also found that these same oncogenes are apparently present in normal mammalian cells. The cells carry on their normal and necessary functions, and are not cancerous, as long as the oncogenes are under control. But control can be lost due to, for example, a virus infection or exposure to a chemical carcinogen. Then the oncogenes are transcribed too often, and the cell becomes cancerous.

Following transcription, the RNA molecules that are produced from DNA may be modified before they are put to use. Ribosomal RNA and tRNA molecules are formed as larger precursors and are then trimmed to the correct size. After transcription, many of the bases in tRNA are modified by methylation, saturation of a double bond, or by isomerization of the ribose-base linkage. This post-transcriptional modification or processing changes the information content of the RNA.

Eucaryotic mRNA may undergo considerable alteration before the message that it carries is ready to guide protein synthesis. These changes may include the elimination of portions of the mRNA molecule, the splicing together of two or more mRNA molecules, or the addition of new bases to one end of the mRNA. During this processing, the message encoded in the mRNA molecule is apparently refined so that it can be correctly read by the ribosome.

Figure 30.12 summarizes the processes by which genetic information is transferred within a cell. These steps culminate in the conversion of a coded nucleotide message into a protein amino acid sequence.

30.9   The Genetic Code

For a long time after the structure of DNA was elucidated, scientists struggled with the problem of how DNA could also be a template for the synthesis of proteins. Since the backbone of the DNA molecule contains a regular structure of repeated and identical phosphate and deoxyribose units, the key to the code had to lie in the four bases—adenine, guanine, cytosine, and thymine.

The code, using only the four nucleotides A, G, C, and T, must be capable of coding at least for the 20 amino acids that occur in proteins. If each nucleotide coded one amino acid, only four amino acids could be represented. If the code used two nucleotides to specify an amino acid, 16 (4×4) combinations would be possible—still not enough. Using three nucleotides we can have 64 ($4 \times 4 \times 4$) possible combinations—which is more than enough to specify the 20 common amino acids in proteins. It has now been determined that each code word requires a sequence of three nucleotides. The code is therefore a triplet code. Each triplet of three nucleotides is called a **codon,** and, in general, each codon specifies one amino acid. Thus, to describe a protein containing 200 amino acid units, a gene containing at least 200 codons, or 600 nucleotides, is required.

codon

In the sequence of biological events, the code from a gene in DNA is first

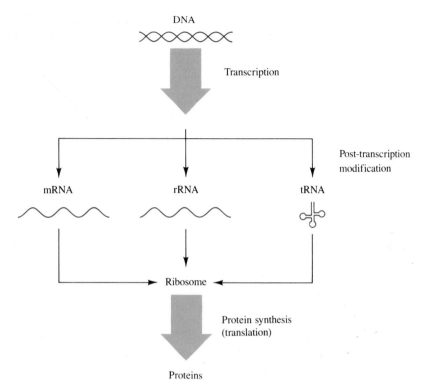

Figure 30.12   A flow diagram representing the processing of cellular genetic information

transcribed to a coded RNA, which, in turn, is used to direct the synthesis of a protein. The 64 possible codons for mRNA are given in Table 30.3. In this table a three-letter sequence (first nucleotide–second nucleotide–third nucleotide) specifies a particular amino acid. For example, the codon CAC (cytosine nucleotide–adenine nucleotide–cytosine nucleotide) is the code for the amino acid histidine (His). You will note that three codons in the table, marked TC, do not encode any amino acids. These are called *nonsense* or *termination codons*. They act as signals to indicate where the synthesis of a protein molecule is to end. The other 61 codons identify 20 amino acids. Methionine and tryptophan have only one codon each. For the other amino acids, the code is redundant; that is, each amino acid is specified by at least two, and sometimes by as many as six, codons.

It is believed that the genetic code is a universal code for all living organisms; that is, the same nucleotide triplet specifies a given amino acid regardless of whether that amino acid is synthesized by a bacterial cell, a pine tree, or a human being.

Recently scientists have developed a machine that automates the sequencing of DNA. This machine can chemically "read" about 500 bases on a nucleic acid polymer per hour. A rapid decoding of genetic information is essential if

Table 30.3 The genetic code for messenger RNA: The sequence of nucleotides in the triplet codons of messenger RNA that specify a given amino acid. (For example, UUU or UUC is the codon for Phe, UCU is a codon for Ser; CAU or CAC is the codon for His.)

First nucleotide	Second nucleotide				Third nucleotide
	U	C	A	G	
U	Phe	Ser	Tyr	Cys	U
	Phe	Ser	Tyr	Cys	C
	Leu	Ser	TC[a]	TC[a]	A
	Leu	Ser	TC[a]	Trp	G
C	Leu	Pro	His	Arg	U
	Leu	Pro	His	Arg	C
	Leu	Pro	Gln	Arg	A
	Leu	Pro	Gln	Arg	G
A	Ile	Thr	Asn	Ser	U
	Ile	Thr	Asn	Ser	C
	Ile	Thr	Lys	Arg	A
	Met	Thr	Lys	Arg	G
G	Val	Ala	Asp	Gly	U
	Val	Ala	Asp	Gly	C
	Val	Ala	Glu	Gly	A
	Val	Ala	Glu	Gly	G

[a] Termination or nonsense codons.

scientists hope finally to understand the human genome, which contains about 3 billion bases.

30.10 Biosynthesis of Proteins

The biosynthesis of proteins is extremely complex, and the following is only a cursory description of the overall process. The production of a polypeptide using an mRNA template is called **translation.** This term is used because it literally means a change from one language to another. The genetic code is *translated* into the primary structure of a polypeptide or a protein.

The biosynthesis of proteins occurs in the ribosomes. Messenger RNA leaves the nucleus of the cell and travels to the cytoplasm, where it becomes associated with a cluster of ribosomes. Each mRNA strand is bound to five or more ribosomes. In the next step, amino acids are activated by ATP and, with the aid of specific enzymes (aminoacyl-tRNA synthetases), are bound to tRNA's to form aminoacyl-tRNA complexes. The amino acid is attached by an ester linkage to a terminal ribose unit of tRNA (see Figure 30.10).

translation

$$R-CH-\overset{\overset{\displaystyle O}{\|}}{C}-OH + tRNA + ATP \xrightarrow[\text{synthetase}]{\text{Aminoacyl-tRNA}}$$

with NH_2 on the R—CH group.

$$R-CH-\overset{\overset{\displaystyle O}{\|}}{C}-tRNA + AMP + HO-\overset{\overset{\displaystyle O}{\|}}{\underset{\underset{\displaystyle OH}{|}}{P}}-O-\overset{\overset{\displaystyle O}{\|}}{\underset{\underset{\displaystyle OH}{|}}{P}}-OH$$

with NH_2 on the R—CH group.

Aminoacyl-tRNA

A different specific enzyme is utilized for binding each of the 20 amino acids to a corresponding tRNA. Although only 20 amino acids are involved, there are about 60 different tRNA molecules in the cells. In summary the function of tRNA is to bring amino acids to the ribosome synthesis site.

The next step in the process is the initiation of polypeptide synthesis. Two codons signal for the start of protein synthesis, AUG and GUG (AUG being the more common). As shown in Table 30.3, these codons also code for incorporation of the amino acids methionine and valine. Most mRNA's have more than one AUG and GUG, and the ribosome must choose at which codon to begin. It appears that the ribosome uses information in addition to the AUG or GUG triplet to choose the correct starting codon for protein synthesis.

Once the correct starting point has been identified, a special initiator tRNA binds to the ribosome. This specific tRNA carries an N-formyl methionine in procaryotic cells:

$$CH_3-S-CH_2CH_2\overset{\overset{\displaystyle HC=O}{\underset{\displaystyle |}{}}\overset{\displaystyle NH}{\underset{\displaystyle |}{}}}{CH}-\overset{\overset{\displaystyle O}{\|}}{C}-tRNA$$

N-formyl methionine-tRNA

Because of the attached formyl group (CHO), a second amino acid will react only with the carboxyl group of methionine, the correct direction for protein synthesis. In eucaryotic cells, the initiator tRNA carries a methionine group.

The next stage involves the elongation or growth of the peptide chain, which is assembled one amino acid at a time. After the initiator tRNA is attached to the mRNA codon, the elongation of the polypeptide chain involves the following steps (see Figure 30.13):

1. The next aminoacyl-tRNA enters the ribosome and becomes attached to mRNA through the hydrogen bonding of the tRNA anticodon to the mRNA codon.
2. The peptide bond between the two amino acids is formed by the transfer of the amino acid from the initial aminoacyl-tRNA to the incoming aminoacyl-tRNA. In this step, which is catalyzed by the enzyme peptidyl transferase, the carboxyl group of the first

Figure 30.13 Biosynthesis of proteins: mRNA from DNA enters and complexes with the ribosomes. tRNA carrying an amino acid (aminoacyl-tRNA) enters the ribosome and attaches to the mRNA at its complementary anticodon. The peptide chain elongates when another aminoacyl-tRNA enters the ribosome and attaches to the mRNA. The peptide bond is then formed by the transfer of the peptide chain from the initial to the incoming aminoacyl-tRNA. The sequence is repeated until a termination codon appears in mRNA.

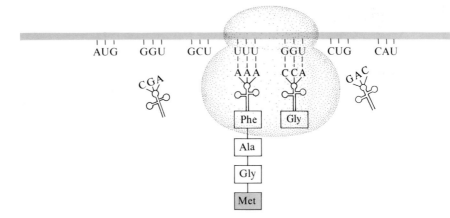

Figure 30.13 (continued)

amino acid separates from its tRNA and forms a peptide bond with the free amino group of the incoming aminoacyl-tRNA.

3. The tRNA carrying the peptide chain (now known as a peptidyl-tRNA) moves over in the ribosome, the free tRNA is ejected, and the next aminoacyl-tRNA enters the ribosome.

The peptide chain is transferred to the incoming amino acid and the sequence is repeated over and over again as the mRNA moves through the ribosome, just like a tape delivering its message. In each step the entire peptide chain is transferred to the incoming amino acid.

The initiation and elongation of polypeptide chains requires cellular energy. The primary source of this energy is the nucleotide guanosine-5′-triphosphate (GTP). At various steps in the growth of the protein chain, a high-energy GTP phosphate anhydride bond is hydrolyzed, yielding GDP and a phosphate group. The energy that is released drives protein synthesis. This reaction is analogous to that involving ATP (see Section 30.4).

The termination of the polypeptide chain occurs when a nonsense or termination codon appears. In normal cells there are no tRNA's that have complementary anticodons to the termination codons. Because there is no new aminoacyl-tRNA to bind to the ribosome, the peptidyl-tRNA is hydrolyzed, and the free polypeptide (protein) is released. All of these amazing, coordinated steps are accomplished at a high rate of speed—about 1 minute for a 150 amino acid chain in hemoglobin and 10–20 seconds for a 300–500 amino acid chain in the species of bacteria known as *Escherichia coli* (*E. coli*). This mechanism of protein synthesis is illustrated in Figure 30.13.

30.11 Mutations

It is known that from time to time a new trait appears in an individual that is not present in either parents or ancestors. These traits, which are generally the result

mutation

of genetic or chromosomal changes, are called **mutations.** Some mutations are beneficial, but most are harmful. Because mutations are genetic, they may be passed on to the next or future generations.

Mutations can occur spontaneously or can be caused by chemical agents or various types of radiation such as X-rays, cosmic rays, and ultraviolet rays. The agent that causes the mutation is called a **mutagen.** Exposure to mutagens may produce changes in the DNA of the sperm or ova. The likelihood of such changes is increased by the intensity and length of exposure to the mutagen. Mutations may then show up as birth defects in the next generation. Common types of genetic alterations include the substitution of one purine or pyrimidine for another during DNA replication. Such a substitution is a change in the genetic code and causes misinformation to be transcribed from the DNA. A mutagen also may alter genetic material by causing a chromosome or chromosome fragment to be added or removed.

mutagen

There is clear evidence that many mutagens are also carcinogens. When these chemicals alter the genome, they may also change genetic controls, causing a cell to become cancerous. Bruce Ames, an American biochemist, made use of this information to develop a sensitive and easy test for potential carcinogens. The Ames test uses specific strains of bacteria that lack some necessary enzymes due to mutation. These bacteria are exposed to a possible cancer-causing substance. If the bacteria regain their missing enzymes, the substance tested has been proven to be a mutagen. By quickly identifying mutagens, this test helps scientists recognize potential carcinogens.

The average person is exposed to many mutagens every day. Yet the frequency of mutation is relatively low. This seeming contradiction can be understood with the knowledge that each cell contains enzymes for repairing damaged DNA. For example, a simple walk on a sunny day exposes the skin cells to ultraviolet radiation, which chemically alters a few of the thymine bases in the DNA. If these changes were allowed to remain, the DNA could not be replicated correctly and a mutation would occur. Fortunately, cellular enzymes locate the damaged DNA, excise the altered thymines, and rebuild the correct nucleotide sequence. Similar repair processes are occurring continuously for most normal cells.

In some cases mutations have weakened the cellular DNA repair machinery. Patients suffering from *xeroderma pigmentosum* lack the enzyme that recognizes chemically altered thymines. For these people sunlight becomes a real danger. Exposure to only small amounts of ultraviolet radiation causes skin ulceration and eventual formation of multiple skin cancers. Although this disease occurs only rarely, it has been estimated that about 1% of all humans are carriers of these mutations.

30.12   Genetic Engineering

Almost since life first evolved, nature has had its own genetic engineers, the viruses. These small particles commonly carry only a few genes surrounded by a protein coat. Viruses are not living cells but exist as parasites within host cells. The virus invades a cell, adds its genetic material to that of the cell, and forces the cell to produce viral genes and proteins. Viruses thus continue to exist by successfully modifying the genetic material of host cells to their own benefit. Pathogenic viruses are generally hard to control because they exist within parasitized cells.

The recently discovered virus that causes the Acquired Immune Deficiency Syndrome (AIDS) acts by invading and altering the transcription of cells (lymphocytes) that are part of the body's immune system. Within the cell the virus releases viral RNA and the enzyme *reverse transcriptase*. The viral RNA is the template and the enzyme is the catalyst for the synthesis of viral DNA. Viral DNA then inserts into the cell DNA, altering cell transcription and forcing the cell to produce new viral RNA's and proteins. The cell has now lost control of its normal transcription and reproductive ability. Progressive damage to the immune system occurs as immune cells produce many new viruses and then die.

In recent years laboratory techniques for the controlled production of genetic changes have been developed. These techniques are known as *genetic engineering* and have already been responsible for considerable progress in medicine and biology. Genetic engineering holds the promise of revolutionary advances in medicine, agriculture, the manufacture of pharmaceuticals, and other fields. Using techniques similar to those used by the viruses, the genetic engineer inserts specific genes into the genome of a host cell. The host cell is thus programmed to produce new or different proteins that may benefit humankind.

Genetic engineering has been made possible by several basic advances in nucleic acid biochemistry. First, scientists have gained the ability to read and then to synthesize specific genetic messages. In addition, many genomes can be broken apart and specific genes isolated.

Second, special enzymes, the *restriction endonucleases*, were discovered. These enzymes split double-stranded DNA at very specific locations. Often the newly formed break has what is termed "sticky ends"; that is, one end of the break can stick to the end of another break via hydrogen bonding between complementary bases.

It was also discovered that a gene from another genome could be processed to have matching sticky ends. With the aid of other enzymes (ligases), the sticky ends of the broken DNA chain can be bonded to the sticky ends of the gene. The resultant modified and repaired DNA chain now contains a new gene. Thus, a new gene can be added to the genome. The product of this addition is a form of recombinant DNA. The term **recombinant DNA** refers to DNA whose genes have been rearranged to contain new or different hereditary information. The process of gene addition to DNA is shown as a diagram in Figure 30.14.

recombinant DNA

Genetic engineering is progressing in a variety of areas. Bacteria have been modified to produce proteins that are relatively scarce. Human insulin and human growth hormone are now synthesized by microorganisms. Bovine rennin, an enzyme needed in large amounts during cheese production, is now partially supplied by genetically modified bacteria.

Presently, natural proteins can be altered to improve specific properties by genetic engineering. For example, the proteolytic enzymes used in detergents are being modified to improve their stability when exposed to bleach and high pH

(a) Breaking DNA chain

(b) Adding or splicing in a new chain

Figure 30.14 Schematic diagram showing (a) breaking of double-stranded DNA chain to obtain "sticky ends" and (b) adding or splicing in a new gene previously processed to have matching sticky ends: Only the nitrogen bases involved in the sticky ends are shown.

(conditions that often exist during a laundry cycle). Lipid digestive enzymes (lipases) are being modified to convert inexpensive oils into the more expensive triacylglycerols.

Genetic engineering is also used to alter the properties of living organisms. An immunity to specific weed killers is being incorporated into plants of commercial importance in order to aid growers. Organisms are being developed that can metabolize and therefore clean up toxic wastes. Thus, in the future it is likely that genetic engineering will have a major impact on our way of life.

QUESTIONS

A. *Review the meanings of the new terms introduced in this chapter.*

1. Nucleoprotein
2. Nucleic acid
3. Nucleoside
4. Nucleotide
5. Ribonucleic acid (RNA)
6. Deoxyribonucleic acid (DNA)
7. Genome
8. Genes
9. Mitosis
10. Meiosis
11. Transcription
12. Codon
13. Translation
14. Mutation
15. Mutagen
16. Recombinant DNA

B. *Review questions*

1. Write the names and structural formulas for the five nitrogen bases found in nucleotides.
2. What is the difference between a nucleoside and a nucleotide?
3. Identify the compounds represented by the following letters:
   (a) A, AMP, ADP, ATP
   (b) G, GMP, GDP, GTP
4. What are the three units that make up a nucleotide?
5. Write structural formulas for the substances represented by
   (a) A   (c) ADP   (e) dGTP
   (b) AMP   (d) ATP   (f) CDP
6. What is the major function of ATP in the body?
7. What are the principal structural differences between DNA and RNA?
8. Draw the structure for a three-nucleotide segment of RNA.
9. Show by structural formulas the hydrogen bonding between adenine and uracil.
10. Briefly describe the structure of DNA as proposed by Watson and Crick.
11. What is meant by the term *complementary bases*?
12. Explain why the ratio of thymine to adenine in DNA is 1:1, but the ratio of thymine to guanine is not necessarily 1:1.
13. Why is DNA considered to be the genetic substance of life?
14. Briefly describe the process of DNA replication.
15. What is the role of DNA in the genetic process?
16. What is the genetic code?
17. Why are at least three nucleotides needed for one unit of the genetic code?
18. List the three kinds of RNA and identify the role of each.
19. What is an oncogene?
20. What is a codon? An anticodon?
21. Explain the relationship between codons and anticodons.
22. There are 146 amino acid residues in the β-polypeptide chain of hemoglobin. How many nucleotides in mRNA are needed to designate this chain. (See Figure 29.4 to review the β-chain.)
23. In RNA does the guanine content have to be equal to the cytosine content? Explain. Do they have to be equal in DNA? Explain

24. Starting with DNA, briefly outline the biosynthesis of proteins.
25. Explain the role of N-formylmethionine in procaryotic protein synthesis.
26. A segment of a DNA strand consists of GCTTAGACCTGA.
   (a) What is the nucleotide order in the complementary mRNA?
   (b) What is the anticodon order in tRNA?
   (c) What is the sequence of amino acids coded by the DNA?
27. What will the anticodon be in tRNA if the codon in mRNA is the following?
   (a) GUC   (d) UUU
   (b) ACC   (e) CCA
   (c) CGA
28. Complete hydrolysis of RNA would yield what compounds?
29. What is a mutation?
30. Why do mutations occur?
31. Briefly describe the Ames test.
32. Does DNA damage always result in a mutation? Explain.
33. Briefly list the basic steps that are often employed in genetic engineering.
34. Which of these statements are correct?
   (a) Adenine and guanine are both purine bases and are found in both DNA and RNA.
   (b) The ratio of adenine to thymine and guanine to cytosine in DNA is about 1:1.
   (c) DNA and RNA are responsible for transmitting genetic information from parent to daughter cells.
   (d) DNA is a polymer made from nucleotides.
   (e) Codons are combinations of the base units in a tRNA molecule.
   (f) The double-helix structure of DNA is held together by peptide linkages.
   (g) Amino acids are linked to tRNA by an ester bond.
   (h) The nucleotide adenosine monophosphate contains adenine, D-ribose, and a phosphate group.
   (i) The letters ATP stand for adenine triphosphate
   (j) Thymine and uracil are both complementary bases to adenine.

(k) Messenger RNA is a transcribed section of DNA.

(l) The ratio of adenine to guanine and thymine to cytosine is 1:1 in DNA.

(m) Genetic information is based on the nucleotide sequence in DNA.

(n) Humans have 46 pairs of chromosomes.

(o) In mitosis the sperm cell and the egg cell, each with 23 chromosomes, unite to give a new cell containing 46 chromosomes.

(p) The genetic code consists of triplets of nucleotides; each triplet codes an amino acid.

(q) Transfer RNA carries the code for the synthesis of proteins.

(r) ADP and ATP contain high-energy phosphate anhydride bonds.

(s) On hydrolysis, DNA yields ribose, phosphoric acid, and the bases adenine, guanine, cytosine, and thymine.

(t) DNA has a double-helix conformation, whereas all RNA's have a single-helix conformation.

31

Nutrition and Digestion

1. Understand the new terms listed in Question A at the end of the chapter.
2. Distinguish a nutrient from a food.
3. Describe the difference between a minimum dietary requirement and a recommended dietary allowance.
4. Discuss the dangers of kwashiorkor.
5. Explain why fats are a more concentrated source of metabolic energy than carbohydrates.
6. List some of the dangers of a high-sucrose diet.
7. Briefly describe the importance of dietary fiber.
8. List the essential fatty acids and essential amino acids.
9. Discuss a major danger inherent in a vegetarian diet.
10. Explain the functions of vitamins in the body.
11. State, in a general way, the results of vitamin deficiencies.
12. List the major mineral elements.
13. Compare the similarities between trace mineral elements and vitamins.
14. Briefly discuss the importance of water in the diet.
15. List four purposes served by food additives.
16. Briefly discuss food additives and their effect on nutrition.
17. List the five principal digestive juices and where they originate in the body.
18. List the principal enzymes of the various digestive juices.
19. Give the main digestive functions of each of the five principal digestive juices.

20. List the classes of products formed when carbohydrates, fats, and proteins are digested.
21. Briefly describe the absorption of nutrients from the digestive tract into the lymph and blood.
22. Discuss the role of the liver in maintaining blood glucose levels.
23. Explain how the liver metabolizes potentially toxic compounds.

31.1 Introduction

Nutrition is a science of practical importance. Every person is concerned with diet. As a child you may have heard "Finish your milk" or "Please eat your vegetables." Do you remember being told that chocolate will cause complexion problems? How many of your friends are watching their weight?

nutrients

The need for choosing the right diet has given rise to the science of nutrition, the study of nutrients—how they are digested, absorbed, metabolized, and excreted. **Nutrients** are components of the food we eat that provide for body growth, maintenance, and repair. Milk is a food, but the calcium from that milk is a nutrient. We eat meat, a food, for protein, a nutrient.

Nutritionists divide nutrients into six broad classes: (1) carbohydrates, (2) lipids, (3) proteins, (4) vitamins, (5) minerals, and (6) water. The first three classes—carbohydrates, lipids, and proteins—are the major sources of the building materials, replacement parts, and energy needs of the cells. The next three classes of nutrients—water, minerals, and vitamins—have functions other than as sources of energy or building materials. Nevertheless they have vital roles in nutrition. Water is absolutely essential to every diet, because most biochemical reactions occur in aqueous solution. Minerals are required to maintain specific concentrations of certain inorganic ions in the cellular and extracellular fluids. They are also utilized in a variety of other ways—for example, calcium and phosphorus in bones and teeth and iron in hemoglobin. Vitamins are components of some enzyme systems that are vital to the cells.

Nutrients supply the needs of the body's many different cells. For example, red blood cells must produce hemoglobin and thus need iron. Muscle cells produce muscle fibers and need much protein. As they do their jobs, cells wear out and must be replaced. Red blood cells, on an average, are renewed every six weeks, whereas the cells lining the digestive tract must be replaced every three days.

The six classes of nutrients provide the basis for a healthy diet. This chapter will describe briefly (1) the relationship between diet and nutrition, (2) some characteristics of each nutrient category, and (3) the processes by which these nutrients are digested.

31.2 Diet

diet

Diet is the food and drink that we consume. Our choice of meals determines the nutrients available to our bodies. Thus, our health depends directly on our diet.

Unfortunately, some dietary choices are not clear. Controversy surrounds many food selections. Are "fast foods" unhealthy? Should we avoid food additives? What about "natural" foods? To make an intelligent decision, we must understand the role of the food nutrients in maintaining good health.

Many nutrients are contained in each foodstuff. For example, a McDonalds' Big Mac contains 13% protein, 16% fat, and 20% carbohydrate. An order of french fries adds primarily carbohydrate (38%) with some fat (18%) and protein (4%). Such a meal might be supplemented with a chocolate shake (23% carbohydrate, 3% fat, 3% protein). These foods provide a variety of nutrients, but does this represent a healthful or an unhealthful diet?

Nutritionists face this difficult problem of deciding the kinds of nutrients that should be in a diet. They often establish dietary need by correlating physical well-being with nutrient consumption. James Lind (1716–1794), a physician in the British Navy during the middle of the 18th century, was one of the first to use this approach. In a study of scurvy, a disease that afflicted sailors on long voyages, he placed seamen who suffered from scurvy on various diets, some of which contained citrus fruits. By observing changes in the conditions of the seamen, Lind was able to conclude that citrus fruits provide a nutrient that prevents scurvy. This and later work eventually led to the requirement of limes and lemons in the diets of the British Merchant Marine (1765) and the British Navy (1795). Scurvy is now recognized as a deficiency disease caused by a lack of vitamin C, ascorbic acid.

As scientists like Lind discovered and studied more nutrients, they also found that the minimum quantities needed for good health varied from person to person. Thus, rather than establishing uniform minimum requirements, nutritionists have established a standard called the recommended dietary allowance. The **recommended dietary allowance** (RDA) for a nutrient is an average value that has been shown to maintain health for large groups of people. Although there is considerable variation in the dietary needs of individuals, RDA's are useful yardsticks in judging healthful diets. RDA's for a variety of nutrients are shown in Table 31.1.

recommended dietary allowance

31.3 Energy in the Diet

An important component of every diet is the energy allowance. Energy-supplying molecules must compensate for energy used by the body. Merely lying down and daydreaming requires about 0.1 kcal per hour per kg (kcal/hr-kg) body weight. Sitting and writing uses about 1 kcal/hr-kg, and strenuous exercise such as swimming or playing tennis may use 5 kcal/hr-kg. The dietary energy allowance will vary with activity, body size, age, and sex (see Table 31.1). Thus a 65 kg male office worker will require a diet that furnishes 2700 kcal/day, whereas a man of similar weight working as a carpenter will require about 3000 kcal/day. Women generally use less energy than men, and energy use decreases with age. [Many nutritionists still use the kilocalorie unit or its synonym, the large Calorie (Cal). Remember, there are 4.184 kilojoules per kilocalorie (or Calorie) (see Section 2.12).]

Table 31.1 Recommended daily dietary allowances[a] (revised 1980): Designed for the maintenance of good nutrition of practically all healthy people in the USA

	Age (years)	Weight (kg)	Weight (lb)	Height (cm)	Height (in)	Protein (g)	Fat-soluble vitamins Vitamin A (μg RE)[b]	Vitamin D (μg)[c]	Vitamin E (mg α-TE)[d]	Water-soluble vitamins Vitamin C (mg)	Thiamin (mg)	Riboflavin (mg)	Niacin (mg)	Vitamin B6 (mg)	Folic acid (μg)	Vitamin B12 (μg)	Minerals Ca (mg)	P (mg)	Mg (mg)	Fe (mg)	Zn (mg)	I (μg)
Infants	0.0–0.5	6	13	60	24	kg × 2.2	420	10	3	35	0.3	0.4	6	0.3	30	0.5	360	240	50	10	3	40
	0.5–1.0	9	20	71	28	kg × 2.0	400	10	4	35	0.5	0.6	8	0.6	45	1.5	540	360	70	15	5	50
Children	1–3	13	29	90	35	23	400	10	5	45	0.7	0.8	9	0.9	100	2.0	800	800	150	15	10	70
	4–6	20	44	112	44	30	500	10	6	45	0.9	1.0	11	1.3	200	2.5	800	800	200	10	10	90
	7–10	28	62	132	52	34	700	10	7	45	1.2	1.4	16	1.6	300	3.0	800	800	250	10	10	120
Males	11–14	45	99	157	62	45	1000	10	8	50	1.4	1.6	18	1.8	400	3.0	1200	1200	350	18	15	150
	15–18	66	145	176	69	56	1000	10	10	60	1.4	1.7	18	2.0	400	3.0	1200	1200	400	18	15	150
	19–22	70	154	177	70	56	1000	7.5	10	60	1.5	1.7	19	2.2	400	3.0	800	800	350	10	15	150
	23–50	70	154	178	70	56	1000	5	10	60	1.4	1.6	18	2.2	400	3.0	800	800	350	10	15	150
	51+	70	154	178	70	56	1000	5	10	60	1.2	1.4	16	2.2	400	3.0	800	800	350	10	15	150
Females	11–14	46	101	157	62	46	800	10	8	50	1.1	1.3	15	1.8	400	3.0	1200	1200	300	18	15	150
	15–18	55	120	163	64	46	800	10	8	60	1.1	1.3	14	2.0	400	3.0	1200	1200	300	18	15	150
	19–22	55	120	163	64	44	800	7.5	8	60	1.1	1.3	14	2.0	400	3.0	800	800	300	18	15	150
	23–50	55	120	163	64	44	800	5	8	60	1.0	1.2	13	2.0	400	3.0	800	800	300	18	15	150
	51+	55	120	163	64	44	800	5	8	60	1.0	1.2	13	2.0	400	3.0	800	800	300	10	15	150
Pregnant						+30	+200	+5	+2	+20	+0.4	+0.3	+2	+0.6	+400	+1.0	+400	+400	+150	—[e]	+5	+25
Lactating						+20	+400	+5	+3	+40	+0.5	+0.5	+5	+0.5	+100	+1.0	+400	+400	+150	—[e]	+10	+50

Reference: *Recommended Dietary Allowances*, 9th ed. Food and Nutrition Board, National Research Council–National Academy of Sciences, 1980.

[a] The allowances are intended to provide for individual variations among most normal persons as they live in the United States under usual environmental stresses. Diets should be based on a variety of common foods in order to provide other nutrients for which human requirements have been less well defined.

[b] Retinol equivalents. 1 retinol equivalent = 1 μg retinol or 6 μg β-carotene.

[c] As cholecalciferol. 10 μg cholecalciferol = 400 IU of vitamin D.

[d] α-Tocopherol equivalents. 1 mg α-tocopherol = 1 α-TE.

[e] The increased requirement during pregnancy cannot be met by the iron content of habitual American diets or by the existing iron stores of many women; therefore the use of 30–60 mg of supplemental iron is recommended.

The balance between energy needs and the energy allowance is of vital importance. Calorie deficiency leads to a condition called *marasmus*, which affects many of the world's poor, particularly children. Marasmus is a wasting disease due to starvation. People suffering from this disease have limited diets that often consist of bulky, carbohydrate-containing foods—for example, sweet potatoes (32% carbohydrate, 1% fat, 2% protein). These foods are not energy-rich (about 160 kcal for a medium-size sweet potato). Children, with their small stomachs, have difficulty consuming enough to satisfy their energy requirements. It is estimated that 15–20% of the people in underdeveloped countries suffer from malnutrition due to insufficient calories.

In contrast, many people in developed countries consume far more calories than they need for health and well-being. Food is available in abundance, much of it rich in energy. For example, the lunch described previously consisting of a Big Mac (563 kcal), french fries (220 kcal) and a chocolate shake (383 kcal) would supply nearly one-half of the daily energy allowance for an adult male. Excess, accumulated calories lead to a condition called *obesity*, which is characterized by an overabundance of fatty tissue and by many attendant health problems.

Each pound of body fat contains about 3500 kcal of energy, or between one and two days' total RDA for energy. Because fat contains so much energy, it is normally accumulated only slowly. Unfortunately, for the same reason, fat is also very difficult to lose. To lose 1 lb of fat, a 65 kg man would have to swim nonstop for about 10 hours, play tennis continuously for about 8 hours, or run for 4 hours. Exercise alone is generally not sufficient to cure obseity without a change in diet as well.

Thus, many people in the affluent, developed countries find it necessary to choose a restricted-calorie diet (to "diet"). The difficulties associated with selecting a restricted-calorie diet have led to the creation of numerous fad diets that fail to provide sound nutrition. Yet nutritionists counsel that successful and nutritionally sound dieting can be accomplished by following these simple guidelines: (1) Reduce calorie intake by only a moderate amount (a 500 kcal/day reduction causes a loss of 1 lb of fat per week) and be prepared to continue the diet for a long time; (2) carefully select foods so that the diet contains adequate amounts of all nutrients. The primary function of any diet is to maintain good health.

31.4 Carbohydrates in the Diet

Carbohydrates are a good source of usable, reduced carbon atoms, which makes them important sources of dietary energy. About half of the average daily calorie requirement derives from carbohydrates.

Dietary carbohydrates are primarily the polysaccharides starch and cellulose, the disaccharides lactose and sucrose, and the monosaccharides glucose and fructose. Seeds are the most common source of starch, grains being about 70% by weight starch, whereas dried peas and beans contain about 40%. A second major source of starch is tuber and root crops such as potatoes, yams, and cassava. The disaccharide lactose is an important component of milk, and sucrose is usually consumed as refined sugar (derived from sugar beets or sugar cane). The monosaccharides are often found in fruits.

The polysaccharides, also termed *complex carbohydrates*, are difficult to digest because of their complex structures (see Section 27.13). Starch is digested only slowly, enabling the body to control distribution of this energy nutrient. Cellulose is not digested by humans; however, it is a major source of *dietary fiber*. As cellulose passes through the digestive tract, it absorbs water and provides dietary bulk. This bulk acts to prevent constipation and diverticulosis, a weakening of the intestinal walls. Many nutritionists recommend a daily fiber intake of 15–30 g, supplied by such foods as whole-wheat bread (1.8 g/slice) and bran cereals (7.5 g/0.5 cup).

Although no RDA has been set for carbohydrate, many nutritionists recommend that a minimum of about 500 kcal/day be derived from this source. In the American diet most of these calories are derived from starch, although in recent years an increasing amount has been coming from sucrose.

The high sucrose content of many modern diets is due primarily to the large amounts of sucrose in commercially prepared foods. In 1900 an American consumed an average of only about 20 lb of sucrose annually in prepared foods and beverages; by 1971 this figure had risen to about 70 lb annually. This large increase was caused mainly by (1) increased consumption of prepared foods and (2) an increased percentage of sucrose added to these foods by the manufacturers in attempts to gain larger shares of the market. (It is well known that many people, especially children, have a preference for sweet foods.) Some breakfast cereals on the market today contain more than 40% sucrose!

The increase in sucrose consumption has troubled many nutritionists for several reasons. First, sucrose is a prime factor in the incidence of dental caries. Because it is readily used by oral bacteria, sucrose promotes growth of the microorganisms that cause tooth decay. Second, ingested sucrose is rapidly hydrolyzed to monosaccharides, which are promptly absorbed from the intestine, leading to a rapid increase in blood-sugar levels. Wide variations in the blood-sugar level may stress the body's hormonal system for controlling blood sugar. Finally, sucrose is said to provide "empty calories." This means that sucrose supplies metabolic energy (calories) but lacks other nutrients. Consequently, nutritionists often recommend starch over sucrose as a major source of dietary carbohydrate.

31.5 Fats in the Diet

Fat is a more concentrated source of dietary energy than carbohydrate. Not only does fat contain more carbons per unit weight than carbohydrate, but the carbons in fats are more reduced. As energy sources fats provide about 9 kcal/g, whereas carbohydrates provide only about 4 kcal/g.

Fats contribute much of the dietary energy of many foods. For example, french fries contain about 18% fat, yet this fat provides about 40% of the kilocalories in the potatoes. A cup of whole milk has 170 kcal, but only 80 kcal come from a cup of skim (nonfat) milk. Many common snack foods have a high fat content. Peanuts roasted in oil contain 50% fat. Potato chips are composed of 40% fat. Many dieters are aware that cutting out snack foods can decrease calorie intake significantly; and many nutritionists counsel that the best way to reduce calorie intake is to eat foods containing less fat.

In a diet, both the kind and the amount of fat are important. Fatty acids from meat and dairy products are relatively saturated, whereas those from plant sources are generally more unsaturated. Because there is a probable link between high consumption of saturated fats and atherosclerosis, the U. S. Department of Agriculture and other agencies concerned with nutrition have recommended that American diets should contain about equal portions of polyunsaturated and saturated fatty acids. Two ways of increasing polyunsaturated fats in the diets are: (1) cook with vegetable oils such as corn or peanut oil and (2) use soft margarine, which usually contains more unsaturated fats than hard or stick margarine or butter.

Polyunsaturated fats generally also contain three essential fatty acids—linoleic acid, linolenic acid, and arachidonic acid:

$$CH_3(CH_2)_4CH{=}CHCH_2CH{=}CH(CH_2)_7CO_2H$$
Linoleic acid

$$CH_3CH_2CH{=}CHCH_2CH{=}CHCH_2CH{=}CH(CH_2)_7CO_2H$$
Linolenic acid

$$CH_3(CH_2)_4CH{=}CHCH_2CH{=}CHCH_2CH{=}CHCH_2CH{=}CH(CH_2)_3CO_2H$$
Arachidonic acid

Each of these nutrients has been shown to relieve the deleterious physiological changes, such as poor growth, skin lesions, kidney damage, and impaired fertility, that result from a totally fat-free diet. One essential biochemical function of these fatty acids is as precursors for prostaglandin synthesis.

31.6 Proteins in the Diet

The third energy-supplying nutrient is protein. The average energy yield is about 4.2 kcal/g protein. This energy is mostly derived from reduced carbons.

Unlike carbohydrates and fats (excluding the essential fatty acids), a specific RDA has been established for dietary protein (see Table 31.1). This nutrient is vital because it provides most of the nitrogen used in cellular synthesis. All enzymes, structural proteins (such as connective tissue and muscle fiber), and nucleic acids contain nitrogen. Because production of these materials is critical for human growth, protein malnutrition, or *kwashiorkor*, is a particularly serious problem.

Kwashiorkor can occur even when calorie intake is sufficient and, thus, is an especially insidious form of malnutrition. In many poverty-ridden areas of the world, the only reliable source of protein for children is mother's milk. After weaning, the children eat a protein-poor grain diet. Although the calorie intake is sufficient, these children show the stunted growth, poor disease resistance, and general body wasting that are charcteristic of kwashiorkor.

Table 31.2 Common dietary amino acids

Essential	*Nonessential*
Isoleucine	Alanine
Leucine	Arginine
Lysine	Asparagine
Methionine	Aspartic acid
Phenylalanine	Cysteine
Threonine	Glutamic acid
Tryptophan	Glutamine
Valine	Glycine
	Histidine
	Proline
	Serine
	Tyrosine

Proteins are obtained from animal sources such as meat, milk, cheese, and eggs, and from plant sources such as cereals, nuts, and legumes (peas, beans, and soybeans). Animal proteins have nutritive values that are generally superior to those of vegetable proteins in that they supply all of the 20 amino acids that the body uses. In contrast, a single vegetable source often will lack several amino acids. This deficiency is critical, because humans cannot synthesize the group of amino acids called the *essential amino acids* (see Section 29.3; Table 31.2). The eight essential amino acids must be obtained from the diet.

complete protein

Nutritionists often speak of a dietary source (or sources) of complete protein. A **complete protein** is one that supplies all of the essential amino acids. Animal products are, in general, sources of complete proteins. However, by either choice or necessity, animal protein is seldom consumed by a significant fraction of the world's population. Besides the moral, ethical, and religious reasons given for limiting consumption of animal protein, these proteins are relatively expensive sources of amino acids. Thus, most of the people of the underdeveloped countries subsist primarily on vegetable protein. A constant danger inherent in a vegetarian diet is that the source of vegetable protein may be deficient in several of the essential amino acids; that is, the protein may be incomplete. For this reason nutritionists recommend that several sources of vegetable protein be included with each meal in a vegetarian diet. As an example, soybeans, which are rich in lysine, might supplement wheat, which is lysine-deficient.

31.7 Vitamins

vitamins

Vitamins are a group of naturally occurring organic compounds that are essential for good nutrition. Animals maintained on a diet of proteins, fats, carbohydrates, and the necessary minerals and water are not able to sustain life. Although vitamins are required in only minute amounts, normal nutrition, growth, and development are not possible without them. The minimum daily adult requirement may be as much as 100 mg for some vitamins and as little as 0.1 μg for others. The human body is unable to synthesize these substances and is dependent on their being supplied in the diet. A substance that functions as a vitamin for one speices does not necessarily function as a vitamin for another species.

A prolonged lack of vitamins in the diet leads to vitamin-deficiency diseases such as beriberi, pellagra, pernicious anemia, rickets, and scurvy. Some of these diseases can be corrected by feeding supplementary amounts of vitamins. However, impaired growth due to a vitamin deficiency may be irreversible. For example, it is difficult to correct the distorted bone structures resulting from a childhood lack of vitamin D. Thus, it is especially important that children receive sufficient vitamins for proper growth and development.

The chemical composition of vitamins varies greatly; some are relatively simple substances, whereas others are extremely complex. On the basis of their solubility, vitamins are generally divided into two groups: fat-soluble and water-soluble. The fat-soluble vitamins include A, D, E, and K. Those classified as water-soluble are vitamin C and the B complex; the latter includes about a

Table 31.3 **Some of the most important vitamins: Alternate names are given in parentheses**

Vitamin	Important dietary sources	Some deficiency symptoms
Vitamin A (Retinol)	Green and yellow vegetables, butter, eggs, nuts, cheese, fish liver oil	Poor teeth and gums, night blindness
Vitamin B_1 (Thiamin)	Meat, whole-grain cereals, liver, yeast, nuts	Beriberi (nervous system disorders, heart disease, fatigue)
Vitamin B_2 (Riboflavin)	Meat, cheese, eggs, fish, meat products, liver	Sores on the tongue and lips, bloodshot eyes, anemia
Vitamin B_6 (Pyridoxine)	Cereals, liver, meat, fresh vegetables	Skin disorders (dermatitis)
Vitamin B_{12} (Cyanocobalamin)	Meat, eggs, liver, milk	Pernicious anemia
Vitamin C (Ascorbic acid)	Citrus fruits, tomatoes, green vegetables	Scurvy (bleeding gums, loose teeth, swollen joints, slow healing of wounds, weight loss)
Vitamin D (Ergocalciferol, D_2; cholecalciferol, D_3)	Egg yolk, milk, fish liver oils; formed from provitamin in the skin when exposed to sunlight	Rickets (low blood-calcium level, soft bones, distorted skeletal structure)
Vitamin E (α-Tocopherol)	Meat, egg yolk, wheat germ oil, green vegetables; widely distributed in foods	Not definitely known in humans
Vitamin K (Phylloquinone, K_1; menaquinone, K_2)	Eggs, liver, green vegetables; produced in the intestines by bacterial reactions	Blood is slow to clot (antihemorrhagic vitamin)
Niacin (Nicotinic acid and amide)	Meat, yeast, whole wheat	Pellagra (dermatitis, diarrhea, mental disorders)
Biotin (Vitamin H)	Liver, yeast, egg yolk	Skin disorders (dermatitis)
Folic acid	Liver extract, wheat germ, yeast, green leaves	Macrocytic anemia, gastrointestinal disorders

dozen different compounds. Table 31.3 lists some of the important vitamins, their main food sources, and deficiency symptoms. The structural formulas of several vitamins are shown in Figure 31.1.

Scientists do not yet completely understand the actions of vitamins. Some vitamins are converted to coenzymes. For example, the B-complex vitamins (riboflavin, niacin, thiamin, and pantothenic acid) form coenzymes that function in carbohydrate and lipid metabolism. But vitamins also serve other biological roles. Vitamin D acts as a regulator of calcium metabolism, and one function of vitamin A is to furnish the pigment that makes vision possible.

Because many vitamin functions are not well understood, miraculous properties are often ascribed to some of these substances, such as vitamins C and E. In

Vitamin A
(Retinol)

Vitamin B$_1$
(Thiamin)

Vitamin K$_1$
(Phylloquinone)

Vitamin C
(Ascorbic acid)

Vitamin E
(α-Tocopherol)

Vitamin D
(Ergocalciferol, D$_2$)

Figure 31.1   The structures of selected vitamins

the absence of conclusive scientific studies, it is difficult to judge the merits of some of these claims.

Although vitamins are required only in small quantities, their natural availability is also low. Nutritionists caution that a diet should be balanced to include adequate sources of vitamins. As you can see from Table 31.3, the dietary sources of vitamins are varied. In general, fruits, vegetables, and meats are rich sources of the water-soluble vitamins; and eggs, milk products, and liver are good sources of the fat-soluble vitamins.

A seemingly balanced diet may be deficient in vitamins due to losses incurred in food processing, storing, and cooking. As much as 50–60% of the water-soluble vitamins in vegetables can be lost during cooking. Vitamin C, for example, can be destroyed by exposure to air. Removal of the outside hull from grains drastically decreases their B-complex content. Thus, when polished rice became a dietary staple in the Orient, beriberi (the thiamin-deficiency disease) grew to epidemic proportions.

31.8　Minerals

A number of inorganic ions are needed in the diet for good health. Those that must be ingested in relatively large amounts, the *major elements*, include sodium, potassium, chloride, calcium, magnesium, and phosphate (phosphorus). Elements in a second group, the *trace elements*, are required in only small amounts. As scientific studies of the body's mineral requirements proceed, the list of needed trace elements constantly lengthens. A recent compilation of these trace elements is given in Table 31.4.

Mineral nutrients differ from organic nutrients in that the body, in general, uses minerals in the ionic form in which they are absorbed. Although these elements are required for good health, they can also be toxic if ingested in quantities that are too large. Nutritionists have established RDA's for some of these minerals and warn against excess intake.

The major minerals—sodium, potassium, and chloride—are responsible for maintaining the appropriate salt levels in body fluids. Many enzyme reactions require an optimum salt concentration of 0.1 to 0.3 M. In addition, individual elements serve specific functions; nerve transmission, for example, requires a supply of extracellular sodium and intracellular potassium. Although there is no RDA for these two elements, 2–4 g/day represent an average NaCl consumption. But because high levels of NaCl can contribute to high blood pressure, many nutritionists advise using salt in moderation.

Calcium and magnesium serve many roles in the body, including being required by some enzymes. Fully 99% of all body calcium and an important percentage of the magnesium are found in the bones and teeth. Calcium also is needed for nerve transmission and blood clotting.

Trace elements are similar to vitamins in that (1) they are required in small amounts and (2) food contains only minute quantities of them. Usually a normal diet contains adequate quantities of all trace elements. The exact function of many trace elements remains unknown.

Table 31.4   Essential trace elements

Element	Function	Human deficiency signs
Fluorine	Structure of teeth, possibly of bones; possible growth effect	Increased incidence of caries; possibly risk factor for osteoporosis
Silicon	Calcification; possible function in connective tissue	Not known
Vanadium	Not known	Not known
Chromium	For efficient use of insulin	Relative insulin resistance, impaired glucose tolerance, elevated serum lipids
Manganese	Mucopolysaccharide metabolism, superoxide dismutase enzyme	Not known
Iron	Oxygen and electron transport	Anemia
Cobalt	Part of vitamin B_{12}	Only as vitamin B_{12} deficiency
Nickel	Interaction with iron absorption	Not known
Copper	Oxidative enzymes; interaction with iron; cross-linking of elastin connective protein	Anemia, changes of ossification; possibly elevated serum cholesterol
Zinc	Numerous enzymes involved in energy metabolism and in transcription and translation	Growth depression, sexual immaturity, skin lesions, depression of immunocompetence, change of taste acuity
Arsenic	Not known	Not known
Selenium	Glutathione peroxidase; interaction with heavy metals	Endemic heart problems conditioned by selenium deficiency
Molybdenum	Xanthine, aldehyde and sulfide oxidase enzymes	Not known
Iodine	Constituent of thyroid hormones	Goiter, depression of thyroid function, cretinism

The most notable exception to the foregoing generalizations is iron. This element is part of hemoglobin, the oxygen-binding protein of the blood. (Iron is also a critical component of some enzymes.) Relatively large amounts of iron are required for hemoglobin replenishment. Unfortunately, many foods are not rich enough in iron to provide the necessary RDA. This is especially true for the higher iron RDA for women. Therefore nutritionists sometimes recommend a daily iron dietary supplement.

31.9 Water

Water is the solvent of life. As such it carries nutrients to the cells, allows biochemical reactions to proceed, and carries waste from the cells. Water makes up approximately 55–60% of the total body weight.

Our bodies are constantly losing water via urine (700–1400 mL/day), feces (150 mL/day), sweat (500–900 mL/day), and expired air (400 mL/day). If dehydration is to be prevented, this water output must be offset by water intake. In the normal diet, liquids provide about 1200–1500 mL of water per day. The remaining increment is derived from food (700–1000 mL/day) and water formed by biochemical reactions (metabolic water; 200–300 mL/day). Water losses vary and depend on the intake and the activity of the individual.

A proper water balance is maintained by control of water intake and water excretion. The kidney is the center for control of water output. Water intake is controlled by the thirst sensation. We feel thirsty when one or both of the two following events occurs: (1) As the body's water stores are depleted, the salt concentration rises. Specific brain cells monitor this salinity and initiate the thirst feeling. (2) As water is drawn away from the salivary glands, the mouth feels dry; this event also leads to the sensation of thirst.

31.10 Processed Foods

Nearly all of the foods available in a supermarket today have been processed to varying degrees. The processing may be very extensive with items such as luncheon meats, TV dinners, breakfast cereals, and so on. Loss of nutrients is a common risk associated with processing.

The short history of flour milling is an apt illustration of the risks of too much processing: In 1840 bread had a rough consistency and the color characteristic of stone-ground wheat flour. Over the years vast improvements in milling technology were made. In 1940 bread had a soft, smooth consistency and the white color characteristic of flour made from only the starchy portion of wheat. Consumers generally preferred this bread over the coarse and sometimes gritty product of previous centuries. It was discovered about this time (1940) that the bread had a very low vitamin content and needed vitamin enrichment. Furthermore, in the early 1970s, it was found that the amount of dietary fiber in bread can be greatly increased by less-selective milling of the wheat. Excessive processing or milling of the wheat had decreased the nutritive value of bread. The most nutritious bread being baked today is very similar to that made from the minimally processed flour of 1840.

Advocates of "natural," "organic," or "health" foods argue that foods should be minimally affected by modern technology to ensure maximum nutrition. They correctly point out the dangers of nutrient loss during food processing. Yet in the eyes of many consumers in today's busy world, the convenience of ready-prepared foods greatly outweighs any possible nutritional risks associated with their use.

Nutritionists have faced this dilemma by establishing procedures for monitoring nutritional values of processed foods. If a food contains an added nutrient (as do most processed foods) or if a food makes a nutritional claim, then the package must contain a nutritional-information panel using the following format:

—Serving or portion size
—Servings or portions per container
—Calorie content per serving
—Protein, grams per serving
—Carbohydrate, grams per serving
—Fat, grams per serving
—Proteins, vitamins, and minerals as percentages of the USRDA.

By using this information, together with a basic knowledge of the nutrients needed for good health, the consumer can make educated choices among processed foods.

31.11   Food Additives

Various substances or chemicals may be added to foods during processing. In fact, more than 3000 of these *food additives* have been given the "generally recognized as safe" (GRAS) rating by the U.S. Food and Drug Administration.

The purpose of these food additives varies. Some additives enhance the nutritional value of a food, such as when a food is vitamin-enriched. Other additives serve as preservatives. For example, sodium benzoate is used to inhibit bacterial growth. BHA (butylated hydroxyanisole) and BHT (butylated hydroxytoluene) are used as antioxidants. Still other additives may be used to improve the appearance and flavor of a food—for example, emulsifiers, thickeners, anticaking agents, flavors, flavor enhancers, nonsugar sweeteners, and colors (see Table 31.5).

There has been and continues to be a great deal of controversy concerning the use of food additives. Due to the nature and complexity of the subject, there is no doubt that this debate will continue into the forseeable future. Controversy centers around the problem of balancing the benefit derived from an additive against the risk to consumers. The use of at least some additives is a necessity in the preparation of many foods. To discover that there is a risk and to assess the degree of risk for an additive requires long, difficult, and expensive research. As a case in point, salting and smoking were used in curing meats for centuries

Table 31.5   Some common food additives

Food additive	Purpose
Sodium benzoate Calcium lactate Sorbic acid	Prevention of food spoilage (antimicrobials)
BHA (Butylated hydroxyanisole) BHT (Butylated hydroxytoluene) EDTA (Ethylenediaminetetraacetic acid)	Prevention of changes in color and flavor (antioxidants)
Calcium silicate Silicon dioxide Sodium silicoaluminate	Keeps powders and salts free-flowing (anticaking agents)
Carrageenan Lecithin	Aids even distribution of suspended particles (emulsifiers)
Pectin Propylene glycol	Imparts body and texture (thickeners)
MSG (Monosodium glutamate) Hydrolyzed vegetable protein	Supplements or modifies taste (flavor enhancers)

before there was any knowledge that these processes might involve a hazard. Research has shown that both processes involve risks to at least some consumers: Salt aggravates certain cardiovascular conditions, and smoke produces carcinogens in the meat. Yet in the eyes of many consumers, these risks are outweighed by the benefits to be had from salted and smoked meats. On the other hand, there would be few consumers, indeed, who would wish to have a compound known to be very carcinogenic used as an additive in their ice cream, even though that compound could improve the flavor of the ice cream remarkably!

Owing to the technical nature of the task, the consumer must rely largely on the judgment and integrity of the professional people who have been assigned the responsibility of protecting our food supply. Consumers also should (1) inform themselves as fully as possible concerning the nature, purpose, and possible hazards of the additives that are used or proposed for us in our foods and (2) as responsible citizens make sure that our government provides adequate support to professionals charged with protecting our food.

31.12 A Balanced Diet

To summarize the preceding sections, carbohydrates, fats, and proteins are a major group of nutrients in our diets. These nutrients supply the molecules that are needed for energy, growth, and maintenance. A typical adult diet includes about 100–200 g each of carbohydrate, fat, and protein daily.

A second group of nutrients—vitamins, minerals, and water—is not used for energy but is nevertheless essential to our existence. Vitamins provide organic molecules that cannot be made in the body; and minerals provide the inorganic ions needed for life. Water is the solvent in which most of the chemical reactions essential to life occur. Vitamins and minerals are required only in small amounts, from a few micrograms to a few milligrams per day. But water must be consumed in large quantities, two to three liters per day.

For health and well-being, each of six groups of nutrients must be in our diet to satisfy the RDA's given in Table 31.1. With the variety of foods that are available, how can we make sure that our diets contain enough of all the needed nutrients? The answer "Eat a balanced diet" leads to another question, "How can we make sure that our diet is balanced?"

To answer this question, nutritionists have divided foods into six groups: (1) milk products, (2) vegetables, (3) fruits, (4) cereal products, (5) meats, and (6) fatty foods. Each group is a good source of one or more nutrients. To obtain a balanced mixture of carbohydrate, fat, and protein, a diet should contain food from several classes. A balanced diet also will assure an adequate supply of essential minerals and vitamins.

A balanced diet must include several food groups, even though each food may contain many nutrients. For example, compare the three breakfasts in Figure 31.2, each of which supplies about 600 kcal of food energy. By choosing only doughnuts (cereal food group) and coffee, the consumer would gain some

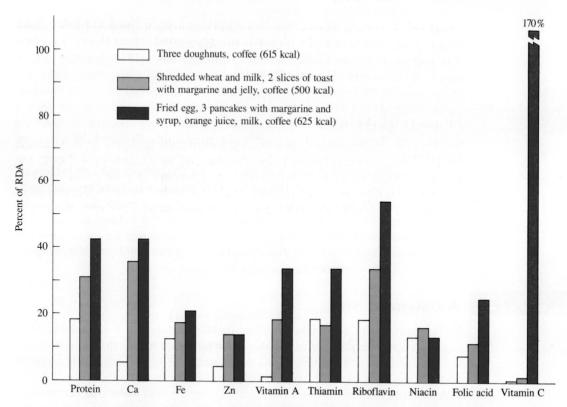

Figure 31.2 A comparison of nutritional values for three breakfasts: (No RDA has been established for carbohydrates and fats.)

nutrients but only in small quantities. A breakfast of cold cereal (cereal group) and milk (milk group), toast (cereal group) with margarine (fatty food group) and jelly, and coffee includes more food groups. Still more food groups are found in a breakfast of orange juice (fruit group), a fried egg (meat group), pancakes (cereal group) with margarine (fatty food group) and syrup, milk (milk group) and coffee. Many other breakfast could be chosen instead, yet an important generalization can be drawn from these three examples: The nutritional value of a meal improves if at least several food groups are included. The third breakfast in this illustration is the most balanced and provides the best nutrition. Although the consumer often does not know the nutrient content of a specific food, overall nutrition can be ensured by choosing a balanced diet.

After the food comprising a balanced diet is eaten, it must be digested, absorbed, and transported in order for the proper nutrients to reach the cells. Eating puts food into the alimentary canal (which includes the mouth, esophagus, stomach, small intestine, and large intestine). In a sense this canal is an extension of our external environment; that is, until food is broken down and processed, it cannot enter our internal environment to reach the cells. After digestion and absorption, the nutrients are transported to the cells by the blood and lymph systems. The liver has a vital role in controlling nutrient levels in the blood and neutralizing toxic substances.

31.13   Human Digestion

digestion

The human digestive tract is shown diagrammatically in Figure 31.3. Although food is broken up mechanically by chewing and by a churning action in the stomach, digestion is a chemical process. **Digestion** is a series of enzyme-catalyzed reactions by which large molecules are hydrolyzed to molecules small enough to be absorbed through the intestinal membranes. Foods are digested to

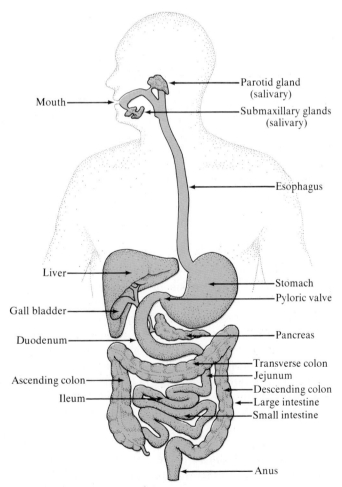

Figure 31.3   The human digestive tract

smaller molecules according to this general scheme:

Carbohydrates $\longrightarrow$ Monosaccharides

$$\text{Fats} \longrightarrow \begin{cases} \text{Fatty acids} \\ \text{Glycerol} \\ \text{Mono- and diesters of glycerol} \end{cases}$$

$$\text{Proteins} \longrightarrow \begin{cases} \text{Amino acids} \\ \text{Dipeptides} \\ \text{Tripeptides} \end{cases}$$

Food passes through the human digestive tract in this sequence:

Mouth $\longrightarrow$ Esophagus $\longrightarrow$ stomach $\longrightarrow$ small intestine (duodenum, jejunum, and ileum) $\longrightarrow$ large intestine (see Figure 31.3).

Five principal digestive juices (or fluids) enter the digestive tract at various points:

1. Saliva from three pairs of salivary glands in the mouth
2. Gastric juice from glands in the walls of the stomach
3. Pancreatic juice, which is secreted by the pancreas and enters the duodenum through the pancreatic duct
4. Bile, which is secreted by the liver and enters the duodenum via a duct from the gall bladder
5. Intestinal juice from intestinal mucosal cells

The main functions and principal enzymes found in each of these fluids are summarized in Table 31.6. The important digestive enzymes occur in gastric, pancreatic, and intestinal juices. An outline of the digestive process follows. (Detailed accounts of the various stages of digestion are to be found in biochemistry and physiology texts.)

Salivary digestion.   Food is chewed (masticated) and mixed with saliva in the mouth, and the hydrolysis of starch begins. The composition of saliva depends on many factors—age, diet, condition of teeth, time of day, and so on. Normal saliva is about 99.5% water. Saliva also contains mucin (a glycoprotein); a number of mineral ions such as K^+, Ca^{2+}, Cl^-, PO_4^{3-}, SCN^-; and one enzyme, salivary amylase (ptyalin). The pH of saliva ranges from slightly acidic to slightly basic, with the optimum pH about 6.6–6.8.

Mucin acts as a lubricant and facilitates the chewing and swallowing of food. The enzyme salivary amylase catalyzes the hydrolysis of starch to maltose:

$$\text{Starch} + \text{Water} \xrightarrow{\text{Salivary amylase}} \text{Maltose}$$

Salivary amylase is inactivated at a pH of 4.0, so it has very little time to act before the food reaches the highly acidic stomach juices.

Saliva is secreted continuously, but the rate of secretion is greatly increased by the sight and odor, or even the thought, of many foods. The mouth-watering

Table 31.6 Digestive fluids

Fluid (volume produced daily)	Source	Principal enzymes and/or function
Saliva (1000–1500 mL)	Salivary glands	Lubricant, aids chewing and swallowing; also contains salivary amylase (ptyalin), which begins the digestion of starch
Gastric juice (2000–3000 mL)	Glands in stomach wall	Pepsin, gastric lipase; pepsin catalyzes partial hydrolysis of proteins to proteoses and peptones in the stomach
Pancreatic juice (500–800 mL)	Pancreas	Trypsinogen, chymotrypsinogen, procarboxypeptidase (converted after secretion to trypsin, chymotrypsin, and carboxypeptidase, respectively, which continue protein digestion); amylopsin (α-amylase, a starch-digestive enzyme), steapsin (a lipase)
Bile (500–1000 mL)	Liver	Contains no enzymes; but contains bile salts, which aid digestion by emulsifying lipids; serves to excrete cholesterol and bile pigments derived from hemoglobin
Intestinal juice	Intestinal mucosal cells	Contains a variety of finishing enzymes: sucrase, maltase, and lactase for carbohydrates; aminopolypeptidase and dipeptidase for final protein breakdown; intestinal lipase; nucleases and phosphatase for hydrolysis of nucleic acids

effect of the sight or thought of pickles is familiar to most of us. This is an example of a *conditioned reflex.*

Gastric digestion. When food is swallowed, it passes through the esophagus to the stomach. In the stomach, mechanical action continues; food particles are reduced in size and are mixed with gastric juices until a material of liquid consistency, known as *chyme*, is obtained.

Gastric juice is a clear, pale yellow, acidic fluid having a pH of about 1.5–2.5. It contains hydrochloric acid; the mineral ions Na^+, K^+, Cl^-, and some phosphates; and the digestive enzymes pepsin and lipase. The flow of gastric juice is accelerated by conditioned reflexes and by the presence of food in the stomach. The secretion of the hormone *gastrin* is triggered by food entering the stomach. This hormone, which is produced by the gastric glands, is absorbed into the bloodstream and returned to the stomach wall where it stimulates the secretion of additional gastric juice. Control of gastric secretion by this hormone is an example of one of the many chemical control systems that exist in the body.

The chief digestive function of the stomach is the partial digestion of protein. The principal enzyme of gastric juice is pepsin, which digests protein. The enzyme is secreted in an inactive form called pepsinogen, which is activated by hydrochloric acid to pepsin. Pepsin catalyzes the hydrolysis of proteins to fragments called proteoses and peptones, which are still fairly large molecules. Pepsin splits the peptide bonds adjacent to only a few amino acid residues, particularly tyrosine and phenylalanine:

$$\text{Protein} + \text{Water} \xrightarrow{\text{Pepsin}} \text{Proteoses} + \text{Peptones}$$

The second enzyme in the stomach, gastric lipase, is a fat-digesting enzyme. Its action in the stomach is slight because the acidity is too high for lipase activity. Food may be retained in the stomach for as long as six hours. It then passes through the pyloric valve into the duodenum.

Intestinal digestion.   The next section of the digestive tract, the small intestine, is where most of the digestion occurs. The stomach contents are first made alkaline by secretions from the pancreatic and bile ducts. The pH of the pancreatic juice is 7.5–8.0, and the pH of bile is 7.1–7.7. The shift in pH is necessary because the enzymes of the pancreatic and intestinal juices are active only in an alkaline medium. Enzymes that digest all three kinds of food—carbohydrates, fats, and proteins—are secreted by the pancreas. Pancreatic secretion is stimulated by hormones that are secreted into the bloodstream by the duodenum and the jejunum.

The enzymes occurring in the small intestine include pancreatic amylases (diastase) that hydrolyze most of the starch to maltose, and carbohydrases (α-amylase, maltase, sucrase, and lactase) that complete the hydrolysis of disaccharides to monosaccharides. The proteolytic enzymes trypsin and chymotrypsin attack proteins, proteoses, and peptones, hydrolyzing them to dipeptides. Then the peptidases—carboxypeptidase, aminopeptidase, and dipeptidase—complete the hydrolysis of proteins to amino acids. Pancreatic lipases catalyze the hydrolysis of almost all fats. Fats are split into fatty acids, glycerol, and mono- and diesters of glycerol by these enzymes.

The liver is another important organ in the digestive system. A fluid known as bile is produced by the liver and stored in the gall bladder, a small organ located on the surface of the liver. When food enters the duodenum, the gall bladder contracts, and the bile enters the duodenum through a duct that is also used by the pancreatic juice. In addition to water, the major constituents of the bile are bile acids (as salts), bile pigments, inorganic salts, and cholesterol. The bile acids are steroid monocarboxylic acids, two of which are shown below:

Cholic acid

Chenodeoxycholic acid

The bile acids are synthesized in the liver from cholesterol, which is also synthesized in the liver. The presence of bile in the intestine is important for the digestion and absorption of fats. When released into the duodenum, the bile acids emulsify the fats, allowing them to be hydrolyzed by the pancreatic lipases. About 90% of the bile salts are reabsorbed in the lower part of the small intestine and are transported back to the liver and used again.

Most of the digested food is absorbed from the small intestine. Undigested and indigestible material passes from the small intestine to the large intestine, where it is retained for varying periods of time before final elimination as feces. Additional chemical breakdown, sometimes with the production of considerable amounts of gases, is brought about by bacteria (or rather by bacterial enzymes) in the large intestine. For a healthy person this additional breakdown is not important from the standpoint of nutrition since absorption of nutrients does not occur from the large intestine. However, large amounts of water, partly from digestive juices, are absorbed from the large intestine so that the contents become more solid before elimination.

31.14 Absorption

absorption

For digested food to be utilized in the body, it must pass from the intestine into the blood and lymph systems. The process by which digested foods pass through the membrane linings of the small intestine and enter the blood and lymph is called **absorption**. Absorption is complicated, and we shall consider only an overview of it.

After the food you have eaten is digested, the body must absorb billions upon billions of nutrient molecules into the bloodstream. The absorption system is in the membranes of the small intestine, which, upon microscopic inspection, are seen to be wrinkled into hundreds of folds. These folds are covered with thousands of small projections called *villi*. Each projection is itself covered by many minute folds called *microvilli*. The small intestine's wrinkles, folds, and projections increase the surface area available for absorption. The average small intestine is about 4 meters (13.3 ft) long and is estimated to contain about 8360 square meters (90,000 sq ft) of absorbing surface.

The inner surface of the small intestine is composed of mucosal cells that produce many enzymes, such as disaccharidases, aminopeptidases, and dipeptidases, needed to complete the digestive process. As digestion is completed, the resulting nutrient molecules are absorbed by the mucosal cells and transferred to the blood and lymph systems. Water-soluble nutrients such as monosaccharides, glycerol, short-chain fatty acids, amino acids, and minerals enter directly into the bloodstream. Fat-soluble nutrients such as long-chain fatty acids and monoacylglycerols first enter the lymph fluid and then enter the bloodstream where the two fluids come together.

An important factor in the absorption process is that the membranes of the intestine are selectively permeable; that is, they prevent the passage of most large molecules but allow the passage of smaller molecules. For example, polysaccharides, disaccharides, and proteins are not ordinarily absorbed, but generally monosaccharides and amino acids are.

31.15   Liver Function

The liver is the largest organ in the body and performs several vital functions. Two of these functions are (1) the regulation of the concentrations of organic nutrients in the blood and (2) the removal of toxic substances from the blood.

The concentration of blood sugar (glucose) is controlled and maintained by processes that occur in the liver. After absorption, excess glucose and other monosaccharides are removed from the blood and converted to glycogen in the liver. The liver is the principal storage organ for glycogen. As glucose is used in other cells, the stored liver glycogen is gradually hydrolyzed to maintain the appropriate blood-glucose concentration. Liver function is under sensitive hormonal control, as are most vital body functions. This regulation will be discussed further in Chapter 33.

A second major function of the liver is the detoxification of harmful and potentially harmful substances. This function apparently developed as higher vertebrates appeared in the evolutionary time scale. The liver is able to deal with most of the toxic molecules that occur in nature. For example, ethanol is oxidized in the liver and nitrogenous metabolic waste products are converted to urea for excretion.

Organic chemists have learned to synthesize new substances that have no counterparts in the biological world. They are used as industrial chemicals, insecticides, drugs, and food additives. When these potentially toxic substances are ingested, even in small amounts, the body is faced with the difficult challenge of metabolizing or destroying substances that are unlike any found in nature.

The liver is actually able to meet this challenge and deal with most of these foreign molecules through an oxidation system located on the endoplasmic reticulum. Bound to these intracellular membranes are enzymes that can catalyze reactions between oxygen and the foreign molecules. As these molecules are oxidized, they become more polar and water-soluble. Finally, the oxidation products of the potential toxins are excreted in the urine or bile fluid.

For example, most automobile antifreeze solutions contain ethylene glycol, a toxic substance. Even though this compound does not occur naturally, the liver can metabolize ethylene glycol. When small amounts are ingested accidentally, the following chemical changes occur:

Thus ethylene glycol is converted by oxidation to two more polar (charged) acid anions that are easily eliminated from the body.

Unfortunately oxidation is not effective for some compounds. Halogenated hydrocarbons, which are particularly inert to oxidation, accumulate in fatty tissue or in the liver itself. Examples of halogenated hydrocarbons are carbon tetrachloride, hexachlorobenzene, DDT, dioxins, and polychlorinated biphenyls (PCB's). Some compounds become more toxic after oxidation. For example, polycyclic hydrocarbons (which can be formed when food is barbecued) become carcinogenic upon partial oxidation. Methanol becomes particularly toxic because it is converted by oxidation to formaldehyde. One of the most serious dangers of environmental pollution lies in the introduction of compounds that the liver cannot detoxify.

In a sense the liver is the final guardian along the pathway by which nutrients pass to the cells. This pathway starts with a balanced diet. Once foods are digested and absorbed, the liver adjusts nutrient levels and removes potential toxins. The blood can then provide nutrients for the cellular biochemistry that constitutes life.

QUESTIONS

A. *Review the meanings of the new terms introduced in this chapter.*

1. Nutrients
2. Diet
3. Recommended dietary allowance
4. Complete protein
5. Vitamins
6. Digestion
7. Absorption

B. *Review questions*

1. Milk is a food. List four nutrients that can be obtained from milk.
2. List the three classes of nutrients that do *not* commonly supply energy for the cell.
3. What is meant by the term *energy allowance*?
4. How does marasmus differ from kwashiorkor?
5. You are told that a new diet will cause you to lose 9 kg (20 lb) of fat in one week. Is this reasonable? Explain.
6. What is meant by the statement that candy provides empty calories?
7. Why is cellulose important in the diet?
8. Explain why a tablespoon of butter (a fatty food) will approximately double the calorie content of a medium-size baked potato (a carbohydrate food).
9. What is meant by the term *essential fatty acid*?
10. What chemical characteristics do the essential fatty acids have in common?
11. List the essential amino acids.
12. How do animal proteins differ from vegetable proteins?
13. Which vitamins are water-soluble? Which are fat-soluble?
14. Why does cooking affect the B-complex vitamin content of vegetables?
15. List three different functions that can be attributed to vitamins.
16. Distinguish the major elements from the trace elements.
17. List two major biological functions for calcium.
18. In what ways are the trace elements similar to vitamins? How do they differ?
19. What percentage of the average water consumption comes from solid foods? How much from liquids?
20. A fruit drink label claims that the juice contains 100% of the RDA for vitamin C. Because of this nutrition claim, what information must be printed on the label by law?
21. List five common categories of food additives.
22. Which federal agency is responsible for regulating the use of food additives?
23. Why must the food of higher animals be digested before it can be utilized?
24. What are the five principal digestive juices?
25. What is chyme?

26. What is the approximate pH of each of the following?
    (a) Saliva   (c) Pancreatic juice
    (b) Gastric juice   (d) Bile
27. What enzymes are present in each of the digestive juices?
28. In what parts of the digestive system are each of the following digested?
    (a) Carbohydrates   (b) Fats   (c) Proteins
29. In what part of the digestive tract does the absorption of food occur?
30. What are the end products of carbohydrate digestion? List the specific compounds that are formed.
31. What is the digestive function of the liver?
32. List the principal digestive enzymes that act on proteins.
33. How do the intestinal mucosal cells aid digestion?
34. How does the liver metabolize toxic compounds and remove them from the blood stream?
35. Which of these statements are correct?
    (a) Water is an essential nutrient.
    (b) Most vegetable proteins are complete proteins.
    (c) Oleic acid is an essential fatty acid.
    (d) A dietary supply of glycine is not needed.
    (e) Of the three classes of energy nutrients, an RDA has been established only for proteins.
    (f) Vitamins are inorganic nutrients.
    (g) Most foods contain a variety of nutrients.
    (h) Calcium is an important trace element.
    (i) The functions of most trace elements are not well understood.
    (j) The main purpose of digestion is to hydrolyze large molecules to smaller ones that can be absorbed through the intestinal membranes.
    (k) Most of the digestion of food occurs in the stomach.
    (l) Gastric juice contains hydrochloric acid and has a pH of 1.5–2.5.
    (m) Digestion in the small intestine occurs in an alkaline medium.
    (n) The function of bile acids is to emulsify carbohydrates; this allows them to be hydrolyzed to monosaccharides.
    (o) The liver functions to reduce potentially toxic compounds.

Bioenergetics

Introduction

bioenergetics

For life to exist, energy must be available. The part of biochemistry that deals with the transformation, distribution, and utilization of energy by living organisms is called **bioenergetics.** Thus, when our muscles undergo physical activity, bioenergetics must have an important role. Let us follow some of the biochemical changes during fairly intense work—for example, cutting grass with a hand-propelled mower on a warm day—as a means of introduction to bioenergetics.

For the most part, bioenergetics occurs inside cells. Consequently, cells must take in needed chemicals from and return waste products to the surrounding fluids. Because of this exchange process, the chemical changes in the fluid surrounding working muscle cells provide important clues concerning the principles of bioenergetics.

As lawn mowing progresses, breathing accelerates; oxygen is taken in and carbon dioxide expelled more rapidly. These gases are transported by the blood stream between the muscles, where bioenergetics is active, and the lungs. In fact, the blood is an important intermediary in bioenergetics.

32.2 ## Oxygen/Carbon Dioxide Exchange

Muscles must have an adequate oxygen supply, especially when a person is pushing a lawn mower or doing any other work. About 5 g of oxygen (3.8 L at 25°C and 1 atm) is required for every minute of strenuous activity by a young adult. The necessary oxygen is supplied to the muscle cells by oxygenated arterial blood. Waste carbon dioxide from the muscle cells is removed by oxygen-deficient venous blood.

Normally the partial pressure of oxygen is about 100 torr in the lungs and 35 torr in the cells. Because gases move spontaneously from regions of higher pressure to regions of lower pressure, oxygen moves toward the cells. But the body must move oxygen at rates far faster than can be attained by simple diffusion. Red blood cells, which contain the oxygen transport protein hemoglobin (Hb) (see Section 29.7), increase the oxygen transport rate by 80–90 times that obtained by simple diffusion.

The amount of oxygen bound by hemoglobin changes as the partial pressure of oxygen changes. Figure 32.1 graphically shows the oxygen-binding characteristics of hemoglobin in the form of a steeply sloped S-shaped curve, known as a *sigmoidal curve.* The solid line represents the behavior of hemoglobin when the body is resting. The steep portion of the curve is in the 35–40 torr partial pressure range of oxygen found in the fluid surrounding the cell. In this steep portion of the curve, a small change in the partial pressure of oxygen will cause a relatively large change in the oxygen bound to hemoglobin. The lowering of the partial pressure of oxygen as hemoglobin moves from the lungs to resting muscle tissue causes the release of about 70% of the hemoglobin-bound oxygen.

When the strenuous work of lawn mowing begins, the muscle cells must have more oxygen to generate the needed energy. The rate of oxygen flow to the cells is

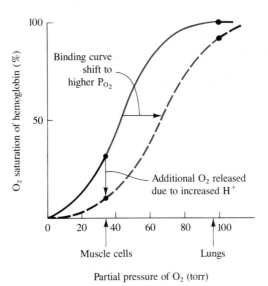

Figure 32.1 The oxygen binding curve for hemoglobin under approximate physiological conditions: As the partial pressure of oxygen is increased, more O_2 binds to hemoglobin. The colored portion of each curve highlights changes in O_2 saturation of hemoglobin as the blood circulates between the lungs and the muscle cells.

speeded up by an increase in the pulse and respiration rates of the person doing the mowing. But more subtle, and very effective, biochemical changes also occur.

First, in hard-working muscle tissue where bioenergetics proceeds rapidly, the partial pressure of oxygen may drop to 10 torr. This decrease in P_{O_2} from 35 torr to 10 torr is small. But because the hemoglobin–oxygen binding curve is steep, the amount of additional oxygen released is large. Hemoglobin may release up to 90% of its oxygen under these conditions.

Second, hydrogen ions are formed as the muscles work (see Section 32.3). These ions bind to oxygenated hemoglobin (HbO_2) and stimulate the release of additional oxygen.

$$H^+ + HbO_2 \longrightarrow HbH^+ + O_2 \tag{1}$$

This acid effect is represented graphically by a shift of the oxygen binding curve toward higher partial pressures of oxygen, as shown in Figure 32.1. This shift, shown by the dashed line, means that more O_2 will be released in the muscles. When muscle cells increase bioenergetics and need more oxygen, the acid produced by this activity triggers the release of more oxygen from HbO_2.

When oxygen is used in the muscle cells, carbon dioxide is produced. This metabolic product must be removed from the cells. The partial pressure of carbon dioxide is highest in the muscle cells, decreases in the venous blood, and is lowest in the lungs. Thus, carbon dioxide tends to move from the cells toward the lungs. But as with oxygen, carbon dioxide must be moved at a faster rate than can be attained by simple diffusion.

For the most part the rapid, efficient removal of carbon dioxide is effected by two methods. In the first method hemoglobin acts as a carrier molecule. Carbon dioxide reacts with amino groups on the hemoglobin molecule to form carbamino ion groups and H^+ ions:

$$Hb—NH_2 + CO_2 \longrightarrow Hb—NH—CO_2^- + H^+ \tag{2}$$
$$\text{Carbamino ion}$$

In the second method of removal, carbon dioxide reacts with water to form highly soluble bicarbonate and hydrogen ions:

$$CO_2 + H_2O \longrightarrow H_2CO_3 \longrightarrow H^+ + HCO_3^- \tag{3}$$

Reactions (2) and (3) occur in the fluid surrounding the muscles. The hydrogen ions produced by these reactions stimulate the further release of oxygen in the muscle tissue by the reaction shown in equation (1).

The hemoglobin carbamino ions, bicarbonate ions, and excess hydrogen ions are transported to the lungs via the venous blood. There the exhalation of carbon dioxide enables the reaction of equations (2) and (3) to reverse, as shown in these equations:

$$Hb—NH—CO_2^- + H^+ \longrightarrow Hb—NH_2 + CO_2 \tag{4}$$

$$HCO_3^- + H^+ \longrightarrow H_2CO_3 \longrightarrow H_2O + CO_2 \tag{5}$$

These reversible reactions serve not only to eliminate CO_2 but also to consume the excess H^+ ions that were formed in the muscle tissue.

As shown in equations (1) to (5), acid (H^+) has an important role in both the delivery of O_2 and the removal of CO_2. In muscle, CO_2 and H^+ are formed. This acid (H^+) causes HbO_2 to release the additional O_2 needed to continue the bioenergetics. In the lungs, CO_2 is exhaled and the blood becomes less acidic, causing Hb to bind more O_2. The overall interrelationships of oxygen, carbon dioxide, and acid can be summarized in this way:

Energy use at the muscle	Gas balance restored at the lungs
O_2 used	O_2 inhaled
CO_2 formed	CO_2 exhaled
Acidity increases	Acidity decreases
More O_2 released from HbO_2	More O_2 bound to Hb

32.3   Hydrogen Ion Production and Control

Acid (H^+ ions) is produced as the muscles perform work. Two products of cellular bioenergetics—carbon dioxide and lactic acid—are the primary sources of this acidity. Both substances produce hydrogen ions in solution:

$$CO_2 + H_2O \longrightarrow H_2CO_3 \longrightarrow H^+ + HCO_3^- \tag{6}$$

$$CH_3CH(OH)COOH \longrightarrow H^+ + CH_3CH(OH)COO^- \tag{7}$$
$$\text{Lactic acid} \qquad\qquad\qquad \text{Lactate ion}$$

To prevent a toxic buildup of acid (abnormally low pH), the excess H^+ ions must be removed from the cells. The lungs provide a short-term partial solution to the problem of increased acidity in the cells and surrounding fluid. When CO_2 is exhaled from the lungs, reaction (6) is reversed and the H^+ ion concentration is reduced in the blood stream. During hard work, the rate of removal of carbon dioxide from the lungs is accelerated by an increase in the respiration and pulse rate. Thus, as the breathing rate increases, the blood acidity decreases.

The liver and kidneys also have an important role in controlling the pH of body fluids. The liver converts lactic acid to glucose and thereby helps to prevent toxic acid buildup. The kidneys transfer water and selected ions from the blood stream to the urine. Hydrogen ions and bicarbonate ions are among those transferred. Because this is a relatively slow process, the kidneys are mainly concerned with the long-term maintenance of correct body fluid pH.

32.4   Metabolism

As we have seen, to do work (for example, to mow a lawn), the muscles must take in extra O_2. This oxygen reacts with nutrients such as carbohydrates or fats. Energy is released as the reduced carbons of the nutrients are converted by a series of reactions into the oxidized carbons of carbon dioxide and lactic acid. These reactions comprise an important fraction of all the chemical reactions that occur in muscle cells.

metabolism

anabolism

catabolism

The sum of all chemical reactions that occur within a living organism is defined as **metabolism.** Many hundreds of different chemical reactions occur in a typical cell. To help make sense of this myriad of reactions, biochemists have subdivided metabolism into two contrasting categories—*anabolism* and *catabolism.* **Anabolism** is the process by which simple substances are synthesized (built up) into complex substances. **Catabolism** is the process by which complex substances are broken down into simpler substances. Anabolic reactions usually involve reduction and consume cellular energy, whereas catabolic reactions usually involve oxidation and produce energy for the cell. The energy needed to mow the lawn is generated from catabolic reactions that occur within muscle cells.

32.5   Metabolism and Cell Structure

procaryote

Cells segregate many of their metabolic reactions into specific, subcellular locations. The simple, procaryotic cells **(procaryotes)**—those without internal membrane-bound bodies—have a minimum amount of spatial organization (see Figure 32.2). The anabolic processes of DNA and RNA synthesis in these cells are localized in the nuclear material, whereas most other metabolic reactions are spread throughout the cytoplasm.

eucaryote

organelle

In contrast, metabolic reactions in the cells of higher plants and animals are often segregated into specialized compartments. These cells, the **eucaryotes,** contain internal, membrane-bound bodies called **organelles** (see Figure 32.2). It is within the organelles that many specific metabolic processes occur.

In the eucaryotic cell, most of the DNA and RNA synthesis are localized in the

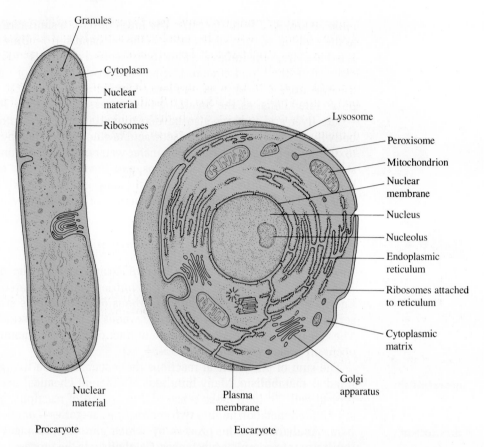

Figure 32.2   A schematic representation of a procaryotic and a eucaryotic cell: The procaryote lacks much of the organized structure and the numerous organelles found in the eucaryote.

nucleus. Anabolism of proteins takes place on the ribosomes, whereas that of carbohydrates and lipids occurs primarily in the cytoplasm.

There are a variety of specialized catabolic organelles within a eucaryotic cell. The lysosome contains the cell's digestive enzymes, and the peroxisome is the site of oxidative reactions that form hydrogen peroxide. Perhaps the most important catabolic organelle is the mitochondrion (plural, mitochondria). This membrane-bound body provides most of the energy for a typical cell. The energy is released by catabolic processes, which oxidize carbon-containing nutrients. Mitochondria (1) consume most of the O_2 that is inhaled and (2) produce most of the CO_2 that is exhaled by the lungs.

32.6   Biochemical Energy Sources

The ultimate source of biological energy on earth is sunlight. Plants capture light energy and transform it to chemical energy by a process called *photosynthesis* (see Section 32.10). This chemical energy is stored in the form of reduced carbon atoms in carbohydrate molecules (see Figure 32.3). It is important to understand that the energy contained in carbohydrates, lipids, and proteins originally came from sunlight. As the reduced carbon atoms are oxidized, energy is released and used by the cell.

Humans, as well as other animals, draw most of their energy from foodstuffs that contain reduced carbons (see Sections 31.3–31.6). For example, after we eat a meal, nutrients such as carbohydrates and fats are transported to our cells. The carbons in these compounds are in a reduced state and thus contain stored energy.

H   OH
| |
—C—   —C—
| |
H   H

Typical fatty   Typical carbohydrate
acid carbon   carbon
(oxidation number = −2)   (oxidation number = 0)

Through the cell's metabolism these reduced carbons are oxidized, step by step, and are eventually converted to carbon dioxide.

$O{=}C{=}O$

Carbon dioxide carbon (oxidation number = +4)

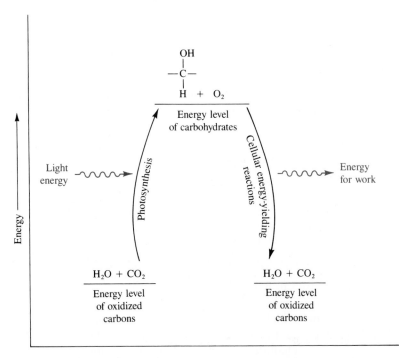

Figure 32.3   Energy flow through metabolism using the important energy nutrients, carbohydrates. Reduction of carbon stores energy while carbon oxidation releases energy.

When we work at a strenuous task, the energy needed to do the work is obtained from this general catabolic process that occurs in our muscle cells. Stored nutrients, such as carbohydrates, are oxidized with the consumption of oxygen. Carbon dioxide and lactic acid are produced. To summarize, an oxidative reaction sequence releases the energy that ultimately powers muscle action.

32.7 Biological Oxidation–Reduction

Biological oxidation–reduction, as with all redox reactions, can be separated into two half-reactions (see Section 17.3). Oxidation, the loss of electrons from a reactant.

$$A \xrightarrow{\text{Oxidation}} A^+ + e^- \qquad (8)$$

is coupled with a second process, reduction, the gain of electrons by a reactant.

$$B^+ + e^- \xrightarrow{\text{Reduction}} B \qquad (9)$$

Reactions (8) and (9) can be combined to give the complete redox reaction if electron transfer is possible:

$$A + B^+ \longrightarrow A^+ + B \qquad (10)$$

Oxidation–reduction reactions are vital to cellular bioenergetics. In eucaryotic cells, specific organelles are present that specialize in redox reactions. For example, the *mitochondria* (see Figure 32.4) (often called the powerhouses of the cell) are the sites for most of the catabolic redox reactions. In the mitochondria an electron transport system completes the transfer of electrons to oxygen, forming water. *Chloroplasts* (see Figure 32.4) are organelles found in higher plants and contain an electron transport system that is responsible for the anabolic redox reactions in photosynthesis (see Section 32.10).

The cells maintain close control over these important electron transport systems by isolating them within organelles. Both the mitochondria and the chloroplasts are packed with membranes within which the electron transport systems are located. These lipid-rich membranes act as insulators and force electrons into pathways that are useful to the cell.

To move electrons from one place to another (often outside of the mitochondrion or chloroplast), the cell uses a set of oxidation–reduction coenzymes. Recall from Section 29.8 that a coenzyme is an organic compound that is used and reused to help an enzyme-catalyzed reaction. The redox coenzymes facilitate reactions by acting as temporary storage places for electrons. The three most common oxidation–reduction coenzymes (nicotinamide adenine dinucleotide, NAD^+; nicotinamide adenine dinucleotide phosphate, $NADP^+$; and flavin adenine dinucleotide, FAD) are shown in Figure 32.5.

The addition or removal of electrons occurs in only one portion of each of these complex molecules. The nicotinamide ring is the reactive component

(a) Chloroplast

Figure 32.4 Schematic representation of (a) a chloroplast and (b) a mitochondrion.

within NAD^+ or $NADP^+$:

NAD⁺ or NADP⁺
(oxidized form)

NADH or NADPH
(reduced form)

(R represents the remainder of each molecule.)

Figure 32.5 Structures of the oxidation–reduction coenzymes (a) nicotinamide adenine dinucleotide (NAD^+), (b) nicotinamide adenine dinucleotide phosphate ($NADP^+$), and (c) flavin adenine dinucleotide (FAD)

For FAD, the flavin ring is the reactive component:

$$+ 2\,e^- + 2\,H^+ \rightleftharpoons$$

FAD
(oxidized form)

$FADH_2$
(reduced form)

(R represents the remainder of each molecule.)

A very important function of these redox coenzymes is to carry electrons to the mitochondrial electron transport system. As the coenzymes are oxidized, molecular oxygen is reduced:

$$2\,FADH_2 + O_2 \xrightarrow[\text{electron transport}]{\text{Mitochondrial}} 2\,FAD + 2\,H_2O$$

$$\begin{array}{c}\text{Reduced} \\ \text{coenzyme}\end{array} \qquad\qquad\qquad \begin{array}{c}\text{Oxidized} \\ \text{coenzyme}\end{array}$$

$$2\,NADH + 2\,H^+ + O_2 \xrightarrow[\text{electron transport}]{\text{Mitochondrial}} 2\,NAD^+ + 2\,H_2O$$

$$\begin{array}{c}\text{Reduced} \\ \text{coenzyme}\end{array} \qquad\qquad\qquad \begin{array}{c}\text{Oxidized} \\ \text{coenzyme}\end{array}$$

With the movement of electrons, energy is released. In fact, over 85% of a typical cell's energy is derived from this redox process. (Remember the mitochondria are the powerhouses of the cell!) However, the released energy is not used immediately by the cell but stored, usually in high-energy phosphate bonds such as those in ATP.

32.8   High-Energy Phosphate Bonds

The cell needs an energy delivery system because most of the cell's energy is produced in the mitochondria. However, energy is required throughout the cell. Molecules containing high-energy phosphate bonds are a transportable form of energy and meet this need. These high-energy phosphate bonds are themselves produced using energy derived from redox reactions (see Figure 32.6).

The most common high-energy phosphate bond within the cell is the phosphate anhydride bond (or phosphoanhydride bond):

(R represents the remainder of each molecule.)

A relatively large amount of energy is required to bond together the two negatively charged phosphate groups. The repulsion between these phosphates causes the phosphate anhydride bond to behave somewhat like a coiled spring. When the bond is broken, the phosphate separate rapidly and energy is released.

The phosphate anhydride bond is an important component of the nucleotide triphosphates, the most important of which is adenosine triphosphate (ATP) (see Section 29.4):

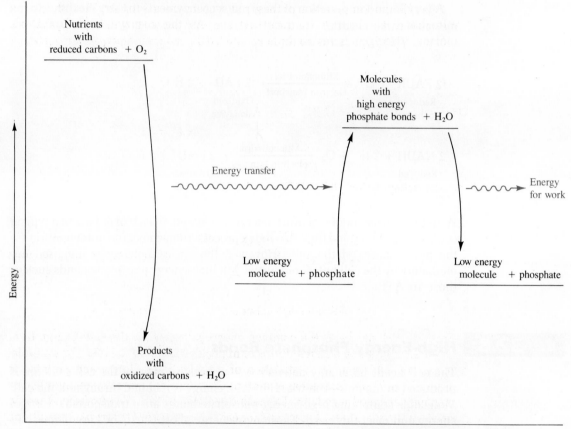

Figure 32.6   Energy flow from nutrients with reduced carbons (energy-yielding nutrients) to high-energy phosphate bonds that are used to do work.

Adenosine triphosphate (ATP)

Adenosine triphosphate plays an important role in all cells, from the simplest to the most complex. ATP functions by storing and transporting the energy in its high-energy phosphate bonds to the places in the cell where energy is needed. ATP is the common intermediary in energy metabolism.

The cell realizes several advantages by storing energy in ATP. First, the stored energy is easily accessible to the cell; it is readily released by a simple hydrolysis reaction yielding adenosine diphosphate (ADP) and an inorganic phosphate ion (P_i):

Adenosine triphosphate (ATP)

Adenosine diphosphate (ADP)   Phosphate ion

Second, ATP serves as the *common energy currency* for the cell. Energy from catabolism of many different kinds of molecules is stored in ATP. For example, the energy obtained from oxidation of carbohydrates, lipids, and proteins is stored in ATP. The oxidation of each of these nutrients requires many different enzyme-catalyzed reactions. To make *direct* use of this energy, the cell would need a separate series of reactions for each different energy source. Instead, the cell channels most of the energy derived from oxidation–reduction reactions into the high-energy bonds of ATP. This process is analogous to an economic system that values all goods and services in terms of a common currency, such as the dollar. Buying and selling within the system is thus greatly simplified. In the cell, energy utilization is greatly simplified by converting all stored energy to ATP, the common energy currency.

32.9 Biological Energy Transformation

To this point we have considered two forms of chemical storage of biological energy: reduced carbon atoms and high-energy phosphate bonds. It is vital that the cell be able to convert each form of stored energy to the other. These energy transformations lie at the heart of cellular metabolism.

There are many examples of energy conversion outside of biology. The chemical energy of gasoline is converted to motion (kinetic energy) of a car. The kinetic energy of a river can be converted to electrical energy. Electrical energy is converted to the heat energy that cooks a meal or heats a room. In each case we can point to a machine or process that transforms energy. For example, an automobile engine converts chemical energy to kinetic energy, and an electric stove transforms electrical energy to heat energy. Similarly, biochemists can point to cellular processes that accomplish energy transformations.

The cell converts energy stored in reduced carbon atoms into energy stored in phosphate anhydride bonds through two biological processes—*substrate-level phosphorylation* and *oxidative phosphorylation*. **Substrate-level phosphorylation** is the process whereby energy derived from the oxidation of reduced carbon atoms is used to form high-energy phosphate bonds on various biochemical molecules (substrates) (Figure 32.7).

substrate-level phosphorylation

$$R\text{—}OH + HO\text{—}\overset{\overset{\displaystyle O^-}{|}}{\underset{\underset{\displaystyle O}{\|}}{P}}\text{—}O^- + \begin{array}{c} \text{Energy} \\ \text{(derived} \\ \text{from redox)} \end{array} \longrightarrow R\text{—}O\text{—}\overset{\overset{\displaystyle O^-}{|}}{\underset{\underset{\displaystyle O}{\|}}{P}}\text{—}O^- + H_2O$$

Substrate   Phosphate ion   Phosphorylated substrate

(R represents the remainder of the substrate molecule.)

In a succeeding reaction, the phosphorylated substrate transfers the phosphate to ADP and forms ATP.

Phosphorylated substrate   Adenine + H⁺ ⟶

Adenosine diphosphate (ADP)

Substrate   Adenine

Adenosine triphosphate (ATP)

This process is called substrate-level phosphorylation because ADP gains a phosphate from a cellular substrate.

Substrate-level phosphorylation is found most commonly in the catabolism of carbohydrates—that is, glycolysis (see Chapter 33.) This process accounts for only a minority of a resting cell's total energy production. However, this means of ATP production does not require oxygen. Under anaerobic conditions (for example, when the blood stream cannot deliver enough O_2 to hardworking muscles), substrate-level phosphorylation may be the cell's principal means of forming ATP.

oxidative phosphorylation

Oxidative phosphorylation is a process that directly uses energy derived from oxidation–reduction reactions to form ATP. This process occurs in the mito-

Figure 32.7 Some biological molecules that contain high-energy phosphate bonds (phosphorylated substrates)

chondria and depends on the mitochondrial electron transport system. The enzyme-catalyzed oxidation and phosphorylation reactions are coupled in such a way that energy released by the oxidation of the coenzyme is used to form ATP via phosphorylation. The overall process is indicated by these equations:

$$\text{FADH}_2 + \tfrac{1}{2}\text{O}_2 \xrightarrow[\text{electron transport}]{\text{Mitochondrial}} \text{FAD} + \text{H}_2\text{O}$$

$$2\ \text{ADP} + 2\ \text{P}_i \xrightarrow[\text{Oxidative phosphorylation}]{\text{Energy}} 2\ \text{ATP} + 2\ \text{H}_2\text{O}$$

$$\text{NADH} + \text{H}^+ + \tfrac{1}{2}\text{O}_2 \xrightarrow[\text{electron transport}]{\text{Mitochondrial}} \text{NAD}^+ + \text{H}_2\text{O}$$

$$3\ \text{ADP} + 3\ \text{P}_i \xrightarrow[\text{Oxidative phosphorylation}]{\text{Energy}} 3\ \text{ATP} + 3\ \text{H}_2\text{O}$$

Note that, for each FADH_2 oxidized, two ATP's are formed; for each NADH oxidized, three ATP's are produced. This combination of mitochondrial electron transport and oxidative phosphorylation creates most cellular ATP.

Several important reaction sequences depend on electron transport and oxidative phosphorylation to produce ATP. Cells can derive energy from fats (see Chapter 34) only when oxidative phosphorylation is functioning. The citric acid cycle (see Chapter 33), which completes oxidation of most nutrients, forms ATP using oxidative phosphorylation. Because electron transport and oxidative phosphorylation require oxygen, the processes that depend on this means of producing ATP are aerobic. Oxygen must be available during oxidative phosphorylation. Thus, the major energy-producing reaction sequences in the cell will function only in the presence of oxygen.

32.10 *Photosynthesis*

photosynthesis

Light from the sun is the original source of nearly all energy for biological systems. Many kinds of cells can transform chemical energy to a form useful for doing work. However, there must also be cells that can transform sunlight into chemical energy. Such cells use **photosynthesis,** a process by which energy from the sun is converted to chemical energy that is stored in chemical bonds.

Photosynthesis is performed by a wide variety of organisms, both eucaryotic and procaryotic. Besides the higher plants, photosynthetic eucaryotes include multicellular green, brown, and red algae and unicellular organisms such as euglena. Photosynthetic procaryotes include the green and purple bacteria and the blue-green algae. Although the photosynthetic importance of higher plants is usually emphasized, it has been estimated that more than half of the world's photosynthesis is carried out by unicellular organisms.

Photosynthesis in higher plants is a complex series of reactions in which carbohydrates are synthesized from atmospheric carbon dioxide and water:

$$6 \, CO_2 + 6 \, H_2O + 2820 \text{ kJ (673 kcal)} \longrightarrow C_6H_{12}O_6 + 6 \, O_2$$
$$\text{Glucose}$$

Sunlight provides the large energy requirement for this process. An important side benefit of photosynthesis is the generation of oxygen, which is crucial to all aerobic metabolism.

The 1961 Nobel prize in chemistry was awarded to the American chemist Melvin Calvin (b. 1911), of the University of California at Berkeley, for his work on photosynthesis. Calvin and his co-workers used radioactive-carbon tracer techniques to discover the details of the complicated sequence of chemical reactions that occur in the overall process of photosynthesis.

Photosynthesis traps light energy by reducing carbons. For eucaryotes the necessary electron-transfer reactions are segregated in the chloroplast (see Figure 32.4). Like the mitochondrion, the chloroplast contains an electron transport system within its internal membranes. Unlike the mitochondrial system, which oxidizes coenzymes to liberate energy, the chloroplast electron transport system reduces coenzymes with an input of energy:

$$NADP^+ + H_2O + \text{Energy} \xrightarrow[\text{electron transport}]{\text{Chloroplast}} NADPH + H^+ + \tfrac{1}{2} O_2$$

$$NADH + H^+ + \tfrac{1}{2} O_2 \xrightarrow[\text{electron transport}]{\text{Mitochondrial}} NAD^+ + H_2O + \text{Energy}$$

$$\text{FADH}_2 + \tfrac{1}{2}\,\text{O}_2 \xrightarrow[\text{electron transport}]{\text{Mitochondrial}} \text{FAD} + \text{H}_2\text{O} + \text{Energy}$$

The chloroplasts capture light energy and place it in chemical storage.

The photosynthetic mechanism is complex, but it can be divided into two general components—the *dark reactions* and the *light reactions*. The dark reactions produce glucose from carbon dioxide, reduced coenzymes, and ATP. No light is needed and, in nature, these reactions continue during the night.

The light reactions of photosynthesis form the ATP and NADPH needed to produce glucose when light energy is present. The mechanism for capturing light energy is unique to the photosynthetic process. Although much research has been devoted to this topic, not all of the details are clear. In general, light is absorbed by colored compounds (pigments) located in the chloroplasts. The most abundant of these pigments is chlorophyll. Once the light energy is absorbed, it is transferred to specific molecules (probably a special chlorophyll), causing the molecules to lose electrons (see Figure 32.8). Two events follow in quick succession: First, the electrons lost by these special molecules are moved through the electron transport system until they reach and reduce molecules of the coenzyme NADP^+. Second, the special chlorophylls that lost electrons now regain them. Water is the electron donor, giving up an electron and producing oxygen gas in the process.

Figure 32.8 A schematic showing the movement of electrons from water to NADP^+ in the photosynthetic electron transport pathway: Note that light energy causes the electrons to become more energetic so that they can reduce NADP^+.

Photosynthesis uses light energy to force electrons to higher energy levels, as shown in Figure 32.8. As noted in the preceding paragraph, these energetic electrons are used to reduce NADP$^+$. But also notice that, when the electron loses energy in the middle of this electron transport process, the released energy is used to make ATP. Thus, the light reactions of photosynthesis supply both the NADPH and ATP needed to make glucose.

QUESTIONS

A. *Review the meanings of the new terms introduced in this chapter.*

1. Bioenergetics
2. Metabolism
3. Anabolism
4. Catabolism
5. Procaryote
6. Eucaryote
7. Organelle
8. Substrate-level phosphorylation
9. Oxidative phosphorylation
10. Photosynthesis

B. *Review questions*

1. Explain how increased carbon dioxide production can create a more acidic environment in muscle tissue.
2. How does rapid breathing (hyperventilation) change the blood pH? Explain.
3. Show a chemical equation for the reaction that produces a bond between hemoglobin and carbon dioxide.
4. What general characteristics are associated with a catabolic pathway? How does this process differ from an anabolic pathway?
5. Why are fats and carbohydrates good sources of cellular energy?
6. Describe the function of the mitochondria in catabolism.
7. Based on the function of the mitochondria, explain why these organelles are composed of about 90% membrane by weight.
8. Could a higher-plant cell survive with chloroplasts but no mitochondria? Explain.
9. Give an example of the most common high-energy phosphate bond found in the cell. With what compound is it generally associated?
10. Why is ATP known as the "common energy currency" of the cell?
11. How much energy would be released if 3 mol of ATP were converted to 3 mol of ADP?
12. Define the term *oxidation–reduction coenzyme.*
13. Draw the ring-structure portion of NAD$^+$ that becomes reduced during metabolism.

14. How does oxidative phosphorylation differ from substrate-level phosphorylation?
15. In what part of the cell does oxidative phosphorylation occur?
16. How many ATP's would be formed from 2 NADH and 3 FADH$_2$ using mitochondrial electron transport and oxidative phosphorylation?
17. The following compound is formed during glucose catabolism:

$$\begin{array}{c} \text{COOH} \\ | \\ \text{C}-\text{O}-\overset{\displaystyle O^-}{\underset{\displaystyle O}{\overset{|}{\underset{||}{P}}}}-\text{O}^- \\ || \\ \text{CH}_2 \end{array}$$

Phosphoenolpyruvate

How many ATP's can be formed from one molecule of this compound during substrate-level phosphorylation?
18. Compare the structural similarities between the chloroplasts and the mitochondria.
19. Explain how the function of the chloroplast differs from that of the mitochondrion.
20. What role do chloroplast pigments serve in photosynthesis?
21. Give the overall reaction for photosynthesis in higher plants.
22. In photosynthesis, electrons reduce NADP$^+$. From what compound are these electrons ultimately obtained?
23. Which of these statements are correct?
    (a) Slowed breathing, induced by a drug overdose, might cause the blood pH to become more acidic.
    (b) Anabolic processes are those in which complex biological substances are broken down into simpler substances.
    (c) Oxidation of reduced carbon atoms provides energy for the cell.
    (d) Typical carbohydrate carbons supply more

energy to the cell than typical fatty acid carbons.

(e) Many reduced carbons are oxidized to carbon dioxide in the mitochondria.

(f) NAD^- and $NADP^+$ are coenzymes that react as oxidizing agents in some metabolic processes.

(g) Carbon dioxide will provide much cellular energy.

(h) A phosphate anhydride bond is considered to be a high-energy phosphate bond.

(i) Mitochondrial electron transport serves to oxidize NADH.

(j) Oxidative phosphorylation occurs in the mitochondria.

(k) The chloroplast produces carbohydrates.

(l) Chlorophyll absorbs light during photosynthesis.

(m) NAD^+ is reduced during photosynthesis.

Carbohydrate Metabolism

After studying Chapter 33, you should be able to

1. Understand the new terms listed in Question A at the end of the chapter.
2. Briefly explain why carbohydrates are known as energy-storage molecules.
3. List two general ways that hormones can control metabolic pathways.
4. Briefly explain why enzymes are of vital importance in metabolism.
5. Explain why the Embden–Meyerhof pathway is catabolic.
6. State the purpose of the final reactions in anaerobic glucose catabolism.
7. Explain why the Embden–Meyerhof pathway is termed anaerobic.
8. Explain the role of glycogen in maintenance of blood-glucose levels.
9. Explain the role of adrenalin, insulin, and glucagon in the control of blood-glucose concentration.
10. Briefly describe how substrate-level phosphorylation is involved in the Embden–Meyerhof pathway.
11. Give an overall description of the Embden–Meyerhof pathway (anaerobic) for metabolism of glucose.
12. Give an overall description of the citric acid cycle (aerobic).
13. Discuss the relationship between electron transport, oxidative phosphorylation, and the citric acid cycle.
14. Compare the amounts of energy formed in the anaerobic and aerobic metabolic pathways of glucose.
15. Describe the function of acetyl-CoA in carbohydrate metabolism.
16. Describe the formation of glucose by gluconeogenesis.

17. Explain the function of hormones in the body.
18. List the blood-glucose levels that are considered to be normal, hyperglycemic, and hypoglycemic.
19. Explain the renal threshold.
20. Predict what might happen to the blood-glucose level if a large overdose of insulin is taken.
21. Describe the glucose-tolerance test and how it ties in with the condition of diabetes mellitus.

33.1 Introduction

Carbohydrates are rich sources of energy for most organisms. The energy is released when a cell subjects a carbohydrate to a series of chemical reactions, called a *metabolic pathway*. Despite the wide diversity of cell types, carbohydrate metabolic pathways vary little from cell to cell and from organism to organism.

Sunlight provides the energy that is stored in carbohydrates:

$$6\ CO_2 + 6\ H_2O + 2820\ kJ \xrightarrow[\text{Light}]{\text{Enzymes/Chlorophyll}} C_6H_{12}O_6 + 6\ O_2 \tag{1}$$

Equation (1) summarizes the production of glucose (a carbohydrate) and oxygen by the endothermic process *photosynthesis*. Note that, in the overall transformation, carbon atoms from carbon dioxide are reduced and oxygen atoms from water are oxidized. The light energy is used to cause a net movement of electrons from water to carbon dioxide. As the carbons become more reduced, more energy is stored. Photosynthesis also supplies free oxygen to the atmosphere.

Equation (2) represents the oxidation of glucose and corresponds to the reversal of the overall photosynthesis reaction. Electrons are moved from carbohydrate carbons to oxygen. Energy stored in the reduced carbon atoms in glucose is released and can then be used by the cell to do work.

$$C_6H_{12}O_6 + 6\ O_2 \xrightarrow{\text{Enzymes}} 6\ CO_2 + 6\ H_2O + 2820\ kJ\ (673\ kcal) \tag{2}$$

Glucose can be burned in oxygen in the laboratory to produce carbon dioxide, water, and heat. But in the living cell, the oxidation of glucose does not proceed directly to carbon dioxide and water. Instead, like photosynthesis, the overall process proceeds by a series of enzyme-catalyzed intermediate reactions. These intermediate steps channel some of the liberated energy into uses other than heat production. Specifically, a portion of the energy is stored in the chemical bonds of ATP.

33.2 Enzymes in Metabolism

Specific enzymes are required for essentially all biochemical reactions. Only when enzymes are present do the reactions of metabolic pathways proceed fast enough to keep a cell alive. In a sense, enzymes can be thought of as the valves of a large pumping plant. As long as the valves are open, metabolic chemicals can be processed. If some valves are closed, or missing, biochemicals are shunted to other reactions within the cell.

Enzymes are used to control metabolism just as valves are used to control pumping. Specific enzymes may be either created or destroyed during hormone-induced metabolic changes (see Section 33.7). For example, during a long fast our bodies must break down muscle proteins for energy. The proteins yield amino acids, which need to be converted to carbohydrates and fats by the liver. Normally this organ does not have the necessary enzyme complement to handle a large influx of amino acids. But under fasting conditions, the adrenal glands release *cortisone*. This hormone signals the liver to synthesize the extra enzymes needed to catabolize amino acids.

Metabolism is also controlled by altering the catalytic activity of enzymes. Changes in the three-dimensional structure of an enzyme can cause the rate of the reaction it catalyzes to increase or decrease (see Section 29.9). For example, calcium ion is known to initiate a process that leads to changes in the structure of the enzyme that converts glycogen to glucose. These changes activate the enzyme and increase the rate of glycogen breakdown. When muscles contract, calcium is released, and the conversion rate of glycogen to glucose is increased. Thus more glucose (and therefore energy) is provided automatically to working muscles.

33.3   Overview of Human Carbohydrate Metabolism

Glucose is the key monosaccharide in carbohydrate metabolism. Most carbohydrates that are consumed in a meal are converted to glucose in the liver. Glucose circulates in the blood, and the concentration is maintained within well-defined limits in a healthy person. When blood glucose is in excess, it is converted to glycogen in the liver and muscle tissue. Glycogen is a storage carbohydrate; it can be quickly hydrolyzed to replace depleted glucose supplies in the blood. The synthesis of glycogen from glucose is called **glycogenesis;** the hydrolysis, or breakdown, of glycogen to glucose is known as **glycogenolysis** (see Figure 33.1).

glycogenesis

glycogenolysis

Energy (stored as ATP) is obtained from glucose via several common metabolic pathways. Under *anaerobic* (oxygen not required) conditions, a general sequence of reactions known as the *Embden–Meyerhof pathway* oxidizes glucose to produce energy. When the final product of this process is lactic acid, the pathway is known as glycolysis. This reaction sequence is especially important for humans (and other animals) during strenuous activity when muscle tissue generates much lactic acid. Part of the lactic acid produced is sent to the liver and is converted to glycogen in the *gluconeogenesis* pathway (see Section 33.6). The rest is converted to carbon dioxide and water via the citric acid cycle, an *aerobic* (free or respiratory oxygen required) sequence. The *citric acid cycle,* also known as the Krebs cycle or the tricarboxylic acid cycle, is much more efficient at ATP production than is the glycolysis pathway. Consequently, the citric acid cycle is the major vehicle for obtaining metabolic energy from carbohydrates.

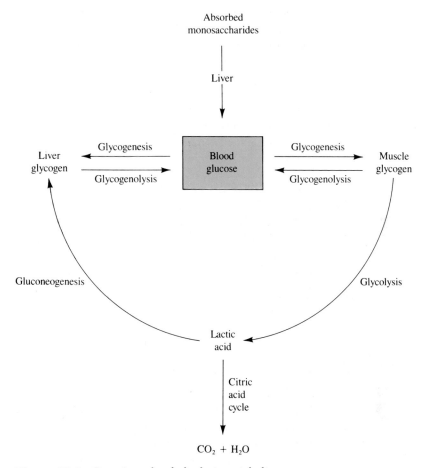

Figure 33.1   Overview of carbohydrate metabolism

The diagram in Figure 33.1 presents a general overview of carbohydrate metabolism. The entire process requires specific enzymes at each reaction stage and is controlled by chemical regulatory compounds.

33.4   Anaerobic Sequence

In the absence of oxygen, glucose in living cells can be converted to lactic acid (in muscle) or to alcohol (in yeast). The sequence of reactions involved is similar in different kinds of cells. At least a dozen reactions, many different enzymes, ATP, and inorganic phosphate (P_i) are required. Such a sequence of reactions from a particular reactant to end products is called a *metabolic pathway*. The key role of glucose in metabolism was established by tracing metabolic pathways.

Figure 33.2 Conversion of glucose to pyruvate via the Embden–Meyerhof pathway (anaerobic sequence). Glycolysis proceeds further, forming lactic acid.

The anaerobic conversion of glucose to pyruvic acid is known as the Embden–Meyerhof pathway (see Figure 33.2). The sequence is a catabolic one in which glucose is oxidatively degraded:

$$C_6H_{12}O_6 \xrightarrow[\text{pathway}]{\text{Embden–Meyerhof}} 2 \; CH_3\overset{\overset{\displaystyle O}{\|}}{C}-COOH$$

D-Glucose   Pyruvic acid

(sum of oxidation numbers   (sum of oxidation numbers
for carbon = 0)   for carbon = +4)

In glucose the sum of the oxidation numbers of the six carbon atoms is zero. After processing one molecule of glucose to two molecules of pyruvic acid by the pathway, the sum of the oxidation numbers of the six carbon atoms is +4.

This makes it evident that an overall oxidation of carbon must occur in the Embden–Meyerhof pathway.

The prime purpose of the Embden–Meyerhof pathway is the production of energy for the cell. As carbon atoms are oxidized, energy is released and stored in the form of ATP. The pathway uses the process of *substrate-level phosphorylation* (see Secton 32.9). It is interesting to note that there is only one oxidation–reduction reaction in the Embden–Meyerhof pathway—the conversion of glyceraldehyde-3-phosphate to 1,3-diphosphoglycerate:

Glyceraldehyde-3-phosphate $+ NAD^+ + HO-P-O^- \longrightarrow NADH + H^+ +$ 1,3-Diphosphoglycerate

Carbon 1 is oxidized from the aldehyde to the carboxylate oxidation state. Simultaneously, the oxidation–reduction coenzyme, NAD^+, is reduced. This single oxidation–reduction supplies most of the energy that is generated by the Embden–Meyerhof pathway. This energy is used to make the following two different high-energy phosphate bonds:

1,3-Diphosphoglycerate   Phosphoenolpyruvate

These high-energy bonds are found on intermediate compounds or *pathway substrates*. Substrate-level phosphorylation is complete when these substrates transfer their high-energy phosphate bonds to ADP, forming ATP:

1,3-Diphosphoglycerate   Adenosine diphosphate (ADP)

Adenosine triphosphate (ATP)   3-Phosphoglycerate

Phosphoenolpyruvate   Adenosine diphosphate (ADP)

Adenosine triphosphate (ATP)   Pyruvate

It is important to note that the Embden–Meyerhof pathway oxidizes carbon and produces ATP in the absence of molecular oxygen. This pathway provides for *anaerobic* energy production. In order for this reaction sequence to continue, the coenzyme NADH must be recycled back to NAD^+; that is, an additional oxidation–reduction reaction is needed to remove electrons from NADH. In the absence of oxygen, pyruvate is used as an electron acceptor. In human muscle cells pyruvate is reduced directly to lactic acid:

$$CH_3\underset{\underset{O}{\|}}{C}COO^- + NADH + H^+ \rightleftharpoons CH_3\underset{\underset{OH}{|}}{C}HCOO^- + NAD^+$$

Pyruvate   Lactate

In yeast cells, pyruvate is converted to acetaldehyde, which is then reduced to ethanol:

$$CH_3\underset{\underset{O}{\|}}{C}COO^- + H^+ \longrightarrow CH_3\overset{\overset{O}{\|}}{C}\!-\!H + CO_2$$

Pyruvate   Acetaldehyde

$$CH_3\overset{\overset{O}{\|}}{C}\!-\!H + NADH + H^+ \rightleftharpoons CH_3CH_2OH + NAD^+$$

Acetaldehyde   Ethanol

In each case NADH is reoxidized to NAD^+, and a carbon atom from pyruvate is reduced. When lactic acid is the final product of anaerobic glucose catabolism, the pathway is termed **glycolysis.** As the Embden–Meyerhof pathway produces equal amounts of pyruvate and NADH, there is just enough pyruvate to recycle all the NADH. This is a good example of an important general characteristic of metabolism: Chemical reactions in the cell are precisely balanced so that there is never a large surplus or a large deficit of any metabolic product. If such a situation does occur, the cell may die.

glycolysis

What glycolysis does for the cell can be summarized with the following net chemical equation:

$$C_6H_{12}O_6 + 2\ ADP + 2\ P_i \longrightarrow 2\ CH_3CH(OH)COOH + 2\ ATP + 150\ kJ\ (36\ kcal)$$

This anaerobic process produces cellular energy. However, it is not very efficient because only two moles of ATP are formed per mole of glucose. In fact, if the energy stored in the two ATP's is summed with the energy released as heat during the Embden–Meyerhof pathway, a total of only about 209 kJ/mol (50 kcal/mol) is found to have been removed from glucose. Compare this result with the complete oxidation of glucose:

$$C_6H_{12}O_6 + 6\ O_2 \longrightarrow 6\ CO_2 + 6\ H_2O + 2820\ kJ \quad (673\ kcal)$$

And we see that the Embden–Meyerhof pathway releases less than one-tenth of the total energy available in glucose. Thus, lactic acid must still contain much energy in its relatively reduced carbon atoms.

33.5 Citric Acid Cycle (Aerobic Sequence)

As discussed previously, only a small fraction of the energy that is potentially available from glucose is liberated during the anaerobic conversion to lactic acid (glycolysis). Consequently, this acid remains valuable to the cells because of its stored energy. The lactic acid formed may be (1) circulated back to the liver and converted to glycogen at the expense of some ATP or (2) converted back to pyruvic acid in order to enter the citric acid cycle.

$$\underset{\text{Lactic acid}}{CH_3\overset{\overset{\displaystyle OH}{|}}{C}HCOOH} + NAD^+ \rightleftharpoons \underset{\text{Pyruvic acid}}{CH_3\overset{\overset{\displaystyle O}{\|}}{C}COOH} + NADH + H^+$$

Pyruvic acid is the link between the anaerobic sequence (Embden–Meyerhof pathway) and the aerobic sequence (citric acid cycle). Pyruvic acid itself does not actually enter into the citric acid cycle. Instead, it is converted to acetyl coenzyme A, (acetyl-CoA) a complex substance that like ATP is of great importance in metabolism:

$$\underset{\text{(Coenzyme A)}}{CH_3\overset{\overset{\displaystyle O}{\|}}{C}-COOH \; + \; CoASH} \; + \; NAD^+ \longrightarrow \underset{\text{Acetyl-CoA}}{CH_3\overset{\overset{\displaystyle O}{\|}}{C}-SCoA} + NADH + H^+ + CO_2$$

Acetyl coenzyme A consists of an acetyl group bonded to a coenzyme A group. Coenzyme A contains the following units: adenine, ribose, diphosphate, pantothenic acid, and thioethanolamine. Coenzyme A is abbreviated as CoASH or CoA. Acetyl coenzyme A is abbreviated as acetyl-CoA or acetyl-SCoA.

| Acetyl | Thioethanolamine | Pantothenic acid | Diphosphate | Ribose | Adenine |

Acetyl-CoA

The acetyl group is the group that is actually oxidized in the citric acid cycle. This group is attached to the large carrier molecule as a thio ester—that is, by an ester linkage in which oxygen is replaced by sulfur:

$$H_3C\overset{\overset{\displaystyle O}{\|}}{-C}-S-CoA$$

Acetyl group ———
Thioester linkage ———
Carrier group

Acetyl-CoA not only is a key component of carbohydrate metabolism but also, as we shall see in Chapter 34, serves to tie the metabolism of fats and that of certain amino acids to the citric acid cycle.

The citric acid cycle was elucidated by Hans A. Krebs (1900–1981), a British biochemist; thus it is also called the Krebs cycle. For his studies in intermediary metabolism, Krebs shared the 1953 Nobel prize in medicine and physiology with

Fritz A. Lipmann (1899–1986), an American biochemist who discovered coenzyme A.

Krebs showed the citric acid cycle to be a series of eight reactions in which the acetyl group of acetyl-CoA is oxidized to carbon dioxide and water, and where many reduced coenzymes (both NADH and $FADH_2$) are formed. These reduced coenzymes then pass electrons through the electron transport system and, in the process, ATP is produced. The citric acid cycle is found in the mitochondria, which are the primary sites for the production of cellular energy.

The sequence of reactions involved in the citric acid cycle is shown in Figure 33.3. It is important to note that this cycle produces little usable cellular energy directly (only one GTP, or guanosine triphosphate, convertible to ATP). However, many ATP's are produced from the oxidation of acetyl-CoA (or from pyruvic acid) because of two other processes—*electron transport* and *oxidative phosphorylation* (see Section 32.9). Electron transport recycles the large number of reduced coenzymes formed by the citric acid cycle. As a consequence, oxidative phosphorylation can produce ATP from ADP and phosphate. Because electron transport requires oxygen and the citric acid cycle depends upon electron transport, the citric acid cycle is termed *aerobic*.

All three processes—the citric acid cycle, electron transport, and oxidative phosphorylation—team up to produce energy for the cell. All three take place in the mitochondria. Overall, these three processes result in the oxidation of one pyruvic acid molecule to three carbon dioxide molecules:

$$CH_3\overset{\displaystyle O}{\overset{\|}{C}}-COOH \longrightarrow 3\ CO_2$$

Because the three carbon atoms are fully oxidized, a large quantity of energy (1260 kJ; about 300 kcal) is available to the cell. Most of this energy is used to produce reduced coenzymes:

$$4\ NAD^+ + FAD + 10\ H \longrightarrow 4\ NADH + 4\ H^+ + FADH_2$$

These coenzymes, in turn, yield a total of 14 ATP molecules via oxidative phosphorylation. Each mole of ATP stores approximately 35 kJ (8.0 kcal) of energy. If we include the single GTP (convertible to ATP) that is formed in the citric acid cycle, the cell obtains about 462 kJ (110 kcal) from each mole of pyruvic acid that is oxidized.

33.6 Gluconeogenesis

A continuous supply of glucose is needed by the body, especially for the brain and the nervous system. But the amount of glucose and glycogen present in the body is sufficient to last for only about four hours at normal metabolic rates. Thus, there is a metabolic need for a pathway that produces glucose from noncarbohydrate sources. The formation of glucose from noncarbohydrate

gluconeogenesis sources is called **gluconeogenesis.**

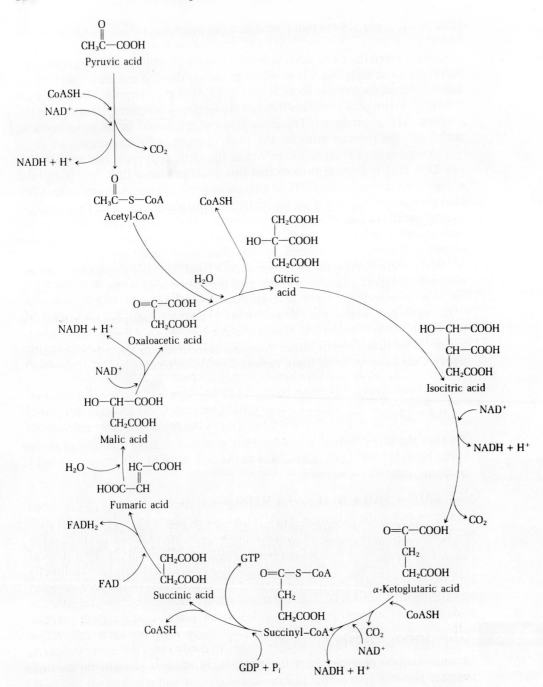

Figure 33.3 The citric acid cycle (Krebs cycle)

Figure 33.4 An overview of gluconeogenesis: All transformations except lactic acid to pyruvic acid require several reactions.

Most of the glucose formed during gluconeogenesis comes from lactic acid, certain amino acids, and the glycerol of fats. In each case, these molecules are converted to Embden–Meyerhof pathway intermediates (see Figure 33.2). As shown previously, lactic acid is converted to pyruvic acid. Amino acids first undergo *deamination* (loss of amino groups) and then are converted to phosphoenolpyruvic acid. Glycerol is converted to glyceraldehyde-3-phosphate (see Figure 33.4). Most of the steps in the Embden–Meyerhof pathway are reversed to transform these pathway intermediates into glucose.

Gluconeogenesis takes place primarily in the liver and also in the kidneys. These organs have the enzymes that catalyze reversal of the Embden–Meyerhof pathway. Because of this capability the liver is the organ primarily responsible for maintaining normal blood-sugar levels.

33.7 Hormones

hormones

Hormones are chemical substances that act as control agents in the body, often regulating metabolic pathways. They help to adjust physiological processes such as digestion, metabolism, growth, and reproduction. For example, the concentration of glucose in the blood is maintained within definite limits by the actions of hormones. Hormones are secreted by the endocrine, or ductless, glands directly into the bloodstream and are transported to various parts of the body to exert specific control functions. The endocrine glands include the thyroid, parathyroid, pancreas, adrenal, pituitary, ovaries, testes, placenta, and certain portions of the gastrointestinal tract. A hormone produced by one species is usually active in some other species. For example, the insulin used to treat diabetes mellitus in humans may be obtained from the pancreas of animals slaughtered in meat packing plants.

Hormones are often referred to as the chemical messengers of the body. They do not fit into any single chemical structural classification. Many are proteins or polypeptides, some are steroids, others are phenol or amino acid derivatives; examples are shown in Figure 33.5. Because a lack of any hormone can produce

Figure 33.5   Structure of selected hormones: Thyroxin is produced in the thyroid gland; oxytocin is a polypeptide produced in the posterior lobe of the pituitary gland; glucagon is a polypeptide produced in the pancreas; testosterone and estradiol are steroid hormones produced in the testes and the ovaries, respectively; adrenalin is produced in the adrenal glands.

serious physiological disorders, many hormones are produced synthetically or are extracted from their natural sources and made available for medical use.

Like the vitamins, hormones are generally needed in only minute amounts. Concentrations range from 10^{-6} M to 10^{-12} M. Unlike vitamins, which must be supplied in the diet, the necessary hormones are produced in the body of a healthy person. A number of hormones and their functions are listed in Table 33.1.

33.8   Glucose Concentration in the Blood

An adequate blood-glucose level must be maintained to ensure good health. To achieve this goal, hormones regulate and coordinate metabolism in specific organs. The hormones control selected enzymes, which, in turn, regulate the rates of reaction within the appropriate metabolic pathways. In the following paragraphs, we will examine some of the physiological mechanisms that maintain proper blood-sugar levels.

Glucose concentrations average about 70 to 90 mg/100 mL of blood under normal fasting conditions—that is, when no nourishment has been taken for several hours. Most people are in a normal fasting condition before eating breakfast. After the ingestion of carbohydrates, the glucose concentration rises above the normal level, and a condition of **hyperglycemia** exists. If the concentration of glucose rises still further, the renal threshold for glucose is eventually

hyperglycemia

Table 33.1   List of selected hormones and their functions

Hormone	Source	Principal functions
Insulin	Pancreas	Controls blood-sugar level and storage of glycogen
Glucagon	Pancreas	Stimulates conversion of glycogen to glucose; raises blood-sugar level
Oxytocin	Pituitary gland	Stimulates contraction of the uterine muscles and secretion of milk by the mammary glands
Vasopressin	Pituitary gland	Controls water excretion by the kidneys; stimulates constriction of the blood vessels
Growth hormone	Pituitary gland	Stimulates growth
Adrenocorticotrophic hormone (ACTH)	Pituitary gland	Stimulates the adrenal cortex, which, in turn, releases several steroid hormones
Prolactin	Pituitary gland	Stimulates milk production by mammary glands after birth of a baby
Epinephrine (adrenalin)	Adrenal glands	Stimulates rise in blood pressure, acceleration of heartbeat, decreased secretion of insulin, and increased blood sugar
Cortisone	Adrenal glands	Helps control carbohydrate metabolism, salt and water balance, formation and storage of glycogen
Thyroxine and triiodothyronine	Thyroid gland	Increase the metabolic rate of carbohydrates and proteins
Calcitonin	Thyroid gland	Prevents the rise of calcium in the blood above the required level
Parathyroid hormone	Parathyroid gland	Regulates the metabolism of calcium and phosphate in the body
Gastrin	Stomach	Stimulates secretion of gastric juices
Secretin	Duodenum	Stimulates secretion of pancreatic juice
Estrogen	Ovaries	Stimulates development and maintenance of female sexual characteristics
Progesterone	Ovaries	Stimulates female sexual characteristics and maintains pregnancy
Testosterone	Testes	Stimulates development and maintenance of male sexual characteristics

renal threshold

reached. The **renal threshold** is the concentration of a substance in the blood above which the kidneys begin to excrete that substance into the urine. The renal threshold for glucose is about 140 to 170 mg/100 mL of blood. Glucose excreted by the kidneys can be detected in the urine by a test for reducing sugars (for example, the Benedict test; see Section 27.11). When the glucose concentra-

hypoglycemia

tion of the blood is below the normal fasting level, **hypoglycemia** exists (see Figure 33.6).

Glucose concentration in the blood is under the control of various hormones. These hormones act as checks on one another and establish an equilibrium

homeostasis

condition called **homeostasis**—that is, self-regulated equilibrium. Three hormones—insulin, epinephrine (adrenalin), and glucagon—are of special significance in maintaining glucose concentration within the proper limits. Insulin, secreted by the islands of Langerhans in the pancreas, acts to reduce blood glucose levels by increasing the rate of glycogen formation. Epinephrine from the adrenal glands and glucagon from the pancreas increase the rate of glycogen

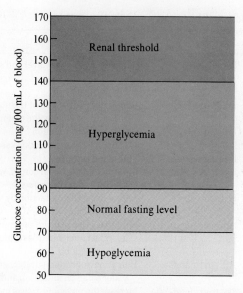

Figure 33.6   Conditions related to concentration of glucose in the blood

breakdown (glycogenolysis) and thereby increase blood-glucose levels. These opposing effects are summarized as follows:

During the digestion of a meal rich in carbohydrates, the blood-glucose level of a healthy person rises into the hyperglycemic range. This stimulates insulin secretion, and the excess glucose is converted to glycogen, thereby returning the glucose level to normal. A large amount of ingested carbohydrates can over-stimulate insulin production and thereby produce a condition of mild hypoglycemia. This in turn triggers the secretion of additional epinephrine and glucagon, and the blood-glucose levels are again restored to normal. The body is able to maintain the normal fasting level of blood glucose for long periods of time without food by drawing on liver glycogen, muscle glycogen, and finally on body fat as glucose replacement sources. Thus, in a normal person neither hyperglycemia nor mild hypoglycemia has serious consequences, since the body is able to correct these conditions. However, either condition, if not corrected, can have very serious consequences. Since the brain is heavily dependent on blood glucose for energy, hypoglycemia affects the brain and the central nervous system. Mild hypoglycemia may result in impaired vision, dizziness, and fainting spells. Severe hypoglycemia produces convulsions and unconsciousness; if prolonged, it may result in permanent brain damage and death.

Hyperglycemia may be induced by fear or anger, because the rate of epinephrine secretion is increased under emotional stress. Glycogen hydrolysis is thereby speeded up and glucose concentration levels rise sharply. This whole sequence readies the individual for the strenuous effort of either fighting or fleeing as the situation demands.

Diabetes mellitus is a serious metabolic disorder characterized by hyperglycemia, glucosuria (glucose in the urine), frequent urination, thirst, weakness, and loss of weight. Prior to 1921 diabetes often resulted in death. In that year Frederick Banting and Charles Best, working at the University of Toronto, discovered insulin and devised methods for extracting the hormone from animal pancreases. For his work on insulin, Banting, with J. J. MacLeod, received the Nobel prize in medicine and physiology in 1923. Insulin is very effective in controlling diabetes. It must be given by injection, because, like any other protein, it would be hydrolyzed to amino acids in the gastrointestinal tract.

People with mild or borderline diabetes may show normal fasting blood-glucose levels, but they are unable to produce sufficient insulin for prompt control of ingested carbohydrates. As a result, their blood glucose rises to an abnormally high level and does not return to normal for a long period of time. Such a person has a decreased tolerance for glucose, which may be diagnosed by a glucose-tolerance test. After fasting for at least 12 hours blood and urine specimens are taken to establish a beginning reference level. The person then drinks a solution containing 100 g of glucose (amount for adults). Blood and urine specimens are then collected at 0.5, 1, 2, and 3 hour intervals and tested for glucose content. In a normal situation the blood-glucose level returns to normal after about 3 hours. Individuals with mild diabetes show a slower drop in glucose levels, and the glucose level in a severe diabetic remains high for the entire 3 hours. Responses to a glucose-tolerance test are shown in Figure 33.7.

The chemical structure of insulin has been determined and biologically active insulin has been synthesized in the laboratory. In 1978 scientists at the City of Hope Medical Center in Duarte, California, announced the production of insulin identical in structure to that made in the human pancreas. Genes containing the codons required to produce the A and B polypeptide chains of insulin were made and attached to the bacteria *Escherichia coli*, which then synthesized the two chains. The A and B chains were extracted and brought together; insulin was formed when the two chains linked together through the two disulfide groups. Although still relatively expensive, insulin produced by this general method is now available in pharmacies. This "genetically engineered" insulin should be a great boon for millions of diabetics throughout the world. It is a boon because, despite the fact that today most insulin is obtained as a by-product of meat packing, there is need for more insulin than can be obtained as a by-product.

33.9 Overview of Complex Metabolic Pathways

When we examine a metabolic pathway such as the Embden–Meyerhof pathway (Figure 33.2) or the citric acid cycle (Figure 33.3), the sheer complexity may be puzzling and overwhelming. We are tempted to ask why so many reactions are

Figure 33.7 Typical responses to a glucose-tolerance test

used by a cell to achieve its goal. This is a question that biochemists have asked for many years. It appears that a physiological design that includes a number of reactions per pathway achieves several vital objectives for the cell.

First, many of the chemicals that are formed in the middle of a pathway, *pathway intermediates,* are used in other metabolic processes within the cell.

$$A \rightleftharpoons B \rightleftharpoons C \rightleftharpoons D$$ Pathway I
(B, C = pathway intermediates)

$$B \rightleftharpoons X \rightleftharpoons Y \rightleftharpoons Z$$ Pathway II

$$C \rightleftharpoons I \rightleftharpoons J \rightleftharpoons K$$ Pathway III

These intermediates are like interchangeable machine parts. Once such machine parts are made, they can be used in more than one machine. And once pathway intermediates are formed, they can be used in several pathways and serve a variety of metabolic functions in the cell.

Second, having multiple-step pathways helps the cell to handle metabolic energy efficiently. For many pathways the total energy available is much greater than the cell can handle in a single reaction. As an example, a one-step complete oxidation of glucose yields enough energy to cook a cell, figuratively speaking. To avoid such disasters the cell extracts only a little energy from glucose at each chemical reaction (Figure 33.8). The quantity of energy released in each step is small enough to be handled by the cell. Thus, in order for a cell to extract the maximum energy, a metabolic pathway must have a number of steps.

Metabolic reaction sequences seem needlessly complex because we see only a

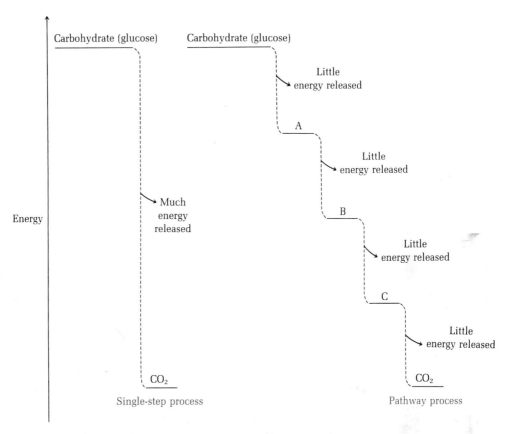

Figure 33.8 A single-step oxidation process compared with a multiple-step process: In the pathway, A, B, and C represent hypothetical pathway intermediates.

small part of the total cellular function. Although the processes must be studied separately, it is important to remember that they are all interrelated.

QUESTIONS

A. *Review the meanings of the new terms introduced in this chapter.*

1. Glycogenesis
2. Glycogenolysis
3. Glycolysis
4. Gluconeogenesis
5. Hormones
6. Hyperglycemia
7. Renal threshold
8. Hypoglycemia
9. Homeostasis

B. *Review questions*

1. Why are carbohydrates considered to be energy-storage molecules?

2. List two general ways in which glucose catabolism differs from photosynthesis.
3. How much energy would be released if three moles of glucose were converted to carbon dioxide?
4. Why are enzymes important in metabolism?
5. What major storage carbohydrate is found in the liver?
6. Draw the structure of the carbohydrate that is produced during glycogenolysis.
7. Define the type of ATP production that occurs in the Embden–Meyerhof pathway.

8. Explain why the Embden–Meyerhof pathway is considered to be anaerobic even though the oxidation of glucose occurs.

9. What are the end products of the anaerobic catabolism of glucose in (a) muscle tissue and (b) yeast cells?

10. What is the purpose of the final reactions in anaerobic glucose catabolism?

11. Explain why the Embden–Meyerhof pathway is considered to be catabolic.

12. How many ATP's would be produced if three glucose molecules were processed through the Embden–Meyerhof pathway?

13. Write the structure of lactic acid. Would you predict that this molecule could provide cellular energy? Briefly explain.

14. How many high-energy phosphate bonds are directly formed in the citric acid cycle? List the number and types of reduced coenzymes that are produced in this cycle.

15. Why are electron transport and oxidative phosphorylation needed when the cell uses the citric acid cycle to produce energy?

16. Compare the amounts of metabolic energy (in the form of ATP) produced per glucose unit via the anaerobic sequence and via the aerobic sequence.

17. Why was the citric acid cycle not involved in the metabolism of life forms that existed before the evolution of photosynthesis?

18. What is acetyl-CoA and what is its function in metabolism?

19. What are the functions of hormones and where are they produced?

20. How does the function of hormones in the body differ from that of enzymes?

21. (a) What is the range of glucose concentration in blood under normal fasting conditions?
    (b) What blood-glucose concentrations are considered to be hyperglycemic? Hypoglycemic?

22. What is meant by the renal threshold?

23. What is meant by normal fasting blood-sugar level?

24. Does the presence of glucose in the urine establish that the condition of diabetes mellitus is present? Explain.

25. Explain how the body maintains blood-glucose concentrations within certain definite limits despite wide variations in the rates of glucose intake and utilization.

26. Why is adrenalin sometimes called the emergency or crisis hormone?

27. Explain how adrenalin and insulin maintain blood glucose within a definite concentration range.

28. Predict what might happen to blood-glucose concentrations if a large overdose of insulin were taken by accident.

29. Why is insulin not effective when taken orally?

30. Describe the glucose-tolerance test.

31. Which of these statements are correct?
    (a) Carbon dioxide is a final product of glucose catabolism.
    (b) In general, only very few metabolic reactions require enzymes.
    (c) Hormonal control often changes an enzyme's function.
    (d) Glycolysis refers to the process of forming glycogen.
    (e) The Embden–Meyerhof pathway uses oxidative phosphorylation to form ATP.
    (f) Lactic acid is one product of glyconeogenesis.
    (g) ATP is produced directly in the citric acid cycle.
    (h) The Embden–Meyerhof metabolic pathway is an anaerobic sequence of reactions.
    (i) In the Embden–Meyerhof metabolic pathway, one mole of glucose is converted to two moles of lactic acid in muscle tissue.
    (j) The citric acid cycle is much more efficient in energy production than is the Embden–Meyerhof pathway.
    (k) Hormones are regulatory agents that are secreted into the stomach and intestine to control metabolism.
    (l) A person with diabetes mellitus suffers from hypoglycemia.
    (m) Hypoglycemia can affect the brain due to low blood-sugar level.
    (n) When the blood-glucose level exceeds the renal threshold, glucose is eliminated through the kidneys into the urine.

34

Metabolism of Lipids and Proteins

After studying Chapter 34, you should be able to

1. Understand the new terms listed in Question A at the end of the chapter.
2. Briefly explain what characteristic of fatty acids allows them to provide large amounts of metabolic energy.
3. Briefly describe Knoop's experiments on fatty acid oxidation and degradation and the conclusions derived from them.
4. Explain what is meant by beta oxidation and beta cleavage in relation to the metabolism of fatty acids.
5. Tell the purpose of ketone-body production and indicate a dangerous side effect.
6. Briefly describe the biosynthesis of fatty acids using palmitic acid as an example.
7. List three major differences between beta oxidation and fatty acid synthesis.
8. Briefly describe how amino acid metabolism differs from carbohydrate and fatty acid metabolism.
9. List the possible metabolic fates of amino acids in humans.
10. Describe the major purpose of transamination.
11. Briefly explain the importance of L-glutamic acid and L-glutamine in nitrogen metabolism.
12. Explain how metabolism of proteins (amino acids) is tied into that of carbohydrates and fats.
13. Explain how a lack of essential amino acids in the diet affects the nitrogen balance.
14. Explain the purpose of the urea cycle.

34.1 Introduction

The ability to produce cellular energy is a vital characteristic of every cell's metabolism. As we have seen, carbohydrates are one of the major sources of cellular energy. The other two are lipids and proteins.

Of all the lipids, fatty acids are the most commonly used for cellular energy. Each fatty acid contains a long chain of reduced carbon atoms that can be oxidized to yield energy.

$$CH_3CH_2CH_2CH_2CH_2CH_2CH_2CH_2CH_2CH_2CH_2CH_2CH_2CH_2CH_2COOH$$
Palmitic acid

The average oxidation number of the carbon atoms in fatty acids is about -2 compared with 0 in carbohydrates. Thus, when catabolized (oxidized), fatty acids yield more energy per carbon atom than do carbohydrates.

Proteins (amino acids) are also a source of reduced carbon atoms that can be catabolized to provide cellular energy. In addition, amino acids provide the major pool of usable nitrogen for cells. Proteins and amino acids also perform diverse other functions. Some of these functions will be considered later in this chapter.

34.2 Fatty Acid Oxidation (Beta Oxidation)

Fats are the most energy-rich class of foods. Palmitic acid derived from fat yields 39.1 kJ (9.36 kcal) per gram when burned to form carbon dioxide and water. By contrast, glucose yields only 15.6 kJ (3.74 kcal) per gram. Of course, fats are not actually burned in the body simply to produce heat. They are broken down in a series of enzyme-catalyzed reactions that also produce useful potential chemical energy in the form of ATP. In complete biochemical oxidation, the carbon and hydrogen of a fat ultimately are combined with oxygen (from respiration) to form carbon dioxide and water.

In 1904 Franz Knoop, a German biochemist, established that the catabolism of fatty acids involved a process whereby their carbon chains are shortened by two carbon atoms at a time. Knoop knew that animals do not metabolize benzene groups to carbon dioxide and water. Instead the benzene nucleus remains attached to at least one carbon atom and is eliminated in the urine as a derivative of either benzoic acid or phenylacetic acid.

Benzoic acid   Phenylacetic acid

Accordingly Knoop prepared a homologous series of straight-chain fatty acids with a phenyl group at one end and a carboxyl group at the other end. He then fed these benzene-tagged acids to test animals. Phenylaceturic acid was identified in the urine of the animals that had eaten acids with an even number of carbon atoms; hippuric acid was present in the urine of the animals that had consumed acids with an odd number of carbon atoms:

$$\text{—CH}_2\text{—}\overset{\displaystyle O}{\overset{\displaystyle \|}{C}}\text{—NHCH}_2\text{COOH}$$

Phenylaceturic acid
(metabolic end product when n is even)

—CH$_2$(CH$_2$)$_n$COOH

$$\text{—}\overset{\displaystyle O}{\overset{\displaystyle \|}{C}}\text{—NHCH}_2\text{COOH}$$

Hippuric acid
(metabolic end product when n is odd)

These results indicated a metabolic pathway for fatty acids in which the carbon chain is shortened by two carbon atoms at each stage.

Knoop's experiments were remarkable for their time. They involved the use of tagged molecules and served as prototypes for modern research that utilizes isotopes to tag molecules.

Knoop postulated that the carbon chain of a fatty acid is shortened by successive removals of acetic acid units. The process involves the oxidation of the beta-carbon atom and cleavage of the chain between the alpha and beta carbons. A six-carbon fatty acid would produce three molecules of acetic acid, thus:

This C is oxidized.

First
reaction   CH$_3$CH$_2$CH$_2$$\overset{\beta}{C}H_2$$\overset{\alpha}{C}H_2$COOH $\longrightarrow$ CH$_3$CH$_2$CH$_2$COOH + CH$_3$COOH
sequence
                                    ↑
                        Chain is cleaved

Caproic acid   Butyric acid   Acetic acid

This C is oxidized.

Second
reaction   CH$_3$$\overset{\beta}{C}H_2$$\overset{\alpha}{C}H_2$COOH $\longrightarrow$ 2 CH$_3$COOH
sequence   ↑
                   Chain is cleaved

Butyric acid   Acetic acid

The general validity of Knoop's theory of beta-carbon atom oxidation has been confirmed. However, the detailed pathway for fatty acid oxidation was not established until about 50 years after his original work. The sequence of reactions involved, like those of the Embden–Meyerhof and citric acid pathways, is another fundamental metabolic pathway. Beta oxidation, or the *two-carbon chop*, is accomplished in a series of reactions whereby the first two carbon atoms of the fatty acid chain become the acetyl group in a molecule of acetyl-CoA.

The catabolism proceeds in this manner: A fatty acid reacts with coenzyme A (CoASH) to form an activated thioester. The energy needed for this step of the catabolism is obtained from ATP.

Step 1. Activation: Formation of thioester with CoA

$$\underset{\text{Fatty acid}}{RCH_2CH_2CH_2\overset{\overset{\displaystyle O}{\|}}{C}OH} + CoASH + ATP \longrightarrow$$

$$\underset{\text{CoA thioester of a fatty acid}}{RCH_2CH_2CH_2\overset{\overset{\displaystyle O}{\|}}{C}—SCoA} + AMP + \underset{\substack{\text{Inorganic}\\\text{phosphate}}}{2\ P_i}$$

The activated thioester next undergoes four more steps in the reaction sequence involving *oxidation, hydration, oxidation,* and *cleavage* to produce acetyl-CoA and an activated thioester shortened by two carbon atoms. The cleavage reaction requires an additional molecule of CoA.

Step 2. Oxidation: Dehydrogenation at carbons 2 and 3 (alpha and beta carbons)

$$RCH_2CH_2CH_2\overset{\overset{\displaystyle O}{\|}}{C}—SCoA + FAD \longrightarrow RCH_2CH{=}CH\overset{\overset{\displaystyle O}{\|}}{C}—SCoA + FADH_2$$

Step 3. Hydration: Conversion to secondary alcohol

$$RCH_2CH{=}CH\overset{\overset{\displaystyle O}{\|}}{C}—SCoA + H_2O \longrightarrow RCH_2\overset{\overset{\displaystyle OH}{|}}{C}HCH_2\overset{\overset{\displaystyle O}{\|}}{C}—SCoA$$

Step 4. Oxidation: Dehydrogenation of carbon 3 (beta carbon) to a keto group

$$RCH_2\overset{\overset{\displaystyle OH}{|}}{C}HCH_2\overset{\overset{\displaystyle O}{\|}}{C}—SCoA + NAD^+ \longrightarrow RCH_2\overset{\overset{\displaystyle O}{\|}}{C}CH_2\overset{\overset{\displaystyle O}{\|}}{C}—SCoA + NADH + H^+$$

Step 5. Carbon-chain cleavage: Reaction with CoA to produce acetyl-CoA and activated thioester of a fatty acid shortened by two carbons

$$RCH_2\overset{\overset{\displaystyle O}{\|}}{C}CH_2\overset{\overset{\displaystyle O}{\|}}{C}—SCoA + CoASH \longrightarrow RCH_2\overset{\overset{\displaystyle O}{\|}}{C}—SCoA + \underset{\text{Acetyl-CoA}}{CH_3\overset{\overset{\displaystyle O}{\|}}{C}—SCoA}$$

The shortened-chain thioester again undergoes the reaction sequence of oxidation, hydration, oxidation, and cleavage to shorten the carbon chain further and produce another molecule of acetyl-CoA. Thus, for example, eight molecules of acetyl-CoA can be produced from one molecule of palmitic acid.

As in the metabolic pathways for glucose, each reaction in the fatty acid oxidation pathway is enzyme catalyzed. No ATP is directly produced during fatty acid catabolism. Instead, ATP is formed when the reduced coenzymes, FADH$_2$ and NADH, are oxidized by the mitochondrial electron transport system in concert with oxidative phosphorylation. Fatty acid oxidation is *aerobic* (requires O_2) because the products, $FADH_2$ and NADH, can only be reoxidized when oxygen is present.

Extreme circumstances such as long-term, continuous exercise, starvation, and untreated diabetes mellitus cause a change in fatty acid metabolism. In such cases the energy obtainable from glucose is severely limited. In response the body produces small molecules from fatty acids, called *ketone bodies*. These molecules include acetoacetic acid and two of its derivatives, β-hydroxybutyric acid and acetone.

| Acetoacetic acid | β-Hydroxybutyric acid | Acetone |

Ketone bodies are highly soluble in blood and are able to provide cellular energy via beta oxidation and the citric acid cycle. As blood glucose becomes less available, ketone bodies partially substitute as energy-supplying molecules. Thus ketone bodies can substitute for glucose when the concentration of glucose is low.

An increase in ketone-body concentration is an emergency response to an extreme circumstance. This response can have dangerous side effects. For example, most ketone bodies are carboxylic acids. When their concentration increases in the blood, the acidity rises, causing a condition called *ketosis*, or *ketoacidosis*. Ketosis can effect respiration and cause a general deterioration of normal body function.

34.3 Fat Storage and Utilization

Fats (triacylglycerols) are stored primarily in adipose tissue, which is widely distributed in the body. Fat tends to accumulate under the skin (subcutaneous fat), in the abdominal region, and around some internal organs, especially the kidneys. Fat is deposited around internal organs as a shock absorber, or cushion. Subcutaneous fat acts as an insulating blanket. It is developed to an extreme degree in mammals such as seals, walruses, and whales that live in cold water.

Fat is the major reserve of potential energy. It is metabolized continuously. Stored fat does not remain in the body unchanged; there is a rapid exchange between the triacylglycerols of the plasma lipoproteins and the triacylglycerols in the adipose tissue. The plasma lipoprotein–bound triacylglycerols are broken down by an enzyme (lipoprotein lipase) that is found on the walls of all capillaries, and the resulting free fatty acids are transported into the adipose cells. When the body needs energy from fat, adipose-cell enzymes hydrolyze triacylglycerols and the fatty acids are exported to other body tissues. This vital process is under careful hormonal control. For example, part of the "fight or flight" response caused by the hormone epinephrine (adrenalin) is an increased fatty acid output from the adipose tissue. Conversely, when there is more energy available in the diet than the body needs, the excess energy is used to make body fat. Continued eating of more food than the body can use results in obesity.

There is some relationship between the diet and the character of body fats. For example, when hogs are fed large amounts of highly unsaturated fats or fatty acids, they produce a relatively unsaturated lard. Conversely, hogs fed large amounts of saturated fats or starch produce a relatively saturated lard.

34.4   Biosynthesis of Fatty Acids (Lipogenesis)

lipogenesis

The biosynthesis of fatty acids from acetyl-CoA is called **lipogenesis.** Acetyl-CoA may be obtained from the catabolism of carbohydrates, fats, or proteins. Fatty acids, in turn, may be combined with glycerol to form triacylglycerols, which are stored in adipose tissue. Consequently, lipogenesis is the pathway by which all three of the major classes of foods may ultimately be converted to body fat.

Is lipogenesis just the reverse of fatty acid oxidation (beta oxidation)? By analogy with carbohydrate metabolism (compare glycolysis with gluconeogenesis, see Chapter 33), we might expect this to be the case. However, fatty acid biosynthesis is not simply a reversal of fatty acid oxidation. The following are the major differences between the two pathways:

1. Fatty acid catabolism occurs in the mitochondria, but fatty acid anabolism (lipogenesis) occurs in the cytoplasm.
2. Lipogenesis requires a set of enzymes that are different from the enzymes used in the catabolism.
3. In the anabolic pathway (lipogenesis), the growing fatty acid chain is linked to a special acyl carrier protein (ACP—SH). ACP—SH acts as a handle to transfer the growing chain from one enzyme to another through the series of enzyme-catalyzed reactions in the pathway. Coenzyme A is the carrier in fatty acid catabolism.
4. A preliminary set of reactions, involving malonyl-CoA, occurs for each two-carbon addition cycle in the synthesis. Malonyl is a three-carbon group and has no counterpart in the catabolic pathway. Malonyl-CoA is synthesized from acetyl-CoA and carbon dioxide in the presence of the enzyme acetyl-CoA carboxylase, ATP, and the vitamin biotin.

$$\underset{\text{Acetyl-CoA}}{CH_3\overset{\overset{\displaystyle O}{\|}}{C}-SCoA} + CO_2 \xrightarrow[\substack{\text{Acetyl-CoA} \\ \text{carboxylase}}]{\text{ATP, biotin}} \underset{\text{Malonyl-CoA}}{HO\overset{\overset{\displaystyle O}{\|}}{C}CH_2\overset{\overset{\displaystyle O}{\|}}{C}-SCoA}$$

The biosynthesis of a fatty acid occurs by addition of successive two-carbon-atom increments to a lengthening chain starting with acetyl-CoA. Each incremental addition follows this five-step pathway or reaction sequence.

Step 1. Acetyl-CoA and malonyl-CoA are linked to separate acyl carrier proteins:

$$\underset{\text{Acetyl-CoA}}{CH_3\overset{\overset{\displaystyle O}{\|}}{C}-SCoA} + \underset{\text{Malonyl-CoA}}{HO\overset{\overset{\displaystyle O}{\|}}{C}CH_2\overset{\overset{\displaystyle O}{\|}}{C}-SCoA} + \underset{\substack{\text{Acyl} \\ \text{protein} \\ \text{carrier}}}{2\ ACP-SH} \longrightarrow \underset{\text{Acetyl-ACP}}{CH_3\overset{\overset{\displaystyle O}{\|}}{C}-SACP} + \underset{\text{Malonyl-ACP}}{HO\overset{\overset{\displaystyle O}{\|}}{C}CH_2\overset{\overset{\displaystyle O}{\|}}{C}-SACP} + 2\ CoASH$$

Step 2. Acetyl-ACP and malonyl-ACP condense, with loss of carbon dioxide (decarboxylation):

$$\underset{\text{Acetyl-ACP}}{CH_3\overset{\overset{\displaystyle O}{\|}}{C}-SACP} + \underset{\text{Malonyl-ACP}}{HO\overset{\overset{\displaystyle O}{\|}}{C}CH_2\overset{\overset{\displaystyle O}{\|}}{C}-SACP} \longrightarrow \underset{\text{Acetoacetyl-ACP}}{CH_3\overset{\overset{\displaystyle O}{\|}}{C}CH_2\overset{\overset{\displaystyle O}{\|}}{C}-SACP} + CO_2 + ACP-SH$$

The three steps that follow are reversals of three steps in fatty acid beta oxidation (Section 34.2).

Step 3. Reduction: Hydrogenation of carbon 3 (β-keto group)

$$CH_3\overset{\overset{\displaystyle O}{\|}}{C}CH_2\overset{\overset{\displaystyle O}{\|}}{C}-SACP + NADPH + H^+ \longrightarrow \underset{\beta\text{-Hydroxybutyryl-ACP}}{CH_3\overset{\overset{\displaystyle OH}{|}}{C}HCH_2\overset{\overset{\displaystyle O}{\|}}{C}-SACP} + NADP^+$$

Step 4. Dehydration: Formation of a double bond between carbons 2 and 3

$$CH_3\overset{\overset{\displaystyle OH}{|}}{C}HCH_2\overset{\overset{\displaystyle O}{\|}}{C}-SACP \longrightarrow \underset{\text{Crotonyl-ACP}}{CH_3CH{=}CH\overset{\overset{\displaystyle O}{\|}}{C}-SACP} + H_2O$$

Step 5. Reduction: Hydrogenation of carbons 2 and 3

$$CH_3CH{=}CH\overset{\overset{\displaystyle O}{\|}}{C}-SACP + NADPH + H^+ \longrightarrow \underset{\text{Butyryl-ACP}}{CH_3CH_2CH_2\overset{\overset{\displaystyle O}{\|}}{C}-SACP} + NADP^+$$

This completes the first cycle of the synthesis; the chain has been lengthened by two carbon atoms. Biosynthesis of longer-chain fatty acids proceeds by a series of such cycles, each lengthening the carbon chain by an increment of two carbon atoms. The next cycle would begin with the reaction of butyryl-ACP and malonyl-ACP, leading to a six-carbon chain, and so on. This synthesis commonly produces palmitic acid (16 carbons) as its end product. The synthesis of palmitic acid from acetyl-CoA and malonyl-CoA requires cycling through the series of steps seven times. The condensed equation for the formation of palmitic acid is

$$\underset{\text{Acetyl-CoA}}{CH_3\overset{\overset{\displaystyle O}{\|}}{C}-SCoA} + 7\,\underset{\text{Malonyl-CoA}}{HO\overset{\overset{\displaystyle O}{\|}}{C}CH_2\overset{\overset{\displaystyle O}{\|}}{C}-SCoA} + 14\,NADPH + 14\,H^+ \longrightarrow$$

$$\underset{\text{Palmitic acid}}{CH_3(CH_2)_{14}COOH} + 7\,CO_2 + 6\,H_2O + 8\,CoASH + 14\,NADP^+$$

Nearly all naturally occurring fatty acids have even numbers of carbon atoms. A sound reason for this fact is that both the catabolism and the synthesis proceed by two-carbon increments.

In conclusion, it should be noted that the metabolism of fats has some features in common with that of carbohydrates. The acetyl-CoA produced in the catabolism of both carbohydrates and fatty acids can be used as a raw material for making other substances and as an energy source. When acetyl-CoA is oxidized via the citric acid cycle, some potential energy is trapped in ATP. The ATP in turn serves as the source of energy needed for the production of other substances, including the synthesis of carbohydrates and fats.

34.5 Amino Acid Metabolism

Amino acids serve an important and unique role in cellular metabolism; they are the building blocks of proteins and also provide most of the nitrogen for other nitrogen-containing compounds.

Amino acid metabolism differs markedly from the biochemistry of carbohydrates or fatty acids. Amino acids always contain nitrogen, and the chemistry of this element presents unique problems for the cell. In addition, there is no structure common to all the carbon skeletons of amino acids. The carbohydrates can share a common metabolic pathway, as can fatty acids, because they share common structures. But the carbon skeletons of amino acids vary widely, and the cell must use a different metabolic pathway for almost every amino acid. Thus the metabolism of the carbon structures of amino acids is complex. In the sections that follow, a brief overview of amino acid metabolism will be presented together with a more detailed examination of nitrogen metabolism.

34.6 Metabolic Nitrogen Acquisition

Nitrogen is an important component of many biochemicals. In addition to being a component of amino acids, nitrogen is found in nucleic acids, hemoglobin, and many vitamins. Every cell must have a continuous nitrogen supply. This supply might seem easy to obtain because the atmosphere contains about 78% free (elemental) nitrogen. Unfortunately, most cells cannot use elemental nitrogen.

Most higher-plant and animal cells require nitrogen that is bonded to other elements before it is biochemically useful. However, most nitrogen on earth exists as N_2 molecules, the two atoms being bonded together by a strong and unreactive triple bond. On an industrial scale, high temperature (400–500°C), high pressure (several hundred atmospheres), and a catalyst are required to react nitrogen gas with the reducing agent, hydrogen, to form ammonia. In the biosphere only a few organisms have the metabolic machinery necessary to use the abundant atmospheric nitrogen. These are procaryotes including *Azobacter* species, *Clostridium pasteurianum*, and *Rhizobium* species. By converting nitrogen gas to compounds, these organisms make nitrogen available to the rest of the biological world.

**nitrogen
fixation**

The conversion of diatomic nitrogen to a biochemically useful form is termed **nitrogen fixation.** Nitrogen is fixed by several methods, including (1) soil bacteria, (2) lightning, (3) Haber synthesis of ammonia, and (4) high-temperature processes such as combustion reactions. Of the procaryotes that are able to catalyze nitrogen fixation, *Rhizobium* bacteria deserve special attention. These bacteria flourish on the roots of legumes, such as clover and soybeans, in a symbiotic relationship. The bacteria have degenerated essentially into nitrogen-fixing machines that are maintained by the plants in root nodules. The legumes even provide a special hemoglobin protein to assist the bacteria in their task.

Currently, in many university and industrial genetic-engineering laboratories, scientists are attempting to transfer the nitrogen-fixation capability of procaryotes to higher plants. To accomplish this transfer, the appropriate genes must be removed from procaryotic cells and spliced into the DNA of higher plants (see Section 30.12). This research is particularly challenging and, if successful, would have potentially great rewards. Success would mean that grains and other commercially important crops could be grown in poor soils using little or no nitrogen fertilizer. This achievement would create a vast increase in the world's food-production capability.

Higher plants use nitrogen compounds primarily to produce proteins, which, in turn, enter the animal food chain. Both plant and animal proteins are important human nutrients.

Protein is digested and absorbed to provide the amino acid dietary requirements (see Chapter 31). Once absorbed, an amino acid can be used in one of the following ways:

1. Be incorporated into a protein
2. Be utilized in the synthesis of other nitrogenous compounds such as nucleic acids
3. Be deaminated to a keto acid, which either can be used to synthesize other compounds or can be oxidized to carbon dioxide and water to provide energy

**amino acid
pool**

Absorbed amino acids enter the amino acid pool. This **amino acid pool** is the total supply of amino acids available for use throughout the body. The amount of amino acids in the pool is maintained in balance with other cellular nitrogen pools (see Figure 34.1).

One particularly important nitrogen pool is composed of the proteins in all the body's tissues. Amino acids continually move back and forth between the amino acid pool and the tissue proteins. In other words, our body proteins are constantly being broken down and resynthesized. The rate of turnover varies with different proteins, but research with tagged (isotopically labeled) amino acids has shown that some proteins from liver and other active tissues have a half-life of less than a week, whereas the half-life of some muscle proteins is about six months.

When there is a dietary deficiency of protein (or amino acids), the tissue protein acts as an emergency source to maintain the amino acid pool. For example, one symptom of chronic undernourishment is a wasting of muscle tissue protein. The tissue protein is broken down to yield amino acids. The

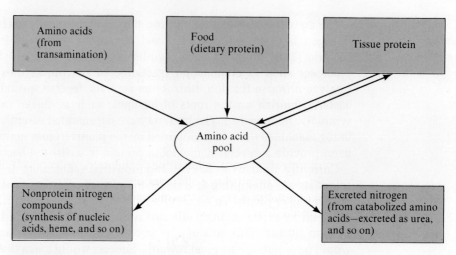

Figure 34.1   Amino acid pool showing nitrogen intake and output factors

amino acids may then be used to supply other nitrogen pools or simply may be converted to cellular energy.

In a healthy, well-nourished adult, the amount of nitrogen excreted is equal to the amount of nitrogen ingested. Such a person is said to be in nitrogen equilibrium, or **nitrogen balance.** In a growing child, the amount of nitrogen excreted is less than that consumed, and the child is in **positive nitrogen balance.** A fasting or starving person or one suffering from certain diseases will excrete more nitrogen than is ingested; such a person is in **negative nitrogen balance.** A person on a diet that lacks one or more essential amino acids will be in negative nitrogen balance. Tissue proteins can be broken down, but resynthesis is blocked if an amino acid that the body cannot synthesize is missing from the diet. More nitrogen is then excreted than consumed, because the body cannot synthesize specific tissue proteins. The nitrogen balance depends on both the amount and the nature of the nitrogen in the diet.

nitrogen balance

positive nitrogen balance

negative nitrogen balance

34.7   Amino Acid Utilization

Many dietary amino acids are incorporated directly into tissue proteins, as described in Section 30.10. Other absorbed amino acids may be utilized in one of the following ways.

Amino acids are important in metabolism as carriers of usable nitrogen. If an amino acid is not directly incorporated into tissue proteins, its nitrogen may be incorporated into a variety of other molecules. These molecules include other amino acids, nucleic acid bases, the heme of hemoglobin, and some lipids.

A process called transamination is responsible for most of the nitrogen transfer to and from amino acids. **Transamination** is the exchange of an oxygen atom for

transamination

an amino group between an α-keto acid and an α-amino acid:

$$RCH-COOH + R'\overset{\overset{\displaystyle O}{\|}}{C}-COOH \rightleftharpoons R\overset{\overset{\displaystyle O}{\|}}{C}-COOH + R'CH-COOH$$
$$\underset{NH_2}{|} \qquad\qquad\qquad\qquad\qquad\qquad \underset{NH_2}{|}$$

α-Amino α-Keto
acid   acid

Transamination may involve many different molecules, with each different transamination requiring a different enzyme (transaminase). For example, one enzyme (glutamic-pyruvic transaminase) catalyzes the conversion of pyruvic acid to L-alanine:

$$CH_3\overset{\overset{\displaystyle O}{\|}}{C}-COOH + NH_2-\overset{\overset{\displaystyle COOH}{|}\overset{\displaystyle CH_2}{|}\overset{\displaystyle CH_2}{|}}{\underset{\underset{\displaystyle H}{|}}{C}}-COOH \rightleftharpoons CH_3CH-COOH + O=\overset{\overset{\displaystyle COOH}{|}\overset{\displaystyle CH_2}{|}\overset{\displaystyle CH_2}{|}}{C}-COOH$$

Pyruvic acid   L-Glutamic acid   L-Alanine α-Ketoglutaric acid

A different enzyme catalyzes the production of L-aspartic acid from oxaloacetic acid:

$$O=\overset{\overset{\displaystyle COOH}{|}\overset{\displaystyle CH_2}{|}}{C}-COOH + NH_2-\overset{\overset{\displaystyle COOH}{|}\overset{\displaystyle CH_2}{|}\overset{\displaystyle CH_2}{|}}{C}HCOOH \rightleftharpoons NH_2-\overset{\overset{\displaystyle COOH}{|}\overset{\displaystyle CH_2}{|}}{C}HCOOH + O=\overset{\overset{\displaystyle COOH}{|}\overset{\displaystyle CH_2}{|}\overset{\displaystyle CH_2}{|}}{C}-COOH$$

Oxaloacetic   L-Glutamic   L-Aspartic α-Ketoglutaric
acid   acid   acid   acid

Note that both of these reactions involve the conversion of L-glutamic acid to α-ketoglutaric acid. In fact, most transaminations use L-glutamic acid. Thus, this amino acid plays a central role in cellular nitrogen transfer.

Transamination is the first step in the conversion of the carbon skeletons of amino acids to energy-storage compounds. Amino acids that are used to produce **glucogenic amino acids** glucose and glycogen are termed **glucogenic amino acids.** Most amino acids are glucogenic (see Table 34.1). But some amino acids are converted to acetyl-CoA. When fed to starving animals, these amino acids cause an increase in the rate of **ketogenic amino acids** ketone-body formation and are, therefore, called **ketogenic amino acids.** Only leucine is completely ketogenic, but a few amino acids can be converted to either glucose or acetyl-CoA and are both ketogenic and glycogenic.

Table 34.1 Classification of amino acids as sources of energy-storage molecules

Glucogenic	Ketogenic and glucogenic	Ketogenic
Alanine	Isoleucine	Leucine
Arginine	Lysine	
Aspartic acid	Phenylalanine	
Asparagine	Tyrosine	
Cysteine		
Glutamic acid		
Glutamine		
Glycine		
Histidine		
Methionine		
Proline		
Serine		
Threonine		
Tryptophan		
Valine		

The amino acid pool of Figure 34.1 can now be described in more detail. At the center of this pool is L-glutamic acid, and other amino acids can either add or remove nitrogen from this central compound. Given the important role of L-glutamic acid, it is not surprising that there are other cellular reactions by which nitrogen is interchanged with this amino acid. L-Glutamic acid can accept a second nitrogen atom and form L-glutamine:

$$NH_3 + \underset{\text{L-Glutamic acid}}{\underset{|}{\overset{\overset{\displaystyle O}{\overset{\displaystyle \|}{C-OH}}}{\underset{|}{\overset{|}{CH_2}}}}-CHCOOH} \rightleftharpoons \underset{\text{L-Glutamine}}{\underset{|}{\overset{\overset{\displaystyle O}{\overset{\displaystyle \|}{C-NH_2}}}{\underset{|}{\overset{|}{CH_2}}}}-CHCOOH} + H_2O$$

Although this reaction can be considered as the simple addition of ammonia to yield an amide, the actual cellular reactions are more complex. The product, L-glutamine, acts as a second central amino acid in biological nitrogen transfer, the amide nitrogen being transferable in a number of cellular reactions.

It is worthwhile to consider the synthesis of L-glutamine in more detail. Ammonia is a base and therefore is toxic to the cell. When ammonia forms an amide bond to L-glutamic acid, the nitrogen becomes less basic and also nontoxic. Thus L-glutamine serves as a safe package for transporting nitrogen. In the human body, L-glutamine is the major compound for transferring nitrogen from one cell to another via the bloodstream.

34.8 Acetyl-CoA, a Central Molecule in Metabolism

Acetyl-CoA is a central molecule in the metabolism of carbon compounds (Figure 34.2). Acetyl-CoA is also a critical intermediate in the processes that form and break down both fats and amino acids. In addition, essentially all compounds that enter the citric acid cycle first must be catabolized to acetyl-CoA. This section will examine the characteristics of acetyl-CoA that make it a central metabolic compound.

Recall that acetyl-CoA consists of a small two-carbon unit (acetyl group) bonded by a thioester linkage to a large organic coenzyme molecule, coenzyme A (CoA):

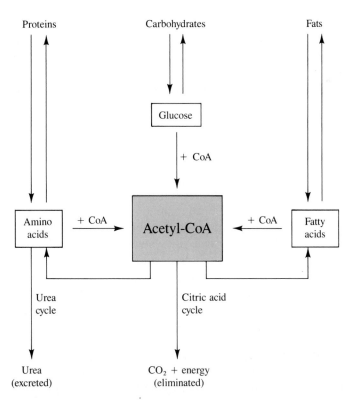

Figure 34.2 Simplified diagram showing acetyl-CoA at the hub of protein, carbohydrate, and fat metabolism

The acetyl group is the principal building block used for making a great number of large biomolecules in the cell. These complex molecules, built up mainly from the simple two-carbon acetyl fragment, have very different shapes and functions and include such diverse compounds as long-chain fatty acids, amino acids, and steroid hormones.

The acetyl group is attached to a CoA molecule by the thioester linkage and moved to a reaction site within the cell. Here the transfer of the acetyl group to become part of a larger molecule is facilitated by the reactive (easily formed and broken) thioester bond. In addition, CoA acts as a kind of handle for the various enzymes that catalyze reactions of the acetyl group. Specific enzymes have active sites that have evolved to fit coenzyme A (Section 29.9). These enzymes bind tightly to the CoA portion of acetyl-CoA and react with the acetyl group. The enzyme is then detached, freeing the CoA to repeat its carrier function by delivering an acetyl group to another enzyme for perhaps a different reaction.

One important function of acetyl-CoA is that of supplying carbons for the citric acid cycle. Carbohydrates, fats, and amino acids all can be used to make acetyl-CoA. The acetyl group is then shunted into the citric acid cycle, taking advantage of the properties of coenzyme A. Oxidation of these carbons by the citric acid cycle supplies most of a cell's total energy needs.

34.9   Nitrogen Excretion and the Urea Cycle

Nitrogen—unlike carbon, hydrogen, and oxygen—is often conserved for reuse by the cell. But the cell excretes nitrogen when it has an excess of this element or when the carbon skeletons of nitrogen-containing compounds are needed for other purposes. Two examples from human nutrition arise: (1) when we consume more protein than is needed (an excess of nitrogen-containing molecules) or (2) when we experience starvation (protein is destroyed to provide reduced carbons for energy). Under normal conditions, adult humans excrete about 20 g of urea nitrogen per day.

The nitrogen-elimination process poses a major problem for the cell. The simplest excretion product is ammonia, but ammonia is basic and, therefore, toxic to the cell. Fish can excrete ammonia through their gills because ammonia is soluble and is swept away by water passing through the gills. Land animals and birds excrete nitrogen in less toxic forms. Birds and reptiles excrete nitrogen as the white solid uric acid, a derivative of the purine bases. Mammals excrete the water-soluble compound urea. Both of these compounds contain a high percentage of nitrogen in a nontoxic form.

Uric acid   Urea

Urea synthesis in mammals follows a pathway called the urea cycle (Figure 34.3), which takes place in the liver. Ammonia is first produced from L-glutamic acid in an oxidation–reduction reaction:

$$
\begin{array}{ccc}
\text{COOH} & & \text{COOH} \\
| & & | \\
\text{CH}_2 & & \text{CH}_2 \\
| & & | \\
\text{CH}_2 & & \text{CH}_2 \\
| & & | \\
\text{NH}_2\text{—CHCOOH} + \text{NAD}^+ + \text{H}_2\text{O} \rightleftharpoons & & \text{O}=\text{C—COOH} + \text{NADH} + \text{H}^+ + \text{NH}_3 \\
\text{L-Glutamic acid} & & \alpha\text{-Ketoglutaric acid}
\end{array}
$$

The ammonia quickly reacts with bicarbonate and ATP to form carbamoyl phosphate:

$$
\text{NH}_3 + \text{HCO}_3^- + 2\ \text{ATP} \rightleftharpoons \underset{\substack{\text{Carbamoyl} \\ \text{phosphate}}}{\text{NH}_2\text{—}\overset{\displaystyle O}{\overset{\|}{\text{C}}}\text{—O—}\overset{\displaystyle O^-}{\underset{\displaystyle \|O}{\text{P}}}\text{—O}^-} + 2\ \text{ADP} + \text{P}_i
$$

Finally, carbamoyl phosphate enters the urea cycle:

$$
\underset{\substack{\text{Carbamoyl} \\ \text{phosphate}}}{\text{NH}_2\text{—}\overset{O}{\overset{\|}{\text{C}}}\text{—O—}\overset{O^-}{\underset{\|O}{\text{P}}}\text{—O}^-} + \underset{\substack{\text{L-Aspartic} \\ \text{acid}}}{\text{NH}_2\text{—}\underset{\text{H}}{\overset{\text{CH}_2\text{COOH}}{\text{C}}}\text{—COOH}} + \text{ATP} \xrightarrow{\text{Urea cycle}}
$$

$$
\underset{\text{Urea}}{\text{NH}_2\text{—}\overset{O}{\overset{\|}{\text{C}}}\text{—NH}_2} + \underset{\text{Fumaric acid}}{\text{HC}\overset{\text{COOH}}{\underset{\text{COOH}}{\|}}\text{CH}} + 3\ \text{P}_i + \text{AMP}
$$

Like the intermediate compounds of the citric acid cycle, the compounds intermediate in the urea cycle do not appear in the overall reactions and serve only a catalytic function in the production of urea. Note that the urea cycle intermediates are α-amino acids. These are amino acids that are rarely used in protein synthesis. Their primary role is in the formation of urea.

Also it is important to recognize that the cell must expend energy, ATP, to produce urea. Formation of a nontoxic nitrogen-excretion product is essential. In fact, impairment of the urea cycle is one of the major problems of liver cirrhosis

Figure 34.3 Urea cycle

caused by alcoholism. As liver function is impaired, more nitrogen is excreted as ammonia, leading to toxic effects.

Finally, let us look at the sources of the nitrogen that is excreted as urea. One nitrogen atom in each urea molecule comes from L-glutamic acid. The other nitrogen atom comes from L-aspartic acid, which may have gained its nitrogen from L-glutamic acid by transamination. Thus, the amino acid that is central to nitrogen transfer reactions is also the major contributor to nitrogen excretion.

QUESTIONS

A. *Review the meanings of the new terms introduced in this chapter.*

1. Lipogenesis
2. Nitrogen fixation
3. Amino acid pool
4. Nitrogen balance
5. Positive nitrogen balance
6. Negative nitrogen balance
7. Transamination
8. Glucogenic amino acids
9. Ketogenic amino acids

B. *Review questions*

1. What major characteristic of a fatty acid allows it to serve as an energy-storage molecule?
2. How is it possible to become obese even though very little fat is included in the diet?
3. Briefly describe Knoop's experiment on fatty acid oxidation and catabolism.
4. What is meant by beta oxidation and beta cleavage in relation to the biochemistry of fatty acids?
5. By means of a diagram, outline how caproic acid is catabolized to butyric acid.
6. Why is the acyl carrier protin (ACP) of importance in fatty acid synthesis?
7. Aside from being the source of certain fatty acids, are fats essential in our diet? Explain your answer.
8. Beta oxidation is used by the cell to produce energy, yet no ATP's are formed in this pathway. Can you explain this seeming contradiction?
9. Give the name and structure of a ketone body that does *not* contain a ketone functional group.
10. How are ketone bodies important in energy metabolism?
11. Define *ketosis.*
12. Is fatty acid synthesis simply the reverse of beta oxidation? Briefly explain.

13. Aside from being a food reserve, what are the two principal functions of body fat?
14. In what way is the citric acid cycle involved in obtaining energy from fats?
15. Why is the ATP yield from a six-carbon fatty acid greater than the ATP yield from a six-carbon hexose (glucose)?
16. Outline the parts played by malonyl-CoA and acetyl-CoA in the biosynthesis of fatty acids.
17. List several reasons why acetyl-CoA is considered to be an important, central intermediate in metabolism.
18. Prepare a diagram showing the principal steps in the conversion of starch to body fat.
19. Briefly describe why soybeans are a crop that will enrich the soil.
20. What are the possible metabolic fates of amino acids?
21. How might a low-protein diet cause a negative nitrogen balance?
22. Give an example of a reaction that is central to metabolic nitrogen transfer.
23. Briefly describe why L-glutamic acid is considered to be the central amino acid of the amino acid pool.
24. Why is L-glutamine a better nitrogen transport molecule than ammonia?
25. Is L-aspartic acid a ketogenic amino acid? Explain.
26. Write the structural formulas of the compounds produced by transamination of the following acids:
    (a) L-Alanine   (c) L-Phenylalanine
    (b) L-Aspartic acid (d) L-Serine
27. Give the structure of urea.
28. How many ATP's are used to produce urea? Why is the production of urea of metabolic importance?

29. Draw the structures of the two common amino acids that contribute nitrogen to the urea cycle.

30. Which of these statements are correct?

    (a) The average carbon in palmitic acid is relatively oxidized, and, thus, this fatty acid contains little stored metabolic energy.

    (b) Carbohydrates provide more metabolic energy than fatty acids on a per-gram basis.

    (c) Based on his experiments, Knoop postulated that fatty acids are broken down via beta oxidation—that is, by a "two-carbon chop."

    (d) Fatty acid oxidation is an anaerobic reaction sequence.

    (e) The beta oxidation pathway directly produces 38 ATP's.

    (f) Acetyl-CoA is a very important product of beta oxidation.

    (g) When energy from glucose is severely limited, the body produces and uses ketone bodies to provide cellular energy.

    (h) Triacylglycerols stored in adipose tissue are continuously exchanged with triacylglycerols of the plasma lipoproteins.

    (i) The catabolism of fatty acids is known as lipogenesis.

    (j) Fatty acid anabolism occurs in the cytoplasm.

    (k) An acyl carrier protein is used in both beta oxidation and fatty acid synthesis.

    (l) Malonyl-CoA is synthesized from acetyl-CoA.

    (m) The biosynthesis of fatty acids occurs by successive additions of two-carbon increments.

    (n) During a dietary deficiency of protein, tissue protein acts as an emergency source to maintain a balanced amino acid pool.

    (o) Most amino acids are glucogenic.

    (p) Nitrogen fixation occurs in higher plants.

    (q) A positive nitrogen balance means more nitrogen is excreted than is consumed.

    (r) A ketogenic amino acid can cause an increase in the rate of ketone-body formation.

    (s) Transamination allows formation of amino acids from α-keto acids.

    (t) Acetyl-CoA can be produced from carbohydrates, fatty acids, and proteins.

    (u) Acetyl-CoA consists of an acetyl group and a coenzyme A molecule linked through a phosphate ester bond.

    (v) Mammals excrete nitrogen in the form of urea.

    (w) Compared with other nitrogen-excretion compounds, urea is especially toxic.

Appendix I
Mathematical Review

1. Multiplication. Multiplication is a process of adding any given number or quantity to itself a certain number of times. Thus, 4 *times* 2 means 4 added two times, or 2 added together four times, to give the product 8. Various ways of expressing multiplication are

$$ab \qquad a \times b \qquad a \cdot b \qquad a(b) \qquad (a)(b)$$

All mean a times b, or a multipled by b, or b times a.

When $a = 16$ and $b = 24$, we have $16 \times 24 = 384$

The expression $°F = (1.8 \times °C) + 32$ means that we are to multiply 1.8 times °C and add 32 to the product. When °C equal 50,

$$°F = (1.8 \times 50) + 32 = 90 + 32 = 122°F$$

The result of multiplying two or more numbers together is known as the *product*.

2. Division. The word *division* has several meanings. As a mathematical expression, it is the process of finding how many times one number or quantity is contained in another. Various ways of expressing division are

$$a \div b \qquad \frac{a}{b} \qquad a/b$$

All mean a divided by b.

When $a = 15$ and $b = 3$,   we have $\dfrac{15}{3} = 5$

The number above the line is called the *numerator*; the number below the line is the *denominator*. Both the horizontal and the slanted (/) division signs also mean *per*. For example, in the expression for density, the mass per unit volume:

$$\text{Density} = \text{Mass/Volume} = \frac{\text{Mass}}{\text{Volume}} = \text{g/mL}$$

The diagonal line still refers to a division of grams by the number of milliliters occupied by that weight.

The result of dividing one number into another is called the *quotient*.

3. Fractions and decimals.   A fraction is an expression of division, showing that the numerator is divided by the denominator. A *proper fraction* is one in which the numerator is smaller than the denominator. In an *improper fraction*, the numerator is the larger number. A decimal or a decimal fraction is a proper fraction in which the denominator is some power of 10. The decimal fraction is determined by carrying out the division of the proper fraction. Examples of proper fractions and their decimal fraction equivalents are shown in the following table.

Proper fraction		Decimal fraction		Proper fraction
$\dfrac{1}{8}$	=	0.125	=	$\dfrac{125}{1000}$
$\dfrac{1}{10}$	=	0.1	=	$\dfrac{1}{10}$
$\dfrac{3}{4}$	=	0.75	=	$\dfrac{75}{100}$
$\dfrac{1}{100}$	=	0.01	=	$\dfrac{1}{100}$
$\dfrac{1}{4}$	=	0.25	=	$\dfrac{25}{100}$

4. Addition of numbers with decimals.   To add numbers with decimals, we use the same procedure as that used when adding whole numbers, but we always line up the decimal points in the same column. For example, add $8.21 + 143.1 + 0.325$:

```
   8.21
+143.1
+  0.325
─────────
 151.635
```

When adding numbers that express units of measurement, we must be certain that the numbers added together represent the same units. For example, what is the total length of three pieces of glass tubing measuring 10.0 cm, 125 mm, and 8.4 cm? If we simply add the numbers, we obtain a value of 143.4, but we are not certain what the unit of measurement is. To add these lengths correctly, first change 125 mm to 12.5 cm. Now all the lengths are expressed in the same units and can be added:

$$\begin{array}{r} 10.0 \text{ cm} \\ 12.5 \text{ cm} \\ \underline{8.4 \text{ cm}} \\ 30.9 \text{ cm} \end{array}$$

5. Subtraction of numbers with decimals.   To subtract numbers containing decimals, we use the same procedure as for subtracting whole numbers, but we always line up the decimal points in the same column. For example, subtract 20.60 from 184.49:

$$\begin{array}{r} 182.49 \\ -\ 20.60 \\ \hline 161.89 \end{array}$$

6. Multiplication of numbers with decimals.   To multiply two or more numbers together that contain decimals, we first multiply as if they were whole numbers. Then, to locate the decimal point in the product, we add together the number of digits to the right of the decimal in all the numbers multiplied together. The product should have this same number of digits to the right of the decimal point.

Multiply 2.05 × 2.05 (total of four digits to the right of the decimal):

$$\begin{array}{r} 2.05 \\ \times 2.05 \\ \hline 1025 \\ \underline{4100} \\ 4.2025 \end{array}$$ (four digits to the right of the decimal)

Here are more examples:

$14.25 \times 6.01 \times 0.75 = 64.231875$ (six digits to the right of the decimal)
$39.26 \times 60 = 2355.60$ (two digits to the right of the decimal)

[Note: When at least one of the numbers that is multiplied is a measurement, the answer must be adjusted to contain the correct number of significant figures. (See Section 2.2 on significant figures.)]

7. Division of numbers with decimals.   To divide numbers containing decimals, we first relocate the decimal points of the numerator and denominator by moving them to the right as many places as needed to make the denominator a whole number. (Move the decimal of both the numerator and the denominator the same amount and in the same direction.) For example,

$$\frac{136.94}{4.1} = \frac{1369.4}{41}$$

The decimal point adjustment in this example is equivalent to multiplying both numerator and denominator by 10. Now we carry out the division normally, locating the decimal point immediately above its position in the dividend.

$$
\begin{array}{r}
33.4 \\
\hline
41\,)\overline{1369.4} \\
123 \\
\hline
139 \\
123 \\
\hline
164 \\
164 \\
\hline
\end{array}
\qquad
\frac{0.441}{26.25} = \frac{44.1}{2625} =
\begin{array}{r}
0.0168 \\
\hline
2625\,)\overline{44.1000} \\
2625 \\
\hline
17850 \\
15750 \\
\hline
21000 \\
21000 \\
\hline
\end{array}
$$

[*Note:* When at least one of the numbers in the division is a measurement, the answer must be adjusted to contain the correct number of significant figures. (See Section 2.2 on significant figures.)]

The foregoing examples are merely guides to the principles used in performing the various mathematical operations illustrated. There are, no doubt, shortcuts and other methods, and the student will discover these with experience. Every student of chemistry should learn to use an electronic calculator for solving mathematical problems. The use of a calculator will save many hours of doing tedious longhand calculations. After solving a problem, the student should check for errors and evaluate the answer to see if it is logical and consistent with the data given.

8. Algebraic equations. Many mathematical problems that are encountered in chemistry fall into the following algebraic forms. Solutions to these problems are simplified by first isolating the desired term on one side of the equation. This rearrangement is accomplished by treating both sides of the equation in an identical manner (so as not to destroy the equality) until the desired term is isolated.

(a) $a = \dfrac{b}{c}$

To solve for a, divide b by c.
To solve for b, multiply both sides of the equation by c.

$$a \times c = \frac{b}{\cancel{c}} \times \cancel{c}$$

$$b = a \times c$$

To solve for c, multiply both sides of the equation by $\dfrac{c}{a}$

$$\cancel{a} \times \frac{c}{\cancel{a}} = \frac{b}{\cancel{c}} \times \frac{\cancel{c}}{a}$$

$$c = \frac{b}{a}$$

(b) $\dfrac{a}{b} = \dfrac{c}{d}$

To solve for a, multiply both sides of the equation by b.

$$\frac{a}{\cancel{b}} \times \cancel{b} = \frac{c}{d} \times b$$

$$a = \frac{c \times b}{d}$$

To solve for b, multiply both sides of the equation by $\dfrac{b \times d}{c}$.

$$\frac{a}{\cancel{b}} \times \frac{\cancel{b} \times d}{c} = \frac{\cancel{c}}{\cancel{d}} \times \frac{b \times \cancel{d}}{\cancel{c}}$$

$$b = \frac{a \times d}{c}$$

(c) $a \times b = c \times d$

To solve for a, divide both sides of the equation by b.

$$\frac{a \times \cancel{b}}{\cancel{b}} = \frac{c \times d}{b}$$

$$a = \frac{c \times d}{b}$$

(d) $\dfrac{(b - c)}{a} = d$

To solve for b, first multiply both sides of the equation by a.

$$\frac{\cancel{a}(b - c)}{\cancel{a}} = d \times a$$

$$b - c = d \times a$$

Then add c to both sides of the equation.

$$b - \cancel{c} + \cancel{c} = d \times a + c$$

$$b = (d \times a) + c$$

When $a = 1.8$, $c = 32$, and $d = 35$,

$$b = (35 \times 1.8) + 32 = 63 + 32 = 95$$

9. Exponents, powers of 10, expression of large and small numbers.

In scientific measurements and calculations, we often encounter very large and very small numbers—for example, 0.00000384 and 602,000,000,000,000,000,000,000. These numbers are troublesome to write and awkward to work with, especially in calculations. A convenient method of expressing these large and small numbers in a simplified form is by means of exponents or powers of 10. This method of expressing numbers is known as **scientific** or **exponential notation.**

An *exponent* is a number written as a superscript following another number; it is also called a *power* of that number, and it indicates how many times the number is used as a factor. In the number 10^2, 2 is the exponent, and the number means 10 squared, or 10 to the second power, or $10 \times 10 = 100$. Three other examples are

$$3^2 = 3 \times 3 = 9$$

$$3^4 = 3 \times 3 \times 3 \times 3 = 81$$

$$10^3 = 10 \times 10 \times 10 = 1000$$

For ease of handling, large and small numbers are expressed in powers of 10. Powers of 10 are used because multiplying or dividing by 10 coincides with moving the decimal point in a number by one place. Thus, a number multiplied by 10^1 would move the decimal point one place to the right; 10^2, two places to the right; 10^{-2}, two places to the left. To express a number in powers of 10, we move the decimal point in the original number to a new position, placing it so that the number is a value between 1 and 10. This new decimal number is multiplied by 10 raised to the proper power. For example, to write the number 42,389 in exponential form (powers of 10), the decimal point is placed between the 4 and the 2 (4.2389), and the number is multiplied by 10^4; thus, the number is 4.2389×10^4:

$$42{,}389 = 4.2389 \times 10^4$$
$$\overset{\curvearrowleft}{\underset{4\ 3\ 2\ 1}{}}$$

The exponent (power) of 10 (4) tells us the number of places that the decimal point has been moved from its original position. If the decimal point is moved to the left, the exponent is a positive number; if it is moved to the right, the exponent is a negative number. To express the number 0.00248 in exponential notation (as a power of 10), the decimal point is moved three places to the right; the exponent of 10 is -3, and the number is 2.48×10^{-3}:

$$0.00248 = 2.48 \times 10^{-3}$$
$$\underset{1\ 2\ 3}{\overset{\curvearrowright}{}}$$

Study the following examples.

$$1237 = 1.237 \times 10^3$$

$$988 = 9.88 \times 10^2$$

$$147.2 = 1.472 \times 10^2$$

$$2{,}200{,}000 = 2.2 \times 10^6$$

$$0.0123 = 1.23 \times 10^{-2}$$

$$0.00005 = 5 \times 10^{-5}$$

$$0.000368 = 3.68 \times 10^{-4}$$

Exponents in multiplication and division. The use of powers of 10 in multiplication and division greatly simplifies locating the decimal point in the answer. In multiplication, first change all numbers to powers of 10, then multiply the numerical portion in the usual manner, and finally add the exponents of 10 algebraically, expressing them as a power of 10 in the product. In multiplication, the exponents (powers of 10) are added algebraically:

$$10^2 \times 10^3 = 10^{(2+3)} = 10^5$$

$$10^2 \times 10^2 \times 10^{-1} = 10^{(2+2-1)} = 10^3$$

Multiply: $40{,}000 \times 4200$

Change to powers of 10: $4 \times 10^4 \times 4.2 \times 10^3$

Rearrange: $4 \times 4.2 \times 10^4 \times 10^3$

                    $16.8 \times 10^{(4+3)}$

                    16.8×10^7 or 1.68×10^8 (Answer)

Multiply: 380×0.00020

          $3.80 \times 10^2 \times 2.0 \times 10^{-4}$

          $3.80 \times 2.0 \times 10^2 \times 10^{-4}$

          $7.6 \times 10^{(2-4)}$

          7.6×10^{-2} or 0.076 (Answer)

Multiply: $125 \times 284 \times 0.150$

          $1.25 \times 10^2 \times 2.84 \times 10^2 \times 1.50 \times 10^{-1}$

          $1.25 \times 2.84 \times 1.50 \times 10^2 \times 10^2 \times 10^{-1}$

          $5.325 \times 10^{(2+2-1)}$

          5.32×10^3 (Answer)

In division, after changing the numbers to powers of 10, move the 10 and its exponent from the denominator to the numerator, changing the sign of the exponent. Carry out the division in the usual manner and evaluate the power of 10. The following is a proof of the equality of moving the power of 10 from the denominator to the numerator.

$$1 \times 10^{-2} = 0.01 = \frac{1}{100} = \frac{1}{10^2} = 1 \times 10^{-2}$$

In division, change the sign(s) of the exponent(s) of 10 in the denominator and move the 10 and its exponent(s) to the numerator. Then add all the exponents of 10 together. For example,

$$\frac{10^5}{10^3} = 10^5 \times 10^{-3} = 10^{(5-3)} = 10^2$$

$$\frac{10^3 \times 10^4}{10^{-2}} = 10^3 \times 10^4 \times 10^2 = 10^{(3+4+2)} = 10^9$$

Divide: $\dfrac{2871}{0.0165}$

Change to powers of 10: $\dfrac{2.871 \times 10^3}{1.65 \times 10^{-2}}$

Move 10^{-2} to the numerator, changing the sign of the exponent. This is mathematically equivalent to multiplying both numerator and denominator by 10^2.

$$\frac{2.871 \times 10^3 \times 10^2}{1.65}$$

$$\frac{2.871 \times 10^{(3+2)}}{1.65} = 1.74 \times 10^5 \quad \text{(Answer)}$$

Divide: $\dfrac{0.000585}{0.00300}$

$$\frac{5.85 \times 10^{-4}}{3.00 \times 10^{-3}}$$

$$\frac{5.85 \times 10^{-4} \times 10^3}{3.00} = \frac{5.85 \times 10^{(-4+3)}}{3.00}$$

$$= 1.95 \times 10^{-1} \quad \text{or} \quad 0.195 \quad \text{(Answer)}$$

Calculate: $\dfrac{760 \times 300 \times 40.0}{700 \times 273}$

$$\frac{7.60 \times 10^2 \times 3.00 \times 10^2 \times 4.00 \times 10^1}{7.00 \times 10^2 \times 2.73 \times 10^2}$$

$$\frac{7.60 \times 3.00 \times 4.00 \times 10^2 \times 10^2 \times 10^1}{7.00 \times 2.73 \times 10^2 \times 10^2}$$

$$= 4.77 \times 10^1 \quad \text{or} \quad 47.7 \quad \text{(Answer)}$$

10. Significant figures in calculations. The result of a calculation based on experimental measurements cannot be more precise than the measurement that has the greatest uncertainty. (See Section 2.5 for additional discussion.)

Addition and subtraction. The result of an addition or subtraction should contain no more digits to the right of the decimal point than are contained in the quantity that has the least number of digits to the right of the decimal point.

Perform the operation indicated and then round off the number to the proper number of significant figures:

```
142.8  g
 18.843 g              93.45 mL
 36.42  g             -18.0  mL
198.063 g              75.45 mL
198.1  g  (Answer)     75.5  mL  (Answer)
```

Multiplication and division. In calculations, involving multiplication or division, the answer should contain the same number of significant figures as the measurement that has the least number of significant figures. In multiplication or division, the position of the decimal point has nothing to do with the number of significant figures in the answer.

Study the following examples:

	Round off to
$2.05 \times 2.05 = 4.2025$	4.20
$18.48 \times 5.2 = 96.096$	96
$0.0126 \times 0.020 = 0.000252$ or	
$1.26 \times 10^{-2} \times 2.0 \times 10^{-2} = 2.520 \times 10^{-4}$	2.5×10^{-4}
$\dfrac{1369.4}{41} = 33.4$	33
$\dfrac{2268}{4.20} = 540$	540

11. Dimensional analysis. Many problems of chemistry can be solved readily by dimensional analysis using the factor-label or conversion-factor method. Dimensional analysis involves the use of proper units of dimensions for all factors that are multiplied, divided, added, or subtracted in setting up and solving a problem. Dimensions are physical quantities such as length, mass, and time, which are expressed in such units as centimeters, grams, and seconds, respectively. In solving a problem, we treat these units mathematically just as though they were numbers, which gives us an answer that contains the correct dimensional units.

A measurement or quantity given in one kind of unit can be converted to any other kind of unit having the same dimension. To convert from one kind of unit to another, the original quantity or measurement is multiplied or divided by a conversion factor. The key to success lies in choosing the correct conversion factor. This general method of calculation is illustrated in the following examples.

Suppose we want to change 24 ft to inches. We need to multiply 24 ft by a conversion factor containing feet and inches. Two such conversion factors can be written relating inches to feet:

$$\frac{12 \text{ in.}}{1 \text{ ft}} \quad \text{or} \quad \frac{1 \text{ ft}}{12 \text{ in.}}$$

We choose the factor that will mathematically cancel feet and leave the answer in inches. Note that the units are treated in the same way we treat numbers, multiplying or dividing as required. Two possibilities then arise to change 24 ft to inches:

$$24 \text{ ft} \times \frac{12 \text{ in.}}{1 \text{ ft}} \quad \text{or} \quad 24 \text{ ft} \times \frac{1 \text{ ft}}{12 \text{ in.}}$$

In the first case (the correct method), feet in the numerator and the denominator cancel, giving us an answer of 288 in. In the second case, the units of the answer are $\text{ft}^2/\text{in.}$, the answer being 2.0 $\text{ft}^2/\text{in.}$ In the first case, the answer is reasonable since it is expressed in units having the proper dimensions. That is, the dimension of length expressed in feet has been converted to length in inches according to the mathematical expression

$$\text{ft} \times \frac{\text{in.}}{\text{ft}} = \text{in.}$$

In the second case, the answer is not reasonable since the units ($\text{ft}^2/\text{in.}$) do not correspond to units of length. The answer is therefore incorrect. The units are the guiding factor for the proper conversion.

The reason we can multiply 24 ft times 12 in./ft and not change the value of the measurement is that the conversion factor is derived from two equivalent quantities. Therefore, the conversion factor 12 in./ft is equal to *unity*. And when you multiply any factor by 1, it does not change the value:

$$12 \text{ in.} = 1 \text{ ft} \quad \text{and} \quad \frac{12 \text{ in.}}{1 \text{ ft}} = 1$$

Convert 16 kg to milligrams. In this problem it is best to proceed in this fashion:

$$kg \rightarrow g \rightarrow mg$$

The possible conversion factors are

$$\frac{1000 \text{ g}}{1 \text{ kg}} \quad \text{or} \quad \frac{1 \text{ kg}}{1000 \text{ g}} \qquad \frac{1000 \text{ mg}}{1 \text{ g}} \quad \text{or} \quad \frac{1 \text{ g}}{1000 \text{ mg}}$$

We use the conversion factor that leaves the proper unit at each step for the next conversion. The calculation is

$$16 \text{ kg} \times \frac{1000 \text{ g}}{1 \text{ kg}} \times \frac{1000 \text{ mg}}{1 \text{ g}} = 1.6 \times 10^7 \text{ mg}$$

Many problems can be solved by a sequence of steps involving unit conversion factors. This sound, basic approach to problem solving, together with neat and orderly setting up of data, will lead to correct answers having the right units, fewer errors, and considerable saving of time.

12. Graphical representation of data.   A graph is often the most convenient way to present or display a set of data. Various kinds of graphs have been devised, but the most common type uses a set of horizontal and vertical coordinates to show the relationship of two variables. It is called an x–y graph because the data of one variable are represented on the horizontal axis, or x-axis (abscissa), and the data of the other variable are represented on the vertical axis, or y-axis (ordinate). (See Figure I.1.)

As a specific example of a simple graph, let us graph the relationship between Celsius and Fahrenheit temperature scales. Assume that initially we have only the information in the following table.

°C	°F
0	32
50	122
100	212

On a set of horizontal and vertical coordinates (graph paper), scale off at least 100 Celsius degrees on the x-axis and at least 212 Fahrenheit degrees on the y-axis. Locate and mark the three points corresponding to the three temperatures given and draw a line connecting these points (see Figure I.2).

Here is how a point is located on the graph: Using the 50°C–122°F data, trace a vertical line up from 50°C on the x-axis and a horizontal line across from 122°F on the y-axis and

Figure I.1

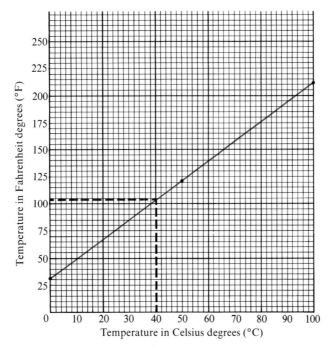

Figure I.2

mark the point where the two lines intersect. This process is called *plotting*. The other two points are plotted on the graph in the same way. [*Note:* The number of degrees per scale division was chosen to give a graph of convenient size. In this case there are 5 Fahrenheit degrees per scale division and 2 Celsius degrees per scale division.]

The graph in Figure I.2 shows that the relationship between Celsius and Fahrenheit temperature is that of a straight line. The Fahrenheit temperature corresponding to any given Celsius temperature between 0° and 100° can be determined from the graph. For example, to find the Fahrenheit temperature corresponding to 40°C, trace a perpendicular line from 40°C on the x-axis to the line plotted on the graph. Now trace a horizontal line from this point on the plotted line to the y-axis and read the corresponding Fahrenheit temperature (104°F). (See the dashed lines in Figure I.2.) In turn, the Celsius temperature corresponding to any Fahrenheit temperature between 32° and 212° can be determined from the graph by tracing a horizontal line from the Fahrenheit temperature to the plotted line and reading the corresponding temperature on the Celsius scale directly below the point of intersection.

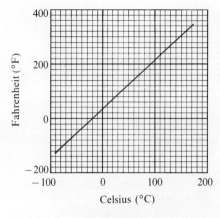

Figure I.3

The mathematical relationship of Fahrenheit and Celsius temperatures is expressed by the equation $°F = 1.8 \times °C + 32$. Figure I.2 is a graph of this equation. Because the graph is a straight line, it can be extended indefinitely at either end. Any desired Celsius temperature can be plotted against the corresponding Fahrenheit temperature by extending the scales along both axes as necessary. Negative, as well as positive, values can be plotted on the graph (see Figure I.3).

Figure I.4 is a graph showing the solubility of potassium chlorate in water at various temperatures. The solubility curve on this graph was plotted from the data in the following table.

Temperature (°C)	Solubility (g KClO$_3$/100 g water)
10	5.0
20	7.4
30	10.5
50	19.3
60	24.5
80	38.5

In contrast to the Celsius–Fahrenheit temperature relationship, there is no known mathematical equation that describes the exact relationship between temperature and the solubility of potassium chlorate. The graph in Figure I.4 was constructed from experimentally determined solubilities at the six temperatures shown. These experimentally determined solubilities are all located on the smooth curve traced by the unbroken line portion of the graph. We are therefore confident that the unbroken line represents a very good approximation of the solubility data for potassium chlorate over the temperature range from 10°C to 80°C. All points on the plotted curve represent the composition of saturated solutions. Any point below the curve represents an unsaturated solution.

The dashed-line portions of the curve are *extrapolations*; that is, they extend the curve above and below the temperature range actually covered by the plotted solubility data. Curves such as this one are often extrapolated a short distance beyond the range of the known data, although the extrapolated portions may not be highly accurate. Extrapolation is justified only in the absence of more reliable information.

The graph in Figure I.4 can be used with confidence to obtain the solubility of KClO$_3$ at any temperature between 10° and 80°C, but the solubilities between 0°C and 10°C and

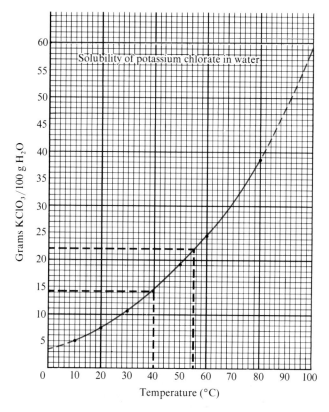

Figure 1.4

between 80°C and 100°C are less reliable. For example, what is the solubility of KClO₃ at 55°C, at 40°C, and at 100°C?

First draw a perpendicular line from each temperature to the plotted solubility curve. Now trace a horizontal line to the solubility axis from each point on the curve and read the corresponding solubilities. The values that we read from the graph are

55°   22.0 g KClO₃/100 g water

40°   14.2 g KClO₃/100 g water

100°   59 g KClO₃/100 g water

Of these solubilities, the one at 55°C is probably the most reliable because experimental points are plotted at 50°C and at 60°C. The 40°C solubility value is a bit less reliable because the nearest plotted points are at 30°C and 50°C. The 100 °C solubility is the least reliable of the three values because it was taken from the extrapolated part of the curve, and the nearest plotted point is 80°C. Actual handbook solubility values are 14.0 g and 57.0 g of KClO₃/100 g of water at 40°C and 100°C, respectively.

The graph in Figure I.4 can also be used to determine whether a solution is saturated or unsaturated. For example, a solution contains 15 g of KClO₃/100 g of water and is at a temperature of 55°C. Is the solution saturated or unsaturated? Answer: The solution is unsaturated because the point corresponding to 15 g and 55°C on the graph is below the solubility curve; all points below the curve represent unsaturated solutions.

Appendix II
Vapor Pressure of Water at Various Temperatures

Temperature (°C)	Vapor pressure (torr)	Temperature (°C)	Vapor pressure (torr)
0	4.6	26	25.2
5	6.5	27	26.7
10	9.2	28	28.3
15	12.8	29	30.0
16	13.6	30	31.8
17	14.5	40	55.3
18	15.5	50	92.5
19	16.5	60	149.4
20	17.5	70	233.7
21	18.6	80	355.1
22	19.8	90	525.8
23	21.2	100	760.0
24	22.4	110	1074.6
25	23.8	—	—

Appendix III
Units of Measurement

Prefixes and numerical values for SI units

Prefix	Symbol	Numerical value	Power of 10 equivalent
exa	E	1,000,000,000,000,000,000	10^{18}
peta	P	1,000,000,000,000,000	10^{15}
tera	T	1,000,000,000,000	10^{12}
giga	G	1,000,000,000	10^{9}
mega	M	1,000,000	10^{6}
kilo	k	1,000	10^{3}
hecto	h	100	10^{2}
deka	da	10	10^{1}
—	—	1	10^{0}
deci	d	0.1	10^{-1}
centi	c	0.01	10^{-2}
milli	m	0.001	10^{-3}
micro	μ	0.000001	10^{-6}
nano	n	0.000000001	10^{-9}
pico	p	0.000000000001	10^{-12}
femto	f	0.000000000000001	10^{-15}
atto	a	0.000000000000000001	10^{-18}

Units of Measurement

Length
1 in. = 2.54 cm
10 mm = 1 cm
100 cm = 1 m
1000 mm = 1 m
1000 m = 1 km
1 mile = 1.61 km
1 Å = 10^{-8} cm

Mass
1 lb = 453.6 g
1000 mg = 1 g
1000 g = 1 kg
1 ounce = 28.3 g
2.2 lb = 1 kg

Volume
1 mL = 1 cm^3
1000 mL = 1 L
1 fluid ounce = 29.6 mL
1 qt = 0.946 L
1 gal = 3.785 L

Temperature
°F = 1.8 × °C + 32
°C = $\dfrac{(\text{°F} - 32)}{1.8}$
K = °C + 273
°F = 1.8(°C + 40) − 40
Absolute zero = −273.18°C, or −459.72°F

Appendix IV
Solubility Table

	F^-	Cl^-	Br^-	I^-	O^{2-}	S^{2-}	OH^-	NO_3^-	CO_3^{2-}	SO_4^{2-}	$C_2H_3O_2^-$
H^+	S	S	S	S	S	s	S	S	s	S	S
Na^+	S	S	S	S	S	S	S	S	S	S	S
K^+	S	S	S	S	S	S	S	S	S	S	S
NH_4^+	S	S	S	S	—	S	S	S	S	S	S
Ag^+	S	I	I	I	I	I	—	S	I	I	I
Mg^{2+}	I	S	S	S	I	d	I	S	I	S	S
Ca^{2+}	I	S	S	S	I	d	I	S	I	I	S
Ba^{2+}	I	S	S	S	s	d	s	S	I	I	S
Fe^{2+}	s	S	S	S	I	I	I	S	s	S	S
Fe^{3+}	I	S	S	—	I	I	I	S	I	S	I
Co^{2+}	S	S	S	S	I	I	I	S	I	S	S
Ni^{2+}	s	S	S	S	I	I	I	S	I	S	S
Cu^{2+}	s	S	S	—	I	I	I	S	I	S	S
Zn^{2+}	s	S	S	S	I	I	I	S	I	S	S
Hg^{2+}	d	S	I	I	I	I	I	S	I	d	S
Cd^{2+}	s	S	S	S	I	I	I	S	I	S	S
Sn^{2+}	S	S	S	s	I	I	I	S	I	S	S
Pb^{2+}	I	I	I	I	I	I	I	S	I	I	S
Mn^{2+}	s	S	S	S	I	I	I	S	I	S	S
Al^{3+}	I	S	S	S	I	d	I	S	—	S	S

Key: S = Soluble in water
        s = Slightly soluble in water

I = Insoluble in water (less than 1 g/100 g H_2O)
d = Decomposes in water

Appendix V
Answers to Selected Problems

Chapter 1

6. The following statements are correct:
   a, b, d, f, g, h, i

Chapter 2

C.8 The following statements are correct:
a, c, d, e, g, h, i, j, l, n, o, r, s.

D.1 (a) 2 (b) 3 (c) 3 (d) 2 (e) 3 (f) 6
(g) 3 (h) 4

D.2 (a) 93.2 (b) 8.87 (c) 0.0285 (d) 21.3
(e) 4.64 (f) 130 (g) 34.3 (h) 2.00×10^6

D.3 (a) 2.9×10^6 (b) 4.56×10^{-2} (c) 5.8×10^{-1}
(d) 4.0822×10^3 (e) 8.40×10^{-3}
(f) 4.030×10^1 (g) 1.2×10^7 (h) 5.5×10^{-6}

D.4 (a) 14.4 (b) 58.5 (c) 1.08×10^8 (d) 40.
(e) 2.0×10^2 (f) 2009 (g) 0.504
(h) 1.79×10^3 (i) 7.18×10^{-3}
(j) 2.49×10^{-4}

D.5 (a) 0.833 (b) 0.429 (c) 0.750 (d) 0.500

D.6 (a) 1.9 (b) 86.7 (c) 2.1 (d) 51.3 (e) 8.93
(f) 0.030

D.7 (a) 100°C (b) 72°F (c) 318 K (d) 4.6 mL

D.8 (a) 0.280 m (b) 1.000 km (c) 92.8 mm

(d) 1.5×10^{-4} km (e) 6.06×10^{-6} km
(f) 4.5×10^8 Å (g) 6.5×10^3 Å
(h) 1.21×10^3 cm (i) 8.0×10^3 m
(j) 31.5 cm (k) 2.5×10^7 mm
(l) 1.2×10^{-6} cm (m) 5.20×10^4 cm
(n) 0.3884 nm (o) 107 cm
(p) 4.1×10^4 in. (q) 811 km (r) 12.9 cm^2
(s) 117 ft (t) 10.2 miles (u) 7.4×10^4 mm^3
(v) 1.25×10^{19} mm^3

D.9 (a) 1.068×10^4 mg (b) 6.8×10^{-2} kg
(c) 8.54×10^{-3} kg (d) 94.3 lb
(e) 0.164 g (f) 6.5×10^5 mg
(g) 5.5×10^3 g (h) 4.3×10^4 g

D.10 (a) 2.50×10^{-2} L (b) 2.24×10^4 mL
(c) 3.3×10^3 mL (d) 1.3×10^3 m^3
(e) 468 mL (f) 9.41 gal (g) 9.0×10^{-3} mL
(h) 75.7 L

D.11 (a) 89 km/hr (b) 81 ft/s

D.12 (a) 33.4 ft/s (b) 22.8 miles/hr

D.13 297 g salt remaining

D.14 (a) 4.7×10^4 miles/hr (b) 7.5×10^4 km/hr

D.15 77.2 kg

D.16 0.32 g

D.17 5.0×10^2 s

D.18 3×10^4 mg

D.19 $0.392/kg

D.20 2.52×10^3

D.21 3.0×10^3 times heavier

D.22 $21

D.23 56 L

D.24 2.3×10^2 L

D.25 7.6×10^4 drops

D.26 1.6×10^2 L

D.27 5.0×10^{-3} mL

D.28 2.83×10^4 mL

D.29 4×10^5 m^2

D.30 (a) 72.2°C (b) −18°C (c) 255 K
(d) −0.40°F (e) 90°F (f) −23°C (g) 546 K
(h) −61°C

D.31 98.6°F

D.32 −100°C is 10°F colder than −138°F

D.33 (a) −40°C = −40°F (b) 11.4°F = −11.4°C

D.34 1.7×10^4 J

D.35 1.9×10^3 J; 4.5×10^2 cal

D.36 0.30 J/g °C

D.37 0.49 J/g °C

D.38 17°C

D.39 41.6°C

D.40 1.565 g/mL

D.41 3.12 g/mL

D.42 7.1 g/mL

D.43 920 g

D.44 1.28 g/mL

D.45 340 g

D.46 76.9 g

D.47 A = magnesium, B = aluminum, C = silver

D.48 3.57×10^3 g

D.49 (a) 0.972 g/mL (b) 1.03 mL/g

D.50 (a) 2.72 g/mL (b) 2.72

D.51 49.8 mL

D.52 Ethyl alcohol; 63 mL versus 50 mL

D.53 18.3 g/cm^3

D.54 4.83×10^3 mL

D.55 Density of liquid = 0.842 g/mL;
density of slug = 2.7 g/mL

D.56 (a) 1.16 (b) 77.7 mL sulfuric acid

D.57 (a) 1.39 (b) 272 mL sulfuric acid

D.58 Specific gravity of gasoline is less than that
of water; sp gr (gasoline) = 0.720;
sp gr (water) = 1.00

Chapter 3

C.20 The following statements are correct:
c, f, g, j, l, n, o, q, t.

D.1 (a) 391 K (b) 244°F

D.2 30.3% iron

D.3 3.50 g copper(II) oxide

D.4 21.9 g copper

D.5 78.7 g mercury

D.6 10.7% fat

D.7 (a) 8.5 g oxygen (b) 40% oxygen

D.8 21.7 g chlorine

D.9 (a) 5.1×10^{14} J; 1.2×10^{14} cal
(b) 4.0×10^8 gal water

Chapter 4

C.30 The following statements are correct:
c, e, g, j, k, m, n, p, r, u, v, w, y.

D.1 9.83 g Na

D.2 36% Zn, 64% Cu

D.3 16.8 g CaO

D.4 2.66 g/mL

D.5 54.5 mL Br$_2$

D.6 (a) 44.4% S (b) Ca (c) 24.0 g S

D.7 18 carat

D.8 75% C

D.9 8.5×10^3 g Au

D.10 1.6×10^3 kg alloy

Chapter 5

C.8 The following statements are correct:
a, b, c, f, g, i.

C.28 The following statements are correct:
a, c, d, e, f, h, i, j, k, l, n, p, q, r.

C.39 The following statements are correct:
b, c, f, g, h, k.

C.43 The following statements are correct: b, d.

D.1 (a) 5.1×10^5 (b) 2.74×10^{-4} (c) 1×10^{-8}
(d) 5.1×10^2

D.2 1st = 2; 2nd = 8; 3rd = 18; 4th = 32; 5th = 50;
6th = 72

D.3 (a) 8   16   O   8   8
(b) 28   58   Ni   28   30
(c) 80   199   Hg   80   119

D.4 131 amu

D.5 107.87 amu

D.6 24.31 amu

Chapter 6

C.39 The following statements are correct:
a, d, e, g, h, i, k, n, o, p, t, v.

Chapter 7

C.31 The following statements are correct:
a, b, e, h, i, j, l, o, q, r, s, t, u, v, w, x, z, bb, cc, gg,
hh, jj.

Chapter 8

30. The following statements are correct:
a, d, f, g, i, j, l, m, o, p, r, u, w, x, y, aa.

Chapter 9

B.15 The following statements are correct:
a, b, e, g, h, k, l, n.
C.1 (a) 212.8   (b) 174.3   (c) 261.3
   (d) 60.0   (e) 90.0   (f) 159.6
   (g) 540.0   (h) 354.0   (i) 96.0   (j) 147.1
C.2 (a) 56.1   (b) 311.9   (c) 158.5
   (d) 187.5   (e) 209.6   (f) 123.0
   (g) 540.0   (h) 329.1   (i) 350.7   (j) 183.9
C.3 (a) 0.344 mol Zn   (b) 2.83×10^{-2} mol Mg
   (c) 7.5×10^{-2} mol Cu   (d) 6.49 mol Co
   (e) 4.6×10^{-4} mol Sn   (f) 28 mol N atoms
C.4 (a) 0.625 mol NaOH   (b) 0.275 mol Br_2
   (c) 7.18×10^{-3} mol $MgCl_2$
   (d) 0.463 mol CH_3OH
   (e) 2.03×10^{-2} mol Na_2SO_4
   (f) 5.97 mol ZnI_2
C.5 (a) 108 g Au   (b) 284 g H_2O (c) 888 g Cl_2
   (d) 252 g NH_4NO_3 (e) 4.17×10^{-2} g H_2SO_4
   (f) 11.5 g CCl_4 (g) 0.122 g Ti
   (h) 8.0×10^{-7} g S
C.6 (a) 7.59×10^{23} molecules O_2
   (b) 3.4×10^{23} molecules C_6H_6
   (c) 6.02×10^{23} molecules CH_4
   (d) 1.65×10^{25} molecules HCl
C.7 (a) 3.441×10^{-22} g Pb
   (b) 1.791×10^{-22} g Ag
   (c) 2.99×10^{-23} g H_2O
   (d) 3.77×10^{-22} g $C_3H_5(NO_3)_3$
C.8 (a) 550 g Cu   (b) 24.6 kg Au
   (c) 1.7×10^{-23} mol C
   (d) 8.3×10^{-21} mol CO_2
   (e) 0.885 mol S
   (f) 42.7 mol NaCl
   (g) 1.05×10^{24} atoms Mg
   (h) 9.47 mol Br_2
C.9 (a) 6.022×10^{23} CS_2 molecules
   (b) 6.022×10^{23} C atoms
   (c) 1.204×10^{24} S atoms
   (d) 1.806×10^{24} total atoms
C.10 8.43×10^{23} atoms P
C.11 5.88 g Na
C.12 10.8 g/at. wt
C.13 5.54×10^{19} m
C.14 1.2×10^{14} dollars per person
C.15 (a) 8.3×10^{16} drops per mile^3

(b) 7.3×10^6 miles^3
C.16 (a) 10.3 cm^3 Ag   (b) 2.18 cm
C.17 (a) 6.02×10^{23} atoms O
   (b) 3.75×10^{23} atoms O
   (c) 3.60×10^{23} atoms O
   (d) 6.0×10^{24} atoms O
   (e) 5.36×10^{24} atoms O
   (f) 5.0×10^{18} atoms O
C.18 (a) 14.4 g Ag   (b) 1.28 g Cl   (c) 266 g N
   (d) 6.74 g O   (e) 6.00 g H
C.19 10.3 mol H_2SO_4
C.20 1.62 mol HNO_3
C.21 (a) H_2O (b) CH_3OH
C.22 41.58 g Fe_2S_3
C.23 (a) 22.4% Na; 77.6% Br
   (b) 39.1% K; 1.0% H; 12.0% C; 48.0% O
   (c) 34.4% Fe; 65.6% Cl
   (d) 16.5% Si; 83.5% Cl
   (e) 15.8% Al; 28.1% S; 56.1% O
   (f) 63.5% Ag; 8.2% N; 28.3% O
C.24 (a) 47.9% Zn; 52.1% Cl
   (b) 18.2% N; 9.1% H; 31.2% C; 41.6% O
   (c) 12.3% Mg; 31.3% P; 56.5% O
   (d) 21.2% N; 6.1% H; 24.3% S; 48.4% O
   (e) 23.1% Fe; 17.4% N; 59.6% O
   (f) 54.4% I; 45.6% Cl
C.25 (a) 77.7% Fe   (b) 69.92% Fe
   (c) 72.3% Fe   (d) 15.2% Fe
C.26 Highest percent Cl, LiCl; lowest, $BaCl_2$
C.27 43.7% P; 56.3% O
C.28 24.2% C; 4.0% H; 71.7% Cl
C.29 8.60 g Li
C.30 (a) 76.98% Hg   (b) 46.4% O   (c) 17.3% N
   (d) 2.72% Mg
C.31 (a) H_2O (b) N_2O_3 (c) Equal   (d) $KClO_3$
   (e) $KHSO_4$ (f) Na_2CrO_4
C.32 (a) N_2O (b) NO   (c) N_2O_5 (d) Na_2CO_3
   (e) $NaClO_4$ (f) Mn_3O_4
C.33 (a) CuCl   (b) $CuCl_2$ (c) Cr_2S_3 (d) K_3PO_4
   (e) $BaCr_2O_7$ (f) PBr_8Cl_3
C.34 SnO_2
C.35 V_2O_5
C.36 No. 19.5 g Zn react with 9.57 g S (only 9.40 g
   S are available).
C.37 $C_6H_6O_2$
C.38 $C_6H_{12}O_6$
C.39 $C_9H_8O_4$
C.40 4.77 g O_2
C.41 GaAs
C.42 (a) CCl_4; CCl_4 (b) CCl_3; C_2Cl_6
   (c) CCl; C_6Cl_6 (d) C_3Cl_8; C_3Cl_8

Chapter 10

C.20 The following statements are correct:
a, d, e, f, h, i, j, l, n, o, p, q.

Chapter 11

B.1 (a) 0.247 mol KNO_3
(b) 0.0658 mol $Ca(NO_3)_2$
(c) 4.4 mol $(NH_4)_2C_2O_4$
(d) 25.0 mol $NaHCO_3$
(e) 3.85×10^{-3} mol $ZnCl_2$
(f) 0.056 mol $NaOH$
(g) 16 mol CO_2
(h) 4.29 mol C_2H_5OH
(i) 0.237 mol H_2SO_4

B.2 (a) 272 g $Fe(OH)_3$ (b) 1.31 g $NiSO_4$
(c) 1.25×10^5 g $CaCO_3$ (d) 3.60 g $HC_2H_3O_2$
(e) 179 g NH_3 (f) 373 g Bi_2S_3
(g) 2.6 g HCl (h) 1.35 g $C_6H_{12}O_6$
(i) 1.56×10^3 g Br_2 (j) 18 g K_2CrO_4

B.3 (a) 10.0 g H_2O (b) 25.0 g HCl

B.4 (a) $\dfrac{6 \text{ mol } CO_2}{2 \text{ mol } C_3H_7OH}$ (b) $\dfrac{2 \text{ mol } C_3H_7OH}{9 \text{ mol } O_2}$
(c) $\dfrac{9 \text{ mol } O_2}{6 \text{ mol } CO_2}$ (d) $\dfrac{8 \text{ mol } H_2O}{2 \text{ mol } C_3H_7OH}$
(e) $\dfrac{6 \text{ mol } CO_2}{8 \text{ mol } H_2O}$ (f) $\dfrac{8 \text{ mol } H_2O}{9 \text{ mol } O_2}$

B.5 (a) $\dfrac{3 \text{ mol } CaCl_2}{1 \text{ mol } Ca_3(PO_4)_2}$ (b) $\dfrac{6 \text{ mol } HCl}{2 \text{ mol } H_3PO_4}$
(c) $\dfrac{3 \text{ mol } CaCl_2}{2 \text{ mol } H_3PO_4}$ (d) $\dfrac{1 \text{ mol } Ca_3(PO_4)_2}{2 \text{ mol } H_3PO_4}$
(e) $\dfrac{6 \text{ mol } HCl}{1 \text{ mol } Ca_3(PO_4)_2}$ (f) $\dfrac{2 \text{ mol } H_3PO_4}{6 \text{ mol } HCl}$

B.6 2.80 mol Cl_2

B.7 540 g $NaOH$

B.8 (a) 8.33 mol H_2O (b) 0.800 mol $Al(OH)_3$

B.9 19.7 g $Zn_3(PO_4)_2$

B.10 (a) 0.500 mol Fe_2O_3 (b) 12.4 mol O_2
(c) 6.20 mol SO_2 (d) 65.6 g SO_2
(e) 0.871 mol O_2 (f) 332 g FeS_2

B.11 4.20 mol HCl

B.12 (a) 2.22 mol H_2 (b) 162 g HCl

B.13 87.4 kg Fe

B.14 117 g steam (H_2O); 271 g Fe

B.15 (a) 52.5 mol O_2 (b) 13.0 g CO_2
(c) 220 g CO_2

B.16 (a) HNO_3 is limiting; KOH in excess
(b) H_2SO_4 is limiting; $NaOH$ in excess
(c) H_2S is limiting; $Bi(NO_3)_3$ in excess
(d) H_2O is limiting; Fe in excess

B.17 (a) 2.0 mol Cu; 2.0 mol $FeSO_4$;
1.0 mol $CuSO_4$ (unreacted)
(b) 15.9 g Cu; 38.1 g $FeSO_4$;
5.97 g Fe (unreacted)

B.18 (a) 3.6 mol CO_2
(b) 12 mol CO_2
(c) 2.4 mol CO_2
(d) 6.0 mol CO_2; 8.0 mol H_2O; 10 mol O_2
(e) 24.8 g CO_2
(f) 75.0 g CO_2
(g) 60.0 g CO_2

B.19 57.8%

B.20 34.3 g CH_3OH (alcohol); 5.71 g H_2 unreacted

B.21 95.0% yield of Cu

B.22 (a) 324 g C_2H_5OH
(b) 1.10×10^3 g $C_6H_{12}O_6$

B.23 522 g C

B.24 77.8% CaC_2

B.25 $MgCl_2$ produces more $AgCl$ than $CaCl_2$.

B.26 3.73×10^2 kg Li_2O

B.27 18 kg of concentrated H_2SO_4

B.28 13 tablets

B.29 67.2% $KClO_3$

B.30 The following statements are correct:
a, c, d, f.

B.31 The following statements are correct:
a, c, e.

Chapter 12

C.13 The following statements are correct:
b, d, f(1, 4), h, i, n, o, p, q, t.

D.1 (a) 0.941 atm (b) 28.1 in. Hg
(c) 13.8 lb/in.^{2} (d) 715 torr
(e) 953 mbar (f) 95.3 kPa

D.2 (a) 0.037 atm (b) 79 atm (c) 1.05 atm
(d) 4.94×10^{-2} atm

D.3 (a) 263 mL (b) 800 mL (c) 132 mL

D.4 (a) 374 mm Hg (b) 711 mm Hg

D.5 1.0×10^2 atm

D.6 (a) 6.60 L (b) 6.17 L (c) 2.42 L (d) 8.35 L

D.7 600 K (or 327°C)

D.8 1.48×10^3 torr

D.9 −62°C

D.10 65 atm

D.11 320°F

D.12 (a) 363 mL (b) 778 mL

D.13 6.10 L

D.14 3.55 atm

D.15 2.4×10^5 L

D.16 33.4 L

D.17 7.39×10^{21} molecules; 2.22×10^{22} atoms; 275 mL at STP

D.18 703 torr

D.19 1200 torr

D.20 2.42 L

D.21 370 torr

D.22 56 L

D.23 (a) 34 mol H_2 (b) 1.2×10^2 g H_2

D.24 4.91 g CO_2

D.25 43.2 g/mol (mol. wt)

D.26 (a) 22.4 L (b) 8.30 L (c) 44.6 L

D.27 2.69×10^{22} molecules NH_3

D.28 44.6 mol Cl_2

D.29 39.9 g/mol (mol. wt)

D.30 (a) 3.74 g/L (b) 0.18 g/L (c) 3.58 g/L
(d) 2.50 g/L

D.31 (a) 1.70 g/L (b) 1.54 g/L

D.32 $-78°C$

D.33 (a) 8.4 L H_2 (b) 8.20 g CH_4 (c) 8.47 g/L
(d) 63.5 g/mol (mol. wt)

D.34 164 g/mol (mol. wt)

D.35 57 L

D.36 123 L

D.37 2.81 K

D.38 0.127 mol

D.39 279 L H_2

D.40 (a) 5.5 mol NH_3 (b) 5.6 mol NH_3
(c) 215 L NO (d) 0.640 L NO
(e) 2.4 L NO (f) 1.1×10^2 g O_2
(g) 9.7 g NH_3

D.41 (a) 308 L O_2 (b) 224 L SO_2

D.42 9.0 atm

D.43 $\dfrac{He}{N_2} = \dfrac{2.6}{1.0}$ (rate of effusion)

D.44 (a) $He/CH_4 = 2:1$
(b) 67 cm from the He end

D.45 C_4H_8 (molecular formula)

D.46 (a) 10 mol CO_2; 3 mol O_2; no CO
(b) 29 atm

D.47 76.0% $KClO_3$

Chapter 13

C.47 The following statements are correct:
a, b, c, f, h, l, m, o, p, s, t, u, w, y.

D.1 (a) 0.420 mol $CoCl_2 \cdot 6H_2O$
(b) 0.262 mol $FeI_2 \cdot 4H_2O$

D.2 (a) 2.52 mol H_2O (b) 1.05 mol H_2O

D.3 51.1% H_2O

D.4 48.6% H_2O

D.5 $Pb(C_2H_3O_2)_2 \cdot 3H_2O$

D.6 $FePO_4 \cdot 4H_2O$

D.7 3.11×10^5 J

D.8 5.5×10^4 J

D.9 1.6×10^5 cal (6.7×10^5 J)

D.10 4.07×10^4 J/mol H_2O

D.11 Yes, sufficient ice

D.12 Not sufficient steam

D.13 2.29×10^6 J

D.14 43.9 kJ

D.15 40.2 g H_2O

D.16 18.0 mL versus 22.4 L

D.17 (a) 6.00 mol O_2 (b) 162 L O_2

D.18 6.2 L O_2

D.19 (a) 18.0 g H_2O (b) 36.0 g H_2O
(c) 0.783 g H_2O (d) 18.0 g H_2O
(e) 0.447 g H_2O (f) 0.167 g H_2O

D.20 6.97×10^{18} molecules/second

D.21 54 g H_2SO_4 added

D.22 (a) Yes, O_2 remains (b) 20.0 mL O_2

Chapter 14

C.31 The following statements are correct:
a, b, f, h, j, k, l, n, p, r, s, t, v, x, y, z.

D.1 (a) 20.0% NaBr (b) 10.7% K_2SO_4
(c) 7.41% $Mg(NO_3)_2$

D.2 (a) 240 g solution (b) 544 g solution

D.3 (a) 23.1% NaCl (b) 22% $HC_2H_3O_2$
(c) 15.3% $C_6H_{12}O_6$; 84.7% H_2O

D.4 (a) 3.3 g KCl (b) 37.5 g K_2CrO_4
(c) 6.4 g $NaHCO_3$

D.5 455 g solution

D.6 (a) 4.5 g NaCl (b) 449 g H_2O

D.7 19 g H_2O needs to evaporate

D.8 (a) 22.0% CH_3OH (b) 33.6% NaCl

D.9 (a) 25.0% CH_3OH (b) 22% CCl_4

D.10 214 mL

D.11 (a) 424 g HNO_3 (b) 1.18 L

D.12 (a) 0.40 M (b) 3.8 M NaCl
(c) 2.5 M HCl (d) 0.59 M $BaCl_2 \cdot 2H_2O$

D.13 (a) 0.327 M Na_2CrO_4
(b) 1.81 M $C_6H_{12}O_6$
(c) 2.19×10^{-3} M $Al_2(SO_4)_3$
(d) 0.172 M $Ca(NO_3)_2$

D.14 (a) 40 mol LiCl (b) 0.075 mol H_2SO_4
(c) 3.5×10^{-4} mol NaOH (d) 16 mol $CoCl_2$

D.15 (a) 8.8×10^3 g NaCl (b) 13 g HCl
(c) 4.6×10^2 g H_2SO_4 (d) 8.58 g $Na_2C_2O_4$

D.16 (a) 1.68×10^3 mL (b) 3.91×10^4 mL
(c) 1.05×10^3 mL (d) 7.81×10^3 mL

D.17 6.72 M HNO_3

D.18 (a) 6.0 M HCl   (b) 0.064 M $ZnSO_4$
       (c) 1.6 M HCl
D.19 (a) 200 mL of 12 M HCl
       (b) 20 mL of 15 M NH_3
       (c) 16 mL of 16 M HNO_3
       (d) 69 mL of 18 M H_2SO_4
D.20 8.2×10^3 mL (8.2 L)
D.21 (a) 0.48 M H_2SO_4 (b) 0.74 M H_2SO_4
       (c) 1.83 M H_2SO_4
D.22 540 mL (water to be added)
D.23 0.32 M HNO_3
D.24 Take 31.3 mL of 5.00 M KOH and dilute with
       water to a volume of 250 mL.
D.25 (a) 7.60 g $BaCrO_4$
       (b) 15 mL of 1.0 M $BaCl_2$
D.26 (a) 33.3 mL of 0.250 M H_3PO_4
       (b) 1.10 g $Mg_3(PO_4)_2$
D.27 (a) 0.300 mol H_2 (b) 7.80 L H_2
D.28 2.08 M HCl
D.29 (a) 0.67 mol KCl
       (b) 0.33 mol $CrCl_3$
       (c) 0.30 mol $FeCl_2$
       (d) 69 mL of 0.060 M $K_2Cr_2O_7$
       (e) 35 mL of 6.0 M HCl
D.30 (a) 1.3 mol Cl_2 (b) 16 mol HCl
       (c) 1.3×10^2 mL of 6.0 M HCl   (d) 3.2 L Cl_2
D.31 (a) HCl: 36.5 g/eq. wt; NaOH: 40.0 g/eq. wt
       (b) HCl: 36.5 g/eq. wt; $Ba(OH)_2$: 85.7 g/eq. wt
       (c) H_2SO_4: 49.1 g/eq. wt;
           $Ca(OH)_2$: 37.1 g/eq. wt
       (d) H_2SO_4: 98.1 g/eq. wt; KOH: 56.1 g/eq. wt
       (e) H_3PO_4: 49.0 g/eq. wt; LiOH: 23.9 g/eq. wt
D.32 (a) 4.0 N HCl   (b) 0.243 N HNO_3
       (c) 6.0 N H_2SO_4 (d) 5.55 N H_3PO_4
       (e) 0.250 N $HC_2H_3O_2$
D.33 1.86 N H_2SO_4
D.34 $Mg(OH)_2$ tablet
D.35 (a) 9.943 mL NaOH   (b) 7.261 mL NaOH
       (c) 20.19 mL NaOH
D.36 (a) 4.38 m CH_3OH (b) 10.0 m C_6H_6
       (c) 5.6 m $C_6H_{12}O_6$
D.37 (a) CH_3OH (b) Both the same
D.38 6.2 m H_2SO_4; 5.0 M H_2SO_4
D.39 Solution will freeze in 20.0°F temperature.
D.40 (a) 101.5°C   (b) 2.9 m $C_{12}H_{22}O_{11}$
D.41 (a) 10.8 m $C_2H_6O_2$ (b) 105.5°C   (c) −20.1°C
D.42 (a) 0.545 m $C_{10}H_8$ (b) 2.7°C   (c) 81.5°C
D.43 153 g/mol
D.44 163 g/mol
D.45 500 g H_2O

D.46 (a) 8.04×10^3 g $C_2H_6O_2$
       (b) 7.24×10^3 mL $C_2H_6O_2$
       (c) −4.0°F
D.47 60 g NaOH solution
D.48 96.5 g NaOH solution
D.49 (a) 1.6×10^2 g sugar (b) 0.47 M (c) 0.516 m
D.50 Molecular formula is $C_8N_4H_2$

Chapter 15

C.36 The following statements are correct:
       a, c, f, i, j, k, l, n, p, r, t, u.
D.1 (a) 0.015 M NaCl = 0.015 M Na^+, 0.015 M Cl^-
       (b) 4.25 M $NaKSO_4$ = 4.25 M Na^+, 4.25 M K^+,
           4.25 M SO_4^{2-}
       (c) 0.75 M $ZnBr_2$ = 0.75 M Zn^{2+}, 1.5 M Br^-
       (d) 1.65 M $Al_2(SO_4)_3$ = 3.30 M Al^{3+},
           4.95 M SO_4^{2-}
       (e) 0.20 M $CaCl_2$ = 0.20 M Ca^{2+}, 0.40 M Cl^-
       (f) 0.265 M K^+, 0.265 M I^-
       (g) 0.682 M NH_4^+, 0.341 M SO_4^{2-}
       (h) 0.0627 M Mg^{2+}, 0.125 M ClO_3^-
D.2 (a) 0.035 g Na^+, 0.053 g Cl^-
       (b) 9.78 g Na^+, 16.6 g K^+, 40.8 g SO_4^{2-}
       (c) 4.9 g Zn^{2+}, 12 g Br^-
       (d) 8.91 g Al^{3+}, 47.6 g SO_4^{2-}
       (e) 0.80 g Ca^{2+}, 1.4 g Cl^-
       (f) 1.04 g K^+, 3.36 g I^-
       (g) 1.23 g NH_4^+, 3.28 g SO_4^{2-}
       (h) 0.152 g Mg^{2+}, 1.04 g ClO_3^-
D.3 0.260 M Ca^{2+}
D.4 (a) 1.0 M Na^+, 1.0 M Cl^-
       (b) 0.50 M Na^+, 0.50 M Cl^-
       (c) 1.0 M K^+, 0.50 M Ca^{2+}, 2.0 M Cl^-
       (d) 0.20 M K^+, 0.20 M H^+, 0.40 M Cl^-
       (e) No ions left in solution
       (f) 0.67 M Na^+, 0.67 M NO_3^-
D.5 3.0×10^3 mL
D.6 (a) 0.684 M HCl   (b) 0.542 M HCl
       (c) 0.367 M HCl   (d) 0.147 M NaOH
       (e) 0.964 M NaOH   (f) 0.4750 M NaOH
D.7 0.309 M $Ba(OH)_2$
D.8 (a) 40.8 mL of 0.245 M HCl
       (b) 1.57×10^3 mL of 0.245 M HCl
D.9 0.201 M HCl
D.10 437 mL HCl
D.11 0.673 g KOH
D.12 88.0% NaOH
D.13 7.0% NaCl
D.14 (a) 0.468 L H_2 (b) 0.936 L H_2

D.15 (a) 2 (b) 0.0 (c) 8.19 (d) 7 (e) 0.30
(f) 4.0

D.16 (a) 3.4 (b) 2.6 (c) 4.3 (d) 10.5

D.17 4

D.18 13.9 L of 18.0 M H_2SO_4

D.19 The solution will be basic.

D.20 0.3586 N NaOH

D.21 22.7 mL of 0.325 N HNO_3

D.22 22.7 mL of 0.325 N H_2SO_4

D.23 0.4536 N H_3PO_4; 0.1512 M H_3PO_4

D.24 (a) 20.0% $CaCl_2$ (b) 2.12 M $CaCl_2$
(c) 2.24 m $CaCl_2$

Chapter 16

C.24 The following statements are correct:
c, d, g, i, j, k, l, n, q, s, t, u, v, z.

D.1 4.20 mol HI

D.2 (a) 3.16 mol HI
(b) 3.4 mol HI; 0.30 mol H_2; 0.57 mol I_2
(c) $K_{eq} = 57$

D.3 2.75 mol H_2; 0.538 mol I_2; 0.500 mol HI

D.4 $K_{eq} = 29$

D.5 128 times as fast

D.6 HClO, 3.5×10^{-8}; $HC_3H_5O_2$, 1.3×10^{-5};
HCN, 4.0×10^{-10}

D.7 (a) $[H^+] = 2.1 \times 10^{-3}$ M (b) pH = 2.7
(c) 0.84% ionized

D.8 $K_a = 2.7 \times 10^{-5}$

D.9 $K_a = 7 \times 10^{-10}$

D.10 (a) 0.42% ionized; pH = 2.4
(b) 1.3% ionized; pH = 2.9
(c) 4.2% ionized; pH = 3.4

D.11 $K_a = 1.1 \times 10^{-7}$

D.12 $K_a = 7.3 \times 10^{-6}$

D.13 $[H^+] = 6.0$ M; $[OH^-] = 1.7 \times 10^{-15}$ M;
pH = −0.78; pOH = 14.78

D.14 (a) pH = 4.0; pOH = 10.0
(b) pOH = 2.0; pH = 12.0
(c) pOH = 2.6; pH = 11.4
(d) pH = 4.2; pOH = 9.8
(e) pOH = 4.9; pH = 9.1

D.15 (a) $[OH^-] = 1.0 \times 10^{-10}$
(b) $[OH^-] = 3.6 \times 10^{-9}$
(c) $[OH^-] = 2.5 \times 10^{-6}$

D.16 (a) $[H^+] = 1.7 \times 10^{-8}$ (b) $[H^+] = 1 \times 10^{-6}$
(c) $[H^+] = 2.2 \times 10^{-9}$

D.17 (a) 1.5×10^{-9} (b) 1.9×10^{-12}
(c) 1.2×10^{-23} (d) 2.6×10^{-13}
(e) 3.1×10^{-70} (f) 1.7×10^{-10}

(g) 2.4×10^{-5} (h) 5.13×10^{-17}
(i) 1.81×10^{-18}

D.18 (a) 4.5×10^{-5} mol/L
(b) 7.6×10^{-10} mol/L
(c) 1.6×10^{-2} mol/L
(d) 1.2×10^{-4} mol/L

D.19 (a) 8.9×10^{-4} g $BaCO_3$
(b) 9.3×10^{-9} g $AlPO_4$
(c) 0.50 g Ag_2SO_4
(d) 7.0×10^{-4} g $Mg(OH)_2$

D.20 (a) 2.1×10^{-4} mol Ca^{2+}/L;
4.2×10^{-4} mol F^-/L
(b) 8.2×10^{-3} g CaF_2

D.21 (a) Precipitate formed
(b) Precipitate formed
(c) No precipitate formed

D.22 (a) 3.0×10^{-8} M SO_4^{2-}
(b) 7.0×10^{-7} g $BaSO_4$

D.23 $BaSO_4$ will precipitate first

D.24 (a) 5.0×10^{-12} mol AgBr
(b) 2.5×10^{-12} mol AgBr

D.25 No precipitate of $PbCl_2$ will form.

D.26 (a) $[H^+] = 3.6 \times 10^{-5}$; pH = 4.4
(b) $[H^+] = 1.8 \times 10^{-5}$; pH = 4.7

D.27 (a) Change in pH = 5.3 units
(b) Change in pH = 0.02 units

Chapter 17

C.17 The following statements are correct:
a, c, e, g, j, k, m, p, q, r, s.

D.1 0.0772 mol NO

D.2 20.2 L Cl_2

D.3 17 g K MnO_4

D.4 66.2 mL $K_2Cr_2O_7$ solution

D.5 10.0 mL $K_2Cr_2O_7$ solution

D.6 91.3% KI

D.7 149 g Cu

D.8 4.22 L NO

D.9 5.56 mol H_2

Chapter 18

C.36 The following statements are correct:
c, e, f, g, j, k, n, o, q, r, t.

D.1 0.0625 mg of Sr-90 remaining

D.2 $380

D.3 2064 A.D.; one-eighth of the starting amount
remains

D.4 1.1×10^4 years old (11,000)

D.5 18 minutes/half-life

D.6 (a) 0.0424 g/mol   (b) 3.9×10^{12} J/mol
D.7 (a) 3.0×10^{-11} J/atom U-235
  (b) 1.8×10^{13} J/mol
  (c) 0.08185% mass loss
D.8 (a) 5.4×10^{11} J/mol   (b) 0.195% mass loss
D.9 7 alpha and 4 beta particles lost

Chapter 19
B.33 The following statements are correct:
  c, d, e, i, j, m, n, o, r, s, t.
C.1 (a) 12.7 kg NaCl   (b) 109 mol Cl_2
C.2 Magnetite
C.3 105 L SO_2
C.4 60 g Cl_2/hr
C.5 0.536 mol Br_2
C.6 (a) 18 M H_2SO_4 (b) 16 M HNO_3
  (c) 12 M HCl

Chapter 20
B.11 422 (Assuming C = 12.0; H = 1.0)
B.22 The following statements are correct: a, b, c, d,
  g, i, j, l, m, p, s.

Chapter 21
B.29 The following statements are correct: a, f, g, h,
  i, j, k, l, m, n, o, q, t, w, x, y.

Chapter 22
B.37 The following statements are correct: a, b, e, g,
  h, i, j, m, o, q.

Chapter 23
B.28 The following statements are correct: b, c, f, h,
  i, k, m, o, p, r, t, u, w, y.

Chapter 24
B.40 The following statements are correct: a, b, f, g,
  h, i, j, m, n, o, p, r, t, w, y, z.

Chapter 25
B.4 8.9×10^2 ethylene units
B.22 The following statements are correct: a, b, d, f,
  i, k.

Chapter 26
B.21 62.5°
B.26 The following statements are correct: a, b, f, g,
  i, k, l.

Chapter 27
B.38 The following statements are correct: c, e, g, h,
  i, l, n, p, q, r, s, v, w.

Chapter 28
B.26 The following statements are correct: d, e, g, j.

Chapter 29
B.47 38% protein
B.48 6.8×10^4 (mol. wt)
B.49 The following statements are correct: b, c, d, f,
  g, i, m, n, p, t.

Chapter 30
B.34 The following statements are correct: a, b, d, g,
  h, j, m, p, r.

Chapter 31
B.35 The following statements are correct: a, d, e, g,
  i, j, l, m.

Chapter 32
B.23 The following statements are correct: a, c, e, f,
  h, i, j, k, l.

Chapter 33
B.31 The following statements are correct: a, c, h, i,
  j, m, n.

Chapter 34
B.30 The following statements are correct: c, f, g, h,
  j, l, m, n, o, r, s, t, v.

Group
1

Periodic Table of the Elements with Group Numbering Recommended by the IUPAC and the American Chemical Society

Period

Atomic number — 11
Name — Sodium | 2
Symbol — **Na** | 8 — Electron structure | 1
22.98977 — Atomic weight

[a] Mass number of most stable or best-known isotope

[b] Mass of the isotope of longest half-life

Transition elements

Period	1	2	3	4	5	6	7	8	9
1	1 Hydrogen **H** 1.0079 (1)								
2	3 Lithium **Li** 6.941 (2,1)	4 Beryllium **Be** 9.01218 (2,2)							
3	11 Sodium **Na** 22.98977 (2,8,1)	12 Magnesium **Mg** 24.305 (2,8,2)							
4	19 Potassium **K** 39.098 (2,8,8,1)	20 Calcium **Ca** 40.08 (2,8,8,2)	21 Scandium **Sc** 44.9559 (2,8,9,2)	22 Titanium **Ti** 47.90 (2,8,10,2)	23 Vanadium **V** 50.9414 (2,8,11,2)	24 Chromium **Cr** 51.996 (2,8,13,1)	25 Manganese **Mn** 54.9380 (2,8,13,2)	26 Iron **Fe** 55.847 (2,8,14,2)	27 Cobalt **Co** 58.9332 (2,8,15,2)
5	37 Rubidium **Rb** 85.4678 (2,8,18,8,1)	38 Strontium **Sr** 87.62 (2,8,18,8,2)	39 Yttrium **Y** 88.9059 (2,8,18,9,2)	40 Zirconium **Zr** 91.22 (2,8,18,10,2)	41 Niobium **Nb** 92.9064 (2,8,18,12,1)	42 Molybdenum **Mo** 95.94 (2,8,18,13,1)	43 Technetium **Tc** 98.9062[b] (2,8,18,14,1)	44 Ruthenium **Ru** 101.07 (2,8,18,15,1)	45 Rhodium **Rh** 102.9055 (2,8,18,16,1)
6	55 Cesium **Cs** 132.9054 (2,8,18,18,8,1)	56 Barium **Ba** 137.34 (2,8,18,18,8,2)	57 Lanthanum **La*** 138.9055 (2,8,18,18,9,2)	72 Hafnium **Hf** 178.49 (2,8,18,32,10,2)	73 Tantalum **Ta** 180.9479 (2,8,18,32,11,2)	74 Wolfram (Tungsten) **W** 183.85 (2,8,18,32,12,2)	75 Rhenium **Re** 186.2 (2,8,18,32,13,2)	76 Osmium **Os** 190.2 (2,8,18,32,14,2)	77 Iridium **Ir** 192.22 (2,8,18,32,17,0)
7	87 Francium **Fr** (223)[a] (2,8,18,32,18,8,1)	88 Radium **Ra** 226.0254[b] (2,8,18,32,18,8,2)	89 Actinium **Ac**** (227)[a] (2,8,18,32,18,9,2)	104 Unnilquadium **Unq** (261)[a] (2,8,18,32,32,10,2)	105 Unnilpentium **Unp** (262)[a] (2,8,18,32,32,11,2)	106 Unnilhexium **Unh** (263)[a] (2,8,18,32,32,12,2)	107 Unnilseptium **Uns**	—	109 Unnilennium **Une**

Lanthanide series — 6

	58 Cerium **Ce** 140.12 (2,8,18,20,8,2)	59 Praseodymium **Pr** 140.9077 (2,8,18,21,8,2)	60 Neodymium **Nd** 144.24 (2,8,18,22,8,2)	61 Promethium **Pm** (145)[a] (2,8,18,23,8,2)	62 Samarium **Sm** 150.4 (2,8,18,24,8,2)

Actinide series — 7

	90 Thorium **Th** 232.0381[b] (2,8,18,32,18,10,2)	91 Protactinium **Pa** 231.0359[b] (2,8,18,32,20,9,2)	92 Uranium **U** 238.029 (2,8,18,32,21,9,2)	93 Neptunium **Np** 237.0482 (2,8,18,32,22,9,2)	94 Plutonium **Pu** (242)[a] (2,8,18,32,23,9,2)

Atomic weights are based on carbon-12. Atomic weights in parentheses indicate the most stable or best-known isotope. Slight disagreement exists as to the exact electronic configuration of several of the high-atomic-number elements.

18

2	
Helium	2
He	
4.00260	

13	**14**	**15**	**16**	**17**
5 Boron **B** 10.81 — 2,3	6 Carbon **C** 12.011 — 2,4	7 Nitrogen **N** 14.0067 — 2,5	8 Oxygen **O** 15.9994 — 2,6	9 Fluorine **F** 18.99840 — 2,7
13 Aluminum **Al** 26.98154 — 2,8,3	14 Silicon **Si** 28.086 — 2,8,4	15 Phosphorus **P** 30.97376 — 2,8,5	16 Sulfur **S** 32.06 — 2,8,6	17 Chlorine **Cl** 35.453 — 2,8,7

10 Neon **Ne** 20.179 — 2,8			
18 Argon **Ar** 39.948 — 2,8,8			

10	**11**	**12**						
28 Nickel **Ni** 58.71 — 2,8,16,2	29 Copper **Cu** 63.546 — 2,8,18,1	30 Zinc **Zn** 65.38 — 2,8,18,2	31 Gallium **Ga** 69.72 — 2,8,18,3	32 Germanium **Ge** 72.59 — 2,8,18,4	33 Arsenic **As** 74.9216 — 2,8,18,5	34 Selenium **Se** 78.96 — 2,8,18,6	35 Bromine **Br** 79.904 — 2,8,18,7	36 Krypton **Kr** 83.80 — 2,8,18,8
46 Palladium **Pd** 106.4 — 2,8,18,18,0	47 Silver **Ag** 107.868 — 2,8,18,18,1	48 Cadmium **Cd** 112.40 — 2,8,18,18,1	49 Indium **In** 114.82 — 2,8,18,18,3	50 Tin **Sn** 118.69 — 2,8,18,18,4	51 Antimony **Sb** 121.75 — 2,8,18,18,5	52 Tellurium **Te** 127.60 — 2,8,18,18,6	53 Iodine **I** 126.9045 — 2,8,18,18,7	54 Xenon **Xe** 131.30 — 2,8,18,18,8
78 Platinum **Pt** 195.09 — 2,8,18,32,17,1	79 Gold **Au** 196.9665 — 2,8,18,32,18,1	80 Mercury **Hg** 200.59 — 2,8,18,32,18,2	81 Thallium **Tl** 204.37 — 2,8,18,32,18,3	82 Lead **Pb** 207.2 — 2,8,18,32,18,4	83 Bismuth **Bi** 208.9804 — 2,8,18,32,18,5	84 Polonium **Po** (210)[a] — 2,8,18,32,18,6	85 Astatine **At** (210)[a] — 2,8,18,32,18,7	86 Radon **Rn** (222)[a] — 2,8,18,32,18,8

Inner transition elements

63 Europium **Eu** 151.96 — 2,8,18,25,8,2	64 Gadolinium **Gd** 157.25 — 2,8,18,25,9,2	65 Terbium **Tb** 158.9254 — 2,8,18,27,8,2	66 Dysprosium **Dy** 162.50 — 2,8,18,28,8,2	67 Holmium **Ho** 164.9304 — 2,8,18,29,8,2	68 Erbium **Er** 167.26 — 2,8,18,30,8,2	69 Thulium **Tm** 168.9342 — 2,8,18,31,8,2	70 Ytterbium **Yb** 173.04 — 2,8,18,32,8,2	71 Lutetium **Lu** 174.97 — 2,8,18,32,9,2
95 Americium **Am** (243)[a] — 2,8,18,32,25,8,2	96 Curium **Cm** (247)[a] — 2,8,18,32,25,9,2	97 Berkelium **Bk** (249)[a] — 2,8,18,32,26,9,2	98 Californium **Cf** (251)[a] — 2,8,18,32,27,9,2	99 Einsteinium **Es** (254)[a] — 2,8,18,32,28,9,2	100 Fermium **Fm** (253)[a] — 2,8,18,32,29,9,2	101 Mendelevium **Md** (256)[a] — 2,8,18,32,30,9,2	102 Nobelium **No** (254)[a] — 2,8,18,32,31,9,2	103 Lawrencium **Lr** (257)[a] — 2,8,18,32,32,9,2

Index

Names and Formulas of Common Ions

Positive Ions		Negative Ions	
Ammonium	NH_4^+	Acetate	$C_2H_3O_2^-$
Copper(I)	Cu^+	Bromate	BrO_3^-
(Cuprous)		Bromide	Br^-
Hydrogen	H^+	Chlorate	ClO_3^-
Potassium	K^+	Chloride	Cl^-
Silver	Ag^+	Chlorite	ClO_2^-
Sodium	Na^+	Cyanide	CN^-
Barium	Ba^{2+}	Fluoride	F^-
Cadmium	Cd^{2+}	Hydride	H^-
Calcium	Ca^{2+}	Bicarbonate	HCO_3^-
Cobalt(II)	Co^{2+}	(Hydrogen carbonate)	
Copper(II)	Cu^{2+}	Bisulfate	HSO_4^-
(Cupric)		(Hydrogen sulfate)	
Iron(II)	Fe^{2+}	Bisulfite	HSO_3^-
(Ferrous)		(Hydrogen sulfite)	
Lead(II)	Pb^{2+}	Hydroxide	OH^-
Magnesium	Mg^{2+}	Hypochlorite	ClO^-
Manganese(II)	Mn^{2+}	Iodate	IO_3^-
Mercury(II)	Hg^{2+}	Iodide	I^-
(Mercuric)		Nitrate	NO_3^-
Nickel(II)	Ni^{2+}	Nitrite	NO_2^-
Tin(II)	Sn^{2+}	Perchlorate	ClO_4^-
(Stannous)		Permanganate	MnO_4^-
Zinc	Zn^{2+}	Thiocyanate	SCN^-
Aluminum	Al^{3+}	Carbonate	CO_3^{2-}
Antimony(III)	Sb^{3+}	Chromate	CrO_4^{2-}
Arsenic(III)	As^{3+}	Dichromate	$Cr_2O_7^{2-}$
Bismuth(III)	Bi^{3+}	Oxalate	$C_2O_4^{2-}$
Chromium(III)	Cr^{3+}	Oxide	O^{2-}
Iron(III)	Fe^{3+}	Peroxide	O_2^{2-}
(Ferric)		Silicate	SiO_3^{2-}
Titanium(III)	Ti^{3+}	Sulfate	SO_4^{2-}
(Titanous)		Sulfide	S^{2-}
Manganese(IV)	Mn^{4+}	Sulfite	SO_3^{2-}
Tin(IV)	Sn^{4+}	Arsenate	AsO_4^{3-}
(Stannic)		Borate	BO_3^{3-}
Titanium(IV)	Ti^{4+}	Phosphate	PO_4^{3-}
(Titanic)		Phosphite	PO_3^{3-}
Antimony(V)	Sb^{5+}		
Arsenic(V)	As^{5+}		